MW00563080

Algebra 1

with CalcChat® and CalcView®

Common Core

Ron Larson
Laurie Boswell

Erie, Pennsylvania
BigIdeasLearning.com

Big Ideas Learning, LLC
1762 Norcross Road
Erie, PA 16510-3838
USA

For product information and customer support, contact Big Ideas Learning at **1-877-552-7766** or visit us at ***BigIdeasLearning.com***.

Cover Image
Dmitriy Rybin/Shutterstock.com

Printed in the U.S.A.

ISBN 13: 978-1-64727-416-0

1 2 3 4 5 6 7 8 9 10—24 23 22 21 20

One Voice From Kindergarten through Algebra 2

Dr. Ron Larson and Dr. Laurie Boswell are a hands-on authorship team that began writing together in 1992. Since that time, they have authored over four dozen textbooks. This successful collaboration allows for one voice from Kindergarten through Algebra 2.

Ron Larson

Ron Larson, Ph.D., is well known as the lead author of a comprehensive program for mathematics that spans school mathematics and college courses. He holds the distinction of Professor Emeritus from Penn State Erie, The Behrend College, where he taught for nearly 40 years. He received his Ph.D. in mathematics from the University of Colorado. Dr. Larson's numerous professional activities keep him actively involved in the mathematics education community and allow him to fully understand the needs of students, teachers, supervisors, and administrators.

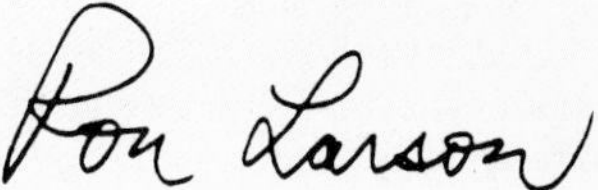

Laurie Boswell

Laurie Boswell, Ed.D., is the former Head of School at Riverside School in Lyndonville, Vermont. In addition to textbook authoring, she provides mathematics consulting and embedded coaching sessions. Dr. Boswell received her Ed.D. from the University of Vermont in 2010. She is a recipient of the Presidential Award for Excellence in Mathematics Teaching and is a Tandy Technology Scholar. Laurie has taught math to students at all levels, elementary through college. In addition, Laurie has served on the NCTM Board of Directors and as a Regional Director for NCSM. Along with Ron, Laurie has co-authored numerous math programs and has become a popular national speaker.

Contributors, Reviewers, and Research

Contributing Specialists and Reviewers

Big Ideas Learning would like to express our gratitude to the mathematics education and instruction experts who served as our advisory panel, contributing specialists, and reviewers during the writing of *Big Ideas Math Algebra 1 Common Core Edition*. Their input was an invaluable asset during the development of this program.

- **Sophie Murphy, Ph.D. Candidate**, Melbourne School of Education, Melbourne, Australia
  Learning Targets and Success Criteria Specialist and Visible Learning Reviewer
- **Michael McDowell, Ed.D.**, Superintendent, Ross, CA
  Project-Based Learning Specialist
- **Nancy Siddens**, Independent Language Teaching Consultant, Las Cruces, NM
  English Language Learner Specialist and Teaching Education Contributor
- **Linda Hall**, Mathematics Educational Consultant, Edmond, OK
  Content Reviewer
- **Beverly Stitzel**, Secondary Mathematics Teacher, Oxford, MI
  Content Reviewer
- **Elizabeth Caccavella, Ed.D.**, Supervisor of Mathematics, Paterson, NJ
  Content Reviewer
- **Matthew L. Beyranevand, Ed.D.**, K–12 Mathematics Coordinator, Chelmsford, MA
  Content Reviewer
- **Jill Kalb**, Secondary Math Content Specialist, Arvada, CO
  Content Reviewer
- **Jason Berkholz**, Mathematics Department Chair, Metropolitan School District of Washington Township, Indianapolis, IN
  Content Reviewer
- **Larry Dorf**, Secondary Mathematics Teacher, Harrisburg, PA
  Content Reviewer

Research

Ron Larson and Laurie Boswell developed this program using the latest in educational research, along with the body of knowledge collected from expert mathematics educators. This program follows the best practices outlined in the most prominent and widely accepted educational research, including:

- *Visible Learning*, John Hattie © 2009
- *Visible Learning for Teachers*, John Hattie © 2012
- *Visible Learning for Mathematics,* John Hattie © 2017
- *Principles to Actions: Ensuring Mathematical Success for All*, NCTM © 2014
- *Adding It Up: Helping Children Learn Mathematics,* National Research Council © 2001
- *Mathematical Mindsets: Unleashing Students' Potential through Creative Math, Inspiring Messages and Innovative Teaching,* Jo Boaler © 2015
- *Classroom Instruction That Works: Research-Based Strategies for Increasing Student Achievement,* Marzano, Pickering, and Pollock © 2001
- *What Works in Schools: Translating Research into Action,* Robert Marzano © 2003
- *Principles and Standards for School Mathematics,* NCTM © 2000
- Common Core State Standards for Mathematics, National Governors Association Center for Best Practices and the Council of Chief State School Officers © 2010
- *Universal Design for Learning Guidelines,* CAST © 2011
- *Rigorous PBL by Design: Three Shifts for Developing Confident and Competent Learners,* Michael McDowell © 2017
- Rigor/Relevance Framework® International Center for Leadership in Education
- *Understanding by Design*, Grant Wiggins and Jay McTighe © 2005
- Achieve, ACT, and The College Board
- *Evaluating the Quality of Learning: The SOLO Taxonomy,* John B. Biggs & Kevin F. Collis © 1982
- *Formative Assessment in the Secondary Classroom,* Shirley Clarke © 2005
- *Improving Student Achievement: A Practical Guide to Assessment for Learning,* Toni Glasson © 2009

Explore Every Chapter Through the Lens of STEM

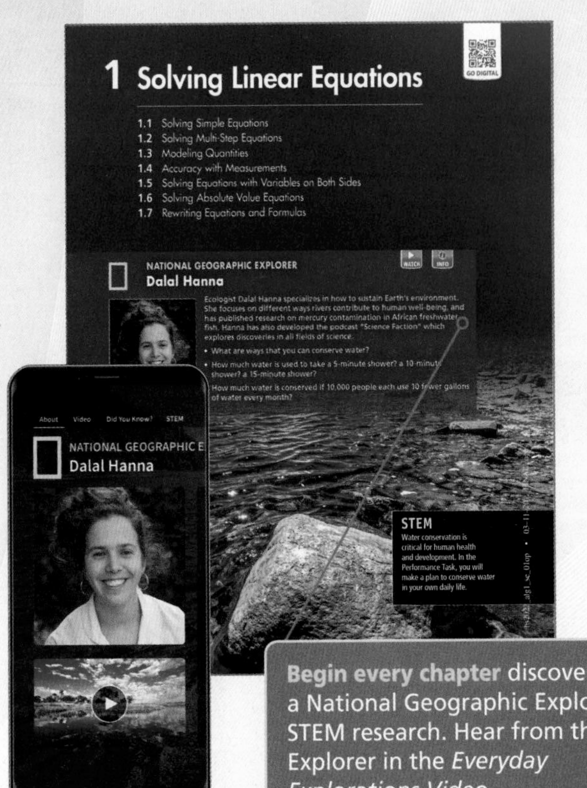

National Geographic Explorers

Meet a National Geographic Explorer at the start of every chapter, and follow the context through the chapter to connect their research to your learning.

Throughout the chapter, revisit the Explorer's field of study to apply the math you are learning.

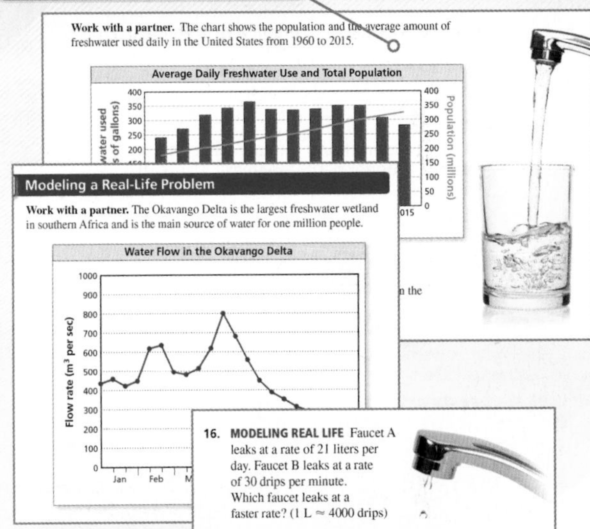

Begin every chapter discovering a National Geographic Explorer's STEM research. Hear from the Explorer in the *Everyday Explorations Video.*

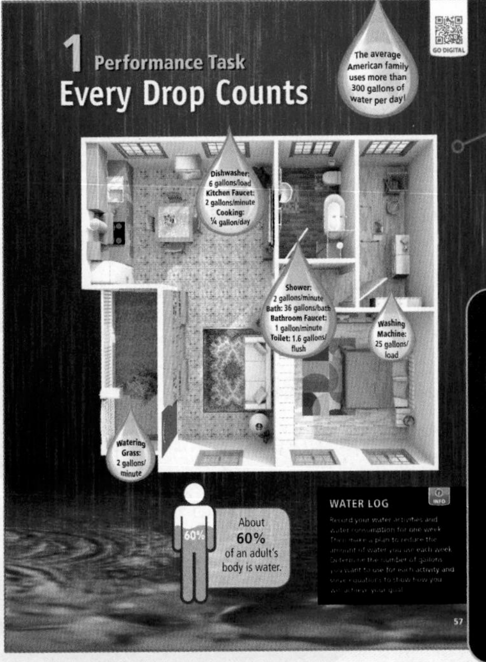

Conclude the chapter with a Performance Task related to the National Geographic Explorer's field of study. Explore the task digitally to experience additional insights.

Focus, Coherence, and Rigor

Instructional Design

A single authorship team from Kindergarten through Algebra 2 results in a seamless articulation of focused topics with meaningful coherence from course to course.

Every chapter and every lesson contain a rigorous balance of conceptual understanding, procedural fluency, and application.

FOCUS

A focused program emphasizes the major work of each course, the widely applicable prerequisites needed for you to be college and career ready.

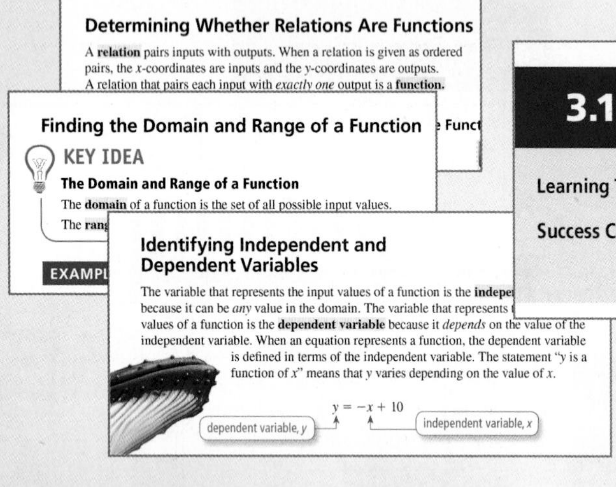

Determining Whether Relations Are Functions

A **relation** pairs inputs with outputs. When a relation is given as ordered pairs, the *x*-coordinates are inputs and the *y*-coordinates are outputs. A relation that pairs each input with *exactly one* output is a **function**.

Finding the Domain and Range of a Function

KEY IDEA

The Domain and Range of a Function

The **domain** of a function is the set of all possible input values.

The ran…

EXAMPL…

Identifying Independent and Dependent Variables

The variable that represents the input values of a function is the **indepe…** because it can be *any* value in the domain. The variable that represents … values of a function is the **dependent variable** because it *depends* on the value of the independent variable. When an equation represents a function, the dependent variable is defined in terms of the independent variable. The statement "*y* is a function of *x*" means that *y* varies depending on the value of *x*.

$y = -x + 10$

3.1 Functions

Learning Target Understand the concept of a function.

Success Criteria

- I can determine whether a relation is a function.
- I can find the domain and range of a function.
- I can distinguish between independent and dependent variables.

Learning targets, success criteria, and content headings through each section focus the learning into manageable chunks.

The authors gave careful thought to how the learning should progress from prior chapters and grades to future ones, as shown in the Teaching Edition progressions charts.

COHERENCE **Through the Grades**

Prior Learning	Current Learning	Future Learning
Middle School • **8.G.A.1, 8.G.A.3** Translate, reflect, and rotate figures in the coordinate plane. • **8.EE.B.6** Use similar triangles to explain why the slope is the same between any two distinct points on a nonvertical line.	**Chapter 3** • **HSF-IF.A.1, HSF-IF.A.2** Understand the definition of a function and use function notation. • **HSF-IF.B.4** Sketch a graph of a function from a verbal description. • **HSF-IF.C.9** Compare properties of two functions each represented in a … way.	**Algebra 1** • **HSA-CED.A.2, HSF-BF.A.1a, HSF-LE.A.1b, HSF-LE.A.2** Create equations of linear functions using points and slopes. • **HSF-IF.C.7a, HSF-IF.C.7b, HSF-IF.C.7e** Graph piecewise, exponential, quadratic, square root …

You have used *linear regression* to find an equation of the line of best fit. Similarly, you can use *exponential regression* to find an exponential function that best fits a data set.

EXAMPLE 6 **Modeling Real Life**  

The table shows the temperatures *y* (in degrees Fahrenheit) of coffee *x* minutes after pouring a cup. Use technology to find a function that fits the data. Predict the temperature of the coffee 10 minutes after it is poured.

SOLUTION

Step 1 Enter the data from the table into a tech… of the data.

Throughout the course, you will build on prior learning as you learn new concepts.

COHERENCE

A coherent program has intentional progression of content between courses (building new understanding on foundations from prior years) and within the course (connecting concepts throughout).

from a Single Authorship Team

RIGOR

A rigorous program provides a balance of three important building blocks.

- **Conceptual Understanding**
  Discovering why
- **Procedural Fluency**
  Learning how
- **Application**
  Knowing when to apply

EXPLORE IT! Describing Relations

Work with a partner. You buy an item from the vending machine.

a. Describe two possible relations associated with the vending machine.

b. Think about each relation in part (a).
- What are the inputs?
- What are the outputs?
- Does each input pair with *exactly* one output? Explain.

In mathematics, a **function** is a relation that pairs each input with exactly one output.

c. How can you use a coordinate plane to represent a relation? What are the inputs? What are the outputs?

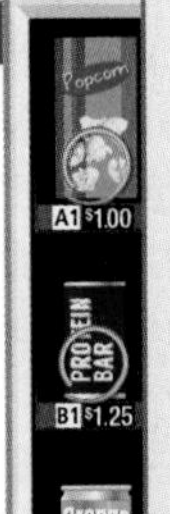

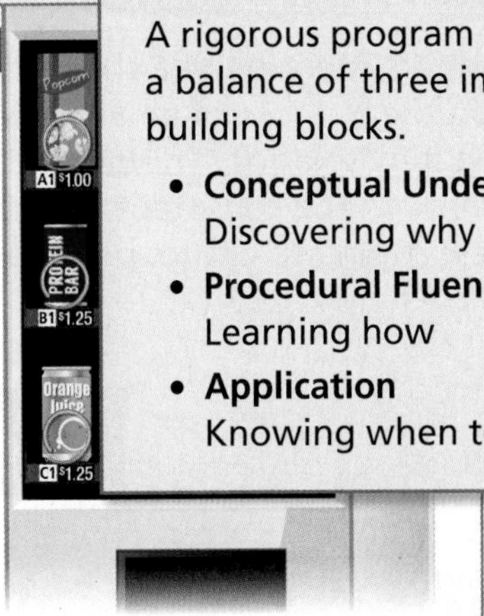

Conceptual Understanding
Explore, question, explain, and persevere as you discover foundational concepts central to the learning target of each section.

Math Practice
Contextualize Relationships
Can you think of any mathematical relations? Are any of these relations functions?

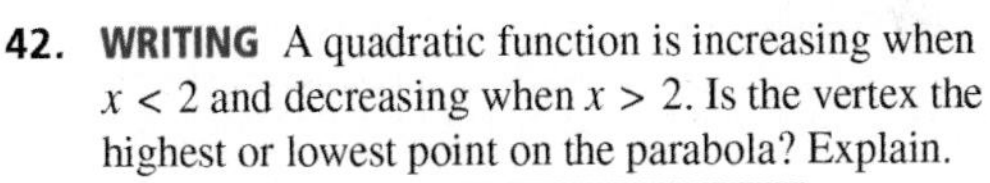
42. WRITING A quadratic function is increasing when $x < 2$ and decreasing when $x > 2$. Is the vertex the highest or lowest point on the parabola? Explain.

53. MP **NUMBER SENSE** Without evaluating, order $(7 \cdot 7)^5$, $(7 \cdot 7)^{-8}$, and $(7 \cdot 7)^0$ from least to greatest. Explain your reasoning.

Conceptual Understanding
Understand the ideas behind key concepts, see them from varied perspectives, and explain their meaning.

EXAMPLE 1 Graphing $f(x) = a(x - p)(x - q)$ 

Graph $f(x) = -(x + 1)(x - 5)$. Find the domain and range.

SOLUTION

Step 1 Identify the x-intercepts. Because the x-intercepts are $p = -1$ and $q = 5$, plot $(-1, 0)$ and $(5, 0)$.

Step 2 Find and graph the axis of symmetry.

$$x = \frac{p + q}{2} = \frac{-1 + 5}{2} = 2$$

Step 3 Find and plot the vertex. The x-coordinate of the vertex is 2. To find the y-coordinate of the vertex, substitute 2 for x and evaluate.

$$f(2) = -(2 + 1)(2 - 5) = 9$$

So, the vertex is $(2, 9)$.

Step 4 Draw a parabola through the vertex and the points where the x-intercepts occur.

▶ The domain is all real numbers. The range is $y \leq 9$.

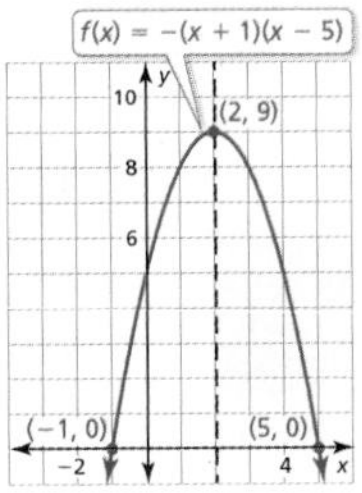

$f(x) = -(x + 1)(x - 5)$ (graph: points $(2, 9)$, $(-1, 0)$, $(5, 0)$)

Procedural Fluency
Learn with clear, stepped-out teaching and examples, and become fluent through *Self-Assessment*, *Practice*, and *Review & Refresh*.

EXAMPLE 6 Modeling Real Life  

A jellyfish emits about 1.25×10^8 particles of light, or photons, in 6.25×10^{-4} second. How many photons does the jellyfish emit each second? Write your answer in scientific notation and in standard form.

SOLUTION

Divide to find the unit rate in photons per second.

$\dfrac{1.25 \times 10^8}{6.25 \times 10^{-4}}$ ← photons / ← seconds — Divide the number of photons by the number of seconds.

$= \dfrac{1.25}{6.25} \times \dfrac{10^8}{10^{-4}}$ — Rewrite.

$= 0.2 \times 10^{12}$ — Simplify.

$= 2 \times 10^{11}$ — Write in scientific notation.

▶ The jellyfish emits 2×10^{11}, or 200,000,000,000 photons per second.

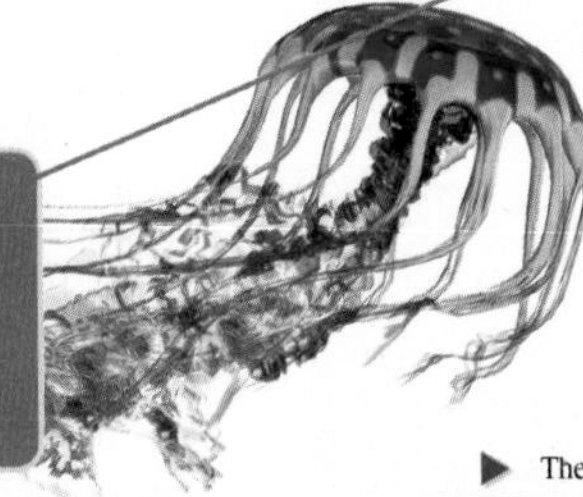

Application
Make meaning of mathematics in problem-solving contexts and real-life applications.

Visible Learning Through Learning Targets,

Making Learning Visible

Knowing the learning intention of a chapter or lesson helps you focus on the purpose of an activity, rather than simply completing it in isolation. This program supports visible learning through the consistent use of learning targets and success criteria to ensure positive outcomes for all students.

Every chapter and section show the learning target and related success criteria, so you know exactly what the learning should look like.

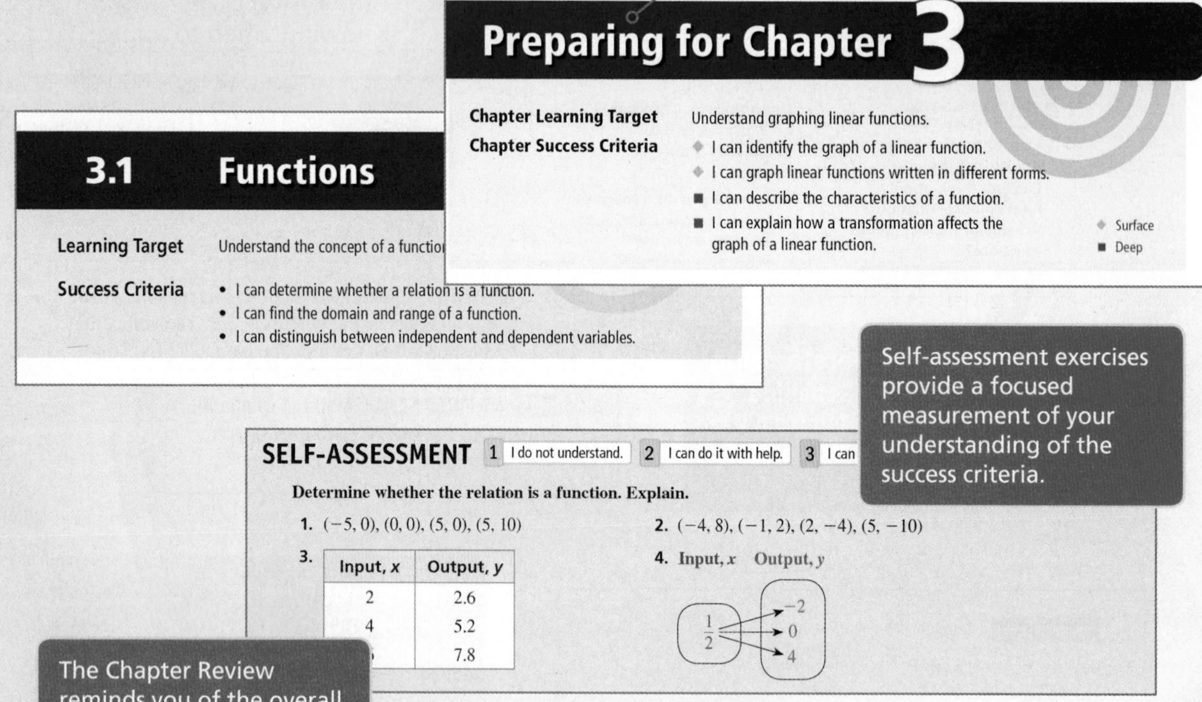

Preparing for Chapter 3
Chapter Learning Target
Understand graphing linear functions.
Chapter Success Criteria
I can identify the graph of a linear function.
I can graph linear functions written in different forms.
I can describe the characteristics of a function.
I can explain how a transformation affects the graph of a linear function.
Surface
Deep
3.1 Functions
Learning Target
Understand the concept of a functio
Success Criteria
I can determine whether a relation is a function.
I can find the domain and range of a function.
I can distinguish between independent and dependent variables.
SELF-ASSESSMENT
1 I do not understand.
2 I can do it with help.
3 I can
Determine whether the relation is a function. Explain.
1. (−5, 0), (0, 0), (5, 0), (5, 10)
2. (−4, 8), (−1, 2), (2, −4), (5, −10)
3.
Input, x
Output, y
2
2.6
4
5.2
7.8
4. Input, x Output, y

Self-assessment exercises provide a focused measurement of your understanding of the success criteria.

The Chapter Review reminds you of the overall learning target and success criteria for the chapter.

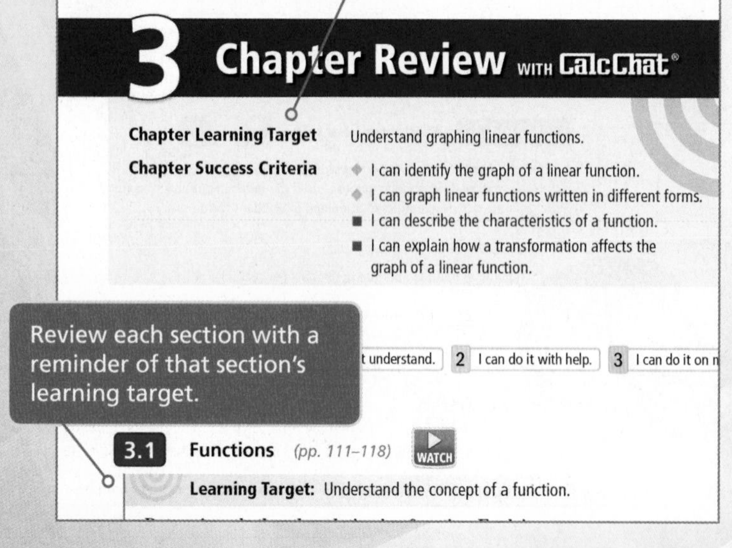

3 Chapter Review WITH CalcChat®
Chapter Learning Target
Understand graphing linear functions.
Chapter Success Criteria
I can identify the graph of a linear function.
I can graph linear functions written in different forms.
I can describe the characteristics of a function.
I can explain how a transformation affects the graph of a linear function.
t understand.
2 I can do it with help.
3 I can do it on
3.1 Functions (pp. 111–118)
WATCH
Learning Target: Understand the concept of a function.

Review each section with a reminder of that section's learning target.

QUESTIONS FOR LEARNERS

As you progress through a section, you should be able to answer the following questions.

1. What am I learning?
2. Why am I learning this?
3. Where am I in my learning?
4. How will I know when I have learned it?
5. Where am I going next?

Success Criteria, and Self-Assessment

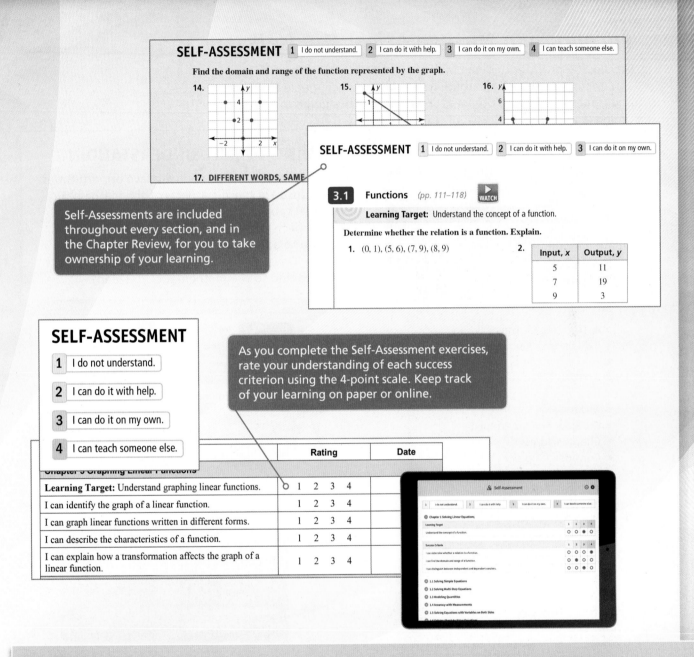

SELF-ASSESSMENT 1 I do not understand. 2 I can do it with help. 3 I can do it on my own. 4 I can teach someone else.

Find the domain and range of the function represented by the graph.

14. **15.** **16.**

17. DIFFERENT WORDS, SAME

SELF-ASSESSMENT 1 I do not understand. 2 I can do it with help. 3 I can do it on my own.

3.1 **Functions** *(pp. 111–118)* WATCH

Learning Target: Understand the concept of a function.

Determine whether the relation is a function. Explain.

1. (0, 1), (5, 6), (7, 9), (8, 9)

2.

Input, *x*	Output, *y*
5	11
7	19
9	3

Self-Assessments are included throughout every section, and in the Chapter Review, for you to take ownership of your learning.

SELF-ASSESSMENT

1 I do not understand.

2 I can do it with help.

3 I can do it on my own.

4 I can teach someone else.

As you complete the Self-Assessment exercises, rate your understanding of each success criterion using the 4-point scale. Keep track of your learning on paper or online.

	Rating	Date
Chapter 3 Graphing Linear Functions		
Learning Target: Understand graphing linear functions.	1 2 3 4	
I can identify the graph of a linear function.	1 2 3 4	
I can graph linear functions written in different forms.	1 2 3 4	
I can describe the characteristics of a function.	1 2 3 4	
I can explain how a transformation affects the graph of a linear function.	1 2 3 4	

Self-Assessment

Chapter 1 Solving Linear Equations

1.1 Solving Simple Equations

1.2 Solving Multi-Step Equations

1.3 Modeling Quantities

1.4 Accuracy with Measurements

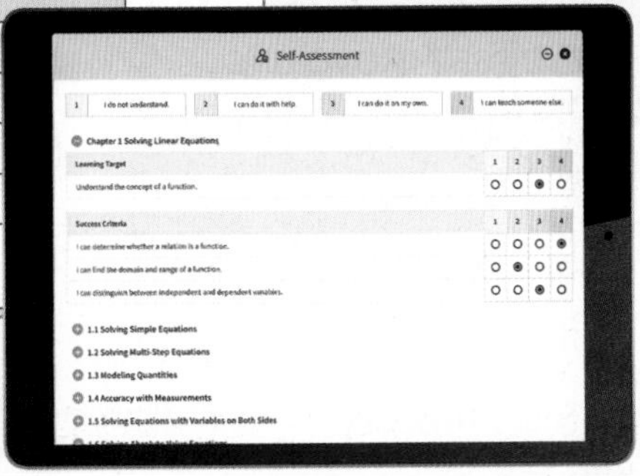

1.5 Solving Equations with Variables on Both Sides

Ensuring Positive Outcomes

John Hattie's *Visible Learning* research consistently shows that using learning targets and success criteria can result in two year's growth in one year, ensuring positive outcomes for student learning and achievement.

Sophie Murphy, M.Ed., wrote the chapter-level learning targets and success criteria for this program. Sophie is currently completing her Ph.D. at the University of Melbourne in Australia with Professor John Hattie as her leading supervisor. Sophie completed her Masters' thesis with Professor John Hattie in 2015. Sophie has over 20 years of experience as a teacher and school leader in private and public-school settings in Australia.

Embedded Mathematical Practices

Encouraging Mathematical Mindsets

Developing proficiency in the **Mathematical Practices** is about becoming a mathematical thinker: learning to ask why and being able to reason and communicate with others as you learn. Use this guide to help you understand more about each practice.

BUILDING TO FULL UNDERSTANDING

Throughout this course, you will have opportunities to demonstrate specific aspects of the mathematical practices. Labels throughout indicate gateways to those aspects. Collectively, these opportunities will lead you to a full understanding of each math practice. Developing these mindsets and habits will give meaning to the mathematics you learn.

1

One way to **Make Sense of Problems and Persevere in Solving Them** is to use the problem-solving plan. Take time to analyze the given information and what the problem is asking to help you to plan a solution pathway.

Look for these labels:

- Explain the Meaning
- Find Entry Points
- Analyze Givens
- Interpret a Solution
- Make a Plan
- Consider Similar Problems
- Check Progress
- Consider Simpler Forms
- PROBLEM SOLVING
- THOUGHT PROVOKING
- DIG DEEPER

EXAMPLE 3 Modeling Real Life WATCH

The function $E(d) = 0.25\sqrt{d}$ approximates the number of seconds it takes a dropped object to fall d feet on Earth. The function $M(d) = 1.6 \cdot E(d)$ approximates the number of seconds it takes a dropped object to fall d feet on Mars. How long does it take a dropped object to fall 64 feet on Mars?

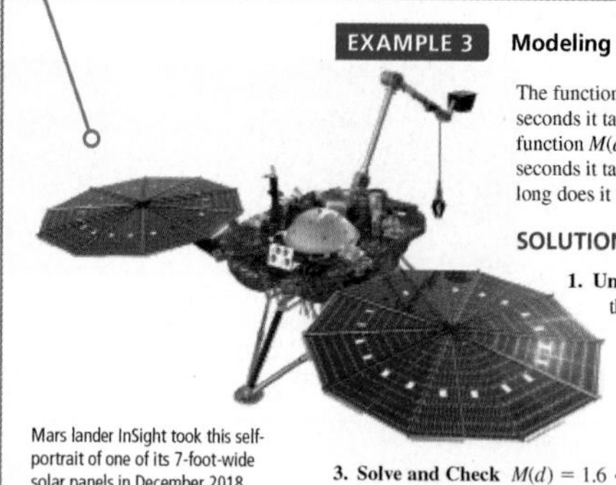

Mars lander InSight took this self-portrait of one of its 7-foot-wide solar panels in December 2018.

SOLUTION

1. **Understand the Problem** You are given functions that represent the number of seconds it takes a dropped object to fall d feet on Earth and on Mars. You are asked how long it takes a dropped object to fall a given distance on Mars.
2. **Make a Plan** Multiply $E(d)$ by 1.6 to write a rule for M. Then find $M(64)$.
3. **Solve and Check** $M(d) = 1.6 \cdot E(d)$

$= 1.6 \cdot 0.25\sqrt{d}$ Substitute $0.25\sqrt{d}$ for $E(d)$.

$= 0.4\sqrt{d}$ Simplify.

2

You **Reason Abstractly** when you explore a concrete example and represent it symbolically. Other times you **Reason Quantitatively** when you see relationships in numbers or symbols and draw conclusions about a concrete example.

EXPLORE IT! Finding a Composition of Functions

Work with a partner. The formulas below represent the temperature F (in degrees Fahrenheit) when the temperature is C degrees Celsius, and the temperature C when the temperature is K (Kelvin).

$F = \frac{9}{5}C + 32$ $\qquad C = K - 273$

a. Write an expression for F in terms of K.

b. Given that

$f(x) = \frac{9}{5}x + 32$

and

$g(x) = x - 273$

write an expression for $f(g(x))$. What does $f(g(x))$ represent in this situation?

Math Practice
Make Sense of Quantities
Does $g(f(x))$ make sense in this context? Explain.

11. MP **REASONING** Explain why a V-shaped graph does *not* represent a linear function.

12. MP **REASONING** How can you tell whether a graph shows a discrete domain or a continuous domain?

Look for these labels:

- Make Sense of Quantities
- Use Equations
- Use Expressions
- Understand Quantities
- Use Operations
- Contextualize Relationships
- Reason Abstractly
- REASONING
- NUMBER SENSE

3

When you **Construct Viable Arguments and Critique the Reasoning of Others**, you make and justify conclusions and decide whether others' arguments are correct or flawed.

25. MAKING AN ARGUMENT Your friend says that a line always represents a function. Is your friend correct? Explain.

Look for these labels:

- Use Assumptions
- Use Definitions
- Use Prior Results
- Make Conjectures
- Build Arguments
- Analyze Conjectures
- Use Counterexamples
- Justify Conclusions
- Compare Arguments
- Construct Arguments
- Listen and Ask Questions
- Critique Reasoning
- MAKING AN ARGUMENT
- LOGIC
- ERROR ANALYSIS
- DIFFERENT WORDS, SAME QUESTION
- WHICH ONE DOESN'T BELONG?

Math Practice

Make Conjectures
Which type of reasoning helps you to make a conjecture? Which type helps you to justify a conjecture? How do you know when to use each type?

Math Practice

Listen and Ask Questions
Ask a few classmates to read their answers to parts (b)–(d). Ask any questions you have about their answers.

4

To **Model with Mathematics**, you apply the math you have learned to a real-life problem, and you interpret mathematical results in the context of the situation.

45. MODELING REAL LIFE Flying fish use their pectoral fins like airplane wings to glide through the air.

a. Write an equation of the form $y = a(x - h)^2 + k$ with vertex $(33, 5)$ that models the flight path, assuming the fish leaves the water at $(0, 0)$.

b. What are the domain and range of the function? What do they represent in this situation?

c. Does the value of a change when the flight path has vertex $(30, 4)$? Justify your answer.

Look for these labels:

- Apply Mathematics
- Simplify a Solution
- Use a Diagram
- Use a Table
- Use a Graph
- Use a Formula
- Analyze Relationships
- Interpret Results
- MODELING REAL LIFE
- PROBLEM SOLVING

43. MP **PROBLEM SOLVING** An online ticket agency charges the amounts shown for basketball tickets. The total cost for an order is \$220.70. How many tickets are purchased?

Charge	Amount
Ticket price	\$32.50 per ticket
Convenience charge	\$3.30 per ticket
Processing charge	\$5.90 per order

Embedded Mathematical Practices (continued)

5

To **Use Appropriate Tools Strategically**, you need to know what tools are available and think about how each tool might help you solve a mathematical problem. You can use a tool for its advantages, while being aware of its limitations.

9. MP **CHOOSE TOOLS** For a large data set, would you use a stem-and-leaf plot or a histogram to show the distribution of the data? Explain.

EXPLORE IT! Reflecting Figures in Lines

Work with a partner. Use technology to draw any scalene triangle and label it $\triangle ABC$. Draw any line, $\overleftrightarrow{DE}$, and another line that is parallel to $\overleftrightarrow{DE}$.

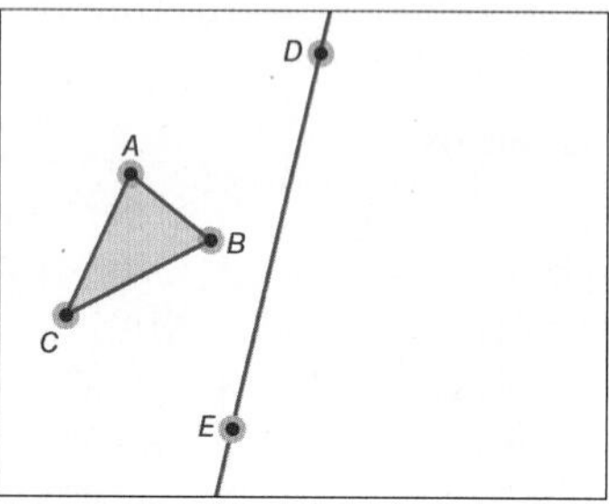

a. Reflect $\triangle ABC$ in $\overleftrightarrow{DE}$, followed by a reflection in the other line to form $\triangle A''B''C''$. What do you notice? Make several observations.

b. Is there a single transformation that maps $\triangle ABC$ to $\triangle A''B''C''$? Explain.

c. Repeat parts (a) and (b) with other figures. What do you notice?

d. Using the same triangle and line $\overleftrightarrow{DE}$, draw line $\overleftrightarrow{DF}$ that intersects $\overleftrightarrow{DE}$ at point D so that $\angle EDF$ is an acute or right angle. Then reflect $\triangle ABC$ in $\overleftrightarrow{DE}$, followed by a reflection in $\overleftrightarrow{DF}$ to form $\triangle A''B''C''$. What do you notice? Make several observations.

Look for these labels:

- Choose Tools
- Recognize Usefulness of Tools
- Use Other Resources
- Use Technology to Explore
- CHOOSE TOOLS
- USING TOOLS

6

When you **Attend to Precision**, you are developing a habit of being careful how you talk about concepts, label your work, and write your answers.

MP **PRECISION** **In Exercises 27–30, determine whether the statement uses the word *function* in a way that is mathematically correct. Explain your reasoning.**

27. The selling price of an item is a function of the cost of making the item.

28. The sales tax on a purchased item in a given state is a function of the selling price.

29. A function pairs each student in your school with a homeroom teacher.

30. A function pairs each chaperone on a school trip with 10 students.

Math Practice

Communicate Precisely
In part (b), for a function $y = f(x)$, explain the meaning of f, x, and $f(x)$.

Look for these labels:

- Communicate Precisely
- Use Clear Definitions
- State the Meaning of Symbols
- Specify Units
- Label Axes
- Calculate Accurately
- Understand Mathematical Terms
- PRECISION

Math Practice

Look for Structure
Why is it helpful to multiply each side by 6? How else could you begin to solve this equation?

b. $\frac{n}{6} = -\frac{n}{6} + \frac{1}{2}$ — Write the equation.

$6 \cdot \frac{n}{6} = 6 \cdot \left(-\frac{n}{6} + \frac{1}{2}\right)$ — Multiplication Property of Equality

$n = -n + 3$ — Simplify.

$+n \quad +n$ — Addition Property of Equality

$2n = 3$ — Simplify.

$\frac{2n}{2} = \frac{3}{2}$ — Division Property of Equality

$n = \frac{3}{2}$

Look for these labels:
- View as Components
- Look for Patterns
- Look for Structure
- STRUCTURE
- PATTERNS

56. **MP STRUCTURE** Use the Quadratic Formula and the numbers below to create a quadratic equation with the solutions $x = \frac{3 \pm \sqrt{89}}{10}$.

$\_\_x^2 + \_\_x + \_\_ = 0$

−5	−4	−3	−2	−1
1	2	3	4	5

7

You **Look For and Make Use of Structure** by looking closely to see structure within a mathematical statement, or stepping back for an overview to see how individual parts make one single object.

Math Practice

View as Components
Notice that the function consists of the product of the principal, 100, and a factor independent of the principal, $(1.005)^{12t}$.

SOLUTION

a. $m(t) = P\left(1 + \frac{r}{n}\right)^{nt}$ — Use the compound interest formula.

$= 100\left(1 + \frac{0.06}{12}\right)^{12t}$ — Substitute 100 for *P*, 0.06 for *r*, and 12 for *n*.

$= 100(1.005)^{12t}$ — Simplify.

Work with a partner. Use a p... Record your data in the table.

a. Measure the length of the rope. Describe your measurement.

b. Make a knot in the rope, then measure the length of the rope again. Continue to make identical knots in the rope, measuring the length of the rope after each knot is tied.

Number of knots	Length of rope
0	
1	
2	
3	
4	
5	
6	
7	
8	

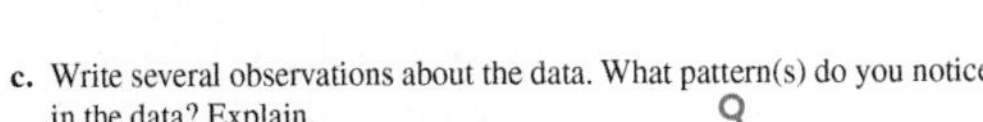

c. Write several observations about the data. What pattern(s) do you notice in the data? Explain.

20. **MP REPEATED REASONING** Use the diagram.

a. Find the perimeter and area of each square.

b. What happens to the area of a square when its perimeter increases by a factor of *n*?

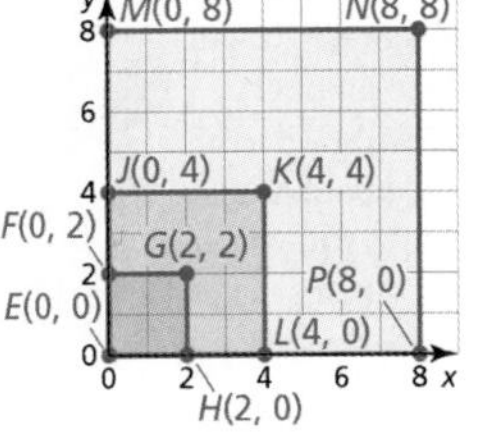

Look for these labels:
- Repeat Calculations
- Find General Methods
- Maintain Oversight
- Evaluate Results
- REPEATED REASONING

When you **Look For and Express Regularity in Repeated Reasoning**, you can notice patterns and make generalizations. Keeping in mind the goal of a problem helps you evaluate reasonableness of answers along the way.

8

The Modeling Process

Modeling Real Life

Learning how to apply the mathematics you learn to model real-life situations is an important part of this course. Here are some ways you may approach the modeling process.

THE PROBLEM-SOLVING PLAN

1. **Understand the Problem**
   Before planning a solution, you must identify what the problem is asking, analyze givens and goals, and think about entry points to a solution.
2. **Make a Plan**
   Plan your solution pathway before jumping in to solve. Identify any variables or relationships and decide on a problem-solving strategy.
   - Use a verbal model
   - Draw a diagram
   - Write an equation
   - Solve a simpler problem
   - Sketch a graph or number line
   - Make a table
   - Make a list
   - Break the problem into parts
3. **Solve and Check**
   As you solve the problem, be sure to monitor and evaluate your progress, and always check your answers. Throughout the problem-solving process, you must continually ask, "Does this make sense?" and be willing to change course if necessary.

66. **PERFORMANCE TASK** The black rhino is a critically endangered species with a current population of about 5500. In the late 1900s, the population decreased by 98% to about 2500. Create a plan to restore the black rhino population. Include the expected annual growth rate and the amount of time it will take to restore the population. Explain how you will determine whether your plan is working over time.

Creating a Model
In a *Performance Task*, you first identify the problem and the variables in a situation and decide what questions to ask or models to create. Any answers you obtain must always be interpreted in the context of the situation to determine whether they are viable.

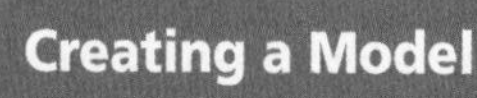

73. **MP PROBLEM SOLVING** When X-rays of a fixed wavelength strike a material x centimeters thick, the intensity $I(x)$ of the X-rays transmitted through the material is given by $I(x) = I_0e^{-\mu x}$, where I_0 is the initial intensity and μ is a value that depends on the type of material and the wavelength of the X-rays. The table shows the values of μ for various materials and X-rays of medium wavelength.

Material	Aluminum	Copper	Lead
Value of μ	0.43	3.2	43

You wear a lead apron to protect you from harmful radiation while your dentist takes X-rays of your teeth. Explain why lead is a better material to use than aluminum or copper.

Interpreting Parameters Within a Context
To be able to interpret the parameters of a situation, you must understand the significance of the variables. Knowing how they relate and affect one another will help you find an entry point and make a plan to solve.

Defining Quantities

In this problem, you know that the side length of the map doubles on each click, and you are given the lengths for the first few clicks. You need to know how many clicks will make the side length 640 miles.

Writing Functions

You know that the side length of the map is related to the number of clicks. Your plan should include writing a function to represent that relationship.

EXAMPLE 5 **Modeling Real Life** 

Clicking the *zoom-out* button on a mapping website doubles the side length of the square map. After how many clicks on the *zoom-out* button is the side length of the map 640 miles?

Zoom-out clicks	1	2	3
Map side length (miles)	5	10	20

SOLUTION

1. **Understand the Problem** You know that the side length of the square map doubles after each click on the *zoom-out* button. So, the side lengths of the map represent the terms of a geometric sequence. You need to find the number of clicks it takes for the side length of the map to be 640 miles.
2. **Make a Plan** Begin by writing a function f for the nth term of the geometric sequence. Then find the value of n for which $f(n) = 640$.
3. **Solve and Check** The first term is 5, and the common ratio is 2.

$f(n) = a_1 r^{n-1}$ Function for a geometric sequence

$f(n) = 5(2)^{n-1}$ Substitute 5 for a_1 and 2 for r.

The function $f(n) = 5(2)^{n-1}$ represents the geometric sequence. Use this function to find the value of n for which $f(n) = 640$. So, use each side of the equation $640 = 5(2)^{n-1}$ to write a function.

$y = 5(2)^{n-1}$

$y = 640$

Then use technology to graph the functions and find the point of intersection. The point of intersection is (8, 640).

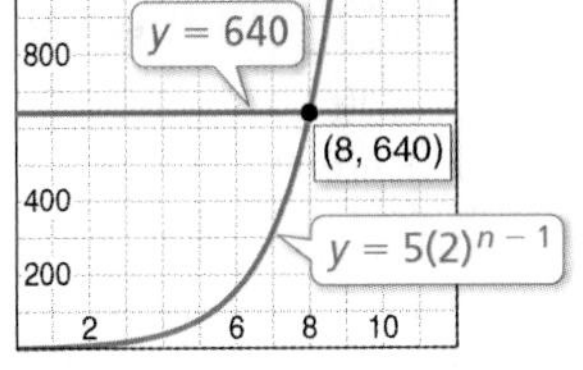

▶ So, after eight clicks, the side length of the map is 640 miles.

Another Method Find the value of n for which $f(n) = 640$ algebraically.

$640 = 5(2)^{n-1}$ Write the equation.

$128 = (2)^{n-1}$ Divide each side by 5.

$2^7 = (2)^{n-1}$ Rewrite 128 as 2^7.

$7 = n - 1$ Equate the exponents.

$8 = n$ ✓ Add 1 to each side.

Analyze Functions Using Different Representations

Graphing your function and the line $y = 640$ allows you to approximate a solution.

Solving an Equation to Solve a Problem

Step 3 of the problem-solving plan must always include checking your results. In this case, you can solve using another method to make sure you get the same answer.

MODELING STANDARDS

For a full list of opportunities to practice all the modeling standards of this course, visit *BigIdeasMath.com*.

How to Use This Program

Scan the QR code on any page to access digital content.

Designed for You

From start to finish, this program was designed with you, the learner, in mind. Let's take a quick tour of a chapter. Look for each **highlighted feature** mentioned below, in your book or online.

GET READY

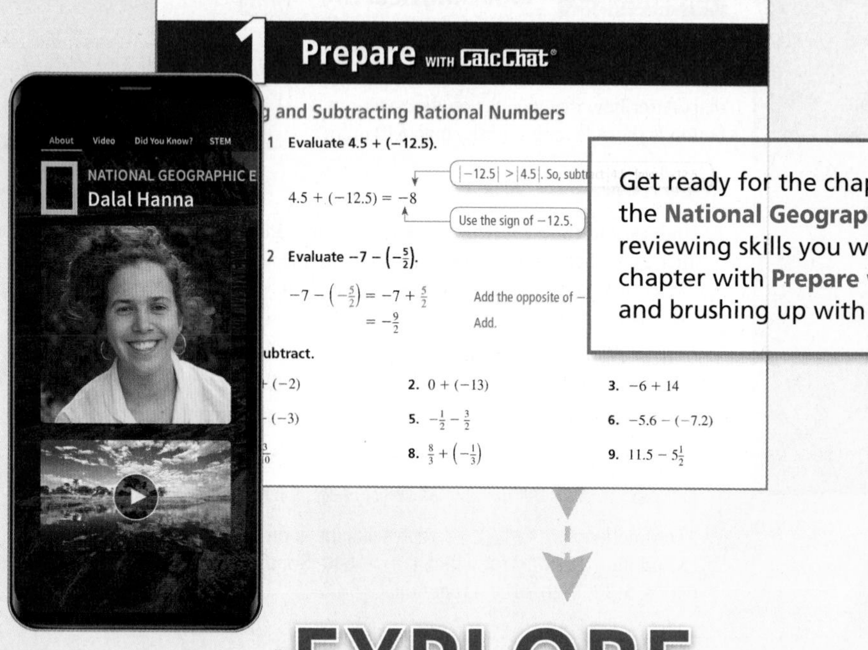

Get ready for the chapter by watching the **National Geographic Explorer** video, reviewing skills you will need for the chapter with **Prepare with CalcChat®**, and brushing up with the **Skills Trainer**.

EXPLORE

Read the **Learning Target and Success Criteria** for each section. Work with a partner to complete the **Explore It!** and discuss the **Math Practice** with your partner.

EXPLORE IT! Reflecting a Polygon

Work with a partner.

a. The diagram shows the *reflection* of $\triangle DEF$ to $\triangle D'E'F'$. How would you define a reflection?

b. Use technology to draw any triangle and label it $\triangle ABC$.

Math Practice

Choose Tools

What other tools can you use to perform reflections of figures?

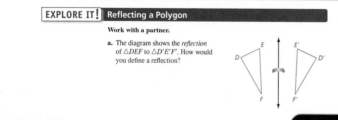

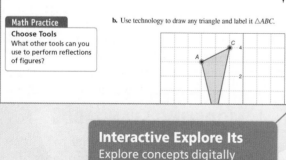

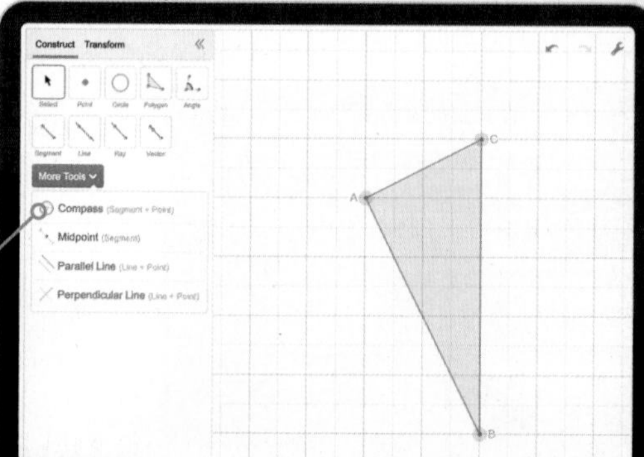

Interactive Explore Its

Explore concepts digitally using **Interactive Tools** in the **Dynamic Student Edition**.

LEARN

Example Support
See a **Digital Example** video of every example in the book, or watch a **Tutorial Video** for a tutor to walk you step-by-step through a similar example.

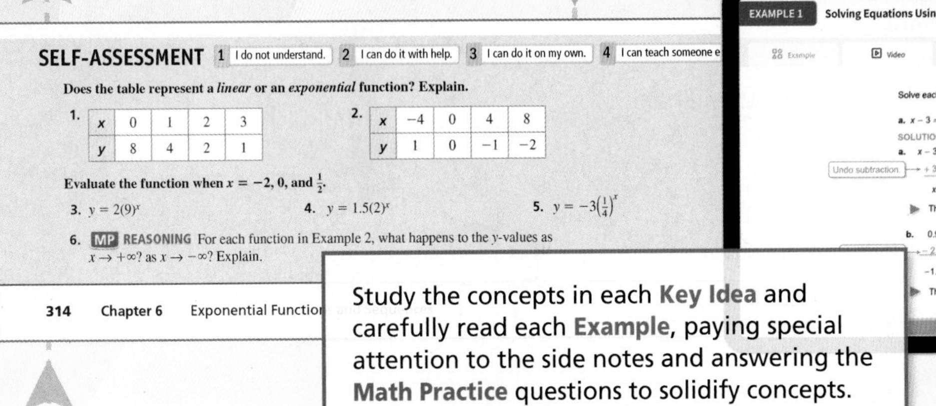

Study the concepts in each **Key Idea** and carefully read each **Example**, paying special attention to the side notes and answering the **Math Practice** questions to solidify concepts. Use the **Self-Assessment** to assess your understanding of the Learning Target and Success Criteria.

PRACTICE and APPLY

In every section, use the **Practice with CalcChat® and CalcView®** to practice and apply your learning and **Review & Refresh** to stay fluent in major topics throughout the course.

At the end of the chapter, use the **Chapter Review with CalcChat®**, take a **Practice Test with CalcChat®**, or complete the **Performance Task** using the concepts of the chapter. Practice questions from current and prior concepts with **College and Career Readiness with CalcChat®** to prepare for high-stakes tests.

How to Study Math

Preparing for College and Career

Math is a cumulative subject. What you learn tomorrow will build on what you learn today. So, to be successful, commit to these positive steps.

- Routinely study
- Practice every day
- Be patient and persevere
- Believe that you can learn

Committing to these habits and mindsets will help you succeed!

In Class

When you are in class, be "all there." Here are some ways to stay focused.

- Actively participate
- Think about what is being said
- Take good notes
- Ask questions

At Home

Practice is an important part of your learning process. Here is where you solidify and apply the concepts you learn.

- Find a quiet location, away from any potential distractions.
- Review your notes and what you learned in class. Talk through them if that helps you remember more.
- Don't be afraid to make mistakes! These are the times that your brain grows and learning happens.
- Lean into challenge. Instead of saying, "I'm not good at this," say, "I can train my brain to figure this out."

Taking Tests

It is completely normal to feel a little nervous about a test! Here are some tips for test-taking success.

Before the test

- Study a little bit each day
- Get a good night's sleep
- Eat breakfast

During the test

- Read the directions and questions carefully
- Answer easy questions first
- Check your work
- Answer every question
- Take your time—You don't have to finish first!
- Take a brain break
- Do your best!

Reinforce Your Studies with CalcChat® and CalcView®

As you complete the exercises throughout the chapter, CalcChat® and CalcView® give you access to solutions and tutor help.

CalcChat®

- View worked-out solutions for select exercises
  - *Prepare with CalcChat®*
  - *Practice with CalcChat® and CalcView®*
  - *Chapter Review with CalcChat®*
  - *Practice Test with CalcChat®*
  - *College and Career Readiness with CalcChat®*
- Chat with a live tutor about the solutions

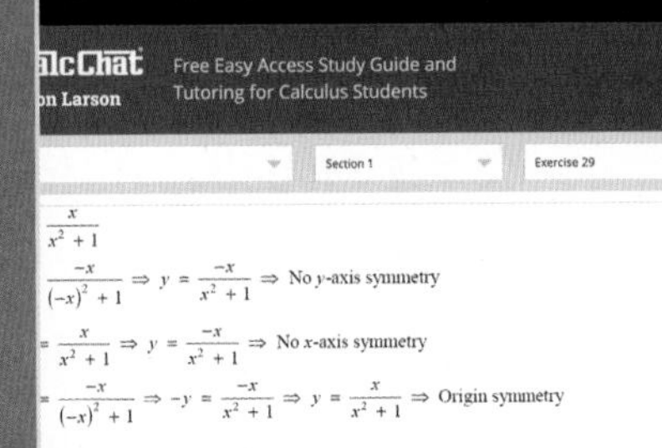

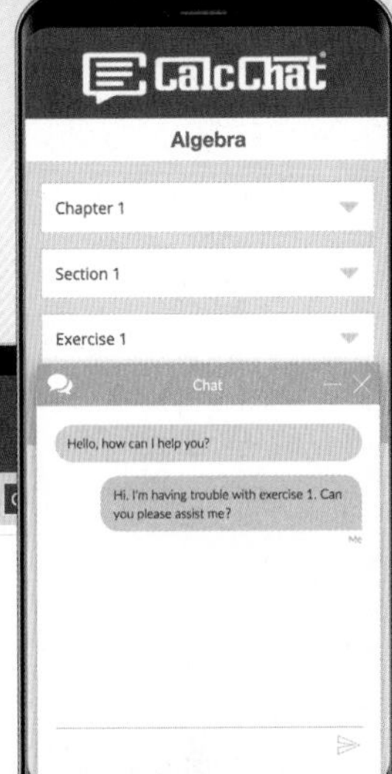

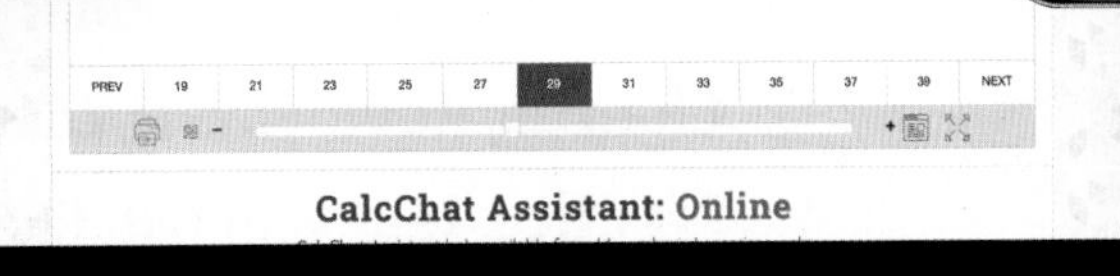

CalcView®

- Watch a video of a worked-out solution for any exercise with a blue exercise number.
- Hear a teacher explain step-by-step how to solve the problem

1.3 Practice WITH CalcChat® AND CalcView®

In Exercises 1–4, solve the proportion.

1. $\frac{x}{6} = \frac{10}{12}$
2. $\frac{36}{8} = \frac{9}{h}$
3. $\frac{13}{p} = \frac{5}{4}$
4. $\frac{4}{15} = \frac{w}{27}$

5. **USING RATIOS** A repairman needs to climb to the top of a building. He takes the measurements shown. The right triangles created by each object and its shadow are similar. Can he use a ladder that reaches heights of up to 28 feet? *Example 1*

In Exercises 13 and 14, complete the statement. Round to the nearest hundredth, if necessary.

13. $\frac{7 \text{ gal}}{\text{min}} \approx \frac{\square \text{ qt}}{\text{sec}}$

14. $\frac{8 \text{ km}}{\text{min}} \approx \frac{\square \text{ mi}}{\text{h}}$

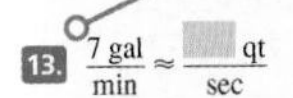

15. **MODELING REAL LIFE** Roller coaster A can reach a top sp... reach... coast...

16. **MOD...** leaks... day. ... of 30... Whic... faste...

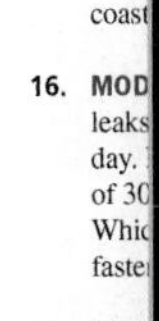

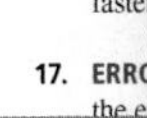

17. **ERRO...** the e...

1 Solving Linear Equations

Water Conservation

Make a plan to conserve water in your own daily life.

Solving Linear Inequalities

2

Mountaineering

Assume the role of an expedition leader and use inequalities to track the progress of climbers on Mount Everest.

3 Graphing Linear Functions

Scuba Diving

Plan a dive by selecting a tank size, depth, and the amount of time you will spend underwater.

Writing Linear Functions

4

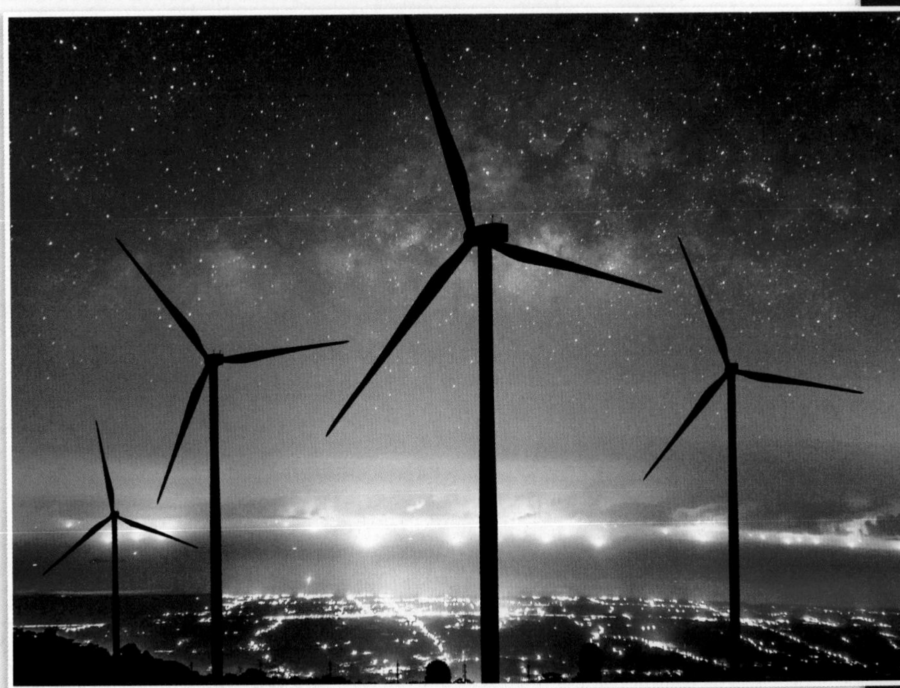

Renewable Energy

Write a proposal for a new wind farm in your community, detailing the size, cost, and energy production of the farm.

5 Solving Systems of Linear Equations

Deep Ocean Exploration

Plan an expedition to the Challenger Deep, including a dive schedule and goals that you hope to accomplish.

Exponential Functions and Sequences

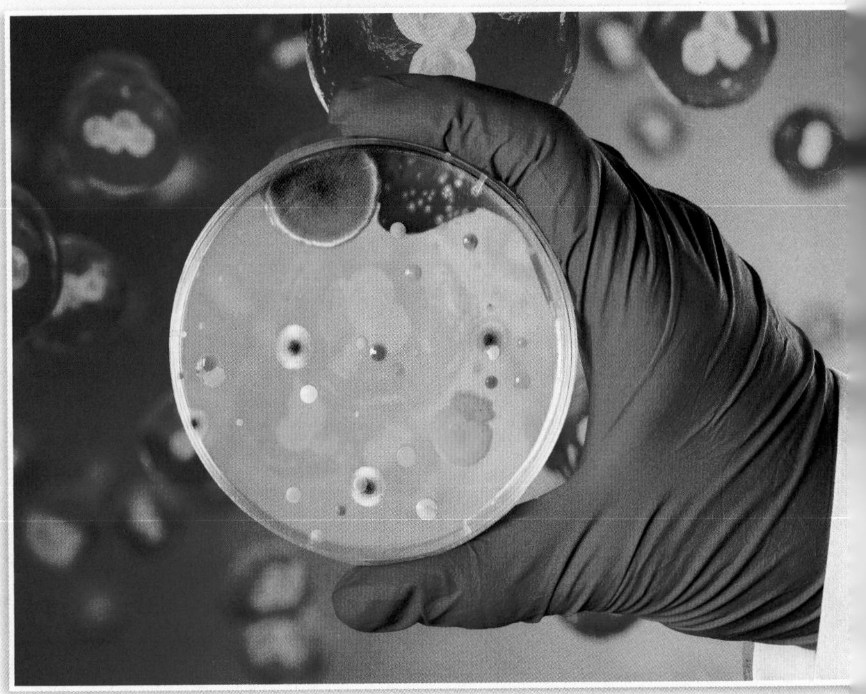

Bacterial and Viral Growth

Write a report for a health organization, forecasting the spread of an Ebola epidemic and recommending steps that can be taken to slow its spread.

7 Polynomial Equations and Factoring

Astronomy
Create a display that demonstrates how gravity affects objects on each planet in our solar system.

Graphing Quadratic Functions

8

Wildlife Conservation

Analyze sea turtle nesting trends in a region. Write a report that includes methods to increase the population.

9 Solving Quadratic Equations

Cosmology

Use a quadratic equation to show the relationship among a star's *luminosity, apparent brightness,* and distance from Earth.

Radical Functions and Equations

10

Marine Conservation

Write a report that describes the *recovery* and *reassembly* of a damaged coral reef.

11 Data Analysis and Displays

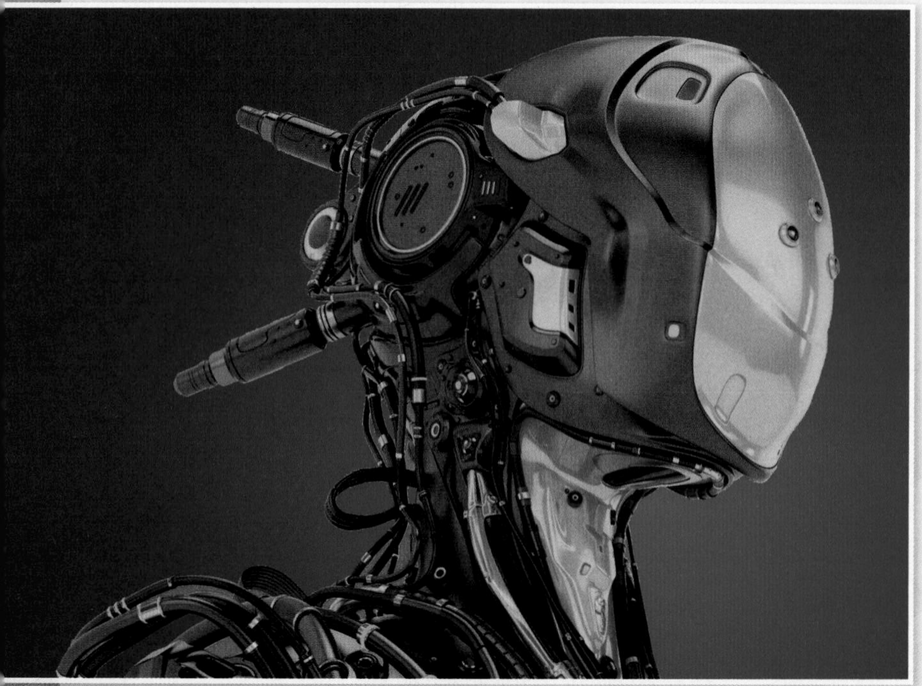

Robotics

Conduct a survey about the use of robotics in everyday life, analyze the data, and use data displays to create a presentation of your findings.

Additional Resources

1 Solving Linear Equations

GO DIGITAL

NATIONAL GEOGRAPHIC EXPLORER

Dalal Hanna

Ecologist Dalal Hanna specializes in how to sustain Earth's environment. She focuses on different ways rivers contribute to human well-being, and has published research on mercury contamination in African freshwater fish. Hanna has also developed the podcast "Science Faction" which explores discoveries in all fields of science.

- What are ways that you can conserve water?
- How much water is used to take a 5-minute shower? a 10-minute shower? a 15-minute shower?
- How much water is conserved if 10,000 people each use 10 fewer gallons of water every month?

STEM

Water conservation is critical for human health and development. In the Performance Task, you will make a plan to conserve water in your own daily life.

Water Conservation

Preparing for Chapter 1

Chapter Learning Target Understand solving linear equations.

Chapter Success Criteria
- ◆ I can solve simple and multi-step equations.
- ◆ I can describe how to solve equations.
- ■ I can analyze the measurements used to solve a problem and judge the level of accuracy appropriate for the solution.
- ■ I can apply equation-solving techniques to solve real-life problems.

◆ Surface
■ Deep

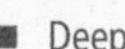

Chapter Vocabulary

Work with a partner. Discuss each of the vocabulary terms.

solution	ratio	rate
equivalent equations	proportion	accuracy

Mathematical Practices

Construct Viable Arguments and Critique the Reasoning of Others

Mathematically proficient students justify conclusions, communicate them to others, and respond to the arguments of others.

Work with a partner. The chart shows the population and the average amount of freshwater used daily in the United States from 1960 to 2015.

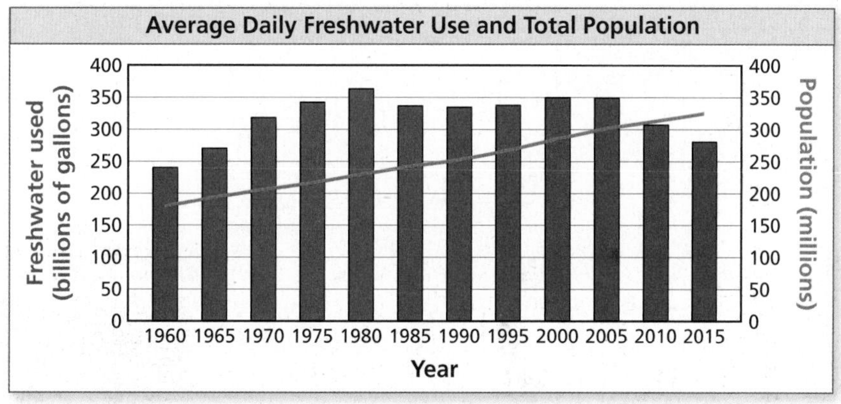

1. Make several observations about the data in the chart.
2. What conclusions can you make about water conservation efforts in the United States? Explain your reasoning to another pair.

1 Prepare WITH CalcChat®

Adding and Subtracting Rational Numbers

Example 1 **Evaluate 4.5 + (−12.5).**

$$4.5 + (-12.5) = -8$$

$|-12.5| > |4.5|$. So, subtract $|4.5|$ from $|-12.5|$.

Use the sign of −12.5.

Example 2 **Evaluate $-7 - \left(-\frac{5}{2}\right)$.**

$-7 - \left(-\frac{5}{2}\right) = -7 + \frac{5}{2}$ Add the opposite of $-\frac{5}{2}$.

$= -\frac{9}{2}$ Add.

Add or subtract.

1. $-5 + (-2)$

2. $0 + (-13)$

3. $-6 + 14$

4. $1.9 - (-3)$

5. $-\frac{1}{2} - \frac{3}{2}$

6. $-5.6 - (-7.2)$

7. $\frac{4}{5} + \frac{3}{10}$

8. $\frac{8}{3} + \left(-\frac{1}{3}\right)$

9. $11.5 - 5\frac{1}{2}$

Multiplying and Dividing Rational Numbers

Example 3 **Evaluate −3.5 • (−5).**

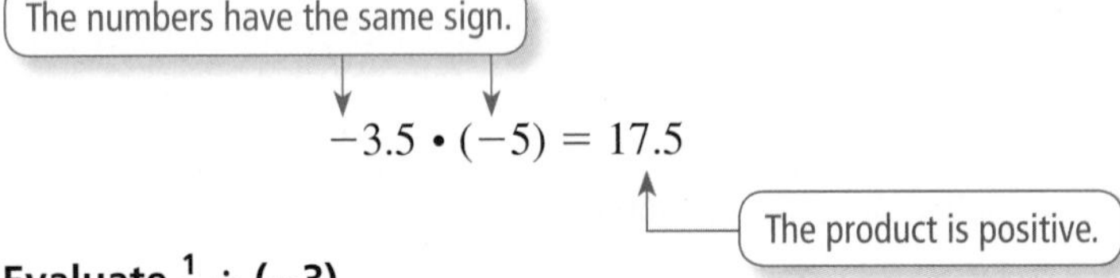

The product is positive.

Example 4 **Evaluate $\frac{1}{5} \div (-3)$.**

The numbers have different signs.

$$\frac{1}{5} \div (-3) = -\frac{1}{15}$$

The quotient is negative.

Multiply or divide.

10. $-3(8)$

11. $-7 \cdot (-9)$

12. $4 \cdot (-7)$

13. $-\frac{1}{4} \div (-6)$

14. $-1.6 \div 2$

15. $1.2 \div (-3)$

16. $\frac{3}{4} \cdot \frac{1}{2}$

17. $\frac{4}{3} \div \frac{4}{9}$

18. $-3.5(-4.25)$

19. **MP LOGIC** Describe the signs of two rational numbers when (a) their sum is positive, (b) their product is positive, and (c) their quotient is positive. Give examples to support your answers.

1.1 Solving Simple Equations

Learning Target Write and solve one-step linear equations.

Success Criteria

- I can apply properties of equality to produce equivalent equations.
- I can solve linear equations using addition, subtraction, multiplication, or division.
- I can write linear equations that model real-life situations.

EXPLORE IT! Modeling a Real-Life Problem

Work with a partner. The Okavango Delta is the largest freshwater wetland in southern Africa and is the main source of water for one million people.

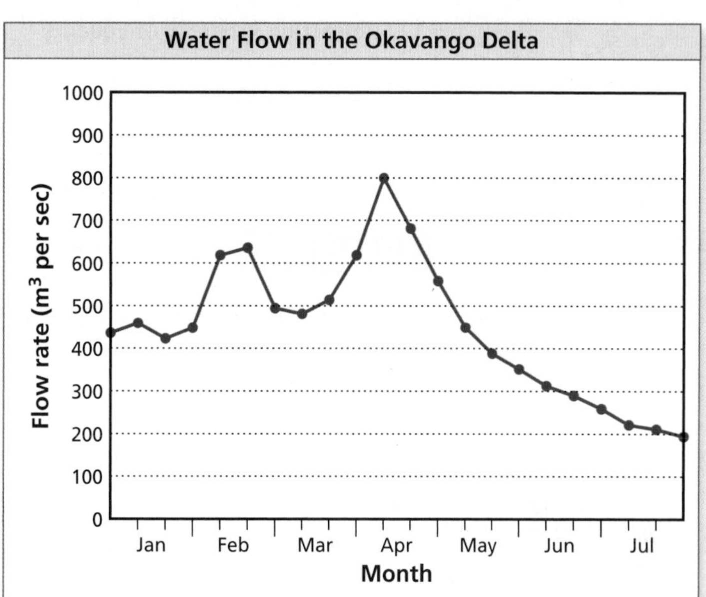

Math Practice

Use a Graph

How can you use the graph to determine the quantities involved and the relationship between the quantities?

a. What does the graph show? Make several observations from the graph.

b. When the water flow was at its peak, about how long did it take 100,000 cubic meters of water to flow past a point in the Okavango Delta? Explain your reasoning.

c. Your friend uses an equation to answer part (b) as shown. Is your friend's reasoning valid? Explain.

$$f = 800t$$

$$100{,}000 = 800t$$

$$\frac{100{,}000}{800} = t$$

$$\frac{1000}{8} = t$$

$$125 \text{ sec} = t \qquad m^3 \div \frac{m^3}{\text{sec}} = m^3 \times \frac{\text{sec}}{m^3} = \text{sec}$$

Solving Equations Using Addition or Subtraction

Vocabulary

equation, *p. 4*
linear equation in one variable, *p. 4*
solution, *p. 4*
equivalent equations, *p. 4*

An **equation** is a statement that two expressions are equal. A **linear equation in one variable** is an equation that can be written in the form $ax + b = 0$, where a and b are constants and $a \neq 0$. When you *solve an equation*, you use properties of real numbers to find a **solution**, which is a value that makes the equation true.

Equivalent equations are equations that have the same solution(s). When you perform the same operation on each side of an equation, you produce an equivalent equation.

KEY IDEA

Addition, Subtraction, and Substitution Properties of Equality

Adding or subtracting the same number on each side of an equation produces an equivalent equation.

Addition Property of Equality If $a = b$, then $a + c = b + c$.

Subtraction Property of Equality If $a = b$, then $a - c = b - c$.

Substitution Property of Equality If $a = b$, then a can be substituted for b (or b for a) in any equation or expression.

REMEMBER

Two operations that undo each other, such as addition and subtraction, are *inverse operations*. Use inverse operations to isolate the variable.

EXAMPLE 1 Solving Equations Using Addition or Subtraction

Solve each equation. Justify each step. Check your solution.

a. $x - 3 = -5$ **b.** $0.9 = y + 2.8$

SOLUTION

a. $x - 3 = -5$ Write the equation.

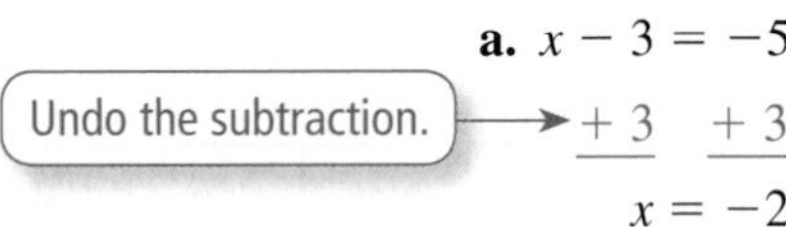

$\underline{+3}\quad\underline{+3}$ Addition Property of Equality

$x = -2$ Simplify.

▶ The solution is $x = -2$.

Check

$x - 3 = -5$

$-2 - 3 \stackrel{?}{=} -5$

$-5 = -5$ ✓

b. $0.9 = y + 2.8$ Write the equation.

Undo the addition. $\underline{-2.8}\quad\underline{-2.8}$ Subtraction Property of Equality

$-1.9 = y$ Simplify.

▶ The solution is $y = -1.9$.

Check

$0.9 = y + 2.8$

$0.9 \stackrel{?}{=} -1.9 + 2.8$

$0.9 = 0.9$ ✓

SELF-ASSESSMENT

1 I do not understand. 2 I can do it with help. 3 I can do it on my own. 4 I can teach someone else.

Solve the equation. Justify each step. Check your solution.

1. $n + 3 = -7$ **2.** $g - \frac{1}{3} = -\frac{2}{3}$ **3.** $-6.5 = p + 3.9$

4. VOCABULARY Are the equations $6x = -5$ and $-1 = 6x + 4$ equivalent? Explain your reasoning.

Solving Equations Using Multiplication or Division

KEY IDEA

Multiplication and Division Properties of Equality

Multiplying or dividing each side of an equation by the same nonzero number produces an equivalent equation.

Multiplication Property of Equality If $a = b$, then $a \cdot c = b \cdot c, c \neq 0$.

Division Property of Equality If $a = b$, then $\frac{a}{c} = \frac{b}{c}, c \neq 0$.

REMEMBER
Multiplication and division are inverse operations.

EXAMPLE 2 Solving Equations Using Multiplication or Division

Solve each equation. Justify each step. Check your solution.

a. $-\frac{n}{5} = -3$ **b.** $\pi x = -2\pi$ **c.** $1.3z = 5.2$

SOLUTION

a. $-\frac{n}{5} = -3$ Write the equation.

Undo the division. → $-5 \cdot \left(-\frac{n}{5}\right) = -5 \cdot (-3)$ Multiplication Property of Equality

$n = 15$ Simplify.

▶ The solution is $n = 15$.

Check
$-\frac{n}{5} = -3$
$-\frac{15}{3} \stackrel{?}{=} -3$
$-3 = -3$ ✓

b. $\pi x = -2\pi$ Write the equation.

Undo the multiplication. → $\frac{\pi x}{\pi} = \frac{-2\pi}{\pi}$ Division Property of Equality

$x = -2$ Simplify.

▶ The solution is $x = -2$.

Check
$\pi x = -2\pi$
$\pi(-2) \stackrel{?}{=} -2\pi$
$-2\pi = -2\pi$ ✓

c. $1.3z = 5.2$ Write the equation.

Undo the multiplication. → $\frac{1.3z}{1.3} = \frac{5.2}{1.3}$ Division Property of Equality

$z = 4$ Simplify.

▶ The solution is $z = 4$.

Check
$1.3z = 5.2$
$1.3(4) \stackrel{?}{=} 5.2$
$5.2 = 5.2$ ✓

SELF-ASSESSMENT 1 I do not understand. 2 I can do it with help. 3 I can do it on my own. 4 I can teach someone else.

Solve the equation. Justify each step. Check your solution.

5. $\frac{y}{3} = -6$ **6.** $z \div 25 = -4.5$ **7.** $9\pi = \pi x$ **8.** $0.05w = 1.4$

9. WHICH ONE DOESN'T BELONG? Which equation does not belong with the other three? Explain your reasoning.

$8 = \frac{x}{2}$ $3 = x \div 4$ $x - 6 = 5$ $\frac{x}{3} = 9$

Solving Real-Life Problems

KEY IDEA

Problem-Solving Plan

1. **Understand the Problem** What is the unknown? What information is given? What is being asked?
2. **Make a Plan** Decide how you will solve the problem. Your plan might involve one or more of the problem-solving strategies shown on the next page.
3. **Solve and Check** Carry out your plan. Examine your solution. Then check that your solution makes sense in the original statement of the problem.

EXAMPLE 3 Modeling Real Life

In the 2016 Olympics, Usain Bolt won the 200-meter dash with a time of 19.78 seconds. Find his average speed to the nearest hundredth of a meter per second.

SOLUTION

1. **Understand the Problem** You know the winning time and the distance of the race. You are asked to find his average speed.
2. **Make a Plan** Use the Distance Formula to write an equation that represents the problem. Then solve the equation.
3. **Solve and Check**

REMEMBER
The formula that relates distance d, rate or speed r, and time t is

$d = rt$.

$d = r \cdot t$ Write the Distance Formula.

$200 = r \cdot 19.78$ Substitute 200 for d and 19.78 for t.

$\frac{200}{19.78} = \frac{19.78r}{19.78}$ Division Property of Equality

$10.11 \approx r$ Simplify.

REMEMBER
The symbol $\approx$ means "approximately equal to."

▶ Bolt's average speed was about 10.11 meters per second.

Check Reasonableness Round Bolt's average speed to 10 meters per second. At this speed, it would take

$$200 \text{ m} \div \frac{10 \text{ m}}{1 \text{ sec}} = 200 \cancel{\text{m}} \times \frac{1 \text{ sec}}{10 \cancel{\text{m}}} = 20 \text{ sec}$$

to run 200 meters. Because 20 is close to 19.78, your solution is reasonable.

SELF-ASSESSMENT 1 I do not understand. 2 I can do it with help. 3 I can do it on my own. 4 I can teach someone else.

10. In 2015, an autonomous vehicle drove from the Golden Gate Bridge to New York City at an average speed of 15.7 miles per hour. The journey took 9 days. About how far did the vehicle travel?

11. In the 2012 Olympics, Usain Bolt ran the 200-meter dash at an average speed of about 10.35 meters per second. Was he faster in 2012 or in 2016? By how many seconds?

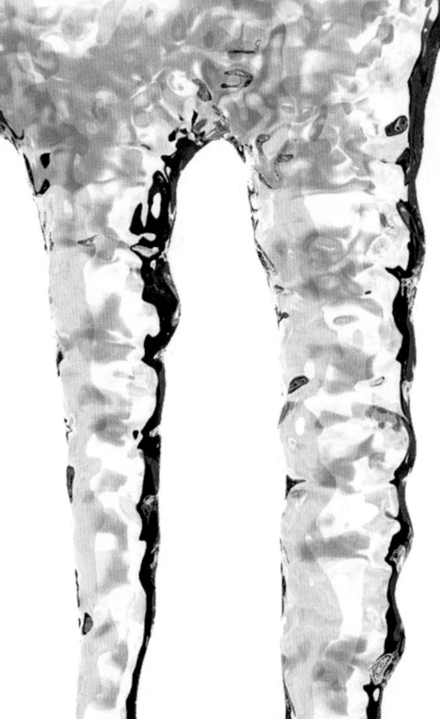

KEY IDEA

Common Problem-Solving Strategies

Use a verbal model.	Guess, check, and revise.
Draw a diagram.	Sketch a graph or number line.
Write an equation.	Make a table.
Look for a pattern.	Make a list.
Work backward.	Break the problem into parts.

EXAMPLE 4 Modeling Real Life

On January 22, 1943, the temperature in Spearfish, South Dakota, fell from 54°F at 9:00 A.M. to −4°F at 9:27 A.M. How many degrees did the temperature fall?

SOLUTION

1. **Understand the Problem** You know the temperature before and after the temperature fell. You are asked to find how many degrees the temperature fell.
2. **Make a Plan** Use a verbal model to write an equation that represents the problem. Then solve the equation.
3. **Solve and Check**

Verbal Model Temperature at 9:27 A.M. = Temperature at 9:00 A.M. − Number of degrees the temperature fell

Variable Let T be the number of degrees Fahrenheit the temperature fell.

Equation $-4 \quad = \quad 54 \quad - \quad T$

$-4 = 54 - T$ Write the equation.

$-4 - 54 = 54 - 54 - T$ Subtraction Property of Equality

$-58 = -T$ Simplify.

$58 = T$ Divide each side by −1.

▶ The temperature fell 58°F.

Check The temperature fell from 54 degrees *above* 0 to 4 degrees *below* 0. You can use a number line to check your solution.

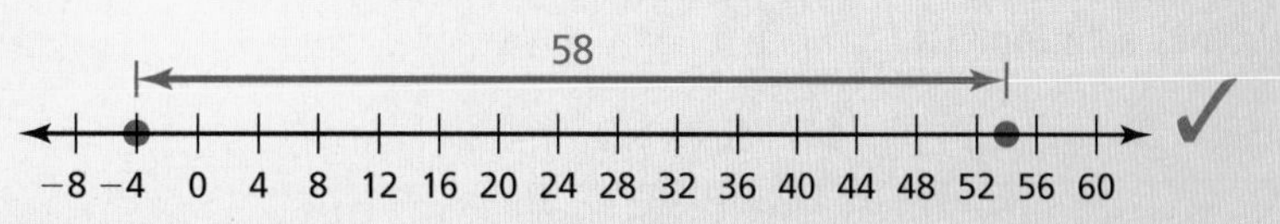

SELF-ASSESSMENT

1 I do not understand. 2 I can do it with help. 3 I can do it on my own. 4 I can teach someone else.

12. You thought the balance in your savings account was \$68.33, but you forgot to record a withdrawal. Your statement lists your balance as \$26.33. How much was the withdrawal that you forgot to record?

13. In one year, a bluefin tuna releases 300% more eggs than an Atlantic sturgeon. The bluefin tuna releases about 10,000,000 eggs. About how many eggs does the Atlantic sturgeon release?

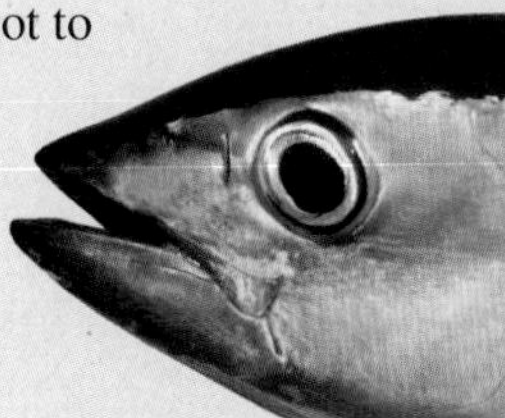

1.1 Practice WITH CalcChat® AND CalcView®

In Exercises 1–10, solve the equation. Justify each step. Check your solution. *Example 1*

1. $x + 5 = 8$
2. $m + 9 = 2$
3. $y - 4 = 3$
4. $s - 2 = 1$
5. $w + 3 = -4$
6. $n - 6 = -7$
7. $5.2 = a - 0.4$
8. $1.7 = 3.1 + c$
9. $\frac{3}{2} + t = \frac{1}{2}$
10. $z - \frac{3}{4} = -\frac{1}{3}$

11. **MODELING REAL LIFE** An amusement park offers a ticket for \$12.95 off the original price p. Write and solve an equation to find the original price.

12. **MODELING REAL LIFE** You and a friend are playing a board game. Your final score x is 12 points less than your friend's final score. Write and solve an equation to find your final score.

	ROUND 9	ROUND 10	FINAL SCORE
Your Friend	22	12	195
You	9	25	?

In Exercises 13–22, solve the equation. Justify each step. Check your solution. *Example 2*

13. $5g = 20$
14. $4q = 52$
15. $p \div 5 = 3$
16. $y \div 7 = 1$
17. $-54 = 9s$
18. $\frac{w}{-3} = 6$
19. $-\frac{x}{6} = 1.4$
20. $-7.8 = -2.6t$
21. $-108\pi = 9\pi r$
22. $5 = \frac{h}{4\pi}$

In Exercises 23–32, solve the equation. Check your solution.

23. $-14 = p - 11$
24. $0 = 4 + q$
25. $-8r = 64$
26. $x \div (-2) = 8$
27. $\frac{3}{7}m = 6$
28. $-\frac{2}{5}y = 4$
29. $-3.8 = d \div 1.5$
30. $2a = \frac{1}{5}$
31. $f + 3\pi = 7\pi$
32. $-3\frac{1}{6} = k - \frac{2}{3}$

ERROR ANALYSIS In Exercises 33 and 34, describe and correct the error in solving the equation.

33.

$$-0.8 + r = 12.6$$
$$r = 12.6 + (-0.8)$$
$$r = 11.8$$

34.

$$-\frac{m}{3} = -4$$
$$3 \cdot \left(-\frac{m}{3}\right) = 3 \cdot (-4)$$
$$m = -12$$

MP USING TOOLS The sum of the angle measures of a quadrilateral is 360°. In Exercises 35 and 36, write and solve an equation to find the value of x. Use a protractor to check the reasonableness of your answer.

35.

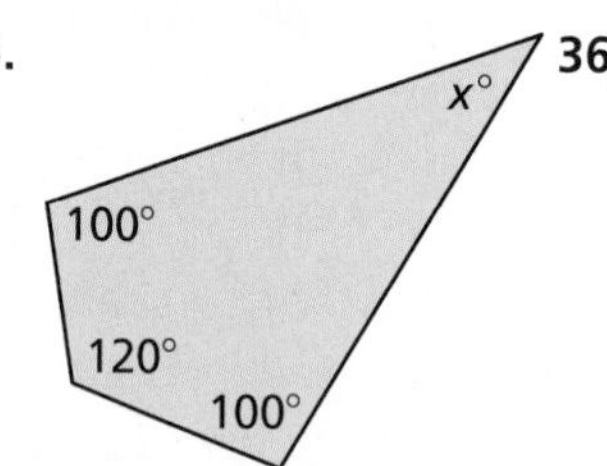

36.

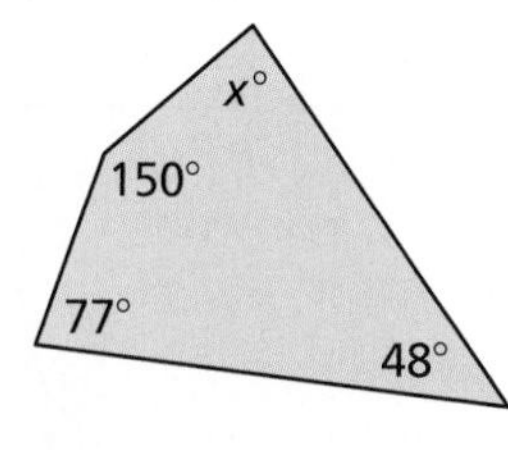

37. **COLLEGE PREP** A baker orders 162 eggs. Each carton contains 18 eggs. Which equation can you use to find the number x of cartons? Explain your reasoning and solve the equation.

Ⓐ $162x = 18$ Ⓑ $\frac{x}{18} = 162$

Ⓒ $18x = 162$ Ⓓ $x + 18 = 162$

38. **MP REASONING** Are the equations equivalent? Explain.

Equation 1	$x - \frac{1}{2} = \frac{x}{4} + 3$
Equation 2	$4x - 2 = x + 12$

MODELING REAL LIFE In Exercises 39–42, write and solve an equation to answer the question.
Examples 3 and 4

39. A swimmer wins the 50-yard freestyle with a time of 24.76 seconds. Find the swimmer's average speed to the nearest hundredth of a yard per second.

40. The length of an American flag is 1.9 times its width. What is the width of the flag?

9.5 ft

41. The temperature at 5 P.M. is 20°F. The temperature at 10 P.M. is −5°F. How many degrees did the temperature fall?

42. The balance of an investment account is $308.32 greater than the balance 4 years ago. The current balance is $4708.57. What was the balance 4 years ago?

43. **MP PROBLEM SOLVING** You spend $8.64 on 12 cans of cat food. Each can costs the same amount and is on sale for 80% of the original price. The following week, the cans are no longer on sale. You have $10. Can you buy 12 more cans? Explain your reasoning.

44. **DIG DEEPER** Tatami mats are used as a floor covering in Japan. One possible layout uses four identical rectangular mats and one square mat, as shown. The area of the square mat is half the area of one of the rectangular mats. The length of a rectangular mat is twice the width. Find the dimensions of one rectangular mat. Justify your answer.

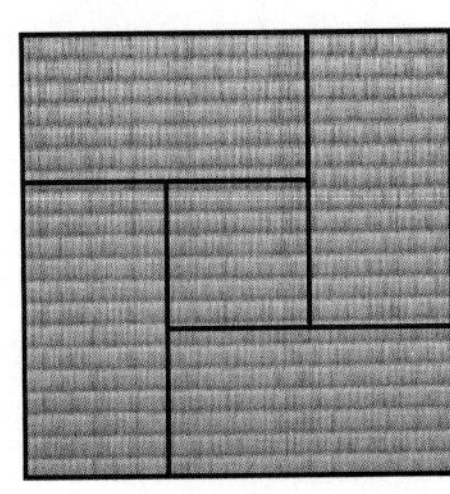
Total area = 81 ft^2

CONNECTING CONCEPTS In Exercises 45–48, find the height h or the area B of the base of the solid.

45.

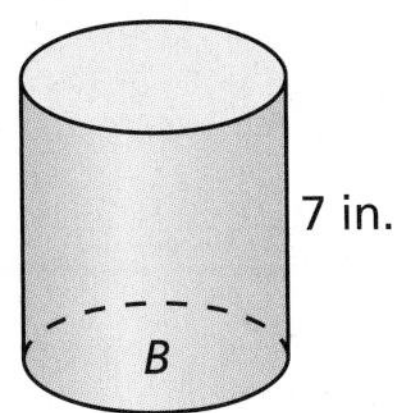

Volume = 84π in.^{3}

46.

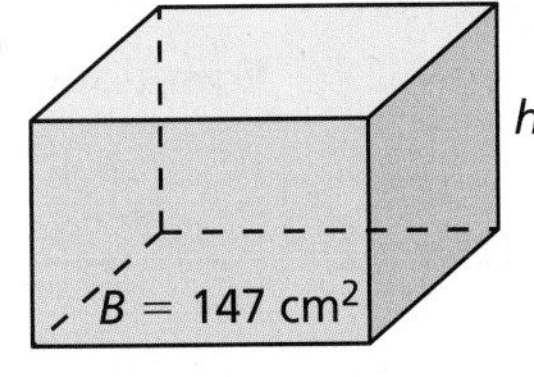

Volume = 1323 cm^3

47.

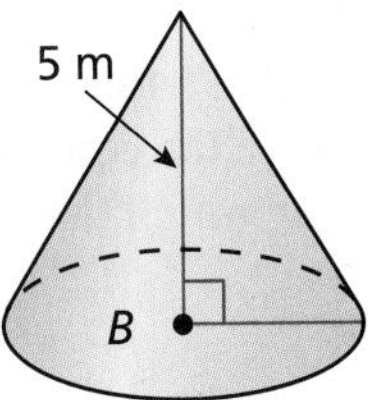

Volume = 15π m^3

48.

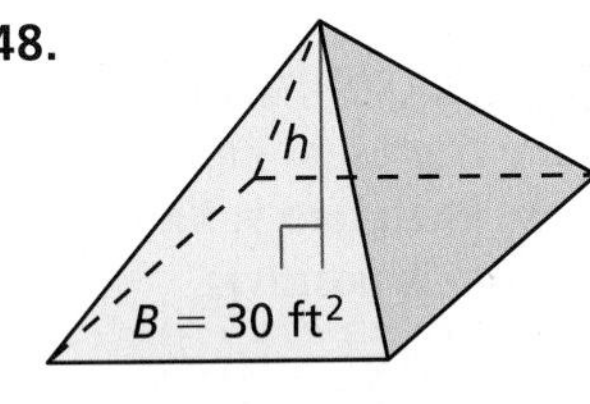

Volume = 35 ft^3

49. **MP STRUCTURE** Use the values −2, 5, 9, and 10 to complete each statement about the equation $ax = b - 5$.

   a. When a = ___ and b = ___, x is a positive integer.

   b. When a = ___ and b = ___, x is a negative integer.

50. **HOW DO YOU SEE IT?**
The circle graph shows the adoptions from a local animal shelter in 1 year. How does the equation $7 + 9 + 5 + 48 + x = 100$ relate to the circle graph? How can you use this equation to find the percent of adoptions that were cats?

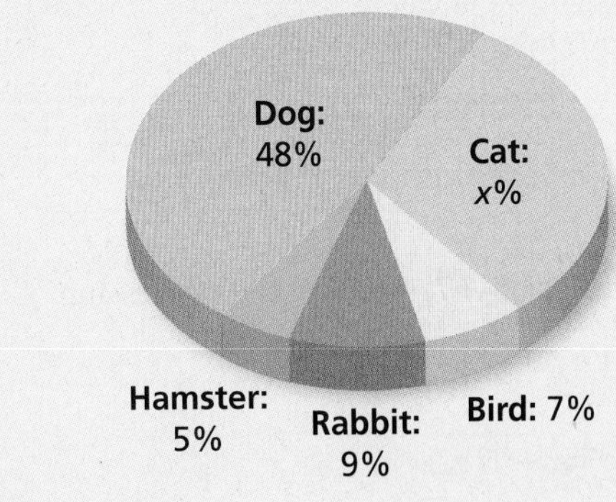

51. **MP REASONING** One-sixth of the girls and two-sevenths of the boys in a school marching band are in the percussion section. The percussion section has 6 girls and 10 boys. How many students are in the marching band? Explain.

52. **ANALYZING RELATIONSHIPS** As c increases, does the value of x *increase, decrease,* or *stay the same* for each equation? Assume c is positive.

Equation	Value of x
$x - c = 0$	
$cx = 1$	
$cx = c$	
$\frac{x}{c} = 1$	

MP REASONING **In Exercises 53–56, the letters a, b, and c represent nonzero constants. Solve the equation for x. Then find values of a, b, and c for which the solution is positive.**

53. $bx = -7$

54. $x + a = \frac{3}{4}$

55. $-\frac{x}{c} = 6.5$

56. $\frac{c}{a}x = -b$

57. **MAKING AN ARGUMENT** In baseball, you calculate a player's batting average by dividing the number of hits by the number of at-bats.

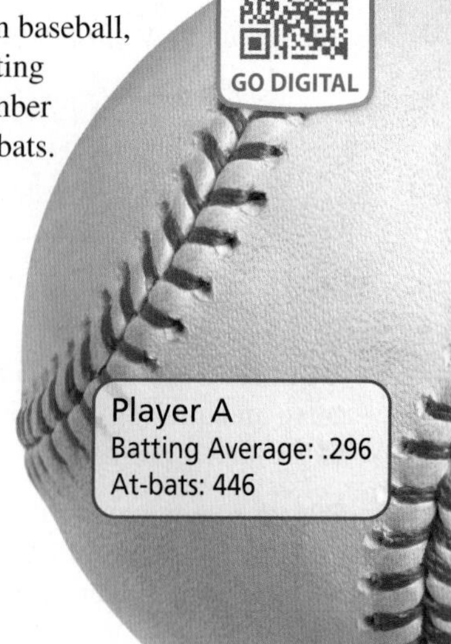

a. How many hits does Player A have?

b. Player B has 33 fewer hits than Player A but has a greater batting average. Your friend concludes that Player B has more at-bats than Player A. Is your friend correct? Explain.

Player A
Batting Average: .296
At-bats: 446

58. **THOUGHT PROVOKING**

Find the value of N such that $x - N = \frac{57}{10}$ and $\frac{x}{N} = -2.8$ are equivalent equations.

REVIEW & REFRESH

WATCH

In Exercises 59–62, multiply or divide.

59. $\frac{3}{5} \cdot \frac{4}{9}$

60. $2\frac{1}{8} \cdot \frac{2}{3}$

61. $\frac{3}{4} \div \frac{9}{10}$

62. $4\frac{1}{3} \div 1\frac{2}{5}$

63. Evaluate $15 - 6(7 + 5) \div 3^2$.

64. Find the missing values in the ratio table. Then write the equivalent ratios.

Calories	50		200	25
Servings	$\frac{1}{2}$	$\frac{3}{2}$		

In Exercises 65–67, simplify the expression.

65. $-5.9x - 4 + 2.3x - 6$

66. $4(-6m + 7)$

67. $-\frac{1}{3}(9y - 12) + 5y$

68. **MODELING REAL LIFE** You have 63 red roses and 45 white roses to make floral arrangements. Each arrangement must be identical. What is the greatest number of arrangements you can make using every flower?

69. Write $\frac{7}{9}$ as a decimal and a percent.

70. **MODELING REAL LIFE** A pizza shop charges \$10.99 for a large cheese pizza and \$1.50 for each topping. Write an expression that represents the cost (in dollars) of a large pizza with n toppings. How much does a large three-topping pizza cost?

71. The expression $14x + 3$ represents the perimeter of the triangle. What is the length of the third side?

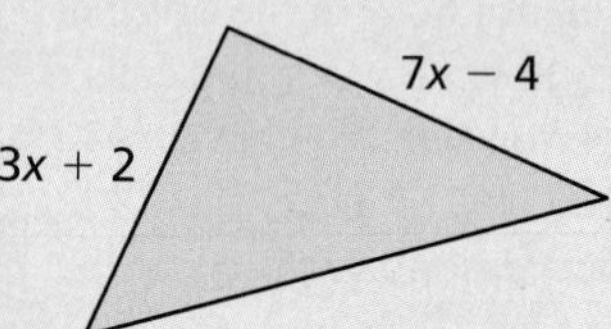

In Exercises 72–75, solve the equation. Justify each step. Check your solution.

72. $7 + x = -5$

73. $-\frac{b}{9} = 3$

74. $-1.8t = -4.5$

75. $w - \frac{1}{4} = -\frac{5}{6}$

76. Find the mean of the data.

Data usage (gigabytes)			
2.5	1.7	3.6	5.4
3.2	1.5	1.8	2.8
4.8	3.5	3.1	4.5

1.2 Solving Multi-Step Equations

Learning Target Write and solve multi-step linear equations.

Success Criteria
- I can apply more than one property of equality to produce equivalent equations.
- I can solve multi-step linear equations using inverse operations.
- I can write multi-step linear equations that model real-life situations.

EXPLORE IT! Solving a Real-Life Problem

Work with a partner. You earn \$9.75 per hour at your part-time job. Your paycheck for last week is shown.

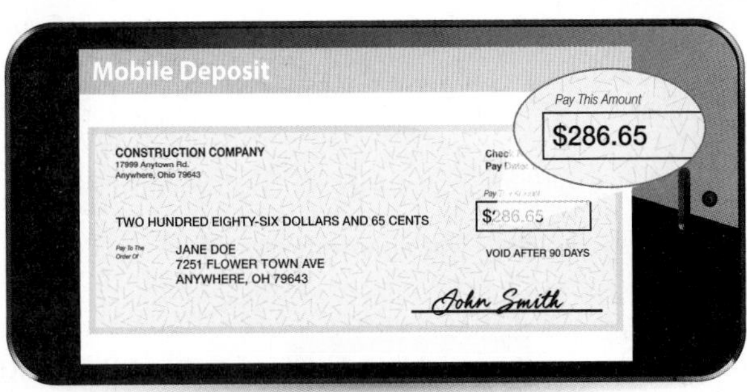

a. How many hours did you work last week? Explain how you found your answer.

b. This week you earn the same amount as last week, but that amount includes \$39 that you earn babysitting. Without solving, determine whether you work more hours at your part-time job this week than last week. Explain your reasoning.

c. Find the number of hours you work this week at your part-time job. Show two different ways to solve.

d. The equation below represents the amount of money you will earn next week. Let h represent the number of hours you work this week.

$$9.75(h + 6) + 39 = 345.15$$

Explain what each part of the equation represents.

i. $h + 6$ **ii.** $9.75(h + 6)$ **iii.** 39

e. Solve the equation in part (d) three different ways using each of the following as the first step.

i. Subtract 39 from each side.

ii. Subtract 345.15 from each side.

iii. Divide each side by 9.75.

Compare the solution methods. Is one solution method more efficient than the other solution methods? Explain your reasoning.

Math Practice

Maintain Oversight
Does it matter which step you perform first when solving?

Solving Multi-Step Linear Equations

KEY IDEA

Solving Multi-Step Equations

To solve a multi-step equation, simplify each side of the equation, if necessary. Then use inverse operations to isolate the variable.

EXAMPLE 1 Solving a Two-Step Equation

Solve $2.5x - 13 = 2$. Check your solution.

SOLUTION

	$2.5x - 13 = 2$	Write the equation.
Undo the subtraction. →	$+13 \quad +13$	Addition Property of Equality
	$2.5x = 15$	Simplify.
Undo the multiplication. →	$\dfrac{2.5x}{2.5} = \dfrac{15}{2.5}$	Division Property of Equality
	$x = 6$	Simplify.

▶ The solution is $x = 6$.

Check

$$2.5x - 13 = 2$$
$$2.5(6) - 13 \stackrel{?}{=} 2$$
$$2 = 2 \checkmark$$

EXAMPLE 2 Combining Like Terms to Solve an Equation

Solve $-12 = 9x - 6x + 15$. Check your solution.

SOLUTION

	$-12 = 9x - 6x + 15$	Write the equation.
	$-12 = 3x + 15$	Combine like terms.
Undo the addition. →	$-15 \quad -15$	Subtraction Property of Equality
	$-27 = 3x$	Simplify.
Undo the multiplication. →	$\dfrac{-27}{3} = \dfrac{3x}{3}$	Division Property of Equality
	$-9 = x$	Simplify.

▶ The solution is $x = -9$.

Check

$$-12 = 9x - 6x + 15$$
$$-12 \stackrel{?}{=} 9(-9) - 6(-9) + 15$$
$$-12 = -12 \checkmark$$

SELF-ASSESSMENT

1 I do not understand. 2 I can do it with help. 3 I can do it on my own. 4 I can teach someone else.

Solve the equation. Check your solution.

1. $-2n + 3 = 9$
2. $-21.5 = \frac{1}{2}c - 11$
3. $-2x - 10x + 12 = 18$
4. **COMPLETE THE SENTENCE** To solve the equation $2x + 3x + 5 = 20$, your friend first combines $2x$ and $3x$ because they are _________.
5. **MP REASONING** In Example 2, explain how you know that $-12 = 9x - 6x + 15$ and $-27 = 3x$ have the same solution.

EXAMPLE 3 Using Structure to Solve a Multi-Step Equation

Solve $2(1 - x) + 3 = -8$. Check your solution.

SOLUTION

Method 1 One way to solve the equation is by using the Distributive Property.

$2(1 - x) + 3 = -8$	Write the equation.
$2(1) - 2(x) + 3 = -8$	Distributive Property
$2 - 2x + 3 = -8$	Multiply.
$-2x + 5 = -8$	Combine like terms.
$\underline{-5} \quad \underline{-5}$	Subtraction Property of Equality
$-2x = -13$	Simplify.
$\frac{-2x}{-2} = \frac{-13}{-2}$	Division Property of Equality
$x = 6.5$	Simplify.

▶ The solution is $x = 6.5$.

Check

$2(1 - x) + 3 = -8$

$2(1 - 6.5) + 3 \stackrel{?}{=} -8$

$-8 = -8$ ✓

REMEMBER

The Distributive Property states the following for real numbers *a*, *b*, and *c*.

Sum

$a(b + c) = ab + ac$

Difference

$a(b - c) = ab - ac$

Method 2 Another way to solve the equation is by interpreting the expression $1 - x$ as a single quantity.

$2(1 - x) + 3 = -8$	Write the equation.
$\underline{-3} \quad \underline{-3}$	Subtraction Property of Equality
$2(1 - x) = -11$	Simplify.
$\frac{2(1 - x)}{2} = \frac{-11}{2}$	Division Property of Equality
$1 - x = -5.5$	Simplify.
$\underline{-1} \quad \underline{-1}$	Subtraction Property of Equality
$-x = -6.5$	Simplify.
$\frac{-x}{-1} = \frac{-6.5}{-1}$	Division Property of Equality
$x = 6.5$	Simplify.

▶ The solution is $x = 6.5$.

Math Practice

Look for Structure

Explain why it is convenient to first solve for the expression $1 - x$, and then solve for *x*. How else could you solve the equation?

SELF-ASSESSMENT

1 I do not understand. 2 I can do it with help. 3 I can do it on my own. 4 I can teach someone else.

Solve the equation. Check your solution.

6. $3(x + 1) + 6 = -9$

7. $17 = 7 + 4(2.2d - 8.5)$

8. $13 = -2(y - 4) + 3y$

9. $2x(5 - 3) - 3x = 5$

10. $-4(2m + 5) - \frac{3}{4}m = 22$

11. $5(3 - x) + 2(3 - x) = 14$

12. MP **REASONING** Solve $2(4x - 11) = 10$ in as many ways as you can. Construct a viable argument to justify each of your solution methods.

Solving Real-Life Problems

EXAMPLE 4 Modeling Real Life

Use the table to find the number of miles you need to bike on Friday so that the mean number of miles biked per day is 5.

Day	Miles
Monday	3.5
Tuesday	5.5
Wednesday	0
Thursday	5

SOLUTION

1. **Understand the Problem** You know how many miles you biked Monday through Thursday. You are asked to find the distance you need to bike on Friday so that the mean number of miles biked per day is 5.
2. **Make a Plan** Use the definition of mean to write an equation that represents the problem. Then solve the equation.
3. **Solve and Check** The mean of a data set is the sum of the data divided by the number of data values. Let x be the number of miles you need to bike on Friday.

$$\frac{3.5 + 5.5 + 0 + 5 + x}{5} = 5 \quad \text{Write the equation.}$$

$$\frac{14 + x}{5} = 5 \quad \text{Combine like terms.}$$

$$5 \cdot \frac{14 + x}{5} = 5 \cdot 5 \quad \text{Multiplication Property of Equality}$$

$$14 + x = 25 \quad \text{Simplify.}$$

$$\underline{-14} \qquad \underline{-14} \quad \text{Subtraction Property of Equality}$$

$$x = 11 \quad \text{Simplify.}$$

▶ You need to bike 11 miles on Friday.

Check Reasonableness Notice that on the days that you did bike, the values are close to the mean. Because you did not bike on Wednesday, you need to bike about twice the mean on Friday. Eleven miles is about twice the mean. So, your solution is reasonable.

SELF-ASSESSMENT 1 I do not understand. 2 I can do it with help. 3 I can do it on my own. 4 I can teach someone else.

13. The formula $d = \frac{1}{2}n + 26$ relates the nozzle pressure n (in pounds per square inch) of a fire hose and the maximum horizontal distance d (in feet) the water reaches. How much pressure is needed to reach a fire 20 yards away?

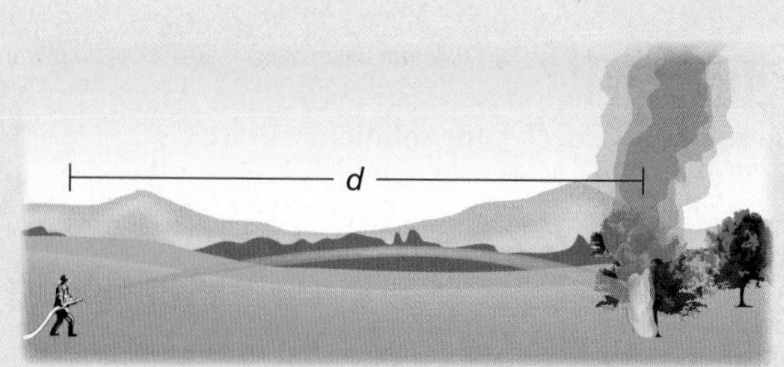

EXAMPLE 5 Modeling Real Life

One person buys a used car in Indiana and pays \$10,195, including 7% sales tax and \$425 in additional fees. Another person buys a used car in Pennsylvania and pays \$9995, including 6% sales tax and \$420 in additional fees. Compare the list prices of the used cars. (The list price is the price of the car before sales tax and fees.)

SOLUTION

1. **Understand the Problem** You know how much each person pays for a car. You also know the sales tax and additional fees in each state. You are asked to compare the list prices of the cars.
2. **Make a Plan** Use a verbal model to write equations that represent the total amount each person pays. Then solve the equations to find each list price.
3. **Solve and Check**

Verbal Model List price + Sales tax rate (written as a decimal) • List price + Other fees = Total amount paid

Variable Let p be the list price (in dollars) of the used car.

Equations

Indiana:		Pennsylvania:
$p + 0.07p + 425 = 10{,}195$	Write the equation.	$p + 0.06p + 420 = 9995$
$1.07p + 425 = 10{,}195$	Combine like terms.	$1.06p + 420 = 9995$
$-425 \quad -425$	Subtraction Property of Equality	$-420 \quad -420$
$1.07p = 9770$	Simplify.	$1.06p = 9575$
$\frac{1.07p}{1.07} = \frac{9770}{1.07}$	Division Property of Equality	$\frac{1.06p}{1.06} = \frac{9575}{1.06}$
$p \approx 9130.84$	Simplify.	$p \approx 9033.02$

REMEMBER
To write a percent as a decimal, remove the percent symbol and divide by 100.

▶ So, the list price of the car in Indiana is about \$9130.84 − \$9033.02 = \$97.82 more than the list price of the car in Pennsylvania.

Check

$p + 0.07p + 425 = 10{,}195$

$9130 + 0.07(9130) + 425 \stackrel{?}{\approx} 10{,}195$

$10{,}194.10 \approx 10{,}195$ ✓

$p + 0.06p + 420 = 9995$

$9030 + 0.06(9030) + 420 \stackrel{?}{\approx} 9995$

$9991.80 \approx 9995$ ✓

SELF-ASSESSMENT

1 I do not understand. 2 I can do it with help. 3 I can do it on my own. 4 I can teach someone else.

14. You have 96 feet of fencing to enclose a rectangular pen for your dog. To provide sufficient running space for your dog to exercise, the pen should be three times as long as it is wide. Find the dimensions of the pen.

15. You are paid 1.2 times your normal hourly rate for each hour you work over 40 hours in a week. You work 46 hours this week and earn \$462.56. What is your normal hourly rate?

1.2 Practice WITH CalcChat® AND CalcView®

In Exercises 1–12, solve the equation. Check your solution. *Examples 1 and 2*

1. $3w + 7 = 19$
2. $2g - 13 = 3$
3. $11 = 12 - q$
4. $10 = 7 - m$
5. $5 = \frac{z}{-4} - 3$
6. $\frac{a}{3} + 4 = 6$
7. $\frac{h+6}{5} = 2$
8. $\frac{d-8}{-2} = 12$
9. $12v + 10v + 14 = 80$
10. $24 = 13n - 4n + 9$
11. $3.8y + 5.6y - 2 = 2.7$
12. $\frac{7}{10}c - 8 - \frac{1}{2}c = -16$

13. **MODELING REAL LIFE** The altitude a (in feet) of a plane t minutes after liftoff is given by $a = 3400t + 600$. How many minutes after liftoff is the plane at an altitude of 21,000 feet?

14. **MODELING REAL LIFE** A repair bill for a car is \$648.45. The parts cost \$265.95. The labor cost is \$85 per hour. Write and solve an equation to find the number of hours of labor spent repairing the car.

In Exercises 15–22, solve the equation. Check your solution. *Example 3*

15. $4(z + 5) = 32$
16. $-2(4g - 3) = 30$
17. $6 + 5(m + 1) = 26$
18. $5h + 2(11 - h) = -5$
19. $-15 = -6(3 + x) + 4(x - 6)$
20. $1 = 5(r + 9) - 2(1 - r)$
21. $83.8 = 8.6c - 7.3(6 - 2c)$
22. $3y - 2\frac{3}{4}\left(\frac{1}{2}y - 4\right) = -2$

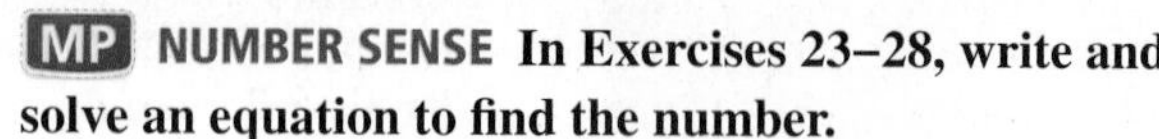

MP NUMBER SENSE In Exercises 23–28, write and solve an equation to find the number.

23. The sum of twice a number and 13 is 75.
24. The difference of three times a number and 4 is -19.
25. Eight plus the quotient of a number and 3 is -2.
26. The sum of twice a number and half the number is 10.
27. Six times the sum of a number and 15 is -42.
28. Four times the difference of a number and 7 is 12.

MP USING TOOLS In Exercises 29 and 30, find the value of the variable. Then find the angle measures of the polygon. Use a protractor to check the reasonableness of your answer.

29.

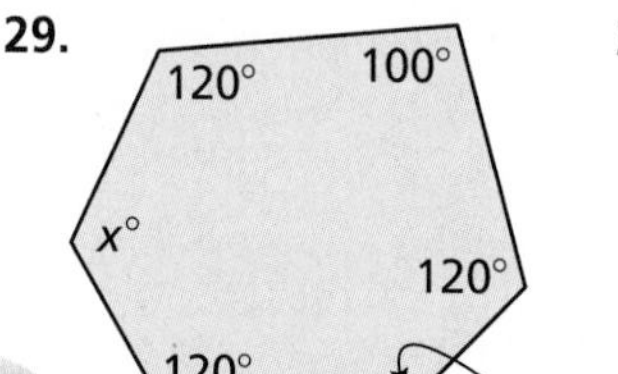

Sum of angle measures: 720°

30.

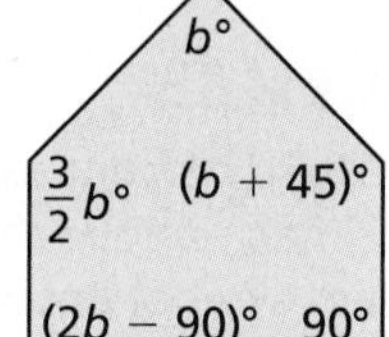

Sum of angle measures: 540°

ERROR ANALYSIS In Exercises 31 and 32, describe and correct the error in solving the equation.

31.

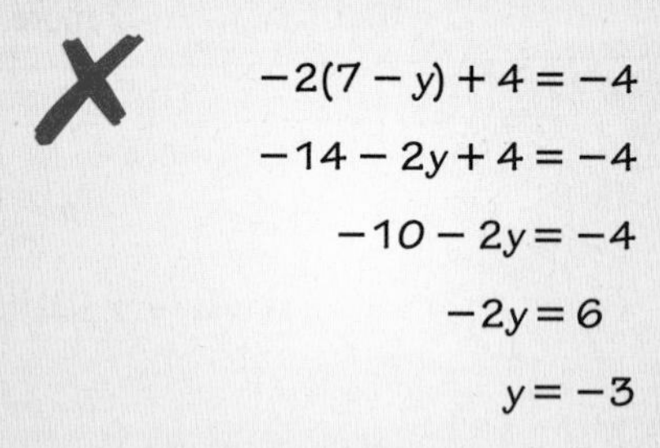

32.

$$\frac{1}{4}(x - 2) + 4 = 12$$
$$\frac{1}{4}(x - 2) = 8$$
$$x - 2 = 2$$
$$x = 4$$

MODELING REAL LIFE **In Exercises 33–36, write and solve an equation to answer the question.**
Examples 4 and 5

33. During the summer, you work 30 hours per week at a gas station and earn \$8.75 per hour. You also work as a landscaper for \$11 per hour and can work as many hours as you want. You want to earn a total of \$400 per week. How many hours must you work as a landscaper?

34. The area of the surface of the swimming pool is 210 square feet. What is the length of the deep end?

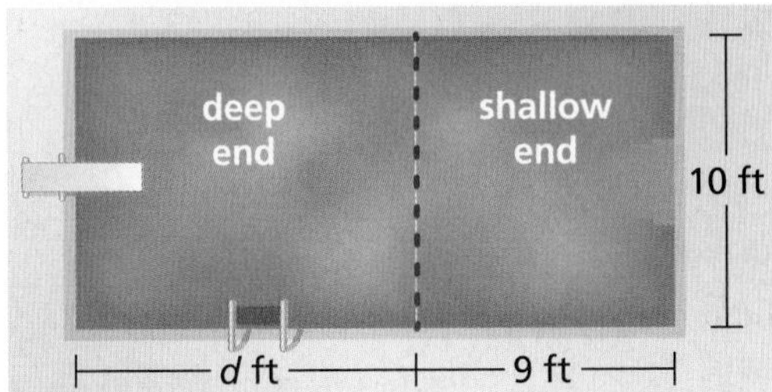

35. Your cell phone has 983.5 MB of free space. You save a 1.4-MB picture and download two songs that are the same size. Your cell phone now has 974.9 MB of free space. What is the size of each song?

36. You order two tacos and a salad. The salad costs \$2.50. You pay 8% sales tax and leave a \$3 tip. You pay a total of \$13.80. How much does one taco cost?

CONNECTING CONCEPTS **In Exercises 37 and 38, write and solve an equation to answer the question.**

37. The perimeter of the Puerto Rican flag is 150 inches. What are the dimensions of the flag?

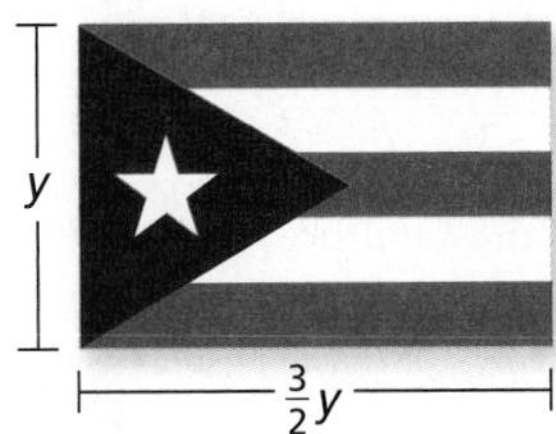

38. The perimeter of the school crossing sign is 102 inches. What is the length of each side?

JUSTIFYING STEPS **In Exercises 39 and 40, justify each step of the solution.**

39. $-\frac{1}{2}(5x - 8) - 1 = 6$ Write the equation.

$-\frac{1}{2}(5x - 8) = 7$

$5x - 8 = -14$

$5x = -6$

$x = -\frac{6}{5}$

40. $2(x + 3) + x = -9$ Write the equation.

$2(x) + 2(3) + x = -9$

$2x + 6 + x = -9$

$3x + 6 = -9$

$3x = -15$

$x = -5$

41. **COMPARING METHODS** Solve the equation $2(4 - 8x) + 6 = -1$ using two different methods. Which method do you prefer? Explain.

42. **HOW DO YOU SEE IT?**
The scatter plot shows the attendance for each meeting of a gaming club.

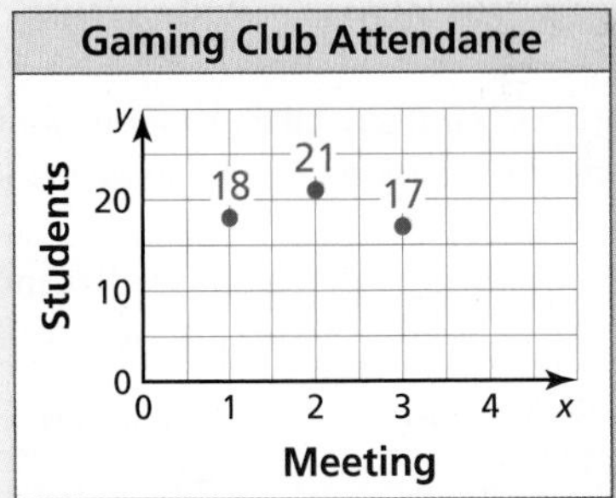

a. The mean attendance for the first four meetings is 20. Is the number of students who attended the fourth meeting greater than or less than 20? Explain.

b. Estimate the number of students who attended the fourth meeting. Describe a way you can check your estimate.

43. **MP PROBLEM SOLVING** An online ticket agency charges the amounts shown for basketball tickets. The total cost for an order is \$220.70. How many tickets are purchased?

Charge	Amount
Ticket price	\$32.50 per ticket
Convenience charge	\$3.30 per ticket
Processing charge	\$5.90 per order

44. **MAKING AN ARGUMENT** You have quarters and dimes that total \$2.80. Your friend says it is possible that the number of quarters is 8 more than the number of dimes. Is your friend correct? Explain.

MP REASONING In Exercises 45–48, the letters a, b, and c represent nonzero constants. Solve the equation for x. Then find values of a, b, and c for which the solution is negative.

45. $ax - b = 12.5$

46. $ax + b = c$

47. $2bx - bx = -8$

48. $cx - 4b = 5b$

49. **DIG DEEPER** Find three consecutive even integers that have a sum of 54. Explain your reasoning.

50. **THOUGHT PROVOKING**
Your math teacher assigns a weight to each component of the class. The weight of the final exam is half your grade, and the weights of the remaining components are equal. What is the least possible score you can receive on the final exam to earn an A (90%) in the class? Explain your reasoning.

Component	Your score	Weight	Score × Weight
Class participation	92%		
Homework	96%		
Quizzes	88%		
Midterm exam	76%		
Final exam			
Total		1	

REVIEW & REFRESH

WATCH

In Exercises 51–54, find the sum or difference.

51. $-3.37 + 4.135$

52. $1\frac{3}{8} - \frac{7}{8}$

53. $18.36 - (-9.04)$

54. $-\frac{5}{12} + \left(-\frac{7}{3}\right)$

55. **MODELING REAL LIFE** About how many times farther from the Sun is Neptune than Mercury?

Planet	Average distance from the Sun (miles)
Mercury	36,000,000
Neptune	2.795×10^9

56. Order the numbers $\frac{11}{20}$, 49%, and 0.5 from least to greatest.

57. Find the perimeter and the area of the figure.

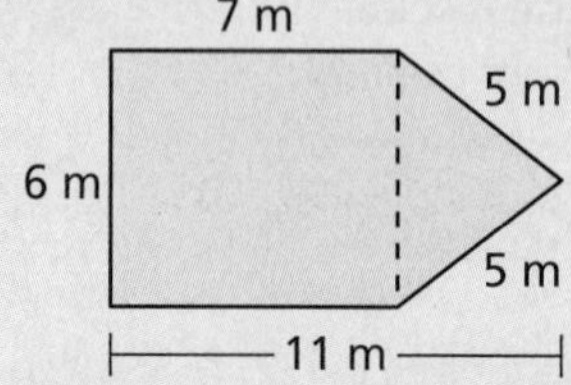

58. **MP NUMBER SENSE** The sum of two-thirds a number and eighteen is twenty-three. What is the number?

In Exercises 59–62, solve the equation. Check your solution.

59. $x + 9 = 7$

60. $8.6 = z - 3.8$

61. $3r + 7 = 11$

62. $26 = 9p - 6 - p$

63. Translate the triangle 1 unit right and 3 units up. What are the coordinates of the image?

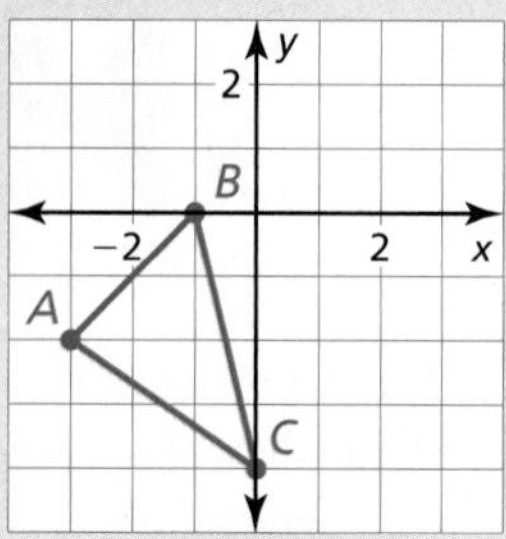

64. **MODELING REAL LIFE** Your friend borrows \$7500 to buy an all-terrain vehicle (ATV). The simple annual interest rate is 6%. She pays off the loan after 5 years of equal monthly payments. How much is each payment?

65. Factor $24x + 32$ using the greatest common factor.

1.3 Modeling Quantities

Learning Target Use proportional reasoning and analyze units when solving problems.

Success Criteria
- I can use ratios to solve real-life problems.
- I can use rates to solve real-life problems.
- I can convert units and rates.

EXPLORE IT! Estimating Quantities

Work with a partner. A freight train that is 1.9 kilometers long is traveling on the Cize-Bolozon viaduct in France.

1.9 km

a. Research the lengths of different types of train cars.

b. Estimate the number of cars in the train. Explain the assumptions that you make to find your estimate.

c. Compare your results with other pairs. Based on these comparisons, do you think you should revise your estimate? Explain your reasoning.

Math Practice

Specify Units

What units of measure did you use in your calculations? Why did you decide to use those units?

Vocabulary AZ VOCAB

ratio, *p. 20*
proportion, *p. 20*
rate, *p. 21*

REMEMBER

The *value of a ratio a : b* is $\frac{a}{b}$. The values of equivalent ratios are equivalent.

Using Ratios and Proportions

GO DIGITAL

A **ratio** is a comparison of two quantities. A **proportion** is an equation stating that two ratios are equivalent.

Equivalent ratios: $a : b$ and $c : d$

Proportion: $\frac{a}{b} = \frac{c}{d}$

EXAMPLE 1 Using Ratios

You take the measurements shown in the diagram. The right triangles created by each object and its shadow are similar. Can the tree fall onto the house?

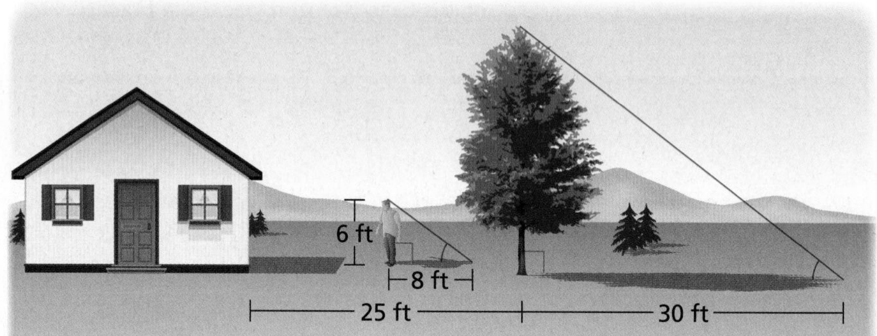

REMEMBER

The triangles created by each object and its shadow have two congruent angles, so the third angles are also congruent and the triangles are similar.

SOLUTION

Ratios of corresponding side lengths in similar triangles are equivalent.

Use a proportion to find the height h (in feet) of the tree.

$\frac{30}{8} = \frac{h}{6}$ Write a proportion.

$6 \cdot \left(\frac{30}{8}\right) = 6 \cdot \left(\frac{h}{6}\right)$ Multiplication Property of Equality

$22.5 = h$ Simplify.

▶ Because 22.5 feet < 25 feet, the tree cannot fall onto the house.

SELF-ASSESSMENT 1 I do not understand. 2 I can do it with help. 3 I can do it on my own. 4 I can teach someone else.

Solve the proportion.

1. $\frac{x}{4} = \frac{9}{12}$ **2.** $\frac{14}{y} = \frac{7}{2}$ **3.** $\frac{5}{3} = \frac{8}{z}$ **4.** $\frac{11}{15} = \frac{n}{10}$

5. MP **REASONING** Are the equations $\frac{a}{b} = \frac{c}{d}$ and $ad = bc$ equivalent? Explain.

6. You are 5 feet 4 inches tall and cast a shadow 3 feet long. At the same time, a nearby water tower casts a shadow 74 feet 3 inches long.

a. Find the height of the water tower.

b. Each additional foot in tower height increases the water pressure at the base of the tower by 0.43 pound per square inch. Estimate the water pressure at the base of the tower.

Using Rates

A **rate** is a ratio of two quantities using different units. You can write rates in many ways. For example, 10 meters per second can be written as $\frac{10 \text{ m}}{\text{sec}}$, $10 \frac{\text{m}}{\text{sec}}$, or 10 m/sec. In real-life situations, you may need to choose your own units to solve a problem.

EXAMPLE 2 Using Rates

The diagram shows statistics for a baseball pitcher. Use rates to compare the pitcher's performance in 2019 to his performance in 2020.

SEASON	INNINGS	HITS	EARNED RUNS	WALKS	STRIKEOUTS
2019	70	54	19	29	100
2020	50	42	15	20	73

SOLUTION

There are many rates you can use to make comparisons. Two that you can use are strikeouts per walk and earned runs per inning.

> **REMEMBER**
> A rate $a : b$ has a unit rate of $\frac{a}{b} : 1$.

Method 1: Compare using strikeouts per walk.

2019: 100 strikeouts to 29 walks

rate: $\frac{100}{29} \approx 3.45$ strikeouts/walk

2020: 73 strikeouts to 20 walks

rate: $\frac{73}{20} = 3.65$ strikeouts/walk

▶ The pitcher had fewer strikeouts per walk in 2019.

Method 2: Compare using earned runs per inning.

2019: 19 earned runs in 70 innings

rate: $\frac{19}{70} \approx 0.27$ earned runs/inning

2020: 15 earned runs in 50 innings

rate: $\frac{15}{50} = 0.3$ earned runs/inning

▶ The pitcher had fewer earned runs per inning in 2019.

SELF-ASSESSMENT

1 I do not understand. 2 I can do it with help. 3 I can do it on my own. 4 I can teach someone else.

7. The table shows enrollment information for two colleges. Use rates to compare the enrollment at the colleges.

College	Students	Athletes	Students with athletic scholarships	Students with academic scholarships
A	4258	288	72	415
B	7120	150	110	826

8. In baseball, a commonly used rate is earned run average (ERA). ERA is a rate of earned runs to a constant number n of innings. In 2020, the pitcher in Example 2 had an ERA of 2.70. Find the value of n. Then explain how to calculate a pitcher's ERA given the number of earned runs and innings pitched.

Using Unit Analysis

In Section 1.1 Example 3, you kept track of units when working with rates.

$$200 \text{ m} \div \frac{10 \text{ m}}{1 \text{ sec}} = 200 \cancel{\text{m}} \times \frac{1 \text{ sec}}{10 \cancel{\text{m}}} = 20 \text{ sec}$$

This is called *unit analysis*. You can use unit analysis to help you convert units.

EXAMPLE 3 Converting Units of Measure

Convert 4.8 gallons to fluid ounces.

SOLUTION

There are 16 cups per gallon and 8 fluid ounces per cup. Use these rates to convert from gallons to fluid ounces.

$$4.8 \text{ gal} = 4.8 \cancel{\text{gal}} \times 16 \frac{\cancel{\text{c}}}{\cancel{\text{gal}}} \times 8 \frac{\text{fl oz}}{\cancel{\text{c}}} = 614.4 \text{ fl oz}$$

▶ So, 4.8 gallons is 614.4 fluid ounces.

EXAMPLE 4 Modeling Real Life

Wind speeds on Jupiter can reach 180 meters per second. Which planet has faster winds, Jupiter or Neptune?

The Voyager 2 performed the first flyby of Neptune in 1989, measuring wind speeds that reached 1200 miles per hour.

SOLUTION

To solve the problem, convert one of the rates so that it has the same units as the other rate. One way is to convert 1200 miles per hour to meters per second.

$$\frac{1200 \text{ mi}}{\text{h}} \approx \frac{1200 \cancel{\text{mi}}}{\cancel{\text{h}}} \times \frac{5280 \cancel{\text{ft}}}{\cancel{\text{mi}}} \times \frac{1 \text{ m}}{3.28 \cancel{\text{ft}}} \times \frac{1 \cancel{\text{h}}}{60 \cancel{\text{min}}} \times \frac{1 \cancel{\text{min}}}{60 \text{ sec}} \approx \frac{537 \text{ m}}{\text{sec}}$$

▶ Because 180 m/sec < 537 m/sec, Neptune's winds reach higher speeds than Jupiter's winds.

SELF-ASSESSMENT

1 I do not understand. 2 I can do it with help. 3 I can do it on my own. 4 I can teach someone else.

9. Convert 2.5 meters to inches. Round to the nearest hundredth, if necessary.

10. Convert 88 gallons per minute to liters per second. Round to the nearest hundredth, if necessary.

11. A solar-powered plane travels around Earth. Its cruising speed is 90 kilometers per hour during the day and 1000 meters per minute at night. Does the plane speed up or slow down at sunrise?

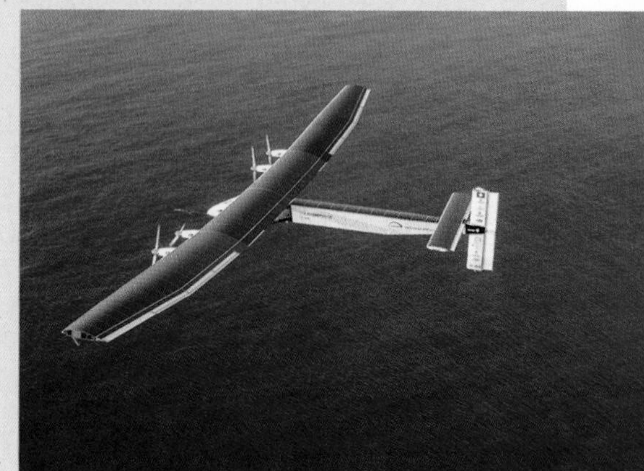

12. MP **REASONING** You buy two kinds of wiring for electrical work. The first costs x dollars per foot and the second costs y dollars per foot. You buy A feet of the first wire and B feet of the second wire. What quantities do the following expressions represent? What are the units?

a. $Ax + By$ **b.** $\dfrac{Ax + By}{A + B}$ **c.** $\dfrac{1 \text{ yd}}{3 \text{ ft}} \times (A + B)$

1.3 Practice WITH CalcChat® AND CalcView®

In Exercises 1–4, solve the proportion.

1. $\frac{x}{6} = \frac{10}{12}$

2. $\frac{36}{8} = \frac{9}{h}$

3. $\frac{13}{p} = \frac{5}{4}$

4. $\frac{4}{15} = \frac{w}{27}$

5. **USING RATIOS** A repairman needs to climb to the top of a building. He takes the measurements shown. The right triangles created by each object and its shadow are similar. Can he use a ladder that reaches heights of up to 28 feet? *Example 1*

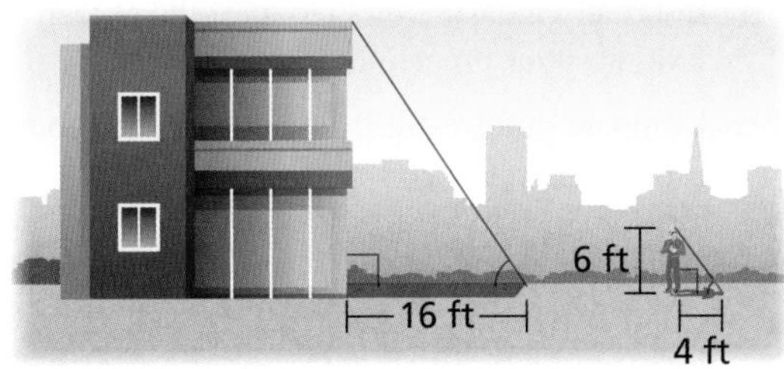

6. **USING RATIOS** An entrepreneur wants to rent a billboard at least 30 feet tall to display an advertisement for her business. She is 5 feet 6 inches tall and casts a shadow 7 feet long. At the same time, a billboard casts a shadow 35 feet long. Is the billboard tall enough?

7. **USING RATES** The table shows the numbers of students and staff at two high schools. Use rates to compare the two schools. *Example 2*

School	Students	Teachers	Support staff
A	2308	144	34
B	1522	85	23

8. **USING RATES** The table shows sales data for two salespeople at a car dealership. Use rates to compare the performances of the salespeople.

Person	Months employed	Sales attempted	Sales made	Sales (millions)
A	10	167	109	\$3.3
B	8	163	97	\$2.7

In Exercises 9–12, complete the statement. Round to the nearest hundredth, if necessary. *Example 3*

9. 160 fl oz = ▭ qt

10. 3.2 km = ▭ cm

11. 30.9 mm ≈ ▭ in.

12. 4.1 kg ≈ ▭ oz

In Exercises 13 and 14, complete the statement. Round to the nearest hundredth, if necessary.

13. $\frac{7 \text{ gal}}{\text{min}} \approx \frac{\square \text{ qt}}{\text{sec}}$

14. $\frac{8 \text{ km}}{\text{min}} \approx \frac{\square \text{ mi}}{\text{h}}$

15. **MODELING REAL LIFE** Roller coaster A can reach a top speed of 110 feet per second. Roller coaster B can reach a top speed of 85 miles per hour. Which roller coaster has a greater top speed? *Example 4*

16. **MODELING REAL LIFE** Faucet A leaks at a rate of 21 liters per day. Faucet B leaks at a rate of 30 drips per minute. Which faucet leaks at a faster rate? (1 L ≈ 4000 drips)

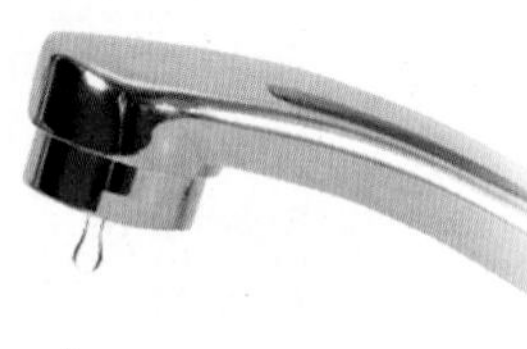

17. **ERROR ANALYSIS** Describe and correct the error in converting 3.5 feet to centimeters.

> ✗ $3.5 \text{ ft} \approx 3.5 \text{ ft} \times 3.28 \frac{\text{m}}{\text{ft}} \times 100 \frac{\text{cm}}{\text{m}}$
>
> $= 1148 \text{ cm}$

18. **MP PROBLEM SOLVING** You travel on the highway at a constant speed of 70 miles per hour for 1 hour 45 minutes. Your vehicle travels 25 miles per gallon and gasoline costs \$2.90 per gallon. How much do you spend on fuel for the trip? Explain your reasoning.

19. **MAKING AN ARGUMENT** Your friend says that when you convert a measurement from yards to meters, the number of meters is greater than the number of yards. Is your friend correct? Explain.

20. **HOW DO YOU SEE IT?** The graph shows the relationship between millimeters and micrometers. Use the graph to convert 5 millimeters to micrometers.

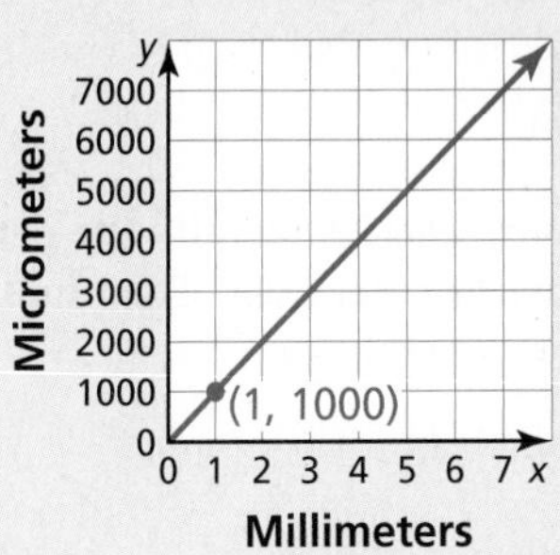

21. **DIG DEEPER** The surface area of a solid is 3240 square inches. Is the surface area greater than 3 square yards? Explain.

22. **THOUGHT PROVOKING**
The table shows statistics for two basketball players during a season. Write an argument supporting that Player A performed better than Player B. Then write an argument supporting that Player B performed better than Player A.

	Player A	Player B
Games played	72	80
Points	1432	1465
Field goals made	505	515
Field goals attempted	1136	1023
Rebounds	490	641
Assists	375	483

23. **MP REASONING** You are standing in a line that is about 200 feet long for a movie premier. Estimate the number of people in the line. Explain your reasoning.

24. **COLLEGE PREP** You make blueberry muffins and banana bread for a bake sale. One batch of blueberry muffins requires m cups of flour, and one batch of banana bread requires n cups of flour. You make A batches of blueberry muffins and B batches of banana bread. Which expression represents the total amount of flour (in cups) you need?

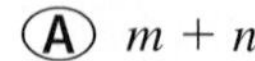

Ⓐ $m + n$ Ⓑ $A + B$

Ⓒ $\frac{A}{m} + \frac{B}{n}$ Ⓓ $Am + Bn$

25. **PERFORMANCE TASK** Choose an object for which you cannot directly measure its height.

a. Visually estimate the height of the object.

b. Indirectly measure the height of the object. Explain your procedure.

c. Compare your result from part (b) with your estimate in part (a).

REVIEW & REFRESH

In Exercises 26 and 27, find the area of the figure.

26.

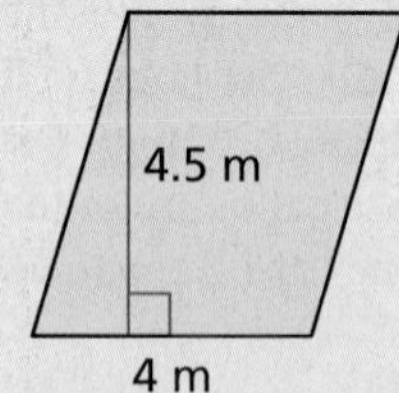

27.

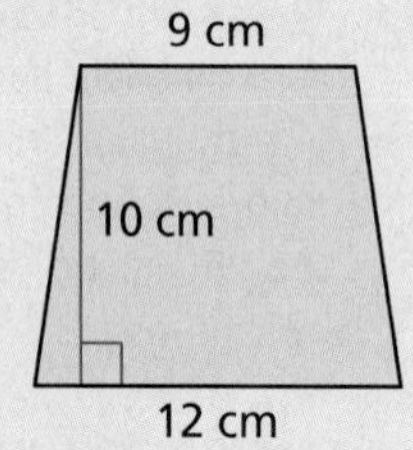

28. The circumference of a circle is 20π inches. What is the area of the circle?

In Exercises 29–31, solve the equation. Check your solution.

29. $2m - 3 = 13$

30. $-21a + 28a - 6 = -10.2$

31. $68 = \frac{1}{5}(20x + 50) + 2$

In Exercises 32 and 33, identify the percent of change as an increase or a decrease. Then find the percent of change.

32. 80 customers to 120 customers

33. 24 points to 18 points

In Exercises 34 and 35, complete the statement. Round to the nearest hundredth, if necessary.

34. 32 c ≈ ___ L

35. 1.6 lb ≈ ___ g

36. **MODELING REAL LIFE** To estimate how many miles you are from a thunderstorm, count the seconds between when you see lightning and when you hear thunder. Then divide by 5. Determine how many seconds you count for a thunderstorm that is 2 miles away.

37. The bar graph shows the results of rolling a six-sided die 50 times. Find the experimental probability of rolling an even number.

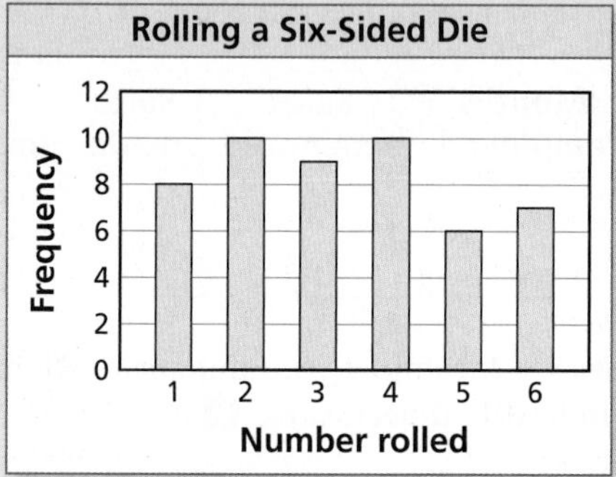

1.4 Accuracy with Measurements

Learning Target Choose an appropriate level of accuracy when calculating with measurements.

Success Criteria
- I can choose an appropriate level of accuracy when measuring to solve real-life problems.
- I can determine where to round numbers when finding estimates.

EXPLORE IT! Measuring Objects

Work with a partner.

a. MP **CHOOSE TOOLS** Measure an object in your classroom or at home. Choose two tools and two different units to find your measurement.

You can measure any object you want. Consider some of the following.

- the height of a doorway
- the length of a table
- the height of a sibling
- the width of a book
- the arm span of a student

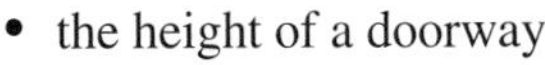

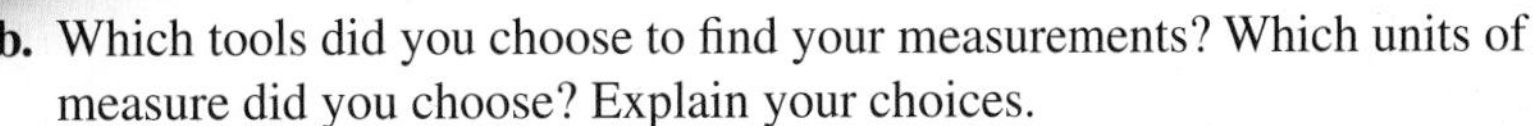

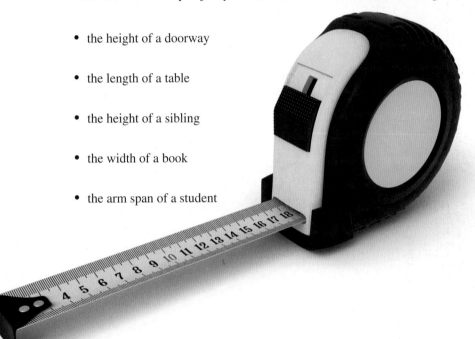

b. Which tools did you choose to find your measurements? Which units of measure did you choose? Explain your choices.

c. Is one measurement more accurate than the other? How can you take another measurement that is more accurate? Explain.

d. Measure the dimensions of the floor of your classroom. Then find the perimeter and area of the floor of your classroom.

e. If someone asks you what the perimeter and area of the floor of your classroom are, how would you answer? Explain your reasoning. Then compare your results with your classmates.

Math Practice

Evaluate Results
What may cause the perimeter and area measurements of your classroom to differ among you and your classmates?

Calculating with Measurements

Vocabulary

precision, *p. 26*
accuracy, *p. 27*

When measuring, **precision** is the level of detail of the measurement. When performing calculations with measurements, the calculated value is no more *precise* than the original measurements.

EXAMPLE 1 Estimating Measurements

You use a centimeter ruler to measure the dimensions of the jewelry box shown. Estimate the volume of the jewelry box.

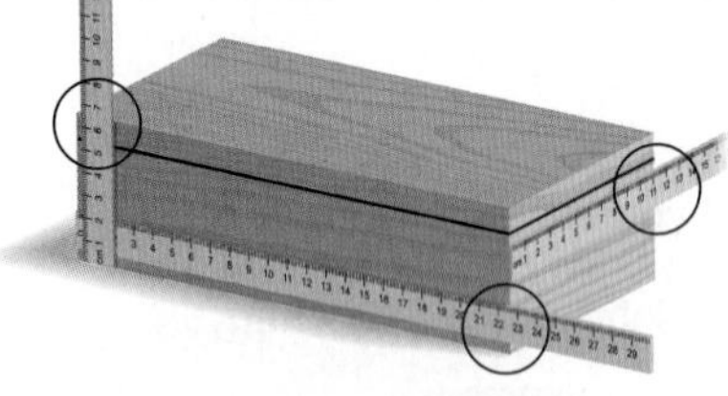

Length

Width

Height

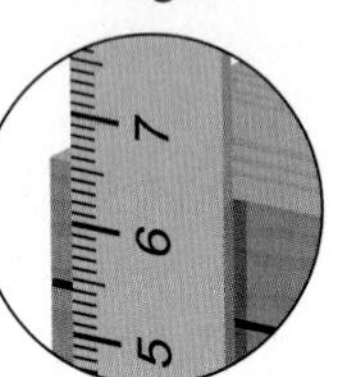

SOLUTION

The length of the jewelry box is about 22.5 centimeters, the width is about 11.3 centimeters, and the height is about 6.5 centimeters. Substitute these values into the formula for the volume of a rectangular prism.

$V = \ell wh$ Volume of a rectangular prism

$= (22.5 \text{ cm})(11.3 \text{ cm})(6.5 \text{ cm})$ Substitute 22.5 for ℓ, 11.3 for w, and 6.5 for h.

$= 1652.625 \text{ cm}^3$ Multiply.

Because the dimensions are measured in tenths of a centimeter, you should not state the volume beyond tenths of a cubic centimeter. The magnitude of the volume is large enough that rounding to 1650 cm^3 is precise enough in this context.

▶ So, the volume is about 1650 cubic centimeters.

SELF-ASSESSMENT

1 I do not understand. 2 I can do it with help. 3 I can do it on my own. 4 I can teach someone else.

1. **MP REASONING** Explain why it is not reasonable to say the volume of the jewelry box in Example 1 is 1652.625 cubic centimeters.

2. You use a centimeter ruler to measure the diameter of the lens of the magnifying glass. Estimate the area of the lens.

3. A chemist is measuring the weight (in ounces) of 15 equal samples of a substance on the electronic balance at once. Estimate the weight of each sample. Explain your reasoning.

The phrase "per capita" means for each person. When you write an amount per capita, you are writing the amount per person.

Accuracy refers to how close a measured value is to the actual value. The accuracy of measurements may affect how you decide to state answers when performing calculations with them.

EXAMPLE 2 Estimating Results

The population of the United States in 2018 was about 328,181,510. The figure below shows the national debt for the United States as reported in 2018.

Estimate the United States national debt per capita.

SOLUTION

The national debt per capita can be thought of as the amount of money each person in the United States would have to pay in order to pay off the entire national debt.

Because the population of the United States and the national debt are constantly increasing, the measured values were accurate for only a moment in time. So, you can round to greater values before making your calculation.

$21,867,237,827,643 \approx 22,000,000,000,000$ Round to nearest trillion.

$328,181,510 \approx 330,000,000$ Round to nearest ten million.

To find the national debt per capita, divide the national debt by the population. Use technology.

$22,000,000,000,000 \div 330,000,000 \approx 66,666.6666...$

▶ Because the measured values are constantly increasing and were rounded, it is not reasonable to express the answer to the nearest cent or nearest dollar. So, you can estimate the national debt per capita to be about $67,000.

STUDY TIP

Due to unknown levels of accuracy in the population and debt figures, it would also be acceptable to estimate this amount as $66,700 or even $70,000 in this context.

SELF-ASSESSMENT

1 I do not understand. 2 I can do it with help. 3 I can do it on my own. 4 I can teach someone else.

4. **MP REASONING** In Example 2, does the place to which you round affect the accuracy of your results? Explain your reasoning.

5. Repeat Example 2 using current statistics. Compare your results. What conclusions can you make?

6. The number of student loan borrowers in the United States is about 44,532,700. The amount of student loan debt held by the borrowers in 2018 is shown. Estimate the student loan debt per student loan borrower.

7. The land area of the entire United States is 3,531,905 square miles. Use the information you found in Exercise 5 to estimate the population per square mile.

Solving Real-Life Problems

EXAMPLE 3 **Modeling Real Life** 

The surface of a city playground is being covered with rubber mulch, which is shredded rubber made from recycled tires. A city worker measures the dimensions of the playground as shown. The recommended depth of the mulch is 6 inches.

a. Estimate the volume of mulch needed to cover the surface.

b. A 1-ton bag of mulch contains about 3 cubic yards of mulch. How many bags of mulch are needed to cover the surface of the playground?

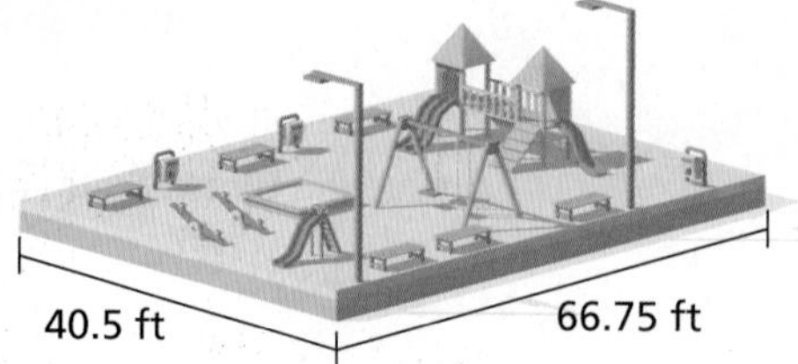

SOLUTION

a. You can use the formula for the volume of a rectangular prism to estimate the volume V (in cubic feet) of mulch needed to cover the surface.

$$V = \ell wh \qquad \text{Volume of a rectangular prism}$$

$$= (66.75 \text{ ft})(40.5 \text{ ft})(0.5 \text{ ft}) \qquad \text{Substitute 66.75 for } \ell\text{, 40.5 for } w\text{, and 0.5 for } h.$$

$$= 1351.6875 \text{ ft}^3 \qquad \text{Multiply.}$$

▶ You can estimate the volume of mulch needed to be about 1350 cubic feet. You are calculating with measured values and 1.6875 cubic feet is a relatively small amount in this context.

b. Convert the amount of mulch in a bag to cubic feet.

$$3 \text{ yd}^3 \times \left(\frac{3 \text{ ft}}{1 \text{ yd}}\right)^3 = 3 \cancel{\text{yd}^3} \times \frac{27 \text{ ft}^3}{1 \cancel{\text{yd}^3}} = 81 \text{ ft}^3$$

You need about 1350 cubic feet of mulch and each bag contains 81 cubic feet. Determine how many bags are needed to fill 1350 cubic feet.

$$1350 \cancel{\text{ft}^3} \times \frac{1 \text{ bag}}{81 \cancel{\text{ft}^3}} = \frac{50}{3}, \text{ or } 16\frac{2}{3} \text{ bags}$$

▶ Because mulch is sold in whole bags, 17 bags are needed to cover the entire surface.

SELF-ASSESSMENT 1 I do not understand. 2 I can do it with help. 3 I can do it on my own. 4 I can teach someone else.

8. **MP REASONING** Another worker measures the dimensions of the playground in meters. Does this change the amount of mulch needed? Explain.

9. **WHAT IF?** How many bags of rubber mulch are needed in Example 3 when the recommended depth of the mulch is 4 inches? Explain.

10. In Example 3, the company's delivery truck can haul at most 8000 pounds. One bag of rubber mulch costs \$375. There is a \$45 delivery charge for each trip the truck makes. What is the total cost for purchasing and delivering the bags of rubber mulch needed for the playground?

1.4 Practice WITH CalcChat® AND CalcView®

1. **ESTIMATING MEASUREMENTS** You use an inch ruler to measure the dimensions of a cylindrical can, as shown. Estimate the volume of the can.
Example 1

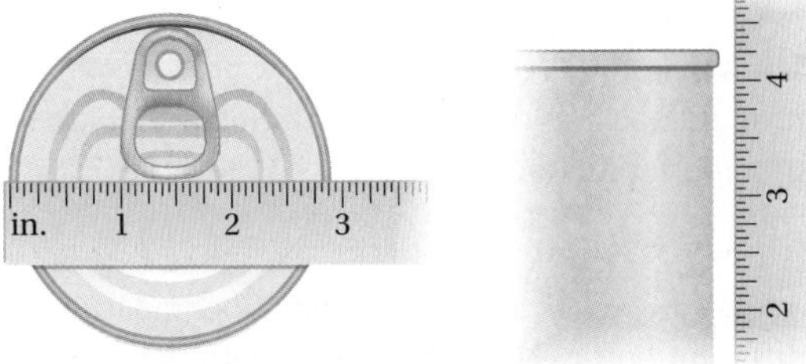

2. **ESTIMATING MEASUREMENTS** You use a tape measure to measure the dimensions of a canvas, as shown. Estimate the area of the canvas.

3. **ESTIMATING RESULTS** The figures show the number of taxpayers and the federal tax revenue for the United States in 2018. Estimate the United States federal tax revenue per taxpayer. *Example 2*

US FEDERAL TAX REVENUE
$3,307,673,720,131

4. **ESTIMATING RESULTS** The circumference of Mercury is about 15,329 kilometers. The circumference of Jupiter is about 439,263 kilometers. About how many times larger is Jupiter than Mercury?

5. **MODELING REAL LIFE** You want to install an in-ground basketball post. You dig a hole with the dimensions shown for the concrete. An 80-pound bag of concrete mix yields 0.6 cubic feet. How many bags do you need to install the basketball post?
Example 3

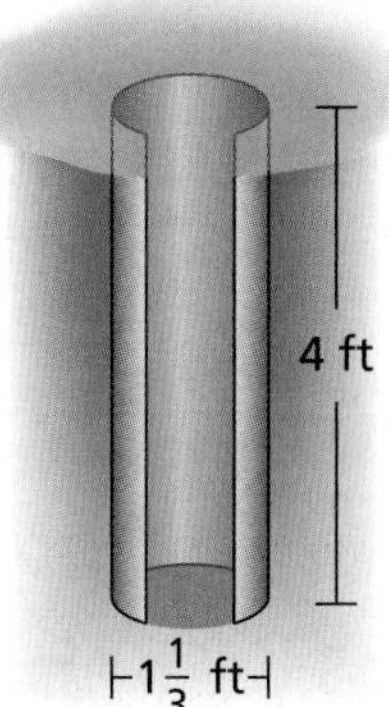

6. **MODELING REAL LIFE** A farmer fills a field with solar panels. The area of the field is 32,374.9 square meters.

a. About how many solar panels of the size shown can fit in the field? Explain.

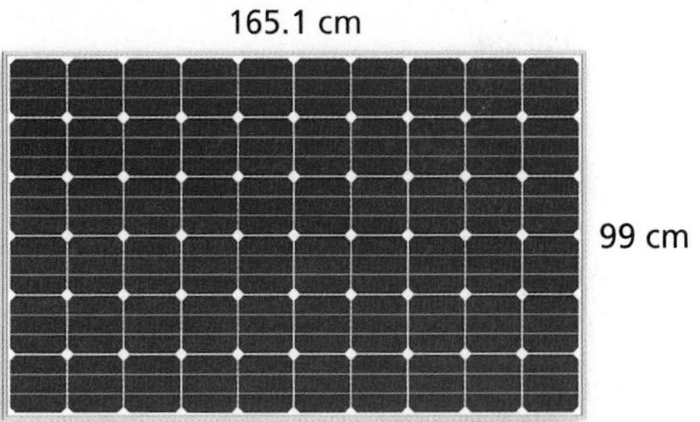

b. One solar panel of this size can produce about 1.06 kilowatt hours of electricity per day. On average, a house uses about 1000 kilowatt hours of electricity per month. Can the field produce enough electricity for 500 houses each month? Explain.

7. **COLLEGE PREP** You measure the dimensions of a gift box as 8.75 inches, 4.75 inches, and 2.5 inches. Which of the following is *not* an appropriate approximation of the volume of the gift box?

Ⓐ 103 in.^{3}

Ⓑ 100 in.^{3}

Ⓒ 103.9 in.^{3}

Ⓓ 103.906 in.^{3}

8. **HOW DO YOU SEE IT?**
A softball weighs about 6.5 ounces. You weigh different numbers of softballs and record the results in the graph.

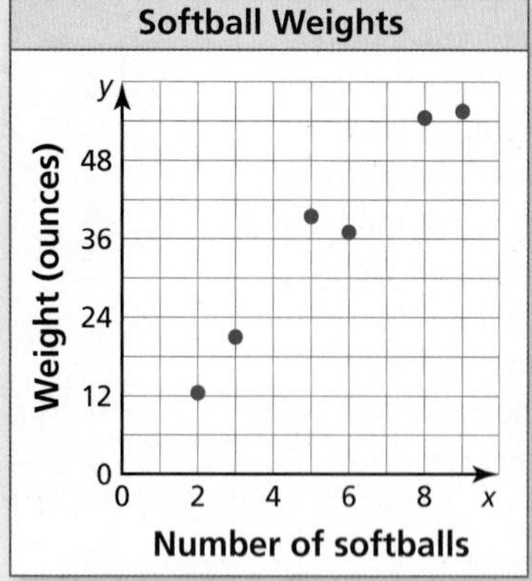

a. Explain how graphing $y = 6.5x$ can help you reason about the accuracy of your results.

b. Which measurement appears to be the least accurate? Why? Explain how this may have occurred.

9. MP **NUMBER SENSE** A substance weighs exactly 1 pound. You use three different scales to measure the weight of the substance. The results are shown in the table. Which measurement is the most accurate?

Scale	1	2	3
Weight (pounds)	1.019	0.9	1.01

10. **MAKING AN ARGUMENT** Your friend measures the circumference of a fitness ball as 2.04 meters and says, "The volume of the ball is 0.1433638009 cubic meters." Do you agree with your friend's statement? Explain.

GO DIGITAL

11. **ANALYZING RELATIONSHIPS** Explain how the choice of a unit of measure can impact the accuracy of the measurement of an object.

12. **THOUGHT PROVOKING**
Explain one way you can determine the accuracy of a thermometer.

13. MP **PROBLEM SOLVING** You are comparing three different bottles of liquid bleach with the same active ingredient. The concentration of active ingredient in each bottle is labeled to the nearest tenth of a percent.

Bleach type	Concentration	Size of bottle (fluid ounces)	Price
Ultra	6.0%	64	\$2.49
Regular	5.3%	128	\$3.99
Concentrated	8.3%	121	\$6.99

a. About how many fluid ounces of active ingredient are in each bottle? Explain the level of accuracy you used in your results.

b. Which bottle is the best buy? the worst buy? Explain.

REVIEW & REFRESH

In Exercises 14 and 15, write the number in scientific notation.

14. 96,400,000

15. 0.00035

16. Evaluate $26 + 9(17 - 3^2) \div 4$.

MP **NUMBER SENSE In Exercises 17 and 18, write and solve an equation to find the number.**

17. The sum of three times a number and 12 is 45.

18. Nine minus the quotient of a number and 7 is -5.

19. **MODELING REAL LIFE** The distance from Earth to the moon is about 238,855 miles. The distance from Earth to Mars is about 140 million miles. About how many trips to the moon are equal to the distance from Earth to Mars?

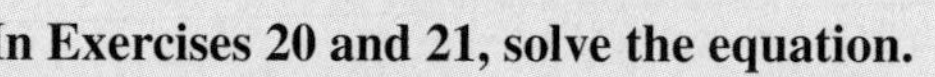

In Exercises 20 and 21, solve the equation.

20. $z - 5.2 = -3.4$

21. $56t = 16$

22. **MODELING REAL LIFE** Which sign shows a greater speed limit? How much greater?

23. The vertices of a trapezoid are $W(1, 4)$, $X(4, 4)$, $Y(4, 1)$, and $Z(-1, 1)$. Draw the figure and its reflection in the x-axis. Identify the coordinates of the image.

1.5 Solving Equations with Variables on Both Sides

GO DIGITAL

Learning Target Write and solve equations with variables on both sides.

Success Criteria
- I can apply properties of equality using variable terms.
- I can solve equations with variables on both sides.
- I can recognize when an equation has zero, one, or infinitely many solutions.

EXPLORE IT! Solving a Real-Life Problem

Work with a partner. You earn \$9.75 per hour at a part-time job. Your friend earns \$9.35 per hour at a part-time job. The only other income you and your friend earn is a weekly allowance.

a. Determine whether it is possible for you and your friend to work the same number of hours and earn the same total amount in a given week for the following situations. Explain your reasoning.

i. Your allowance is \$20 per week and your friend's allowance is \$10 per week.

ii. Your allowance is \$10 per week and your friend's allowance is \$20 per week.

iii. Your allowance is \$10 per week, your friend's allowance is \$20 per week, and your friend receives a \$0.40 raise.

iv. Your allowance is \$20 per week, your friend's allowance is \$20 per week, and your friend receives a \$0.40 raise.

b. The following equation represents one of the situations in part (a).

$$9.75p + 10 = 9.35p + 20$$

Interpret each term and each side of the equation. Which situation does it represent?

c. Solve the equation in part (b). Explain how you solved the equation and what the solution represents. Can you start with a different first step?

d. Write and solve an equation for each of the other three situations in part (a). Compare your solutions to your answers in part (a). What do you notice?

Math Practice

Look for Structure
What do you notice about the coefficients of the variable terms in each equation? What do they tell you about the number of solutions an equation may have?

Solving Equations with Variables on Both Sides

Vocabulary 

identity, *p. 33*

KEY IDEA

Solving Equations with Variables on Both Sides

To solve an equation with variables on both sides, use inverse operations to collect the variable terms on one side and the constant terms on the other side. Then isolate the variable.

EXAMPLE 1 Solving an Equation with Variables on Both Sides

Solve $10 - 4x = -9x$. Check your solution.

SOLUTION

$10 - 4x = -9x$	Write the equation.
$\underline{+4x} \quad \underline{+4x}$	Addition Property of Equality
$10 = -5x$	Simplify.
$\dfrac{10}{-5} = \dfrac{-5x}{-5}$	Division Property of Equality
$-2 = x$	Simplify.

▶ The solution is $x = -2$.

Check

$$10 - 4x = -9x$$

$$10 - 4(-2) \stackrel{?}{=} -9(-2)$$

$$18 = 18 \checkmark$$

EXAMPLE 2 Solving an Equation with Grouping Symbols

Solve $3(3x - 4) = \frac{1}{4}(32x + 24)$.

SOLUTION

$3(3x - 4) = \frac{1}{4}(32x + 24)$	Write the equation.
$9x - 12 = 8x + 6$	Distributive Property
$\underline{+12} \quad \underline{+12}$	Addition Property of Equality
$9x = 8x + 18$	Simplify.
$\underline{-8x} \quad \underline{-8x}$	Subtraction Property of Equality
$x = 18$	Simplify.

▶ The solution is $x = 18$.

SELF-ASSESSMENT

1 I do not understand. 2 I can do it with help. 3 I can do it on my own. 4 I can teach someone else.

Solve the equation. Check your solution.

1. $-2x = 3x + 10$
2. $0.5(6h - 4) = -5h + 1$
3. $-\frac{3}{4}(8n + 12) = 3(n - 3)$
4. **WRITING** Describe the steps in solving the linear equation $3(3x - 8) = 4x + 6$. Explain why the steps produce a valid solution.
5. **MP REASONING** Your friend first multiplies each side of $\frac{1}{2}(x + 9) = \frac{3}{4}(5x + 1)$ by 4 when solving the equation. Why might your friend do this?

Identifying the Number of Solutions

Equations do not always have one solution. An equation that is true for all values of the variable is an **identity** and has *infinitely many solutions.* All real numbers are solutions of any identity. An equation that is not true for any value of the variable has *no solution.*

WORDS AND MATH

Think about the meaning of *identity* in everyday life. Your identity is who you are. It can be the name, distinguishing characteristics, or personality that identifies you. Your identity is the same no matter what changes in your day.

EXAMPLE 3 **Solving Equations with Variables on Both Sides**

Solve each equation.

a. $3(5x + 2) = 15x$ **b.** $\frac{n}{6} = -\frac{n}{6} + \frac{1}{2}$ **c.** $-2(4y + 1) = -8y - 2$

SOLUTION

a.

$3(5x + 2) = 15x$	Write the equation.
$15x + 6 = 15x$	Distributive Property
$\underline{-15x} \quad \underline{-15x}$	Subtraction Property of Equality
$6 = 0$ ✗	Simplify.

▶ The statement $6 = 0$ is never true. So, the equation has no solution.

b.

$\frac{n}{6} = -\frac{n}{6} + \frac{1}{2}$	Write the equation.
$6 \cdot \frac{n}{6} = 6 \cdot \left(-\frac{n}{6} + \frac{1}{2}\right)$	Multiplication Property of Equality
$n = -n + 3$	Simplify.
$\underline{+n} \quad \underline{+n}$	Addition Property of Equality
$2n = 3$	Simplify.
$\frac{2n}{2} = \frac{3}{2}$	Division Property of Equality
$n = \frac{3}{2}$	Simplify.

▶ The only solution is $n = \frac{3}{2}$.

Math Practice

Look for Structure
Why is it helpful to multiply each side by 6? How else could you begin to solve this equation?

c.

$-2(4y + 1) = -8y - 2$	Write the equation.
$-8y - 2 = -8y - 2$	Distributive Property
$\underline{+8y} \quad \underline{+8y}$	Addition Property of Equality
$-2 = -2$	Simplify.

▶ Because the statement $-2 = -2$ is always true, the original equation is an identity and has infinitely many solutions. So, the solution is all real numbers.

SELF-ASSESSMENT 1 I do not understand. 2 I can do it with help. 3 I can do it on my own. 4 I can teach someone else.

Solve the equation.

6. $6m - m = \frac{5}{6}(-6m - 30)$ **7.** $10k + 7 = -3 + 10k$ **8.** $3(2a - 2) = 2(3a - 3)$

9. VOCABULARY Is the equation $-2(4 - x) = 2x + 8$ an identity? Explain your reasoning.

10. WRITING In Example 3, your friend says that there is enough information to determine the numbers of solutions of the equations in parts (a) and (c) once you obtain $15x + 6 = 15x$ and $-8y - 2 = -8y - 2$. Is your friend correct? Explain.

Solving Real-Life Problems

EXAMPLE 4 **Modeling Real Life**  

A boat leaves New Orleans and travels upstream on the Mississippi River for 4 hours. The return trip takes only 2.8 hours because the boat travels 3 miles per hour faster downstream due to the current. How far does the boat travel upstream?

SOLUTION

1. **Understand the Problem** You are given the amounts of time the boat travels and the difference in speeds for each direction. You are asked to find the distance the boat travels upstream.
2. **Make a Plan** Use the Distance Formula to write expressions that represent the problem. Because the distance the boat travels in both directions is the same, you can use expressions for the distance to write an equation.
3. **Solve and Check** The distance is equal to the product of speed and time.

Verbal Model Distance upstream = Distance downstream

Variable Let x be the speed (in miles per hour) of the boat traveling upstream.

Equation

$x \cdot 4 = (x + 3) \cdot 2.8$	Write the equation.
$4x = 2.8x + 8.4$	Distributive Property
$-2.8x \quad -2.8x$	Subtraction Property of Equality
$1.2x = 8.4$	Simplify.
$\frac{1.2x}{1.2} = \frac{8.4}{1.2}$	Division Property of Equality
$x = 7$	Simplify.

▶ So, the boat travels 7 miles per hour upstream. To determine how far the boat travels upstream, multiply 7 miles per hour by 4 hours to obtain 28 miles.

Check Because the speed upstream is 7 miles per hour, the speed downstream is $7 + 3 = 10$ miles per hour. When you substitute each speed and time into the Distance Formula, you get the same distance upstream and downstream.

Upstream

$$\text{Distance} = \frac{7 \text{ mi}}{1 \text{ h}} \cdot 4 \text{ h} = 28 \text{ mi}$$

Downstream

$$\text{Distance} = \frac{10 \text{ mi}}{1 \text{ h}} \cdot 2.8 \text{ h} = 28 \text{ mi} \checkmark$$

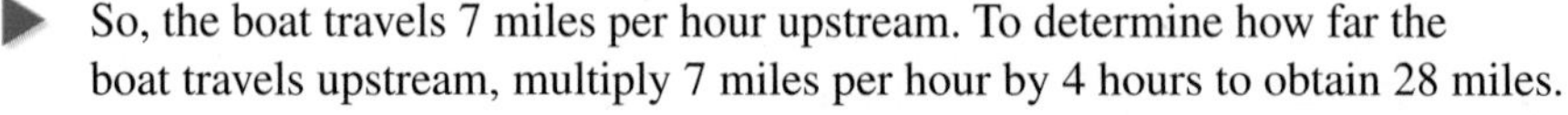

SELF-ASSESSMENT 1 I do not understand. 2 I can do it with help. 3 I can do it on my own. 4 I can teach someone else.

11. A boat travels upstream on the Missouri River for 3.5 hours. The return trip only takes 2.5 hours because the boat travels 2 miles per hour faster downstream due to the current. How far does the boat travel downstream?

12. You ask a deli clerk for x pounds of ham and x pounds of cheese. You end up getting 4 extra ounces of ham and 3 fewer ounces of cheese. The ham costs \$6.24 per pound and the cheese costs \$4.80 per pound. You spend twice as much on ham as you do on cheese. How much do you spend in total?

1.5 Practice WITH CalcChat® AND CalcView®

In Exercises 1–14, solve the equation. Check your solution. *Examples 1 and 2*

1. $15 - 2x = 3x$
2. $26 - 4s = 9s$
3. $5p - 9 = 2p + 12$
4. $8g + 10 = 35 + 3g$
5. $5t + 16 = 6 - 5t$
6. $-3r + 10 = 15r - 8$
7. $7 + 3x - 12x = 3x + 1$
8. $w - 2 + 2w = 6 + 5w$
9. $10(g + 5) = 2(g + 9)$
10. $-9(t - 2) = 4(t - 15)$
11. $\frac{2}{3}(3x + 9) = -2(2x + 6)$
12. $2(2t + 4) = \frac{3}{4}(24 - 8t)$
13. $1.5(3y + 2) - y = 2(8y - 6)$
14. $\frac{1}{2}(4x + 5) = 9x - 12(x - 1)$

In Exercises 15–22, solve the equation. *Example 3*

15. $3t + 4 = 12 + 3t$
16. $6d + 8 = 14 + 3d$
17. $2(h + 1) = 5h - 7$
18. $12y + 6 = 6(2y + 1)$
19. $-\frac{w}{5} = \frac{w}{5} - \frac{1}{10}$
20. $\frac{x}{12} + 1 = \frac{x}{3} - \frac{x}{4}$
21. $3(4g + 6) = 2(6g + 9)$
22. $5(1 + 2m) = \frac{1}{2}(8 + 20m)$

23. **MODELING REAL LIFE** You and your friend drive toward each other. The equation $50h = 190 - 45h$ represents the number h of hours until you and your friend meet. After how many hours will you meet?

24. **ERROR ANALYSIS** Describe and correct the error in solving the equation.

$$6(2y + 6) = 4(9 + 3y)$$
$$12y + 36 = 36 + 12y$$
$$12y = 12y$$
$$0 = 0$$

The equation has no solution.

25. **MODELING REAL LIFE** A cheetah that is running 90 feet per second is 120 feet behind an antelope that is running 60 feet per second. How long will it take the cheetah to catch up to the antelope? *Example 4*

26. **MAKING AN ARGUMENT** A cheetah can run at top speed for only about 20 seconds. If an antelope is too far away for a cheetah to catch it in 20 seconds, the antelope is probably safe. Your friend claims the antelope in Exercise 25 will not be safe if the cheetah starts running 650 feet behind it. Is your friend correct? Explain.

27. **MODELING REAL LIFE** You want to create a piece of pottery at an art studio. The total cost is the cost of the piece plus an hourly studio fee. The costs at two studios are shown.

   a. After how many hours are the total costs the same at both studios? Justify your answer.

   b. Studio B increases its hourly studio fee by $1.50. How does this affect your answer in part (a)? Explain.

28. **MP PROBLEM SOLVING** One serving of granola provides 4% of the protein you need daily. You must get the remaining 48 grams of protein from other sources. How many grams of protein do you need daily?

MP REASONING In Exercises 29 and 30, find the value of *a* for which the equation is an identity. Explain your reasoning.

29. $a(2x + 3) = 9x + 15 + x$
30. $8x - 8 + 3ax = 5ax - 2a$

31. **DIG DEEPER** Two times the greater of two consecutive integers is 9 less than three times the lesser integer. What are the integers?

32. HOW DO YOU SEE IT?
The table and the graph show information about students at a high school.

	Students enrolled this year	Average rate of change
Spanish	355	9 fewer students each year
French	229	12 more students each year

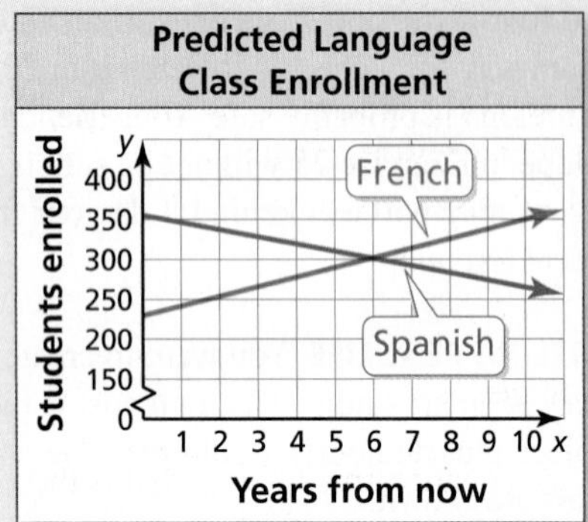

a. Use the graph to determine after how many years there will be equal enrollment in both classes.

b. How does the equation $355 - 9x = 229 + 12x$ relate to the table and the graph? How can you use this equation to determine whether your answer in part (a) is reasonable?

33. MP REASONING Without solving, determine whether the equation $3n + 5 = 3n - 5$ has *one solution, no solution,* or *infinitely many solutions*. Explain your reasoning.

GO DIGITAL

34. CONNECTING CONCEPTS Cylinder A has a radius of 6 feet and a height that is 5.5 feet less than Cylinder B. The cylinders have the same surface area. Find the height of each cylinder.

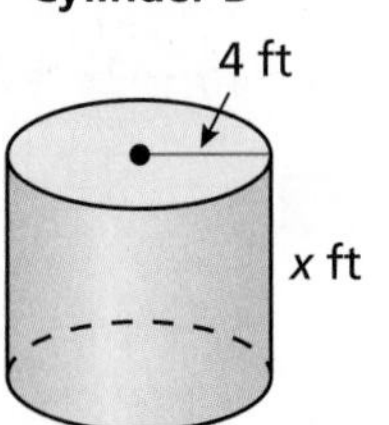

35. COLLEGE PREP For which of the following values of c and d does the equation $cx - 2 = 7x + d$ have no solution? Select all that apply.

Ⓐ $c = -7, d = -2$
Ⓑ $c = 7, d = -2$
Ⓒ $c = 7, d = 0$
Ⓓ $c = 7, d = 2$

36. THOUGHT PROVOKING
Draw a different figure that has the same perimeter as the triangle shown. Explain why your figure has the same perimeter.

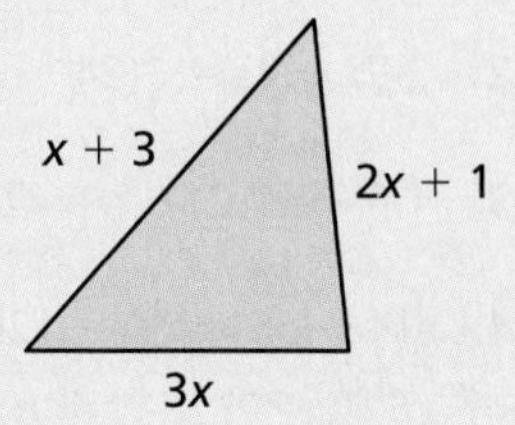

REVIEW & REFRESH

37. You measure the diameter of a circular watch face to be 3.2 centimeters. Estimate the area of the watch face.

In Exercises 38–43, solve the equation. Check your solution.

38. $5 = 10 - v$

39. $2k - 3(2k - 3) = 45$

40. $x - \frac{1}{5} = -\frac{4}{5}$

41. $\frac{n}{7} = 4.5$

42. $7t - 20 = -50 - 8t$

43. $\frac{1}{2}(6c + 2) = -3(c - 1)$

44. Find the area of the kite.

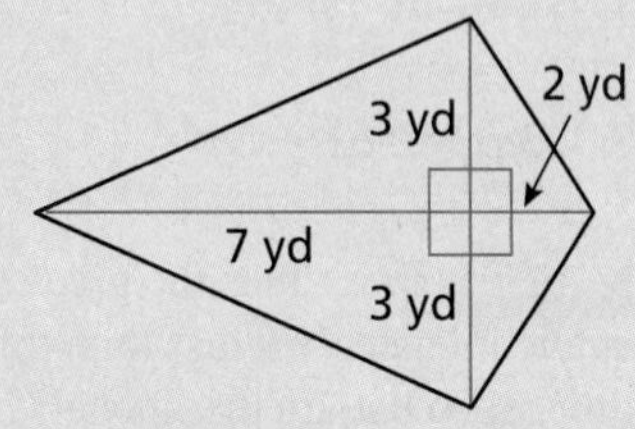

45. You type 168 words in $3\frac{1}{2}$ minutes. How many words do you type per minute?

46. Order the values from least to greatest.

$$|-32|, 22, -16, -|21|, |-10|$$

47. You want to find the height of a drop tower at an amusement park. You take the measurements shown in the diagram. The right triangles created by each object and its shadow are similar. How tall is the drop tower?

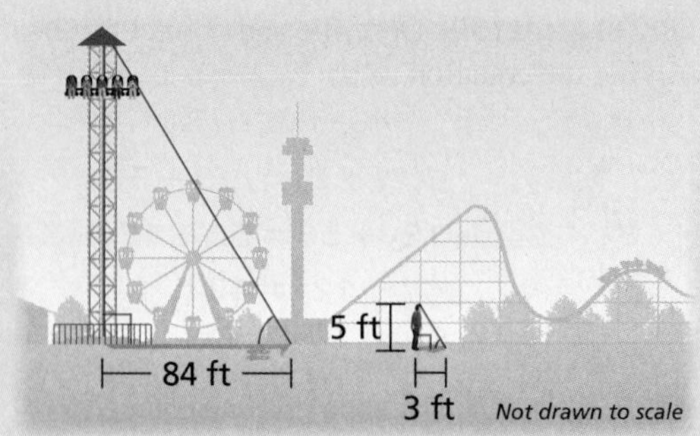

1.6 Solving Absolute Value Equations

Learning Target Write and solve equations involving absolute value.

Success Criteria
- I can write the two linear equations related to a given absolute value equation.
- I can solve equations involving one or two absolute values.
- I can identify special solutions of absolute value equations.

EXPLORE IT! Solving an Absolute Value Equation

Work with a partner. Consider the absolute value equation

$$|x + 2| = 3.$$

a. Explain what you think this equation means.

b. Can you find a number that makes the equation true? If so, what is the number?

c. Do you think there is another number that makes the equation true? If so, find that number. Compare your answer with your classmates.

Math Practice

Construct Arguments Construct a viable argument as to why you think there is or is not more than one solution to the absolute value equation.

d. On the real number line below, locate the point for which the expression $|x + 2|$ is equal to 0.

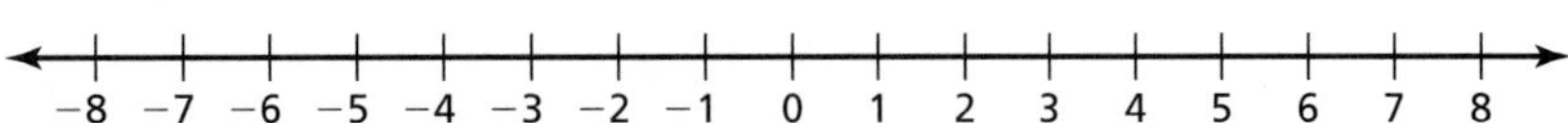

Then locate the numbers you found in parts (b) and (c) on the real number line. What do you notice?

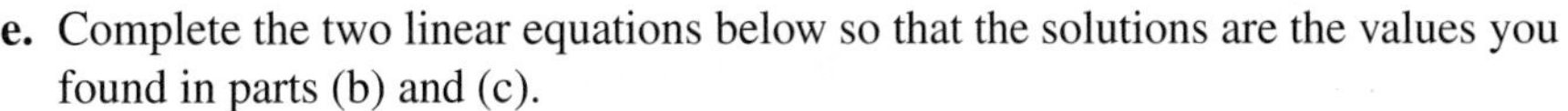

e. Complete the two linear equations below so that the solutions are the values you found in parts (b) and (c).

$x + 2 =$ _____ $\qquad x + 2 =$ _____

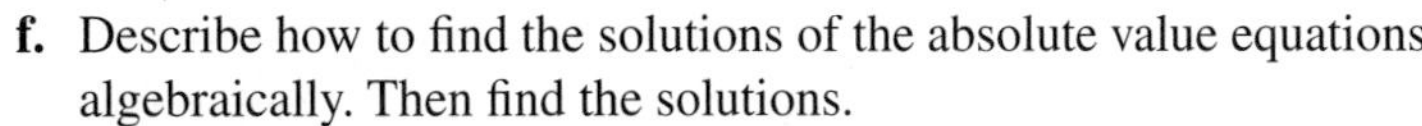

f. Describe how to find the solutions of the absolute value equations algebraically. Then find the solutions.

i. $|x + 2| = 5$

ii. $|x - 3| = 1$

g. Use a spreadsheet to solve the absolute value equations in part (f). Explain your method.

	A	B
1	*x*	|*x* + 2|
2	−8	6
3	−7	
4	−6	
5	−5	
6	−4	
7	−3	
8	−2	
9	−1	
10	0	

=abs(A2 + 2)

Solving Absolute Value Equations

GO DIGITAL

Vocabulary 

absolute value equation, *p. 38*
extraneous solution, *p. 41*

An **absolute value equation** is an equation that contains an absolute value expression. You can solve these types of equations by solving two related linear equations.

KEY IDEAS

Properties of Absolute Value

Let a and b be real numbers. Then the following properties are true.

1. $|a| \geq 0$

2. $|-a| = |a|$

3. $|ab| = |a|\,|b|$

4. $\left|\dfrac{a}{b}\right| = \dfrac{|a|}{|b|}, b \neq 0$

Solving Absolute Value Equations

To solve $|ax + b| = c$ when $c \geq 0$, solve the related linear equations

$$ax + b = c \quad or \quad ax + b = -c.$$

When $c < 0$, the absolute value equation $|ax + b| = c$ has no solution because absolute value represents a distance and cannot be negative.

EXAMPLE 1 Solving Absolute Value Equations

Solve each equation. Graph the solutions, if possible.

a. $|x - 4| = 6$

b. $|3x + 1| = -5$

SOLUTION

a. Write the two related linear equations for $|x - 4| = 6$. Then solve.

$x - 4 = 6$	*or*	$x - 4 = -6$	Write related linear equations.
$x = 10$		$x = -2$	Add 4 to each side.

▶ The solutions are $x = 10$ and $x = -2$.

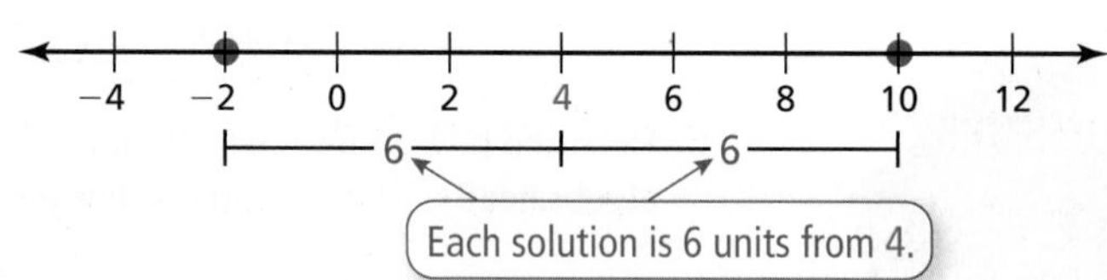

b. The absolute value of an expression must be greater than or equal to 0. The expression $|3x + 1|$ cannot equal -5.

▶ So, the equation has no solution.

SELF-ASSESSMENT 1 I do not understand. 2 I can do it with help. 3 I can do it on my own. 4 I can teach someone else.

Solve the equation. Graph the solutions, if possible.

1. $|x| = 10$

2. $|x - 1| = 4$

3. $|3 + x| = -\frac{1}{2}$

4. **MP REASONING** How do you know that the equation $|4x - 7| = -1$ has no solution?

EXAMPLE 2 Solving a Multi-Step Absolute Value Equation

Solve $|3x + 9| - 10 = -4$.

SOLUTION

First isolate the absolute value expression on one side of the equation.

$\lvert 3x + 9\rvert - 10 = -4$	Write the equation.
$\lvert 3x + 9\rvert = 6$	Add 10 to each side.

Now write the two related linear equations for $|3x + 9| = 6$. Then solve.

$3x + 9 = 6$	*or*	$3x + 9 = -6$	Write related linear equations.
$3x = -3$		$3x = -15$	Subtract 9 from each side.
$x = -1$		$x = -5$	Divide each side by 3.

▶ The solutions are $x = -1$ and $x = -5$.

ANOTHER WAY

Using the Product Property of Absolute Value, $|ab| = |a|\,|b|$, you can first rewrite the equation as

$$3|x + 3| - 10 = -4$$

and then solve.

EXAMPLE 3 Modeling Real Life

You are driving on a highway and are about 250 miles from your state's border. You set your cruise control at 60 miles per hour and plan to turn it off within 30 miles of the border on either side. Find the minimum and maximum numbers of hours you will have cruise control on.

SOLUTION

One way to solve is to write an absolute value equation that models the number x of hours you will have cruise control on. You know that the distance you travel will be within 30 miles of 250 miles.

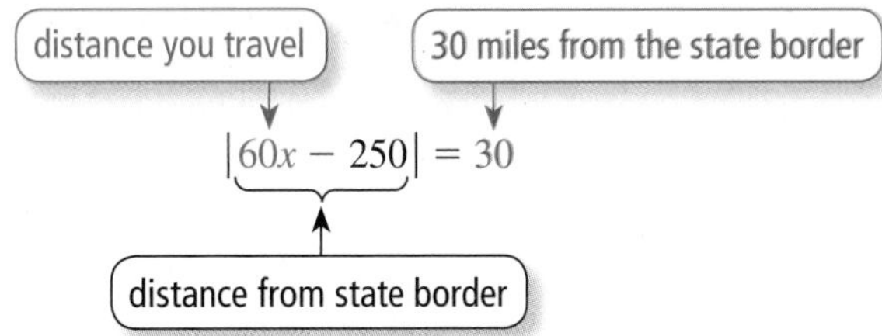

Write the two related linear equations for $|60x - 250| = 30$. Then solve.

$60x - 250 = 30$	*or*	$60x - 250 = -30$	Write related linear equations.
$60x = 280$		$60x = 220$	Add 250 to each side.
$x = 4\frac{2}{3}$		$x = 3\frac{2}{3}$	Divide each side by 60.

The solutions are $x = 3\frac{2}{3}$ and $x = 4\frac{2}{3}$.

▶ So, you will travel at least $3\frac{2}{3}$ hours and at most $4\frac{2}{3}$ hours with cruise control on.

Check

Minimum

$$60\left(3\tfrac{2}{3}\right) - 250 \stackrel{?}{=} -30$$

$$-30 = -30 \checkmark$$

Maximum

$$60\left(4\tfrac{2}{3}\right) - 250 \stackrel{?}{=} 30$$

$$30 = 30 \checkmark$$

SELF-ASSESSMENT

1 I do not understand. 2 I can do it with help. 3 I can do it on my own. 4 I can teach someone else.

Solve the equation. Check your solutions.

5. $|x - 2| + 5 = 9$ **6.** $4|2x + 7| = 16$ **7.** $-2|5x - 1| - 3 = -11$

8. A plane is flying at a speed of 150 miles per hour. The pilot plans on flying at this speed for the next 160 miles, plus or minus 25 miles. Write an absolute value equation to find the minimum and maximum number of hours the plane will travel at that speed.

Solving Equations with Two Absolute Values

If the absolute values of two algebraic expressions are equal, then they must either be equal to each other or be opposites of each other.

KEY IDEA

Solving Equations with Two Absolute Values

To solve $|ax + b| = |cx + d|$, solve the related linear equations

$$ax + b = cx + d \quad or \quad ax + b = -(cx + d).$$

EXAMPLE 4 **Solving Equations with Two Absolute Values**

Solve (a) $|3x - 4| = |x|$ and (b) $|4x - 10| = 2|3x + 1|$.

SOLUTION

a. Write the two related linear equations for $|3x - 4| = |x|$. Then solve.

$$\begin{array}{rlcrl} 3x - 4 = & x & or & 3x - 4 = & -x \\ \underline{-x} & \underline{-x} & & \underline{+x} & \underline{+x} \\ 2x - 4 = & 0 & & 4x - 4 = & 0 \\ \underline{+4} & \underline{+4} & & \underline{+4} & \underline{+4} \\ 2x = & 4 & & 4x = & 4 \\ \frac{2x}{2} = & \frac{4}{2} & & \frac{4x}{4} = & \frac{4}{4} \\ x = & 2 & & x = & 1 \end{array}$$

▶ The solutions are $x = 2$ and $x = 1$.

Check

$|3x - 4| = |x|$

$|3(2) - 4| \stackrel{?}{=} |2|$

$|2| \stackrel{?}{=} |2|$

$2 = 2$ ✓

$|3x - 4| = |x|$

$|3(1) - 4| \stackrel{?}{=} |1|$

$|-1| \stackrel{?}{=} |1|$

$1 = 1$ ✓

b. Write the two related linear equations for $|4x - 10| = 2|3x + 1|$. Then solve.

$$\begin{array}{rlcrl} 4x - 10 = & 2(3x + 1) & or & 4x - 10 = & 2[-(3x + 1)] \\ 4x - 10 = & 6x + 2 & & 4x - 10 = & 2(-3x - 1) \\ \underline{-6x} & \underline{-6x} & & 4x - 10 = & -6x - 2 \\ -2x - 10 = & 2 & & \underline{+6x} & \underline{+6x} \\ \underline{+10} & \underline{+10} & & 10x - 10 = & -2 \\ -2x = & 12 & & \underline{+10} & \underline{+10} \\ \frac{-2x}{-2} = & \frac{12}{-2} & & 10x = & 8 \\ x = & -6 & & \frac{10x}{10} = & \frac{8}{10} \\ & & & x = & 0.8 \end{array}$$

▶ The solutions are $x = -6$ and $x = 0.8$.

SELF-ASSESSMENT 1 I do not understand. 2 I can do it with help. 3 I can do it on my own. 4 I can teach someone else.

Solve the equation. Check your solutions.

9. $|x + 8| = |2x + 1|$

10. $3|x - 4| = |2x + 5|$

11. $\frac{1}{2}|x + 8| = |4x - 1|$

Identifying Special Solutions

GO DIGITAL

When you solve an absolute value equation, it is possible for a solution to be *extraneous*. An **extraneous solution** is an apparent solution that must be rejected because it does not satisfy the original equation.

WORDS AND MATH

The word *extraneous* contains the prefix *extra-*, which means "more than is necessary." Extraneous information is information that is not relevant or essential.

EXAMPLE 5 Identifying Extraneous Solutions

Solve $|2x + 12| = 4x$. Check your solutions.

SOLUTION

Write the two related linear equations for $|2x + 12| = 4x$. Then solve.

$2x + 12 = 4x$	*or*	$2x + 12 = -4x$	Write related linear equations.
$12 = 2x$		$12 = -6x$	Subtract $2x$ from each side.
$6 = x$		$-2 = x$	Solve for x.

Check the apparent solutions to see if either is extraneous.

▶ The solution is $x = 6$. Reject $x = -2$ because it is extraneous.

Check

$|2x + 12| = 4x$

$|2(6) + 12| \stackrel{?}{=} 4(6)$

$|24| \stackrel{?}{=} 24$

$24 = 24$ ✓

$|2x + 12| = 4x$

$|2(-2) + 12| \stackrel{?}{=} 4(-2)$

$|8| \stackrel{?}{=} -8$

$8 \neq -8$ ✗

When solving equations of the form $|ax + b| = |cx + d|$, it is possible that one of the related linear equations will not have a solution.

EXAMPLE 6 Solving an Equation with Two Absolute Values

Solve $|x + 5| = |x + 11|$.

SOLUTION

By equating the expression $x + 5$ and the opposite of $x + 11$, you obtain

$x + 5 = -(x + 11)$	Write related linear equation.
$x + 5 = -x - 11$	Distributive Property
$2x + 5 = -11$	Add x to each side.
$2x = -16$	Subtract 5 from each side.
$x = -8.$	Divide each side by 2.

However, by equating the expressions $x + 5$ and $x + 11$, you obtain

$x + 5 = x + 11$	Write related linear equation.
$x = x + 6$	Subtract 5 from each side.
$0 = 6$ ✗	Subtract x from each side.

which is a false statement. So, the original equation has only one solution.

▶ The solution is $x = -8$.

REMEMBER

Always check your solutions in the original equation to make sure they are not extraneous.

SELF-ASSESSMENT

1 I do not understand. 2 I can do it with help. 3 I can do it on my own. 4 I can teach someone else.

Solve the equation. Check your solutions.

12. $|x + 6| = 2x$

13. $|3x - 2| = x$

14. $|2 + x| = |x - 8|$

15. $|5x - 2| = |5x + 4|$

16. WRITING How is solving an absolute value equation similar to solving an equation without an absolute value? How is it different?

1.6 Practice WITH CalcChat® AND CalcView®

In Exercises 1–8, simplify the expression.

1. $|-9|$
2. $-|15|$
3. $|14| - |-14|$
4. $|-3| + |3|$
5. $-|-5 \cdot (-7)|$
6. $|-0.8 \cdot 10|$
7. $\left|\frac{27}{-3}\right|$
8. $\left|-\frac{-12}{4}\right|$

In Exercises 9–22, solve the equation. Graph the solution(s), if possible. *Examples 1 and 2*

9. $|r| = -2$
10. $|x| = 13.4$
11. $|m + 3| = 7$
12. $|q - 8| = 14$
13. $\left|\frac{t}{2}\right| = 6$
14. $|-3.5d| = 15.4$
15. $|4b - 5| = 19$
16. $|x - 1| + 5 = 2$
17. $2|-8w + 6| = 76$
18. $\left|\frac{1}{3}y - 2\right| - 7 = 3$
19. $-4|8 - 5n| = 13$
20. $-3\left|1 - \frac{2}{3}v\right| = -9$
21. $3 = -2\left|\frac{1}{4}s - 5\right| + 3$
22. $9|4p + 2| + 8 = 35$

23. **MODELING REAL LIFE** The average distance from Earth to the Sun is 92.95 million miles. The actual distance varies from the average by up to 1.55 million miles. Write and solve an absolute value equation to find the minimum and maximum distance from Earth to the Sun. *Example 3*

24. **MODELING REAL LIFE** The recommended mass of a soccer ball is 0.43 kilogram. The actual mass is allowed to vary by up to 20 grams.
    a. Write and solve an absolute value equation to find the minimum and maximum acceptable soccer ball masses.
    b. A soccer ball has a mass of 423 grams. The soccer ball loses 0.016 kilogram of mass over time. Is the mass now acceptable? Explain.

MP STRUCTURE In Exercises 25–28, match the absolute value equation with its graph without solving the equation.

25. $|x + 2| = 4$
26. $|x - 4| = 2$
27. $|x - 2| = 4$
28. $|x + 4| = 2$

A. 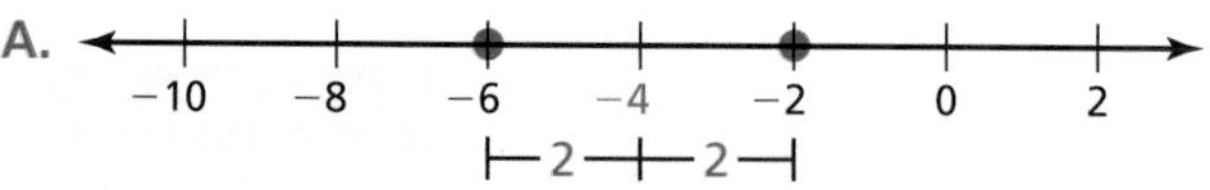

B. 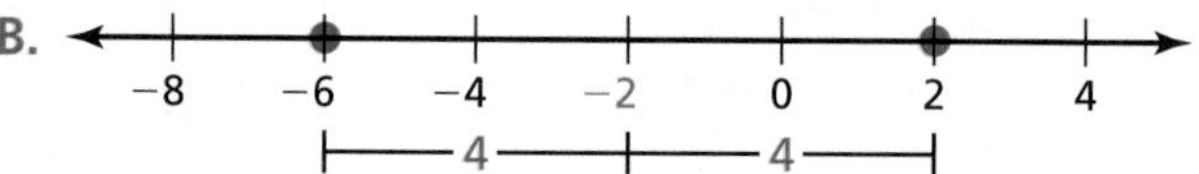

C. 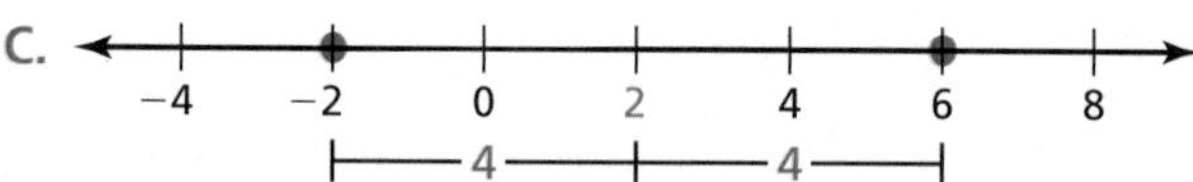

D. 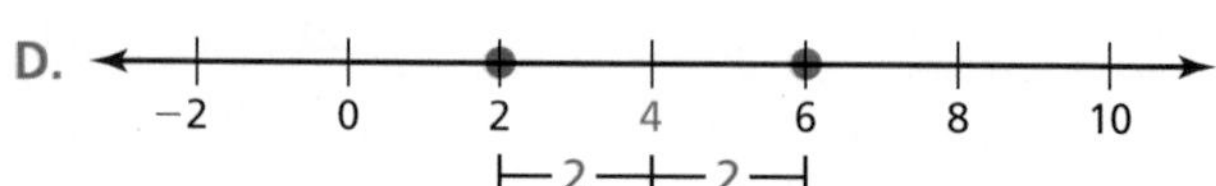

In Exercises 29–38, solve the equation. Check your solutions. *Examples 4, 5, and 6*

29. $|4n - 15| = |n|$
30. $|2c + 8| = |10c|$
31. $|3k - 2| = 2|k + 2|$
32. $\left|\frac{1}{2}b - 8\right| = \left|\frac{1}{4}b - 1\right|$
33. $4|p - 3| = |2p + 8|$
34. $2|4w - 1| = 3|4w + 2|$
35. $|3h + 1| = 7h$
36. $|6a - 5| = 4a$
37. $\left|f - \frac{4}{3}\right| = \left|f + \frac{1}{6}\right|$
38. $|3x - 4| = |3x - 5|$

MP REASONING **In Exercises 39–42, write an absolute value equation that has the given solutions.**

39. $x = 8$ and $x = 18$ **40.** $x = -6$ and $x = 10$

41. $x = 1.5$ and $x = 8.5$ **42.** $x = -10$ and $x = -5$

ERROR ANALYSIS **In Exercises 43 and 44, describe and correct the error in solving the equation.**

43.

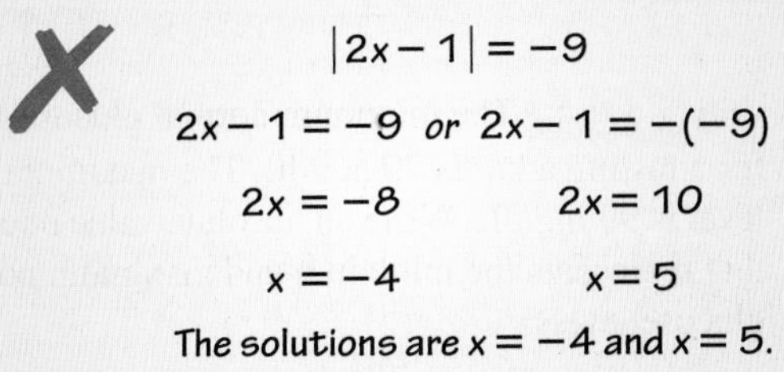

✗

$|2x - 1| = -9$

$2x - 1 = -9$ *or* $2x - 1 = -(-9)$

$2x = -8$ $2x = 10$

$x = -4$ $x = 5$

The solutions are $x = -4$ and $x = 5$.

44.

✗

$|5x + 8| = x$

$5x + 8 = x$ *or* $5x + 8 = -x$

$4x + 8 = 0$ $6x + 8 = 0$

$4x = -8$ $6x = -8$

$x = -2$ $x = -\frac{4}{3}$

The solutions are $x = -2$ and $x = -\frac{4}{3}$.

45. MODELING REAL LIFE Starting from 300 feet away, a car drives toward you. It then passes by you at a constant speed of 48 feet per second. The distance d (in feet) of the car from you after t seconds is given by the equation $d = |300 - 48t|$.

a. Explain what $48t$ represents in the given equation.

b. At what times is the car 60 feet from you?

46. MP REASONING Without solving completely, place each equation into one of the three categories. Explain your reasoning.

No solution	One solution	Two solutions

$|x - 2| + 6 = 0$ $|x + 3| - 1 = 0$

$|x + 8| + 2 = 7$ $|x - 1| + 4 = 4$

$|x - 6| - 5 = -9$ $|x + 5| - 8 = -8$

47. MAKING AN ARGUMENT Your friend says that the absolute value equation $|3x + 8| - 9 = -5$ has no solution because the constant on the right side of the equation is negative. Is your friend correct? Explain.

GO DIGITAL

48. HOW DO YOU SEE IT?
The circle graph shows the results of a survey of registered voters the day of an election.

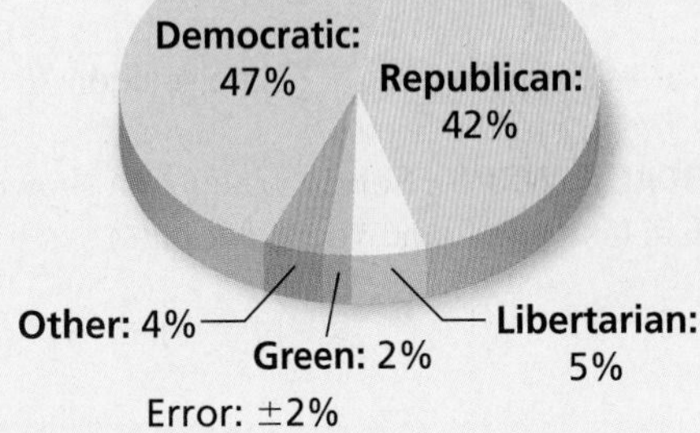

The error given in the graph means that the actual percent could be 2% more or 2% less than the percent reported by the survey.

a. What does the survey predict are the minimum and maximum percents of voters who will vote Republican? Green?

b. Write absolute value equations to represent your answers in part (a).

c. One candidate receives 44% of the vote. Which party do you think the candidate belongs to? Explain.

ABSTRACT REASONING **In Exercises 49–52, complete the statement with *always*, *sometimes*, or *never*. Explain your reasoning.**

49. If $x^2 = a^2$, then $|x|$ is ________ equal to $|a|$.

50. If a and b are real numbers, then $|a - b|$ is ________ equal to $|b - a|$.

51. For any real number p, the equation $|x - 4| = p$ will ________ have two solutions.

52. For any real number p, the equation $|x - p| = 4$ will ________ have two solutions.

53. WRITING Explain why absolute value equations can have no solution, one solution, or two solutions. Give an example of each case.

54. **MP STRUCTURE** Complete the equation $|x - \square| = \square$ with a, b, c, or d so that the equation is graphed correctly.

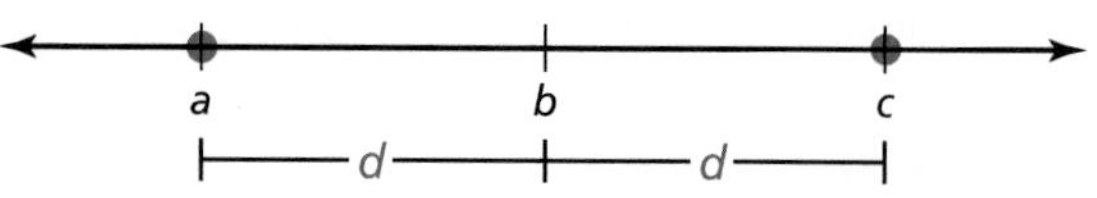

55. **COLLEGE PREP** Which values are solutions of the equation $5 = -\frac{2}{3}|4x - 7| + 11$? Select all that apply.

Ⓐ $x = -\frac{1}{2}$ Ⓑ $x = \frac{1}{2}$

Ⓒ $x = \frac{3}{4}$ Ⓓ $x = \frac{11}{4}$

Ⓔ $x = 4$ Ⓕ no solution

56. **CRITICAL THINKING** Solve the equation shown. Explain how you found your solution(s).

$$8|x + 2| - 6 = 5|x + 2| + 3$$

57. **OPEN-ENDED** Describe a real-life situation that can be modeled by an absolute value equation with the solutions $x = 62$ and $x = 72$.

58. **THOUGHT PROVOKING**

What is the maximum number of solutions an equation of the form $\big||ax - b| + c\big| = d$ can have? Justify your reasoning with an example.

59. **DIG DEEPER** The minimum normal glucose level for a fasting adult is 70 mg/dL. The maximum normal level is 99 mg/dL. Write an absolute value equation that represents the minimum and maximum normal glucose levels.

60. **ABSTRACT REASONING** How many solutions does the equation $a|x + b| + c = d$ have when $a > 0$ and $c = d$? when $a < 0$ and $c > d$? Explain your reasoning.

REVIEW & REFRESH

In Exercises 61–64, solve the equation. Check your solution(s).

61. $3c + 1 = c + 1$

62. $4(6k + 9) = 8(3k - 2)$

63. $-10 - 12g = -4(3g + 2.5)$

64. $|y - 4| = |y + 10|$

65. **MODELING REAL LIFE** An outdoor music festival provides 4000 square yards of land for the audience. Attendees are permitted to reserve a section using a rectangular tarp with a length of 12 feet and a width of 10 feet. About how many sections can be reserved at the music festival?

66. Simplify $12 + 5h - 3.5 + 8h$.

In Exercises 67 and 68, write the number in standard form.

67. 7×10^{-8}

68. 2.59×10^3

In Exercises 69 and 70, find the volume of the figure. Round your answer to the nearest tenth.

69.

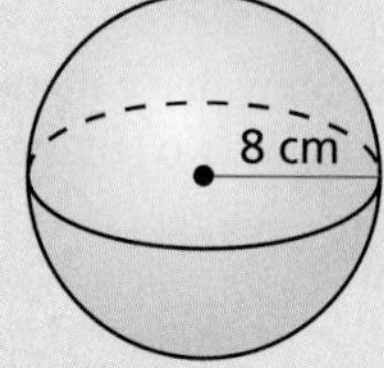

70.

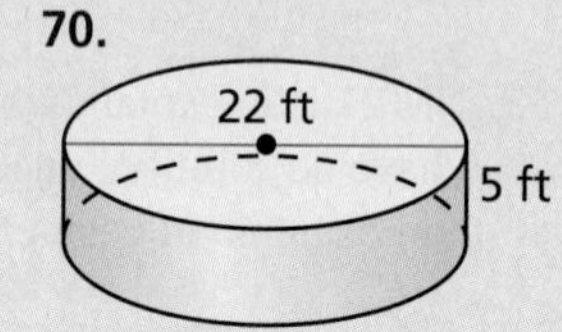

JUSTIFYING STEPS In Exercises 71 and 72, identify the property of equality that makes Equation 1 and Equation 2 equivalent.

71.

Equation 1	$3x + 8 = x - 1$
Equation 2	$3x + 9 = x$

72.

Equation 1	$4y = 28$
Equation 2	$y = 7$

73. A circle has an area of 36π square inches. Find the radius.

74. A triangle has a height of 8 feet and an area of 48 square feet. Find the base.

75. **MODELING REAL LIFE** You are driving your moped to school. The drive is about 12.5 miles, but the distance varies by up to 1.25 miles, depending on the route you take. You drive at a constant speed of 25 miles per hour. Find the minimum and maximum number of minutes it will take you to travel to school.

In Exercises 76–79, complete the statement. Round to the nearest hundredth, if necessary.

76. 9900 sec = $\square$ h

77. 0.25 T = $\square$ oz

78. 11.5 qt ≈ $\square$ mL

79. 49.6 cm ≈ $\square$ ft

1.7 Rewriting Equations and Formulas

Learning Target Solve literal equations for given variables.

Success Criteria

- I can identify a literal equation.
- I can use properties of equality to rewrite literal equations.
- I can use rewritten formulas to solve problems.

EXPLORE IT! Using Multiple Equations to Relate Quantities

Work with a partner. A landscaper purchases gasoline for various lawn care equipment. Consider the following quantities involved in this situation.

Number of gallons of gasoline

Price per gallon of gasoline

Total cost of gasoline

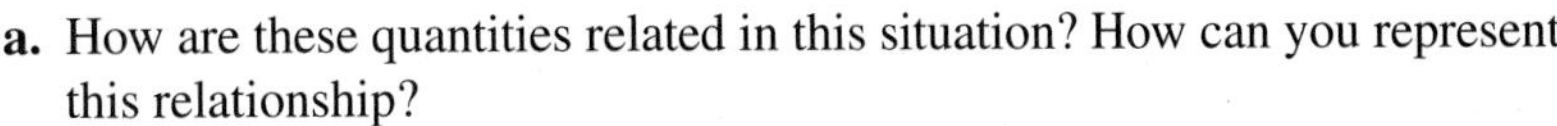

a. How are these quantities related in this situation? How can you represent this relationship?

b. Write an equation that represents the relationship among the three quantities.

Total cost of gasoline = ?

c. Write two more equations that represent the same relationship. How did you write these equations?

Price per gallon of gasoline = ?

Number of gallons of gasoline = ?

d. Why do you think it is beneficial to have solved an equation for each quantity?

e. After pumping gasoline, the landscaper sees the screen shown on the pump. Which quantity is missing? Find the missing quantity and explain how you found it.

Math Practice

Calculate Accurately
How many decimal places did you use in your answer in part (e)? Explain your reasoning.

Rewriting Literal Equations

Vocabulary
literal equation, *p. 46*
formula, *p. 47*

An equation that has two or more variables is called a **literal equation**. To rewrite a literal equation, solve for one variable in terms of the other variable(s).

EXAMPLE 1 **Rewriting a Literal Equation**

Solve the literal equation $3y + 4x = 9$ for y.

SOLUTION

$3y + 4x = 9$	Write the equation.
$3y + 4x - 4x = 9 - 4x$	Subtraction Property of Equality
$3y = 9 - 4x$	Simplify.
$\frac{3y}{3} = \frac{9 - 4x}{3}$	Division Property of Equality
$y = 3 - \frac{4}{3}x$	Simplify.

▶ The rewritten literal equation is $y = 3 - \frac{4}{3}x$.

EXAMPLE 2 **Rewriting a Literal Equation**

Solve the literal equation $y = 3x + 5xz$ for x.

SOLUTION

$y = 3x + 5xz$	Write the equation.
$y = x(3 + 5z)$	Distributive Property
$\frac{y}{3 + 5z} = \frac{x(3 + 5z)}{3 + 5z}$	Division Property of Equality
$\frac{y}{3 + 5z} = x$	Simplify.

▶ The rewritten literal equation is $x = \frac{y}{3 + 5z}$.

REMEMBER
Division by 0 is undefined.

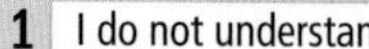

In Example 2, you must assume that $z \neq -\frac{3}{5}$ in order to divide by $3 + 5z$. In general, when dividing by a variable or variable expression to rewrite a literal equation, assume that the variable or variable expression does not equal 0.

SELF-ASSESSMENT 1 I do not understand. 2 I can do it with help. 3 I can do it on my own. 4 I can teach someone else.

Solve the literal equation for *y*.

1. $3y - x = 9$ **2.** $2x - 2y = 5$ **3.** $20 = 8x + 4y$

Solve the literal equation for *x*.

4. $y = 5x - 4x$ **5.** $2x + kx = m$ **6.** $3 + 5x - kx = y$

7. DIFFERENT WORDS, SAME QUESTION Which is different? Find "both" answers.

Solve $3x + 6y = 24$ for x.

Solve $24 - 3x = 6y$ for x.

Solve $6y = 24 - 3x$ for y in terms of x.

Solve $24 - 6y = 3x$ for x in terms of y.

Rewriting and Using Formulas for Area

A **formula** shows how one variable is related to one or more other variables. A formula is a type of literal equation.

EXAMPLE 3 Rewriting a Formula for Surface Area

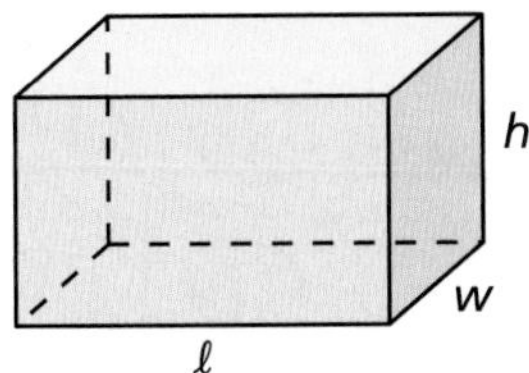

The formula for the surface area S of a rectangular prism is $S = 2\ell w + 2\ell h + 2wh$. Solve the formula for the length ℓ.

SOLUTION

$$S = 2\ell w + 2\ell h + 2wh$$ Write the equation.

$$S - 2wh = 2\ell w + 2\ell h + 2wh - 2wh$$ Subtraction Property of Equality

$$S - 2wh = 2\ell w + 2\ell h$$ Simplify.

$$S - 2wh = \ell(2w + 2h)$$ Distributive Property

$$\frac{S - 2wh}{2w + 2h} = \frac{\ell(2w + 2h)}{2w + 2h}$$ Division Property of Equality

$$\frac{S - 2wh}{2w + 2h} = \ell$$ Simplify.

▶ When you solve the formula for ℓ, you obtain $\ell = \dfrac{S - 2wh}{2w + 2h}$.

EXAMPLE 4 Modeling Real Life

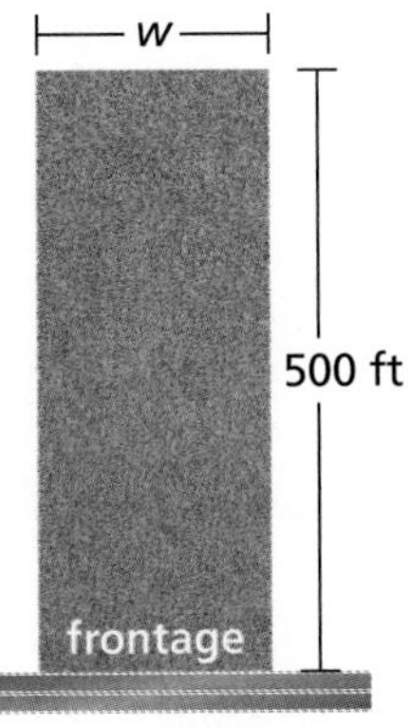

You own a rectangular lot that is 500 feet deep. It has an area of 100,000 square feet. To pay for a new water system, you are assessed $5.50 per foot of lot frontage. How much are you assessed for the new water system?

SOLUTION

To find the amount assessed, first find the frontage of your lot. In the formula for the area of a rectangle, let the width w represent the lot frontage.

$$A = \ell w$$ Write the formula for area of a rectangle.

$$\frac{A}{\ell} = w$$ Divide each side by ℓ to solve for w.

$$\frac{100{,}000}{500} = w$$ Substitute 100,000 for A and 500 for ℓ.

$$200 = w$$ Simplify.

Your frontage is 200 feet. Multiply this by the cost of frontage, $5.50 per foot.

$$\frac{\$5.50}{1\ \cancel{ft}} \cdot 200\ \cancel{ft} = \$1100$$

▶ So, you are assessed $1100 for the new water system.

SELF-ASSESSMENT 1 I do not understand. 2 I can do it with help. 3 I can do it on my own. 4 I can teach someone else.

Solve the formula for the indicated variable.

8. Area of a triangle: $A = \frac{1}{2}bh$; Solve for h.

9. Surface area of a cone: $S = \pi r^2 + \pi r\ell$; Solve for ℓ.

10. You want to enclose a rectangular region with an area of 1200 square feet and a length of 40 feet, 50 feet, or 60 feet. Find the perimeter for each possible region. Explain why you might rewrite the area formula to find the solutions.

Rewriting and Using Other Common Formulas

KEY IDEA

Common Formulas

Temperature F = degrees Fahrenheit, C = degrees Celsius

$C = \frac{5}{9}(F - 32)$

Simple Interest I = interest, P = principal,

r = annual interest rate (decimal form),

t = time (years)

$I = Prt$

Distance d = distance traveled, r = rate, t = time

$d = rt$

Mercury 427°C

Venus 864°F

EXAMPLE 5 Rewriting the Formula for Temperature

Solve the temperature formula for F.

SOLUTION

$C = \frac{5}{9}(F - 32)$ Write the temperature formula.

$\frac{9}{5}C = F - 32$ Multiply each side by $\frac{9}{5}$.

$\frac{9}{5}C + 32 = F$ Add 32 to each side.

▶ The rewritten formula is $F = \frac{9}{5}C + 32$.

EXAMPLE 6 Modeling Real Life

Which has the greater surface temperature: Mercury or Venus?

SOLUTION

Convert the Celsius temperature of Mercury to degrees Fahrenheit.

$F = \frac{9}{5}C + 32$ Write the rewritten formula from Example 5.

$= \frac{9}{5}(427) + 32$ Substitute 427 for C.

$= 768.6 + 32$ Multiply.

$= 800.6$ Add.

▶ The surface temperature of Mercury is 800.6°F. Because 864°F is greater than 800.6°F, Venus has the greater surface temperature.

SELF-ASSESSMENT 1 I do not understand. 2 I can do it with help. 3 I can do it on my own. 4 I can teach someone else.

11. A fever is generally considered to be a body temperature greater than 100°F. Your friend has a temperature of 37°C. Does your friend have a fever when the temperature increases by 1°F? 1°C?

EXAMPLE 7 Modeling Real Life

You deposit \$5000 in an account that earns simple interest. After 6 months, the account earns \$162.50 in interest. What is the annual interest rate?

SOLUTION

COMMON ERROR
The unit of t is years. Be sure to convert months to years.

$$\frac{1 \text{ yr}}{12 \text{ mo}} \cdot 6 \text{ mo} = 0.5 \text{ yr}$$

One way to find the annual interest rate is to solve the simple interest formula for r.

$I = Prt$	Write the simple interest formula.
$\frac{I}{Pt} = r$	Divide each side by Pt to solve for r.
$\frac{162.50}{(5000)(0.5)} = r$	Substitute 162.50 for I, 5000 for P, and 0.5 for t.
$0.065 = r$	Simplify.

▶ The annual interest rate is 0.065, or 6.5%.

EXAMPLE 8 Modeling Real Life

A truck driver averages 60 miles per hour while delivering freight to a customer. On the return trip, the driver averages 50 miles per hour due to construction. The total driving time is 6 hours and 36 minutes. How long does each trip take?

SOLUTION

Step 1 Rewrite the Distance Formula to write expressions that represent the two trip times. Solving the formula $d = rt$ for t, you obtain $t = \frac{d}{r}$. So, $\frac{d}{60}$ represents the delivery time, and $\frac{d}{50}$ represents the return trip time.

Step 2 Use these expressions and the total driving time to write and solve an equation to find the distance one way.

$\frac{d}{60} + \frac{d}{50} = 6.6$	Total driving time: $6 \text{ h} + \frac{36}{60} \text{ h} = 6.6 \text{ h}$
$\frac{11d}{300} = 6.6$	Add the fractions using a common denominator of 300.
$11d = 1980$	Multiply each side by 300.
$d = 180$	Divide each side by 11.

The distance one way is 180 miles.

Check Check that the sum of the driving times is equal to the total driving time.

$$\begin{array}{r} 3 \text{ h} \\ + 3 \text{ h } 36 \text{ min} \\ \hline 6 \text{ h } 36 \text{ min} \end{array} \checkmark$$

Step 3 Use the expressions from Step 1 to find the two trip times.

▶ So, the delivery takes $180 \text{ mi} \div \frac{60 \text{ mi}}{1 \text{ h}} = 3$ hours and the return trip takes $180 \text{ mi} \div \frac{50 \text{ mi}}{1 \text{ h}} = 3.6$ hours, or 3 hours and 36 minutes.

SELF-ASSESSMENT
1 I do not understand. 2 I can do it with help. 3 I can do it on my own. 4 I can teach someone else.

12. How much money must you deposit in a simple interest account to earn \$500 in interest in 5 years at 4% annual interest?

13. A truck driver averages 60 miles per hour while delivering freight and 45 miles per hour on the return trip. The total driving time is 7 hours. How much longer does the return trip take than the delivery?

1.7 Practice WITH CalcChat® AND CalcView®

In Exercises 1–10, solve the literal equation for y. *Example 1*

1. $y - 3x = 13$
2. $2x + y = 7$
3. $2y - 18x = -26$
4. $20x + 5y = 15$
5. $9x - y = 45$
6. $6x - 3y = -6$
7. $4x - 5 = 7 + 4y$
8. $16x + 9 = 9y - 2x$
9. $2 + \frac{1}{6}y = 3x + 4$
10. $11 - \frac{1}{2}y = 3 + 6x$

In Exercises 11–20, solve the literal equation for x. *Example 2*

11. $y = 4x + 8x$
12. $m = 10x - x$
13. $a = 2x + 6xz$
14. $y = 3bx - 7x$
15. $y = 4x + rx + 6$
16. $z = 8 + 6x - px$
17. $sx + tx = r$
18. $a = bx + cx + d$
19. $12 - 5x - 4kx = y$
20. $x - 9 + 2wx = y$

21. **MODELING REAL LIFE** The total cost C (in dollars) to participate in a ski club is given by $C = 85x + 60$, where x is the number of ski trips you take.

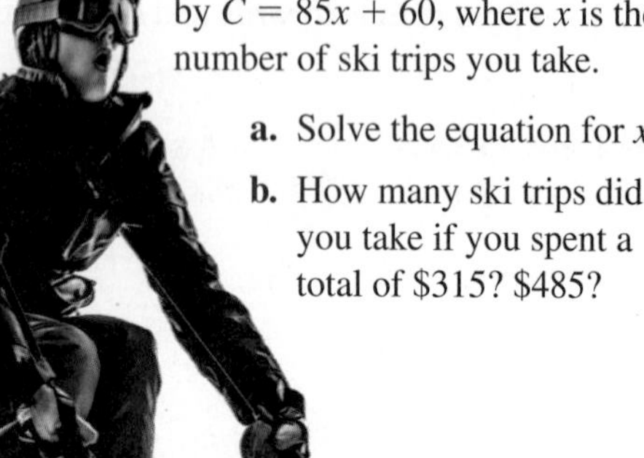

   a. Solve the equation for x.

   b. How many ski trips did you take if you spent a total of \$315? \$485?

22. **MODELING REAL LIFE** The penny size of a nail indicates the length of the nail. The penny size d of a nail that is 1 to 3 inches long is given by $d = 4n - 2$, where n is the length (in inches) of the nail.

   a. Solve the equation for n.

   b. Find the lengths of nails with the following penny sizes: 3, 6, and 10.

ERROR ANALYSIS In Exercises 23 and 24, describe and correct the error in solving the equation for x.

23.

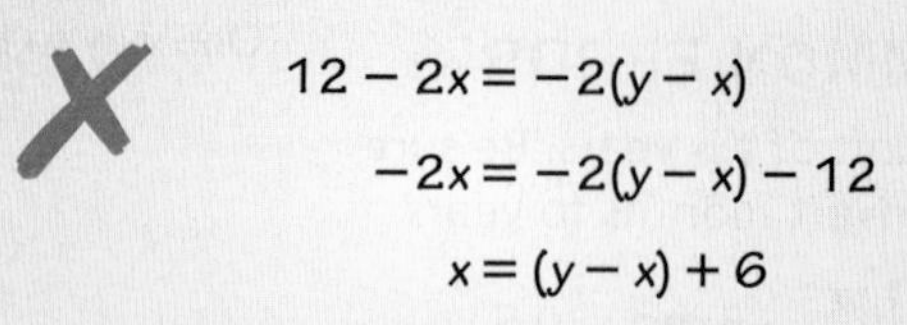

$$12 - 2x = -2(y - x)$$
$$-2x = -2(y - x) - 12$$
$$x = (y - x) + 6$$

24.

$$10 = ax - 3b$$
$$10 = x(a - 3b)$$
$$\frac{10}{a - 3b} = x$$

In Exercises 25–28, solve the formula for the indicated variable. *Examples 3 and 5*

25. Profit: $P = R - C$; Solve for C.

26. Surface area of a cylinder: $S = 2\pi r^2 + 2\pi rh$; Solve for h.

27. Area of a trapezoid: $A = \frac{1}{2}h(b_1 + b_2)$; Solve for b_2.

28. Average acceleration of an object: $a = \frac{v_1 - v_0}{t}$; Solve for v_1.

29. **REWRITING A FORMULA** A common statistic used in professional football is the quarterback rating. This rating is made up of four major factors. One factor is the completion rating given by the formula

$$R = 5\left(\frac{C}{A} - 0.3\right)$$

where C is the number of completed passes and A is the number of attempted passes. Solve the formula for C.

30. **REWRITING A FORMULA** Newton's law of gravitation is given by the formula

$$F = G\left(\frac{m_1 m_2}{d^2}\right)$$

where F is the force between two objects of masses m_1 and m_2, G is the gravitational constant, and d is the distance between the two objects. Solve the formula for m_1.

31. **MODELING REAL LIFE** The sale price S (in dollars) of an item is given by the formula $S = L - rL$, where L is the list price (in dollars) and r is the percent of discount (in decimal form). *Examples 4 and 6*

a. Solve the formula for r.

b. The list price of the shirt is \$21.50. What is the percent of discount?

32. **MODELING REAL LIFE** The density d of a substance is given by the formula $d = \frac{m}{V}$, where m is its mass and V is its volume.

a. Solve the formula for each of the other two variables.

b. Find the mass of the pyrite sample. Explain how you found the mass.

33. **MAKING AN ARGUMENT** Your friend claims that Thermometer A displays a greater temperature than Thermometer B. Is your friend correct? Explain your reasoning.

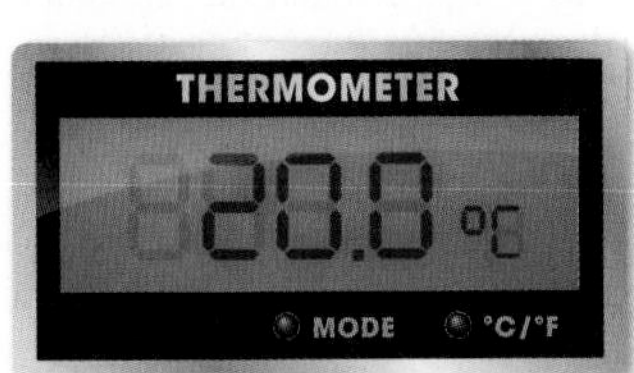

Thermometer A

Thermometer B

34. **MODELING REAL LIFE** You deposit \$2000 in an account that earns simple interest at an annual rate of 4%. How long must you leave the money in the account to earn \$500 in interest? *Example 7*

35. **MODELING REAL LIFE** A flight averages 460 miles per hour. The return flight averages 500 miles per hour due to a tailwind. The total flying time is 4 hours and 48 minutes. How long is each flight? Explain. *Example 8*

36. **MODELING REAL LIFE** An athletic facility is building an indoor track. The track is composed of a rectangle and two semicircles, as shown.

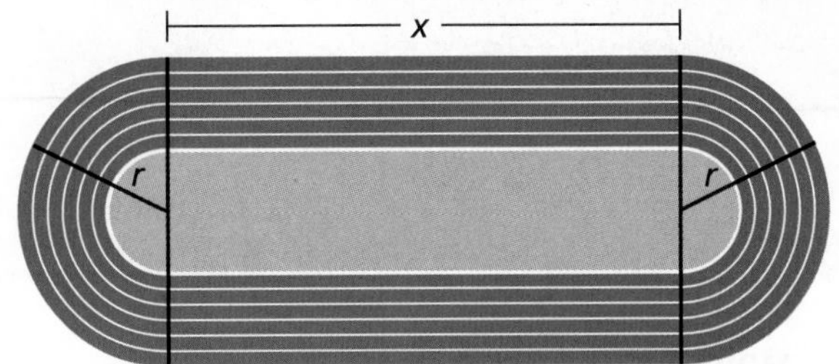

a. Write a formula for the perimeter of the indoor track. Then solve the formula for x.

b. The perimeter of the track is 660 feet, and r is 50 feet. Find x. Round your answer to the nearest foot.

37. **MODELING REAL LIFE** A vehicle travels 55 miles per hour and 20 miles per gallon.

a. Write an equation that represents the distance d (in miles) that the vehicle travels in t hours. Then write an equation that represents the distance d (in miles) that the vehicle travels using g gallons of gasoline.

b. Write an equation that relates g and t. Then solve the equation for g.

c. The vehicle travels for 6 hours. How many gallons of gasoline does the vehicle use? How far does it travel? Explain.

38. **HOW DO YOU SEE IT?**
The rectangular prism shown has square bases.

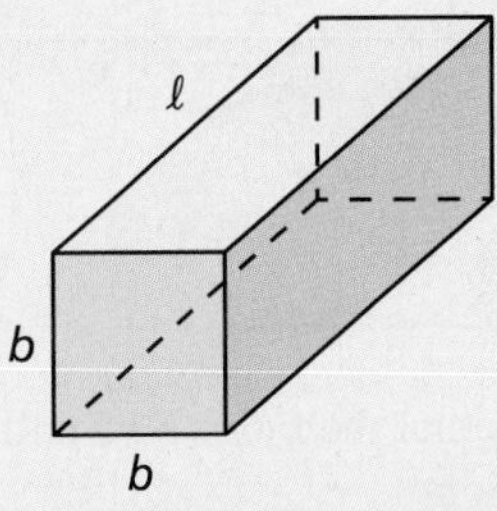

a. Use the figure to write a formula for the surface area S of the prism.

b. Your teacher asks you to solve the formula for either b or ℓ. Which would you choose? Explain.

DIG DEEPER In Exercises 39 and 40, solve the literal equation for a.

39. $x = \frac{a + b + c}{ab}$

40. $y = x\left(\frac{ab}{a - b}\right)$

41. **MODELING REAL LIFE** One type of stone formation found in Carlsbad Caverns in New Mexico is called a column. This stone formation connects to the ceiling and the floor of a cave.

   a. What is the radius (to the nearest tenth of a foot) of a cylindrical column that has a circumference of 7 feet? 8 feet? 9 feet?

   b. Explain why you might rewrite the circumference formula to find the solutions in part (a).

42. **THOUGHT PROVOKING** Give a possible value for h. Justify your answer. Draw and label the figure using your chosen value of h.

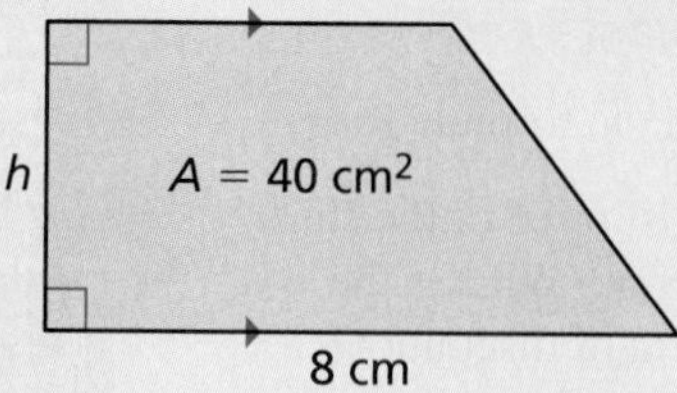

CONNECTING CONCEPTS In Exercises 43 and 44, write a formula for the area of the regular polygon. Solve the formula for the height h.

43.
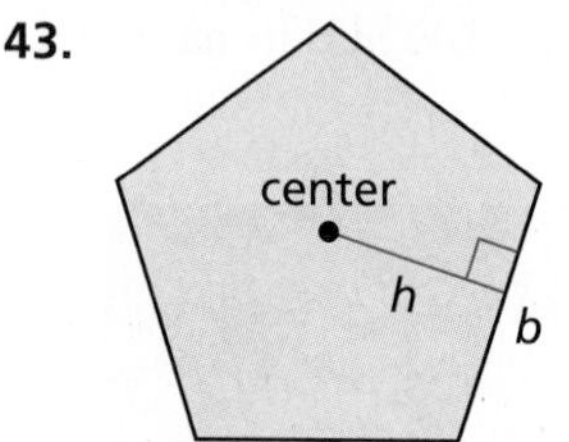

44.
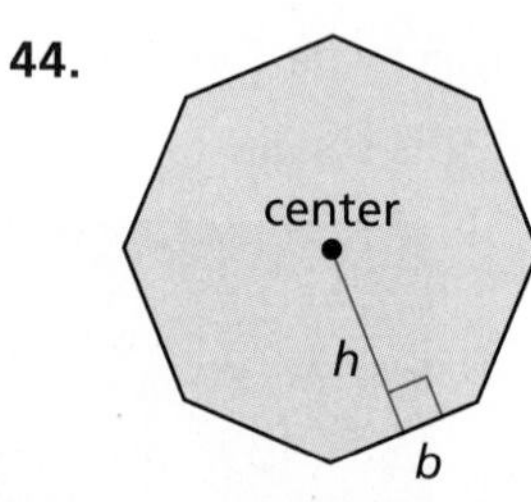

REVIEW & REFRESH

In Exercises 45–48, evaluate the expression when $a = 5$ and $b = 2$.

45. $a^2 + 12$

46. $9b - 4$

47. $\frac{a}{b} - \frac{3}{4}$

48. $3b\left(16 - \frac{1}{10}a\right)$

49. Solve the literal equation $6x - y = 12$ for y.

50. Find the surface area of the cylinder.

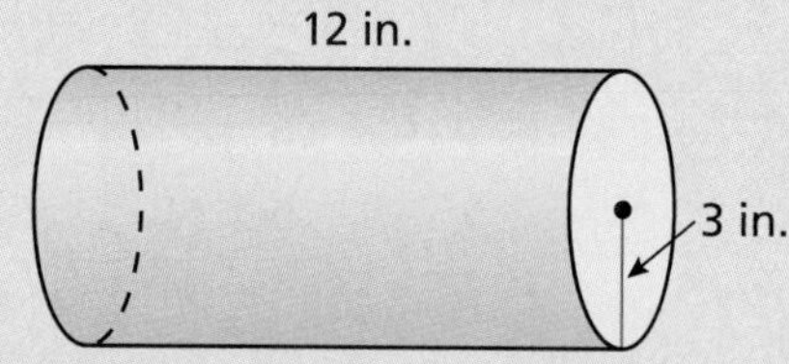

51. Tell whether the ratios 6 : 8 and 4 : 6 form a proportion.

52. **MODELING REAL LIFE** The volume G of an aquarium (in gallons) is given by the formula $G = \frac{\ell wh}{231}$, where ℓ is the length of the aquarium (in inches), w is the width (in inches), and h is the height (in inches).

   a. Solve the formula for h.

   b. Find the height of a 20-gallon aquarium with a length of 24 inches and a width of 12 inches.

In Exercises 53–56, solve the equation. Graph the solutions, if possible.

53. $|x - 3| = 5$

54. $|3y - 12| - 7 = 2$

55. $2|2r + 4| = -16$

56. $-4|s + 9| = -24$

57. Tell whether the points $(-2, 3)$, $(2, 1)$, and $(3, 3)$ form a right triangle.

58. **MODELING REAL LIFE** You want to rent a kayak from one of the two rental companies shown. After how many hours is the total rental cost the same at each company?

KAYAK RENTALS
COMPANY A
KAYAK RENTAL FEE: $20
COST PER HOUR: $15
COMPANY B
KAYAK RENTAL FEE: $5
COST PER HOUR: $20

In Exercises 59–61, solve the equation. Check your solution.

59. $\frac{z}{-5} + 2 = -4$

60. $1.9t = -5.7$

61. $27 = -3(8y - 7) + 20y$

1 Chapter Review WITH CalcChat®

Chapter Learning Target Understand solving linear equations.

Chapter Success Criteria
- ◆ Solve simple and multi-step equations.
- ◆ Describe how to solve equations.
- ■ Analyze the measurements used to solve a problem and judge the level of accuracy appropriate for the solution.
- ■ Apply equation-solving techniques to solve real-life problems.

◆ Surface
■ Deep

SELF-ASSESSMENT 1 I do not understand. 2 I can do it with help. 3 I can do it on my own. 4 I can teach someone else.

1.1 Solving Simple Equations (pp. 3–10) WATCH

Learning Target: Write and solve one-step linear equations.

Vocabulary VOCAB
equation
linear equation in one variable
solution
equivalent equations

Solve the equation. Justify each step. Check your solution.

1. $z + 3 = -6$
2. $2.6 = -0.2t$
3. $-\frac{n}{5} = -2$
4. $5.9 = y - 2.7$
5. $\pi b = -\frac{1}{9}$
6. $3\frac{3}{10} = w + 1\frac{4}{5}$
7. Which property of equality should you use to solve the equation $\frac{a}{b} + x = c$, where a and b are negative numbers? Explain your reasoning.
8. You have \$175.29 in a savings account. You deposit an additional \$48.75. How much more do you need to save to buy the cell phone?

1.2 Solving Multi-Step Equations (pp. 11–18)

Learning Target: Write and solve multi-step linear equations.

Solve the equation. Check your solution.

9. $3y + 11 = -16$
10. $6 = 1 - b$
11. $n + 5n + 7 = 43$
12. $-4(2z + 6) - 12 = 4$
13. $\frac{3}{2}(x - 2) - 5 = 19$
14. $6 = \frac{1}{5}w + \frac{7}{5}w - 4$
15. What happens to the value of x in the equation $\frac{x}{b} + 8 = 15$ as the value of b decreases? Explain your reasoning.
16. Find three consecutive odd integers that have a sum of 75.

1.3 Modeling Quantities (pp. 19–24)

WATCH

Learning Target: Use proportional reasoning and analyze units when solving problems.

Vocabulary
ratio
proportion
rate

Solve the proportion.

17. $\frac{12}{d} = \frac{9}{3}$

18. $\frac{6}{15} = \frac{m}{10}$

19. $\frac{3}{8} = \frac{12}{b}$

20. Convert 4.75 miles to meters. Round your answer to the nearest hundredth, if necessary.

21. The table shows data collected by a musician after two concerts. Use rates to compare the data for each concert.

Concert	Tickets sold	Attendance	Merchandise sales	Social media posts
A	275	264	\$1760	66
B	325	299	\$1794	104

1.4 Accuracy with Measurements (pp. 25–30)

Learning Target: Choose an appropriate level of accuracy when calculating with measurements.

Vocabulary
precision
accuracy

22. You use an inch ruler to measure the dimensions of the photograph. Estimate the area of the photograph.

23. The land area of China is 9,326,410 square kilometers. According to United Nations estimates, the population of China in 2015 was 1,397,029,000. Estimate the population per square kilometer.

1.5 Solving Equations with Variables on Both Sides (pp. 31–36)

Learning Target: Write and solve equations with variables on both sides.

Solve the equation. Check your solution.

24. $3n - 3 = 4n + 1$

25. $2y - 16 = \frac{1}{3}(y - 3)$

26. $5(1 + x) = 5x + 5$

27. $3(n + 4) = \frac{1}{2}(6n + 4)$

28. An airplane leaves Los Angeles and travels 5 hours to New York City. The return trip travels along the same route and takes 6 hours and 15 minutes because the plane travels 99 miles per hour slower due to a headwind. Find the distance that the plane flies between the two cities.

29. Determine whether the equation $mx + 4 = \frac{1}{2}nx + 8$ *always*, *sometimes*, or *never* has a solution when (a) $m < n$, (b) $m = n$, and (c) $m > n$.

1.6 Solving Absolute Value Equations (pp. 37–44)

Learning Target: Write and solve equations involving absolute value.

Vocabulary
absolute value equation
extraneous solution

Solve the equation. Check your solutions.

30. $|y + 3| = 17$

31. $2|k - 3| = 18$

32. $|16g - 40| = -4|4g - 10|$

33. $-|b + 6| = |3b - 2|$

34. $-2|5w - 7| + 9 = -7$

35. $|x - 2| = |4 + x|$

36. The minimum sustained wind speed of a Category 1 hurricane is 74 miles per hour. The maximum sustained wind speed is 95 miles per hour. Write an absolute value equation that represents the minimum and maximum speeds.

1.7 Rewriting Equations and Formulas (pp. 45–52)

Learning Target: Solve literal equations for given variables.

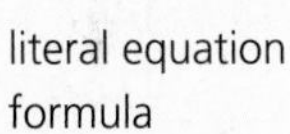
Vocabulary
literal equation
formula

Solve the literal equation for *y*.

37. $2x - 4y = 20$

38. $8x - 3 = 5 + 4y$

39. $3(2x + y) = -4x - y$

40. $a = 9y + 3yx$

41. The formula $F = \frac{9}{5}(K - 273.15) + 32$ converts a temperature from kelvin K to degrees Fahrenheit F.

a. Solve the formula for K.

b. Convert 180°F to kelvin. Round your answer to the nearest hundredth.

Mathematical Practices

Construct Viable Arguments and Critique the Reasoning of Others

Mathematically proficient students justify conclusions, communicate them to others, and respond to the arguments of others.

1. In Exercise 37 on page 51, explain why you are able to write an equation that relates the number of gallons g of gasoline and the time t.

2. Your friend says that Equation 1 and Equation 2 are equivalent. Is your friend correct? If so, explain why the equations are equivalent. If not, correct your friend's reasoning.

   Equation 1: $8x + 18 = 4x - 32$

   Equation 2: $2x + 18 = x - 32$

3. Write instructions to teach someone how to use properties of equality to solve a literal equation for a given variable.

1 Practice Test WITH CalcChat®

Solve the equation.

1. $x - 7 = 15$
2. $\frac{2}{3}x + 5 = 3$
3. $2|x - 3| - 5 = 7$
4. $|2x - 19| = 4x + 1$
5. $-2 + 5x - 7 = 3x - 9 + 2x$
6. $\frac{1}{3}(6x + 12) - 2(x - 7) = 19$

Describe the values of c for which the equation has no solution. Explain your reasoning.

7. $3x - 5 = 3x - c$
8. $|x - 7| = c$

9. A safety regulation states that the minimum height of a handrail is 30 inches. The maximum height is 38 inches. Write an absolute value equation that represents the minimum and maximum heights.

10. The fastest recorded speed in a standing position on a skateboard is about 146.7 kilometers per hour. The fastest recorded speed on inline skates is about 113.6 feet per second. Which speed is faster?

11. The perimeter P (in yards) of a soccer field is represented by the formula $P = 2\ell + 2w$, where ℓ is the length (in yards) and w is the width (in yards).

    a. Solve the formula for w.

    b. The perimeter of the soccer field is 330 yards. Find the width of the field.

    c. About what percent of the field is inside the circle?

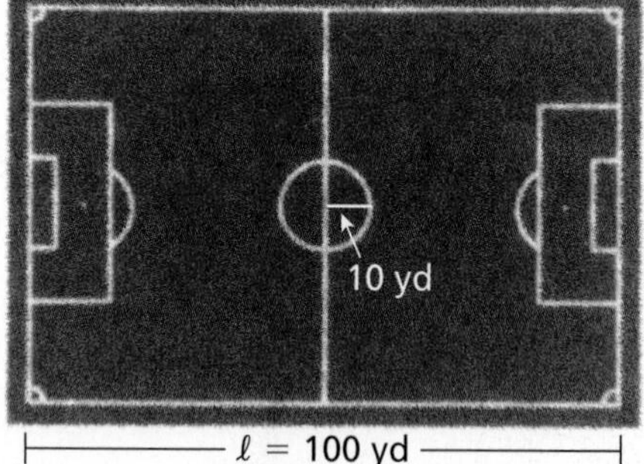

12. Your car needs new brakes. You call a dealership and a local mechanic for prices.

	Cost of parts	Labor cost per hour
Dealership	\$24	\$99
Local mechanic	\$45	\$89

    a. After how many hours are the total costs the same at both places? Justify your answer.

    b. When do the repairs cost less at the dealership? at the local mechanic? Explain.

13. The speed of light is 11,176,920 miles per minute and the distance from Earth to the Sun at a specific time is 92,955,807 miles. About how long does it take for sunlight to reach Earth?

14. Consider the equation $|4x + 20| = 6x$. Without solving, how do you know that $x = -2$ is an extraneous solution?

1 Performance Task
Every Drop Counts

The average American family uses more than 300 gallons of water per day!

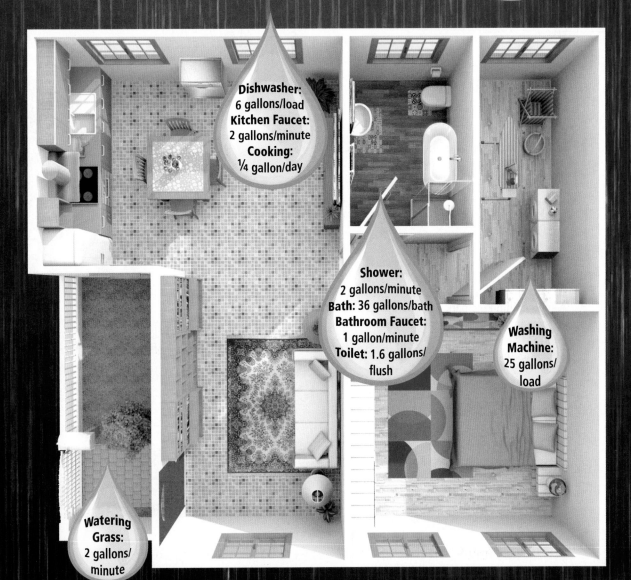

Dishwasher: 6 gallons/load
Kitchen Faucet: 2 gallons/minute
Cooking: $\frac{1}{4}$ gallon/day

Shower: 2 gallons/minute
Bath: 36 gallons/bath
Bathroom Faucet: 1 gallon/minute
Toilet: 1.6 gallons/flush

Washing Machine: 25 gallons/load

Watering Grass: 2 gallons/minute

About **60%** of an adult's body is water.

WATER LOG

Record your water activities and water consumption for one week. Then make a plan to reduce the amount of water you use each week. Determine the number of gallons you want to use for each activity and solve equations to show how you will achieve your goal.

1 College and Career Readiness WITH CalcChat®

Tutorial videos are available for each exercise.

1. Which equation is equivalent to the formula for the area A of a trapezoid, $A = \frac{1}{2}h(b_1 + b_2)$?

Ⓐ $h = \dfrac{A}{2(b_1 + b_2)}$

Ⓑ $h = 2A - (b_1 + b_2)$

Ⓒ $h = \dfrac{2A - b_2}{b_1}$

Ⓓ $h = \dfrac{2A}{b_1 + b_2}$

2. Which equation is *not* equivalent to $cx - a = b$?

Ⓐ $cx - a + b = 2b$

Ⓑ $cx - a + b = 0$

Ⓒ $2cx - 2a = 2b$

Ⓓ $b + a = cx$

3. A mountain biking park has 48 trails, 37.5% of which are beginner trails. The rest are divided evenly between intermediate and expert trails. How many of each kind of trail are in the park?

4. Let N represent the number of solutions of the equation $3(x - a) = 3x - 6$. Complete each statement with the symbol <, >, or =.

a. When $a = 3$, N ____ 1.

b. When $a = -3$, N ____ 1.

c. When $a = 2$, N ____ 1.

d. When $a = -2$, N ____ 1.

e. When $a = x$, N ____ 1.

f. When $a = -x$, N ____ 1.

5. Which of the equations are equivalent?

$6x + 6 = -14$	$8x + 6 = -2x - 14$
$5x + 3 = -7$	$7x + 3 = 2x - 13$

6. You are painting your dining room white and your living room blue. You spend \$132 on 5 cans of paint. The white paint costs \$24 per can, and the blue paint costs \$28 per can.

   a. Write an equation that you can use to find the number of cans of each color that you buy.

   b. How much would you save by switching the colors of the dining room and living room? Explain.

7. The perimeter of the triangle is 13 inches. What is the length of the shortest side?

Ⓐ 3 in.

Ⓑ 4 in.

Ⓒ 6 in.

Ⓓ 8 in.

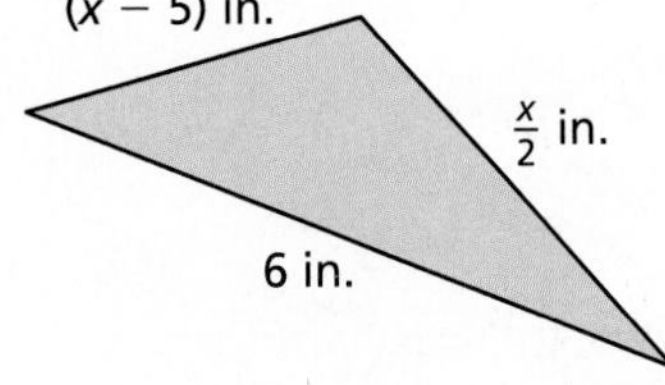

8. You pay \$45 per month for cable TV. Your friend buys a satellite TV receiver for \$99 and pays \$36 per month for satellite TV. Your friend claims that the expenses for a year of satellite TV are less than the expenses for one year of cable. Is your friend correct? Explain.

9. Which table represents a proportional relationship?

Ⓐ

x	1	2	3	4
y	18	15	12	9

Ⓑ

x	2	4	5	8
y	7	14	17.5	28

Ⓒ

x	1	2	3	4
y	5	5	5	5

Ⓓ

x	40	20	10	5
y	1	2	4	8

10. Place each equation into one of the four categories.

No solution	One solution	Two solutions	Infinitely many solutions

$\lvert 8x + 3 \rvert = 0$	$-6 = 5x - 9$	$3x - 12 = 3(x - 4) + 1$
$-2x + 4 = 2x + 4$	$0 = \lvert x + 13 \rvert + 2$	$-4(x + 4) = -4x - 16$
$12x - 2x = 10x - 8$	$9 = 3\lvert 2x - 11 \rvert$	$7 - 2x = 3 - 2(x - 2)$

11. A car travels 1100 feet in 12.5 seconds. How fast does the car travel in miles per hour?

Ⓐ $\frac{1}{60}$ mi/h

Ⓑ 1 mi/h

Ⓒ 60 mi/h

Ⓓ 88 mi/h

2 Solving Linear Inequalities

GO DIGITAL

NATIONAL GEOGRAPHIC EXPLORER

Jimmy Kuo Wei Chin

Jimmy Chin is a photographer and mountain sports athlete known for his ability to capture extraordinary imagery while climbing and skiing in high-risk environments. In 2002, he was the cinematographer for a National Geographic trek across Tibet's Chang Tang Plateau. In 2006, he was part of the first American team to ski off the summit of Mount Everest.

- As elevation increases, the *effective oxygen level* decreases. What is the meaning of *effective oxygen level*?
- What is the effective oxygen level (in percent) at an elevation of 0 feet? 4000 feet? 8000 feet? 12,000 feet?
- What is the atmospheric pressure (in atmospheres) at an elevation of 0 feet? 4000 feet? 8000 feet? Do atmospheric pressure and elevation have a linear relationship?

STEM

Mountain climbing is one of the most dangerous sports in the world. In the Performance Task, you will assume the role of an expedition leader and use inequalities to track the progress of climbers on Mount Everest.

Mountaineering

Preparing for Chapter 2

Chapter Learning Target Understand solving linear inequalities.

Chapter Success Criteria

- ◆ I can solve simple and multi-step inequalities.
- ◆ I can describe how to solve inequalities.
- ■ I can compare and contrast solving inequalities with solving equations.
- ■ I can apply techniques for solving inequalities to solve real-life applications.

◆ Surface
■ Deep

Chapter Vocabulary

Work with a partner. Discuss each of the vocabulary terms.

inequality
solution of an inequality
equivalent inequalities
compound inequality
absolute value inequality

Mathematical Practices

Make Sense of Problems and Persevere in Solving Them

Mathematically proficient students make conjectures about the form and meaning of the solution.

Work with a partner. For every increase in elevation of 1000 feet, the temperature decreases about 3.5°F. A climber on K2 records a temperature of 1°F at an elevation of 17,700 feet.

1. Which inequality represents the elevations h (in feet) for which the temperature is less than −20°F?

$1 - 3.5h \leq -20$

$1 - 3.5\left(\frac{h - 17{,}700}{1000}\right) < -20$

$1 - 3.5h < -20$

$1 - 3.5\left(\frac{h - 17{,}700}{1000}\right) \leq -20$

2. What conclusions can you make about the values of h that make the inequality true?

3. Your friend says that the solution of the inequality is $h < 23{,}700$. Is your friend correct? Explain your reasoning.

The summit of K2 is the second highest point on Earth, with an elevation of 28,251 feet.

2 Prepare WITH CalcChat®

Graphing Numbers on a Number Line

Example 1 Graph each number.

a. 3

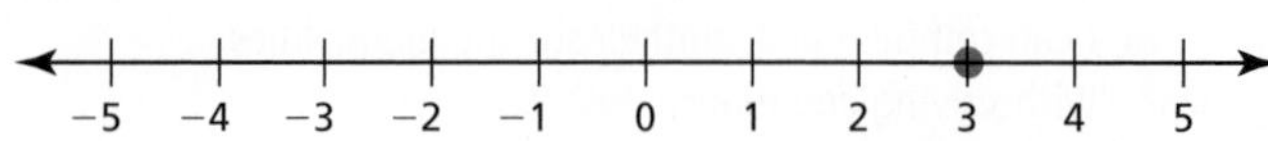

b. -0.2

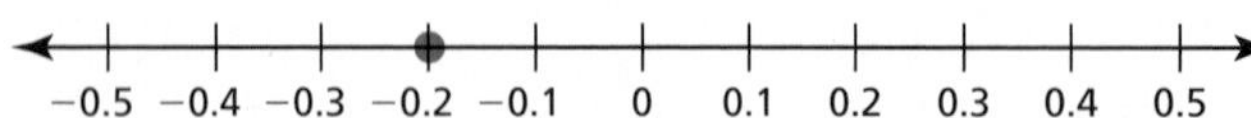

Example 2 Graph each number.

a. $|4|$

The absolute value of a positive number is positive.

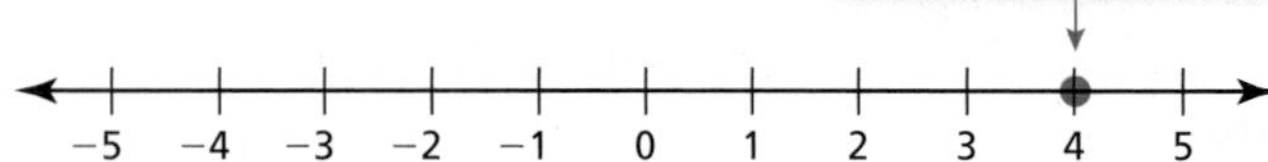

b. $\left|-1\frac{1}{3}\right|$

The absolute value of a negative number is positive.

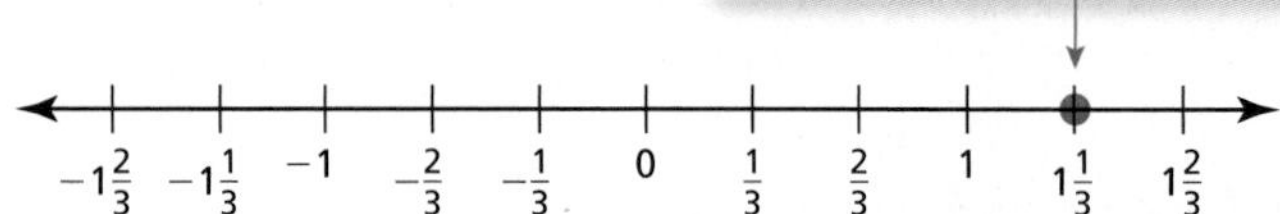

Graph the number.

1. 6

2. -5

3. $-\frac{1}{4}$

4. $|2|$

5. $|-1|$

6. $-|-2.2|$

Comparing Real Numbers

Example 3 Complete the statement -1 ▢ -5 with <, >, or =.

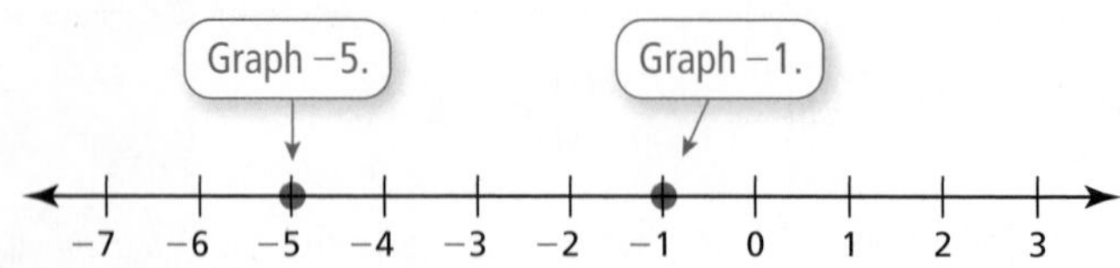

▶ -1 is to the right of -5. So, $-1 > -5$.

Complete the statement with <, >, or =.

7. 2 ▢ 9

8. -6 ▢ 5

9. $-\frac{1}{2}$ ▢ -4

10. -7 ▢ -7.5

11. $|-8|$ ▢ $|8|$

12. $-1\frac{2}{5}$ ▢ $\left|-3\frac{5}{8}\right|$

13. **MP NUMBER SENSE** A number a is to the left of a number b on a number line. How do the numbers $-a$ and $-b$ compare?

2.1 Writing and Graphing Inequalities

Learning Target Write inequalities and represent solutions of inequalities on number lines.

Success Criteria
- I can write word sentences as inequalities.
- I can determine whether a value is a solution of an inequality.
- I can graph and interpret inequalities.

EXPLORE IT! Interpreting a Diagram

Work with a partner. Use the diagram shown.

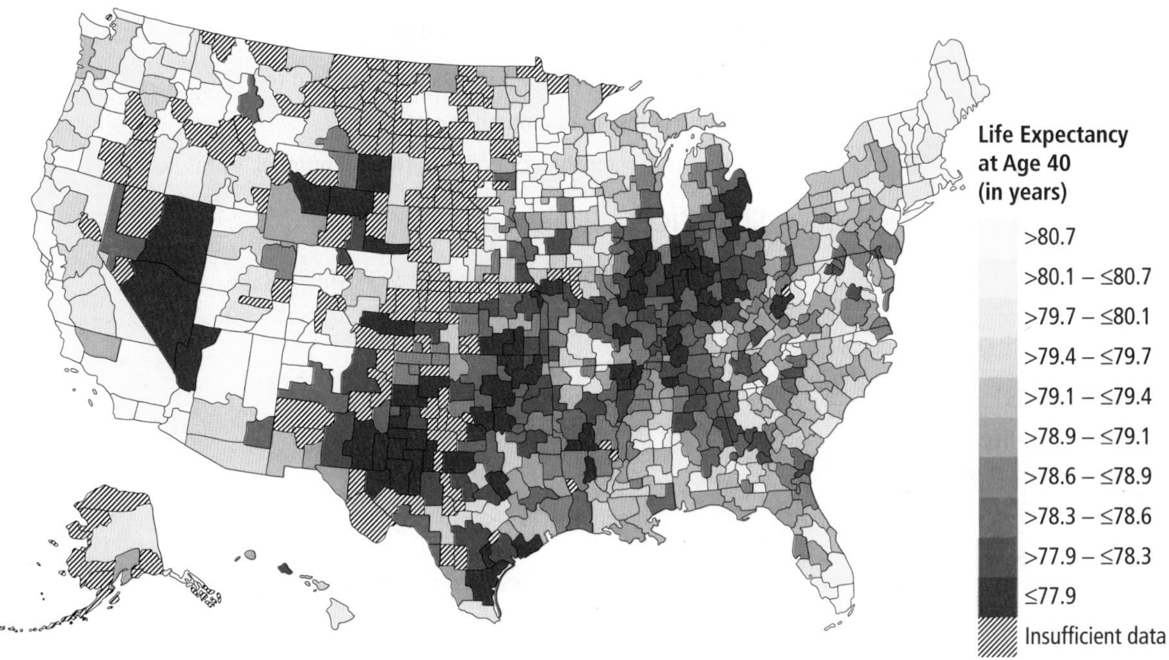

Math Practice

Use a Diagram
Why is it important to be able to interpret real-life data sets that are represented by maps, diagrams, and other data displays?

a. Explain what the diagram represents in your own words.

b. Which state do you think has the highest life expectancy for lower-income people at age 40? Which state do you think has the lowest? Explain your reasoning.

c. Which city do you think has a higher life expectancy for lower-income people at age 40, Detroit or Boston? Explain your reasoning.

d. Write several other observations you can make from the diagram.

e. Explain how you can represent one piece of information from the diagram graphically.

f. MP **CHOOSE TOOLS** Use the Internet or some other reference to find a real-life data set represented by a data display that uses inequalities.

Writing Linear Inequalities

Vocabulary

inequality, *p. 64*
solution of an inequality, *p. 65*
solution set, *p. 65*
graph of an inequality, *p. 66*

An **inequality** is a mathematical sentence that compares expressions. An inequality contains the symbol <, >, ≤, or ≥. To write an inequality, look for the following phrases to determine which inequality symbol to use.

Inequality Symbols

Symbol	<	>	≤	≥
Key phrases	• is less than • is fewer than	• is greater than • is more than	• is less than or equal to • is at most • is no more than	• is greater than or equal to • is at least • is no less than

EXAMPLE 1 Writing Inequalities

Write each sentence as an inequality.

a. A number w minus 3.5 is less than or equal to −2.

b. Three is less than a number n plus 5.

c. Zero is greater than or equal to twice a number x plus 1.

SOLUTION

a. A number w minus 3.5 is less than or equal to −2.

$w - 3.5$  ≤  −2

▶ An inequality is $w - 3.5 \le -2$.

REMEMBER

The inequality $3 < n + 5$ is the same as $n + 5 > 3$.

b. Three is less than a number n plus 5.

3  < $n + 5$

▶ An inequality is $3 < n + 5$.

c. Zero is greater than or equal to twice a number x plus 1.

 0  ≥ $2x + 1$

▶ An inequality is $0 \ge 2x + 1$.

SELF-ASSESSMENT

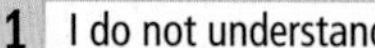

1 I do not understand. 2 I can do it with help. 3 I can do it on my own. 4 I can teach someone else.

Write the sentence as an inequality.

1. A number b is fewer than 30.4.

2. Eleven is more than a number y divided by 4.

3. $-\frac{7}{10}$ is at least twice a number k minus 4.

4. The sum of a number z and 16.2 is at most 30.

5. COMPLETE THE SENTENCE A mathematical sentence using the symbols <, >, ≤, or ≥ is called a(n)_______.

6. DIFFERENT WORDS, SAME QUESTION Which is different? Write "both" inequalities.

w is greater than or equal to −7.	w is no less than −7.
w is no more than −7.	w is at least −7.

Sketching Graphs of Linear Inequalities

A **solution of an inequality** is a value that makes the inequality true. An inequality can have more than one solution. The set of all solutions of an inequality is called the **solution set**.

WORDS AND MATH

The word *set* can mean a collection of similar things that belong together, such as a train set, a set of dishes, or a set of cards.

Value of x	$x + 5 \geq -2$	Is the inequality true?
-6	$-6 + 5 \overset{?}{\geq} -2$ $-1 \geq -2$ ✓	yes
-7	$-7 + 5 \overset{?}{\geq} -2$ $-2 \geq -2$ ✓	yes
-8	$-8 + 5 \overset{?}{\geq} -2$ $-3 \ngeq -2$ ✗	no

REMEMBER

Recall that a diagonal line through an inequality symbol means the inequality is not true. For instance, the symbol $\ngeq$ means "is not greater than or equal to."

EXAMPLE 2 Checking Solutions of Inequalities

Tell whether -4 is a solution of each inequality.

a. $x + 8 < -3$

b. $-4.5x > -21$

SOLUTION

a. $x + 8 < -3$ Write the inequality.

$-4 + 8 \overset{?}{<} -3$ Substitute -4 for x.

$4 \nless -3$ ✗ Simplify.

▶ So, -4 is *not* a solution of the inequality.

b. $-4.5x > -21$ Write the inequality.

$-4.5(-4) \overset{?}{>} -21$ Substitute -4 for x.

$18 > -21$ ✓ Simplify.

▶ So, -4 is a solution of the inequality.

SELF-ASSESSMENT 1 I do not understand. 2 I can do it with help. 3 I can do it on my own. 4 I can teach someone else.

7. **VOCABULARY** Is 5 in the solution set of $x + 3 > 8$? Explain.

Tell whether -6 is a solution of the inequality.

8. $c + 4 < -1$
9. $10 \leq 3 - m$
10. $21 \div x \geq -3.5$
11. $4x - 25 > -2$
12. $-\frac{7}{5}d < -8$
13. $5 \leq -\frac{33}{h}$

14. **MP REASONING** List four solutions of the inequality in Exercise 11.

GO DIGITAL

The **graph of an inequality** shows the solution set of the inequality on a number line. An open circle, ○, is used when a number is *not* a solution. A closed circle, ●, is used when a number is a solution. An arrow to the left or right shows that the graph continues in that direction.

EXAMPLE 3 Graphing Inequalities

WATCH

Graph each inequality.

a. $y \leq -3$ **b.** $\frac{5}{2} < x$ **c.** $z > 0$

SOLUTION

a. Test a number to the left of -3. $y = -4$ is a solution.

Test a number to the right of -3. $y = 0$ is *not* a solution.

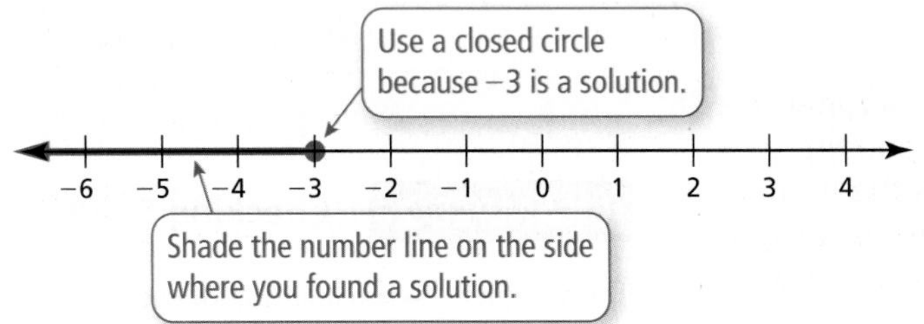
Use a closed circle because −3 is a solution.
−6 −5 −4 −3 −2 −1 0 1 2 3 4
Shade the number line on the side where you found a solution.

ANOTHER WAY

Another way to represent the solutions of an inequality is to use *set-builder notation*. In Example 3(a), the solutions can be written as

$\{y \mid y \leq -3\}$,

which is read as "the set of all numbers y such that y is less than or equal to -3."

b. Test a number to the left of $\frac{5}{2}$. $x = 0$ is *not* a solution.

Test a number to the right of $\frac{5}{2}$. $x = 4$ is a solution.

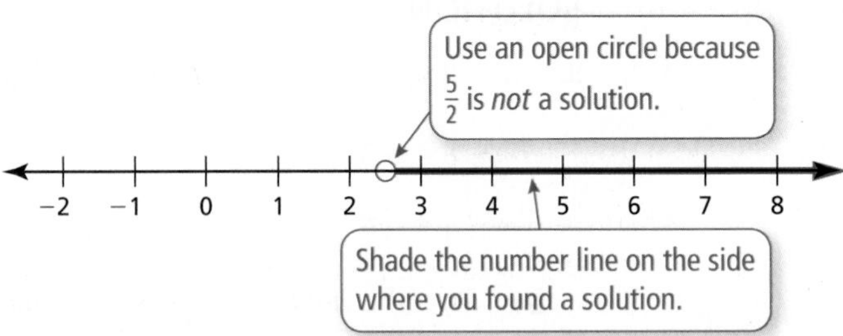
Use an open circle because 5/2 is not a solution.
−2 −1 0 1 2 3 4 5 6 7 8
Shade the number line on the side where you found a solution.

c. Just by looking at the inequality, you can see that it represents the set of all positive numbers.

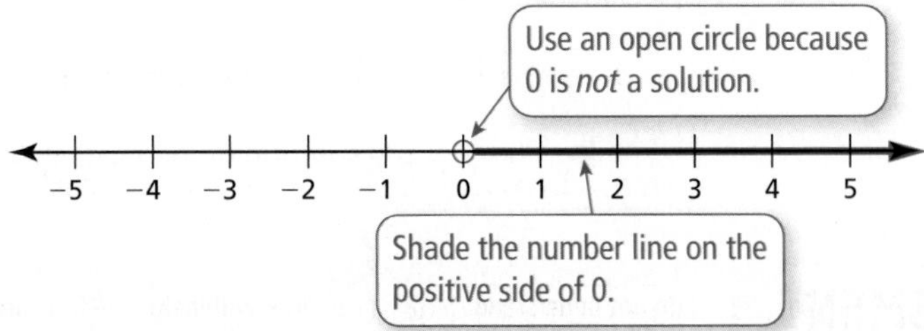
Use an open circle because 0 is not a solution.
−5 −4 −3 −2 −1 0 1 2 3 4 5
Shade the number line on the positive side of 0.

SELF-ASSESSMENT

1 I do not understand. 2 I can do it with help. 3 I can do it on my own. 4 I can teach someone else.

15. MP **PRECISION** Describe how to graph an inequality.

Graph the inequality.

16. $b > -8$ **17.** $1.4 \geq g$ **18.** $r < \frac{1}{2}$ **19.** $v \geq \sqrt{36}$

20. MP **REASONING** How are the graphs of $k < 0$ and $k \leq 0$ alike? How are they different?

Writing and Interpreting Inequalities

EXAMPLE 4 Writing an Inequality from a Graph

The graph shows the height restriction h (in inches) for a ride at an amusement park. Write and interpret an inequality that represents the height restriction for the ride.

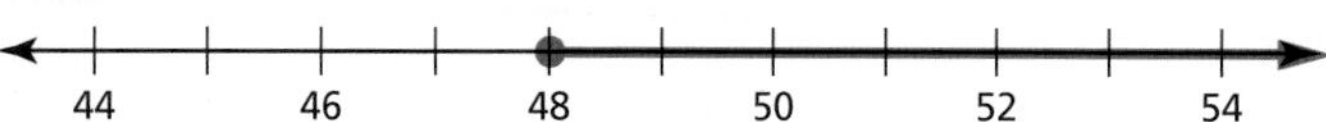

SOLUTION

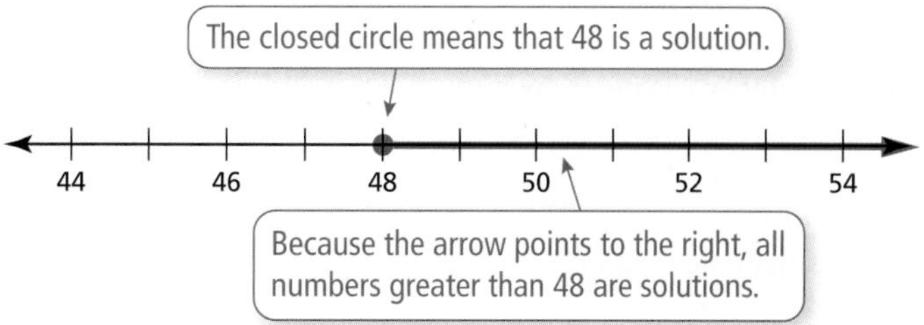

▶ So, $h \geq 48$ represents the height restriction for the ride. This means that you must be at least 48 inches tall to go on the ride.

EXAMPLE 5 Interpreting an Inequality

Let A represent the number of students in the school band. Let B represent the number of students in the school choir, where B is less than A. Interpret the inequality and tell whether it is true.

$$\frac{A + B}{2} < \frac{A}{A + B}$$

SOLUTION

The sum $A + B$ represents the total number of students in the band and the choir. The mean number of students in the band and choir is $A + B$ divided by 2.

So, $\frac{A + B}{2}$ is a number between B and A.

The quantity $\frac{A}{A + B}$ relates the number of band students to the number of students in both the band and the choir.

Because $A < A + B$, you can conclude that $\frac{A}{A + B}$ is less than 1.

▶ Because $\frac{A + B}{2} \not< \frac{A}{A + B}$, the inequality is not true.

SELF-ASSESSMENT

1 I do not understand. 2 I can do it with help. 3 I can do it on my own. 4 I can teach someone else.

21. The graph shows the height restriction h (in inches) for a ride at a water park. Write and interpret an inequality that represents the height restriction for the ride.

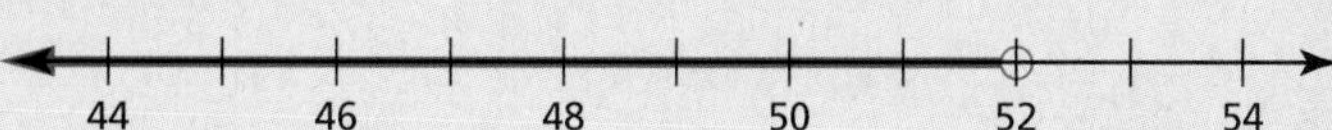

22. Use the information in Example 5 to interpret the inequality and tell whether it is true. Explain your reasoning.

a. $\frac{A}{B} < \frac{B}{A}$

b. $\frac{B}{A + B} \geq \frac{1}{2}$

2.1 Practice WITH CalcChat® AND CalcView®

In Exercises 1–8, write the sentence as an inequality. *Example 1*

1. A number x is greater than 3.

2. A number n plus 7 is less than or equal to 9.

3. Fifteen is no more than a number t divided by 5.

4. One-half of a number y is more than 22.

5. The sum of a number v and 6.2 is at least -4.7.

6. Four is no less than the quotient of a number x and 2.1.

7. Three times a number k minus $\frac{5}{3}$ is no more than $\frac{4}{9}$.

8. $-\frac{7}{8}$ is at most the difference of twice a number m and $\frac{5}{4}$.

In Exercises 9–18, tell whether the value is a solution of the inequality. *Example 2*

9. $r + 4 > 8;\ r = 2$

10. $5 - x < 8;\ x = -3$

11. $3s \le 19;\ s = -6$

12. $17 \ge 2y;\ y = 7$

13. $-1 > -\frac{x}{2};\ x = 3$

14. $\frac{4}{z} \ge 3;\ z = 2$

15. $20 \le \frac{10}{2z} + 20;\ z = 5$

16. $\frac{3m}{6} - 2 > 3;\ m = 8$

17. $10.4 \ge -2n + 4.6;\ n = -2.9$

18. $-5q - \frac{7}{4} + 8q < \frac{5}{8};\ q = \frac{5}{6}$

19. **MODELING REAL LIFE** The Xianren Bridge is located in Guangxi Province, China. This arch is the world's longest natural arch, with a length of 400 feet. Write an inequality that represents the possible lengths ℓ (in *inches*) of all other natural arches.

20. **DRAWING CONCLUSIONS** The winner of a weight-lifting competition bench-pressed 400 pounds. The other competitors all bench-pressed at least 23 pounds less.

    a. Write an inequality that represents the weights that the other competitors bench-pressed.

    b. Was one of the other competitors able to bench-press 379 pounds? Explain.

OPEN-ENDED In Exercises 21 and 22, describe a real-life situation that can be modeled by the inequality.

21. $12x \ge 60$

22. $23 + x \le 31$

In Exercises 23–30, graph the inequality. *Example 3*

23. $x \ge 2$

24. $z \le 5$

25. $-1 > t$

26. $-2 < w$

27. $v \le -4.8$

28. $s < \frac{3}{2}$

29. $\frac{1}{4} < p$

30. $r \ge -|5|$

ERROR ANALYSIS In Exercises 31 and 32, describe and correct the error in graphing the inequality.

31.

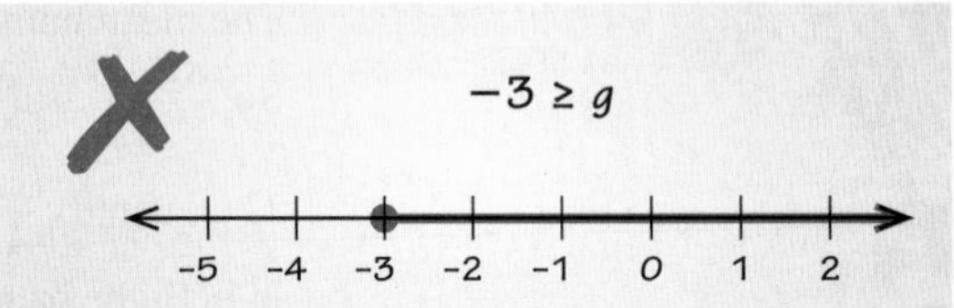

32.

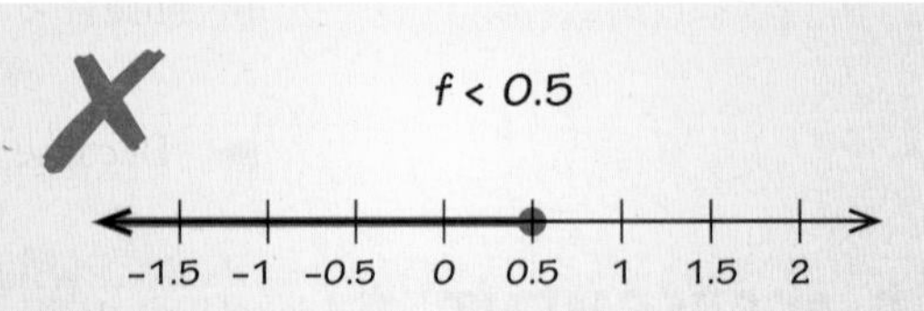

In Exercises 33–38, write and graph an inequality for the given solution set.

33. $\{x \mid x < 7\}$

34. $\{n \mid n \ge -2\}$

35. $\{z \mid 1.3 \le z\}$

36. $\{w \mid 5.2 > w\}$

37. $\left\{k \mid k \le \frac{9}{5}\right\}$

38. $\left\{m \mid \frac{3}{8} < m\right\}$

In Exercises 39 and 40, write an inequality that represents the graph.

39. 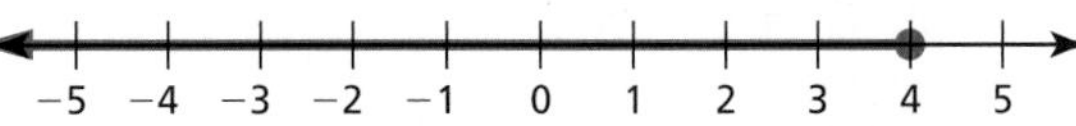

40. 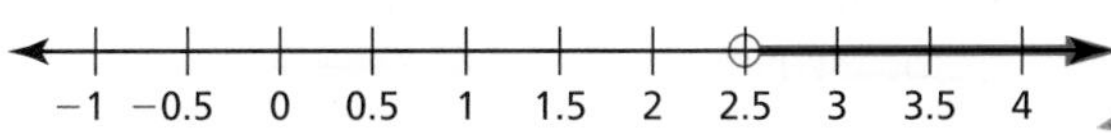

41. MODELING REAL LIFE The graph shows the hourly wage requirement m (in dollars) for employees in a state. Write and interpret an inequality that represents the state's hourly wage requirement. *Example 4*

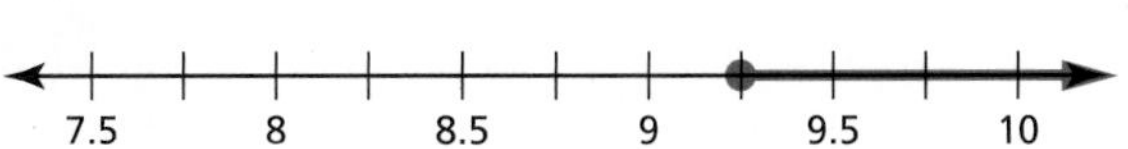

42. MODELING REAL LIFE The graphs show the weight restrictions w (in tons) for vehicles with (a) 2 axles, (b) 3 axles, and (c) 4 axles traveling on state roads. For each type of vehicle, write and interpret an inequality that represents the weight restriction (in pounds).

a. 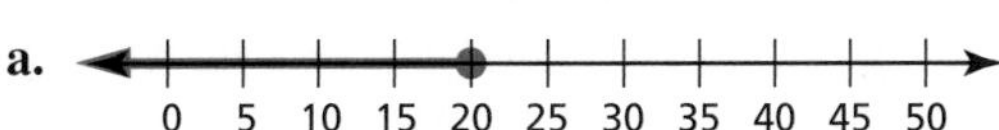

b. 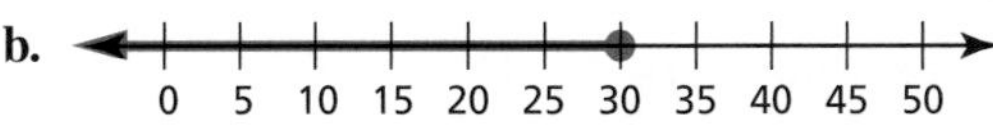

c. 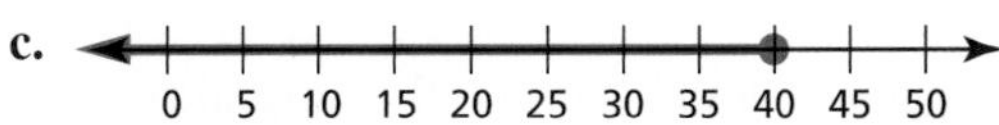

43. COLLEGE PREP The water temperature of a swimming pool must be no less than 76°F. The temperature is currently 74°F. Which graph shows how much the temperature must increase to meet the requirement? Explain your reasoning.

Ⓐ 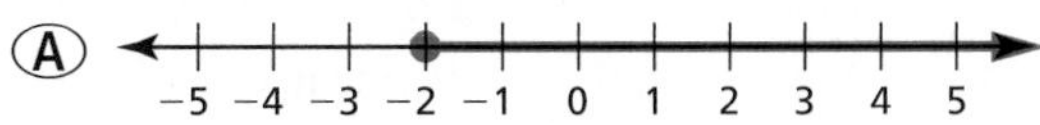

Ⓑ 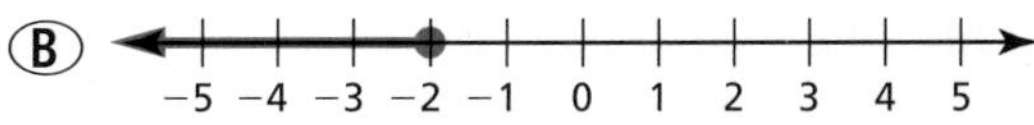

Ⓒ 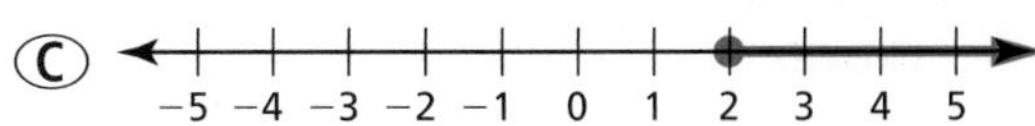

Ⓓ 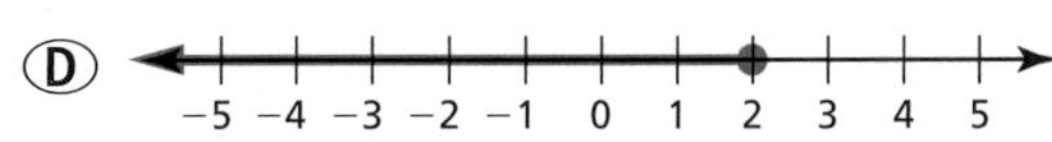

44. MP PROBLEM SOLVING An elevation more than 18,000 feet above sea level is considered extremely high altitude. Supplementary oxygen is recommended when climbing at extremely high altitudes. A mountaineer plans to climb a mountain with an elevation of 6282 meters. Is supplementary oxygen recommended for the climb? Explain.

In Exercises 45–48, let X and Y represent the populations of two cities, where X is greater than Y. Interpret the inequality and tell whether it is true. *Example 5*

45. $2Y > X + Y$

46. $\frac{X + Y}{X} < \frac{X + Y}{Y}$

47. $\frac{Y}{X + Y} < \frac{X}{Y}$

48. $\frac{1}{2}(X - Y) \geq X - \frac{Y}{2}$

49. MP REASONING Complete the inequality $2 \; \square \; |x + 5|$ with $<$, $\leq$, $>$, or $\geq$ so that $x = 3$ and $x = -3$ are both solutions of the inequality.

50. HOW DO YOU SEE IT?
The graph represents the known melting points of all metallic elements (in degrees Celsius).

−38.93 −38.91 −38.89 −38.87 −38.85 −38.83

a. Write an inequality represented by the graph.

b. Write an inequality for the set of all numbers *not* represented by the graph. What does the inequality represent in this context?

CONNECTING CONCEPTS In Exercises 51 and 52, write an inequality that represents the missing dimension x.

51. The area is less than 18 square centimeters.

52. The area is greater than or equal to 8 square feet.

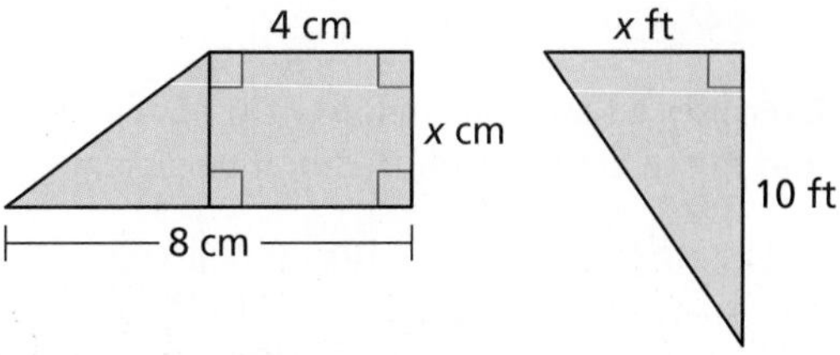

53. **MP PROBLEM SOLVING** A one-way bus ride costs \$1.65. A monthly pass costs \$52. You ride the bus twice each weekday. Should you buy the monthly pass? Explain.

54. **THOUGHT PROVOKING**
A company charges A dollars per unit for x units, plus an initial fee B (in dollars) for a product, where B is greater than A. Explain what $\frac{Ax + B}{x}$ represents and write an inequality that represents its possible values.

55. **DIG DEEPER** A runner finishes a 200-meter dash in 35 seconds. Let r represent any speed (in meters per second) faster than the runner's speed.

a. Write an inequality that represents r. Then graph the inequality.

b. Every point on the graph in part (a) represents a speed faster than the runner's speed. Explain why every point may not represent the speed of a runner.

c. Show how you can use a second inequality to alter the graph in part (a) so that every point represents a possible speed of a runner.

REVIEW & REFRESH

In Exercises 56–61, solve the equation. Check your solution.

56. $x + 2 = 3$

57. $-12 = y - 11$

58. $\frac{z}{6} = \frac{4}{3}$

59. $10 = 2.5w$

60. $3.4v - 7 + 4.6v = 17$

61. $3(5s + 2) - 9s = -42$

62. Determine whether the solids are similar.

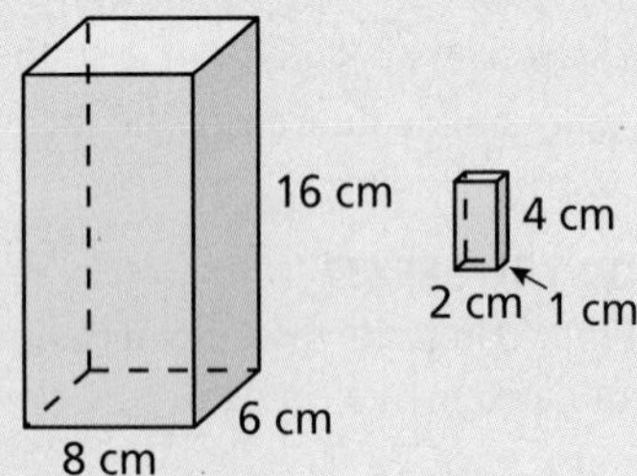

63. **OPEN-ENDED** Write an equation that has (a) one solution, (b) no solution, and (c) infinitely many solutions.

In Exercises 64–67, solve the equation. Check your solutions.

64. $|2a - 3| = 15$

65. $\frac{1}{4}|7 + d| - \frac{5}{2} = -5$

66. $|4g + 16| = 8g$

67. $|3h - 1| = |7 + 3h|$

68. **MODELING REAL LIFE** A store pays \$95 for a drone. What is the selling price when the markup is 25%?

In Exercises 69 and 70, complete the statement. Round to the nearest hundredth, if necessary.

69. 84 c = ___ gal

70. 3.6 m = ___ mm

In Exercises 71–74, solve the literal equation for x.

71. $v = x \cdot y \cdot z$

72. $s = 2r + 3x$

73. $w = 5 + 3(x - 1)$

74. $n = \frac{2x + 1}{2}$

75. **MP NUMBER SENSE** A wood plank is exactly 12 feet long. You use three different laser measuring devices to measure the length of the plank. The results are shown in the table. Which measurement is the most accurate?

Laser measure	1	2	3
Length (feet)	12.01	11.989	12.1

In Exercises 76 and 77, graph the inequality.

76. $q \leq -4$

77. $p > 1$

78. **MODELING REAL LIFE** The tallest person who ever lived was 8 feet 11.1 inches tall.

a. Write an inequality that represents the possible heights of every other person who has ever lived.

b. Is 9 feet a solution of the inequality? Explain.

79. Find the missing values in the ratio table. Then write the equivalent ratios.

Baseballs	12		72	
Gloves	3	6		9

In Exercises 80 and 81, write the sentence as an inequality.

80. Eight is less than or equal to a number z.

81. The difference of a number p and 1 is greater than 6.

2.2 Solving Inequalities Using Addition or Subtraction

Learning Target Write and solve inequalities using addition or subtraction.

Success Criteria
- I can apply the Addition and Subtraction Properties of Inequality to produce equivalent inequalities.
- I can solve inequalities using addition or subtraction.
- I can use inequalities to model real-life problems.

EXPLORE IT! Quarterback Passing Efficiency

Work with a partner. The National Collegiate Athletic Association (NCAA) uses the following formula to rank the passing efficiencies P of quarterbacks.

Math Practice

Make Sense of Quantities

Which has a greater effect on the value of P, a touchdown or an interception? How do you know?

$$P = \frac{8.4Y + 100C + 330T - 200N}{A}$$

Y = total length of all completed passes (in Yards)

C = Completed passes

T = passes resulting in a Touchdown

N = iNtercepted passes

A = Attempted passes

M = incoMplete passes

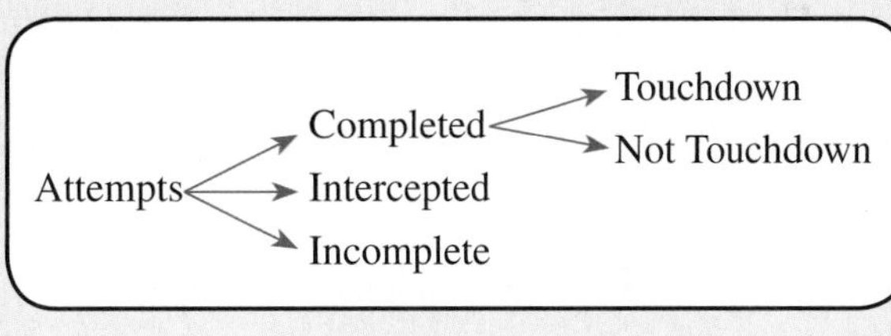

a. Determine whether each inequality must be true. Explain your reasoning.

i. $T < C$ **ii.** $C + N \leq A$

iii. $N < A$ **iv.** $A - C \geq M$

b. You have used properties of equality to solve equations involving addition or subtraction. Can you use similar properties to solve inequalities involving addition or subtraction? Explain your reasoning.

c. Use $C + N \leq A$ and $A - C \geq M$ from part (a) to support your answer in part (b).

d. For each inequality below, complete a table with passing statistics that satisfy the inequality. Then describe the values of P that make each inequality true.

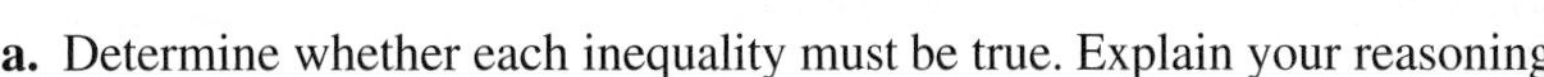

i. $P < 0$ **ii.** $P + 100 \geq 250$ **iii.** $P - 250 > -80$

Attempts	
Completions	
Yards	
Touchdowns	
Interceptions	

Solving Inequalities Using Addition

Vocabulary

equivalent inequalities, *p. 72*

Just as you used the properties of equality to produce equivalent equations, you can use the properties of inequality to produce equivalent inequalities. **Equivalent inequalities** are inequalities that have the same solutions.

KEY IDEA

Addition Property of Inequality

Words Adding the same number to each side of an inequality produces an equivalent inequality.

Numbers

$$\begin{array}{rcl} -3 & < & 2 \\ +4 & & +4 \\ \hline 1 & < & 6 \end{array} \qquad \begin{array}{rcl} -3 & \geq & -10 \\ +3 & & +3 \\ \hline 0 & \geq & -7 \end{array}$$

Algebra If $a > b$, then $a + c > b + c$. If $a \geq b$, then $a + c \geq b + c$.

If $a < b$, then $a + c < b + c$. If $a \leq b$, then $a + c \leq b + c$.

The diagram shows one way to visualize the Addition Property of Inequality when $c > 0$.

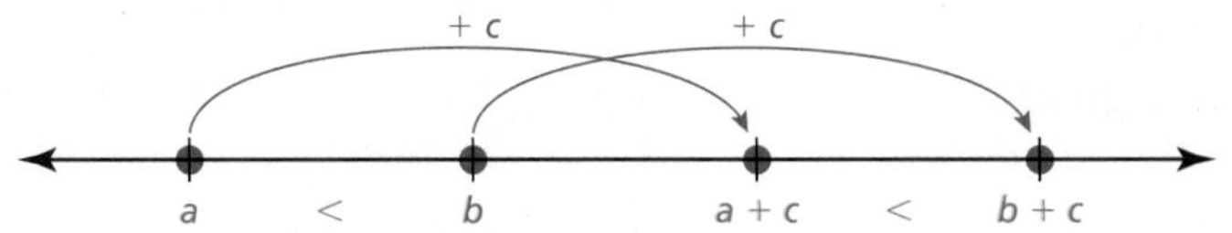

EXAMPLE 1 Solving an Inequality Using Addition

Solve $x - 6 \geq -10$. Graph the solution.

SOLUTION

$x - 6 \geq -10$	Write the inequality.
$\underline{+6} \quad \underline{+6}$	Addition Property of Inequality
$x \geq -4$	Simplify.

Undo the subtraction.

▶ The solution is $x \geq -4$.

REMEMBER

To check this solution, substitute numbers to the left and right of −4 into the original inequality.

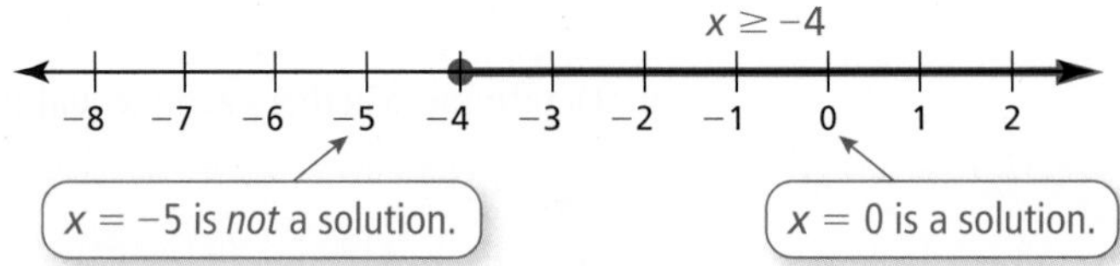

SELF-ASSESSMENT 1 I do not understand. 2 I can do it with help. 3 I can do it on my own. 4 I can teach someone else.

Solve the inequality. Graph the solution.

1. $b - 2 > -9$
2. $m - 3 \leq 5$
3. $\frac{1}{4} > y - \frac{1}{4}$
4. $0.07 \leq -4.05 + z$

5. **VOCABULARY** Is the inequality $x \leq 6$ equivalent to the inequality $x - 5 \leq 6 - 5$? Explain your reasoning.

6. **MP REASONING** The possible values of x are given by $x - 4 \geq -1$. What is the greatest possible value of $-5x$? Explain your reasoning.

Solving Inequalities Using Subtraction

KEY IDEA

Subtraction Property of Inequality

Words Subtracting the same number from each side of an inequality produces an equivalent inequality.

Numbers

$$\begin{array}{rcr} -3 & \le & 1 \\ \underline{-5} & & \underline{-5} \\ -8 & \le & -4 \end{array} \qquad \begin{array}{rcr} 7 & > & -20 \\ \underline{-7} & & \underline{-7} \\ 0 & > & -27 \end{array}$$

Algebra If $a > b$, then $a - c > b - c$. If $a \ge b$, then $a - c \ge b - c$.

If $a < b$, then $a - c < b - c$. If $a \le b$, then $a - c \le b - c$.

The diagram shows one way to visualize the Subtraction Property of Inequality when $c > 0$.

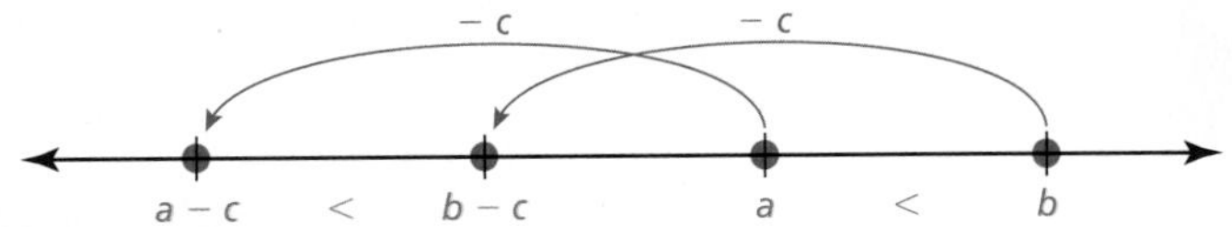

EXAMPLE 2 Solving Inequalities Using Subtraction

Solve each inequality. Graph each solution.

a. $y + 8 \le 5$ **b.** $-8 < 1.4 + m$

SOLUTION

a.

$$\begin{array}{rcrl} y + 8 & \le & 5 & \text{Write the inequality.} \\ \underline{-8} & & \underline{-8} & \text{Subtraction Property of Inequality} \\ y & \le & -3 & \text{Simplify.} \end{array}$$

Undo the addition.

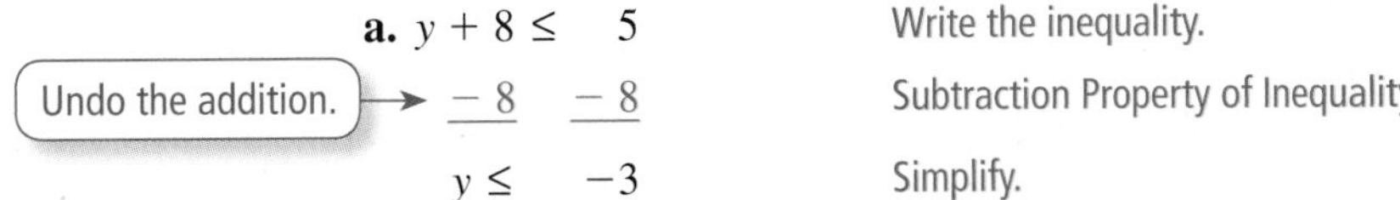

▶ The solution is $y \le -3$.

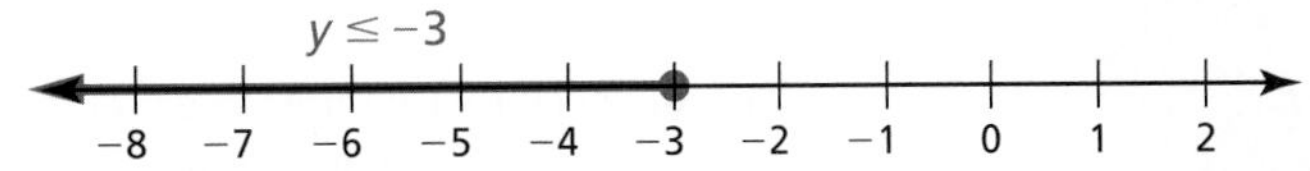

b.

$$\begin{array}{rcrl} -8 & < & 1.4 + m & \text{Write the inequality.} \\ \underline{-1.4} & & \underline{-1.4} & \text{Subtraction Property of Inequality} \\ -9.4 & < & m & \text{Simplify.} \end{array}$$

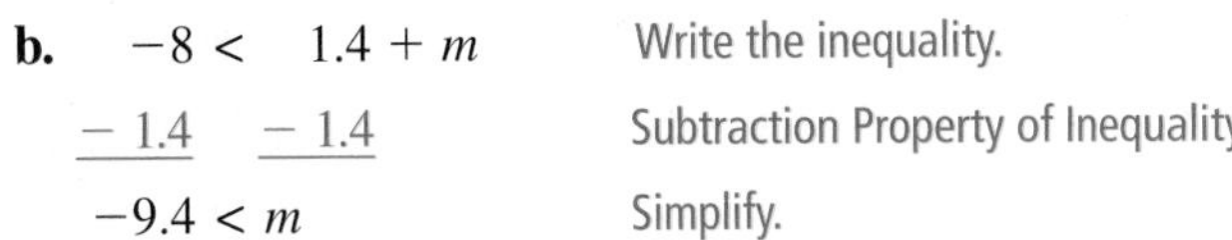

▶ The solution is $m > -9.4$.

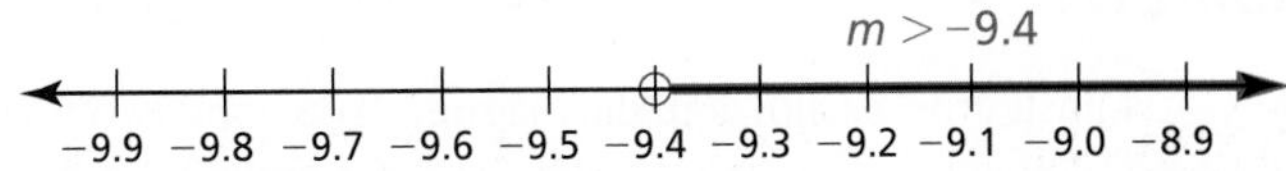

SELF-ASSESSMENT

1 I do not understand. 2 I can do it with help. 3 I can do it on my own. 4 I can teach someone else.

Solve the inequality. Graph the solution.

7. $k + 5 \le -3$

8. $75 < 58 + w$

9. $\frac{5}{6} \le z + \frac{1}{6}$

10. $p + 0.7 > -2.3$

11. OPEN-ENDED Write two inequalities that have a solution of $y \ge -3$. One must require using subtraction to solve the inequality and the other must require using addition.

Solving Real-Life Problems

EXAMPLE 3 **Modeling Real Life**

GO DIGITAL

A circuit overloads at 1800 watts of electricity. You plug an amplifier that uses 900 watts of electricity into the circuit. In addition to the amplifier, which of the following equipment can you plug into the circuit at the same time without overloading the circuit?

Equipment	Watts
Lighting	600
Fog machine 1	450
Fog machine 2	450
Television	200

SOLUTION

1. **Understand the Problem** You know that a circuit overloads at 1800 watts. You also know the numbers of watts used by several pieces of equipment. You are asked to determine what you can plug in without overloading the circuit.
2. **Make a Plan** Use a verbal model to write an inequality that represents the numbers of watts you can add without overloading the circuit. Then solve the inequality and identify other equipment that you can plug in without overloading the circuit.
3. **Solve and Check**

Verbal Model Watts used by amplifier + Additional watts < Overload wattage

Variable Let w be the additional watts you can add to the circuit.

Inequality $900 + w < 1800$

$900 + w < 1800$ Write the inequality.

$-900 \quad\quad -900$ Subtraction Property of Inequality

$w < 900$ Simplify.

▶ You can add up to 900 watts to the circuit. So, you can also plug in the lighting and the television, one of the fog machines and the television, or any individual piece of equipment.

Check

You can check that your answer is correct by adding the numbers of watts used by each grouping of equipment.

$900 + 600 + 200 = 1700$ $\quad\quad$ $900 + 450 + 200 = 1550$

The circuit will not overload because the total wattage is less than 1800 watts. 

SELF-ASSESSMENT 1 I do not understand. 2 I can do it with help. 3 I can do it on my own. 4 I can teach someone else.

12. The capacity of a flash drive is shown in the diagram. You copy two files to the flash drive, one of which is 1.92 gigabytes (GB) and the other 3.4 gigabytes. Which of the following folders can you also copy to the flash drive?

1.81 GB

Miscellaneous

5.2 GB

Photos

2.84 GB

Music

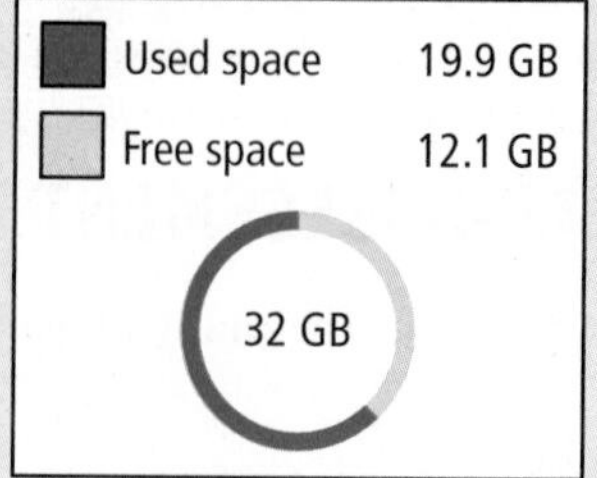

13. **MP REASONING** In Example 3, explain why you cannot plug in both fog machines along with the amplifier.

2.2 Practice WITH CalcChat® AND CalcView®

In Exercises 1–14, solve the inequality. Graph the solution. *Examples 1 and 2*

1. $x - 4 < -5$
2. $1 \le s - 8$
3. $6 \ge m - 1$
4. $c - 12 > -4$
5. $r + 4 < 5$
6. $-8 \le 8 + y$
7. $9 + w > 7$
8. $15 \ge q + 3$
9. $h - (-2) \ge 10$
10. $-6 > t - (-13)$
11. $j + 1.7 < -2.1$
12. $-5.2 + y \ge -7.4$
13. $-\frac{4}{5} \ge p - \frac{2}{5}$
14. $\frac{1}{6} + z > 2\frac{2}{3}$

In Exercises 15–18, write the sentence as an inequality. Then solve the inequality.

15. A number plus 8 is greater than 11.
16. A number minus 3 is at least -5.
17. The difference of a number and 9 is fewer than 4.
18. Six is less than or equal to the sum of a number and $3\frac{1}{4}$.

19. **MODELING REAL LIFE** An NHL hockey player has 59 goals so far in a season. What are the possible numbers of additional goals the player can score to break the NHL record of 92 goals in a season?

20. **MODELING REAL LIFE** You want your daily sodium intake to be less than 2300 milligrams. For breakfast, you eat a cereal bar with the nutrition label shown. What are the possible amounts of sodium you can eat during the rest of the day?

Nutrition Facts
Serving Size 1 Bar (37g)
Servings Per Container 8

Amount Per Serving	
Calories 120	Calories from Fat 30
	% Daily Value*
Total Fat 3g	5%
Saturated Fat 0.5g	3%
Trans Fat 0g	
Cholesterol 0mg	0%
Sodium 125mg	5%

ERROR ANALYSIS In Exercises 21 and 22, describe and correct the error in solving the inequality and graphing the solution.

21.

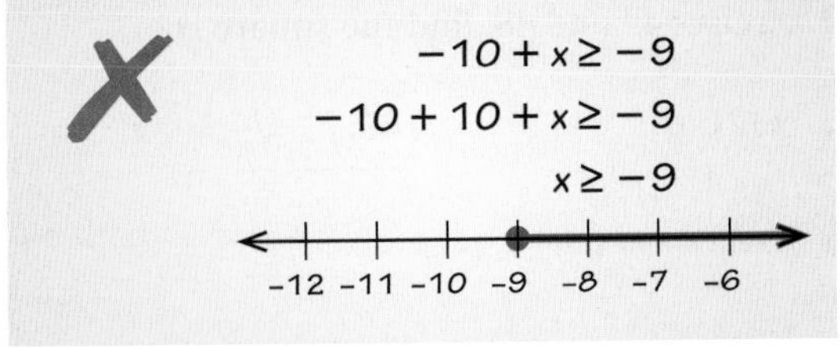

22.

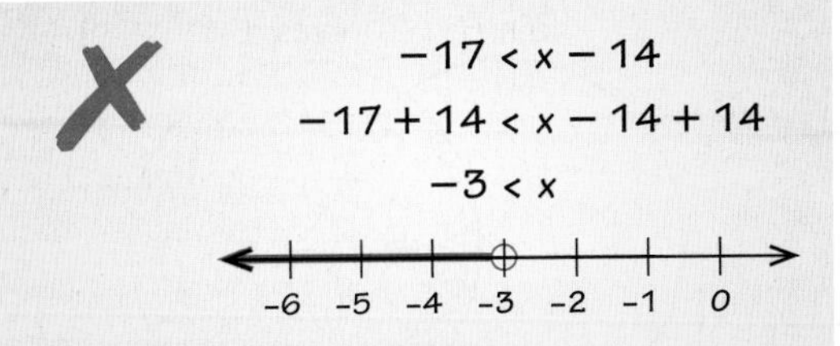

23. **MODELING REAL LIFE** An airline charges an extra fee for a checked bag that weighs more than 50 pounds. Your bag weighs 44.9 pounds. You have a 2.5-pound hair dryer, a 1.3-pound souvenir, and a 3.6-pound pair of boots. Which items can you add to the bag without paying the extra fee? *Example 3*

24. **MODELING REAL LIFE** A website offers free shipping on orders of \$75 or more. You have items totaling \$34.95 in your shopping cart. You want to add one sweater and one shirt to your cart. With which combination can you get free shipping and also spend the least amount of money?

Sweater	Price
A	\$29.95
B	\$24.50

Shirt	Price
A	\$15.75
B	\$12.95

CONNECTING CONCEPTS In Exercises 25 and 26, write and solve an inequality to find the possible values of x.

25. Perimeter < 51.3 in.
26. Perimeter ≤ 18.7 ft

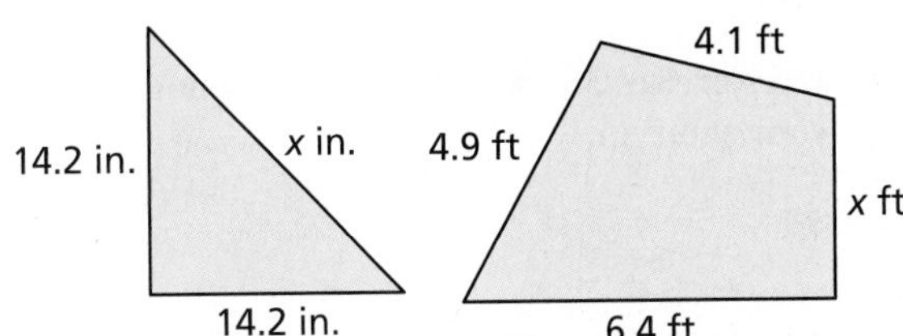

27. **MAKING AN ARGUMENT** In an aerial ski competition, you perform two acrobatic ski jumps. The scores on the two jumps are then added together.

Ski jump	Competitor's score	Your score
1	117.1	119.5
2	119.8	

a. Describe the possible scores that you can earn on your second jump to beat your competitor.

b. Your coach says that you will beat your competitor if you score 118.4 points. A teammate says that you only need 117.5 points. Who is correct? Explain.

28. **HOW DO YOU SEE IT?**
The diagram represents the numbers of students in a school with brown eyes, brown hair, or both.

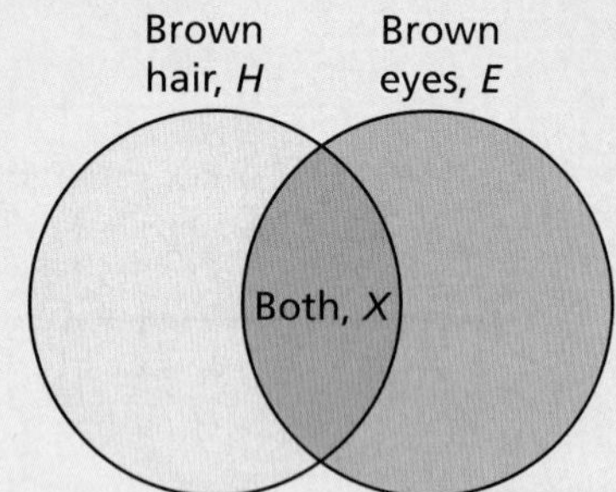

Determine whether each inequality must be true. Explain your reasoning.

a. $H \geq E$ **b.** $H + 10 \geq E$

c. $H \geq X$ **d.** $H + 10 \geq X$

e. $H > X$ **f.** $H + 10 > X$

29. **MP REASONING** Write and graph an inequality that represents the numbers that are *not* solutions of each inequality.

a. $x + 8 < 14$ **b.** $x - 12 \geq 5.7$

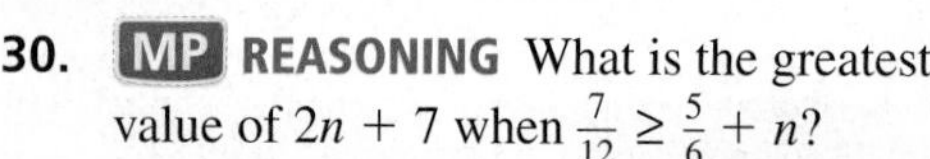

30. **MP REASONING** What is the greatest value of $2n + 7$ when $\frac{7}{12} \geq \frac{5}{6} + n$?

31. **COLLEGE PREP** Which of the following inequalities are equivalent to the inequality $x - b < 3$, where b is a constant? Select all that apply.

Ⓐ $x - b - 3 < 0$ Ⓑ $0 > b - x + 3$

Ⓒ $x < 3 - b$ Ⓓ $-3 < b - x$

32. **THOUGHT PROVOKING**
Use the inequalities

$$c - 3 \geq d,\ b + 4 < a + 1, \text{ and } a - 2 \leq d - 7$$

to order a, b, c, and d from least to greatest.

33. **DIG DEEPER** Write an inequality that requires using addition or subtraction to solve and has the solution shown in the graph. Then describe a real-life situation that can be modeled by the inequality.

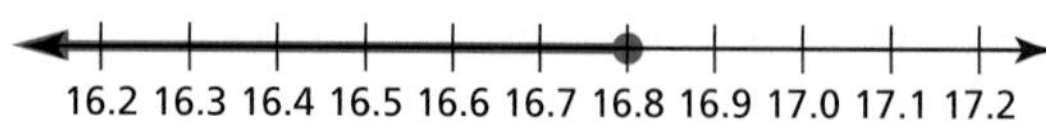

REVIEW & REFRESH

In Exercises 34–37, find the product or quotient.

34. $7 \cdot (-9)$ 35. $-11 \cdot (-12)$

36. $-27 \div (-3)$ 37. $20 \div (-5)$

In Exercises 38 and 39, solve the equation. Check your solution.

38. $-3y = -18$ 39. $\frac{n}{4} = -7.3$

40. **MODELING REAL LIFE** The graph shows the age requirement x (in years) for obtaining a driver's license in a state. Write and interpret an inequality that represents the age requirement.

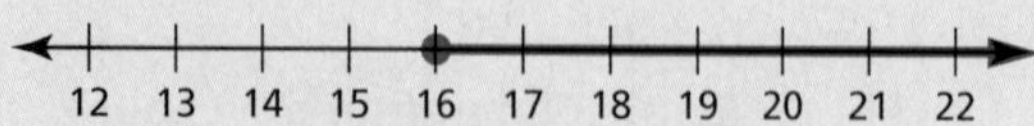

41. Solve the equation $2|x + 5| = |3x - 2|$. Check your solutions.

42. **MP REASONING** Describe the values of a for which the equation $|x + 12| - 10 = a$ has no solution.

43. You randomly choose one of the letters shown. What is the theoretical probability of choosing a vowel?

In Exercises 44 and 45, solve the inequality. Graph the solution.

44. $6 \geq w + 11$ 45. $x - 4.5 > -1.8$

46. **MODELING REAL LIFE** You average 55 miles per hour while driving to a relative's house. On the return trip, you average 50 miles per hour due to bad weather. The total driving time is 5 hours and 15 minutes. How long does each trip take?

In Exercises 47 and 48, find the square root.

47. $\sqrt{121}$ 48. $-\sqrt{\frac{4}{81}}$

2.3 Solving Inequalities Using Multiplication or Division

Learning Target Write and solve inequalities using multiplication or division.

Success Criteria
- I can apply the Multiplication and Division Properties of Inequality to produce equivalent inequalities.
- I can solve inequalities using multiplication or division.
- I can recognize when to reverse an inequality symbol while solving an inequality.

EXPLORE IT! Solving Inequalities

Work with a partner.

a. Which graph represents the solutions of $-6 > 3x$? Does the other graph represent the solutions of $6 < -3x$? Explain your reasoning.

i.
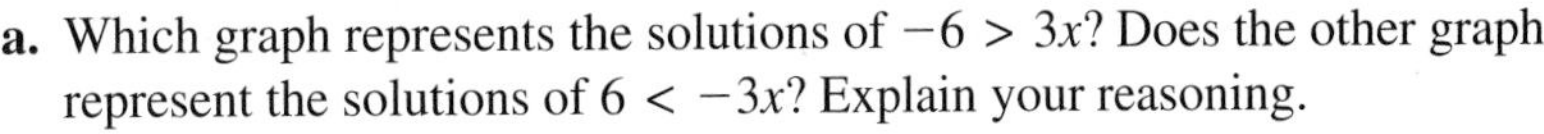

ii.
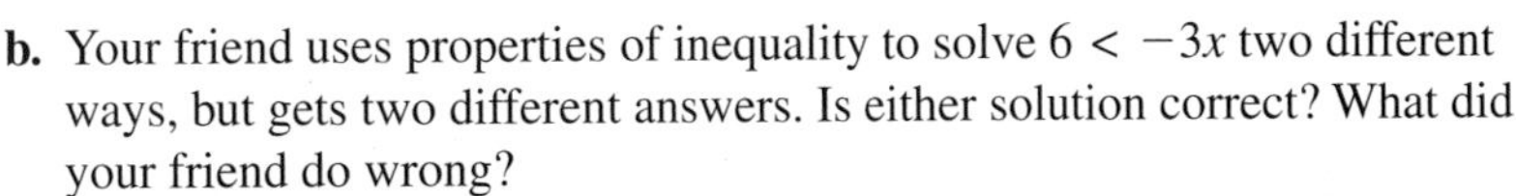

b. Your friend uses properties of inequality to solve $6 < -3x$ two different ways, but gets two different answers. Is either solution correct? What did your friend do wrong?

Solution Method #1

$6 < -3x$	Write the inequality.
$-2 < x$	Divide each side by -3.

The solution is $x > -2$.

Solution Method #2

$6 < -3x$	Write the inequality.
$3x + 6 < 0$	Add $3x$ to each side.
$3x < -6$	Subtract 6 from each side.
$x < -2$	Divide each side by 3.

The solution is $x < -2$.

c. Write a rule that describes how to solve an inequality of the form $ax < b$ when a is positive and when a is negative. Explain.

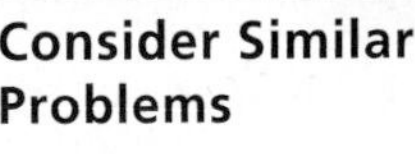

Math Practice

Consider Similar Problems

How can you use a number line to convince a friend that your rules for solving $ax < b$ are valid?

Multiplying or Dividing by Positive Numbers

KEY IDEA

Multiplication and Division Properties of Inequality (c is positive)

Words Multiplying or dividing each side of an inequality by the same *positive* number produces an equivalent inequality.

Numbers

$-6 < 8$ | $6 > -8$
$2 \cdot (-6) < 2 \cdot 8$ | $\frac{6}{2} > \frac{-8}{2}$
$-12 < 16$ | $3 > -4$

Algebra If $a > b$ and c is positive, then $ac > bc$. If $a > b$ and c is positive, then $\frac{a}{c} > \frac{b}{c}$.

If $a < b$ and c is positive, then $ac < bc$. If $a < b$ and c is positive, then $\frac{a}{c} < \frac{b}{c}$.

These properties are also true for ≤ and ≥.

EXAMPLE 1 Multiplying or Dividing by Positive Numbers

Solve (a) $\frac{x}{8} > -5$ and (b) $-27 \geq 6x$. Graph each solution.

SOLUTION

a. $\frac{x}{8} > -5$ Write the inequality.

Undo the division.

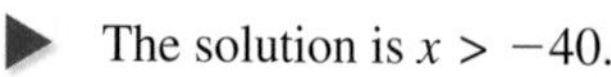

$8 \cdot \frac{x}{8} > 8 \cdot (-5)$ Multiplication Property of Inequality

$x > -40$ Simplify.

▶ The solution is $x > -40$.

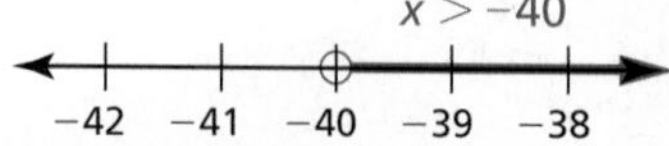

b. $-27 \geq 6x$ Write the inequality.

Undo the multiplication.

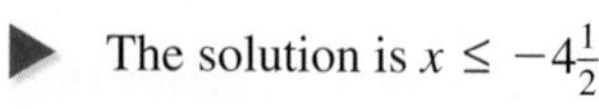

$\frac{-27}{6} \geq \frac{6x}{6}$ Division Property of Inequality

$-4\frac{1}{2} \geq x$ Simplify.

▶ The solution is $x \leq -4\frac{1}{2}$.

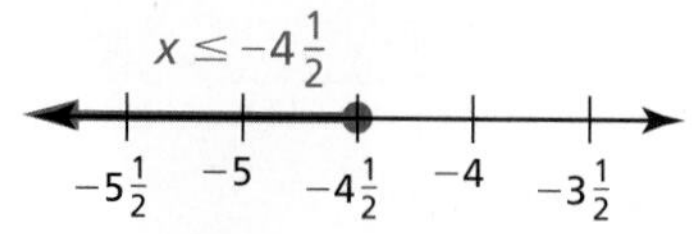

SELF-ASSESSMENT 1 I do not understand. 2 I can do it with help. 3 I can do it on my own. 4 I can teach someone else.

Solve the inequality. Graph the solution.

1. $\frac{n}{7} \geq -1$

2. $-6 \geq \frac{1}{5}w$

3. $4b \geq 39$

4. $-18 > 1.5q$

5. MP **REASONING** Can you use the Multiplication Property of Inequality to solve $8m > -\frac{1}{10}$? Can you use the Division Property of Inequality to solve $-\frac{9}{2} > \frac{3}{2}n$? Explain your reasoning.

Multiplying or Dividing by Negative Numbers

KEY IDEA

Multiplication and Division Properties of Inequality (*c* is negative)

Words When multiplying or dividing each side of an inequality by the same *negative* number, the direction of the inequality symbol must be reversed to produce an equivalent inequality.

Numbers

$$-6 < 8 \qquad\qquad 6 > -8$$

$$-2 \cdot (-6) > -2 \cdot 8 \qquad\qquad \frac{6}{-2} < \frac{-8}{-2}$$

$$12 > -16 \qquad\qquad -3 < 4$$

Algebra If $a > b$ and c is negative, then $ac < bc$. If $a > b$ and c is negative, then $\frac{a}{c} < \frac{b}{c}$.

If $a < b$ and c is negative, then $ac > bc$. If $a < b$ and c is negative, then $\frac{a}{c} > \frac{b}{c}$.

These properties are also true for ≤ and ≥.

COMMON ERROR

A negative sign in an inequality does not necessarily mean you must reverse the inequality symbol, as shown in Example 1.

Only reverse the inequality symbol when you multiply or divide each side by a negative number.

EXAMPLE 2 **Multiplying or Dividing by Negative Numbers**

Solve each inequality. Graph each solution.

a. $2 < \frac{y}{-3}$ **b.** $-7y \le -35$

SOLUTION

a. $2 < \frac{y}{-3}$ Write the inequality.

$-3 \cdot 2 > -3 \cdot \frac{y}{-3}$ Use the Multiplication Property of Inequality. Reverse the inequality symbol.

$-6 > y$ Simplify.

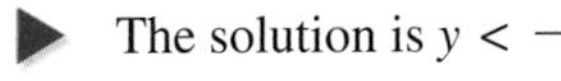

▶ The solution is $y < -6$.

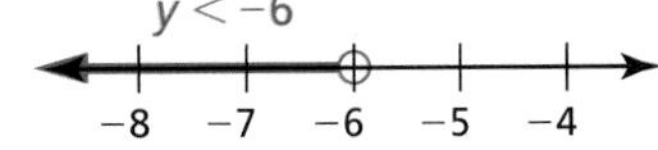

b. $-7y \le -35$ Write the inequality.

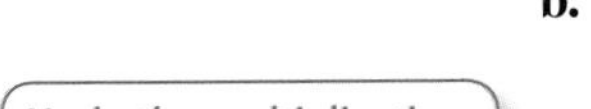

$\frac{-7y}{-7} \ge \frac{-35}{-7}$ Use the Division Property of Inequality. Reverse the inequality symbol.

$y \ge 5$ Simplify.

▶ The solution is $y \ge 5$.

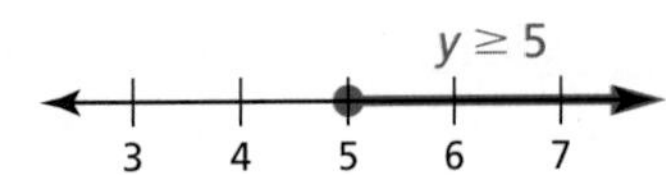

SELF-ASSESSMENT 1 I do not understand. 2 I can do it with help. 3 I can do it on my own. 4 I can teach someone else.

Solve the inequality. Graph the solution.

6. $\frac{x}{-5} \le -5$ **7.** $1 \ge -\frac{1}{10}z$ **8.** $-9m > 67.5$ **9.** $-0.4y \ge -12$

10. WRITING Explain how solving $200x < -800$ is different from solving $-200x < 800$.

Solving Real-Life Problems

GO DIGITAL

EXAMPLE 3 **Modeling Real Life**

Your friend saves \$150 each month to buy a down suit needed for a high-altitude mountain-climbing trip. Describe the numbers of months your friend needs to save to buy the suit.

Mountainwear Down Suit
\$1249.95

SOLUTION

1. **Understand the Problem** You know how much your friend saves each month and how much the suit costs. You are asked how long your friend needs to save in order to buy the suit.
2. **Make a Plan** Use a verbal model to write an inequality. Then solve the inequality and interpret the solution.
3. **Solve and Check**

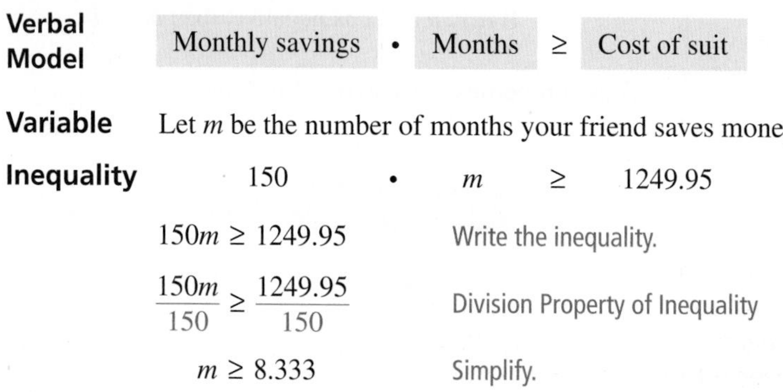

Verbal Model Monthly savings • Months ≥ Cost of suit

Variable Let m be the number of months your friend saves money.

Inequality $150 \cdot m \geq 1249.95$

$150m \geq 1249.95$ Write the inequality.

$\frac{150m}{150} \geq \frac{1249.95}{150}$ Division Property of Inequality

$m \geq 8.333$ Simplify.

▶ Your friend needs to save for more than 8 months, or at least 9 months, to buy the suit.

Math Practice

Interpret Results
Why is the solution rounded up to 9 months in this situation?

Check Reasonableness In 10 months, your friend would save

$\frac{\$150}{\text{mo}} \times 10 \text{ mo} = \$1500.$

Your friend would have a few hundred dollars more than the amount needed. So, your answer of 9 months or more is reasonable.

SELF-ASSESSMENT 1 I do not understand. 2 I can do it with help. 3 I can do it on my own. 4 I can teach someone else.

11. You have at most \$2.85 for a parking meter. Each 15-minute interval costs \$0.25. Describe the amounts of time that you can park.

12. The photograph shows the speed limit for cars on a highway during the day and at night.

a. How many hours does it take a car traveling at the speed limit to travel 175 miles during the day?

b. The car in part (a) travels at or below the nighttime speed limit on the return trip. Describe how much longer the return trip could take.

2.3 Practice WITH CalcChat® AND CalcView®

In Exercises 1–16, solve the inequality. Graph the solution. ▶ *Examples 1 and 2*

1. $3y \le -9$
2. $-6t < 12$
3. $-15 \le -3c$
4. $-9y > 27$
5. $-20 \le 10n$
6. $4x < 14$
7. $29.6 < 7.4t$
8. $-\frac{5}{6} \ge -10z$
9. $\frac{x}{2} > -2$
10. $\frac{w}{-5} \le 16$
11. $-16 \le \frac{8}{3}t$
12. $\frac{a}{4} < 10.2$
13. $22 \ge \frac{4}{5}w$
14. $-6 > -\frac{2}{3}y$
15. $-\frac{n}{3} \ge 0.75$
16. $-7.6 < -\frac{5}{4}m$

17. **MODELING REAL LIFE** A weather forecaster predicts that the temperature in Antarctica will decrease 8°F each hour for the next 6 hours. How many hours will it take for the temperature to drop at least 36°F? ▶ *Example 3*

18. **MODELING REAL LIFE** You have \$25 to purchase apps on your cell phone. Each app that you want costs \$3.99. Describe the numbers of apps you can purchase.

19. **ERROR ANALYSIS** Describe and correct the error in solving the inequality.

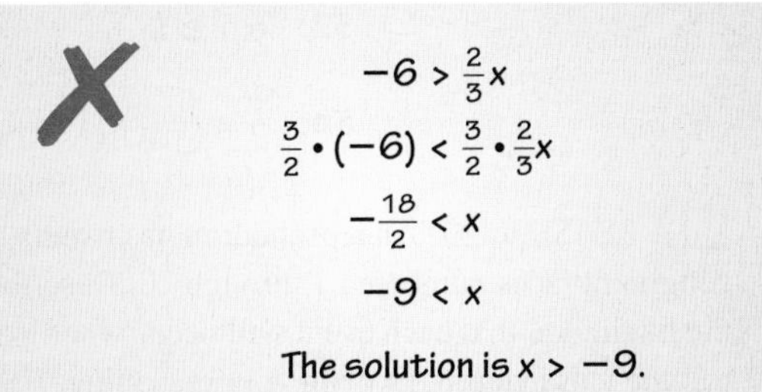

$$-6 > \frac{2}{3}x$$
$$\frac{3}{2} \cdot (-6) < \frac{3}{2} \cdot \frac{2}{3}x$$
$$-\frac{18}{2} < x$$
$$-9 < x$$

The solution is $x > -9$.

20. **MAKING AN ARGUMENT** Your friend says that the inequalities $x \le \frac{4}{3}$ and $-6x \le -8$ are equivalent. Is your friend correct? Explain.

MP USING TOOLS In Exercises 21–24, solve the inequality. Use technology to verify your answer.

21. $36 < 3y$
22. $17v \ge 51$
23. $4 > \frac{n}{-4}$
24. $1.1y < 4.4$

25. **MODELING REAL LIFE** The U.S. Mint pays \$0.11 to produce every \$5 bill. How many \$5 bills are produced when the U.S. Mint pays more than \$5.5 million in production costs for \$5 bills?

26. **HOW DO YOU SEE IT?**
Let $m > 0$. Match each inequality with its graph. Explain your reasoning.

a. $\frac{x}{m} < -1$ b. $\frac{x}{m} > 1$

c. $\frac{x}{m} < 1$ d. $-\frac{x}{m} < 1$

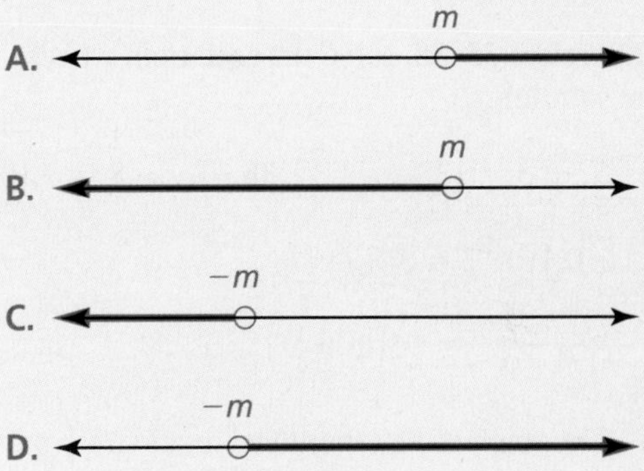

A.
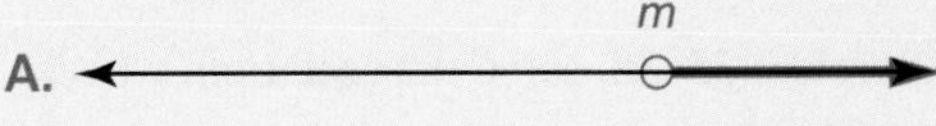

B. (number line, open circle at m)

C. (number line, open circle at $-m$)

D. (number line, open circle at $-m$)

27. **DIG DEEPER** Your class wants to raise at least \$100 for a charity by collecting bottles. Each glass bottle earns \$0.05. Each plastic bottle earns \$0.10.
   a. Describe the numbers of glass bottles your class needs to collect if no plastic bottles are collected.
   b. Describe the numbers of plastic bottles your class needs to collect if no glass bottles are collected.
   c. Write an inequality that represents how many of each type of bottle your class can collect to reach the goal.

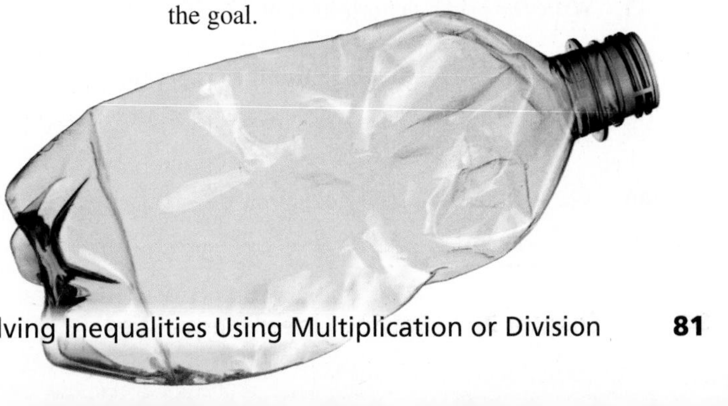

28. THOUGHT PROVOKING
The inequality $\frac{x}{4} \leq 5$ has a solution of $x = p$. Write a second inequality that also has a solution of $x = p$.

29. MP PROBLEM SOLVING You run for 2 hours at a speed no faster than 6.3 miles per hour. You want to run a marathon, which is 26.2 miles, in less than 4 hours. If you continue to run at the same speed, will you reach your goal? Explain.

30. MP STRUCTURE Use the number line shown to explain why the direction of the inequality symbol must be reversed when multiplying or dividing each side of an inequality by the same negative number.

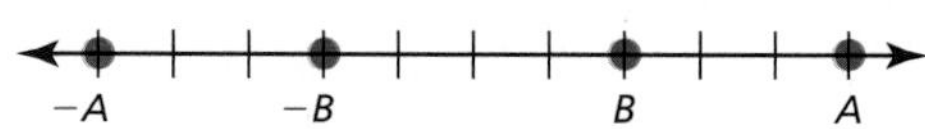

31. MP REASONING Explain why solving the inequality $\frac{4}{x} \geq 2$ by first multiplying each side by x might lead to an error. Assume $x \neq 0$.

32. CONNECTING CONCEPTS The radius of a circle is represented by the formula $r = \frac{C}{2\pi}$. Describe the circumferences C of circles with radii greater than 5.

33. CRITICAL THINKING A water-skiing instructor recommends that a boat pulling a beginning skier has a speed less than 18 miles per hour. Describe the possible distances (in miles) that a beginner can travel in 45 minutes of practice time.

34. CRITICAL THINKING A local zoo employs 36 people to take care of the animals each day. At most, 24 of the employees work full time. Describe the fraction of employees who work part time.

REVIEW & REFRESH

WATCH

In Exercises 35–38, solve the equation. Check your solution.

35. $5x + 3 = 13$

36. $\frac{1}{2}y - 8 = -10$

37. $-0.4x + 2 = 3 - \frac{2}{5}x$

38. $\frac{1}{4}(6x + 8) = -5\left(2 + \frac{1}{2}x\right)$

39. The graph of a proportional relationship passes through the points (2, 56) and (x, 154). Find x.

40. MODELING REAL LIFE You deposit \$2000 in an account that earns simple interest at an annual rate of 3.5%. How long must you leave the money in the account to earn \$175 in interest?

In Exercises 41 and 42, solve the inequality. Graph the solution.

41. $-4d < 18$

42. $7 \geq \frac{c}{3}$

43. Write the prime factorization of 72.

In Exercises 44–47, tell which number is greater.

44. 0.8, 85%

45. $\frac{7}{30}$, 25%

46. 120%, 0.12

47. 0.6%, $\frac{2}{3}$

48. MODELING REAL LIFE You have \$15 to spend on a movie ticket, a drink, and snacks. The ticket costs \$6.99. Describe how much money you can spend on a drink and snacks.

49. The vertices of a trapezoid are $A(-4, 1)$, $B(-1, 3)$, $C(-1, -4)$, and $D(-4, -3)$. Rotate the trapezoid 90° counterclockwise about the origin. What are the coordinates of the image?

50. MP LOGIC One-fifth of the greater of two consecutive integers is 7 less than one-half of the lesser integer. What are the integers?

In Exercises 51–54, graph the inequality.

51. $y > -2$

52. $6.5 \geq k$

53. $\frac{3}{8} \leq m$

54. $p < \left|-\frac{9}{5}\right|$

55. MP REASONING An icosahedron has twenty congruent faces numbered 1 through 20. Describe the likelihood that each event will occur when you roll the icosahedron. Explain your reasoning.

a. rolling a 20

b. rolling a one-digit number

c. rolling a multiple of 4

2.4 Solving Multi-Step Inequalities

Learning Target Write and solve multi-step inequalities.

Success Criteria
- I can use more than one property of inequality to generate equivalent inequalities.
- I can solve multi-step inequalities using inverse operations.
- I can apply multi-step inequalities to solve real-life problems.

EXPLORE IT! Solving Multi-Step Inequalities

Work with a partner.

- Use what you already know about solving equations and inequalities to solve each inequality. Construct a viable argument to justify each solution.
- Match each inequality with its graph.

a. $2x + 3 \leq x + 5$

b. $-2x + 3 > x + 9$

c. $27 \geq 5x + 4x$

d. $-8x + 2x - 16 < -5x + 7x$

e. $3(x - 3) - 5x > -3x - 6$

f. $-5x - 6x \leq 8 - 8x - x$

A. 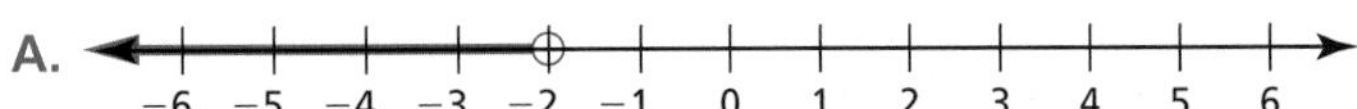

B. 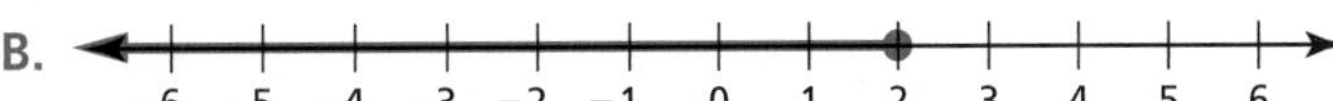

C. 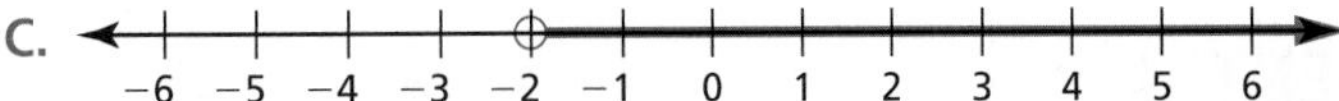

D. 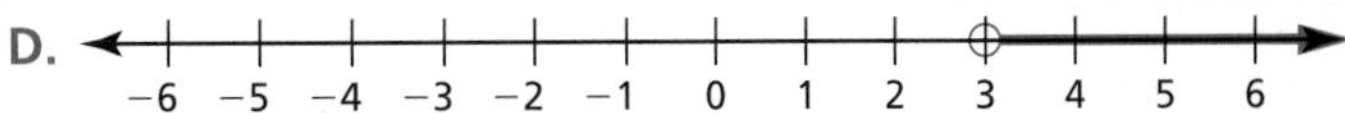

E. 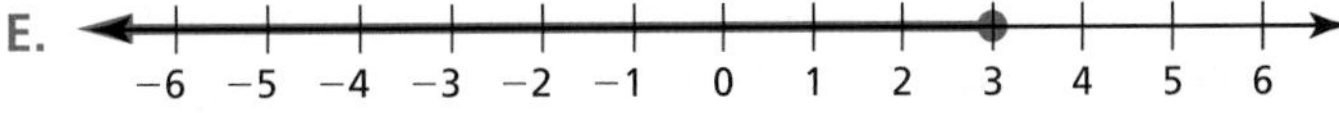

F. 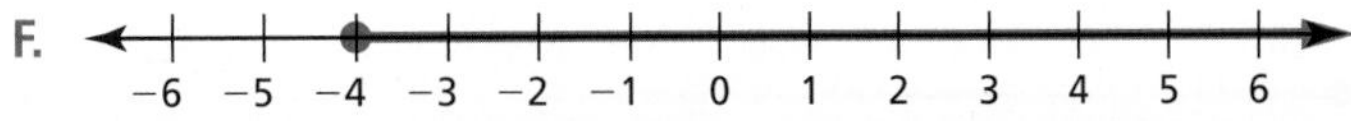

Math Practice

Construct Arguments
Do you think it is possible for an inequality to have no solution? Do you think it is possible for an inequality to have all real numbers as its solution?

Solving Multi-Step Inequalities

To solve multi-step inequalities, use inverse operations to isolate the variable.

EXAMPLE 1 **Solving Multi-Step Inequalities** 

Solve each inequality. Graph each solution.

a. $\frac{y}{-6} + 7 < 9$ **b.** $2v - 4 \geq 5$

SOLUTION

a. $\frac{y}{-6} + 7 < 9$ Write the inequality.

$\underline{-7} \quad \underline{-7}$ Subtraction Property of Inequality

$\frac{y}{-6} < 2$ Simplify.

$-6 \cdot \frac{y}{-6} > -6 \cdot 2$ Use the Multiplication Property of Inequality. Reverse the inequality symbol.

$y > -12$ Simplify.

REMEMBER
Be sure to reverse the inequality symbol when multiplying or dividing by a negative number.

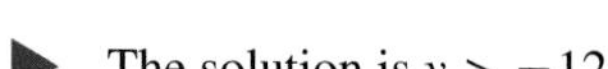

▶ The solution is $y > -12$.

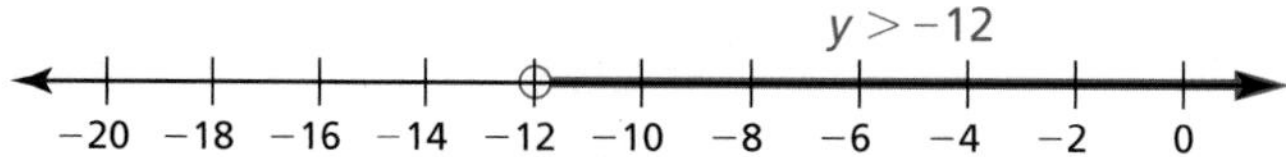

b. $2v - 4 \geq 5$ Write the inequality.

$\underline{+4} \quad \underline{+4}$ Addition Property of Inequality

$2v \geq 9$ Simplify.

$\frac{2v}{2} \geq \frac{9}{2}$ Division Property of Inequality

$v \geq \frac{9}{2}$ Simplify.

▶ The solution is $v \geq \frac{9}{2}$.

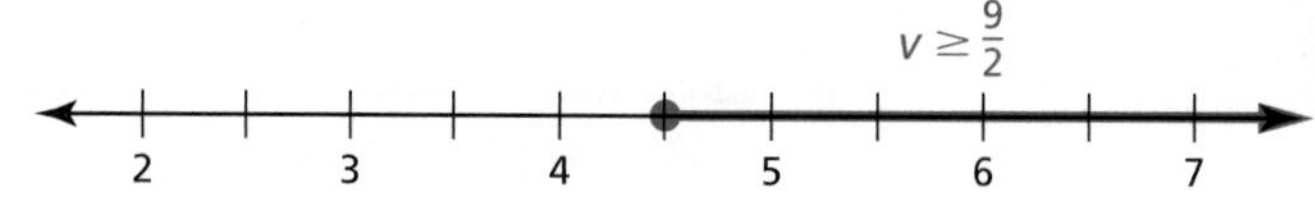

SELF-ASSESSMENT 1 I do not understand. 2 I can do it with help. 3 I can do it on my own. 4 I can teach someone else.

Solve the inequality. Graph the solution.

1. $4b - 1 < 7$

2. $8 - 9c \geq -16$

3. $\frac{n}{-2} + 11 > 12$

4. $6 \geq 5 - \frac{v}{3}$

5. OPEN-ENDED Write two different multi-step inequalities whose solutions are represented by the graph.

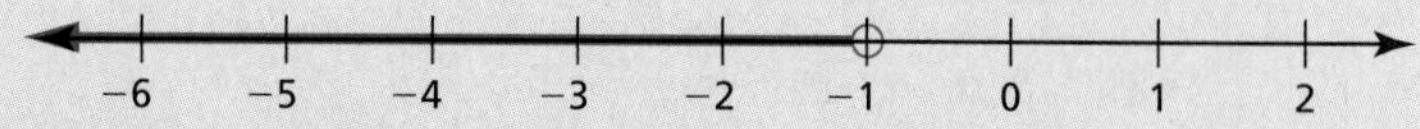

EXAMPLE 2 Solving an Inequality with Variables on Both Sides

Solve $6x - 5 < 2x + 11$.

SOLUTION

$6x - 5 < 2x + 11$	Write the inequality.
$\underline{+5} \quad \underline{+5}$	Addition Property of Inequality
$6x < 2x + 16$	Simplify.
$\underline{-2x} \quad \underline{-2x}$	Subtraction Property of Inequality
$4x < 16$	Simplify.
$\frac{4x}{4} < \frac{16}{4}$	Division Property of Inequality
$x < 4$	Simplify.

▶ The solution is $x < 4$.

When solving an inequality, if you obtain an equivalent inequality that is always true, such as $-5 < 0$, the solutions of the inequality are *all real numbers*. If you obtain an equivalent inequality that is false, such as $3 \leq -2$, the inequality has *no solution*.

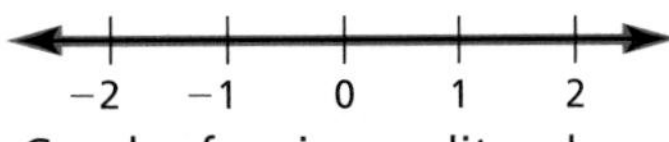

Graph of an inequality whose solutions are all real numbers

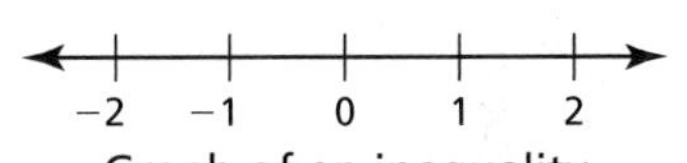

Graph of an inequality that has no solution

EXAMPLE 3 Inequalities with Special Solutions

Solve (a) $8b - 3 > 4(2b + 3)$ and (b) $2(5w - 1.2) \leq 7 + 10w$.

SOLUTION

a.

$8b - 3 > 4(2b + 3)$	Write the inequality.
$8b - 3 > 8b + 12$	Distributive Property
$\underline{-8b} \quad \underline{-8b}$	Subtraction Property of Inequality
$-3 > 12$ ✗	Simplify.

▶ The inequality $-3 > 12$ is false. So, the inequality has no solution.

b.

$2(5w - 1.2) \leq 7 + 10w$	Write the inequality.
$10w - 2.4 \leq 7 + 10w$	Distributive Property
$\underline{-10w} \quad \underline{-10w}$	Subtraction Property of Inequality
$-2.4 \leq 7$	Simplify.

▶ The inequality $-2.4 \leq 7$ is always true. So, all real numbers are solutions.

Math Practice

Maintain Oversight
When the variable terms on each side of an inequality are the same, how can you use inspection to determine whether the inequality is true or false?

SELF-ASSESSMENT

1 I do not understand. 2 I can do it with help. 3 I can do it on my own. 4 I can teach someone else.

Solve the inequality. Graph the solution, if possible.

6. $5x - 12 \leq 3x - 4$

7. $2(k - 5) < 2k + 5$

8. $-4(3n - 1) > -12n + 5.2$

9. $3(2a - 1) \geq \frac{3}{4}a - 17$

10. WRITING Without solving, how can you tell that the inequality $4x + 8 \leq 4x - 3$ has no solution?

Solving Real-Life Problems

GO DIGITAL

EXAMPLE 4 Modeling Real Life

You are playing a trivia game on your cell phone. You need a mean score of at least 90 points to advance to the next round. What scores in the fifth game will allow you to advance?

REMEMBER

The mean in Example 4 is equal to the sum of the game scores divided by the number of games.

SOLUTION

1. **Understand the Problem** You know the scores of your first four games. You are asked to find the scores in the fifth game that will allow you to advance.
2. **Make a Plan** Use the definition of the mean of a set of numbers to write an inequality. Then solve the inequality and answer the question.
3. **Solve and Check** Let x be your score in the fifth game.

$$\frac{95 + 91 + 77 + 89 + x}{5} \geq 90 \quad \text{Write an inequality.}$$

$$\frac{352 + x}{5} \geq 90 \quad \text{Simplify.}$$

$$5 \cdot \frac{352 + x}{5} \geq 5 \cdot 90 \quad \text{Multiplication Property of Inequality}$$

$$352 + x \geq 450 \quad \text{Simplify.}$$

$$\underline{-352} \qquad \underline{-352} \quad \text{Subtraction Property of Inequality}$$

$$x \geq 98 \quad \text{Simplify.}$$

▶ A score of at least 98 points will allow you to advance.

Check

You can draw a diagram to check your answer. The horizontal bar graph shows the differences between the game scores and the desired mean of 90.

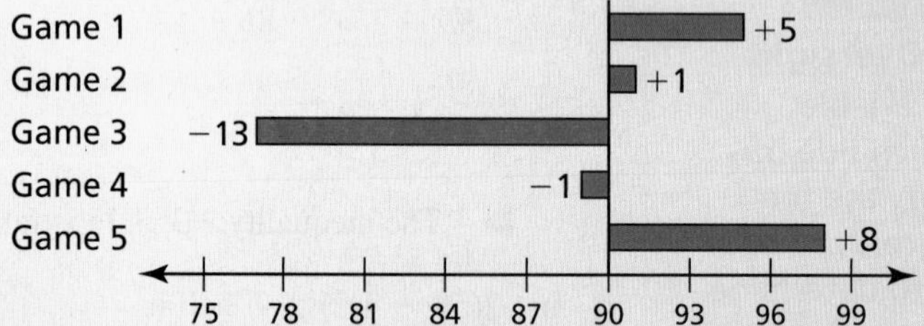

To have a mean of 90, the sum of the differences must be zero.

$$5 + 1 + (-13) + (-1) + 8 = 0 \checkmark$$

SELF-ASSESSMENT 1 I do not understand. 2 I can do it with help. 3 I can do it on my own. 4 I can teach someone else.

11. **WHAT IF?** You need a mean score of at least 85 points to advance to the next round. What scores in the fifth game will allow you to advance?

12. For what amounts of sales do you earn more in the first year with Job Offer A? with Job Offer B?

Job Offer A	
Base salary	$46,975
Commission	4.5% of sales

Job Offer B	
Base salary	$42,550
Commission	6.5% of sales
Sign-on bonus	$2500

2.4 Practice WITH CalcChat® AND CalcView®

In Exercises 1–10, solve the inequality. Graph the solution. *Example 1*

1. $2x - 3 > 7$
2. $5y + 9 \leq 4$
3. $-3 \leq 1 - 8v$
4. $-8 > -3t - 10$
5. $\frac{w}{2} + 4 > 5$
6. $1 + \frac{m}{3} \leq 6$
7. $\frac{p}{-8} - \frac{2}{5} > \frac{8}{5}$
8. $\frac{1}{2} + \frac{r}{-4} \leq \frac{5}{6}$
9. $12.6 \geq -6(a + 2)$
10. $14.7 \leq 3.5(b - 4)$

In Exercises 11–22, solve the inequality. Graph the solution, if possible. *Examples 2 and 3*

11. $4 - 2m > 7 - 3m$
12. $8n + 2 \leq 8n - 9$
13. $-2d - 2 < 3d + 8$
14. $8 + 10f > 14 - 2f$
15. $8g - 5g - 4 \leq -3 + 3g$
16. $3w - 5 > 2w + w - 7$
17. $6(\ell + 3) < 3(2\ell + 6)$
18. $2(5c - 7) \geq 10(c - 3)$
19. $4\left(\frac{1}{2}t - 2\right) > 2(t - 3)$
20. $15\left(\frac{1}{3}b + 3\right) \leq 6(b + 9)$
21. $9j - 4.5 + 6j \geq 3(5j - 1.5)$
22. $6h - 6 + 3.4h < 2(4.7h - 3)$

ERROR ANALYSIS In Exercises 23 and 24, describe and correct the error in solving the inequality.

23.

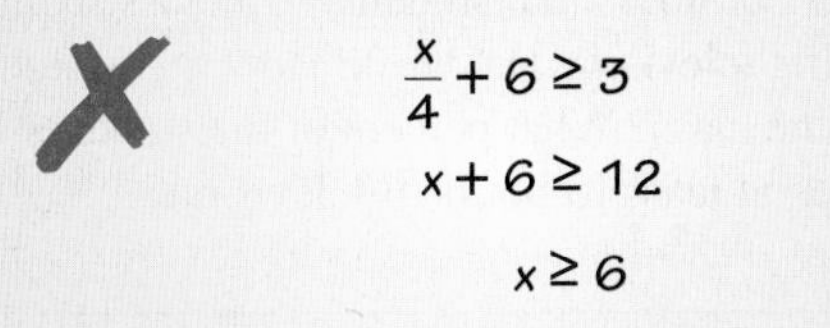

24.

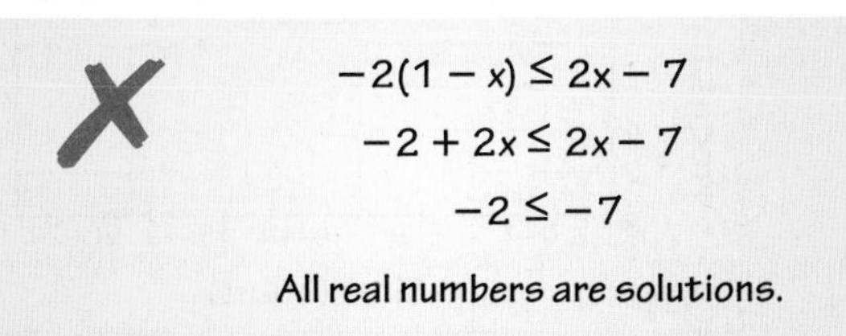

25. **MODELING REAL LIFE** You want an average of at least 30 active minutes each day during the week. How many active minutes do you need on Sunday to achieve your goal? Make an argument for your answer using a bar graph. *Example 4*

Day	Minutes exercising	Day	Minutes exercising
Monday	15	Thursday	0
Tuesday	45	Friday	60
Wednesday	20	Saturday	30

26. **MODELING REAL LIFE** Bowling alley A charges \$3.75 to rent shoes and \$4 per game. Bowling alley B charges \$2.50 to rent shoes and \$4.50 per game.
   a. For what numbers of games is the total cost, including a pair of rental shoes, less at bowling alley A? at bowling alley B?
   b. Bowling alley A increases the cost per game by \$0.50. How does this affect your answer in part (a)? Explain.

27. **CONNECTING CONCEPTS** The area of the rectangle is greater than 60 square feet. Find the possible values of x.

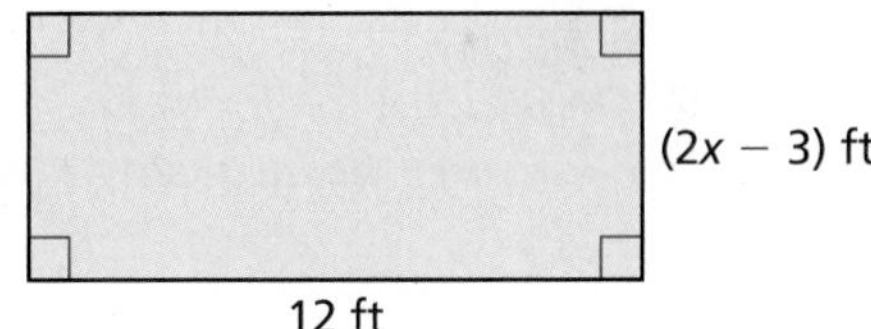

28. **MAKING AN ARGUMENT** Your friend says that the inequality $5x - 2 > 5x - 4$ has no solution because the equation $5x - 2 = 5x - 4$ has no solution. Is your friend correct? Explain.

MP REASONING In Exercises 29 and 30, find the value of *a* for which the solutions of the inequality are all real numbers.

29. $a(x + 3) < 5x + 15 - x$
30. $3x + 8 + 2ax \geq 3ax - 4a$

31. **MP STRUCTURE** Complete the inequality so that it has no solution.

$$-3(2x + 1) < \square x + \square x + \square$$

32. HOW DO YOU SEE IT?
The graph shows your budget and the total cost of x gallons of gasoline and a car wash. You want to determine the possible amounts (in gallons) of gasoline you can buy within your budget.

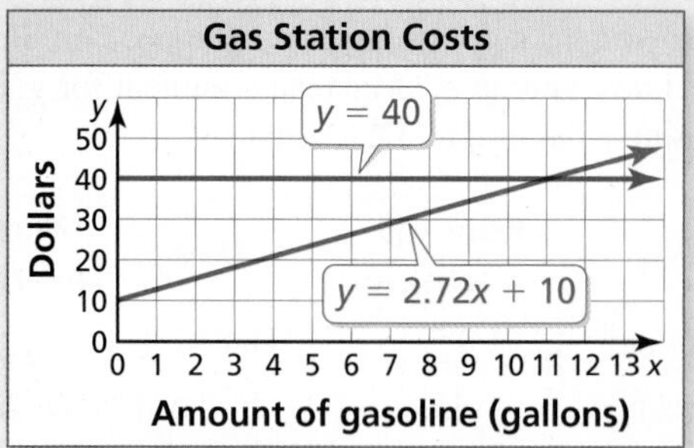

a. What is your budget?

b. How much does a gallon of gasoline cost? How much does a car wash cost?

c. Write an inequality that represents the possible amounts of gasoline you can buy.

d. Use the graph to estimate the solution of your inequality in part (c).

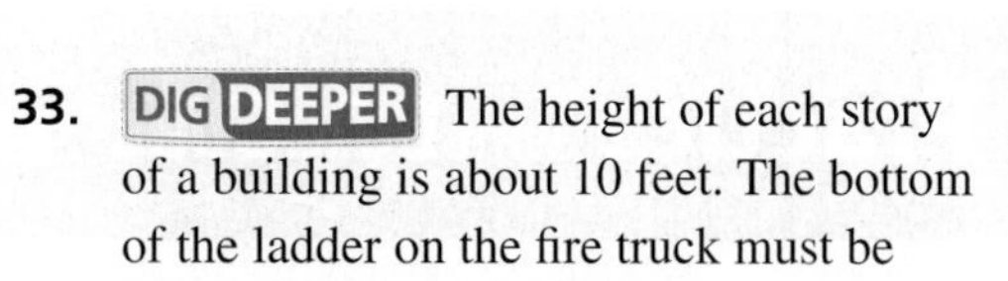

33. **DIG DEEPER** The height of each story of a building is about 10 feet. The bottom of the ladder on the fire truck must be at least 24 feet away from the building. How many stories can the ladder reach? Justify your answer.

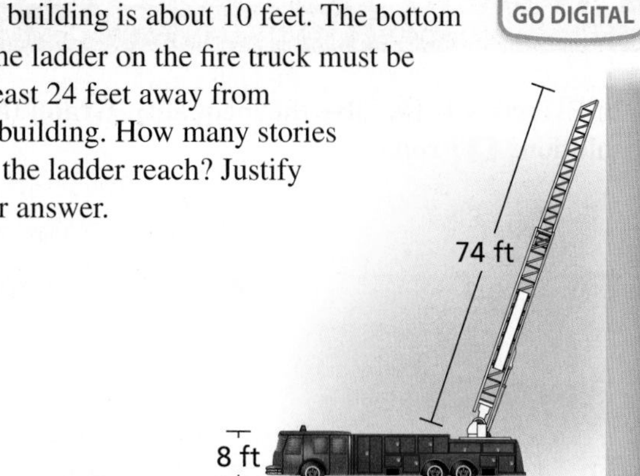

34. THOUGHT PROVOKING
A runner's times (in minutes) in the four races he has completed are 25.5, 24.3, 24.8, and 23.5. The runner plans to run at least two more races and wants to have an average time of less than 24 minutes. Write and solve an inequality to show how the runner can achieve his goal.

REVIEW & REFRESH

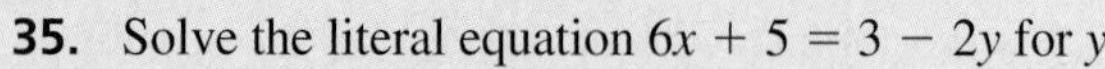

35. Solve the literal equation $6x + 5 = 3 - 2y$ for y.

36. Solve $\frac{10}{x} = \frac{25}{20}$.

In Exercises 37–40, solve the inequality. Graph the solution.

37. $n - 13 \geq -20$

38. $4 < \frac{b}{-3.8}$

39. $x + \frac{3}{7} < \frac{2}{7}$

40. $8(3g - 2) \leq 12(2g + 1)$

41. MODELING REAL LIFE You save \$20 each week to buy a smart watch that costs \$229.95.

a. Describe the numbers of months you need to save to buy the smart watch.

b. Your parents give you \$50 to help you buy the smart watch. How does this affect your answer in part (a)? Use an inequality to justify your answer.

42. Tell whether x and y are proportional.

x	3	6	9	12
y	2	4	6	8

In Exercises 43 and 44, write the sentence as an inequality.

43. Six times a number y is less than or equal to 10.

44. A number p plus 7 is greater than 24.8.

In Exercises 45 and 46, solve the equation.

45. $\frac{z}{8} + \frac{1}{4} = -\frac{z}{8}$

46. $4.9k + 6 - 1.2k = 8 + 3.7k$

47. MODELING REAL LIFE The histogram shows the numbers of hours that students in a class spent watching television last week. How many students are in the class? What percent of the students watched at least 15 hours of television?

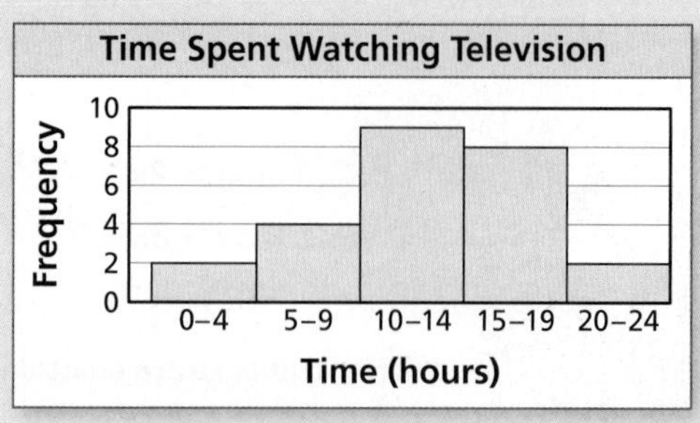

2.5 Solving Compound Inequalities

Learning Target Write and solve compound inequalities.

Success Criteria
- I can write word sentences as compound inequalities.
- I can solve compound inequalities.
- I can graph solutions of compound inequalities.

EXPLORE IT! Describing Intervals on the Real Number Line

Work with a partner. In parts (a)–(h), use two inequalities to describe the interval. Explain your reasoning.

Half-Open Interval

a. 

b. 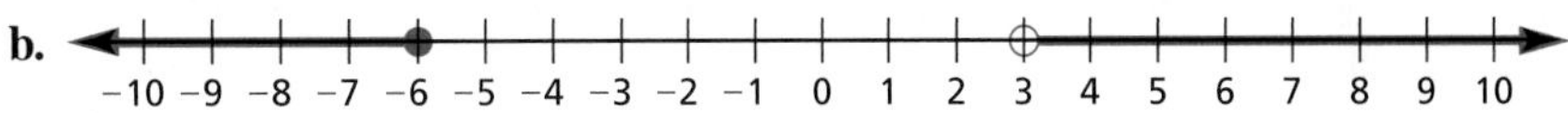

Half-Open Interval

c. 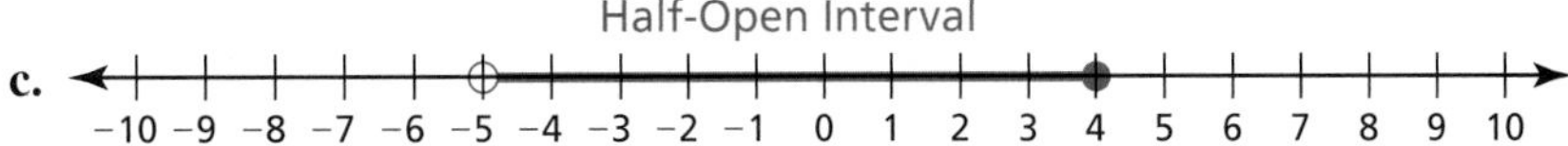

d. 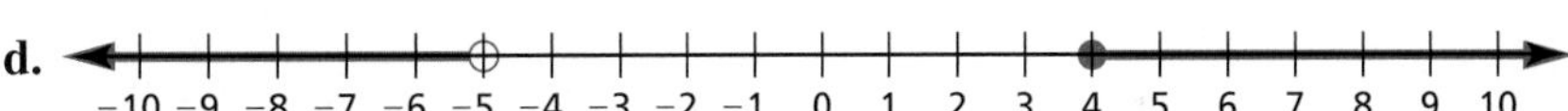

Closed Interval

e. 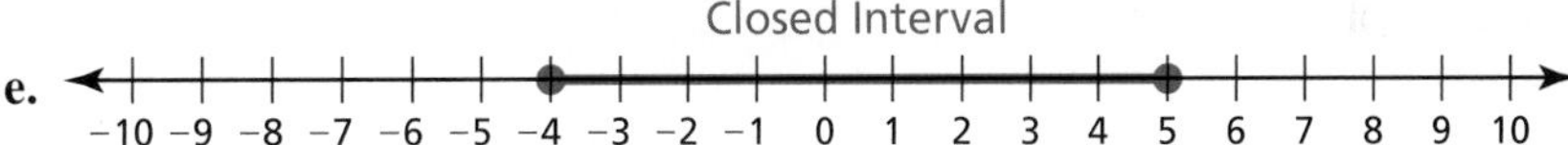

f. 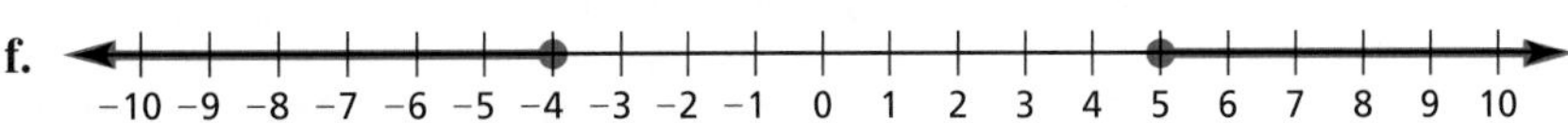

Open Interval

g. 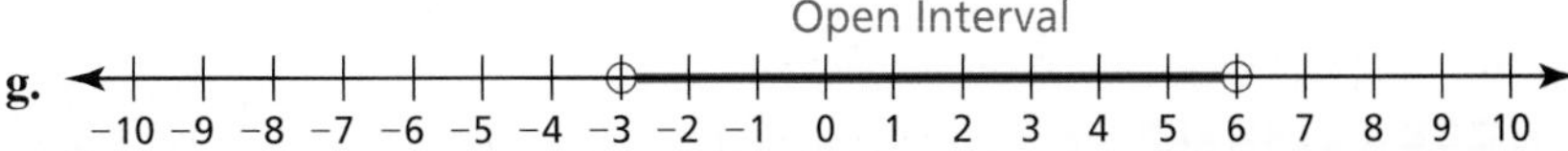

h. 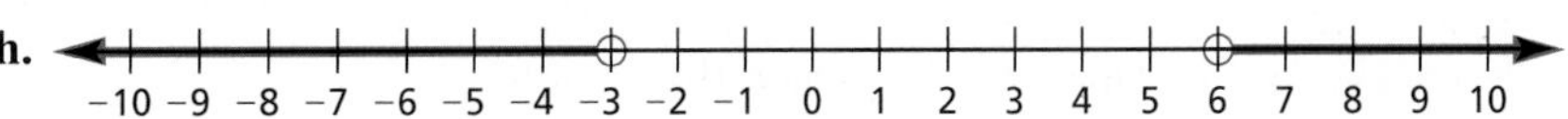

i. Do you use "and" or "or" when writing the inequalities for each graph?

Math Practice

Communicate Precisely
Describe the difference between a closed interval and an open interval.

Writing and Graphing Compound Inequalities

GO DIGITAL

A **compound inequality** is an inequality formed by joining two inequalities with the word "and" or the word "or."

WORDS AND MATH

The word *compound* can have many meanings, such as a chemical mixture, a group of buildings, or a word made from more than one word. All of these meanings have something in common—they represent something that is made from more than one thing.

The graph of a compound inequality with "and" is the *intersection* of the graphs of the inequalities. The graph shows numbers that are solutions of *both* inequalities.

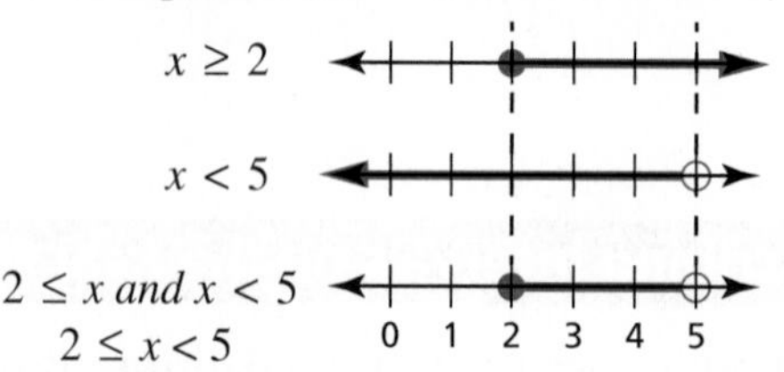

The graph of a compound inequality with "or" is the *union* of the graphs of the inequalities. The graph shows numbers that are solutions of *either* inequality.

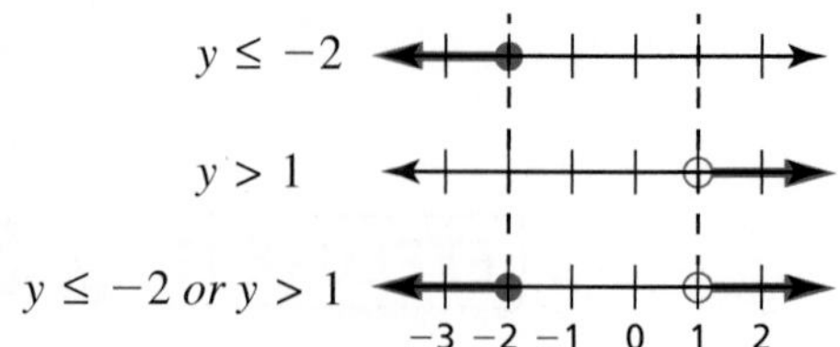

Vocabulary

compound inequality, *p. 90*

EXAMPLE 1 Writing and Graphing Compound Inequalities

Write each sentence as an inequality. Graph each inequality.

a. A number x is greater than -8 and less than or equal to 4.

b. A number y is at most 0 or at least $\frac{3}{2}$.

SOLUTION

a. A number x is greater than -8 and less than or equal to 4.

$x > -8$ *and* $x \leq 4$

▶ An inequality is $-8 < x \leq 4$.

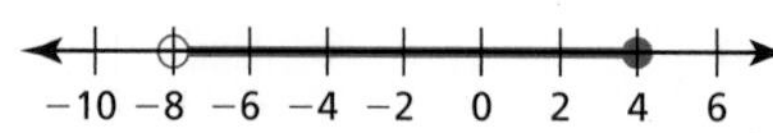

Graph the intersection of the graphs of $x > -8$ and $x \leq 4$.

b. A number y is at most 0 or at least $\frac{3}{2}$.

$y \leq 0$ *or* $y \geq \frac{3}{2}$

▶ An inequality is $y \leq 0$ *or* $y \geq \frac{3}{2}$.

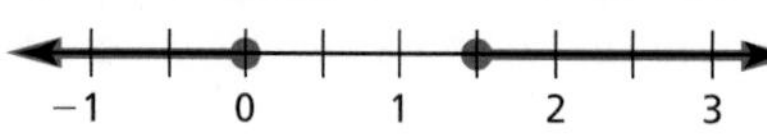

Graph the union of the graphs of $y \leq 0$ and $y \geq \frac{3}{2}$.

SELF-ASSESSMENT

1 I do not understand. 2 I can do it with help. 3 I can do it on my own. 4 I can teach someone else.

Write the sentence as an inequality. Graph the inequality.

1. A number d is more than 0 and less than 10.
2. A number a is fewer than -6 or no less than -3.
3. **WRITING** Compare the graph of $-6 \leq x \leq -4$ with the graph of $x \leq -6$ *or* $x \geq -4$.
4. **WHICH ONE DOESN'T BELONG?** Which compound inequality does *not* belong with the other three? Explain your reasoning.

$a > 4$ *or* $a < -3$	$a < -2$ *or* $a > 8$	$a > 7$ *or* $a < -5$	$a < 6$ *or* $a > -9$

GO DIGITAL

Solving Compound Inequalities

You can solve a compound inequality by solving two inequalities separately. When a compound inequality with "and" is written as a single inequality, you can solve the inequality by performing the same operation on each expression.

EXAMPLE 2 Solving Compound Inequalities with "And"

Solve each inequality. Graph each solution.

a. $-4 < x - 2 < 3$ **b.** $-3 < -2x + 1 \leq 9$

SOLUTION

a. Separate the compound inequality into two inequalities, then solve.

$-4 < x - 2$	*and*	$x - 2 < 3$	Write two inequalities.
$+2 \quad +2$		$+2 \quad +2$	Addition Property of Inequality
$-2 < x$	*and*	$x < 5$	Simplify.

▶ The solution is $-2 < x < 5$.

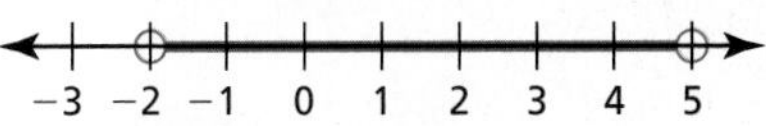

b.

$-3 < -2x + 1 \leq 9$	Write the inequality.
$-1 \qquad -1 \quad -1$	Subtraction Property of Inequality
$-4 < -2x \leq 8$	Simplify.
$\frac{-4}{-2} > \frac{-2x}{-2} \geq \frac{8}{-2}$	Use the Division Property of Inequality. Reverse each inequality symbol.
$2 > x \geq -4$	Simplify.

▶ The solution is $-4 \leq x < 2$.

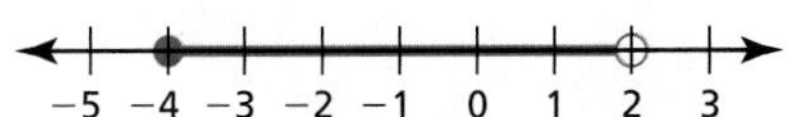

Math Practice

Look for Structure
In the inequality $-4 < x - 2 < 3$, what do you know about the quantity $x - 2$? How does this help you begin to solve?

EXAMPLE 3 Solving a Compound Inequality with "Or"

Solve $3y - 5 < -8$ *or* $2y - 1 > 5$. Graph the solution.

SOLUTION

$3y - 5 < -8$	*or*	$2y - 1 > 5$	Write the inequality.
$+5 \quad +5$		$+1 \quad +1$	Addition Property of Inequality
$3y < -3$		$2y > 6$	Simplify.
$\frac{3y}{3} < \frac{-3}{3}$		$\frac{2y}{2} > \frac{6}{2}$	Division Property of Inequality
$y < -1$	*or*	$y > 3$	Simplify.

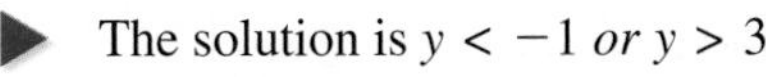

▶ The solution is $y < -1$ *or* $y > 3$.

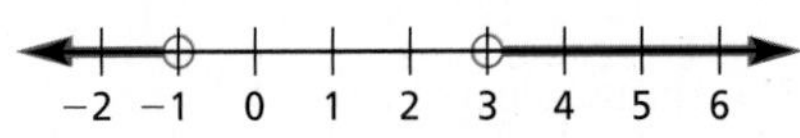

SELF-ASSESSMENT 1 I do not understand. 2 I can do it with help. 3 I can do it on my own. 4 I can teach someone else.

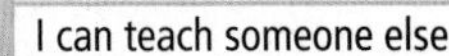

Solve the inequality. Graph the solution.

5. $5 \leq m + 4 < 10$

6. $-3 < \frac{2}{3}k - 5 < 0$

7. $4c + 3 \leq -5$ *or* $c - 8 > -1$

8. $2p + 1 < -4$ *or* $3 - 8p \leq -1$

9. OPEN-ENDED Write a compound inequality that has a solution of all real numbers except $x = 0$.

Operating temperature:
0°C to 35°C

Solving Real-Life Problems

GO DIGITAL

EXAMPLE 4 **Modeling Real Life**  

An electronic device may fail outside of its operating temperature range. Write an inequality that represents the possible operating temperatures (in degrees Fahrenheit) of the smartphone. Then describe a situation in which the phone may be outside of the operating range.

SOLUTION

1. **Understand the Problem** You know the operating temperature range in degrees Celsius. You are asked to represent the range in degrees Fahrenheit and to describe a situation outside of this range.
2. **Make a Plan** Write a compound inequality in degrees Celsius C. Use the formula $C = \frac{5}{9}(F - 32)$ to rewrite the inequality in degrees Fahrenheit F. Then solve the inequality and describe a situation outside of this range.
3. **Solve and Check**

$0 \le C \le 35$ Write the inequality using C.

$0 \le \frac{5}{9}(F - 32) \le 35$ Substitute $\frac{5}{9}(F - 32)$ for C.

$\frac{9}{5} \cdot 0 \le \frac{9}{5} \cdot \frac{5}{9}(F - 32) \le \frac{9}{5} \cdot 35$ Multiplication Property of Inequality

$0 \le F - 32 \le 63$ Simplify.

$+32 \quad +32 \quad +32$ Addition Property of Inequality

$32 \le F \le 95$ Simplify.

▶ A solution is $32 \le F \le 95$. So, the operating temperature range of the smartphone is 32°F to 95°F. Someone might leave the phone in a car on a hot day, where temperatures can exceed 150°F.

Check
You can use the formula $C = \frac{5}{9}(F - 32)$ to check that your answer is correct. Substitute 32 and 95 for F in the formula to verify that 0°C and 35°C are the minimum and maximum operating temperatures in degrees Celsius. ✓

SELF-ASSESSMENT

1 I do not understand. 2 I can do it with help. 3 I can do it on my own. 4 I can teach someone else.

10. A pair of winter boots are rated for temperatures from −40°C to 15°C. Write an inequality that represents the temperature rating (in degrees Fahrenheit) of the boots.

11. Birdwatchers record the types of birds they see or hear. The graph shows results from a location in Canada. Write an inequality that represents the range in the percents of birdwatchers who saw or heard a Black-and-white Warbler from July 1 to September 15.

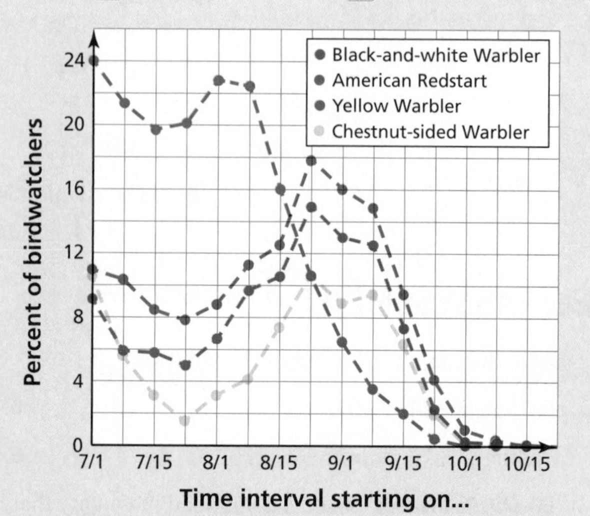

2.5 Practice WITH CalcChat® AND CalcView®

In Exercises 1–4, write the sentence as an inequality. Graph the inequality. *Example 1*

1. A number p is less than 6 and greater than 2.

2. A number n is less than or equal to -7 or greater than 12.

3. A number m is more than $-7\frac{2}{3}$ or at most -10.

4. A number r is no less than -1.5 and fewer than 9.5.

In Exercises 5–12, solve the inequality. Graph the solution. *Examples 2 and 3*

5. $6 < x + 5 \leq 11$

6. $24 > -3r \geq -9$

7. $v + 8 < 3$ *or* $-8v < -40$

8. $-14 > w + 3$ *or* $3w \geq -27$

9. $\frac{1}{2}r + 3 < \frac{7}{4}$ *or* $-r + \frac{3}{4} \leq \frac{3}{8}$

10. $-6.2 < 2n + 8.6 < 21.4$

11. $-12 < \frac{1}{2}(4x + 16) < 18$

12. $35 < 7(2 - b)$ *or* $\frac{1}{3}(15b - 12) \geq 21$

13. **MODELING REAL LIFE** The life zones on Mount Rainier, a mountain in Washington, can be approximately classified by elevation, as follows.

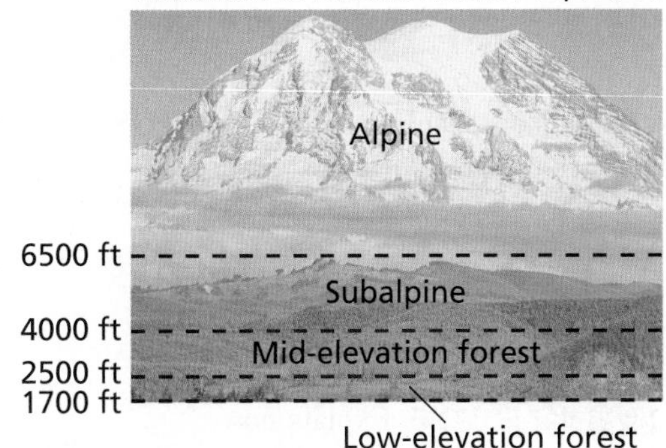

Write an inequality that represents the elevation range for each type of plant life.

a. trees in the low-elevation forest zone

b. flowers in the subalpine and alpine zones

14. **ERROR ANALYSIS** Describe and correct the error in solving the inequality and graphing the solution.

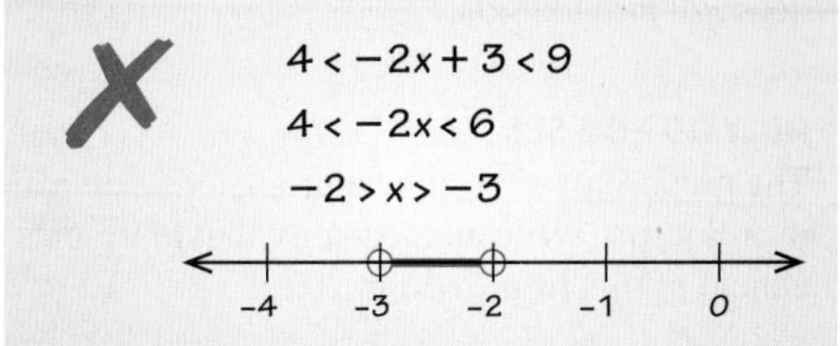

15. **MODELING REAL LIFE** Write an inequality that represents the temperatures (in degrees Fahrenheit) of the interior of the iceberg. *Example 4*

16. **MODELING REAL LIFE** A melting point is the temperature at which a solid melts to become a liquid. A boiling point is the temperature at which a liquid boils to become a gas. The table shows the melting and boiling points of several elements.

Element	Melting point (°C)	Boiling point (°C)
Gold	1064	2807
Silver	962	2212
Copper	1083	2567

a. Write an inequality that represents the temperatures (in degrees Fahrenheit) of each element as a liquid.

b. Describe a situation in which someone might need to know the melting point of one of these elements.

In Exercises 17–22, solve the inequality. Graph the solution, if possible.

17. $22 < -3c + 4 < 14$

18. $2m - 1 \geq 5$ *or* $5m > -25$

19. $-y + 3 \leq 8$ *and* $y + 2 > 9$

20. $x - 8 \leq 4$ *or* $2x + 3 > 9$

21. $\frac{3}{2}n + 19 \leq 10 + \frac{1}{2}n$ *or* $-\frac{2}{3}n + 3 < -\frac{1}{3}n + 12$

22. $3.5x - 18 < 4.5x - 23$ *and* $9.5x - 16 < 22$

23. **MP PROBLEM SOLVING** A ski shop sells skis with lengths ranging from 150 centimeters to 220 centimeters. The shop says the length of the skis should be about 1.16 times a skier's height (in centimeters). Write an inequality that represents the heights of skiers (in inches) for which the shop does *not* provide skis.

24. **HOW DO YOU SEE IT?**
The graph shows the annual profits of a company over 8 years. Write an inequality that represents the annual profits from 2013 to 2020.

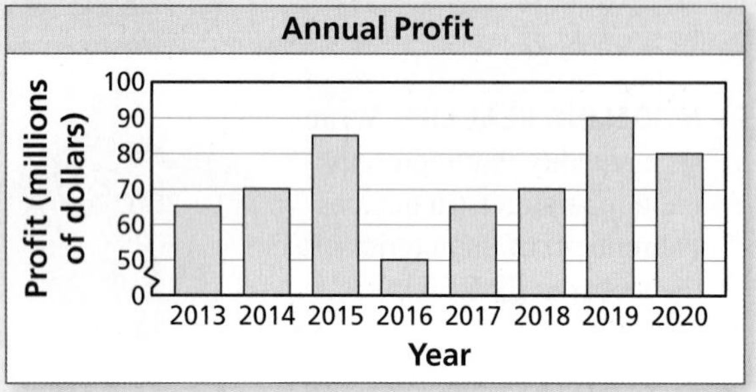

25. **DIG DEEPER** Determine the value of k for which the inequality $0.5 < -4x + k \leq 12 - k$ has the solution set $\{x \mid 1.25 \leq x < 2\}$.

26. **THOUGHT PROVOKING**
Complete the inequality

$4(x - 6) \quad \square \quad 2(x - 10)$

and

$5(x + 2) \geq 2(x + 8)$

with $<$, $\leq$, $>$, or $\geq$ so that the solution is only one value.

27. **MAKING AN ARGUMENT**
The sum of the lengths of any two sides of a triangle is greater than the length of the third side. Write three inequalities that represent the possible values of x. Your friend claims the value of x can be 1.5. Is your friend correct? Explain.

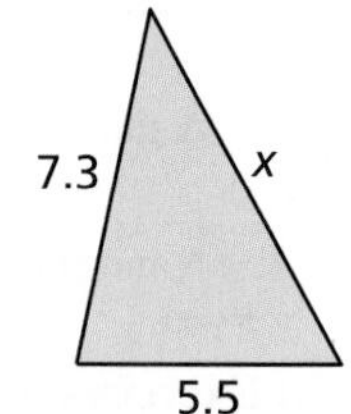

28. **PERFORMANCE TASK** You and your friends want to go on a road trip. You establish a round-trip fuel budget of $100, and plan to use a car with a fuel range of 25–34 miles per gallon. Use current gasoline prices to determine the distances you can travel. Then plan a trip to a city within the allotted distance from your location. Use inequalities to represent how much you will spend on gasoline, the maximum speeds at which you can travel, and how long the trip will take.

REVIEW & REFRESH

In Exercises 29–32, solve the equation. Graph the solutions, if possible.

29. $\left|\frac{d}{9}\right| = 6$

30. $7|5p - 7| = -21$

31. $|r + 2| = 9.4$

32. $\left|\frac{1}{2}w - 6\right| = |w + 7|$

33. The data shows the ages (in months) of children in a daycare group. Find and interpret the mean absolute deviation of the data.

24, 32, 36, 30, 28, 30, 34, 32, 26, 28

34. **MODELING REAL LIFE** You have quarters, nickels, and dimes that total $1.85. You have twice as many nickels as dimes, and 2 more quarters than dimes. How many of each coin do you have?

In Exercises 35 and 36, write an inequality that represents the graph.

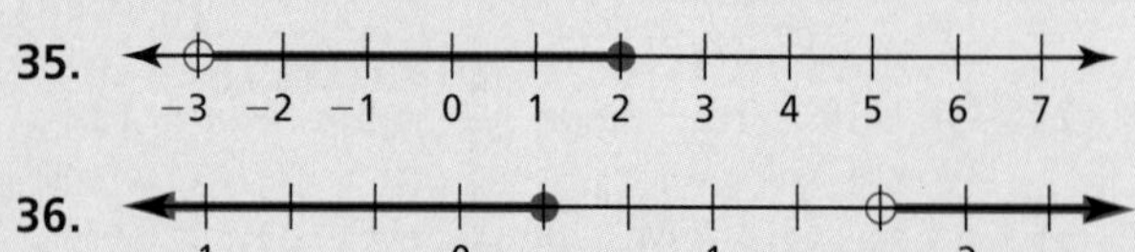

37. **MODELING REAL LIFE** You need an average exam score of at least 84% to receive a B in a class. For what scores on the fourth exam will you receive a B in the class?

Exam	Score
1	78%
2	93%
3	82%

In Exercises 38–41, solve the inequality. Graph the solution.

38. $9.4 + q \leq 15.2$

39. $z - \left(-\frac{3}{5}\right) > \frac{7}{20}$

40. $2 \leq -\frac{2}{9}x$

41. $2x \geq \frac{3}{4}$

42. **MP REASONING** Explain how you could predict the number of times you will spin a 4 in 50 spins on the spinner shown.

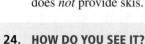

2.6 Solving Absolute Value Inequalities

Learning Target Write and solve inequalities involving absolute value.

Success Criteria
- I can write a compound inequality related to a given absolute value inequality.
- I can solve absolute value inequalities.
- I can use absolute value inequalities to solve real-life problems.

EXPLORE IT! Solving an Absolute Value Inequality

Work with a partner. Consider the absolute value inequality

$|x + 2| \leq 3.$

a. Explain what you think this inequality means.

b. Can you find a number that makes the inequality true? If so, what is the number?

c. Do you think there are other numbers that make the inequality true? If so, find several of them. Compare your answers with your classmates.

d. On the real number line below, locate the point for which the expression $|x + 2|$ is equal to 0.

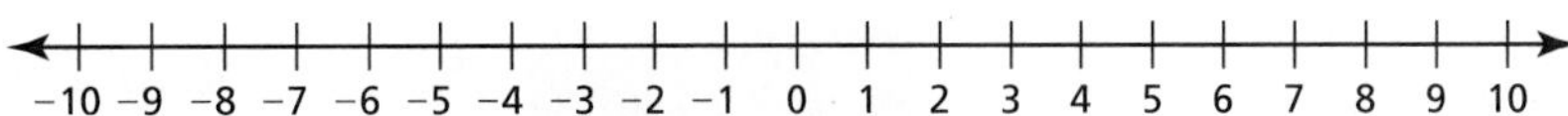

Then locate the numbers you found in parts (b) and (c) on the real number line. What do you notice?

e. Can you write two linear inequalities that use the expression $x + 2$ to represent the solutions of $|x + 2| \leq 3$? Explain.

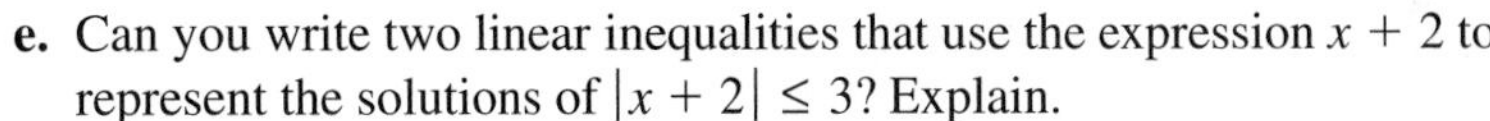

f. Repeat parts (b)–(e) for the inequality $|x + 2| \geq 3$. Compare your results with those for the inequality $|x + 2| \leq 3$.

g. Describe how to find the solutions of the absolute value inequalities algebraically. Then find the solutions.

i. $|x - 4| \leq 2$

ii. $|x - 4| \geq 2$

h. MP **CHOOSE TOOLS** Solve the absolute value inequalities in part (g) in a different way. Explain your method.

x_1	$|x_1 - 4|$
−6	10
−5	9
−4	
−3	
−2	
−1	
0	
1	
2	

Math Practice

Maintain Oversight
How can you change one of the absolute value inequalities shown so that it has no solution?

Solving Absolute Value Inequalities

Vocabulary

absolute value inequality, *p. 96*
absolute deviation, *p. 98*

An **absolute value inequality** is an inequality that contains an absolute value expression. For example, $|x| < 2$ and $|x| > 2$ are absolute value inequalities. Recall that $|x| = 2$ means the distance between x and 0 is 2.

The inequality $|x| < 2$ means the distance between x and 0 is *less than* 2.

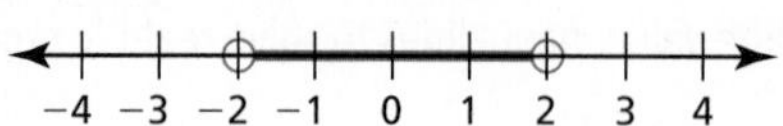

The graph of $|x| < 2$ is the graph of $x > -2$ *and* $x < 2$.

The inequality $|x| > 2$ means the distance between x and 0 is *greater than* 2.

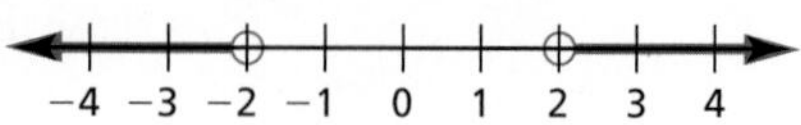

The graph of $|x| > 2$ is the graph of $x < -2$ *or* $x > 2$.

You can solve these types of inequalities by solving a compound inequality.

KEY IDEA

Solving Absolute Value Inequalities

Let c be a positive real number.

To solve $|ax + b| < c$, solve the compound inequality

$ax + b > -c$ *and* $ax + b < c$.

To solve $|ax + b| > c$, solve the compound inequality

$ax + b < -c$ *or* $ax + b > c$.

In the inequalities above, you can replace $<$ with $\leq$ and $>$ with $\geq$.

EXAMPLE 1 Solving Absolute Value Inequalities

Solve each inequality. Graph each solution, if possible.

a. $|x + 7| \leq 2$

b. $|8x - 11| < 0$

SOLUTION

a. Use $|x + 7| \leq 2$ to write a compound inequality. Then solve.

$x + 7 \geq -2$	*and*	$x + 7 \leq 2$	Write a compound inequality.
$\underline{-7 \quad -7}$		$\underline{-7 \quad -7}$	Subtraction Property of Inequality
$x \geq -9$	*and*	$x \leq -5$	Simplify.

REMEMBER
A compound inequality with "and" can be written as a single inequality.

▶ The solution is $-9 \leq x \leq -5$.

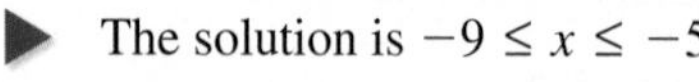

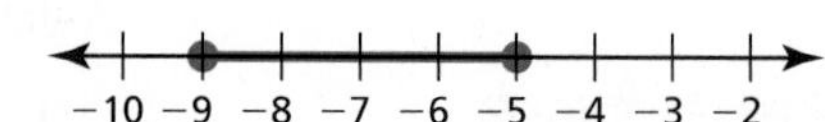

b. By definition, the absolute value of an expression must be greater than or equal to 0. The expression $|8x - 11|$ cannot be less than 0.

▶ So, the inequality has no solution.

SELF-ASSESSMENT 1 I do not understand. 2 I can do it with help. 3 I can do it on my own. 4 I can teach someone else.

1. **WRITING** How do you determine whether to use a compound inequality with "and" or a compound inequality with "or" when solving an absolute value inequality?

Solve the inequality. Graph the solution, if possible.

2. $|x| \leq 3.5$

3. $|k - 3| < -1$

4. $\left|\frac{1}{2}w - 1\right| < 11$

EXAMPLE 2 Solving Absolute Value Inequalities

Solve each inequality. Graph each solution.

a. $|c - 1| \geq 5$ **b.** $|10 - m| \geq -2$ **c.** $4|2x - 3| + 1 > 17$

SOLUTION

a. Use $|c - 1| \geq 5$ to write a compound inequality. Then solve.

$c - 1 \leq -5$	*or*	$c - 1 \geq 5$	Write a compound inequality.
$\underline{+1} \quad \underline{+1}$		$\underline{+1} \quad \underline{+1}$	Addition Property of Inequality
$c \leq -4$	*or*	$c \geq 6$	Simplify.

▶ The solution is $c \leq -4$ *or* $c \geq 6$.

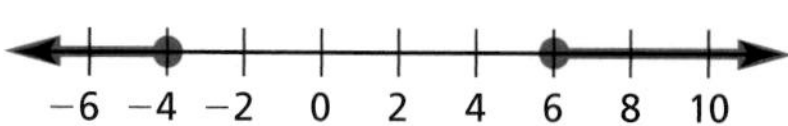

b. By definition, the absolute value of an expression must be greater than or equal to 0. The expression $|10 - m|$ will always be greater than -2.

▶ So, all real numbers are solutions.

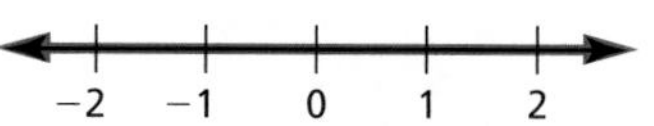

c. First isolate the absolute value expression on one side of the inequality.

$4|2x - 3| + 1 > 17$	Write the inequality.
$\underline{-1} \quad \underline{-1}$	Subtraction Property of Inequality
$4|2x - 3| > 16$	Simplify.
$\frac{4|2x - 3|}{4} > \frac{16}{4}$	Division Property of Inequality
$|2x - 3| > 4$	Simplify.

Use $|2x - 3| > 4$ to write a compound inequality. Then solve.

$2x - 3 < -4$	*or*	$2x - 3 > 4$	Write a compound inequality.
$\underline{+3} \quad \underline{+3}$		$\underline{+3} \quad \underline{+3}$	Addition Property of Inequality
$2x < -1$		$2x > 7$	Simplify.
$\frac{2x}{2} < \frac{-1}{2}$		$\frac{2x}{2} > \frac{7}{2}$	Division Property of Inequality
$x < -\frac{1}{2}$	*or*	$x > \frac{7}{2}$	Simplify.

▶ The solution is $x < -\frac{1}{2}$ *or* $x > \frac{7}{2}$.

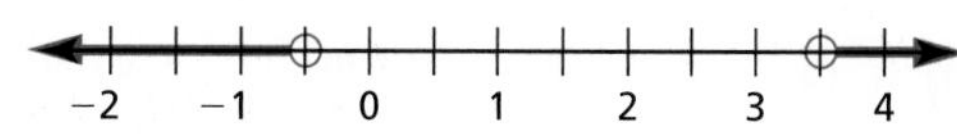

SELF-ASSESSMENT

1 I do not understand. **2** I can do it with help. **3** I can do it on my own. **4** I can teach someone else.

Solve the inequality. Graph the solution.

5. $|x + 3| > 8$ **6.** $|n + 2| - 3.7 \geq -6$ **7.** $3|d + 1| - 7 \geq -2$

8. WRITING Describe how solving $|w - 9| \leq 2$ is different from solving $|w - 9| = 2$.

9. MP REASONING What is the solution of the inequality $|ax + b| < c$, where $c < 0$? What is the solution of the inequality $|ax + b| > c$, where $c < 0$? Explain.

GO DIGITAL

Solving Real-Life Problems

WORDS AND MATH

A *deviation* is something that is different from the expected norm. In mathematics, *absolute deviation* represents how far a number deviates from a specific value.

The **absolute deviation** of a number x from a given value is the absolute value of the difference of x and the given value.

$$\text{absolute deviation} = |x - \text{given value}|$$

EXAMPLE 3 Modeling Real Life

WATCH

INFO

A mountain climber wants to buy a new camera drone to help map out a safe route to a mountain's summit. The table shows the prices of several camera drones. The climber is willing to pay the mean price with an absolute deviation of at most \$100. How many of the camera drone prices meet this condition?

Camera Drone Prices	
\$890	\$750
\$650	\$370
\$660	\$670
\$450	\$650
\$725	\$825

SOLUTION

1. **Understand the Problem** You know the prices of 10 camera drones. You are asked to find how many drones are at most \$100 from the mean price.
2. **Make a Plan** Calculate the mean price by dividing the sum of the prices by the number of prices. Use the absolute deviation and the mean price to write an absolute value inequality. Then solve the inequality and use it to answer the question.
3. **Solve and Check**

The mean price is $\frac{6640}{10} = \$664$. Let x represent a price the climber is willing to pay.

$|x - 664| \leq 100$ Write the absolute value inequality.

$-100 \leq x - 664 \leq 100$ Write a compound inequality.

$564 \leq x \leq 764$ Add 664 to each expression and simplify.

▶ The prices the climber is willing to pay are at least \$564 and at most \$764. Six prices meet this condition: \$750, \$650, \$660, \$670, \$650, and \$725.

STUDY TIP

The absolute deviation of at most \$100 from the mean, \$664, is given by the inequality $|x - 664| \leq 100$.

Check Reasonableness You can check that your answer is correct by graphing the drone prices and the mean on a number line. Any point within 100 of 664 represents a price that the climber is willing to pay.

SELF-ASSESSMENT

1 I do not understand. 2 I can do it with help. 3 I can do it on my own. 4 I can teach someone else.

10. **WHAT IF?** The climber is willing to pay the mean price with an absolute deviation of at most \$75. Do you expect the number of prices that meet this condition to increase or decrease? Explain your reasoning. How many of the camera drone prices meet this condition?

11. A softball team is participating in a tournament where the team will spend three nights at a hotel. Each hotel offers a 50% discount for the third night. The coach wants to keep the total cost for each player at \$225 with an absolute deviation of at most \$25. Write and solve an absolute value inequality to find which hotels meet this condition.

Hotel	Price per night
Hotel A	\$80
Hotel B	\$105
Hotel C	\$75
Hotel D	\$90

2.6 Practice WITH CalcChat® AND CalcView®

In Exercises 1–16, solve the inequality. Graph the solution, if possible. *Examples 1 and 2*

1. $|x| < 3$
2. $|y| \geq 4.5$
3. $|d + 9| > 3$
4. $|h - 5| \leq 10$
5. $|2s - 7| \geq -1$
6. $|4c + 5| > 7$
7. $|5p + 2| < -4$
8. $|9 - 4n| < 5$
9. $|6t - 7| - 8 \geq 3$
10. $|3j - 1| + 6 < 0$
11. $3|14 - m| > 18$
12. $-4|6b - 8| \leq 12$
13. $2|3w + 8| - 12.5 \leq -4.5$
14. $-3|2 - 4u| + 5.5 < -4.1$
15. $6\left|-\frac{1}{4}f + 3\right| + 7 > 7$
16. $\frac{2}{3}|4v + 6| - 2 \leq 10$

In Exercises 17 and 18, write the sentence as an absolute value inequality. Then solve the inequality.

17. A number is less than 6 units from 0.
18. Twice a number is no less than 10 units from −1.

19. **MODELING REAL LIFE** The rules for an essay contest require that entries can have 500 words with an absolute deviation of at most 30 words. Write and solve an absolute value inequality that represents the acceptable numbers of words.

20. **MODELING REAL LIFE** The normal body temperature of a camel is 37°C. This temperature varies by up to 3°C throughout the day. Write and solve an absolute value inequality that represents the range of normal body temperatures (in degrees Celsius) of a camel throughout the day.

ERROR ANALYSIS In Exercises 21 and 22, describe and correct the error in solving the absolute value inequality.

21.

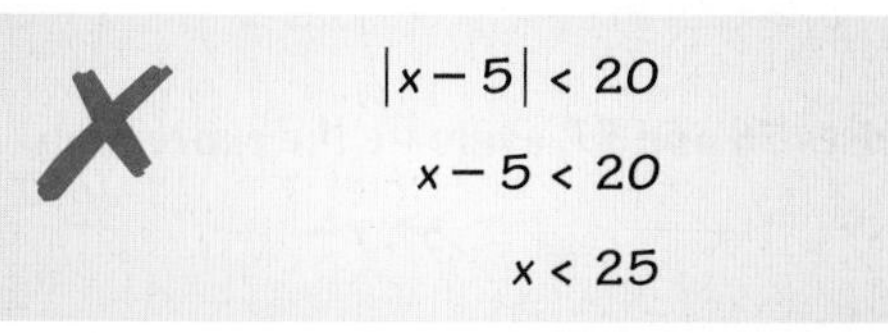

$$|x - 5| < 20$$
$$x - 5 < 20$$
$$x < 25$$

22.

$$|x + 4| > 13$$
$$x + 4 > -13 \quad \text{and} \quad x + 4 < 13$$
$$x > -17 \quad \text{and} \quad x < 9$$
$$-17 < x < 9$$

23. **MODELING REAL LIFE** A manufacturer throws out gaskets with weights that have an absolute deviation of more than 0.06 pound from the mean weight of the batch. The weights (in pounds) of the gaskets in a batch are 0.58, 0.63, 0.65, 0.53, and 0.61. Which gaskets should be thrown out? Use an absolute value inequality to justify your answer. *Example 3*

24. **MODELING REAL LIFE** The table shows the total distances of four trails. You want to complete a trail in $1\frac{1}{2}$ hours with an absolute deviation of at most 15 minutes. You hike at a rate of 3 miles per hour. Which trails can you hike? Use an absolute value inequality to justify your answer.

Trail	Miles
A	$5\frac{1}{4}$
B	$4\frac{3}{4}$
C	$3\frac{1}{2}$
D	4

CONNECTING CONCEPTS In Exercises 25 and 26, write and solve an absolute value inequality that represents the situation.

25. The difference between the areas of the figures is less than 2.

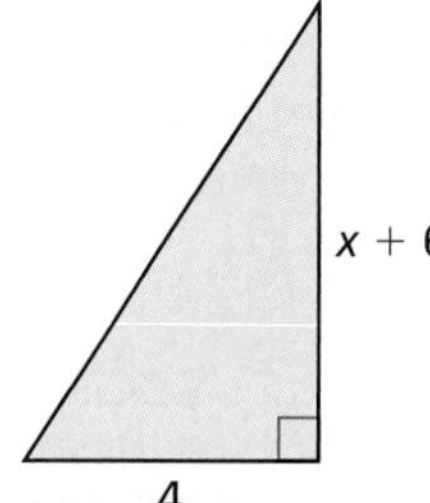

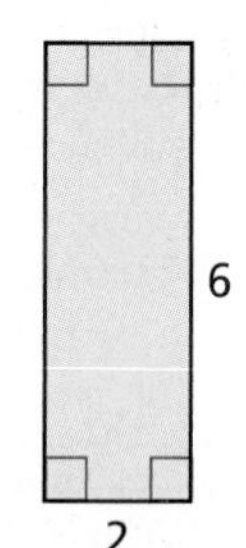

26. The difference between the perimeters of the figures is less than or equal to 3.

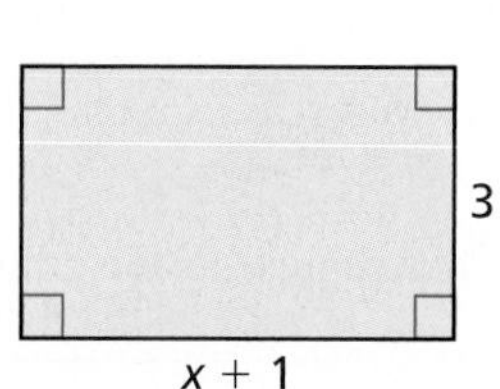

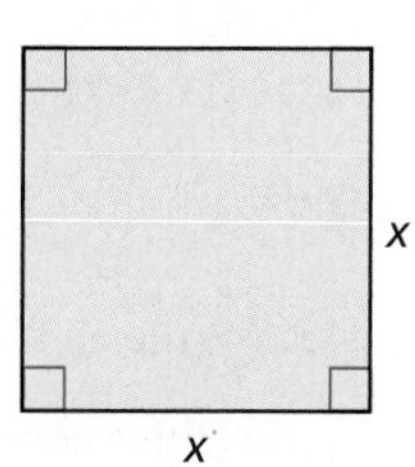

27. **MP PROBLEM SOLVING** Six students measure the acceleration (in meters per second per second) of an object in free fall. The measured values are shown. The students want to state that the absolute deviation of each measured value x from the mean is at most d. Find the value of d.

10.56, 9.52, 9.73, 9.80, 9.78, 10.91

28. **HOW DO YOU SEE IT?**
Write an absolute value inequality for each graph.

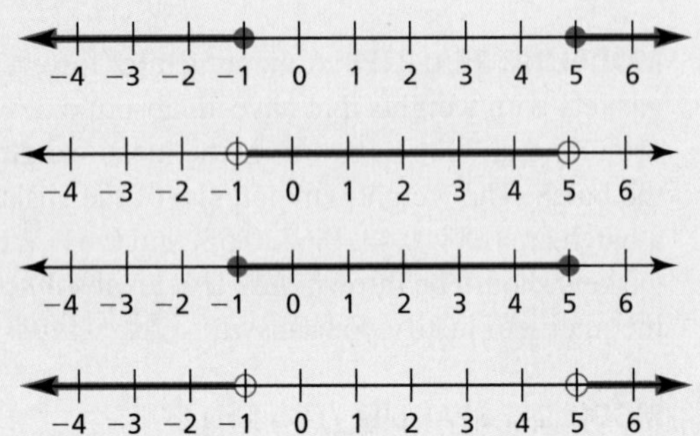

How did you decide which inequality symbol to use for each inequality?

MP REASONING In Exercises 29–32, tell whether the statement is *true* or *false*. If it is false, explain why.

29. If a is a solution of $|x + 3| \leq 8$, then a is also a solution of $x + 3 \geq -8$.

30. If a is a solution of $|x + 3| > 8$, then a is also a solution of $x + 3 > 8$.

31. If a is a solution of $|x + 3| \geq 8$, then a is also a solution of $x + 3 \geq -8$.

32. If a is a solution of $x + 3 \leq -8$, then a is also a solution of $|x + 3| \geq 8$.

33. **MAKING AN ARGUMENT** One of your classmates claims that the solution of $|n| > 0$ is all real numbers. Is your classmate correct? Explain your reasoning.

34. **THOUGHT PROVOKING**
Draw and label a geometric figure so that the perimeter P of the figure is a solution of the inequality $|P - 60| \leq 12$.

35. **DIG DEEPER** Solve the compound inequality $|x - 3| < 4$ *and* $|x + 2| > 8$. Describe your steps.

REVIEW & REFRESH

In Exercises 36–39, plot the ordered pair in a coordinate plane. Describe the location of the point.

36. $A(1, 3)$

37. $B(0, -3)$

38. $C(-4, -2)$

39. $D(-1, 2)$

40. **MP REASONING** Can you determine the solution of $|4x - 2| \geq -6$ without solving? Explain.

41. Complete the table.

x	0	1	2	3	4
$5x + 1$					

In Exercises 42–44, solve the equation.

42. $3(5m - 1) - 7m = -9$

43. $|2x + 7| - 8 = -5$

44. $-\frac{1}{2}(4h - 3) = \frac{1}{4}(6 - 8h)$

45. Write an inequality that represents the graph.

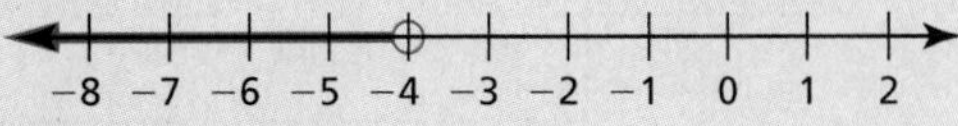

MP REASONING In Exercises 46 and 47, let $c > 0$. Solve the inequality for x.

46. $\frac{x}{c} > -7$

47. $-cx \geq 10.5$

In Exercises 48 and 49, find the cube root.

48. $\sqrt[3]{-216}$

49. $\sqrt[3]{\frac{8}{125}}$

50. **MODELING REAL LIFE** You bike at a speed of 12 miles per hour. Your friend bikes at a speed of 270 meters per minute. Who bikes faster?

In Exercises 51–55, solve the inequality. Graph the solution.

51. $\frac{t}{-5} - 2 \geq 1.7$

52. $15x + 3 < 6(4x + 5)$

53. $-3 < 4y + 5 \leq 9$

54. $6|3x + 2| > 60$

55. $b + \frac{1}{3} \leq \frac{5}{3}$ *or* $1 - 3b \leq -5$

In Exercises 56 and 57, evaluate the expression.

56. $(-3)^4$

57. -10^2

2 Chapter Review WITH CalcChat®

Chapter Learning Target Understand solving linear inequalities.

Chapter Success Criteria

- ◆ I can solve simple and multi-step inequalities.
- ◆ I can describe how to solve inequalities.
- ■ I can compare and contrast solving inequalities with solving equations.
- ■ I can apply techniques for solving inequalities to solve real-life applications.

◆ Surface
■ Deep

SELF-ASSESSMENT 1 I do not understand. 2 I can do it with help. 3 I can do it on my own. 4 I can teach someone else.

2.1 Writing and Graphing Inequalities (pp. 63–70)

Learning Target: Write inequalities and represent solutions of inequalities on number lines.

Vocabulary

inequality
solution of an inequality
solution set
graph of an inequality

Write the sentence as an inequality.

1. A number d minus 2 is less than -1.

2. Ten is at least the product of a number h and 5.

Tell whether -5 is a solution of the inequality.

3. $b + 6 > 1$

4. $\frac{3}{5}d \geq -3$

5. $w - 2.5 > -8$

Graph the inequality.

6. $x > 4$

7. $y \leq 2$

8. $-1.5 \geq z$

9. $w < \frac{2}{3}$

Write an inequality that represents the graph.

10.

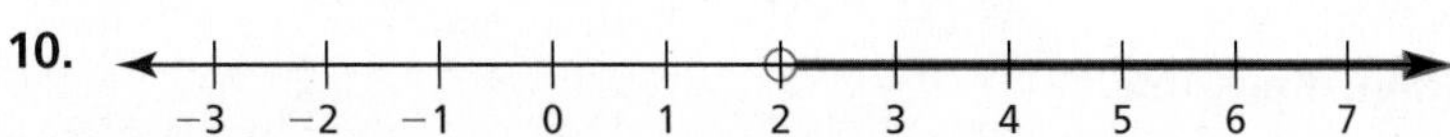

11. 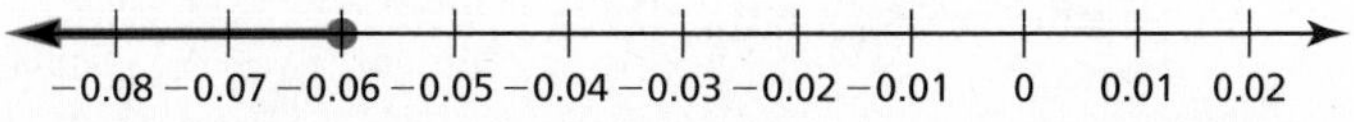 −0.08 −0.07 −0.06 −0.05 −0.04 −0.03 −0.02 −0.01 0 0.01 0.02

12. Three requirements for a lifeguard training course are shown.
   a. Write and graph three inequalities that represent the requirements.
   b. You can swim 250 feet, tread water for 6 minutes, and swim 35 feet underwater without taking a breath. Do you satisfy the requirements of the course? Explain.

13. Given that $M > N$, determine whether the inequality $\frac{M}{N} > \frac{N}{M}$ is *always*, *sometimes*, or *never* true. Explain your reasoning.

LIFEGUARDS NEEDED

Lifeguard Training Requirements

- Swim at least 100 yards.
- Tread water for at least 5 minutes.
- Swim 10 yards or more underwater without taking a breath.

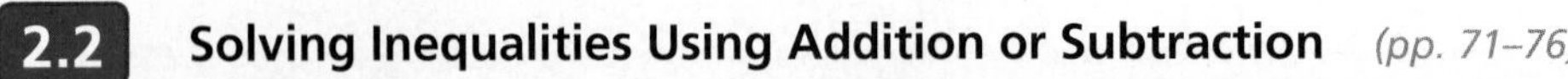

2.2 Solving Inequalities Using Addition or Subtraction (pp. 71–76)

WATCH

Learning Target: Write and solve inequalities using addition or subtraction.

Vocabulary

equivalent inequalities

Solve the inequality. Graph the solution.

14. $p + 4 < 10$

15. $r - 4 > -6$

16. $2.1 \geq m - 6.7$

17. $x + 2.5 \leq -8$

18. Write an inequality that requires using addition or subtraction to solve and has a solution of $-\frac{2}{3} > b$.

19. The Douglas Sea Scale describes the roughness of a sea for navigation. Waves currently reach a height of 12.82 meters. By what amounts can the wave heights increase for the sea to be described as *phenomenal*?

Wave height (m)	2.50–4.00	4.01–6.00	6.01–9.00	9.01–14.00	> 14.00
Description	Rough	Very Rough	High	Very High	Phenomenal

2.3 Solving Inequalities Using Multiplication or Division (pp. 77–82)

Learning Target: Write and solve inequalities using multiplication or division.

Solve the inequality. Graph the solution.

20. $3x > -21$

21. $-4 \leq \frac{g}{5}$

22. $-\frac{3}{4}n \leq 3$

23. $\frac{s}{-8} \geq 11$

24. $36 < 2q$

25. $-1.2k > 6$

26. Write an inequality that requires using multiplication or division to solve and has a solution of $h \geq 3.25$.

2.4 Solving Multi-Step Inequalities (pp. 83–88)

Learning Target: Write and solve multi-step inequalities.

Solve the inequality. Graph the solution, if possible.

27. $3x - 4 > 11$

28. $-4 < \frac{b}{2} + 9$

29. $7.5 - n \leq n + 3$

30. $2(-4s + 2) \geq -5s - 10$

31. $6(2t + 9) \leq 12t - 1$

32. $2r - 8 > \frac{3}{4}(r - 6)$

33. You want to subscribe to an online streaming service for live television. For what numbers of months is the total cost of Channel Champ less than the total cost of TV Mania?

2.5 Solving Compound Inequalities (pp. 89–94)

Learning Target: Write and solve compound inequalities.

34. A number x is more than -6 and at most 8. Write this sentence as an inequality. Graph the inequality.

Solve the inequality. Graph the solution.

35. $19 \geq 3z + 1 \geq -5$

36. $-3p \geq -6$ *or* $4p + 1 > 13$

37. $\frac{r}{4} < -5$ *or* $-2r - 7 \leq 3$

38. $-1 \leq -2d + 7 < 10$

39. Mount Everest has an elevation of about 8850 meters. Any location above 8000 meters is in the *death zone*, which is the elevation at which there is not enough oxygen to sustain human life. Write an inequality that represents the possible elevations of climbers in the death zone on Mount Everest.

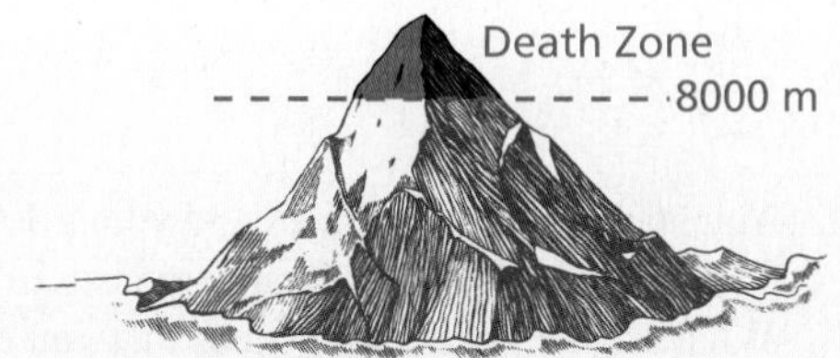

40. A highway has a minimum speed limit of 45 miles per hour and a maximum speed limit of 70 miles per hour. Write and solve an inequality that represents the legal driving speeds in kilometers per hour.

2.6 Solving Absolute Value Inequalities (pp. 95–100)

Learning Target: Write and solve inequalities involving absolute value.

Vocabulary
absolute value inequality
absolute deviation

Solve the inequality. Graph the solution, if possible.

41. $|m| \geq 10$

42. $|k - 9| < -4$

43. $|-1.5g - 2| + 1 < 6$

44. $|9 - 2j| + 10 \geq 2$

45. A safety regulation states that the height of a guardrail should be 106 centimeters with an absolute deviation of no more than 7 centimeters. Write and solve an absolute value inequality that represents the acceptable heights of a guardrail.

Mathematical Practices

Make Sense of Problems and Persevere in Solving Them

Mathematically proficient students make conjectures about the form and meaning of the solution.

1. In Exercise 43 on page 69, how does reasoning about the meaning of the solution help you choose the correct graph?

2. In Exercise 31 on page 87, what assumption did you make about both sides of the inequality? How did this help you complete the inequality?

3. An inequality can be used to represent the normal weights of Golden Retrievers. Make a conjecture about the inequality and its graph. Explain your reasoning.

2 Practice Test WITH CalcChat®

Write the sentence as an inequality.

1. The sum of a number y and 9 is at least -1.
2. A number k is less than 3 units from 10.

Solve the inequality. Graph the solution, if possible.

3. $6m \leq -42$
4. $\frac{x}{2} - 5 \geq -9$
5. $4p + 3 \geq 2(2p + 1)$
6. $-2 \leq 4 - 3a \leq 13$
7. $-7.5 < 2 - h$ *or* $6h + 5 > 71$
8. $4|-3b + 5| - 9 < 7$

9. You start a baking business and your goal is to earn a profit of at least $250 in the first month. Your expenses in the first month are $155. What are the possible revenues that you can earn to meet your goal?

10. A manufacturer of bicycle parts makes chains that have widths of 0.3 inch with an absolute deviation of at most 0.0003 inch. Write and solve an absolute value inequality that represents the possible widths.

11. Write and graph an inequality that represents the numbers that are *not* solutions of the inequality represented by the graph. Explain your reasoning.

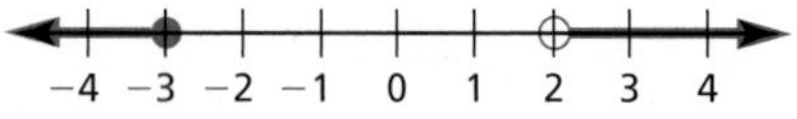

(Number line from −4 to 4: closed dot at −3 with arrow left; open dot at 2 with arrow right.)

−4 −3 −2 −1 0 1 2 3 4

12. In a diving competition, scores range from 0 to 10. When there are three judges, the number of points awarded is calculated by multiplying the sum of the scores by the degree of difficulty. Your opponent earns 40.8 points on a dive. You perform a dive with a degree of difficulty of 2.4. Two of your scores are shown. What scores from the third judge will give you more points than your opponent?

Judge 1	Judge 2	Judge 3
$4\frac{1}{2}$	$6\frac{1}{2}$	?

13. You jog at a rate of 6 miles per hour. Your friend is 55 feet ahead of you and jogs at a rate of 6.6 feet per second. Write and solve an inequality that represents the amounts of time that your friend is ahead of you.

14. A state imposes a sales tax on items of clothing that cost more than $175. The tax applies only to the difference of the price of the item and $175.

    a. Use the receipt shown to find the tax rate.

    b. A shopper has $430 to spend on a winter coat. Find the prices p of coats that the shopper can buy. Assume that $p \geq 175$.

    c. Another state imposes a 5% sales tax on the entire price of an item of clothing. For which prices is paying the 5% tax cheaper than paying the tax described above? Justify your answer.

SHOPPING CENTER

03/07/2020 10:45AM

19-728	Suit	$295.00
TAX		$7.50
TOTAL		$302.50

THANK YOU!

2 Performance Task
Summiting Everest

Summit
29,035 ft

The South Summit
28,500 ft

The Balcony
27,500 ft

The Hillary Step
28,839 ft

South Col
26,300 ft

Most expeditions leave from the South Col around **midnight** on "Summit Day."

A round trip from the South Col to the summit usually takes less than **20 hours**.

Approximate Time Frames
Ascent: **9–13 hours**
Descent: **4–7 hours**

Climbers usually set an **early-afternoon** turnaround time to guard against running out of oxygen or descending in the dark.

George Mallory was a leading member of the first British expeditions to Mount Everest in the early 1920s. In 1923, when asked why he wanted to climb the mountain, he famously responded, "Because it's there."

EXPEDITION LEADER

You are leading an expedition to the summit of Mount Everest. As the leader, you have the authority to send climbers down the mountain if they are too far behind schedule. You must set a departure time and a turnaround time, and then monitor the progress of your climbers. Use inequalities to show how you will know that the climbers are not falling behind schedule during the ascent.

2 College and Career Readiness WITH CalcChat®

Tutorial videos are available for each exercise.

1. The expected attendance at a school event is 65 people. The actual attendance can vary by up to 30 people. Which equation can you use to find the minimum and maximum possible attendances?

   Ⓐ $|x - 65| = 30$ Ⓑ $|x + 65| = 30$

   Ⓒ $|x - 30| = 65$ Ⓓ $|x + 30| = 65$

2. Complete each statement for the inequality $ax + 4 \leq 3x + b$.

   a. When $a = 5$ and $b =$ _____, $x \leq -3$.

   b. When $a =$ _____ and $b =$ _____, the solution of the inequality is all real numbers.

   c. When $a =$ _____ and $b =$ _____, the inequality has no solution.

3. A round of golf costs \$45. A season pass costs \$1200. Which inequality represents the numbers x of rounds of golf you can play in order to spend less money by purchasing the season pass?

   Ⓐ $45x < 1200$ Ⓑ $45x \geq 1200$

   Ⓒ $1200 \geq 45x$ Ⓓ $1200 < 45x$

4. Select each value of a that makes the solution of the equation $3(2x - 4) = 4(ax - 2)$ positive.

−2	−1	0	1	2	3	4	5

5. A student solved the inequality $\frac{-x+4}{3} > \frac{x+1}{2}$ as shown. Which statement accurately describes the student's work? Select all that apply.

$$\frac{-x+4}{3} > \frac{x+1}{2}$$

Step 1: $\frac{2}{2} \cdot \frac{-x+4}{3} > \frac{3}{3} \cdot \frac{x+1}{2}$

Step 2: $\frac{-2x+4}{6} > \frac{3x+1}{6}$

Step 3: $-2x + 4 > 3x + 1$

Step 4: $-5x > -3$

Step 5: $x > \frac{3}{5}$

   Ⓐ The student made an error in Step 1. Ⓑ The student made an error in Step 2.

   Ⓒ The student made an error in Step 3. Ⓓ The student made an error in Step 4.

   Ⓔ The student made an error in Step 5. Ⓕ The student's work is correct.

6. Which equation is *not* equivalent to $\frac{4}{3}x - \frac{1}{2} = \frac{y}{6} + 1$?

Ⓐ $4x - \frac{3}{2} = \frac{y}{2} + 3$

Ⓑ $x = \frac{y + 9}{8}$

Ⓒ $x - \frac{2}{3} = \frac{2}{9}y + \frac{4}{3}$

Ⓓ $8x - 3 = y + 6$

7. Complete the compound inequality with <, ≤, ≥, or > so the solution is represented by the graph.

$$4x - 18 \; \square \; -x - 3 \; \textit{and} \; -3x - 9 \; \square \; -3$$

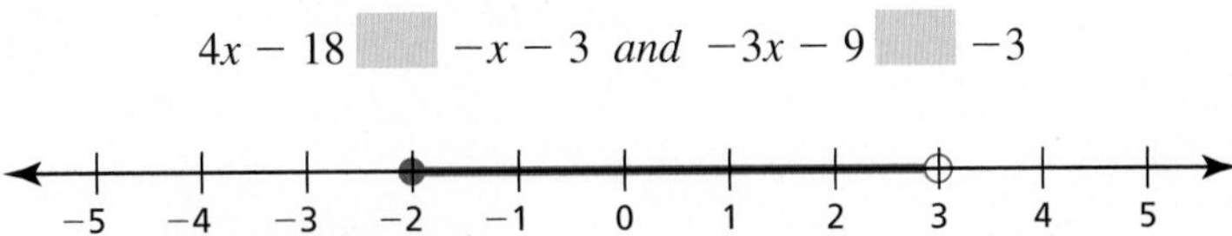

8. Which expression can you use to convert 50 inches per day to centimeters per hour?

Ⓐ $\frac{50 \text{ in.}}{1 \text{ day}} \times \frac{2.54 \text{ cm}}{1 \text{ in.}} \times \frac{1 \text{ day}}{24 \text{ h}}$

Ⓑ $\frac{50 \text{ in.}}{1 \text{ day}} \times \frac{1 \text{ cm}}{2.54 \text{ in.}} \times \frac{1 \text{ day}}{24 \text{ h}}$

Ⓒ $\frac{50 \text{ in.}}{1 \text{ day}} \times \frac{24 \text{ h}}{1 \text{ day}} \times \frac{2.54 \text{ cm}}{1 \text{ in.}}$

Ⓓ $\frac{50 \text{ in.}}{1 \text{ day}} \times \frac{1 \text{ in.}}{2.54 \text{ cm}} \times \frac{1 \text{ day}}{24 \text{ h}}$

9. You have a \$250 gift card to use at a department store.

a. Write an inequality that represents the possible numbers of pairs of socks you can buy when you buy 2 pairs of sneakers. Can you buy 8 pairs of socks? Explain.

b. Describe what the inequality $60 + 80x \leq 250$ represents in this context.

10. Consider the equation shown, where *a*, *b*, *c*, and *d* are integers.

$$ax + b = cx + d$$

Student A claims the equation will always have one solution. Student B claims the equation will always have no solution.

a. Select values for *a*, *b*, *c*, and *d* to create an equation that supports Student A's claim.

b. Select values for *a*, *b*, *c*, and *d* to create an equation that supports Student B's claim.

c. Select values for *a*, *b*, *c*, and *d* to create an equation that shows both Student A and Student B are incorrect.

3 Graphing Linear Functions

NATIONAL GEOGRAPHIC EXPLORER

Rhian G. Waller

Dr. Rhian Waller is a professor of Marine Sciences at the University of Maine. She has led several scuba diving expeditions to some of the most remote locations in the world. Dr. Waller specializes in the ecology of cold-water organisms, with a passion for the conservation of deep-sea and polar ecosystems.

- What are some examples of deep-sea or cold-water organisms?
- What can scuba divers learn by studying some of the least accessible locations on the planet?
- How might scuba divers use mathematics when planning a diving expedition?

STEM

Divers must be sure that their scuba tank provides enough oxygen for their dive. In the Performance Task you will plan a dive by selecting a tank size, depth, and the amount of time you will spend underwater.

Preparing for Chapter 3

Chapter Learning Target Understand graphing linear functions.

Chapter Success Criteria
- ◆ I can identify the graph of a linear function.
- ◆ I can graph linear functions written in different forms.
- ■ I can describe the characteristics of a function.
- ■ I can explain how a transformation affects the graph of a linear function.

◆ Surface
■ Deep

Chapter Vocabulary

Work with a partner. Discuss each of the vocabulary terms.

relation	dependent variable	linear function
function	*x*-intercept	nonlinear function
independent variable	*y*-intercept	

Mathematical Practices

Use Appropriate Tools Strategically

Mathematically proficient students use technological tools to explore concepts and solve problems.

Work with a partner. The equation $d = 90 - 15t$ represents the depth d (in feet) of a scuba diver t minutes after beginning an ascent to the surface. How long does it take the scuba diver to reach the surface?

1. Solve the problem using each tool.
   a. pencil and paper
   b. online or graphing calculator
   c. spreadsheet
2. Describe the advantages and disadvantages of using each tool.
3. Why is it important to know how to choose appropriate tools to solve mathematical problems?

3 Prepare WITH CalcChat®

Plotting Points

Example 1 **Plot the point $A(-3, 4)$ in a coordinate plane. Describe the location of the point.**

Start at the origin. Move 3 units left and 4 units up. Then plot the point. The point is in Quadrant II.

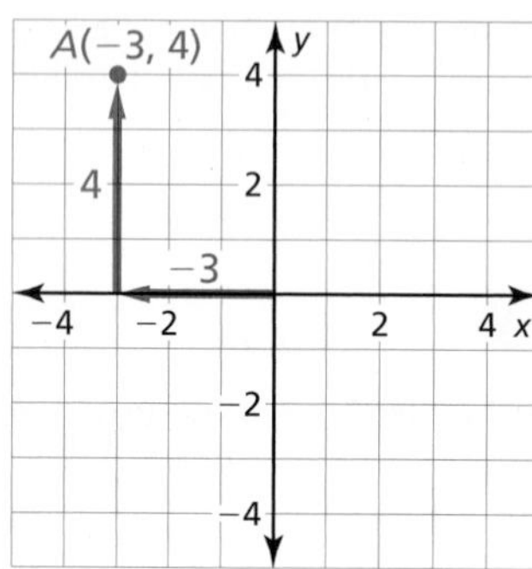

Plot the point in a coordinate plane. Describe the location of the point.

1. $A(3, 2)$
2. $B(-5, 1)$
3. $C(0, 3)$
4. $D\left(-2\frac{1}{2}, -4\right)$
5. $E(-6.5, 0)$
6. $F\left(\frac{5}{2}, -\frac{3}{2}\right)$

Evaluating Expressions

Example 2 **Evaluate $4x - 5$ when $x = 3$.**

$4x - 5 = 4(3) - 5$	Substitute 3 for x.
$= 12 - 5$	Multiply.
$= 7$	Subtract.

Example 3 **Evaluate $-2x + 9$ when $x = -8.5$.**

$-2x + 9 = -2(-8.5) + 9$	Substitute -8.5 for x.
$= 17 + 9$	Multiply.
$= 26$	Add.

Evaluate the expression for the given value of x.

7. $3x - 4; x = 7$
8. $-5x + 8; x = 3$
9. $10x + 18; x = \frac{1}{5}$
10. $-9x - 2; x = -4$
11. $24 - 8x; x = -2.25$
12. $15x + 9; x = -\frac{1}{10}$
13. **MP PRECISION** Let a and b be positive real numbers. Describe how to plot (a, b), $(-a, b)$, $(a, -b)$, and $(-a, -b)$.

3.1 Functions

Learning Target Understand the concept of a function.

Success Criteria

- I can determine whether a relation is a function.
- I can find the domain and range of a function.
- I can distinguish between independent and dependent variables.

A **relation** pairs inputs with outputs. For example, the number of hours you work *and* the pay you receive form a relation. The inputs are the hours worked and the outputs are the pay amounts. Can you think of other relations?

WORDS AND MATH

Think about the meanings of the compound words *input* and *output* by analyzing their prefixes and the root word *put*.

EXPLORE IT! Describing Relations

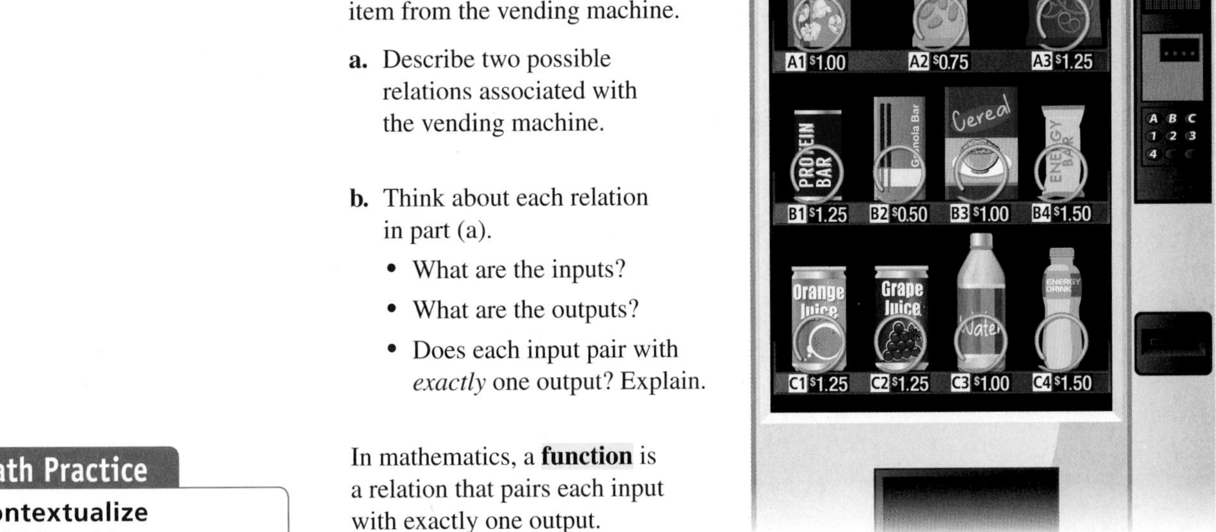

Work with a partner. You buy an item from the vending machine.

a. Describe two possible relations associated with the vending machine.

b. Think about each relation in part (a).

- What are the inputs?
- What are the outputs?
- Does each input pair with *exactly* one output? Explain.

In mathematics, a **function** is a relation that pairs each input with exactly one output.

Math Practice

Contextualize Relationships

Can you think of any mathematical relations? Are any of these relations functions?

c. How can you use a coordinate plane to represent a relation? What are the inputs? What are the outputs?

d. The graph shows a relation. Is the relation a function? Explain your reasoning.

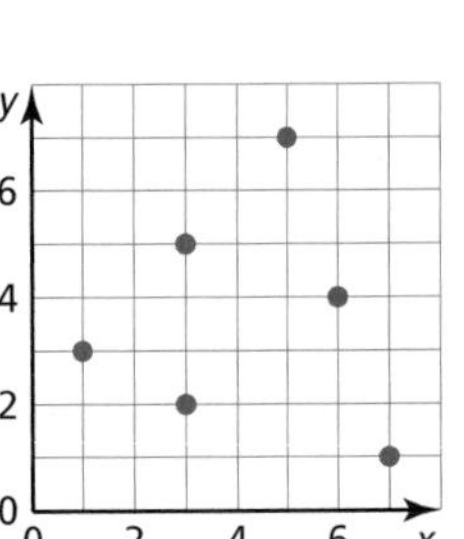

e. Draw two more graphs that represent relations, one that is a function and one that is not a function. Compare your graphs with other students in your class.

Determining Whether Relations Are Functions

Vocabulary

relation, *p. 112*
function, *p. 112*
domain, *p. 114*
range, *p. 114*
independent variable, *p. 115*
dependent variable, *p. 115*

A **relation** pairs inputs with outputs. When a relation is given as ordered pairs, the x-coordinates are inputs and the y-coordinates are outputs. A relation that pairs each input with *exactly one* output is a **function.**

EXAMPLE 1 Determining Whether Relations Are Functions

Determine whether each relation is a function. Explain.

a. $(-2, 2), (-1, 2), (0, 2), (1, 0), (2, 0)$

b. $(4, 0), (8, 7), (6, 4), (4, 3), (5, 2)$

c.

Input, x	-2	-1	0	0	1	2
Output, y	3	4	5	6	7	8

REMEMBER
A relation can be represented by a mapping diagram.

d. **Input, x** **Output, y**

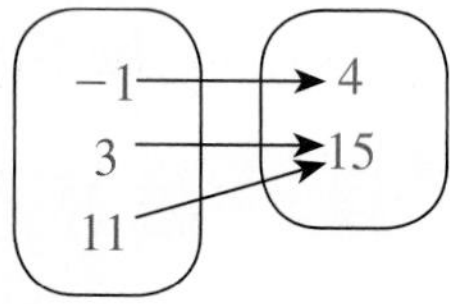

SOLUTION

a. Every input has exactly one output.

▶ So, the relation is a function.

b. The input 4 has two outputs, 0 and 3.

▶ So, the relation is *not* a function.

c. The input 0 has two outputs, 5 and 6.

▶ So, the relation is *not* a function.

d. Every input has exactly one output.

▶ So, the relation is a function.

SELF-ASSESSMENT

1 I do not understand. **2** I can do it with help. **3** I can do it on my own. **4** I can teach someone else.

Determine whether the relation is a function. Explain.

1. $(-5, 0), (0, 0), (5, 0), (5, 10)$

2. $(-4, 8), (-1, 2), (2, -4), (5, -10)$

3.

Input, x	**Output, y**
2	2.6
4	5.2
6	7.8

4. **Input, x** **Output, y**

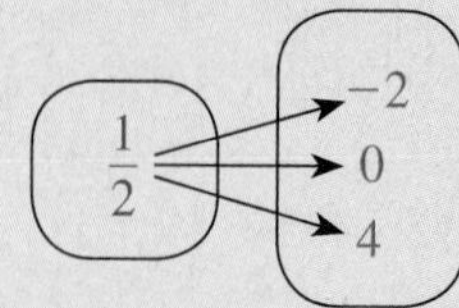

5. OPEN-ENDED Write a relation that is not a function. How can you change the relation so that it is a function?

6. MP **REASONING** Two quantities x and y are in a proportional relationship. Do the ordered pairs (x, y) represent a function? Explain your reasoning.

KEY IDEA

Vertical Line Test

Words A graph represents a function when no vertical line passes through more than one point on the graph.

Examples Function | Not a function

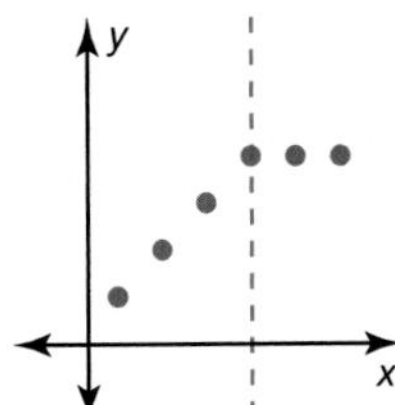

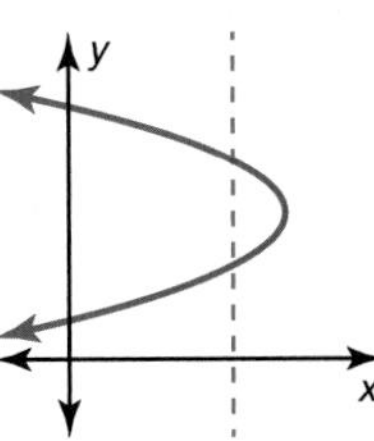

EXAMPLE 2 Using the Vertical Line Test

Determine whether each graph represents a function. Explain.

a.

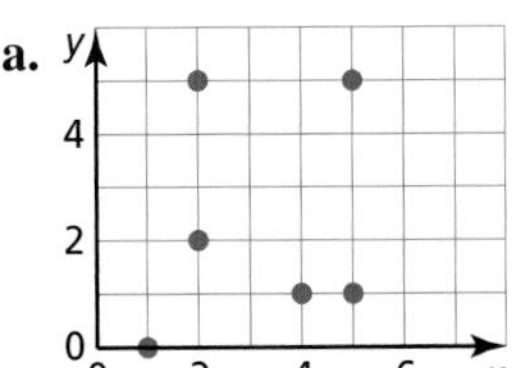

b.

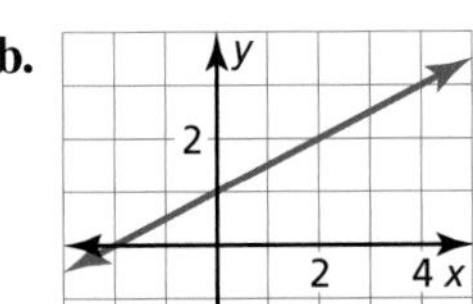

SOLUTION

a. You can draw a vertical line through (2, 2) and (2, 5).

▶ So, the graph does *not* represent a function.

b. No vertical line can be drawn through more than one point on the graph.

▶ So, the graph represents a function.

SELF-ASSESSMENT

1 I do not understand. 2 I can do it with help. 3 I can do it on my own. 4 I can teach someone else.

Determine whether the graph represents a function. Explain.

7.

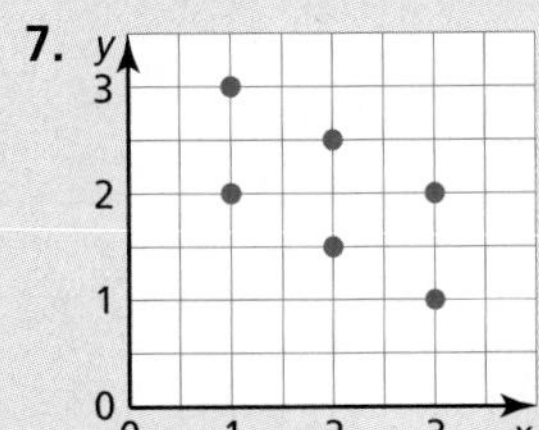

8.

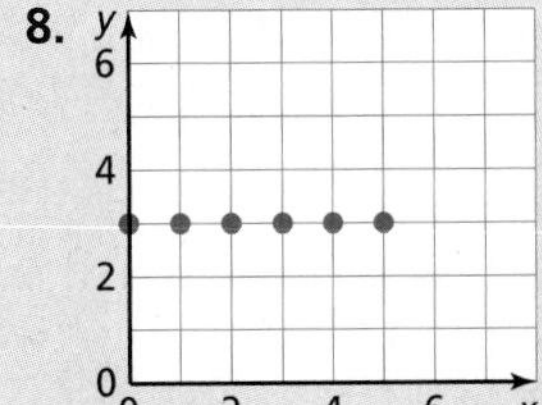

9.

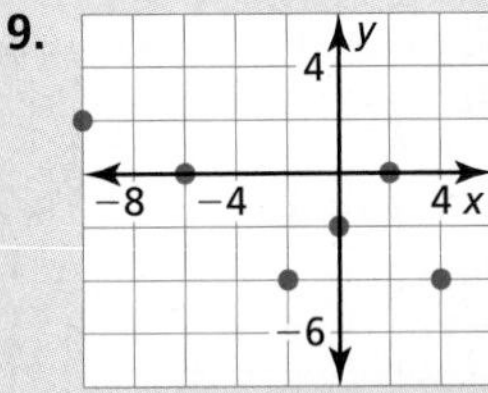

10.

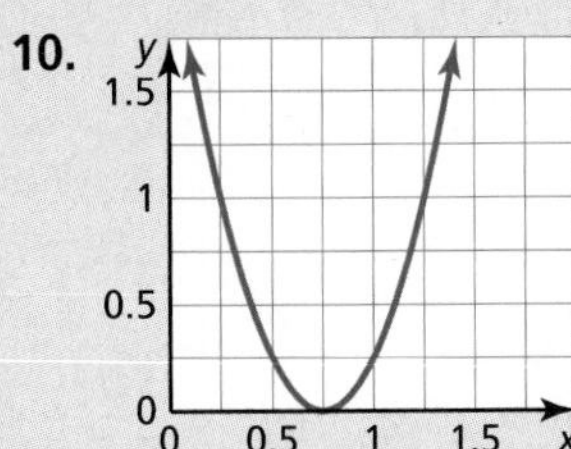

11.

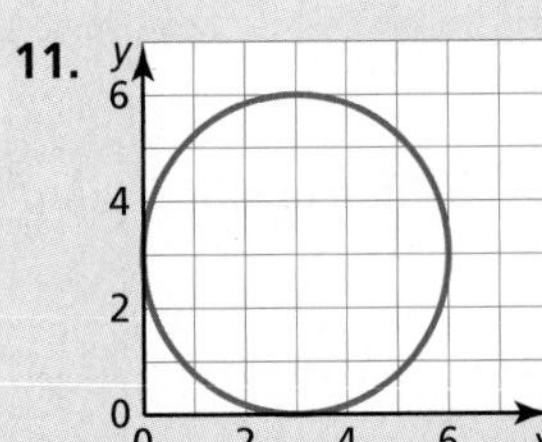

12.

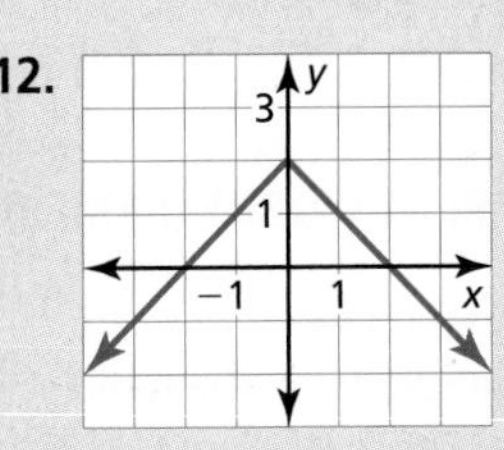

13. WRITING Explain why you can use vertical lines to determine whether a graph represents a function.

Finding the Domain and Range of a Function

KEY IDEA

The Domain and Range of a Function

The **domain** of a function is the set of all possible input values.

The **range** of a function is the set of all possible output values.

EXAMPLE 3 **Finding the Domain and Range from a Graph**

Find the domain and range of the function represented by the graph.

a.

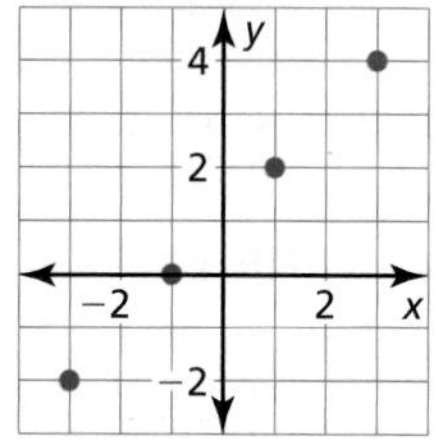

b.

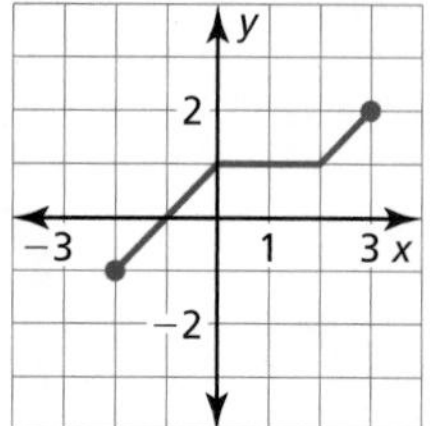

SOLUTION

a. Write the ordered pairs. Identify the inputs and outputs.

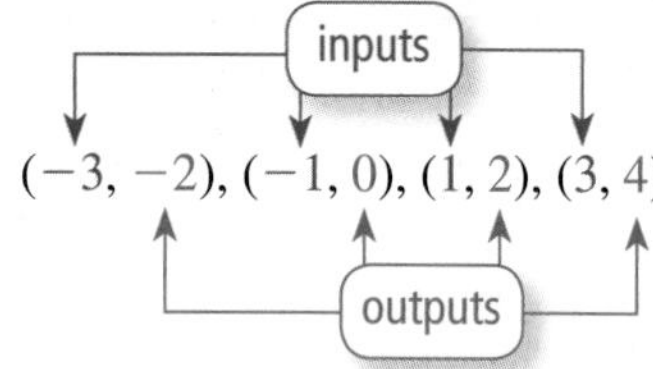

▶ The domain is −3, −1, 1, and 3.
The range is −2, 0, 2, and 4.

b. Identify the x- and y-values represented by the graph.

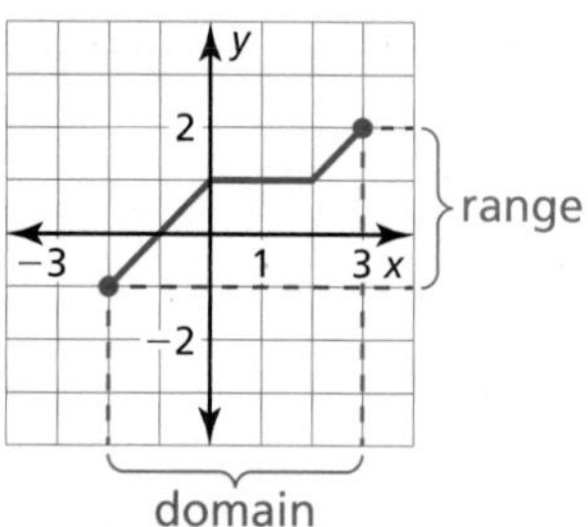

▶ The domain is $-2 \le x \le 3$.
The range is $-1 \le y \le 2$.

SELF-ASSESSMENT

1 I do not understand. 2 I can do it with help. 3 I can do it on my own. 4 I can teach someone else.

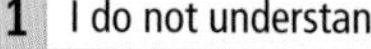

Find the domain and range of the function represented by the graph.

14.

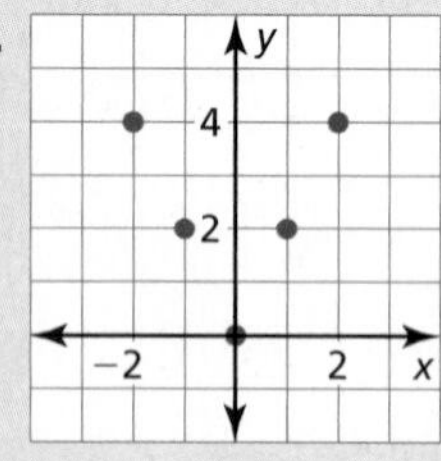

15.

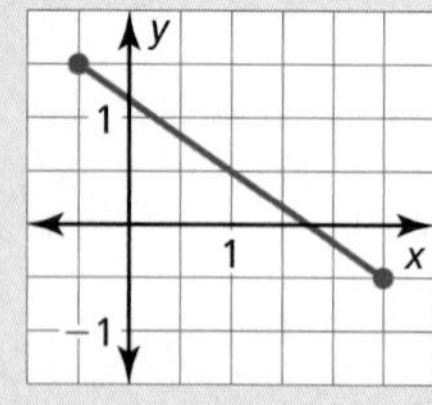

16.

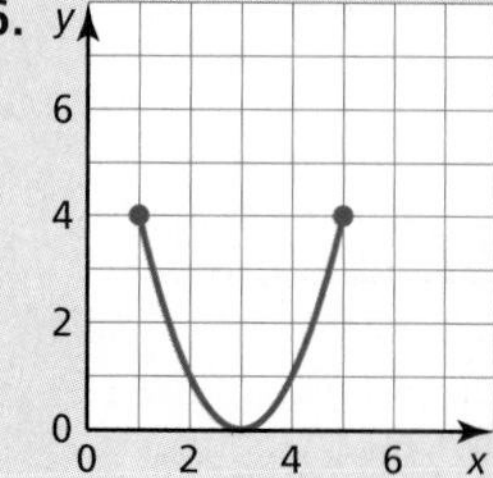

17. DIFFERENT WORDS, SAME QUESTION Which is different? Find "both" answers.

Find the range of the function represented by the table.

Find the x-values of the function represented by (−1, 7), (0, 5), and (1, −1).

Find the inputs of the function represented by the table.

Find the domain of the function represented by (−1, 7), (0, 5), and (1, −1).

x	y
−1	7
0	5
1	−1

Identifying Independent and Dependent Variables

The variable that represents the input values of a function is the **independent variable** because it can be *any* value in the domain. The variable that represents the output values of a function is the **dependent variable** because it *depends* on the value of the independent variable. When an equation represents a function, the dependent variable is defined in terms of the independent variable. The statement "y is a function of x" means that y varies depending on the value of x.

A whale's rib cage safely collapses at pressures that can snap human bones.

$$y = -x + 10$$

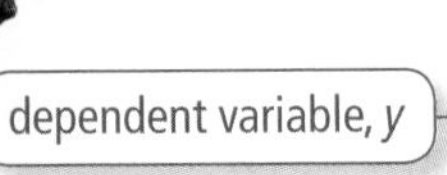

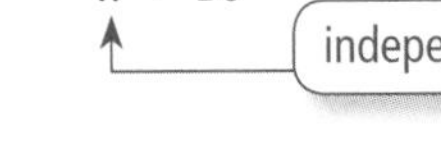

EXAMPLE 4 Modeling Real Life

Water pressure is 0 psi (pounds per square inch) at sea level and increases by about 0.44 psi for every foot an object descends in water.

a. Does the situation represent a function? If so, identify the independent and dependent variables.

b. A whale dives from 1000 feet to 3500 feet. Find the domain and range.

SOLUTION

a. The water pressure depends on the depth of the water. Because the water pressure changes with any change in depth, each input has exactly one output.

▶ So, the situation represents a function in which the water pressure is the dependent variable and depth is the independent variable.

b. The whale dives from 1000 feet to 3500 feet, so the domain is any depth from 1000 feet to 3500 feet.

Because water pressure is 0 psi at sea level and increases at a constant rate, water pressure is proportional to depth. So, the water pressure y (in psi) at a depth of x feet can be represented by $y = 0.44x$. To find the range, find y when $x = 1000$ and when $x = 3500$.

REMEMBER

A proportional relationship can be represented by $y = kx$, where k is the constant of proportionality.

Input, x	$0.44x$	Output, y
1000	0.44(1000)	440
3500	0.44(3500)	1540

▶ So, the domain is $1000 \le x \le 3500$ and the range is $440 \le y \le 1540$.

SELF-ASSESSMENT

1 I do not understand. 2 I can do it with help. 3 I can do it on my own. 4 I can teach someone else.

18. You arrange coins in stacks so that each stack has twice as many coins as the previous stack. The first stack has 2 coins.

a. Does the situation represent a function? If so, identify the independent and dependent variables.

b. You have 6 stacks of coins. Find the domain and range.

19. The total pressure exerted on an object in water is the sum of air pressure at sea level and water pressure. You are scuba diving at a depth where the total pressure is three times the air pressure at sea level. Use the information in Example 4 to find your depth. Explain how you found your answer.

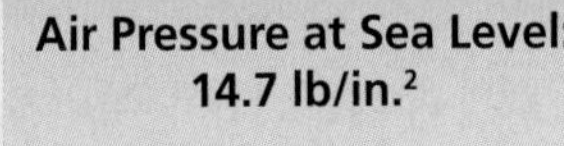

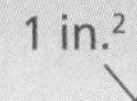

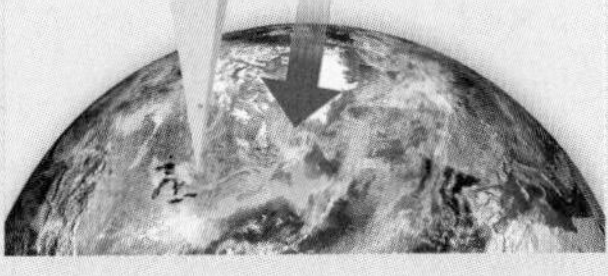

3.1 Practice WITH CalcChat® AND CalcView®

In Exercises 1–6, determine whether the relation is a function. Explain. *Example 1*

1. (1, −2), (2, 1), (3, 6), (4, 13), (5, 22)

2. (7, 4), (5, −1), (3, −8), (1, −5), (3, 6)

3. Input, x Output, y

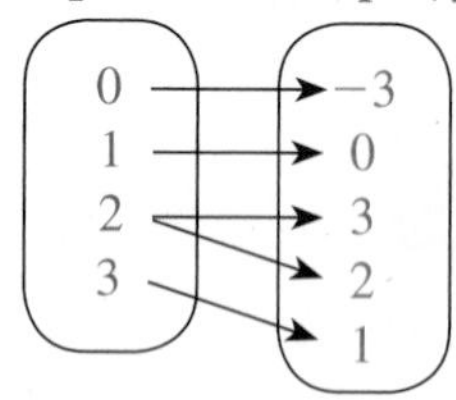

4. Input, x Output, y

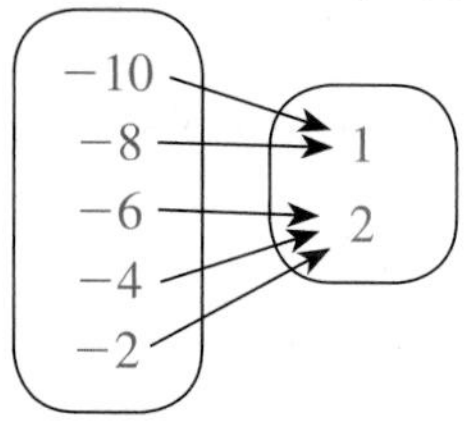

5.

Input, x	16	1	0	1	16
Output, y	−2	−1	0	1	2

6.

Input, x	−3	0	3	6	9
Output, y	$\frac{2}{3}$	$\frac{1}{3}$	0	$-\frac{1}{3}$	$-\frac{2}{3}$

In Exercises 7–10, determine whether the graph represents a function. Explain. *Example 2*

7.

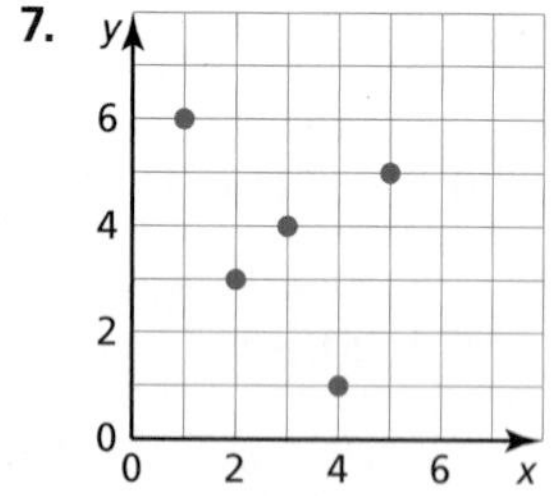

8.

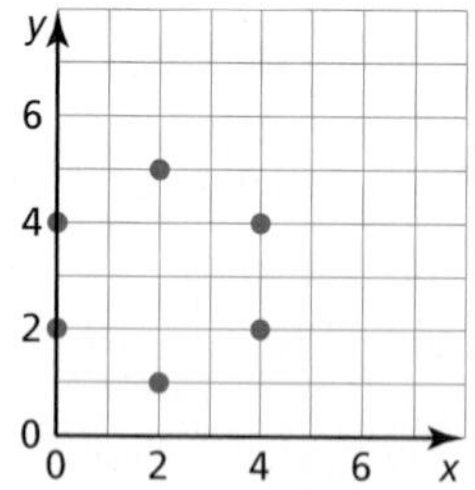

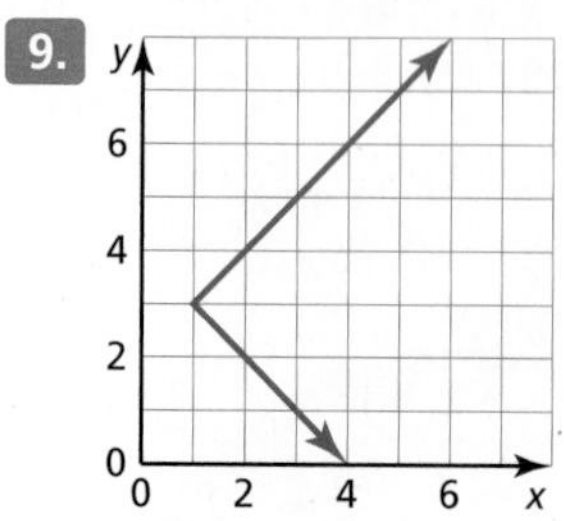

9.

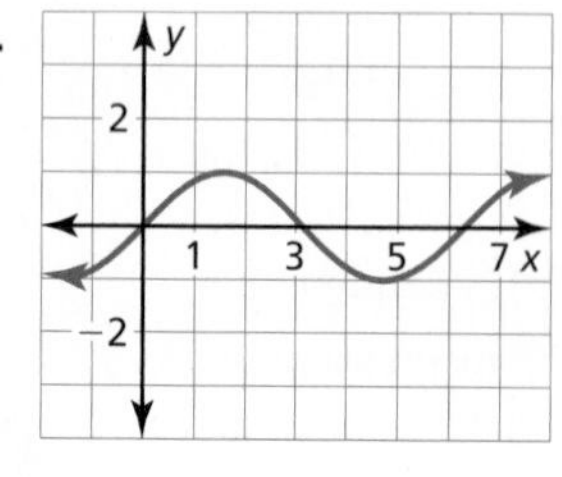

10.

In Exercises 11–14, find the domain and range of the function represented by the graph. *Example 3*

11.

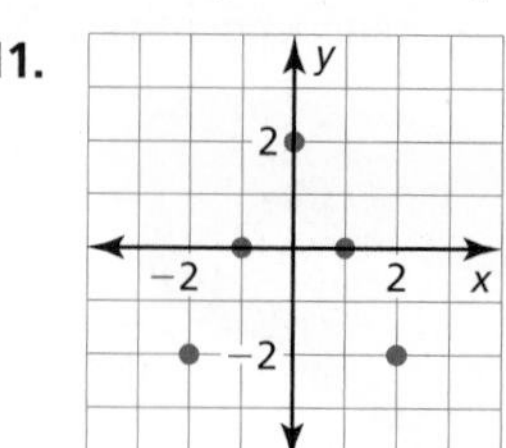

12.

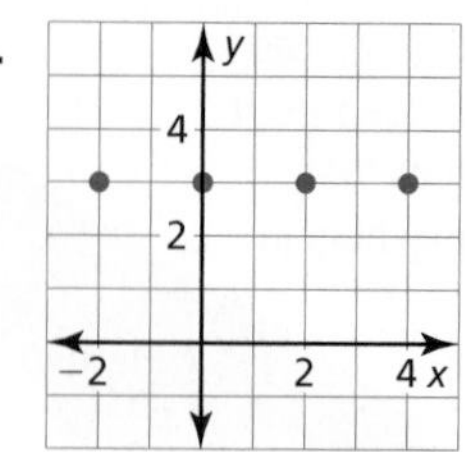

13.

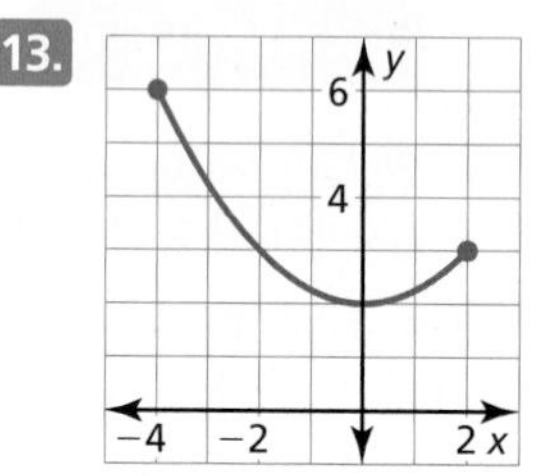

14.

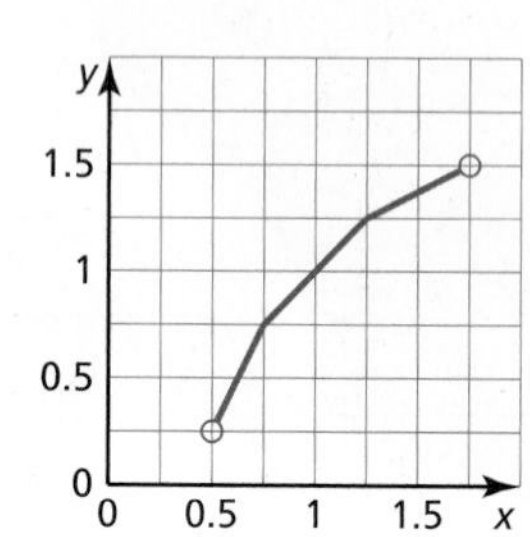

ANALYZING RELATIONSHIPS In Exercises 15 and 16, identify the independent and dependent variables.

15. the number of quarters you put into a parking meter and the amount of time on the meter

16. the amount of gasoline in a car's fuel tank and the amount of time spent driving

17. **MODELING REAL LIFE** A cell phone plan costs \$30 for each line. *Example 4*

a. Does the situation represent a function? If so, identify the independent and dependent variables.

b. You can have a maximum of four lines on a plan. Find the domain and range.

18. **MODELING REAL LIFE** A taxi company charges an initial fee of \$2.80 plus \$3.50 per mile traveled.

a. Does the situation represent a function? If so, identify the independent and dependent variables.

b. You have enough money to travel at most 20 miles in the taxi. Find the domain and range.

ERROR ANALYSIS In Exercises 19 and 20, describe and correct the error in the statement about the relation shown in the table.

Input, x	1	2	3	4	5
Output, y	$6\frac{1}{2}$	$7\frac{1}{2}$	$8\frac{1}{2}$	$6\frac{1}{2}$	$9\frac{1}{2}$

19. 
The relation is *not* a function. One output is paired with two inputs.

20. 
The relation is a function. The range is 1, 2, 3, 4, and 5.

21. **MULTIPLE REPRESENTATIONS** The table shows the balance of a savings account over time. Represent the situation in words and in a coordinate plane. Does the situation represent a function? Explain.

Month, x	0	1	2	3	4
Balance (dollars), y	100	125	150	175	200

22. **MULTIPLE REPRESENTATIONS** The equation $1.5x + 0.5y = 12$ represents the number x of hardcover books and the number y of softcover books you can buy at a used book sale. Represent the situation in a table and in a coordinate plane. Does the situation represent a function? Explain.

23. **MP PRECISION** The graph represents a function. Find the input value corresponding to an output of 2.

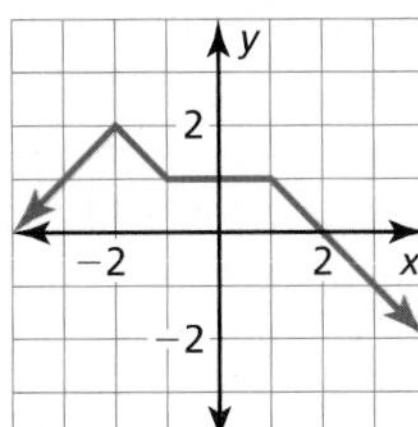

24. **OPEN-ENDED** Complete the table so that when t is the independent variable, the relation is a function, and when t is the dependent variable, the relation is not a function.

t				
v				

25. **MAKING AN ARGUMENT** Your friend says that a line always represents a function. Is your friend correct? Explain.

26. **HOW DO YOU SEE IT?**
The graph represents the height h of a projectile after t seconds.

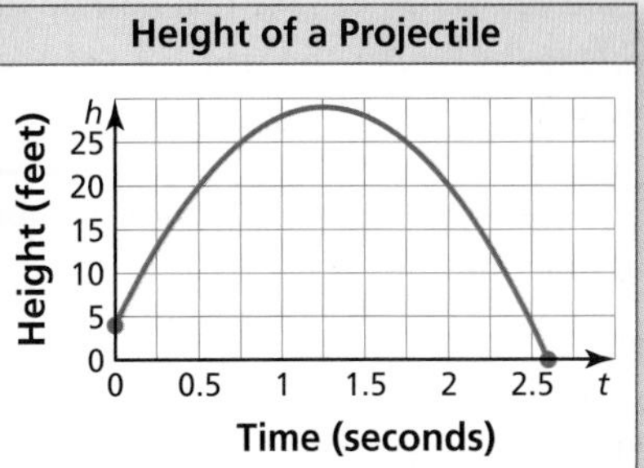

a. Is h a function of t? Explain.

b. Approximate the height of the projectile after 0.5 second and after 1.25 seconds.

c. Approximate the domain and range.

d. Is t a function of h? Explain.

MP PRECISION In Exercises 27–30, determine whether the statement uses the word *function* in a way that is mathematically correct. Explain your reasoning.

27. The selling price of an item is a function of the cost of making the item.

28. The sales tax on a purchased item in a given state is a function of the selling price.

29. A function pairs each student in your school with a homeroom teacher.

30. A function pairs each chaperone on a school trip with 10 students.

MP REASONING In Exercises 31–34, tell whether the statement is *true* or *false*. If it is false, explain why.

31. Every function is a relation.

32. Every relation is a function.

33. When you switch the inputs and outputs of any function, the resulting relation is a function.

34. When the domain of a function has an infinite number of values, the range always has an infinite number of values.

35. **COLLEGE PREP** Which of the following values of x and y make the relation a function? Select all that apply.

$$(-3, 7), (-2, 3), (0, 8), (1, -1), (x, y)$$

Ⓐ $x = -4, y = 0$ Ⓑ $x = 1, y = -2$

Ⓒ $x = 5, y = -1$ Ⓓ $x = 2, y = 8$

36. THOUGHT PROVOKING
Describe a function in which the inputs and/or the outputs are not numbers. Identify the independent and dependent variables. Then find the domain and range of the function.

DIG DEEPER **In Exercises 37–40, find the domain and range of the function.**

37. $y = |x|$

38. $y = -|x|$

39. $y = |x| - 6$

40. $y = 4 - |x|$

41. CONNECTING CONCEPTS Find the domain and range of a function that represents the perimeter of the triangle shown.

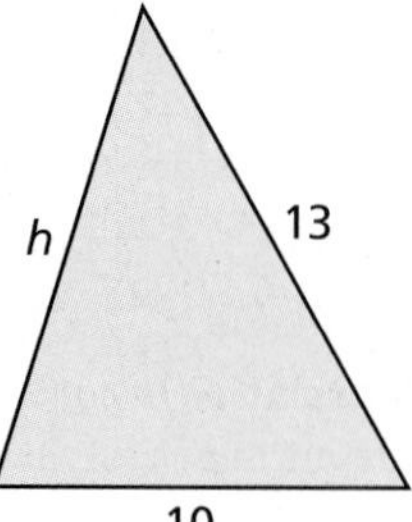

REVIEW & REFRESH

WATCH

42. Tell whether x and y are proportional.

x	4	6	12	16
y	6	8	16	20

43. What number is 60% of 35?

44. 27 is what percent of 75?

In Exercises 45–48, solve the equation.

45. $n - 5.3 = -7.4$

46. $|2x + 5| = 3x$

47. $7c + 10 - 12c = -11 - 2c$

48. $-\frac{1}{2}(3h + 8) + 2 = 13$

49. Determine whether the relation is a function. Explain.

$$(0, -6), (1, -3), (3, 2), (5, 1), (2, -3)$$

50. Write the sentence as an inequality.

Seven is at most the quotient of a number d and -5.

51. MODELING REAL LIFE There is a 6% sales tax on your clothing purchase. You pay $1.80 in tax. What is the total amount you pay?

In Exercises 52–57, solve the inequality. Graph the solution.

52. $z + 9 < 5$

53. $-5y + 9.2 \geq -18.3$

54. $\frac{x}{-7} \leq 2$

55. $7w + 6 > 3(-2 + w)$

56. $2|t - 5| + 3 \geq 9$

57. $-12 \leq 2m + 8 < 4$

58. Find the domain and range of the function represented by the graph.

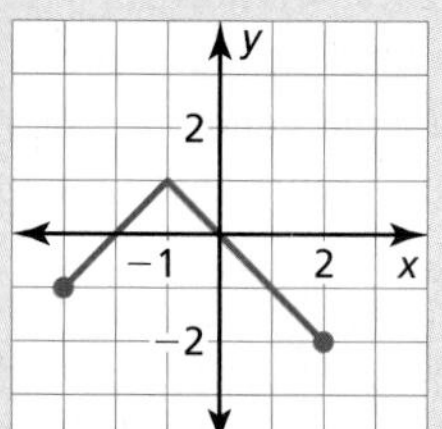

59. MP REASONING Find the value of a for which the equation

$$12x - 15 = a(5 - 4x)$$

is an identity.

60. Write an inequality that represents the graph.

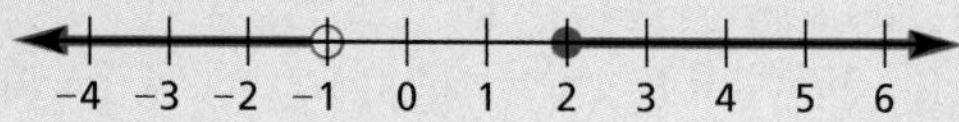

61. MODELING REAL LIFE You want to score an average of at least 10 points per game in the last six basketball games of the season. In five of the six remaining games, you score 8, 14, 6, 12, and 8 points. How many points do you need to score in the sixth game to achieve your goal?

62. Solve the literal equation $3x - 6y = 18$ for y.

63. The volume of the rectangular prism is 105 cubic yards. What is the surface area of the prism in square feet?

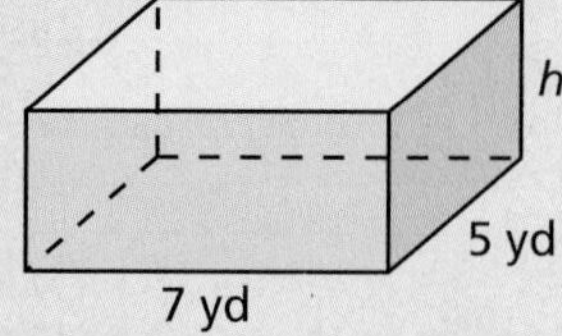

3.2 Characteristics of Functions

Learning Target Describe characteristics of functions.

Success Criteria
- I can estimate intercepts of a graph of a function.
- I can approximate when a function is positive, negative, increasing, or decreasing.
- I can sketch a graph of a function from a verbal description.

EXPLORE IT! Describing Characteristics of Functions

Work with a partner. Consider the function $y = x^3 - 3x$.

a. What do you think it means for a function to be *positive*? *negative*? *increasing*? *decreasing*?

b. Write a pair of numbers greater than 50 and a pair of numbers less than -50 to use as inputs for the function.

NUMBERS GREATER THAN 50	NUMBERS LESS THAN −50
First Number: ________	First Number: ________
Second Number: ________	Second Number: ________

Find the outputs for each pair of inputs. Do you think the function is increasing? decreasing? Explain your reasoning using your input-output pairs.

c. The graph of the function is shown below. Approximate when the function is positive, negative, increasing, or decreasing over its entire domain.

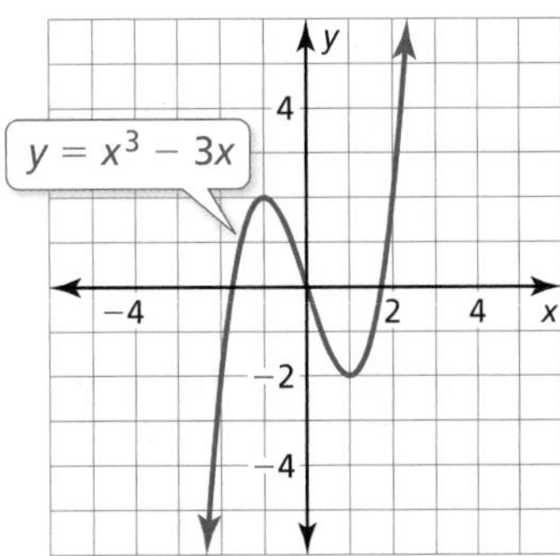

d. Explain whether it is possible for a graph to be decreasing over its entire domain but never negative. Justify your answer using a sketch.

Math Practice

Use Technology to Explore

How can you use technology to identify characteristics of a function?

Intercepts of Graphs of Functions

Vocabulary 

x-intercept, *p. 120*
y-intercept, *p. 120*
increasing, *p. 121*
decreasing, *p. 121*
end behavior, *p. 121*

KEY IDEA

Intercepts

An ***x*-intercept** of a graph is the x-coordinate of a point where the graph intersects the x-axis. It occurs when $y = 0$.

A ***y*-intercept** of a graph is the y-coordinate of a point where the graph intersects the y-axis. It occurs when $x = 0$.

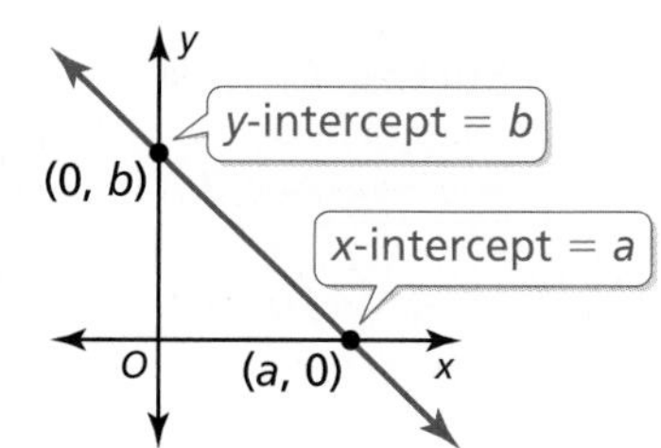

EXAMPLE 1 Estimating Intercepts

Estimate the intercepts of the graph of each function.

a. 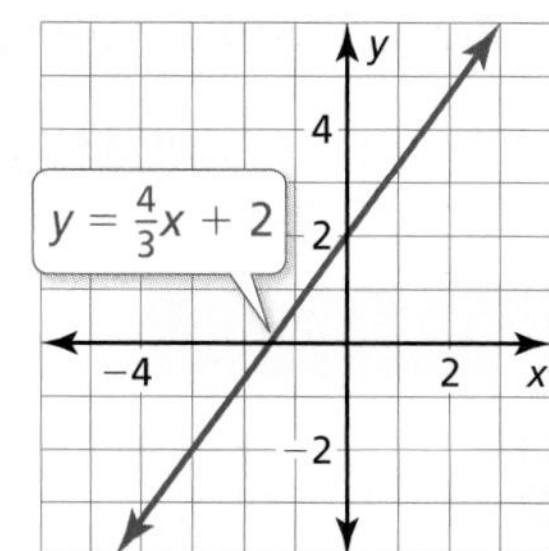

b. 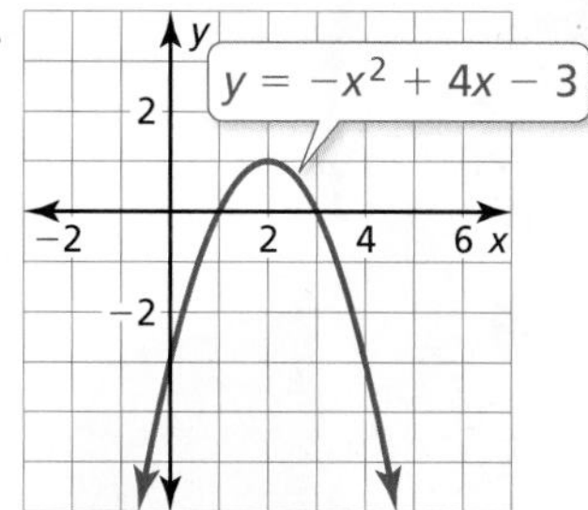

STUDY TIP

You can use a graph to estimate intercepts, but your estimates may not be exact. Substitute your estimates into the equation to check whether they are exact.

SOLUTION

a. The graph appears to intersect the x-axis at $(-1.5, 0)$. It appears to intersect the y-axis at $(0, 2)$.

▶ So, the x-intercept is about -1.5, and the y-intercept is about 2.

b. The graph appears to intersect the x-axis at $(1, 0)$ and $(3, 0)$. It appears to intersect the y-axis at $(0, -3)$.

▶ So, the x-intercepts are about 1 and 3, and the y-intercept is about -3.

SELF-ASSESSMENT 1 I do not understand. 2 I can do it with help. 3 I can do it on my own. 4 I can teach someone else.

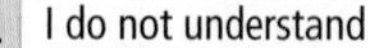

Estimate the intercepts of the graph of the function.

1. 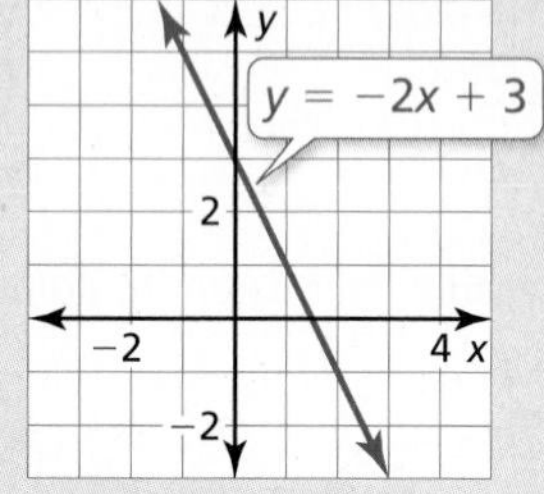

2. 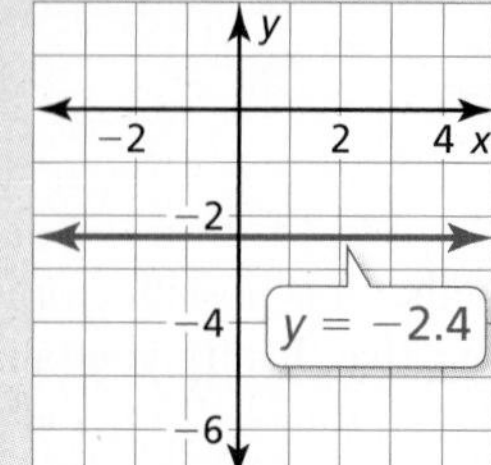

3. 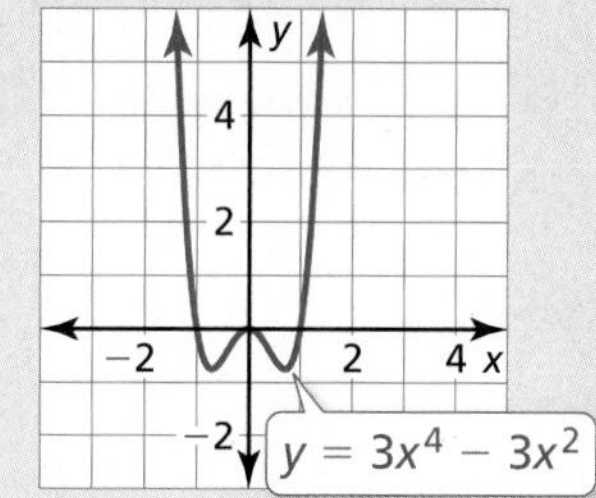

4. **MP REASONING** Can the graph of a function have more than one y-intercept? Can the graph of a function have an infinite number of x-intercepts? Explain your reasoning.

Other Characteristics of Functions

KEY IDEAS

Positive, Negative, Increasing, Decreasing, and End Behavior

A function is *positive* when its graph lies above the x-axis. A function is *negative* when its graph lies below the x-axis.

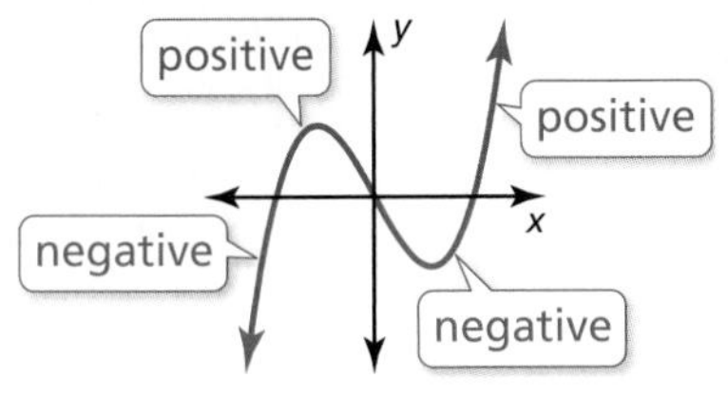

A function is **increasing** when its graph moves up as x moves to the right. A function is **decreasing** when its graph moves down as x moves to the right.

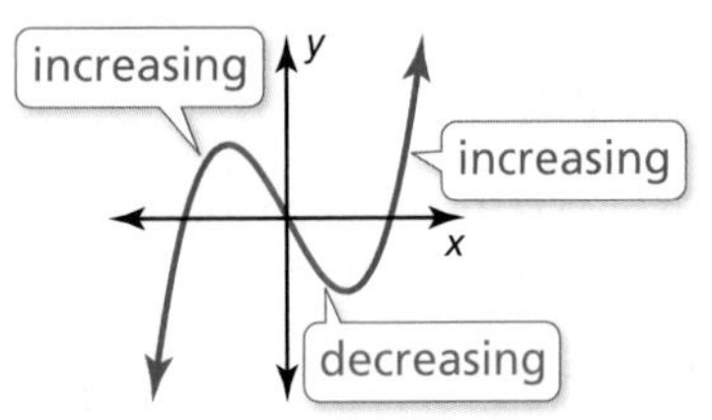

The **end behavior** of a function is the behavior of the graph as x approaches positive infinity ($+\infty$) or negative infinity ($-\infty$).

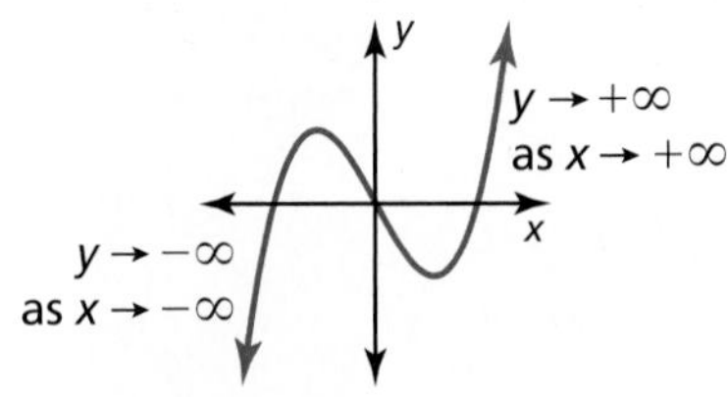

EXAMPLE 2 Describing Characteristics

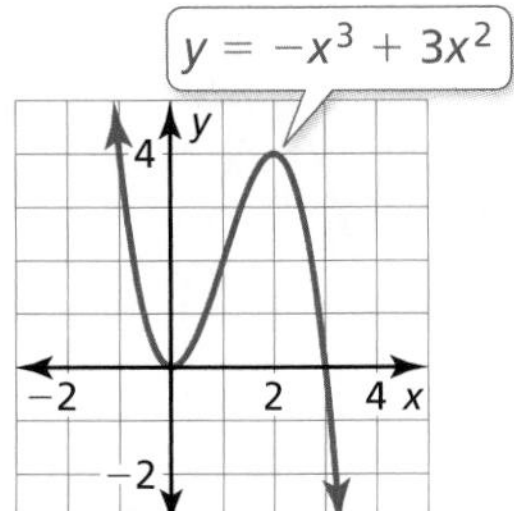

Approximate when the function $y = -x^3 + 3x^2$ is positive, negative, increasing, or decreasing. Then describe the end behavior of the function.

SOLUTION

Positive and Negative:
The function appears to be positive when $x < 0$, positive when $0 < x < 3$, and negative when $x > 3$.

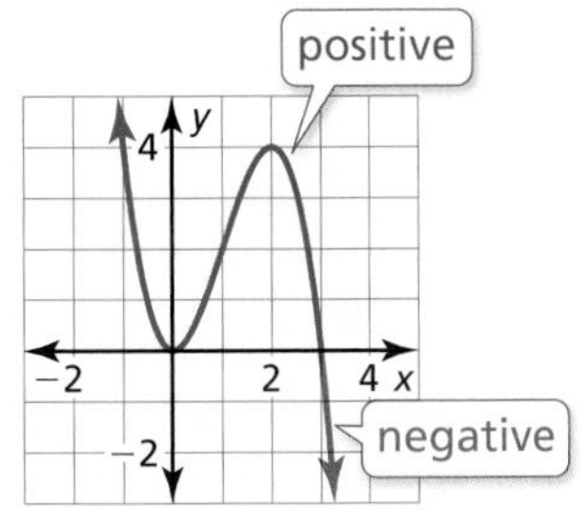

Increasing and Decreasing:
The function appears to be decreasing when $x < 0$, increasing when $0 < x < 2$, and decreasing when $x > 2$.

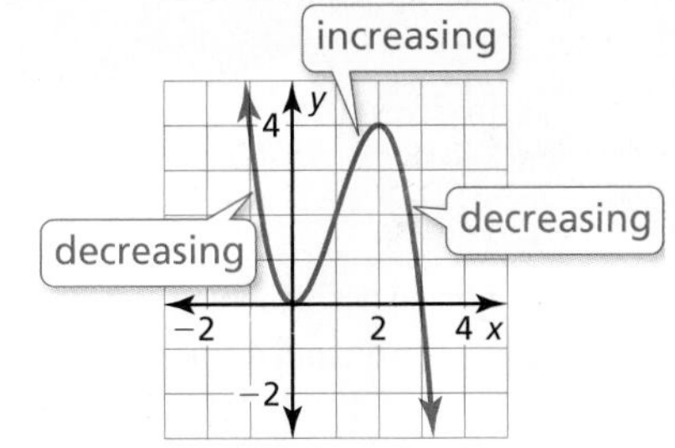

End behavior: The graph shows that the function values increase as x approaches negative infinity and the function values decrease as x approaches positive infinity. So, $y \to +\infty$ as $x \to -\infty$ and $y \to -\infty$ as $x \to +\infty$.

SELF-ASSESSMENT

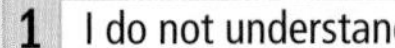

1 I do not understand. 2 I can do it with help. 3 I can do it on my own. 4 I can teach someone else.

Approximate when the function is positive, negative, increasing, or decreasing. Then describe the end behavior of the function.

5. 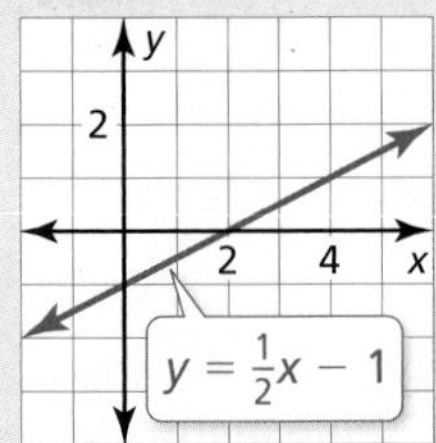

6. 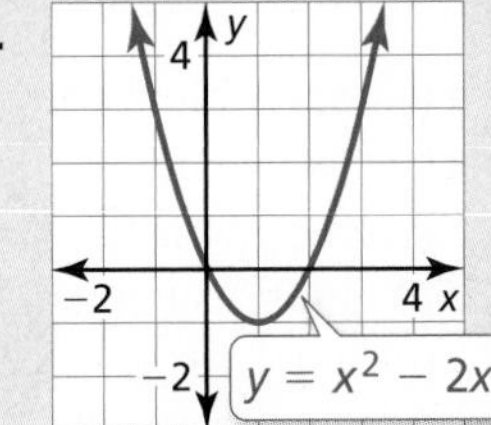

7. 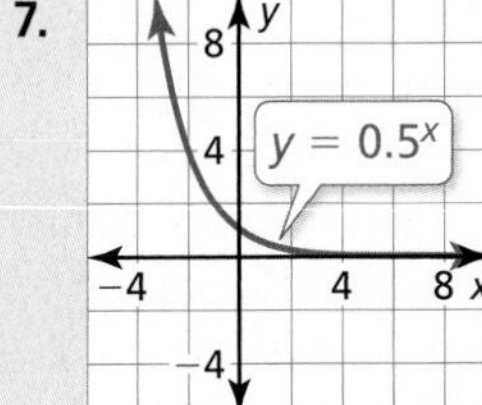

Solving Real-Life Problems

EXAMPLE 3 **Modeling Real Life**

Researchers send two robots to explore an asteroid. The robots move by "hopping" between locations. The graph shows the path of Robot A's first hop. Robot B lands 60 feet from where it starts its first hop, reaching a maximum height of 48 feet after traveling a horizontal distance of 30 feet. Compare the two hops.

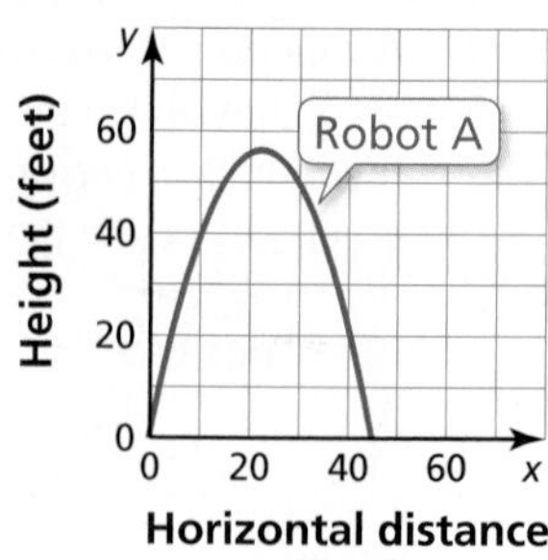

SOLUTION

Use the verbal description to sketch a graph that represents Robot B's hop. First identify several points on the graph.

- the start of the hop: (0, 0)
- the maximum height of the hop: (30, 48)
- the end of the hop: (60, 0)

So, the graph increases from (0, 0) to (30, 48) and then decreases to (60, 0). Sketch the graph using a curve similar to the graph that represents Robot A's hop.

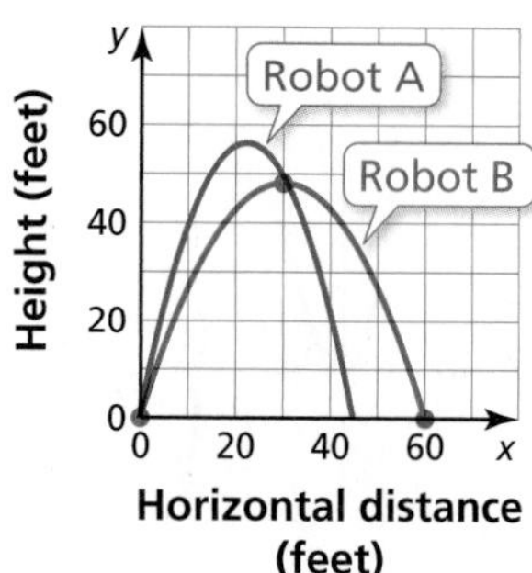

▶ **Intercepts:** Robot A's hop has x-intercepts of about 0 and 45. So, the robot lands about 45 feet from where it starts. This is about $60 - 45 = 15$ feet shorter than Robot B's hop.

Increasing and decreasing: Each hop reaches its maximum height when the height changes from increasing to decreasing. The graph shows that the maximum height of Robot A's hop is between 50 and 60, or about 55. So, Robot A's hop is about $55 - 48 = 7$ feet higher than Robot B's hop at its maximum height.

A Japanese mission used hopping robots to conduct experiments on an asteroid. Because of the asteroid's low gravity, a single hop can last 15 minutes or more.

SELF-ASSESSMENT 1 I do not understand. 2 I can do it with help. 3 I can do it on my own. 4 I can teach someone else.

8. The graph shows your distance from home while out on a walk. The next day, you jog the same route twice at a constant speed. The entire jog takes 1 hour. Compare your walk to your jog.

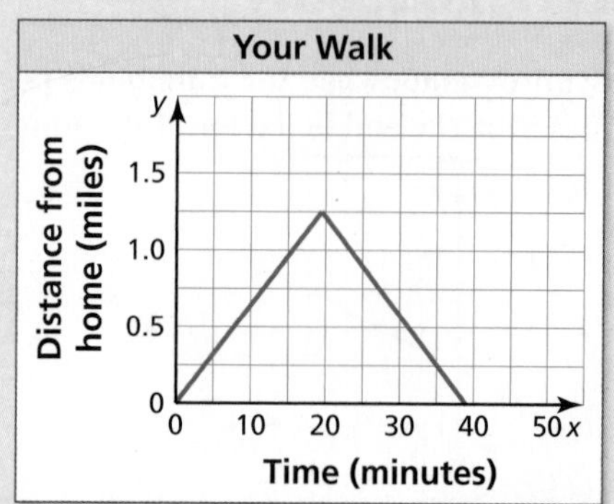

9. **MP REASONING** You throw a ball straight up into the air and notice that the speed of the ball decreases as it approaches its maximum height, then increases again on the way down. Sketch a graph that represents the relationship between time and height in this situation. Explain your reasoning.

3.2 Practice WITH CalcChat® AND CalcView®

In Exercises 1–4, estimate the intercepts of the graph of the function. ▶ *Example 1*

1. 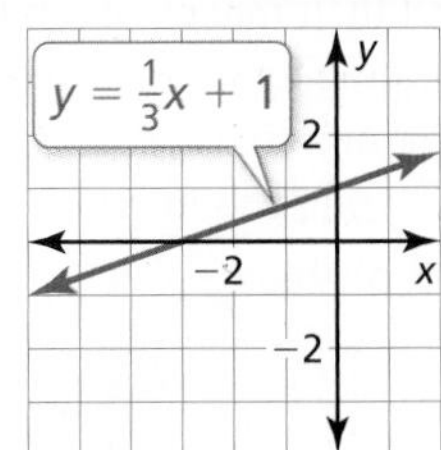

2. 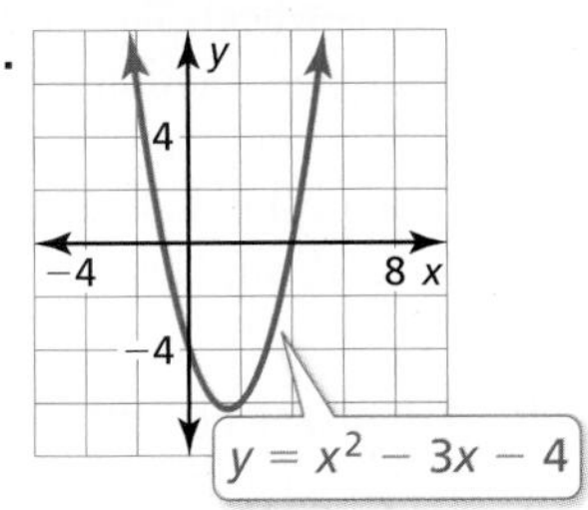

3. 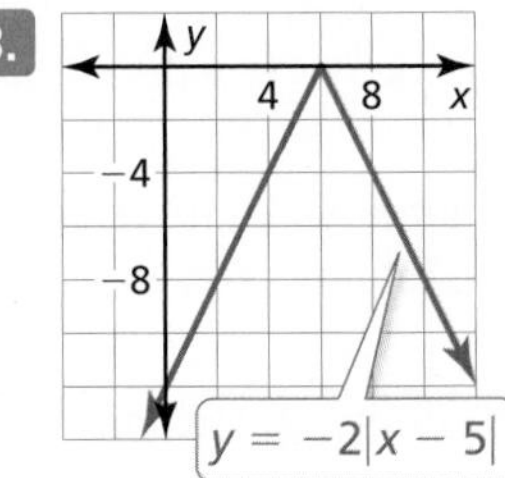

4. 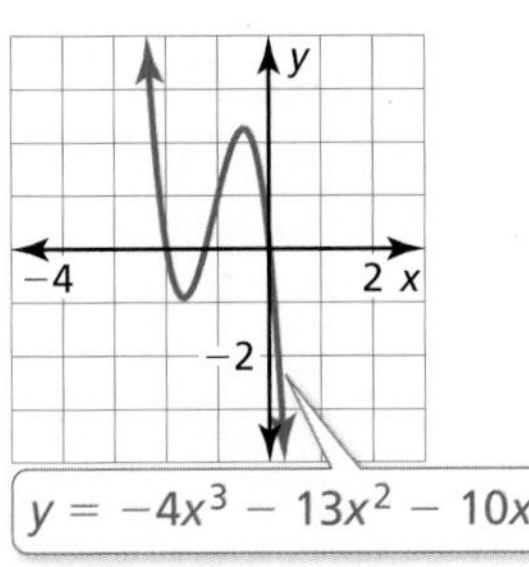

In Exercises 5–10, approximate when the function is positive, negative, increasing, or decreasing. Then describe the end behavior of the function. ▶ *Example 2*

5. 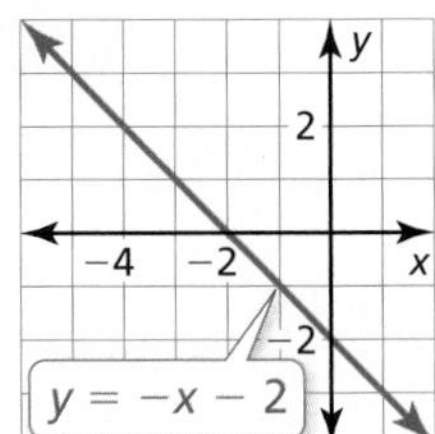

6. 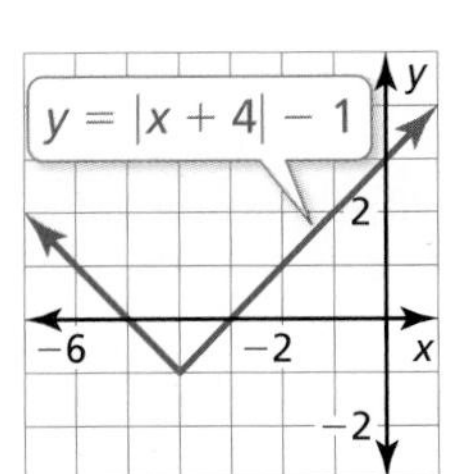

7. 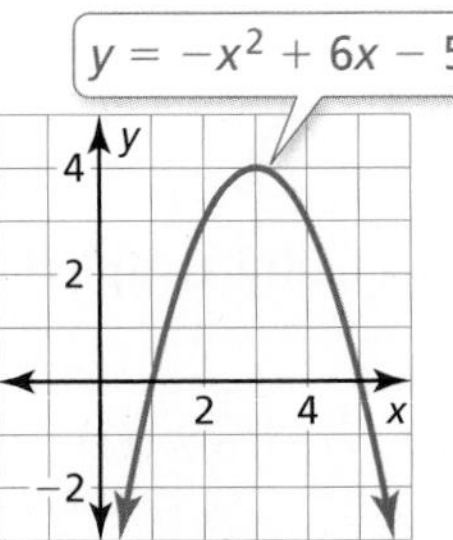

8. 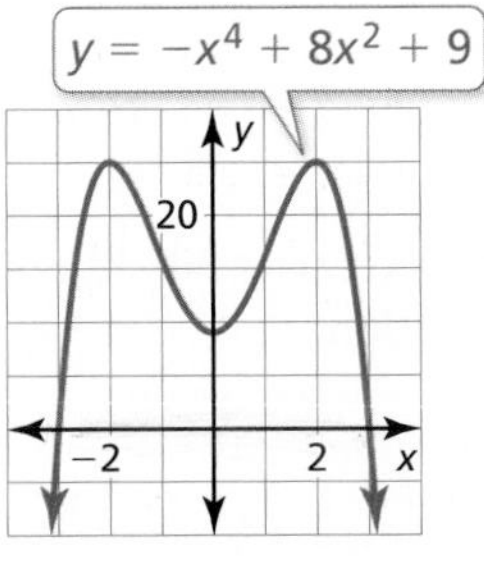

9. 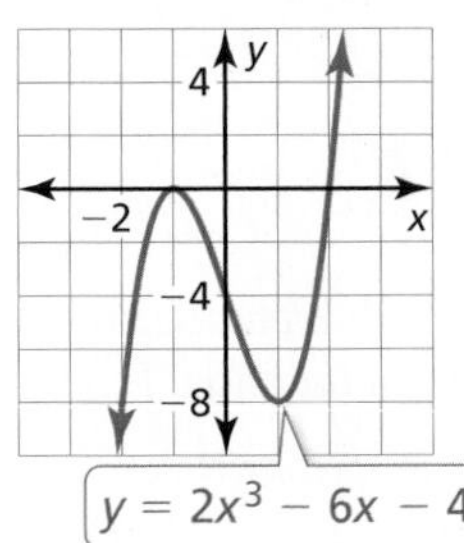

10. 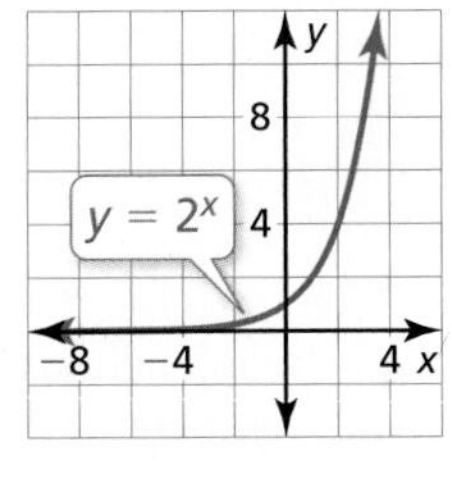

In Exercises 11 and 12, sketch a graph of a function with the given characteristics.

11. • The function is increasing when $x < -6$ and decreasing when $x > -6$.
  • The function is negative when $x < -8$, positive when $-8 < x < -4$, and negative when $x > -4$.

12. • The x-intercepts are -0.5, 1, and 3.25.
  • $y \to +\infty$ as $x \to -\infty$ and $y \to -\infty$ as $x \to +\infty$.

13. **MODELING REAL LIFE** The graph shows the speed of a blue car after the driver applies the brakes. The driver of a red car applies the brakes while traveling 30 miles per hour. The speed of the red car decreases at a constant rate until the car comes to a complete stop 4 seconds later. Compare the initial speeds and stopping times. ▶ *Example 3*

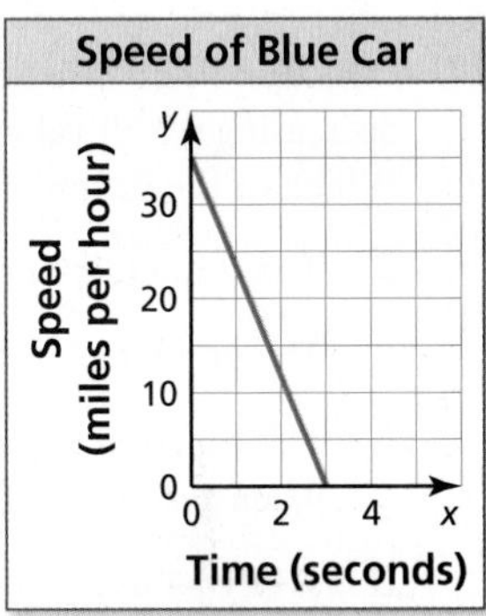

14. **MODELING REAL LIFE** The graph shows the path of a home run. During a second home run, a baseball player hits the baseball when it is 3 feet above home plate. The ball lands on the ground 402 feet from home plate, reaching a maximum height of 93 feet after traveling a horizontal distance of 199 feet. Compare the two home runs.

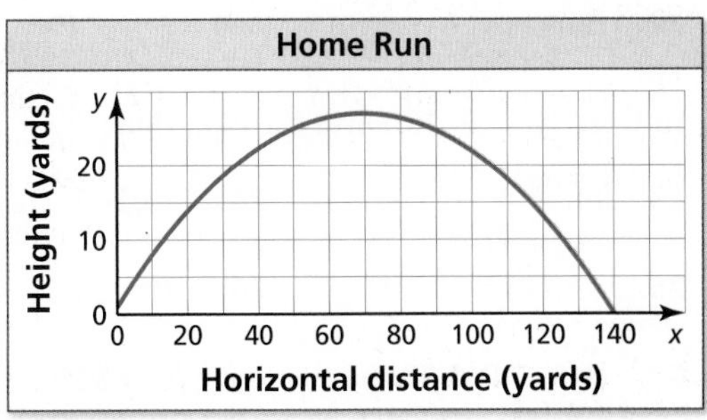

15. **ERROR ANALYSIS** Describe and correct the error in describing characteristics of the function.

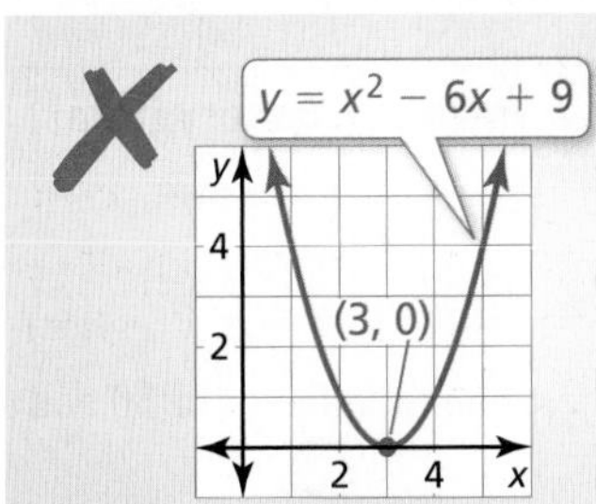

The function is positive for all values of x. The function is decreasing when x < 3 and increasing when x > 3.

16. **HOW DO YOU SEE IT?**
The graph of a function is shown.

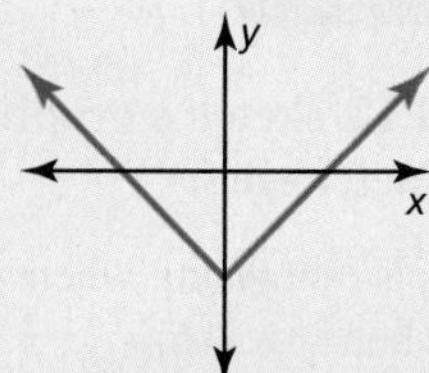

a. How many x-intercepts does the graph have? Is the y-intercept *positive* or *negative*?

b. Is the function *increasing* or *decreasing* when $x < 0$? $x > 0$?

17. **COLLEGE PREP** The graph of a function is a line that is decreasing for all values of x and has an x-intercept of 4. Which of the following are true? Select all that apply.

Ⓐ The y-intercept is negative.

Ⓑ The graph has only one x-intercept.

Ⓒ The function is positive when $x < 4$ and negative when $x > 4$.

Ⓓ $y \to -\infty$ as $x \to -\infty$ and $y \to +\infty$ as $x \to +\infty$.

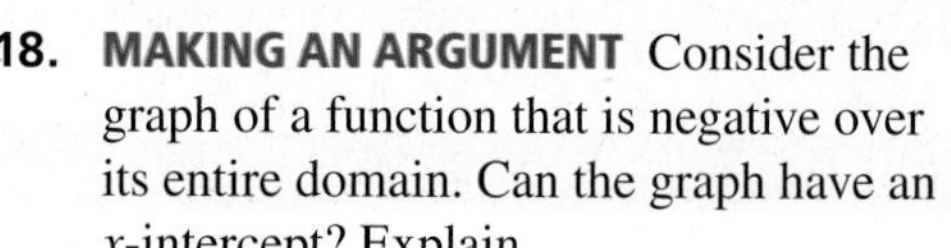

18. **MAKING AN ARGUMENT** Consider the graph of a function that is negative over its entire domain. Can the graph have an x-intercept? Explain.

19. **DIG DEEPER** You board a car at the bottom of a Ferris wheel. The Ferris wheel then makes several complete rotations before stopping again to let you off where you boarded. Sketch a graph that represents the relationship between time and your height above the ground, and describe the relationship.

20. **THOUGHT PROVOKING**
Sketch a graph of a function with the given characteristics.
- The function is decreasing for $x < 0$ and increasing for $x > 0$.
- As x approaches negative infinity, the function does *not* approach positive infinity or negative infinity.
- As x approaches positive infinity, the function does *not* approach positive infinity or negative infinity.
- The graph does *not* have a y-intercept.

REVIEW & REFRESH

In Exercises 21 and 22, write the sentence as an inequality. Graph the inequality.

21. A number n is greater than or equal to -5 and less than -1.

22. A number k is no more than $-\frac{1}{2}$ or at least $2\frac{1}{2}$.

In Exercises 23–26, solve the equation.

23. $7 + b = -21$

24. $-3.2x = 16$

25. $-3(t - 5) = 14$

26. $30 = 2m - 8m + 12$

27. **MODELING REAL LIFE** You have a \$25 gift card to a coffee shop. You have already used \$19.85. You want to purchase one drink and one bakery item. Which pairs of items can you purchase with the amount left on the gift card?

Drink	Price
Coffee	\$2.09
Cappuccino	\$3.79

Bakery item	Price
Muffin	\$2.59
Bagel	\$1.49

28. Find the greatest common factor of 30 and 42.

29. Estimate the intercepts of the graph of the function.

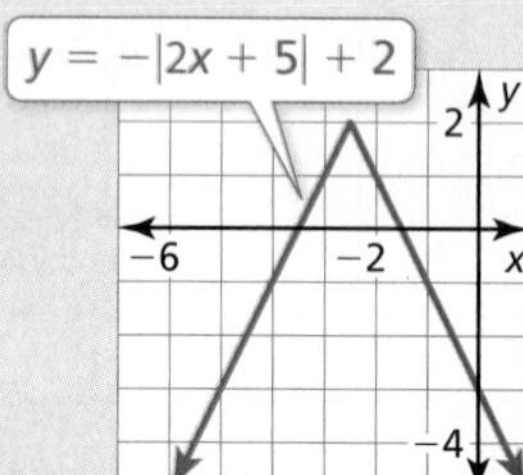

In Exercises 30–33, solve the inequality. Graph the solution.

30. $5a > 20$

31. $\frac{r}{-2} + 6 \leq 11$

32. $1.5x + 7 - 5x > 11 - 3x$

33. $\left|\frac{1}{3}x + 6\right| + 2 > 3$

34. **MP REASONING** Complete the relation so that it is (a) a function and (b) *not* a function. Explain your reasoning.

$(-6, -1), (-4, 0), (-2, 1), (2, 2),$ ▭

3.3 Linear Functions

Learning Target Identify and graph linear functions.

Success Criteria
- I can identify linear functions using graphs, tables, and equations.
- I can graph linear functions with discrete and continuous domains.
- I can write real-life problems that correspond to discrete or continuous data.

EXPLORE IT! Finding a Pattern

Work with a partner. Use a piece of rope that is at least 100 centimeters long. Record your data in the table.

a. Measure the length of the rope. Describe your measurement.

b. Make a knot in the rope, then measure the length of the rope again. Continue to make identical knots in the rope, measuring the length of the rope after each knot is tied.

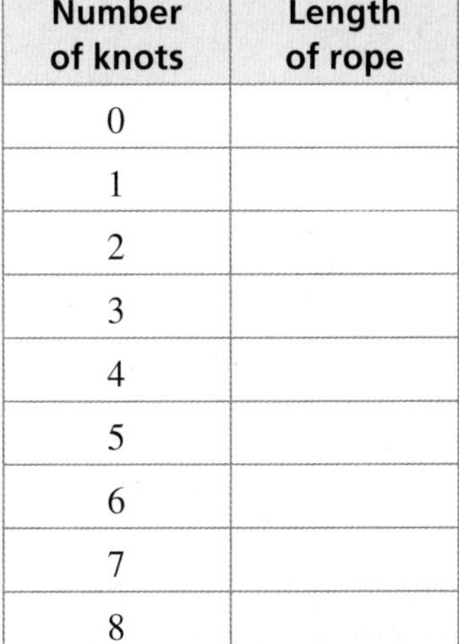

Number of knots	Length of rope
0	
1	
2	
3	
4	
5	
6	
7	
8	

c. Write several observations about the data. What pattern(s) do you notice in the data? Explain.

d. Make a scatter plot of the data. What pattern(s) do you notice in the scatter plot? Explain.

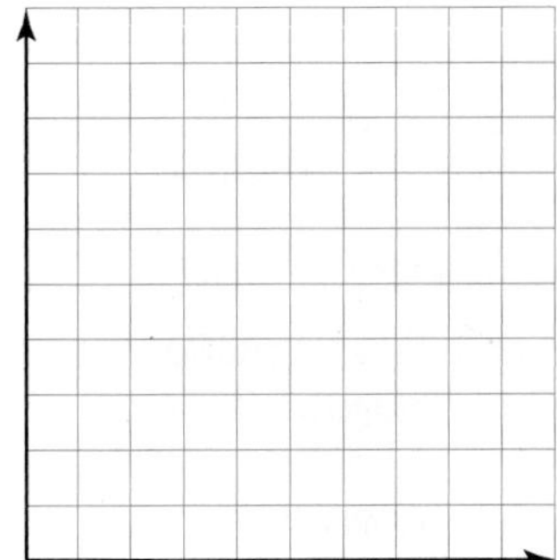

e. How can you predict the length of the rope when it has 10 knots? Explain your reasoning.

f. Does it matter where you tie the knots on the rope? Is there a maximum number of knots you can tie? Does the thickness of the rope or the type of knot you tie affect your results? Explain your reasoning.

Math Practice

Label Axes
How do you determine the labels and scale for each axis?

Identifying Linear Functions

A **linear equation in two variables**, x and y, is an equation that can be written in the form

$$y = mx + b$$

where m and b are constants. The graph of a linear equation is a line. Likewise, a **linear function** is a function whose graph is a nonvertical line. A linear function has a constant rate of change and can be represented by a linear equation in two variables. A **nonlinear function** does not have a constant rate of change. So, its graph is *not* a line.

Vocabulary (AZ VOCAB)

- linear equation in two variables, *p. 126*
- linear function, *p. 126*
- nonlinear function, *p. 126*
- solution of a linear equation in two variables, *p. 128*
- discrete domain, *p. 128*
- continuous domain, *p. 128*

EXAMPLE 1 Identifying Linear Functions Using Graphs

Does the graph represent a *linear* or *nonlinear* function? Explain.

a.

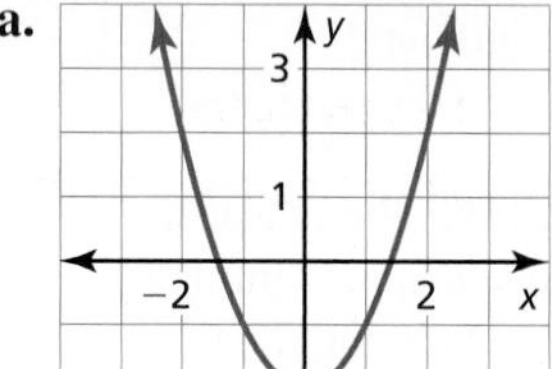

b.

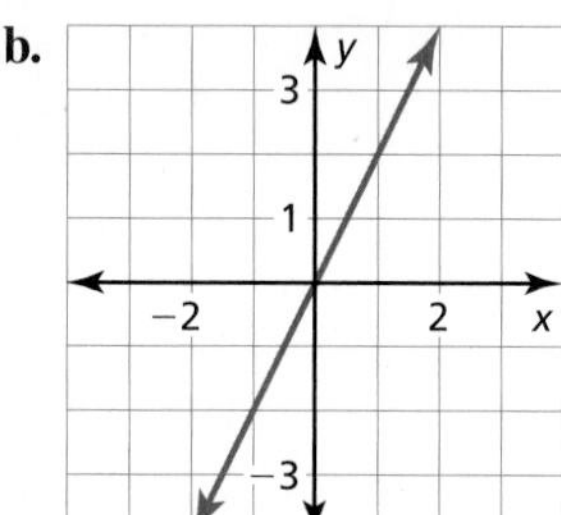

SOLUTION

a. The graph is *not* a line.

▶ So, the function is nonlinear.

b. The graph is a nonvertical line.

▶ So, the function is linear.

EXAMPLE 2 Identifying Linear Functions Using Tables

Does the table represent a *linear* or *nonlinear* function? Explain.

a.

x	3	6	9	12
y	36	30	24	18

b.

x	1	3.5	6	8.5
y	2	9	20	35

SOLUTION

a.

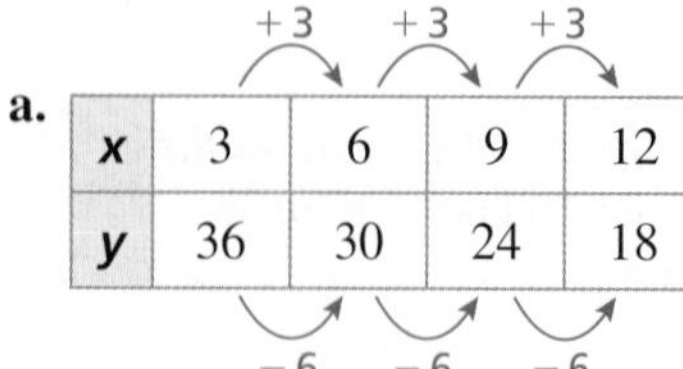

x	3	6	9	12
y	36	30	24	18

As x increases by 3, y decreases by 6. The rate of change is constant.

▶ So, the function is linear.

b.

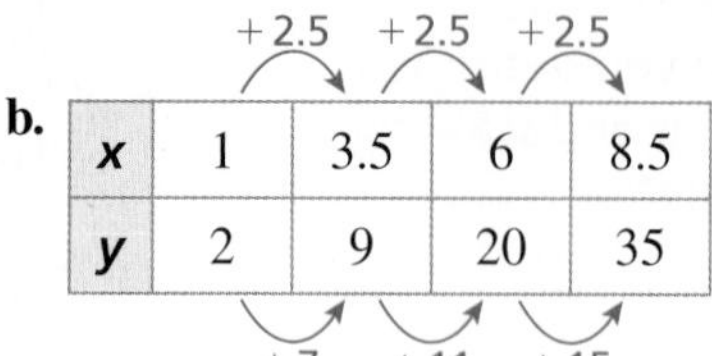

x	1	3.5	6	8.5
y	2	9	20	35

As x increases by 2.5, y increases by different amounts. The rate of change is *not* constant.

▶ So, the function is nonlinear.

STUDY TIP

A constant rate of change describes a quantity that changes by equal amounts over equal intervals.

EXAMPLE 3 Identifying Linear Functions Using Equations

Which of the following equations represent linear functions? Explain.

$y = 3.8$ $y = \sqrt{x}$ $y = 3^x$ $y = \frac{2}{x}$ $y = 6(x - 1)$ $x^2 - y = 0$

SOLUTION

You cannot rewrite the equations $y = \sqrt{x}$, $y = 3^x$, $y = \frac{2}{x}$, and $x^2 - y = 0$ in the form $y = mx + b$. These functions do not have a constant rate of change. So, they cannot represent linear functions.

▶ You can rewrite the equation $y = 3.8$ as $y = 0x + 3.8$ and the equation $y = 6(x - 1)$ as $y = 6x - 6$. These functions have a constant rate of change. So, they represent linear functions.

CONCEPT SUMMARY

Representations of Functions

Words An output is 3 more than the input.

Equation $y = x + 3$

Input-Output Table

Input, x	Output, y
−1	2
0	3
1	4
2	5

Mapping Diagram

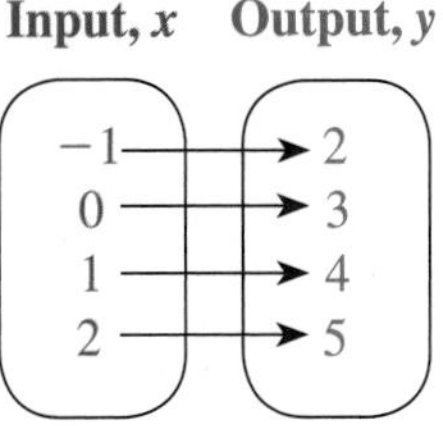

Graph

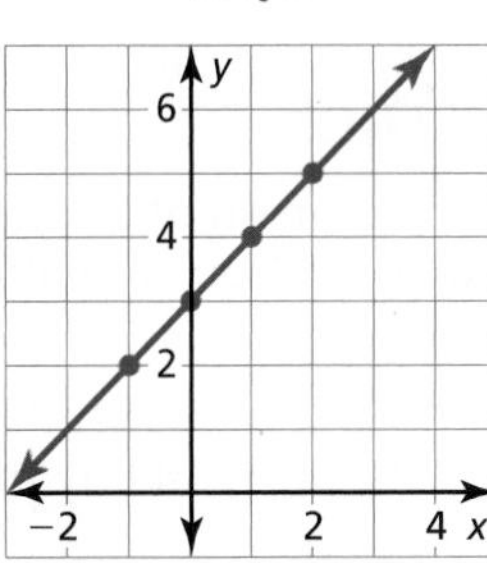

SELF-ASSESSMENT

1 I do not understand. **2** I can do it with help. **3** I can do it on my own. **4** I can teach someone else.

Does the graph or table represent a *linear* or *nonlinear* function? Explain.

1.

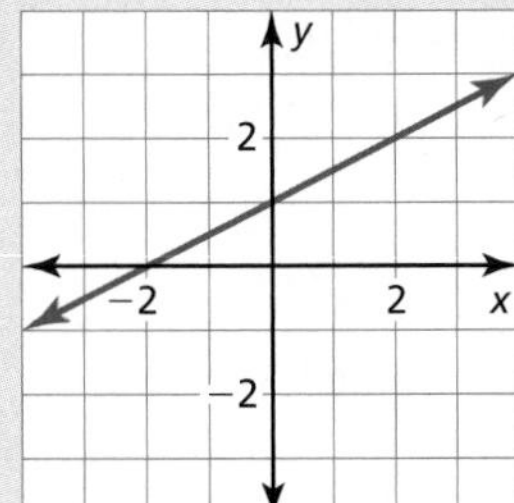

2.

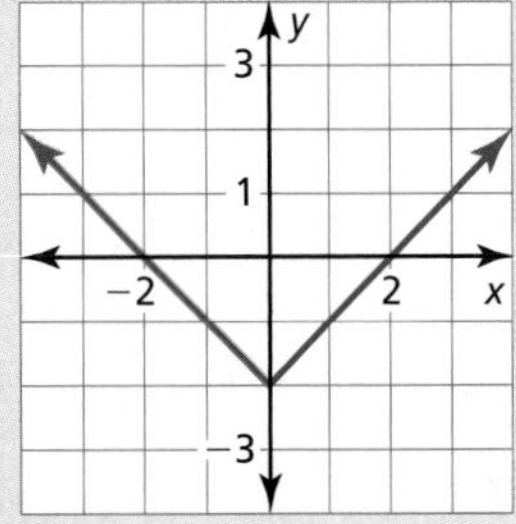

3.

x	0	1	2	3
y	3	5	7	9

4.

x	1	2	3	4
y	$\frac{1}{16}$	$\frac{1}{8}$	$\frac{1}{4}$	$\frac{1}{2}$

5. WRITING Compare linear functions and nonlinear functions.

Does the equation represent a *linear* or *nonlinear* function? Explain.

6. $y = x + 9$

7. $y = \frac{3x}{5}$

8. $y = 5 - 2x^2$

Graphing Linear Functions

A **solution of a linear equation in two variables** is an ordered pair (x, y) that makes the equation true. The graph of a linear equation in two variables is the set of points (x, y) in a coordinate plane that represents all solutions of the equation. Sometimes the points are distinct, and other times the points are connected.

KEY IDEA

Discrete and Continuous Domains

A **discrete domain** is a set of input values that consists of only certain numbers in an interval.

Example: Integers from 1 to 5

A **continuous domain** is a set of input values that consists of all numbers in an interval.

Example: All numbers from 1 to 5

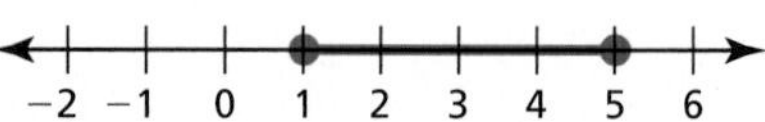

EXAMPLE 4 Graphing Discrete Data

The linear function $y = 15.95x$ represents the cost y (in dollars) of x tickets for a museum. Each customer can buy a maximum of four tickets.

a. Find the domain of the function. Is the domain discrete or continuous? Explain.

b. Graph the function using its domain.

STUDY TIP

The domain of a function depends on the real-life context of the function, not just the equation that represents the function.

SOLUTION

a. You cannot buy part of a ticket, only a certain number of tickets. Because x represents the number of tickets, it must be a whole number. The maximum number of tickets a customer can buy is four.

▶ So, the domain is 0, 1, 2, 3, and 4, and it is discrete.

b. Step 1 Make an input-output table to find the ordered pairs.

Input, x	$15.95x$	Output, y	(x, y)
0	15.95(0)	0	(0, 0)
1	15.95(1)	15.95	(1, 15.95)
2	15.95(2)	31.9	(2, 31.9)
3	15.95(3)	47.85	(3, 47.85)
4	15.95(4)	63.8	(4, 63.8)

Step 2 Plot the ordered pairs. The domain is discrete. So, the graph consists of individual points.

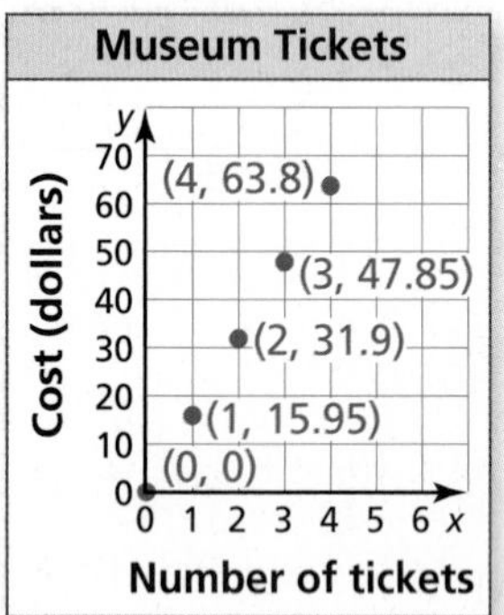

SELF-ASSESSMENT 1 I do not understand. 2 I can do it with help. 3 I can do it on my own. 4 I can teach someone else.

9. The linear function $m = 50 - 9d$ represents the amount m (in dollars) of money you have left after buying d DVDs.

a. Interpret the terms and coefficient in the equation.

b. Find the domain of the function. Is the domain discrete or continuous? Explain.

c. Graph the function using its domain.

EXAMPLE 5 Graphing Continuous Data

An anteater consumes about 35,000 insects each day.

a. Explain why the number of insects consumed is a function of the number of days.

b. Find the domain of the function. Is the domain discrete or continuous? Explain.

c. Graph the function using its domain.

STUDY TIP

When the domain of a linear function is not specified or cannot be obtained from a real-life context, it is understood to be all real numbers.

SOLUTION

a. As the number d of days increases by 1, the number n of insects consumed increases by 35,000. The rate of change is constant.

▶ So, this situation represents a linear function.

b. An anteater eats insects throughout each day. The number d of days can be any value greater than or equal to 0.

▶ So, the domain is $d \geq 0$, and it is continuous.

c. Step 1 Make an input-output table to find ordered pairs.

Input, d	Output, n	(d, n)
0	0	(0, 0)
1	35,000	(1, 35,000)
2	70,000	(2, 70,000)
3	105,000	(3, 105,000)
4	140,000	(4, 140,000)

An anteater can flick its tongue up to 160 times each minute when eating insects.

Step 2 Plot the ordered pairs.

Step 3 Draw a line through the points. The line should start at (0, 0) and continue to the right. Use an arrow to indicate that the line continues without end, as shown. The domain is continuous. So, the graph is a line with a domain of $d \geq 0$.

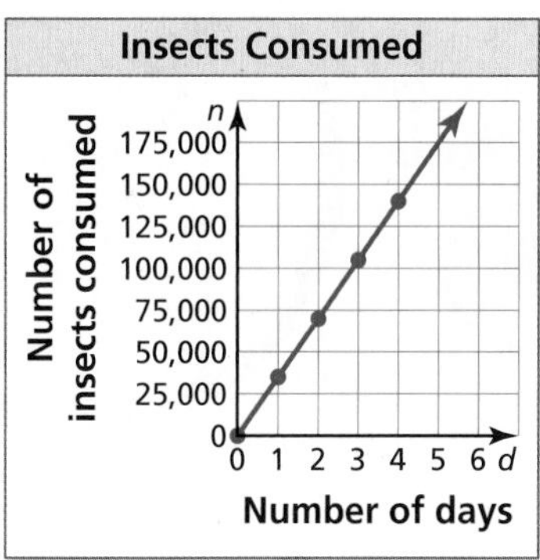

SELF-ASSESSMENT 1 I do not understand. 2 I can do it with help. 3 I can do it on my own. 4 I can teach someone else.

10. A 20-gallon bathtub is draining at a rate of 2.5 gallons per minute.

a. Explain why the number of gallons remaining is a function of the number of minutes.

b. Find the domain of the function. Is the domain discrete or continuous? Explain.

c. Graph the function using its domain.

11. When feeding, a juvenile whale shark filters about 600 cubic meters of water through its mouth each hour. About 2.8 kilograms of food are filtered out from the water each hour.

a. Graph the function that represents the amount a of water filtered by the whale shark as a function of the number m of minutes.

b. The whale shark feeds for 7.5 hours each day. Graph the function that represents the amount f of food (in pounds) filtered by the whale shark as a function of the number d of days.

Writing Real-Life Problems

EXAMPLE 6 **Writing Real-Life Problems**

Write a real-life problem to fit the data shown in each graph. Is the domain of each function *discrete* or *continuous*? Explain.

a.

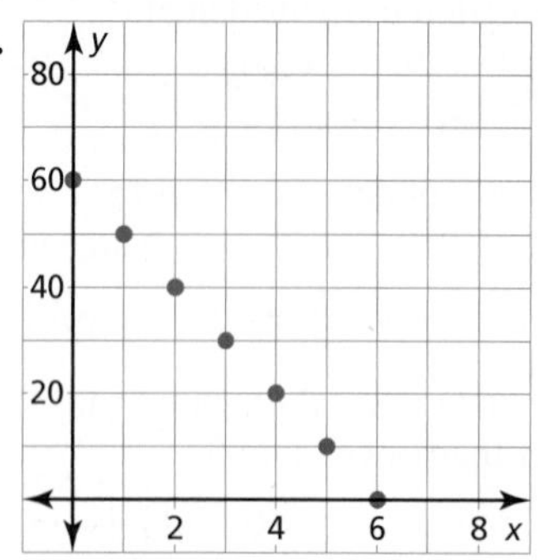

b.

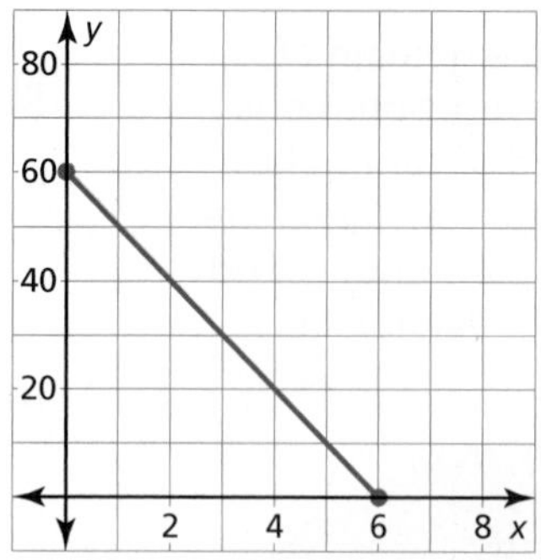

SOLUTION

a. Using the graph, notice that the variable x is a whole number from 0 to 6 and the variable y is a multiple of 10 that starts at 60 and decreases to 0.

x	0	1	2	3	4	5	6
y	60	50	40	30	20	10	0

Discrete domain

▶ One possibility is a person on a game show answering questions and earning money, where x is the number of questions answered incorrectly and y is the total amount of money earned. Because it is not possible to answer part of a question incorrectly, the domain is discrete.

b. Using the graph, notice that the variable x can be any real number from 0 to 6 and the variable y can be any real number from 0 to 60.

▶ One possibility is a person biking a total distance of 60 miles at a rate of 10 miles per hour over a period of 6 hours, where x is the number of hours biking and y is the number of miles remaining. Because it is possible to bike a portion of an hour, the domain is continuous.

SELF-ASSESSMENT

1 I do not understand. 2 I can do it with help. 3 I can do it on my own. 4 I can teach someone else.

Write a real-life problem to fit the data shown in the graph. Is the domain of the function *discrete* or *continuous*? Explain.

12.

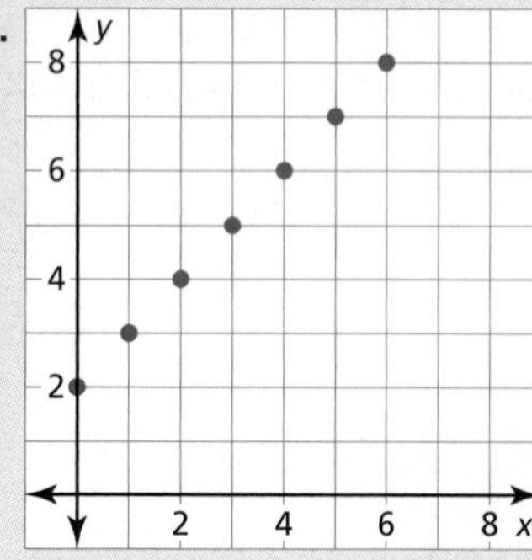

13.

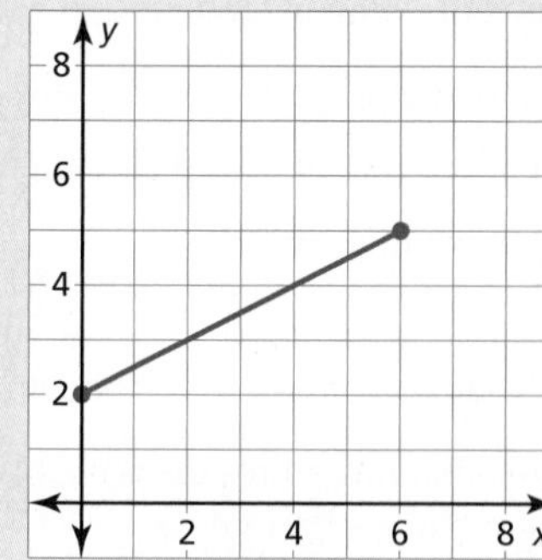

14. OPEN-ENDED Describe a real-life situation that can be represented by a function with a continuous domain and outputs that are all negative numbers.

3.3 Practice WITH CalcChat® AND CalcView®

GO DIGITAL

In Exercises 1–6, determine whether the graph represents a *linear* or *nonlinear* function. Explain. *Example 1*

1.

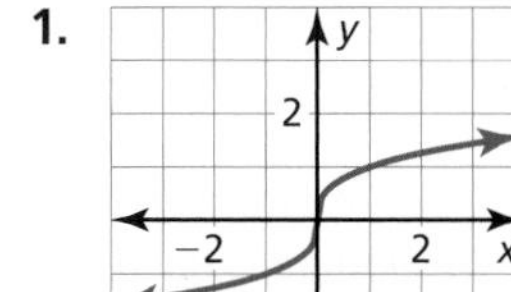

2.

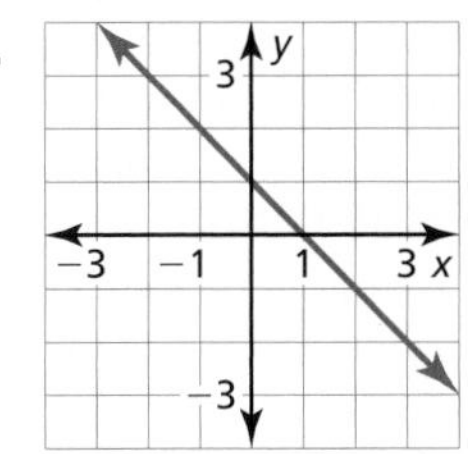

3.

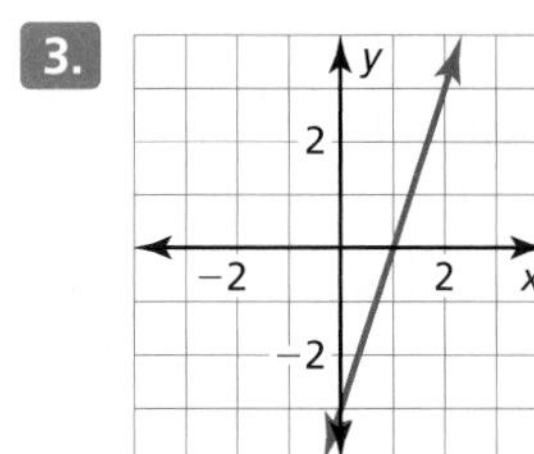

4.

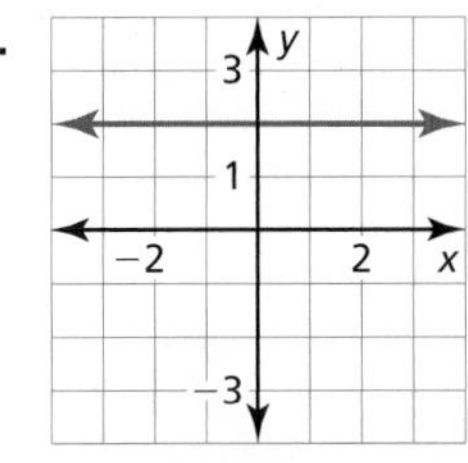

5.

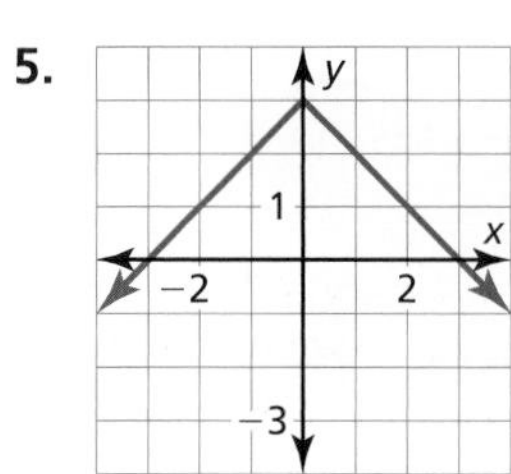

6.

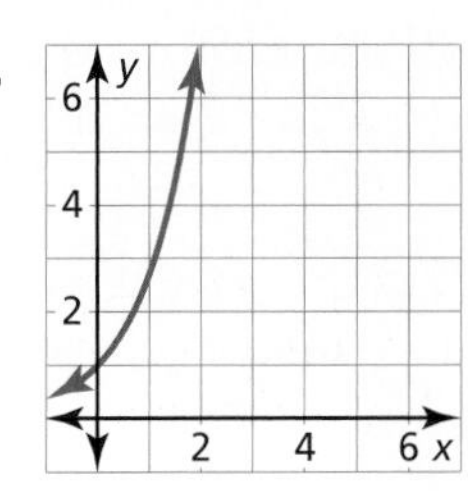

In Exercises 7–10, determine whether the table represents a *linear* or *nonlinear* function. Explain. *Example 2*

7.

x	1	2	3	4
y	5	10	15	20

8.

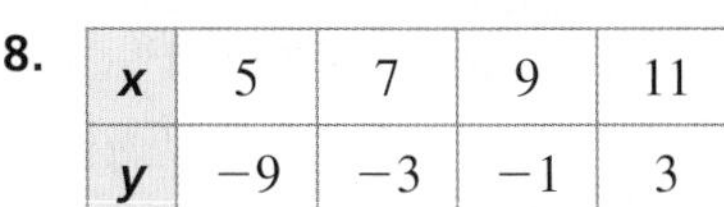

x	5	7	9	11
y	−9	−3	−1	3

9.

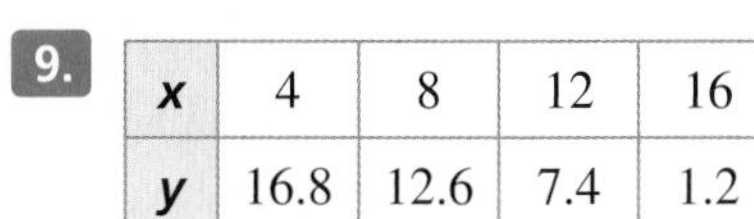

x	4	8	12	16
y	16.8	12.6	7.4	1.2

10.

x	−1	0	1	2
y	35	20	5	−10

11. MP **REASONING** Explain why a V-shaped graph does *not* represent a linear function.

12. MP **REASONING** How can you tell whether a graph shows a discrete domain or a continuous domain?

ERROR ANALYSIS In Exercises 13 and 14, describe and correct the error in determining whether the table or graph represents a linear function.

13.

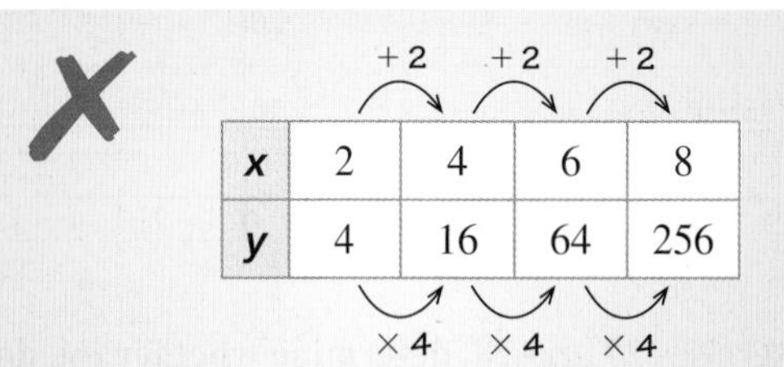

x	2	4	6	8
y	4	16	64	256

+2 +2 +2
×4 ×4 ×4
As x increases by 2, y increases by a constant factor of 4. So, the function is linear.

14.

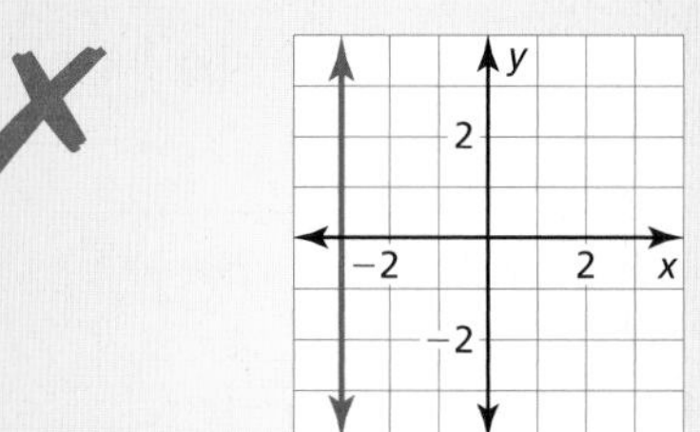

The graph is a line. So, the graph represents a linear function.

In Exercises 15–22, determine whether the equation represents a *linear* or *nonlinear* function. Explain. *Example 3*

15. $y = x^2 + 13$

16. $y = 7 - 3x$

17. $y = \sqrt[3]{8} - x$

18. $y = 4x(8 - x)$

19. $2 + \frac{1}{6}y = 3x + 4$

20. $y - x = 2x - \frac{2}{3}y$

21. $18x - 2y = 26$

22. $2x + 3y = 9xy$

23. **COLLEGE PREP** Which of the following equations do *not* represent linear functions? Select all that apply.

Ⓐ $12 = 2x^2 + 4y^2$

Ⓑ $y - x + 3 = x$

Ⓒ $x = 8$

Ⓓ $x = 9 - \frac{3}{4}y$

Ⓔ $y = \frac{5x}{11}$

Ⓕ $y = \sqrt{x} + 3$

24. **WRITING** Compare discrete domains and continuous domains.

In Exercises 25 and 26, find the domain of the function represented by the graph. Determine whether the domain is *discrete* or *continuous*. Explain.

25.

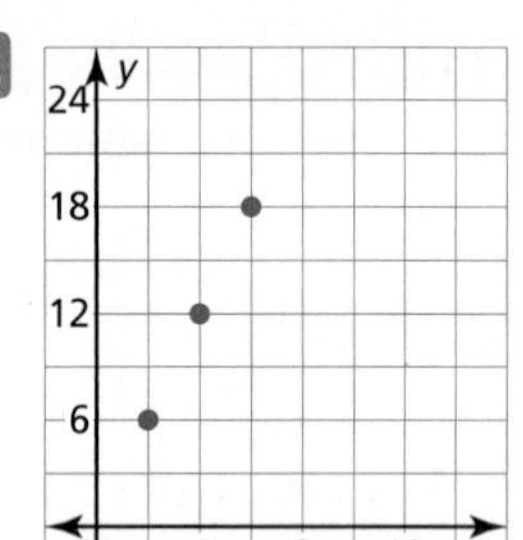

26.

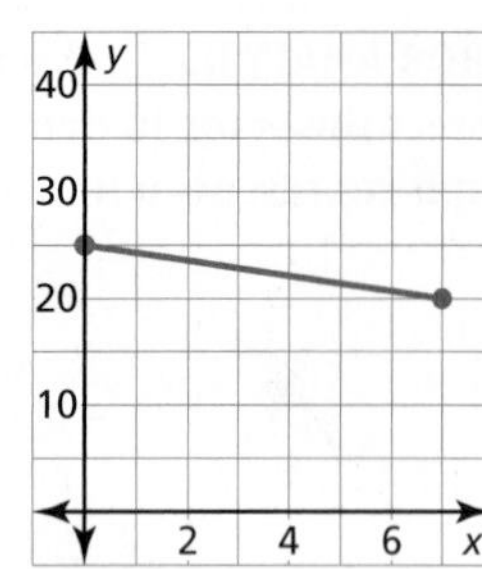

In Exercises 27 and 28, determine whether the domain is *discrete* or *continuous*. Explain.

27.

Input Time (hours), x	3	6	9
Output Distance (miles), y	150	300	450

28.

Input Relay teams, x	0	1	2
Output Athletes, y	0	4	8

29. MODELING REAL LIFE The linear function $m = 10 - 1.44p$ represents the amount m (in dollars) of money that you have after printing p photographs. *Example 4*

a. Interpret the terms and coefficient in the equation.

b. Find the domain of the function. Is the domain discrete or continuous? Explain.

c. Graph the function using its domain.

30. MODELING REAL LIFE The linear function $y = 145 + 30x$ represents the cost y (in dollars) of an airline ticket after adding x checked bags. At most 5 bags can be checked.

a. Interpret the terms and coefficient in the equation.

b. Find the domain of the function. Is the domain discrete or continuous? Explain.

c. Graph the function using its domain.

31. MODELING REAL LIFE You fill a swimming pool with water at a rate of 17 gallons per minute. *Example 5*

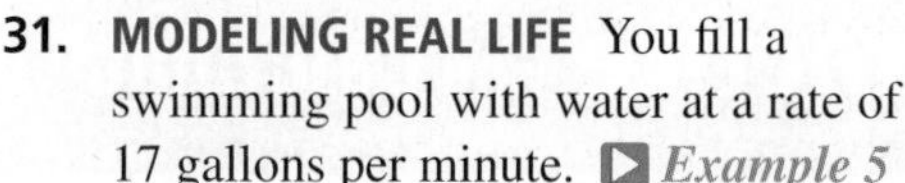

a. Is the amount of water in the pool a function of the number of minutes? Explain.

b. Find the domain of the function. Is the domain discrete or continuous? Explain.

c. Graph the function using its domain.

32. MODELING REAL LIFE The amount of air in a scuba diving tank with a capacity of 2400 liters is decreasing at a rate of 48 liters per minute.

a. Is the amount of air in the tank a function of the number of minutes? Explain.

b. Find the domain of the function. Is the domain discrete or continuous? Explain.

c. Graph the function using its domain.

33. MP STRUCTURE Complete the table so it represents a linear function.

x	5	10	15	20	25
y	-1				11

34. MULTIPLE REPRESENTATIONS You are researching the speed of sound waves in dry air at 86°F. The linear function $d = 0.217t$ represents the distances d (in miles) sound waves travel in t seconds.

a. Represent the situation using a table and a graph.

b. Which of the three representations would you use to find how long it takes sound waves to travel 0.1 mile in dry air at 86°F? Explain.

35. MP REASONING Is the function represented by the ordered pairs linear or nonlinear? Explain your reasoning.

(0, 2), (3, 14), (5, 22), (9, 38), (11, 46)

36. WRITING Describe the end behavior of an increasing linear function and a decreasing linear function.

WRITING **In Exercises 37 and 38, write a real-life problem to fit the data shown in the graph. Determine whether the domain of the function is *discrete* or *continuous*. Explain.** *Example 6*

37.

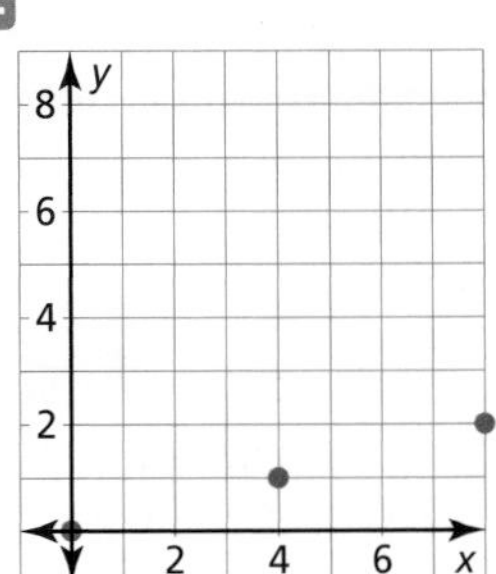

38.

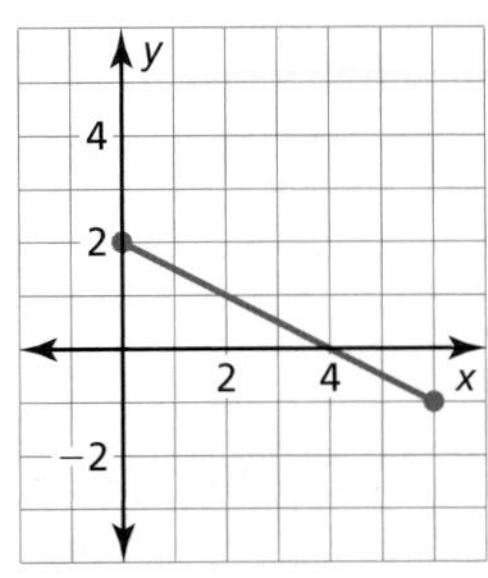

39. **MP STRUCTURE** The table shows your earnings y (in dollars) for working x hours. You work no more than 18 hours each week.

a. What is your hourly pay rate?

b. Find the domain and range of the function.

Time (hours), x	Earnings (dollars), y
4	40.80
5	51.00
6	61.20
7	71.40

40. **MAKING AN ARGUMENT** The linear function $d = 50t$ represents the distance d (in miles) Car A is from a car rental store after t hours. The table shows the distances Car B is from the rental store.

a. Does the table represent a linear or nonlinear function? Explain.

b. Which car is moving at a faster rate? Explain.

Time (hours), t	Distance (miles), d
1	60
3	180
5	310
7	450
9	540

41. **MP REASONING** A water company fills two different-sized jugs. The first jug can hold x gallons of water. The second jug can hold y gallons of water. The company fills A jugs of the first size and B jugs of the second size. What does each expression represent? Does each expression represent a set of discrete or continuous values?

a. $x + y$

b. $A + B$

c. Ax

d. $Ax + By$

42. **HOW DO YOU SEE IT?**
You and your friend go running. The graph shows the distances you and your friend run.

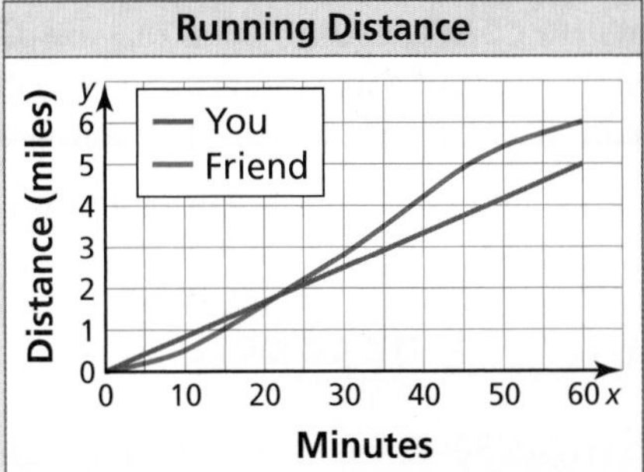

a. Describe your run and your friend's run. Who runs at a constant rate? How do you know? Why might a person not run at a constant rate?

b. Find the domain of each function. Describe the domains using the context of the problem.

43. **PERFORMANCE TASK** You are ordering T-shirts for a school fundraiser and receive bids from three options. You are not sure exactly how many T-shirts you need, but you know it will be no more than 200 shirts. Create a proposal for the school principal. Include the number of T-shirts, which option you chose, and the cost per T-shirt.

Option 1

Charge includes an initial fee plus a cost per T-shirt. Sample pricing is shown in the table.

Number of shirts	Price (dollars)
40	200
80	340
120	480
160	620
200	760

Option 2

Cost for x T-shirts: $c = 2x + 80$

Option 3

Cost is \$5 per T-shirt.

44. **THOUGHT PROVOKING**
A movie complex is open from 10:00 A.M. to 2:00 A.M. daily. It contains 8 theaters, each of which has 225 seats. The number of viewers in the theaters is a function of the number of hours after 10:00 A.M. each day. Describe a reasonable domain and range of the function. Then determine whether the function must be linear. Explain.

45. **MP REASONING** Is a linear function always increasing or always decreasing? Explain.

46. **ANALYZING RELATIONSHIPS** Explain the relationship between an equation and its graph. Why does the graph of a linear equation form a line?

47. **DRAWING CONCLUSIONS** What can you determine about the range of a linear function with a discrete domain? a continuous domain? Explain.

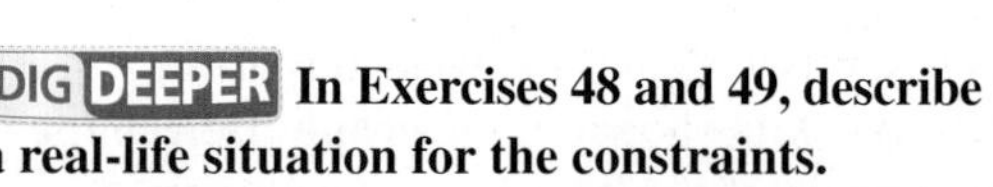

In Exercises 48 and 49, describe a real-life situation for the constraints.

48. The function has at least one negative number in the domain. The domain is continuous.

49. The function gives at least one negative number as an output. The domain is discrete.

REVIEW & REFRESH

In Exercises 50–53, solve the equation. Check your solution.

50. $h + 6 = -7$

51. $15 = 24 - 3y$

52. $9g - 12 = 6g$

53. $-18 = -2|w + 3|$

In Exercises 54–57, multiply or divide.

54. $\frac{3}{2} \cdot \frac{4}{7}$

55. $2\frac{5}{8} \cdot 3\frac{1}{3}$

56. $\frac{7}{8} \div \frac{1}{16}$

57. $\frac{8}{9} \div 4$

58. Tell whether x and y are proportional. Explain your reasoning.

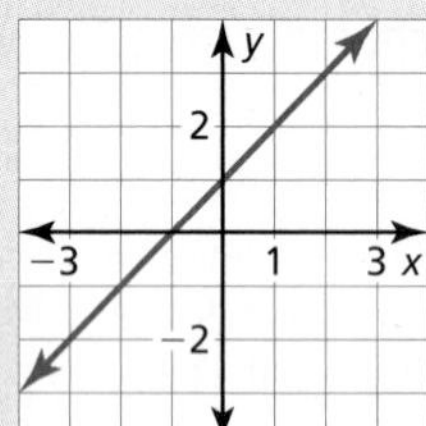

59. Write the sentence as an inequality. Then graph the inequality.

The sum of a number and 12 is at least 35.

In Exercises 60 and 61, determine whether the relation is a function.

60. $(-5, 6), (0, 3), (2, 10), (4, -3), (-5, -2)$

61. $(-3, 4), (-1, -1), (1, 6), (2, 2), (4, -1)$

62. Is the domain discrete or continuous? Explain.

Input Number of stories, x	1	2	3
Output Height of building (feet), y	12	24	36

63. **OPEN-ENDED** Write an inequality that can be solved using the Division Property of Inequality where the inequality symbol needs to be reversed.

64. **MODELING REAL LIFE** An event center charges \$59.95 for each concert ticket.

a. Does this situation represent a function? If so, identify the independent and dependent variables.

b. There are 9350 seats in the arena. Find the domain and range. Is the domain discrete or continuous? Explain.

65. Approximate when the function is positive, negative, increasing, or decreasing. Then describe the end behavior of the function.

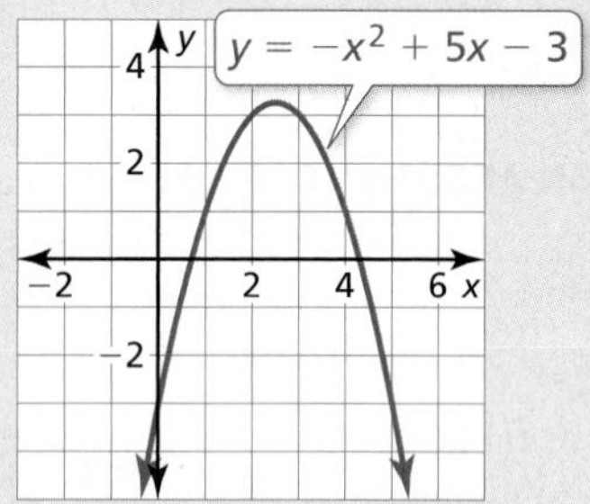

In Exercises 66–69, solve the inequality. Graph the solution.

66. $-4 < -2x + 9 \leq 32$

67. $-1 \leq q - 6$ *or* $\frac{1}{8}q < -\frac{3}{4}$

68. $|8y + 3| > -1$

69. $4|3 - 2z| - 9 \leq 3$

70. Does the graph represent a *linear* or *nonlinear* function? Explain.

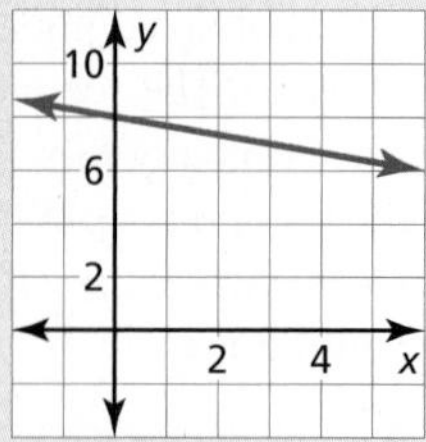

In Exercises 71 and 72, write the number in scientific notation.

71. 107,000,000

72. 0.000002

3.4 Function Notation

Learning Target Understand and use function notation.

Success Criteria
- I can evaluate functions using function notation.
- I can interpret statements that use function notation.
- I can graph functions represented using function notation.

EXPLORE IT! Using Function Notation

Math Practice

Communicate Precisely

In part (b), for a function $y = f(x)$, explain the meaning of f, x, and $f(x)$.

Work with a partner. Consider the functions f and g represented by the graph below.

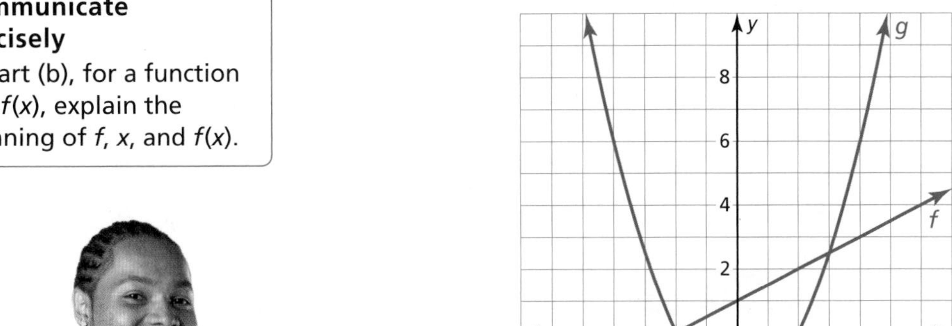

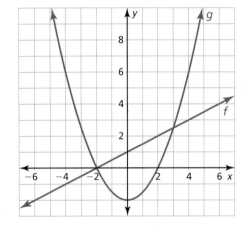

a. Find a point on g and explain how you found the point.

b. Find a point on f and explain what $f(x) = y$ means.

c. Find the points on the appropriate graph(s) at which

- $f(0) = 1$.
- $g(-2) = 0$ and $g(2) = 0$.
- $f(3) = g(3)$.
- $g(x) < f(x)$.

d. Why is it helpful to use f and g to describe the functions instead of using y?

e. Use function notation and inequalities to complete each definition.

- A function h is positive when __________ and negative when __________.
- A function h is increasing on an interval when, for any two numbers x_1 and x_2 in the interval, $x_1 < x_2$ implies __________.
- A function h is decreasing on an interval when, for any two numbers x_1 and x_2 in the interval, $x_1 < x_2$ implies__________.

GO DIGITAL

Using Function Notation to Evaluate and Interpret

Vocabulary 
function notation, *p. 136*

You learned that a linear function can be written in the form $y = mx + b$. By naming a linear function f, you can also write the function using **function notation**.

$f(x) = mx + b$ Function notation

The notation $f(x)$ is another name for y. If f is a function, and x is in its domain, then $f(x)$ represents the output of f corresponding to the input x. You can use letters other than f to name a function, such as g or h.

READING
The notation $f(x)$ is read as "the value of f at x" or "f of x." It does not mean "f times x."

EXAMPLE 1 Evaluating a Function 

Evaluate $f(x) = -4x + 7$ when $x = 2$ and $x = -2$.

SOLUTION

$f(x) = -4x + 7$	Write the function.	$f(x) = -4x + 7$
$f(2) = -4(2) + 7$	Substitute for x.	$f(-2) = -4(-2) + 7$
$= -8 + 7$	Multiply.	$= 8 + 7$
$= -1$	Add.	$= 15$

▶ When $x = 2$, $f(x) = -1$, and when $x = -2$, $f(x) = 15$.

EXAMPLE 2 Interpreting Function Notation 

Let $f(t)$ be the outside temperature (in degrees Fahrenheit) t hours after 6 A.M. Explain the meaning of each statement.

a. $f(0) = 58$ **b.** $f(6) = n$ **c.** $f(3.5) < f(9)$

SOLUTION

a. The initial value of the function is 58. So, the temperature at 6 A.M. is 58°F.

b. The output of f when $t = 6$ is n. So, the temperature at noon (6 hours after 6 A.M.) is n°F.

c. The output of f when $t = 3.5$ is less than the output of f when $t = 9$. So, the temperature at 9:30 A.M. (3 hours and 30 minutes after 6 A.M.) is less than the temperature at 3 P.M. (9 hours after 6 A.M.).

READING
The *initial value* of f is the value of the function when $x = 0$.

SELF-ASSESSMENT

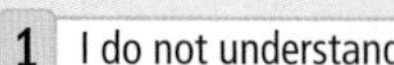
1 I do not understand. 2 I can do it with help.
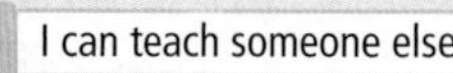
3 I can do it on my own. 4 I can teach someone else.

Evaluate the function when $x = -4, 0$, and $\frac{1}{2}$.

1. $f(x) = 2x + 1$ **2.** $g(x) = -x - 1$ **3.** $n(x) = \frac{1}{2} - \frac{5}{6}x$

4. You cook a turkey in an oven for 3 hours and 45 minutes. Let $f(t)$ be the temperature (in degrees Fahrenheit) of the turkey t hours after being placed in the oven. Explain the meaning of each statement.

a. $f(0) = 67$ **b.** $f(3.75) = 165$

c. $f(3) = f(4)$ **d.** $f(3.75) > f(4)$

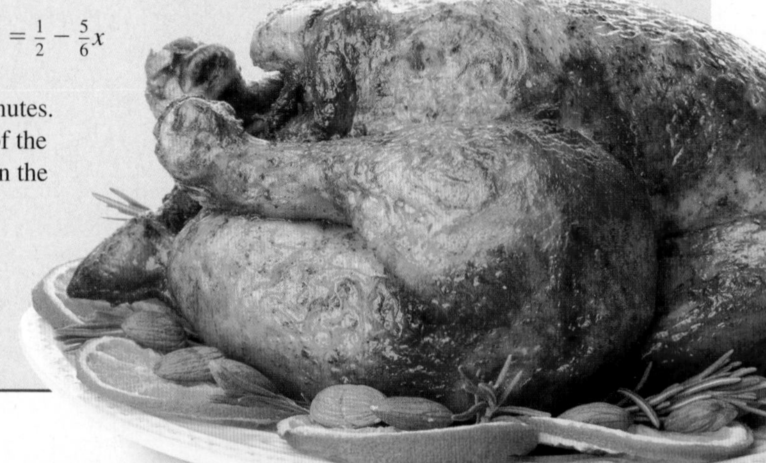

Using Function Notation to Solve and Graph

EXAMPLE 3 Solving for the Independent Variable

For $h(x) = \frac{2}{3}x - 5$, find the value of x for which $h(x) = -7$.

SOLUTION

$h(x) = \frac{2}{3}x - 5$ Write the function.

$-7 = \frac{2}{3}x - 5$ Substitute -7 for $h(x)$.

$-2 = \frac{2}{3}x$ Add 5 to each side.

$-3 = x$ Multiply each side by $\frac{3}{2}$.

▶ When $x = -3$, $h(x) = -7$.

EXAMPLE 4 Graphing a Linear Function in Function Notation

Graph $f(x) = 2x + 5$.

SOLUTION

Step 1 Make an input-output table to find ordered pairs.

x	-2	-1	0	1	2
$f(x)$	1	3	5	7	9

STUDY TIP

The graph of $y = f(x)$ consists of the points $(x, f(x))$.

Step 2 Plot the ordered pairs.

Step 3 Draw a line through the points.

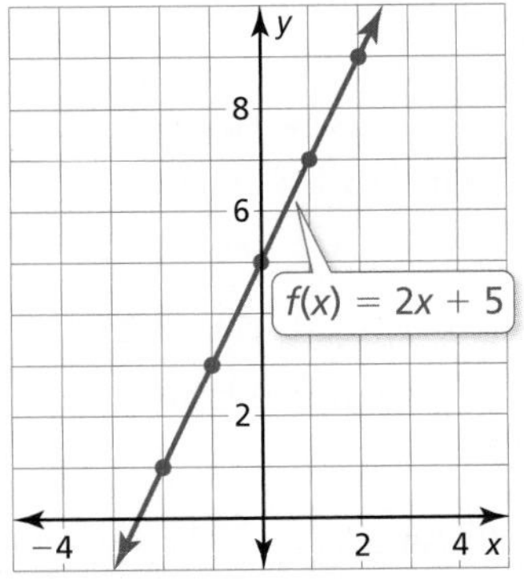

SELF-ASSESSMENT

1 I do not understand. 2 I can do it with help. 3 I can do it on my own. 4 I can teach someone else.

Find the value of x so that the function has the given value.

5. $f(x) = 6x + 9$; $f(x) = 21$

6. $g(x) = -\frac{1}{2}x + 3$; $g(x) = -1$

Graph the linear function.

7. $f(x) = 3x - 2$

8. $g(x) = 4 - x$

9. $h(x) = -\frac{3}{4}x - 1$

10. **MP REASONING** Let g be a function.

a. Given that $13 = g(-5)$, find a point that is on the graph of g.

b. Given that $-\frac{1}{2}$ is a solution of $g(x) = 4$, find a point that is on the graph of g.

Solving Real-Life Problems

EXAMPLE 5 **Modeling Real Life** 

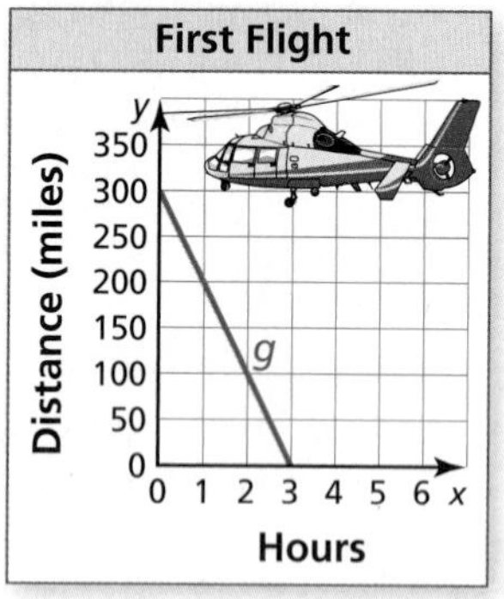

The graph of g shows how far a helicopter is from its destination after taking off. The function $f(x) = 350 - 125x$ represents a second flight, where $f(x)$ is the number of miles the helicopter is from its destination after x hours. Which flight takes less time?

First Flight

(Graph: Distance (miles) vs. Hours; line g from (0, 350) to (3, 0).)

SOLUTION

1. **Understand the Problem** You are given a graph of the first flight and an equation of the second flight. You are asked to determine which flight takes less time.
2. **Make a Plan** Graph the function that represents the second flight. Because both flights involve the same quantities with the same units, you can compare the graphs to determine which flight takes less time. The x-values that correspond to $f(x) = 0$ and $g(x) = 0$ represent the total flight times.
3. **Solve and Check** Graph $f(x) = 350 - 125x$.

Step 1 Make an input-output table to find the ordered pairs.

x	0	1	2	3
$f(x)$	350	225	100	−25

Step 2 Plot the ordered pairs. Draw a line through the points. Note that the function only makes sense when x and $f(x)$ are nonnegative. So, draw the line in the first quadrant only.

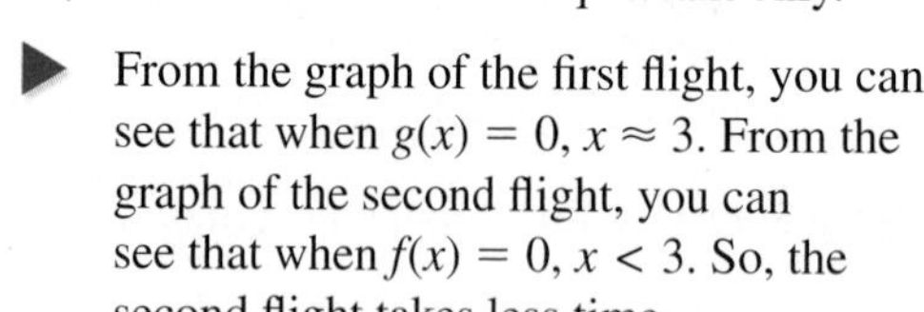

▶ From the graph of the first flight, you can see that when $g(x) = 0$, $x \approx 3$. From the graph of the second flight, you can see that when $f(x) = 0$, $x < 3$. So, the second flight takes less time.

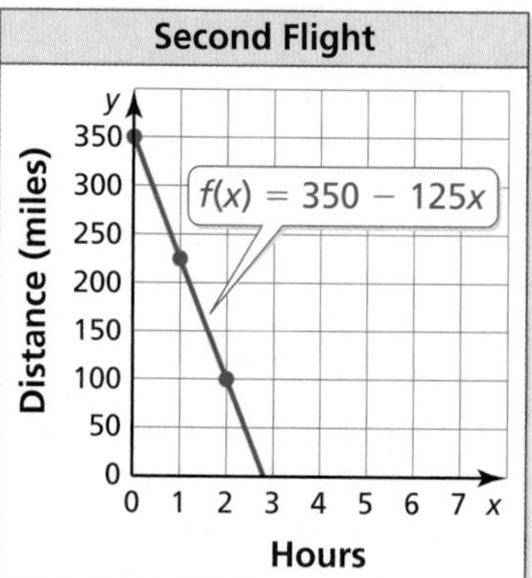

Math Practice

Interpret Results
What happens to $f(x)$ as x increases from 2 to 3? What does this tell you about the time it takes the helicopter to reach its destination?

Another Way For the second flight, use the equation to find the value of x for which $f(x) = 0$.

$f(x) = 350 - 125x$	Write the function.
$0 = 350 - 125x$	Substitute 0 for $f(x)$.
$-350 = -125x$	Subtract 350 from each side.
$2.8 = x$	Divide each side by −125.

Because $2.8 < 3$, the second flight takes less time.

SELF-ASSESSMENT 1 I do not understand. 2 I can do it with help. 3 I can do it on my own. 4 I can teach someone else.

11. **WHAT IF?** Let $f(x) = 250 - 75x$ represent the second flight in Example 5, where $f(x)$ is the number of miles the helicopter is from its destination after x hours. Which flight takes less time? Explain.

12. You stand at zero on a number line and flip a coin. When the coin is heads, you move one unit to the right. When the coin is tails, you move one unit to the left. After each flip, you record your position on the number line. Let g represent your position after the nth flip.
    a. Explain why g is a function.
    b. What does $g(5) = 3$ represent?
    c. What is the probability that $g(3) = 0$? Explain your reasoning.

3.4 Practice WITH CalcChat® AND CalcView®

In Exercises 1–8, evaluate the function when $x = -2, 0,$ and 5. *Example 1*

1. $f(x) = x + 6$
2. $g(x) = 3x$
3. $h(x) = -2x + 9$
4. $r(x) = -x - 7$
5. $p(x) = -3 + \frac{1}{4}x$
6. $b(x) = 18 - 0.5x$
7. $v(x) = 12 - 2x - 5.8$
8. $n(x) = -1 - \frac{1}{3}x + 1\frac{2}{3}$

9. **INTERPRETING FUNCTION NOTATION** Let $c(t)$ be the number of customers in a restaurant t hours after 8 A.M. Explain the meaning of each statement. *Example 2*

   a. $c(0) = 0$ b. $c(3) = c(8)$

   c. $c(n) = 29$ d. $c(13.5) < c(12)$

10. **INTERPRETING FUNCTION NOTATION** Let $H(x)$ be the percent of U.S. households with Internet use x years after 1980. Explain the meaning of each statement.

    a. $H(27) = 61.7$ b. $H(4) = k$

    c. $H(37) > H(30)$ d. $H(17) + H(21) \approx H(29)$

In Exercises 11–16, find the value of x so that the function has the given value. *Example 3*

11. $h(x) = -7x;\ h(x) = 63$
12. $t(x) = 3x;\ t(x) = 24$
13. $m(x) = 4x + 15;\ m(x) = 7$
14. $k(x) = 6x - 12;\ k(x) = 15$
15. $q(x) = 0.5x - 3;\ q(x) = -4$
16. $j(x) = -\frac{4}{5}x + 7;\ j(x) = -5$

In Exercises 17 and 18, find the value of x so that $f(x) = 7$.

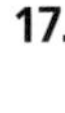

17. 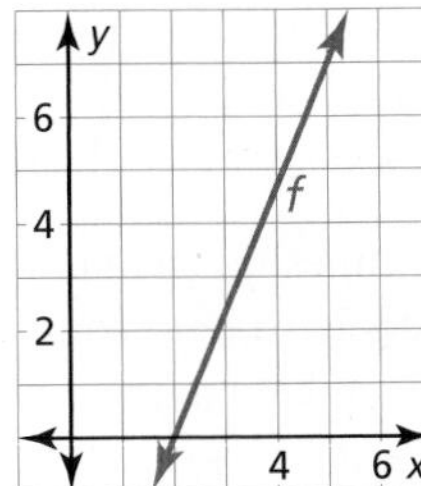

18. 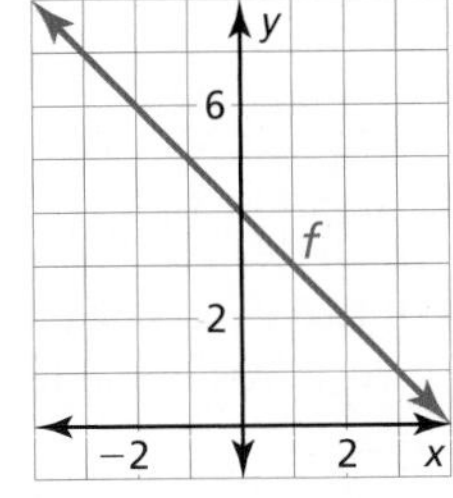

19. **MODELING REAL LIFE** The function $C(x) = 17.5x - 10$ represents the cost (in dollars) of buying x tickets to the orchestra with a \$10 coupon. How much does it cost to buy five tickets?

The distance from the Sun to Earth varies from 91.4 to 94.5 million miles.

20. **MODELING REAL LIFE** Thefunction $d(t) = 300{,}000t$ represents the distance (in kilometers) that light travelsin t seconds.

    a. How far does light travel in 15 seconds?

    b. How long does it take light to travel from the Sun to Earth?

In Exercises 21–26, graph the linear function. *Example 4*

21. $p(x) = 4x$
22. $h(x) = -5x$
23. $d(x) = -\frac{1}{2}x - 3$
24. $w(x) = 0.6x + 2$
25. $g(x) = -4 + 7x$
26. $f(x) = 3 - 6x$

27. **MODELING REAL LIFE** The graph of g shows the percent of battery power remaining on a laptop after it is turned on. The function $f(x) = 0.75 - 0.125x$ represents the percent (in decimal form) of battery power remaining on a tablet x hours after it is turned on. Which device stays on longer? Explain. *(See Example 5.)*

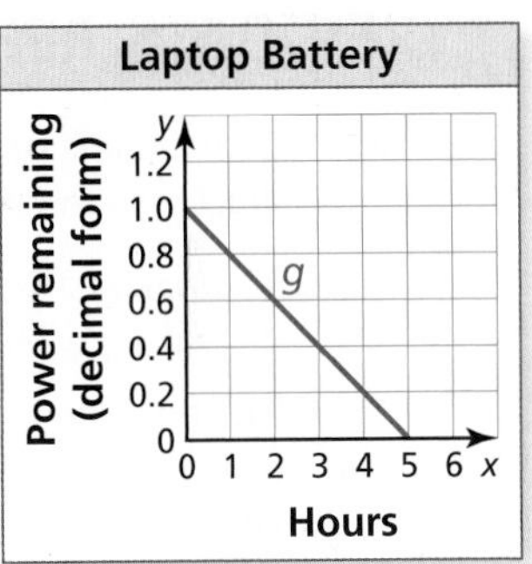

28. **MP PROBLEM SOLVING** The function $C(x) = 25x + 50$ represents the labor cost (in dollars) for Contractor A to build a deck, where x is the number of hours of labor. The table shows sample labor costs from its main competitor, Contractor B. The deck is estimated to take 8 hours of labor. Which contractor would you hire? Explain.

Hours	Cost
2	\$130
4	\$160
6	\$190

29. **MP REASONING** Let f be a function. Use each statement to find a point on the graph of f.

    a. $f(5)$ is equal to 9.

    b. A solution of the equation $f(n) = -3$ is 5.

30. HOW DO YOU SEE IT?
The function A represents the attendance at a high school since the beginning of a flu outbreak. The graph of the function is shown.

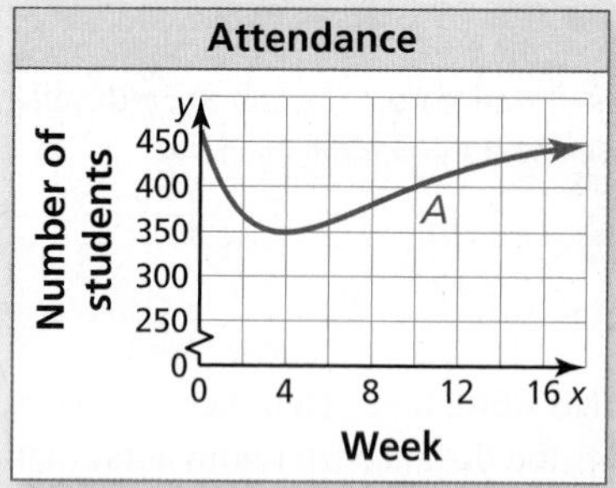

a. What happens to the school's attendance during the flu outbreak?

b. Estimate $A(13)$ and explain its meaning.

c. Use the graph to estimate the solution(s) of the equation $A(x) = 400$. Explain the meaning of the solution(s).

d. What was the least attendance? When did that occur?

e. How many students do you think are enrolled at this high school? Explain your reasoning.

31. DRAWING CONCLUSIONS A student's height can be represented by a function h, where the input is the student's age.

a. What does $h(14)$ represent? Can you determine the units for height? Explain.

b. What does $h(15) = 58$ represent? What can you conclude about the units for height?

32. THOUGHT PROVOKING
Let $B(t)$ be your bank account balance after t days. Describe a situation in which $B(0) < B(4) < B(2)$.

33. **MP REASONING** Given a function f, tell whether the statement

$$f(a + b) = f(a) + f(b)$$

is true or false for all values of a and b. If it is false, explain why.

34. **DIG DEEPER** Let $f(x) = -5 - 10x$ and $g(x) = \frac{1}{5}x + 1$. Find $f(g(x))$. Simplify the expression.

REVIEW & REFRESH

35. Sketch a graph of a function with the given characteristics.

- The function is decreasing when $x < 1$ and increasing when $x > 1$.
- The function is positive when $x < -2.5$, negative when $-2.5 < x < 4.5$, and positive when $x > 4.5$.

In Exercises 36 and 37, solve the inequality. Graph the solution.

36. $5a < -35$ *or* $a - 14 > 1$

37. $-16 \leq 6k + 2 < 0$

38. Determine whether the relation is a function. Explain.

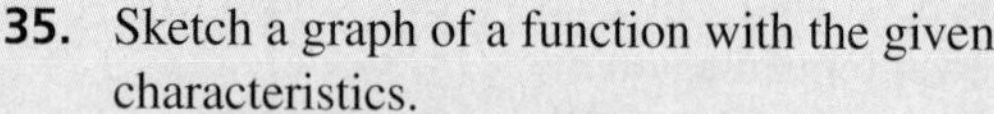

Input, *x*	−1	0	1	2	3
Output, *y*	0	1	4	4	8

39. Write the sentence as an inequality.

Four times a number n minus 10.5 is no less than -1.5.

40. For $g(x) = 10 - 8x$, find the value of x for which $g(x) = 42$.

41. Solve the literal equation $m = 5x + 6xy$ for x.

42. MODELING REAL LIFE You order two hamburgers and a drink. The drink costs \$1.50. You pay a total of \$5.83, including a 6% sales tax. How much does one hamburger cost?

43. Determine whether the graph represents a *linear* or *nonlinear* function. Explain.

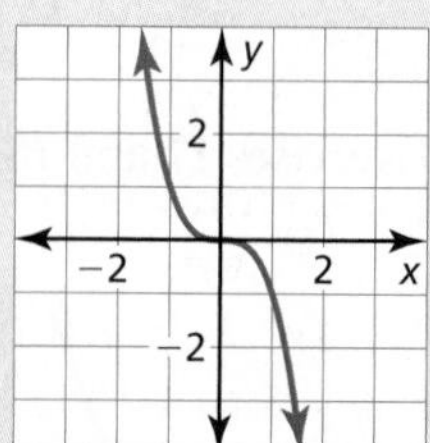

44. **MP NUMBER SENSE** Three times the greater of two consecutive odd integers is 15 less than two-thirds of the lesser integer. What are the integers?

45. Write $1\frac{3}{11}$ as a decimal.

46. Graph $f(x) = \frac{3}{2}x - 1$.

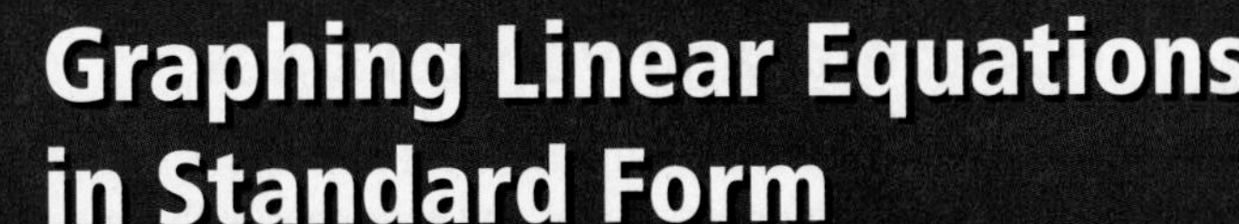

3.5 Graphing Linear Equations in Standard Form

Learning Target Graph and interpret linear equations written in standard form.

Success Criteria
- I can graph equations of horizontal and vertical lines.
- I can graph linear equations written in standard form using intercepts.
- I can solve real-life problems using linear equations in standard form.

EXPLORE IT! Analyzing and Graphing a Linear Equation

Work with a partner. You sold a total of \$80 in tickets to a fundraiser. You lost track of how many of each type of ticket you sold. Adult tickets are \$4 each. Child tickets are \$2 each.

a. Use the verbal model to write an equation that relates the number x of adult tickets and the number y of child tickets. What do you know about the equation you wrote?

$\frac{\square}{\text{adult}}$ • Number of adult tickets + $\frac{\square}{\text{child}}$ • Number of child tickets = $\square$

b. If you sold a large quantity of adult tickets, does that mean you also sold a large quantity of child tickets? Explain.

c. Construct a table of values to show different combinations of tickets you might have sold. Then plot the points and describe any patterns you notice.

x					
y					

d. Graph the equation in part (a). Find the intercepts. Explain the meanings of the intercepts in the context of the problem.

e. Use technology to check your results in parts (c) and (d). Describe the characteristics of the graph.

f. If you know how many adult tickets you sold, can you determine how many child tickets you sold? Explain your reasoning.

g. Determine whether each statement is correct. Explain your reasoning.

i. As the value of x increases, the value of $2y$ decreases.

ii. As the value of y decreases, the value of $4x$ decreases.

iii. For $x < 10$, $y > 20$.

iv. $x = 20$ makes the equation true.

Math Practice

Use Technology to Explore

How can you use technology to describe the graph of the equation $Ax + By = C$ and explore its characteristics?

Horizontal and Vertical Lines

Vocabulary

standard form, *p. 142*

The **standard form** of a linear equation is $Ax + By = C$, where A, B, and C are real numbers and A and B are not both zero.

Consider what happens when $A = 0$ or when $B = 0$. When $A = 0$, the equation becomes $By = C$, or $y = \frac{C}{B}$. Because $\frac{C}{B}$ is a constant, you can write $y = b$. Similarly, when $B = 0$, the equation becomes $Ax = C$, or $x = \frac{C}{A}$, and you can write $x = a$.

KEY IDEAS

Horizontal and Vertical Lines

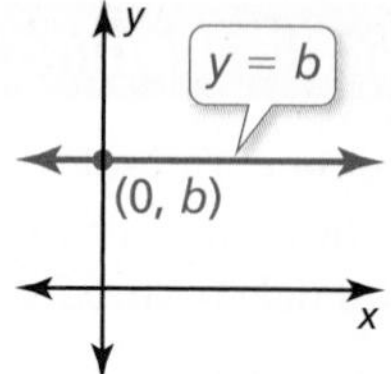

The graph of $y = b$ is a horizontal line. The line passes through the point $(0, b)$.

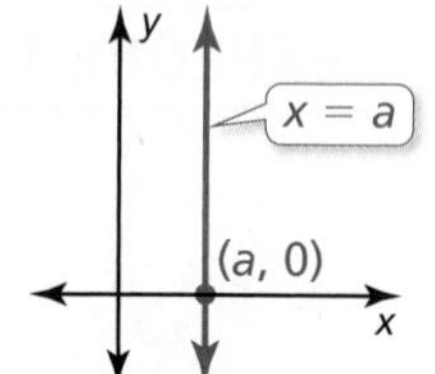

The graph of $x = a$ is a vertical line. The line passes through the point $(a, 0)$.

STUDY TIP

For a horizontal line, notice that for every value of x, the value of y is b.

For a vertical line, notice that for every value of y, the value of x is a.

EXAMPLE 1 Graphing Horizontal and Vertical Lines

Graph each linear equation.

a. $y = 4$

b. $x = -2$

SOLUTION

a. For every value of x, the value of y is 4. The graph of the equation $y = 4$ is a horizontal line 4 units above the x-axis.

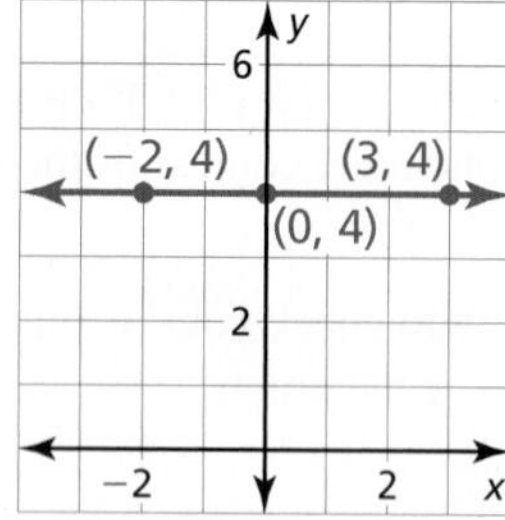

b. For every value of y, the value of x is -2. The graph of the equation $x = -2$ is a vertical line 2 units to the left of the y-axis.

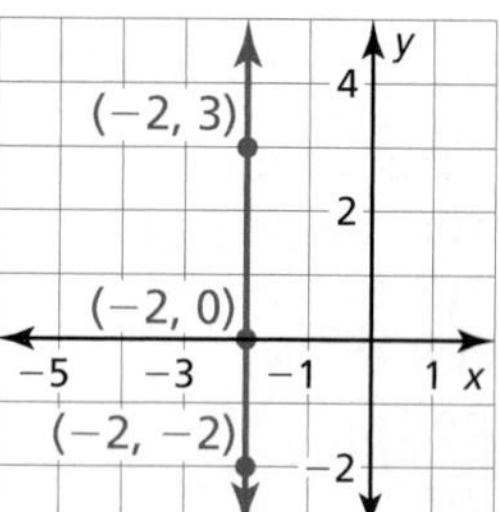

STUDY TIP

For every value of x, the ordered pair $(x, 4)$ is a solution of $y = 4$.

SELF-ASSESSMENT

1 I do not understand. 2 I can do it with help. 3 I can do it on my own. 4 I can teach someone else.

Graph the linear equation.

1. $y = -2.5$

2. $x = 5$

3. $x = -\frac{4}{3}$

4. $y = 18$

5. WRITING Describe the x- and y-intercepts of the horizontal line that passes through the origin and the vertical line that passes through the origin.

6. MP **REASONING** Graph $x = -1$ and $y = -1$. Does each graph represent a function? If so, find the domain and range.

Using Intercepts to Graph Linear Equations

You can use the fact that two points determine a line to graph a linear equation. Two convenient points are the x- and y-intercepts.

KEY IDEA

Using Intercepts to Graph Equations

To graph the linear equation $Ax + By = C$ using intercepts, find the intercepts and draw the line that passes through them.

- To find the x-intercept, let $y = 0$ and solve for x.
- To find the y-intercept, let $x = 0$ and solve for y.

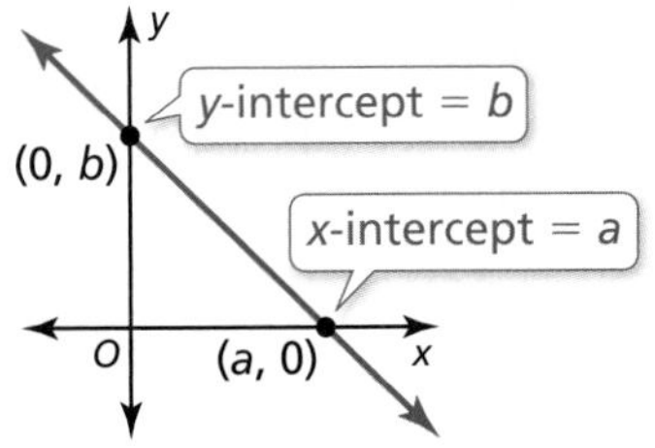

EXAMPLE 2 Using Intercepts to Graph a Linear Equation

Use intercepts to graph the equation $3x + 4y = 12$.

SOLUTION

Step 1 Find the intercepts.

To find the x-intercept, substitute 0 for y and solve for x.

$3x + 4y = 12$	Write the original equation.
$3x + 4(0) = 12$	Substitute 0 for y.
$x = 4$	Solve for x.

To find the y-intercept, substitute 0 for x and solve for y.

$3x + 4y = 12$	Write the original equation.
$3(0) + 4y = 12$	Substitute 0 for x.
$y = 3$	Solve for y.

Step 2 Plot the points and draw the line.

The x-intercept is 4, so plot the point (4, 0).
The y-intercept is 3, so plot the point (0, 3).
Draw a line through the points.

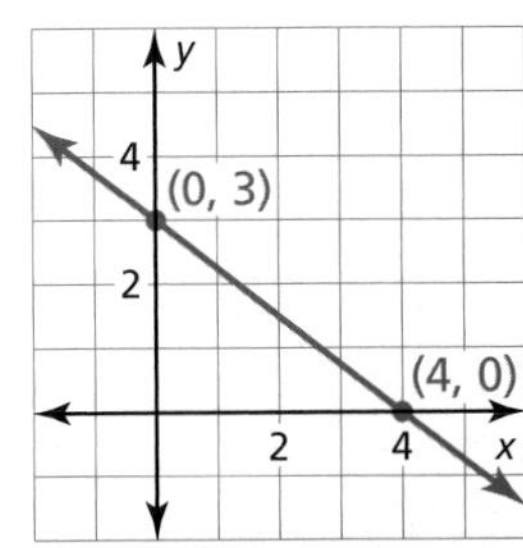

STUDY TIP

You can check your answer by finding other solutions of the equation and verifying that the corresponding points are on the graph.

SELF-ASSESSMENT 1 I do not understand. 2 I can do it with help. 3 I can do it on my own. 4 I can teach someone else.

7. **WRITING** What are some advantages of using the standard form of a linear equation?

Use intercepts to graph the linear equation. Label the points corresponding to the intercepts.

8. $2x - y = 4$

9. $x + 3y = -9$

10. $\frac{3}{4}x + 2y = 6$

11. **WRITING** Describe the graph of a linear equation written in the form $Ax + By = C$ when $C = 0$.

Solving Real-Life Problems

EXAMPLE 3 **Modeling Real Life** 

Math Practice

Understand Quantities

What do the terms $6x$ and $10y$ represent in this situation?

You are planning an awards banquet and need to rent tables to seat 180 people. There are two table sizes available. Small tables seat 6 people, and large tables seat 10 people. The equation $6x + 10y = 180$ models this situation, where x is the number of small tables and y is the number of large tables.

a. Graph the equation. Interpret the intercepts.

b. Find three possible solutions in the context of the problem.

SOLUTION

a. Use intercepts to graph the equation. Neither x nor y can be negative, so only graph the equation in the first quadrant.

STUDY TIP

Although x and y represent discrete data, it is convenient to draw a line segment that includes points whose coordinates are not whole numbers.

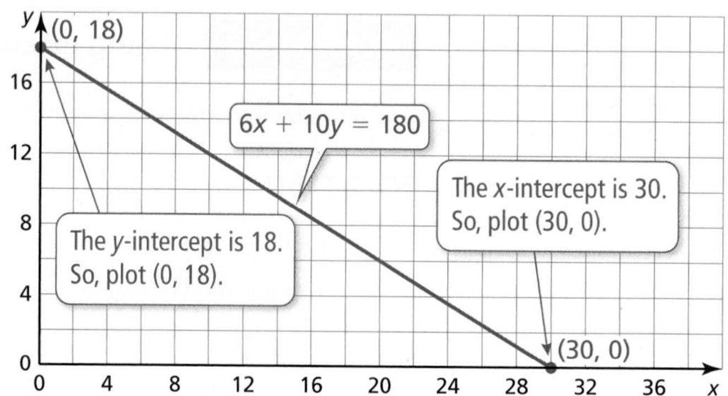

Use the graph to interpret the intercepts.

▶ The x-intercept shows that you can rent 30 small tables when you do not rent any large tables. The y-intercept shows that you can rent 18 large tables when you do not rent any small tables.

b. Only whole-number values of x and y make sense in the context of the problem. Besides the intercepts, it appears that the line passes through the point (10, 12). To verify that this point is a solution, check it in the equation.

$$6x + 10y = 180$$

$$6(10) + 10(12) \stackrel{?}{=} 180$$

$$180 = 180 \checkmark$$

▶ So, three possible combinations of tables that will seat 180 people are 0 small and 18 large, 10 small and 12 large, and 30 small and 0 large.

SELF-ASSESSMENT 1 I do not understand. 2 I can do it with help. 3 I can do it on my own. 4 I can teach someone else.

12. WHAT IF? You decide to rent tables from a different company. The situation can be modeled by the equation $4x + 6y = 180$, where x is the number of small tables and y is the number of large tables.

a. Interpret the terms and coefficients in the equation.

b. Graph the equation. Interpret the intercepts.

c. Find three possible solutions in the context of the problem.

13. The number of people attending the banquet in Example 3 increases by 25%. Your friend claims that not all of the tables will be completely filled. Is your friend correct? Explain.

3.5 Practice WITH CalcChat® AND CalcView®

In Exercises 1–4, graph the linear equation. *Example 1*

1. $x = 4$
2. $y = -3$
3. $y = \frac{1}{2}$
4. $x = -1.5$

In Exercises 5–8, find the x- and y-intercepts of the graph of the linear equation.

5. $2x + 3y = 12$
6. $-6x + 9y = -18$
7. $3x = 6y + 2$
8. $\frac{3}{4} + x = \frac{1}{2}y$

In Exercises 9–18, use intercepts to graph the linear equation. Label the points corresponding to the intercepts. *Example 2*

9. $5x + 3y = 30$
10. $4x + 6y = 12$
11. $-12x + 3y = 24$
12. $-2x + 6y = 18$
13. $-4x + 3y = -30$
14. $-2x + 7y = -21$
15. $2y - x = 7$
16. $3x + 5 = y$
17. $\frac{4}{3} + \frac{2}{3}x = \frac{1}{6}y$
18. $y = \frac{1}{4} - \frac{5}{2}x$

MULTIPLE REPRESENTATIONS In Exercises 19–22, match the equation with its graph.

19. $5x + 3y = 30$
20. $5x + 3y = -30$
21. $5x - 3y = 30$
22. $5x - 3y = -30$

A.

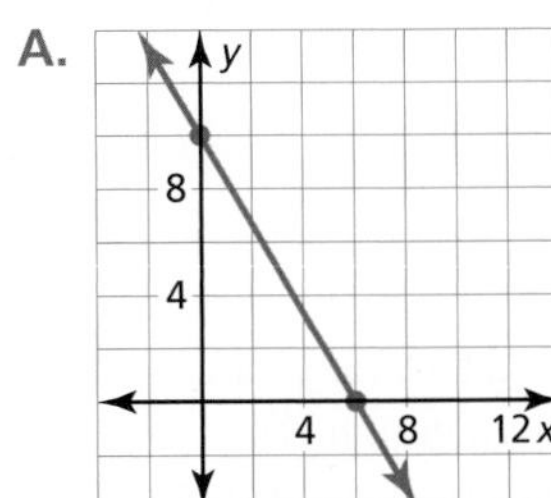

B.

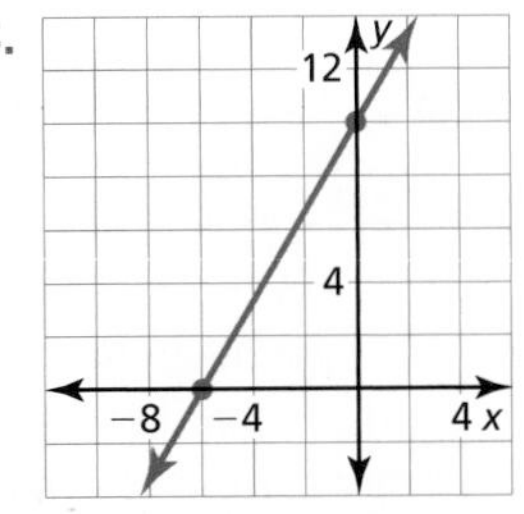

C.

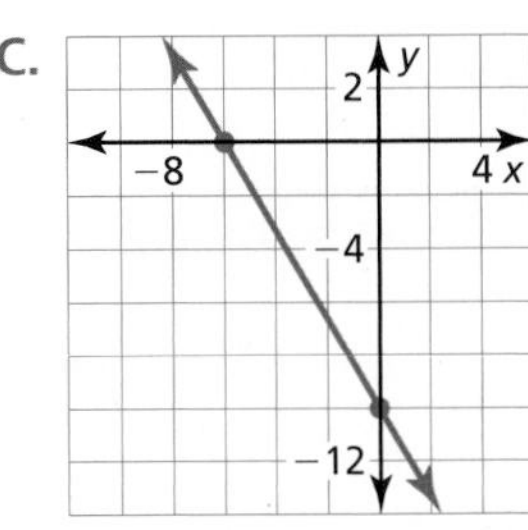

D.

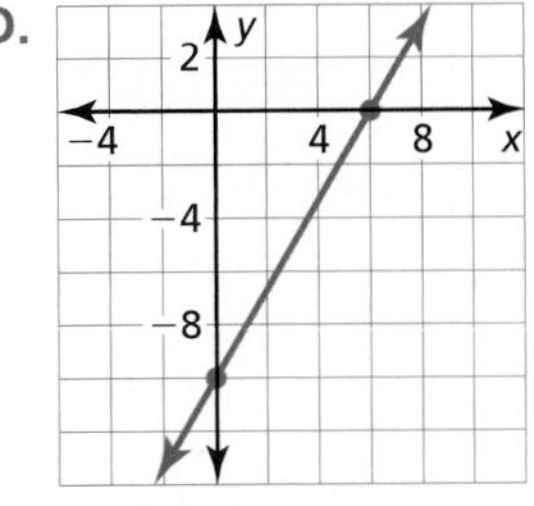

23. **MODELING REAL LIFE** You have a budget of \$300 to order shirts for a math club. The equation $10x + 12y = 300$ models the total cost, where x is the number of short-sleeved shirts and y is the number of long-sleeved shirts. *Example 3*
    a. Interpret the terms and coefficients in the equation.
    b. Graph the equation. Interpret the intercepts.
    c. Find three possible solutions in the context of the problem.

24. **MODELING REAL LIFE** Your goal is to bike and jog a total of 150 miles this month. The equation $12.5x + 6y = 150$ models this situation, where x is the number of hours you bike and y is the number of hours you jog.
    a. Interpret the terms and coefficients in the equation.
    b. Graph the equation. Interpret the intercepts.
    c. You bike for 9 hours this month. How many hours must you jog to reach your goal? How many miles do you bike? jog?

25. **ERROR ANALYSIS** Describe and correct the error in using intercepts to graph the linear equation $4x + 10y = 20$.

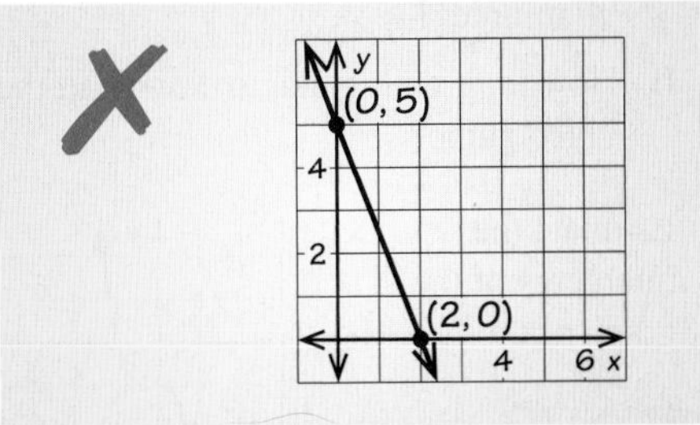

26. **MAKING AN ARGUMENT** To find the x-intercept of the graph of a linear equation, can you substitute 0 for x and solve the equation? Explain.

CONNECTING CONCEPTS In Exercises 27–30, write a set of linear equations that intersect to form the enclosed shape.

27. rectangle
28. square
29. right triangle
30. trapezoid

31. **MP REASONING** Are the equations of horizontal and vertical lines written in standard form? Explain.

32. **HOW DO YOU SEE IT?**
An artist wants to earn a revenue of \$2700 by selling paintings for \$30 each and sculptures for \$45 each.

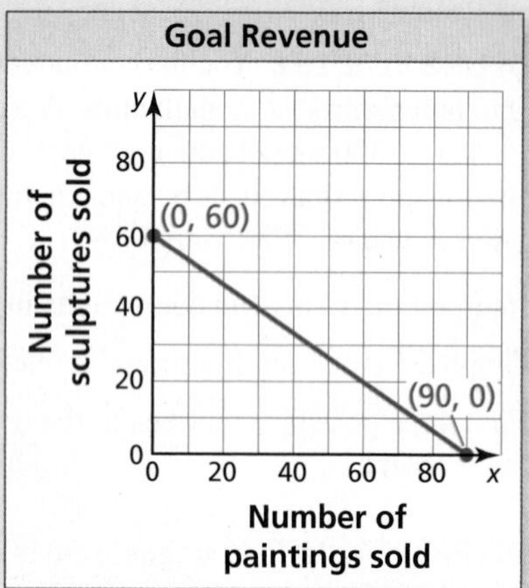

a. Interpret the intercepts of the graph.

b. Describe the domain and range in the context of the problem.

33. **COLLEGE PREP** Which of the following is *not* true about the graph of $-\frac{2}{5}x + \frac{1}{10}y = -\frac{4}{5}$?

GO DIGITAL

Ⓐ The x-intercept is 2 and the y-intercept is -8.

Ⓑ The function is decreasing when $x < 2$ and increasing when $x > 2$.

Ⓒ The graph passes through $(1, -4)$ and $(5, 12)$.

Ⓓ $y \to -\infty$ as $x \to -\infty$ and $y \to +\infty$ as $x \to +\infty$.

34. **THOUGHT PROVOKING**
The x- and y-intercepts of the graph of $ax + by = k$ are integers. Describe the possible values of k. Explain your reasoning.

35. **DIG DEEPER** You have \$99 to buy stamps and envelopes. A sheet of 20 stamps costs \$11. A box of 50 envelopes costs \$7.50.

a. Write an equation in standard form that models this situation. Do the intercepts of the graph make sense in this context? Explain.

b. Can you use all of the money to buy the same numbers of stamps and envelopes? Explain.

REVIEW & REFRESH

36. **MODELING REAL LIFE** The function $D(t) = 75 - 0.3t$ represents the number of gigabytes left after downloading a video game for t minutes.

a. How many gigabytes are left to download after 90 minutes?

b. How long will it take to download the entire video game?

37. Estimate the intercepts of the graph of the function.

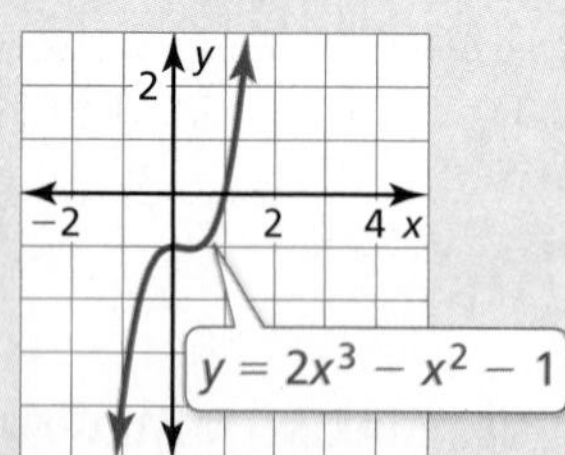

38. **WRITING** Explain how you can determine whether a graph represents a *linear* or a *nonlinear* function.

39. Determine whether the equation $y = x(2 - x)$ represents a *linear* or *nonlinear* function. Explain.

In Exercises 40 and 41, solve the inequality. Graph the solution.

40. $b + 5 \leq -12$

41. $-\frac{c}{3} > -15$

42. **MP REASONING** Complete the equation $\square x + \square y = 30$ so that the x-intercept of the graph is -10 and the y-intercept of the graph is 5.

In Exercises 43–46, solve the equation. Check your solutions.

43. $6.8 + g = 14.1$

44. $-11 = 7 - 3(h + 2)$

45. $3(4 - 8k) = -4(6k - 3)$

46. $5|6n - 9| + 4 = 29$

47. The tape diagram represents the ratio of rare cards to common cards in a collection. There are 9 rare cards. How many common cards are in the collection?

Rare
Common

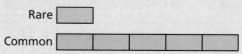

48. For $f(x) = -\frac{2}{3}x + 1$, find the value of x for which $f(x) = 9$.

49. Find the x- and y-intercepts of the graph of $-4x + 8y = -16$.

3.6 Graphing Linear Equations in Slope-Intercept Form

Learning Target Find the slope of a line and use slope-intercept form.

Success Criteria
- I can find the slope of a line.
- I can use the slope-intercept form of a linear equation.
- I can solve real-life problems using slopes and y-intercepts.

Slope is the rate of change between any two points on a line. It is the measure of the *steepness* of the line.

To find the slope of a line, find the value of the ratio of the change in y (vertical change) to the change in x (horizontal change).

$$\text{slope} = \frac{\text{change in } y}{\text{change in } x}$$

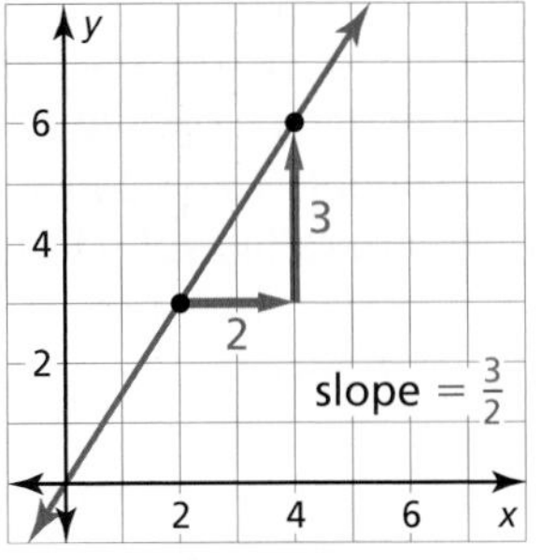

EXPLORE IT! Analyzing Linear Equations

Work with a partner.

Math Practice

Repeat Calculations
If you complete a similar table for a line with a negative or fractional slope or y-intercept, do your results change?

a. Complete the table for $y = 2x$. What do you notice about the values in Columns 2 and 4?

x	Change in x	y	Change in y
1	---	2	---
2	1	4	2
3			
4			
5			

b. Complete a similar table for each equation. Interpret your results.

i. $y = 2x + 1$

ii. $y = 4x - 3$

iii. $y = px + q$

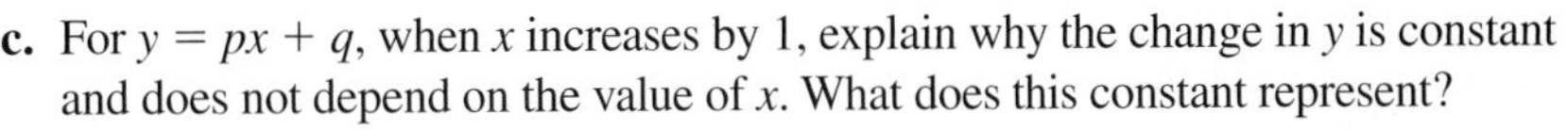

c. For $y = px + q$, when x increases by 1, explain why the change in y is constant and does not depend on the value of x. What does this constant represent?

d. Complete the table for each of the equations in part (a) and part (b). What do you notice?

x	Change in x	y	Change in y
1	---		---
3			
5			
7			

e. For $y = px + q$, when x increases by a constant c, explain why the change in y is constant and does not depend on the value of x. What does this constant represent?

f. What is the relationship between the graph of $y = px + q$ and the values of p and q?

The Slope of a Line

Vocabulary

slope, *p. 148*
rise, *p. 148*
run, *p. 148*
slope-intercept form, *p. 150*
constant function, *p. 150*

READING

In the slope formula, x_1 is read as "*x* sub one" and y_2 is read as "*y* sub two." The numbers 1 and 2 in x_1 and y_2 are called *subscripts*.

KEY IDEA

Slope

The **slope** m of a nonvertical line passing through two points (x_1, y_1) and (x_2, y_2) is the value of the ratio of the **rise** (change in y) to the **run** (change in x).

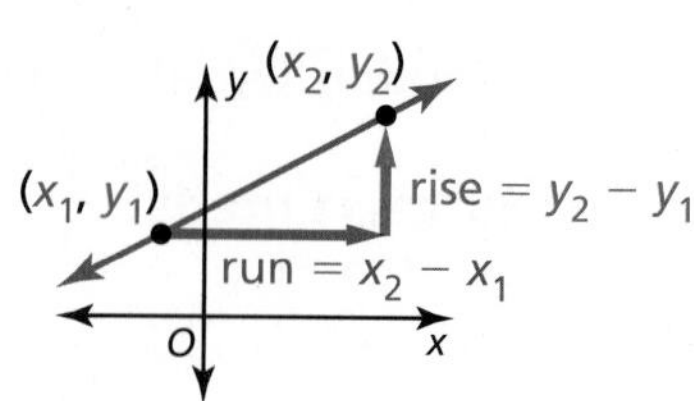

$$\text{slope} = m = \frac{\text{rise}}{\text{run}} = \frac{\text{change in } y}{\text{change in } x} = \frac{y_2 - y_1}{x_2 - x_1}$$

When the line rises from left to right, the slope is positive. When the line falls from left to right, the slope is negative.

EXAMPLE 1 Finding Slopes of Lines

Describe the slope of each line. Then find the slope.

a. 

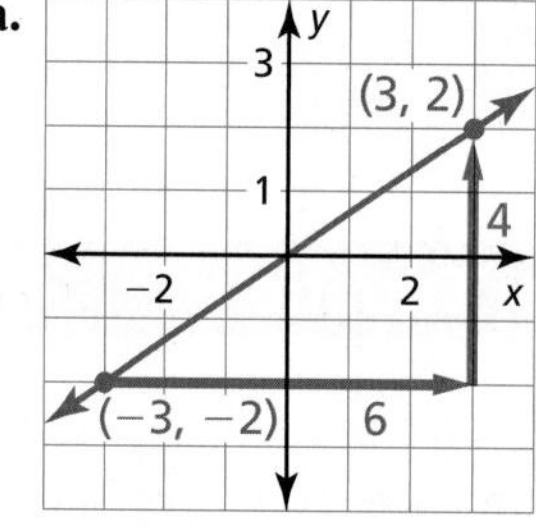

b. 

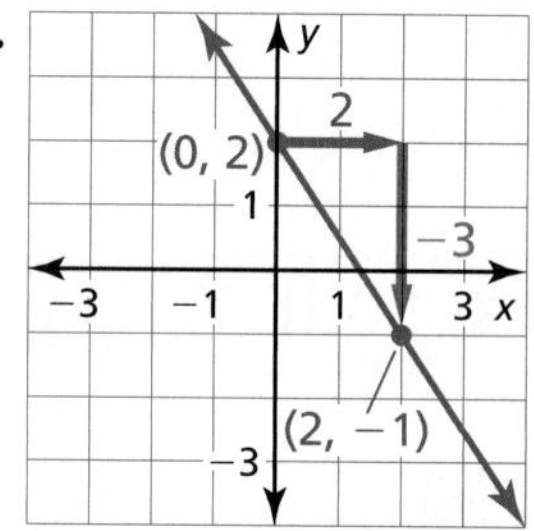

SOLUTION

a. The line rises from left to right. So, the slope is positive. Let $(x_1, y_1) = (-3, -2)$ and $(x_2, y_2) = (3, 2)$.

$$m = \frac{y_2 - y_1}{x_2 - x_1} = \frac{2 - (-2)}{3 - (-3)} = \frac{4}{6} = \frac{2}{3}$$

b. The line falls from left to right. So, the slope is negative. Let $(x_1, y_1) = (0, 2)$ and $(x_2, y_2) = (2, -1)$.

$$m = \frac{y_2 - y_1}{x_2 - x_1} = \frac{-1 - 2}{2 - 0} = \frac{-3}{2} = -\frac{3}{2}$$

SELF-ASSESSMENT

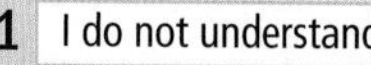

2 I can do it with help. 3 I can do it on my own. 4 I can teach someone else.

Describe the slope of the line. Then find the slope.

1. 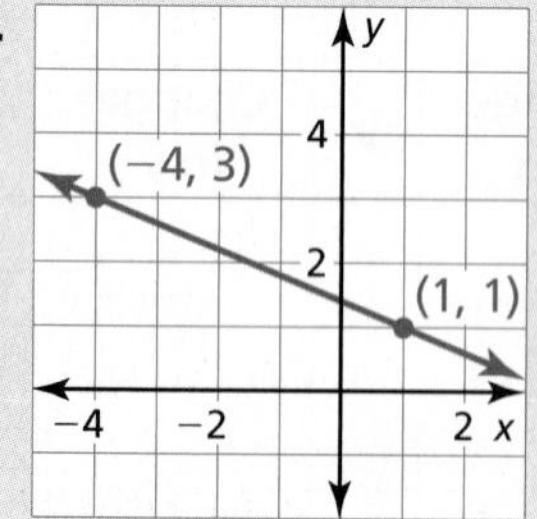

2. 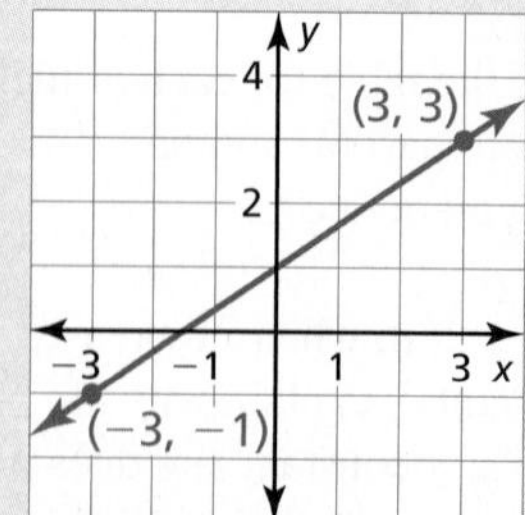

3. 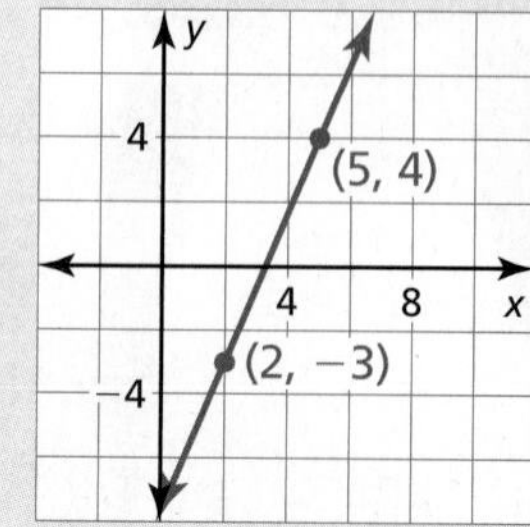

4. **MP STRUCTURE** When finding slope, can you label either point as (x_1, y_1) and (x_2, y_2)? Explain.
5. **WRITING** When the graph of a line is not horizontal or vertical, how can you tell whether the graph has a positive or a negative slope?
6. **MP REASONING** Line p has a slope of -4. Line q has a slope of $\frac{7}{4}$. Which line is steeper? Explain your reasoning.

GO DIGITAL

EXAMPLE 2 Finding Slopes from Tables

The points represented by each table lie on a line. How can you find the slope of each line from the table? What is the slope of each line?

a.

x	y
4	20
7	14
10	8
13	2

b.

x	y
−1	2
1	2
3	2
5	2

c.

x	y
−3	−3
−3	0
−3	6
−3	9

SOLUTION

Choose any two points from the table and use the slope formula.

a. Let $(x_1, y_1) = (4, 20)$ and $(x_2, y_2) = (7, 14)$.

$$m = \frac{y_2 - y_1}{x_2 - x_1} = \frac{14 - 20}{7 - 4} = \frac{-6}{3}, \text{ or } -2$$

▶ The slope is −2.

STUDY TIP

As a check, you can plot the points represented by the table to verify that the line through the points has a slope of −2.

b. Let $(x_1, y_1) = (-1, 2)$ and $(x_2, y_2) = (5, 2)$.

$$m = \frac{y_2 - y_1}{x_2 - x_1} = \frac{2 - 2}{5 - (-1)} = \frac{0}{6}, \text{ or } 0$$

The change in y is 0.

▶ The slope is 0.

c. Let $(x_1, y_1) = (-3, 0)$ and $(x_2, y_2) = (-3, 6)$.

$$m = \frac{y_2 - y_1}{x_2 - x_1} = \frac{6 - 0}{-3 - (-3)} = \frac{6}{0} \;\text{✗}$$

The change in x is 0.

▶ Because division by zero is undefined, the slope of the line is undefined.

CONCEPT SUMMARY

Slope

Positive slope

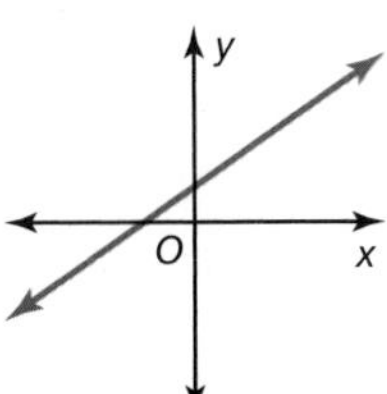

The line rises from left to right.

Negative slope

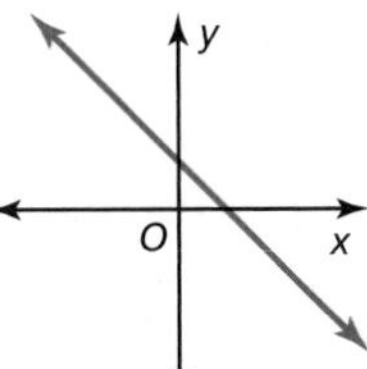

The line falls from left to right.

Slope of 0

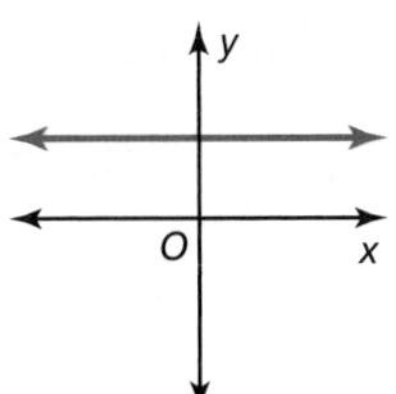

The line is horizontal.

Undefined slope

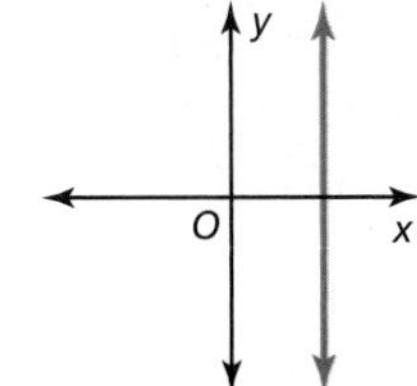

The line is vertical.

SELF-ASSESSMENT

1 I do not understand. 2 I can do it with help. 3 I can do it on my own. 4 I can teach someone else.

The points represented by each table lie on a line. How can you find the slope of each line from the table? What is the slope of each line?

7.

x	2	4	6	8
y	10	15	20	25

8.

x	5	5	5	5
y	−12	−9	−6	−3

Using the Slope-Intercept Form of a Linear Equation

KEY IDEA

Slope-Intercept Form

Words A linear equation written in the form $y = mx + b$ is in **slope-intercept form**. The slope of the line is m, and the y-intercept of the line is b.

Algebra $y = mx + b$

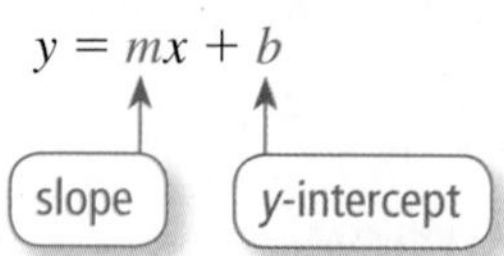

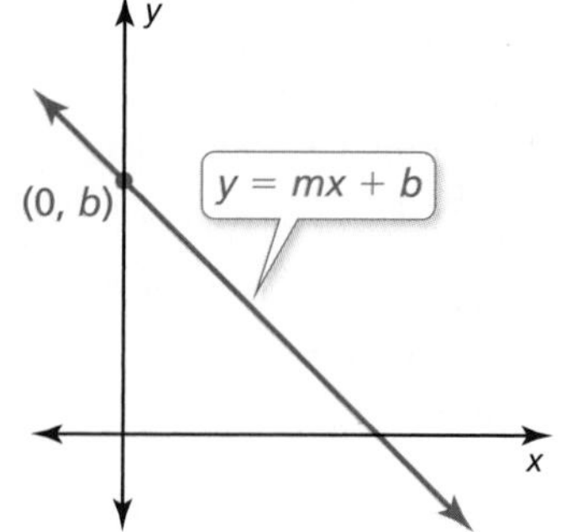

A linear equation written in the form $y = 0x + b$, or $y = b$, is a **constant function**. The graph of a constant function is a horizontal line.

EXAMPLE 3 Identifying Slopes and y-Intercepts

Find the slope and the y-intercept of the graph of each linear equation.

a. $y = 3x - 4$ **b.** $y = 6.5$ **c.** $-5x - y = -2$

SOLUTION

a. $y = mx + b$ Write the slope-intercept form.

slope y-intercept

$y = 3x + (-4)$ Rewrite the original equation in slope-intercept form.

▶ The slope is 3, and the y-intercept is -4.

b. The equation represents a constant function. The equation can also be written as $y = 0x + 6.5$.

▶ The slope is 0, and the y-intercept is 6.5.

c. Rewrite the equation in slope-intercept form by solving for y.

$-5x - y = -2$ Write the original equation.

$-y = 5x - 2$ Add $5x$ to each side.

$y = -5x + 2$ Divide each side by -1.

▶ The slope is -5, and the y-intercept is 2.

STUDY TIP

For a constant function, every input has the same output. For instance, in Example 3(b), every input has an output of 6.5.

STUDY TIP

When you rewrite a linear equation in slope-intercept form, you are expressing y as a function of x.

SELF-ASSESSMENT

1 I do not understand. 2 I can do it with help. 3 I can do it on my own. 4 I can teach someone else.

Find the slope and the y-intercept of the graph of the linear equation.

9. $y = -6x + 1$ **10.** $y = -\frac{1}{2}$ **11.** $x + 4y = -10$

12. WHICH ONE DOESN'T BELONG? Which equation does *not* belong with the other three? Explain your reasoning.

$y = -5x - 1$ $2x - y = 8$ $y = x + 4$ $y = -3x + 13$

EXAMPLE 4 Using Slope-Intercept Form to Graph an Equation

STUDY TIP

You can use the slope to find points on a line in either direction. In Example 4, note that the slope can be written as $\frac{2}{-1}$. So, you can move 1 unit left and 2 units up from (0, 4) to find the point (−1, 6).

Graph $2x + y = 4$. Identify the x-intercept.

SOLUTION

Step 1 Rewrite the equation in slope-intercept form.

$$y = -2x + 4$$

Step 2 Find the slope and the y-intercept.

$$m = -2 \text{ and } b = 4$$

Step 3 The y-intercept is 4. So, plot (0, 4).

Step 4 Use the slope to find another point on the line.

$$\text{slope} = \frac{\text{rise}}{\text{run}} = \frac{-2}{1}$$

Plot the point that is 1 unit right and 2 units down from (0, 4). Draw a line through the two points.

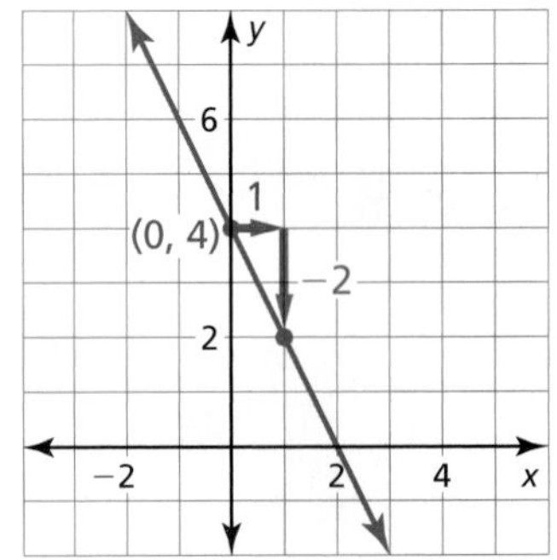

▶ The line appears to intersect the x-axis at (2, 0). So, the x-intercept is 2.

ANOTHER WAY

You can also find the x-intercept by substituting 0 for y in the equation $2x + y = 4$ and solving for x.

EXAMPLE 5 Graphing from a Verbal Description

A linear function g models a relationship in which the dependent variable increases 3 units for every 1 unit the independent variable increases. Graph g when $g(0) = 3$. Identify the slope and the intercepts of the graph.

SOLUTION

Because the function g is linear, it has a constant rate of change. Let x represent the independent variable and y represent the dependent variable.

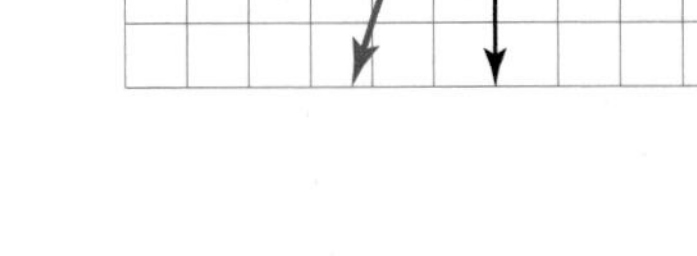

Step 1 Find the slope. When the dependent variable increases by 3, the change in y is +3. When the independent variable increases by 1, the change in x is +1.

So, the slope is $\frac{3}{1}$, or 3.

Step 2 Find the y-intercept. The statement $g(0) = 3$ indicates that when $x = 0$, $y = 3$. So, the y-intercept is 3. Plot (0, 3).

Step 3 Use the slope to find another point on the line. A slope of 3 can be written as $\frac{-3}{-1}$. Plot the point that is 1 unit left and 3 units down from (0, 3). Draw a line through the two points. The line crosses the x-axis at (−1, 0). So, the x-intercept is −1.

▶ The slope is 3, the y-intercept is 3, and the x-intercept is −1.

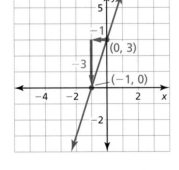

SELF-ASSESSMENT

1 I do not understand. 2 I can do it with help. 3 I can do it on my own. 4 I can teach someone else.

Graph the linear equation. Identify the x-intercept.

13. $y = 4x - 4$ **14.** $3x + y = -3$ **15.** $x + 2y = 6$

16. A linear function h models a relationship in which the dependent variable decreases 2 units for every 5 units the independent variable increases. Graph h when $h(0) = 4$. Identify the slope and the intercepts of the graph.

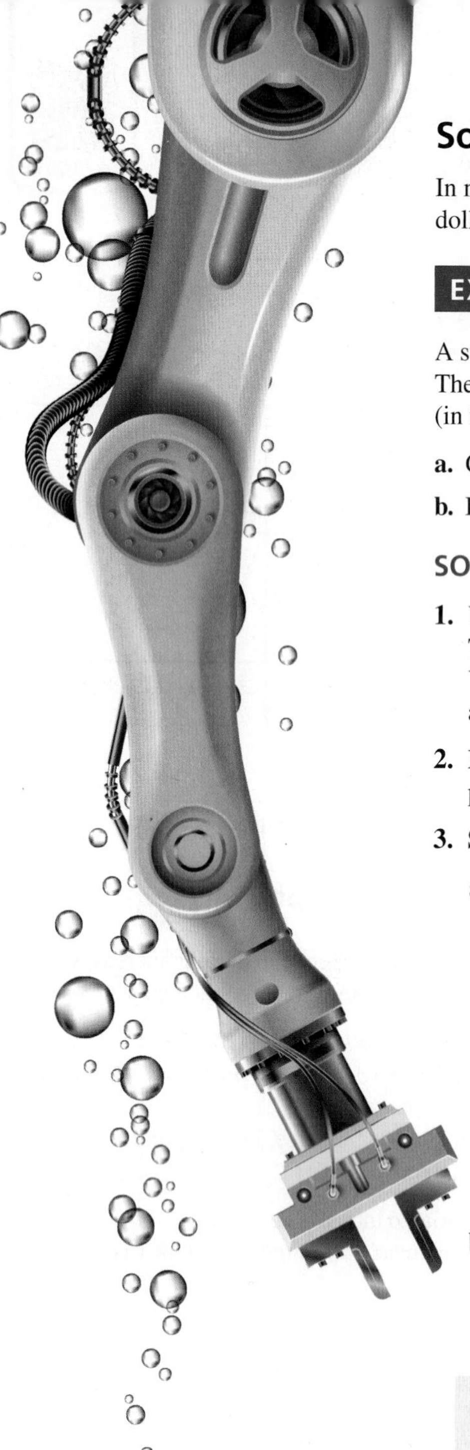

Solving Real-Life Problems

In most real-life problems, slope indicates a rate, such as miles per hour, dollars per hour, or people per year.

EXAMPLE 6 Modeling Real Life

A submersible that is exploring the ocean floor begins to ascend to the surface. The function $h(t) = 650t - 13{,}000$ models the situation, where $h(t)$ is the elevation (in feet) of the submersible t minutes from the time it begins to ascend.

a. Graph the function and find its domain and range.

b. Interpret the slope and the intercepts of the graph.

SOLUTION

1. **Understand the Problem** You know the function that models the elevation. The term $650t$ represents how many feet the submersible ascends after t minutes. You are asked to graph the function and find its domain and range. Then you are asked to interpret the slope and intercepts of the graph.

2. **Make a Plan** Graph the function using values that make sense in the context of the problem. Examine the graph to interpret the slope and the intercepts.

3. **Solve and Check**

a. The time t must be greater than or equal to 0. The elevation $h(t)$ is below sea level and must be less than or equal to 0. Use the slope of 650 and the y-intercept of $-13{,}000$ to graph the function in Quadrant IV.

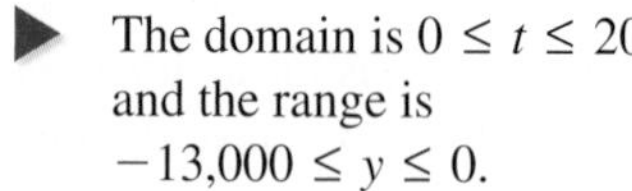

▶ The domain is $0 \le t \le 20$, and the range is $-13{,}000 \le y \le 0$.

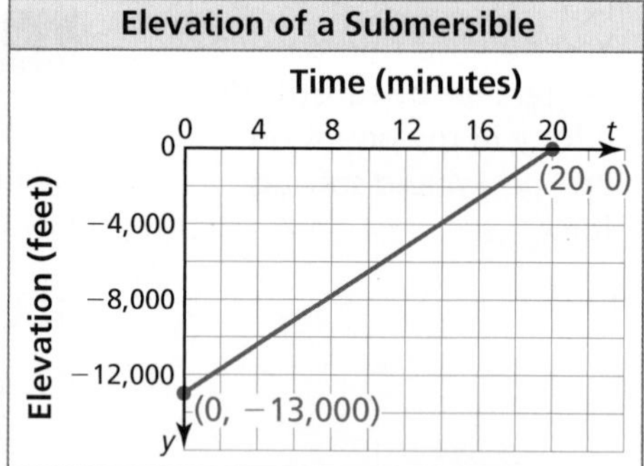

b. The slope is 650. So, the submersible ascends at a rate of 650 feet per minute. The term $-13{,}000$ is the y-intercept. So, the elevation of the submersible after 0 minutes, or when the ascent begins, is $-13{,}000$ feet. The t-intercept is 20. So, the submersible takes 20 minutes to reach an elevation of 0 feet, or sea level.

Check You can check that your graph is correct by substituting the t-intercept for t in the function. If $h(20) = 0$, then the graph is correct.

$h(20) = 650(20) - 13{,}000$ Substitute 20 for t in the original equation.

$h(20) = 0$ ✓ Simplify.

SELF-ASSESSMENT

1 I do not understand. 2 I can do it with help. 3 I can do it on my own. 4 I can teach someone else.

17. A linear function p models the elevation of a submersible as it begins to ascend to the surface. The table shows the elevation $p(t)$ (in meters), where t is the time (in minutes) since the submersible began to ascend.

a. Does this submersible ascend faster than the submersible in Example 6? Use a graph to justify your answer.

b. Both submersibles begin to ascend at the same time. Which one reaches the surface first? Explain.

Time (minutes), t	Elevation (meters), $p(t)$
0	−3200
5	−2450
10	−1700

3.6 Practice WITH CalcChat® AND CalcView®

In Exercises 1–4, describe the slope of the line. Then find the slope. *Example 1*

1.
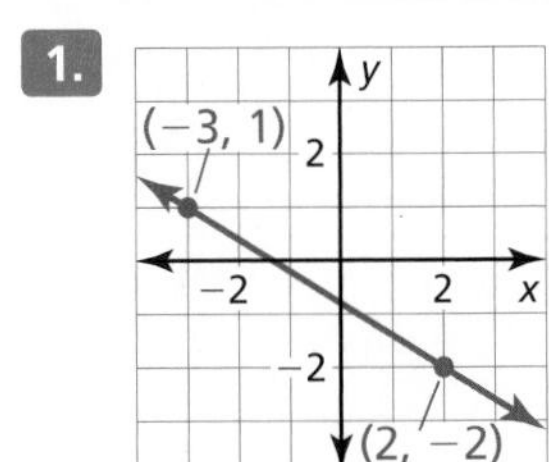

2.
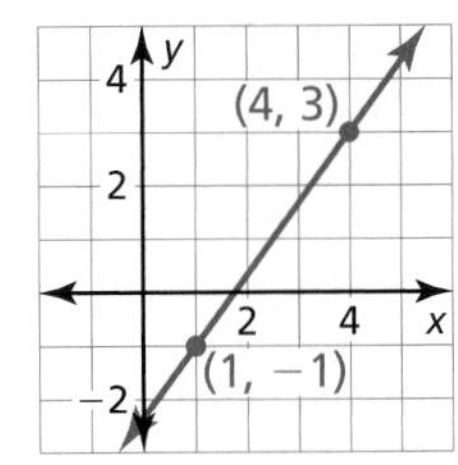

3.
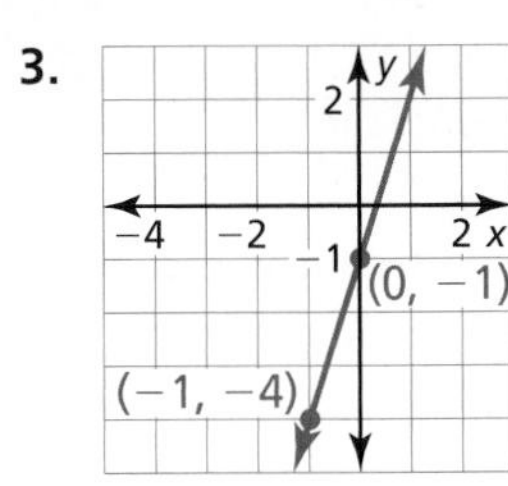

4.
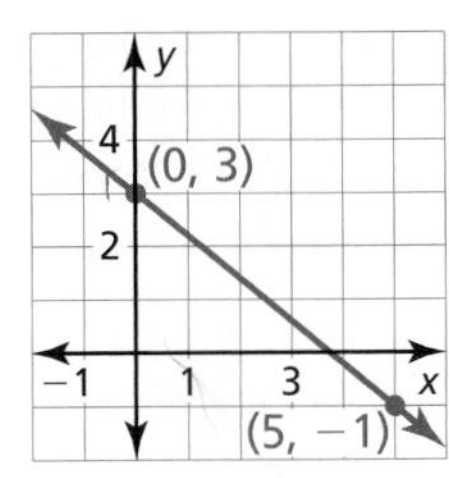

In Exercises 5 and 6, find the slope of the line that passes through the given points.

5. $(1, 4), (3, -6)$

6. $(2, -2), (-7, -5)$

In Exercises 7–10, the points represented by the table lie on a line. Find the slope of the line. *Example 2*

7.
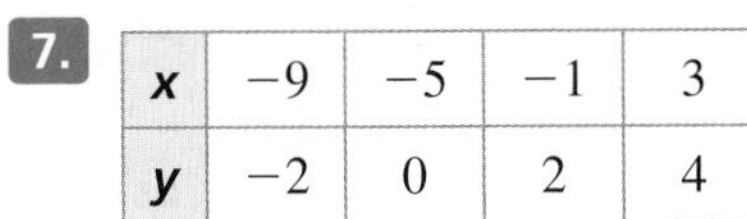

x	−9	−5	−1	3
y	−2	0	2	4

8.

x	−1	2	5	8
y	−6	−6	−6	−6

9.

x	0	0	0	0
y	−4	0	4	8

10.

x	−4	−3	−2	−1
y	2	−5	−12	−19

11. ANALYZING A GRAPH The graph shows the distance y (in miles) that a bus travels in x hours. Find and interpret the slope of the line.

Bus Trip

(2, 120)
(1, 60)
Distance (miles)
Time (hours)

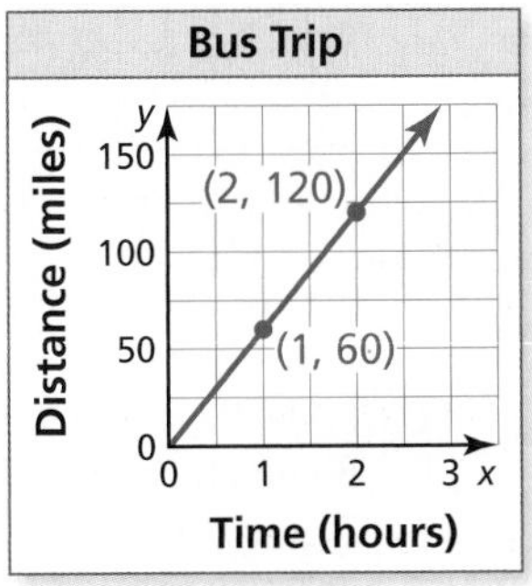

12. ANALYZING A TABLE The table shows the amount x (in hours) of time you spend at a theme park and the admission fee y (in dollars) to the park. The points represented by the table lie on a line. Find and interpret the slope of the line.

Time (hours), x	Admission (dollars), y
6	54.99
7	54.99
8	54.99

In Exercises 13–20, find the slope and the y-intercept of the graph of the linear equation. *Example 3*

13. $y = -3x + 2$

14. $y = 4x - 7$

15. $y = 6x$

16. $y = -1$

17. $-0.75x + y = 4$

18. $x + y = -6\frac{1}{2}$

19. $\frac{1}{6}x = \frac{1}{3} - y$

20. $0 = 4.5 - 2y + 4.8x$

ERROR ANALYSIS In Exercises 21 and 22, describe and correct the error in finding the slope and the y-intercept of the graph of the equation.

21.
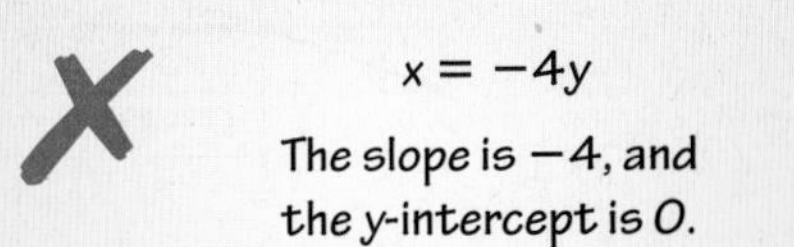

22.
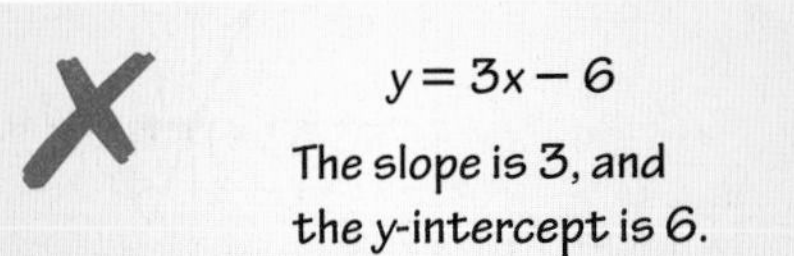

In Exercises 23–30, graph the linear equation. Identify the x-intercept. *Example 4*

23. $y = -x + 7$

24. $y = \frac{1}{2}x + 3$

25. $y = 2x$

26. $y = -x$

27. $3x + y = -1$

28. $x + 4y = 8$

29. $-y + \frac{3}{5}x = 0$

30. $2.5x - y - 7.5 = 0$

In Exercises 31 and 32, graph the function with the given description. Identify the slope and the intercepts of the graph. *Example 5*

31. A linear function f models a relationship in which the dependent variable decreases 4 units for every 2 units the independent variable increases, and $f(0) = -2$.

32. A linear function h models a relationship in which the dependent variable increases 1 unit for every 5 units the independent variable decreases, and $h(0) = 3$.

33. MODELING REAL LIFE A linear function r models the growth of your right index fingernail. The length of the fingernail increases 0.7 millimeter every week. Graph r when $r(0) = 12$. Identify the slope and interpret the y-intercept of the graph.

34. MODELING REAL LIFE A linear function m models the amount of milk sold by a farm per month. The amount decreases 500 gallons for every \$1 increase in price. Graph m when $m(0) = 3000$. Identify the slope and interpret the intercepts of the graph.

ERROR ANALYSIS In Exercises 35 and 36, describe and correct the error in graphing the function.

35.

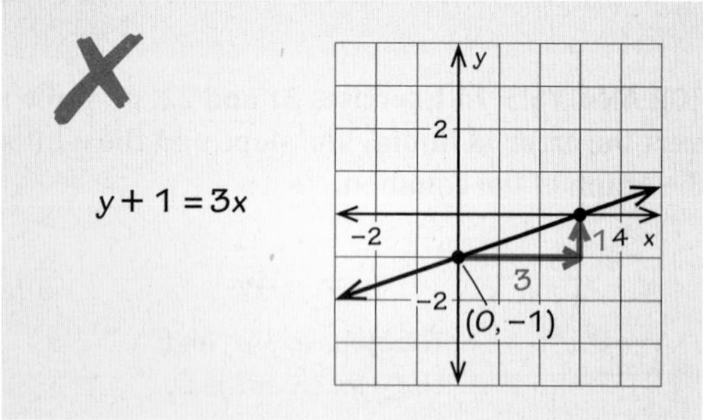

36.

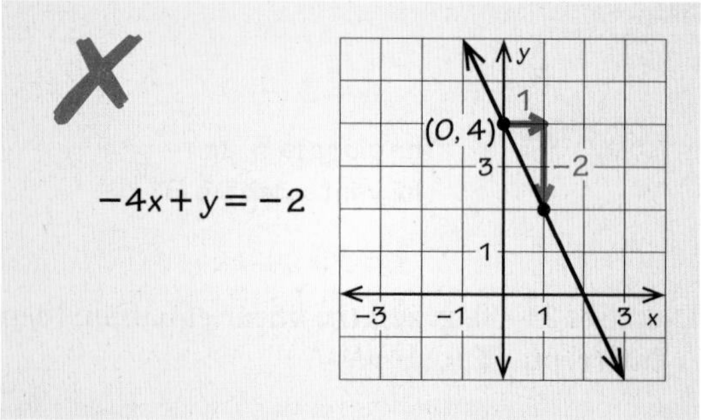

37. MODELING REAL LIFE The function $d(t) = \frac{1}{2}t + 6$ represents the depth (in inches) of snow on the ground during a 9-hour snowfall, where t is the time (in hours) after the snowfall begins. *Example 6*

a. Graph the function and find its domain and range.

b. Interpret the terms and coefficient in the equation.

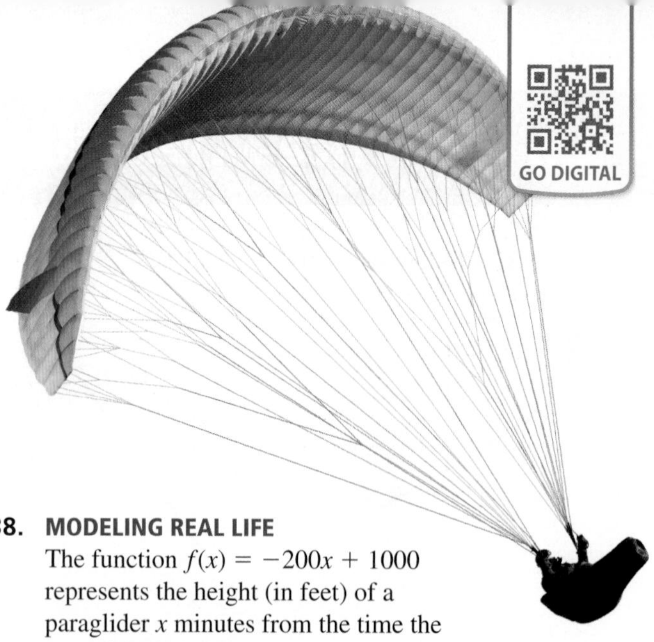

GO DIGITAL

38. MODELING REAL LIFE
The function $f(x) = -200x + 1000$ represents the height (in feet) of a paraglider x minutes from the time the paraglider begins to descend.

a. Graph the function and find its domain and range.

b. Interpret the terms and coefficient in the equation, and the x-intercept of the graph.

39. COMPARING METHODS Describe two ways to graph the equation $4x - 6y = 18$. Which method do you prefer? Explain.

40. COMPARING FUNCTIONS A linear function models the cost of renting a truck from Moving Company A. The table shows the cost y (in dollars) when you drive the truck x miles. The function $c(x) = 0.5x + 70$ represents the cost (in dollars) of renting a truck from Moving Company B, where x is the number of miles you drive the truck. Graph each function. Which company charges a greater initial fee? Which company charges more per mile?

Miles, x	Cost (dollars), y
0	40
50	80
100	120

41. COLLEGE PREP Which of the following linear functions has a slope of $-\frac{2}{3}$ and a y-intercept of 2? Select all that apply.

Ⓐ

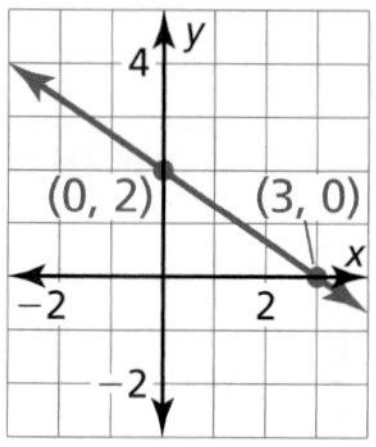

Ⓑ

x	y
−2	6
0	3
2	0
4	−3

Ⓒ $f(x)$ decreases by 3 units for every 2 units x increases, and $f(0) = 2$.

Ⓓ $-y + 2 = \frac{2}{3}x$

42. WRITING Describe the end behavior of the function $y = mx + b$ when (a) $m > 0$ and (b) $m < 0$.

43. CONNECTING CONCEPTS The graph shows the relationship between the width y (in inches) and the length x (in inches) of a rectangle. The perimeter of a second rectangle is 10 inches less than the perimeter of the first rectangle.

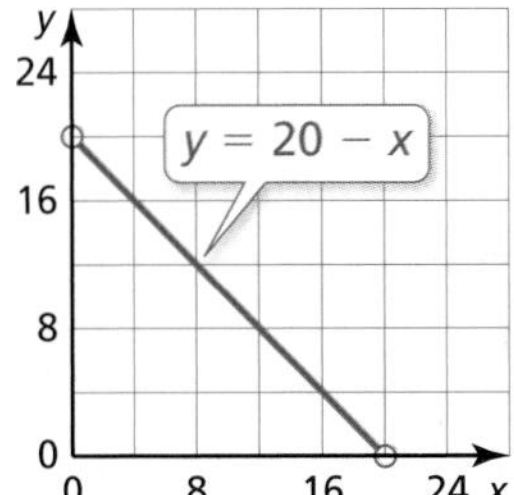

a. Graph the relationship between the width and length of the second rectangle.

b. How does your graph in part (a) compare to the graph shown?

44. CONNECTING CONCEPTS The graph shows the relationship between the base length x (in meters) and the lengths y (in meters) of the two equal sides of an isosceles triangle. The perimeter of a second isosceles triangle is 8 meters more than the perimeter of the first triangle.

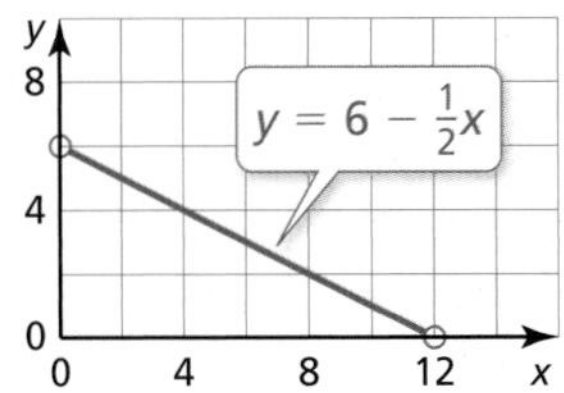

a. Graph the relationship between the base length and the side lengths of the second triangle.

b. How does your graph in part (a) compare to the graph shown?

45. CONNECTING CONCEPTS Graph the equations in the same coordinate plane. What is the area of the enclosed figure?

$3y = -9$

$2y - 14 = 4x$

$-4x + 5 - y = 0$

$y - 1 = 0$

46. MAKING AN ARGUMENT Your friend says that you can write the equation of any line in slope-intercept form. Is your friend correct? Explain your reasoning.

47. ANALYZING EQUATIONS Which equations could be represented by each graph? (The graphs are not drawn to scale.)

$y = -3x + 8$	$y = -x - \frac{4}{3}$
$y = -7x$	$y = 2x - 4$
$y = \frac{7}{4}x - \frac{1}{4}$	$y = \frac{1}{3}x + 5$
$y = -4x - 9$	$y = 6$

a. **b.** **c.** **d.**

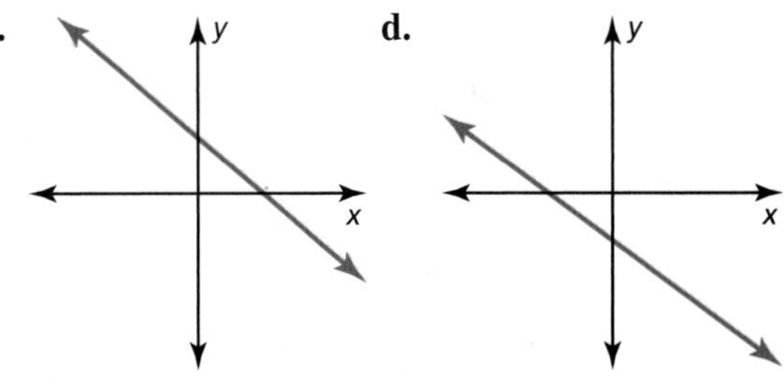

48. HOW DO YOU SEE IT?

You commute to school by walking and by riding a bus. The graph represents your commute.

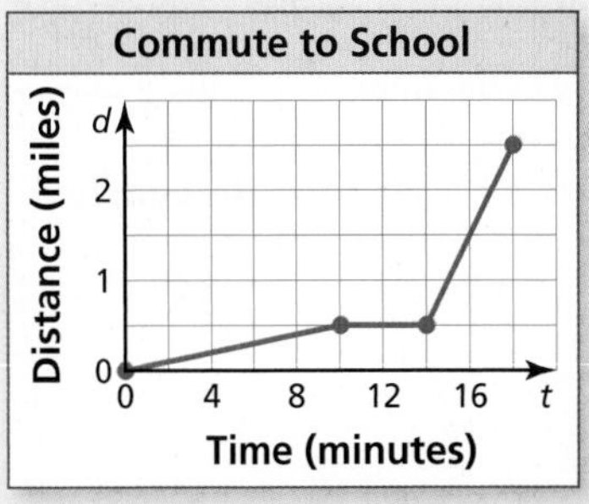

a. Describe your commute in words.

b. Calculate and interpret the slopes of the different parts of the graph.

MP PROBLEM SOLVING **In Exercises 49 and 50, find the value of k so that the graph of the equation has the given slope or y-intercept.**

49. $16kx - 4y = 20;\ m = \frac{1}{2}$

50. $\frac{2}{3}x + 2y - \frac{5}{3}k = 0;\ b = -10$

51. ABSTRACT REASONING To show that the slope of a line is constant, let (x_1, y_1) and (x_2, y_2) be any two points on the line $y = mx + b$. Use the equation of the line to express y_1 in terms of x_1 and y_2 in terms of x_2. Then show that the slope between the points is m.

52. THOUGHT PROVOKING
Your family goes on vacation to a beach 300 miles from your house. You stop along the way and reach your destination 6 hours after departing. Draw a graph that describes your trip. Explain what each part of your graph represents.

53. DIG DEEPER The graphs of the functions $g(x) = 6x + a$ and $h(x) = 2x + b$, where a and b are constants, are shown. They intersect at the point (p, q). Which is greater, $g(p + 2)$ or $h(p + 2)$? How much greater? Explain your reasoning.

GO DIGITAL

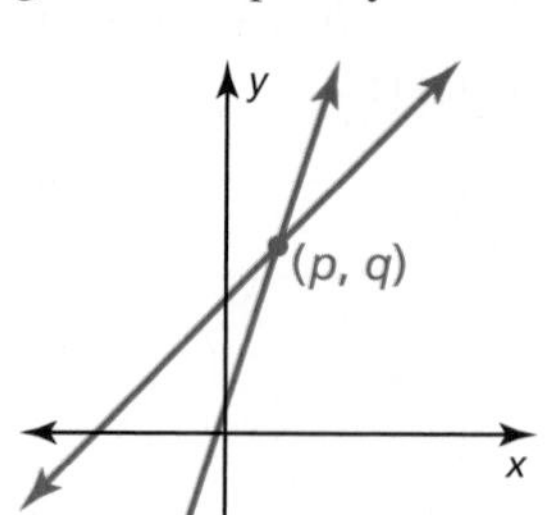

REVIEW & REFRESH

WATCH

In Exercises 54–56, find the coordinates of the figure after the transformation.

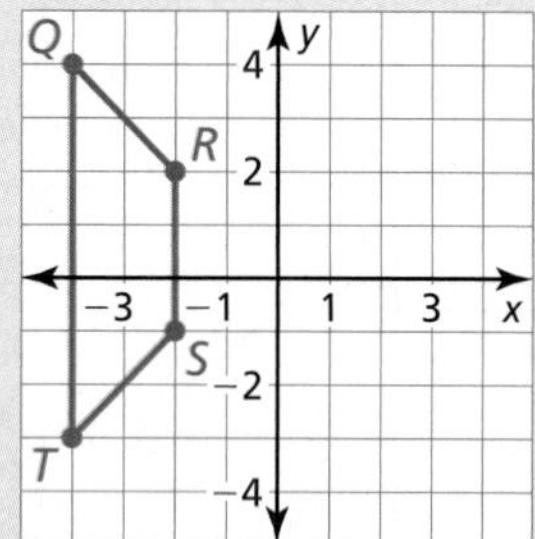

54. Translate the trapezoid 3 units right.

55. Dilate the trapezoid with respect to the origin using a scale factor of $\frac{1}{2}$.

56. Reflect the trapezoid in the y-axis.

In Exercises 57–60, solve the equation.

57. $-\frac{x}{7} = 2.5$

58. $\frac{1}{3}n - 4 = -4 + \frac{1}{3}n$

59. $-4(7 - a) + 10 = -12$

60. $5(2q - 1) = -3(q + 6)$

61. Find the slope and y-intercept of the graph of $7x - 4y = 10$.

62. The circumference of the circle is at least 14π centimeters. Find the possible values of r.

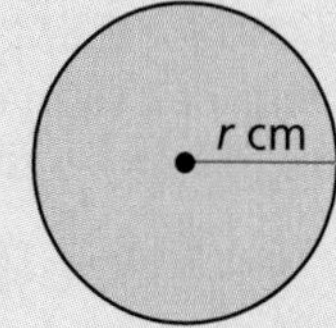

63. MP REASONING Let f be a function. Use each statement to write a point on the graph of f.

a. $f(3)$ is equal to -8.

b. A solution of the equation $f(x) = \frac{3}{4}$ is -1.

64. Graph $y = -\frac{3}{2}x - 6$. Identify the x-intercept.

In Exercises 65 and 66, determine whether the table or equation represents a *linear* or *nonlinear* function. Explain.

65.

x	−2	−1	0	1
y	−4	−1	3	8

66. $\frac{x}{4} + \frac{y}{12} = 1$

67. MODELING REAL LIFE
The table shows the prices of four video games. You have a coupon for 20% off one game, and you want to spend a total of \$30 with an absolute deviation of at most \$5. Which video games can you buy? Use an absolute value inequality to justify your answer.

Video game	Price
A	\$44.99
B	\$41.99
C	\$49.99
D	\$39.99

68. Use intercepts to graph the equation $-3x + 2y = 9$. Label the points corresponding to the intercepts.

In Exercises 69 and 70, graph the inequality.

69. $h < -4$

70. $\frac{9}{2} \leq t$

3.7 Transformations of Linear Functions

Learning Target Graph transformations of linear functions.

Success Criteria
- I can identify a transformation of a linear graph.
- I can graph transformations of linear functions.
- I can explain how translations, reflections, stretches, and shrinks affect graphs of functions.

EXPLORE IT! Comparing Graphs of Functions

Work with a partner.

a. MP CHOOSE TOOLS The graph of $f(x) = x$ is shown. Graph f and g on the same set of coordinate axes. Compare the graphs of f and g.

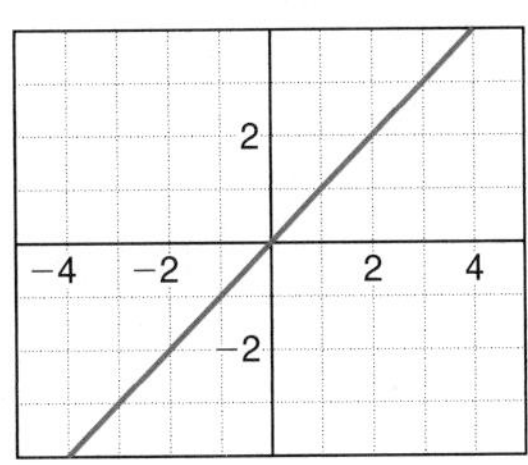

i. $g(x) = x + 4$ **ii.** $g(x) = 2x$ **iii.** $g(x) = -x$

b. Write any linear function m in terms of x. Compare the graphs of m and n. Explain your reasoning.

i. $n(x) = m(x) + 3$ **ii.** $n(x) = m(x) - 3$

iii. $n(x) = \frac{1}{3} \cdot m(x)$ **iv.** $n(x) = 3 \cdot m(x)$

v. $n(x) = -m(x)$ **vi.** $n(x) = m(-x)$

c. Discuss your results in part (b) with other students. What do you notice?

d. How does the graph of a function p compare to the graph of each of the following functions? Explain your reasoning.

i. $q(x) = p(x) + k$ **ii.** $q(x) = k \cdot p(x)$, where $k > 0$

iii. $q(x) = -p(x)$ **iv.** $q(x) = p(-x)$

Math Practice

Look for Structure
How can you use the right side of each equation in part (b) to compare the values of $n(x)$ and $m(x)$? What does this tell you about the graph of n?

Translations and Reflections

A **family of functions** is a group of functions with similar characteristics. The most basic function in a family of functions is the **parent function**. For nonconstant linear functions, the parent function is $f(x) = x$. The graphs of all other nonconstant linear functions are *transformations* of the graph of the parent function. A **transformation** changes the size, shape, position, or orientation of a graph.

WORDS AND MATH

Used as an adjective, *parent* can refer to "being the original source." A *parent function* is the original source of the family of functions.

Vocabulary

KEY IDEAS

A **translation** is a transformation that shifts a graph horizontally or vertically.

Horizontal Translations

The graph of $y = f(x - h)$ is a horizontal translation of the graph of $y = f(x)$, where $h \neq 0$.

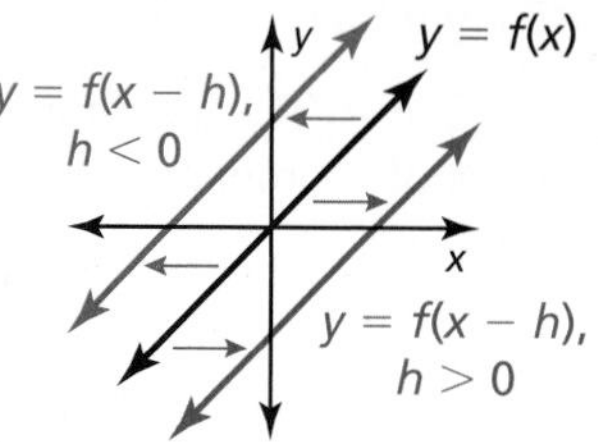

Subtracting h from the *inputs* before evaluating the function shifts the graph left when $h < 0$ and right when $h > 0$.

Vertical Translations

The graph of $y = f(x) + k$ is a vertical translation of the graph of $y = f(x)$, where $k \neq 0$.

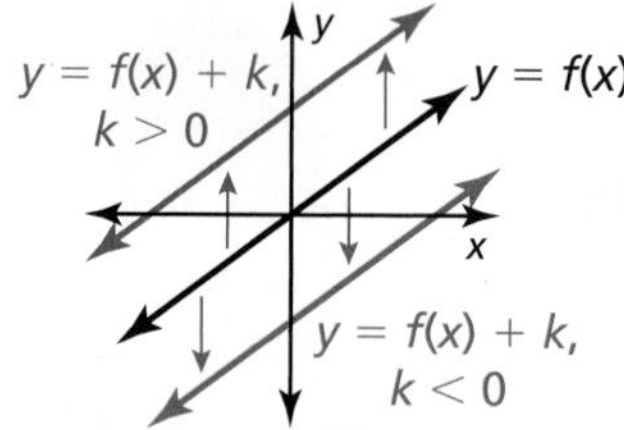

Adding k to the *outputs* shifts the graph down when $k < 0$ and up when $k > 0$.

EXAMPLE 1 Describing Horizontal and Vertical Translations

Let $f(x) = 2x - 1$. Graph (a) $g(x) = f(x) + 3$ and (b) $t(x) = f(x + 3)$. Describe the transformations from the graph of f to the graphs of g and t.

SOLUTION

a. The function g is of the form $y = f(x) + k$, where $k = 3$. So, the graph of g is a vertical translation 3 units up of the graph of f.

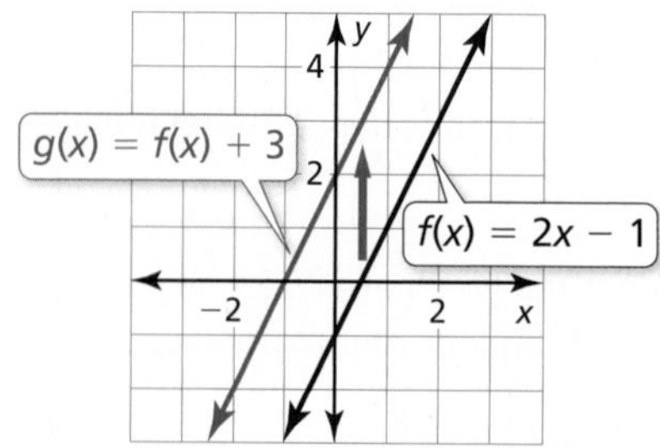

b. The function t is of the form $y = f(x - h)$, where $h = -3$. So, the graph of t is a horizontal translation 3 units left of the graph of f.

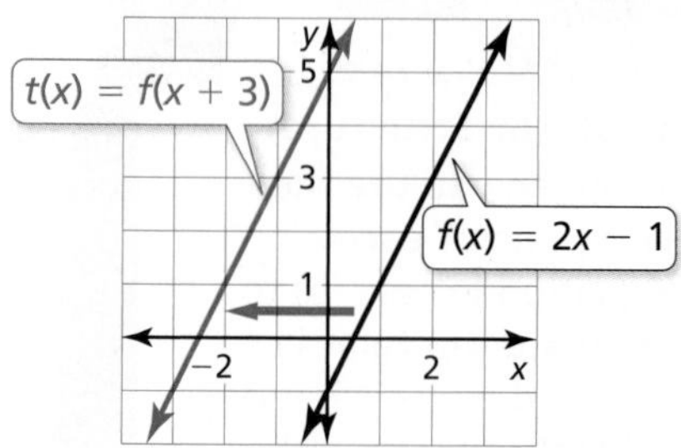

SELF-ASSESSMENT 1 I do not understand. 2 I can do it with help. 3 I can do it on my own. 4 I can teach someone else.

Using f, graph (a) g and (b) h. Describe the transformations from the graph of f to the graphs of g and h.

1. $f(x) = 3x + 1$; $g(x) = f(x) - 2$; $h(x) = f(x - 2)$

2. $f(x) = -2x$; $g(x) = f(x) + 1$; $h(x) = f(x + 1)$

KEY IDEAS

A **reflection** is a transformation that flips a graph over a line called the *line of reflection.*

STUDY TIP

A reflected point is the same distance from the line of reflection as the original point but on the opposite side of the line.

Reflections in the x-Axis

The graph of $y = -f(x)$ is a reflection in the x-axis of the graph of $y = f(x)$.

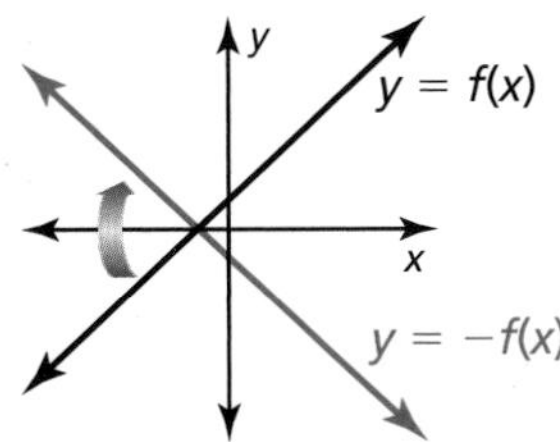

Multiplying the outputs by -1 changes their signs.

Reflections in the y-Axis

The graph of $y = f(-x)$ is a reflection in the y-axis of the graph of $y = f(x)$.

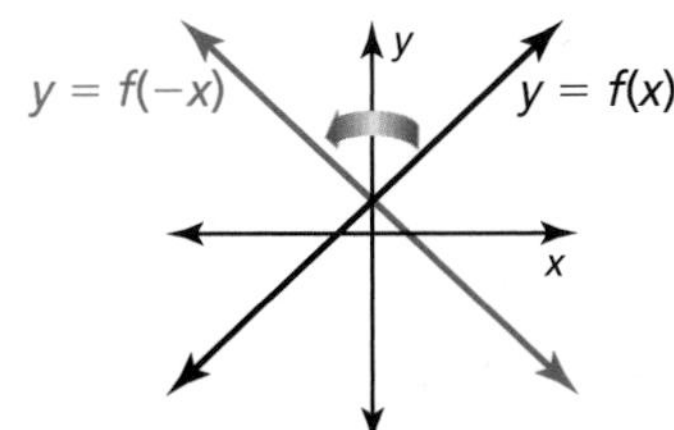

Multiplying the inputs by -1 changes their signs.

EXAMPLE 2 Describing Reflections in the x-Axis and the y-Axis

Let $f(x) = \frac{1}{2}x + 1$. Graph (a) $g(x) = -f(x)$ and (b) $t(x) = f(-x)$. Describe the transformations from the graph of f to the graphs of g and t.

SOLUTION

a. To find the outputs of g, multiply the outputs of f by -1. The graph of g consists of the points $(x, -f(x))$.

x	-4	-2	0
$f(x)$	-1	0	1
$-f(x)$	1	0	-1

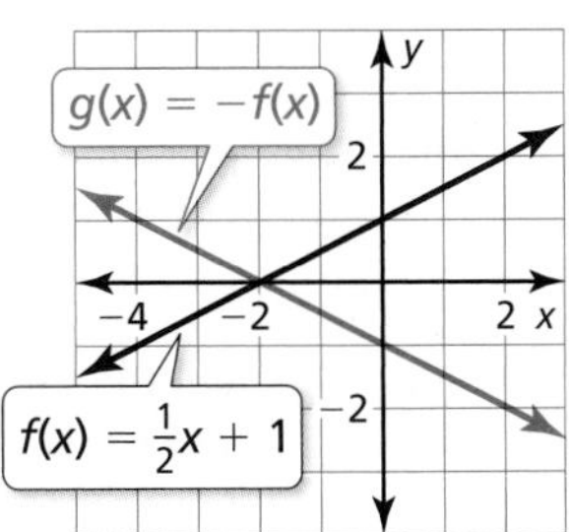

▶ The graph of g is a reflection in the x-axis of the graph of f.

b. To find the outputs of t, multiply the inputs by -1 and then evaluate f. The graph of t consists of the points $(x, f(-x))$.

x	-2	0	2
$-x$	2	0	-2
$f(-x)$	2	1	0

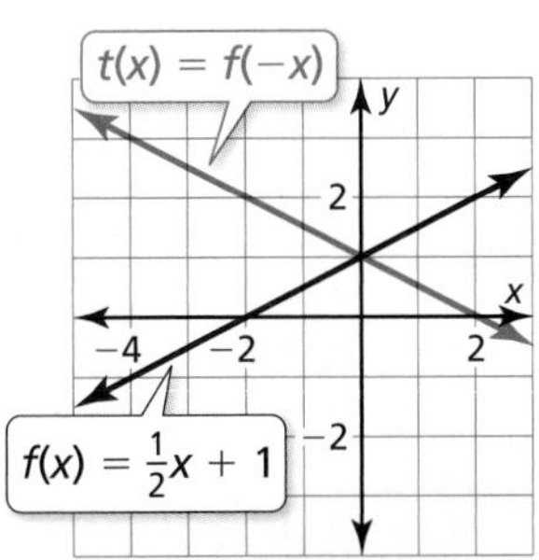

▶ The graph of t is a reflection in the y-axis of the graph of f.

SELF-ASSESSMENT

1 I do not understand. 2 I can do it with help. 3 I can do it on my own. 4 I can teach someone else.

Using f, graph g. Describe the transformation from the graph of f to the graph of g.

3. $f(x) = \frac{3}{2}x + 2$; $g(x) = -f(x)$

4. $f(x) = -4x - 2$; $g(x) = f(-x)$

5. **OPEN-ENDED** Write a linear function for which a reflection in the x-axis has the same graph as a reflection in the y-axis.

Stretches and Shrinks

You can transform a function by multiplying all the inputs (x-coordinates) by the same factor a. When $a > 1$, the transformation is a **horizontal shrink** because the graph shrinks toward the y-axis. When $0 < a < 1$, the transformation is a **horizontal stretch** because the graph stretches away from the y-axis. In each case, the y-intercept stays the same.

You can also transform a function by multiplying all the outputs (y-coordinates) by the same factor a. When $a > 1$, the transformation is a **vertical stretch** because the graph stretches away from the x-axis. When $0 < a < 1$, the transformation is a **vertical shrink** because the graph shrinks toward the x-axis. In each case, the x-intercept stays the same.

KEY IDEAS

Horizontal Stretches and Shrinks

The graph of $y = f(ax)$ is a horizontal stretch or shrink by a factor of $\frac{1}{a}$ of the graph of $y = f(x)$, where $a > 0$ and $a \neq 1$.

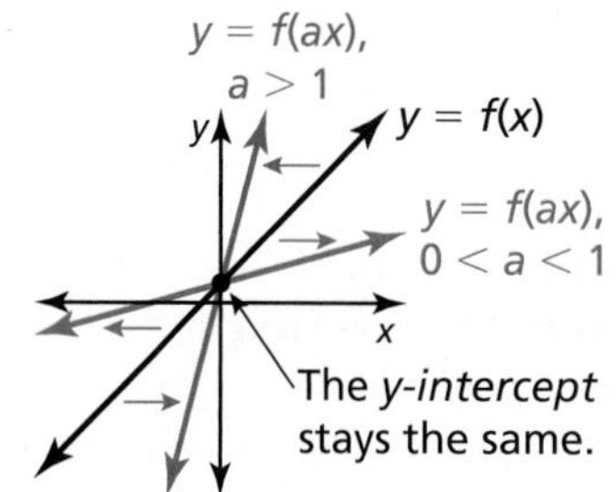

Vertical Stretches and Shrinks

The graph of $y = a \cdot f(x)$ is a vertical stretch or shrink by a factor of a of the graph of $y = f(x)$, where $a > 0$ and $a \neq 1$.

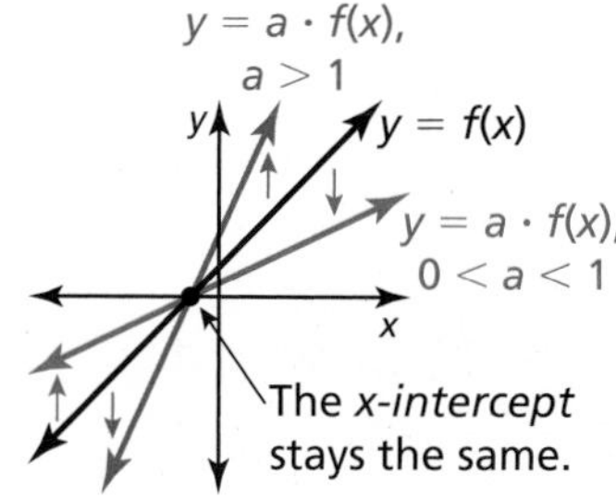

STUDY TIP

The graphs of $y = f(-ax)$ and $y = -a \cdot f(x)$ represent a stretch or shrink *and* a reflection in the x- or y-axis of the graph of $y = f(x)$.

EXAMPLE 3 Describing Horizontal and Vertical Stretches

Let $f(x) = x - 1$. Graph (a) $g(x) = f\left(\frac{1}{3}x\right)$ and (b) $h(x) = 3f(x)$. Describe the transformations from the graph of f to the graphs of g and h.

SOLUTION

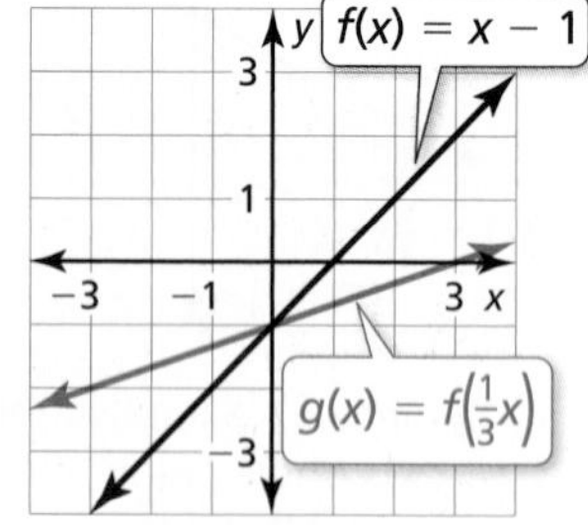

a. To find the outputs of g, multiply the inputs by $\frac{1}{3}$. Then evaluate f. The graph of g consists of the points $\left(x, f\left(\frac{1}{3}x\right)\right)$.

x	-3	0	3
$\frac{1}{3}x$	-1	0	1
$f\left(\frac{1}{3}x\right)$	-2	-1	0

▶ The graph of g is a horizontal stretch of the graph of f by a factor of $1 \div \frac{1}{3} = 3$.

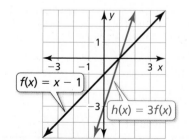

b. To find the outputs of h, multiply the outputs of f by 3. The graph of h consists of the points $(x, 3f(x))$.

x	0	1	2
$f(x)$	-1	0	1
$3f(x)$	-3	0	3

▶ The graph of h is a vertical stretch of the graph of f by a factor of 3.

EXAMPLE 4 Describing Horizontal and Vertical Shrinks

Let $f(x) = x + 2$. Graph (a) $g(x) = f(2x)$ and (b) $h(x) = \frac{1}{4}f(x)$. Describe the transformations from the graph of f to the graphs of g and h.

SOLUTION

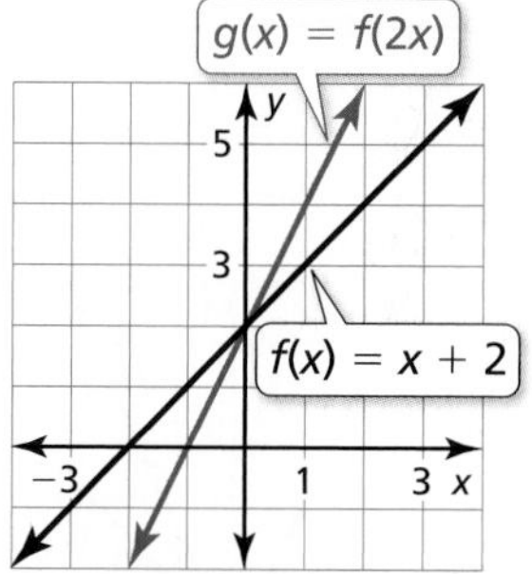

a. To find the outputs of g, multiply the inputs by 2. Then evaluate f. The graph of g consists of the points $(x, f(2x))$.

▶ The graph of g is a horizontal shrink of the graph of f by a factor of $\frac{1}{2}$.

x	−1	0	1
$2x$	−2	0	2
$f(2x)$	0	2	4

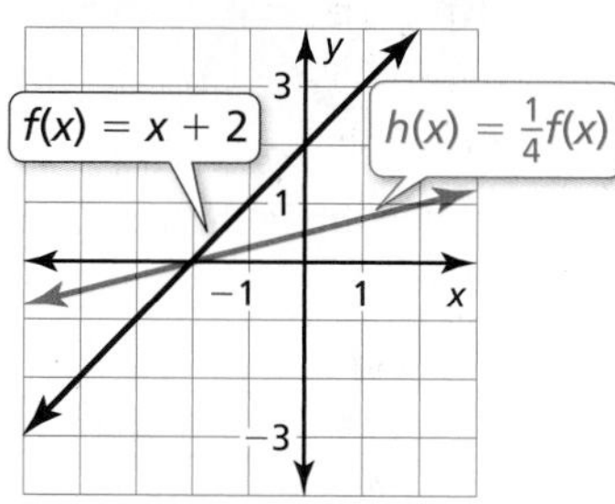

b. To find the outputs of h, multiply the outputs of f by $\frac{1}{4}$. The graph of h consists of the points $\left(x, \frac{1}{4}f(x)\right)$.

▶ The graph of h is a vertical shrink of the graph of f by a factor of $\frac{1}{4}$.

x	−2	0	2
$f(x)$	0	2	4
$\frac{1}{4}f(x)$	0	$\frac{1}{2}$	1

SELF-ASSESSMENT

1 I do not understand. 2 I can do it with help. 3 I can do it on my own. 4 I can teach someone else.

Using f, graph (a) g and (b) h. Describe the transformations from the graph of f to the graphs of g and h.

6. $f(x) = 4x - 2$; $g(x) = f\left(\frac{1}{2}x\right)$; $h(x) = 2f(x)$

7. $f(x) = -3x + 4$; $g(x) = f(3x)$; $h(x) = \frac{1}{2}f(x)$

8. WRITING How does the value of a in the equation $y = h(ax)$ affect the graph of $y = h(x)$? How does the value of a in the equation $y = a \cdot h(x)$ affect the graph of $y = h(x)$?

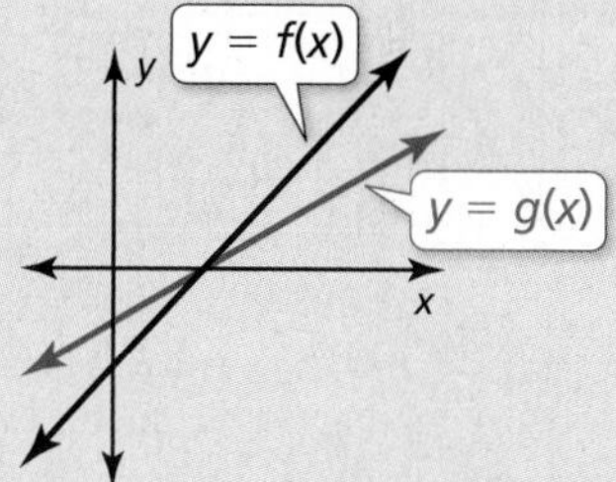

9. MP REASONING The functions f and g are linear functions. The graph of g is a vertical shrink of the graph of f. What can you say about the intercepts of the graphs of f and g? Is this always true? Explain.

Combining Transformations

KEY IDEA

Transformations of Graphs

The graph of $y = a \cdot f(x - h) + k$ or the graph of $y = f(ax - h) + k$ can be obtained from the graph of $y = f(x)$ by performing these steps.

Step 1 Translate the graph of $y = f(x)$ horizontally h units.

Step 2 Use $|a|$ to stretch or shrink the resulting graph from Step 1.

Step 3 Reflect the resulting graph from Step 2 when $a < 0$.

Step 4 Translate the resulting graph from Step 3 vertically k units.

STUDY TIP

You can perform transformations on the graph of *any* function f using these steps.

EXAMPLE 5 Combining Transformations

GO DIGITAL

Graph $f(x) = x$ and $g(x) = -2x + 3$. Describe the transformations from the graph of f to the graph of g.

SOLUTION

Note that you can rewrite g as $g(x) = -2f(x) + 3$.

ANOTHER WAY

You can also rewrite g as $g(x) = f(-2x) + 3$. So, you can write a different combination of transformations that results in the same graph in Example 5.

Step 1 There is no horizontal translation from the graph of f to the graph of g.

Step 2 Stretch the graph of f vertically by a factor of 2 to get the graph of $h(x) = 2x$.

Step 3 Reflect the graph of h in the x-axis to get the graph of $r(x) = -2x$.

Step 4 Translate the graph of r vertically 3 units up to get the graph of $g(x) = -2x + 3$.

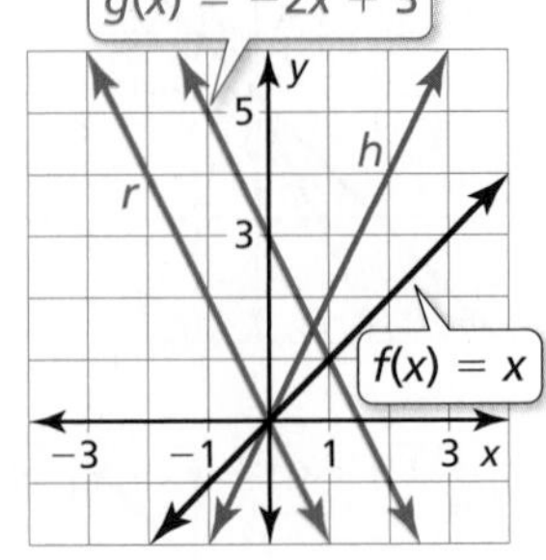

▶ The graph of g is a vertical stretch by a factor of 2, a reflection in the x-axis, and a translation 3 units up of the graph of f.

EXAMPLE 6 Modeling Real Life

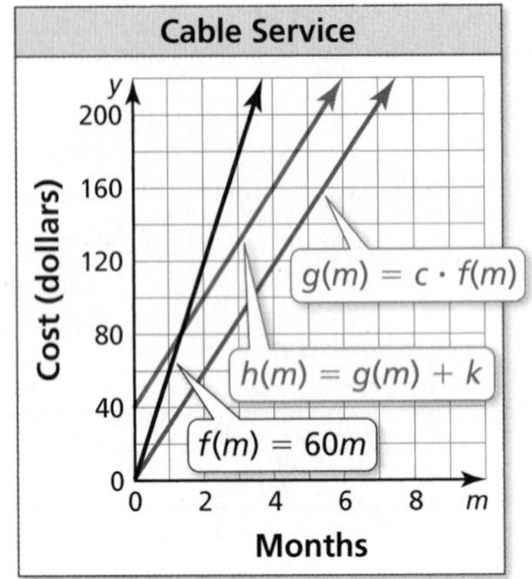

The cost (in dollars) of cable service for m months is represented by the function f. To attract new customers, the cable company multiplies the monthly fee by a factor of c. The company then adds an installation fee of k dollars. Use the graph to find and interpret the values of c and k.

SOLUTION

To find c, compare f and g. The function $g(m) = c \cdot f(m)$ indicates that the graph of g is a vertical stretch or shrink of the graph of f. The graphs of f and g show that for any number of months, the new cost is one-half of the original cost. For example, the cost for two months ($m = 2$) decreases from \$120 to \$60. So, $c = \frac{1}{2}$.

To find k, compare g and h. The function $h(m) = g(m) + k$ indicates that the graph of h is a vertical translation of the graph of g. The graphs of g and h show that for any number of months, the cost increases \$40. For example, the cost for two months increases from \$60 to \$100. So, $k = 40$.

▶ The factor $c = \frac{1}{2}$ indicates that the monthly price is halved. The constant $k = 40$ indicates that the installation fee is \$40.

SELF-ASSESSMENT

1 I do not understand. 2 I can do it with help. 3 I can do it on my own. 4 I can teach someone else.

10. Graph $f(x) = x$ and $h(x) = \frac{1}{4}x - 2$. Describe the transformations from the graph of f to the graph of h.

11. A company pays x dollars per unit for a product. The selling price is represented by the function p.

a. What does $f(x) = x$ represent in this situation? Describe transformations of the graph of f that result in the graph of p.

b. How does the company determine the selling price of a product?

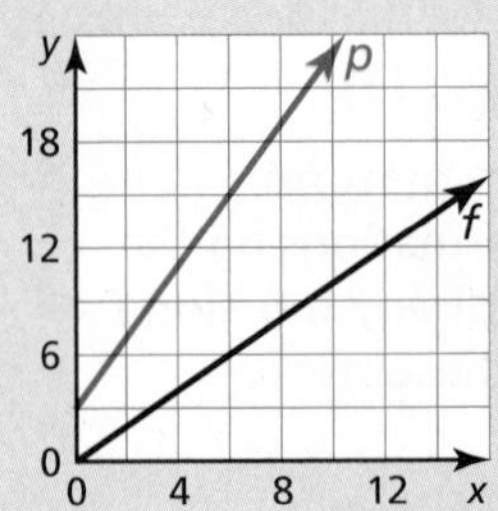

3.7 Practice WITH CalcChat® AND CalcView®

In Exercises 1–6, use the graphs of *f* and *g* to describe the transformation from the graph of *f* to the graph of *g*. *Example 1*

1.

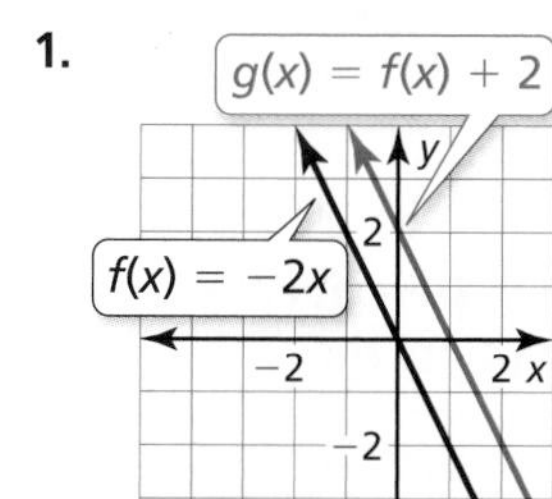

2.

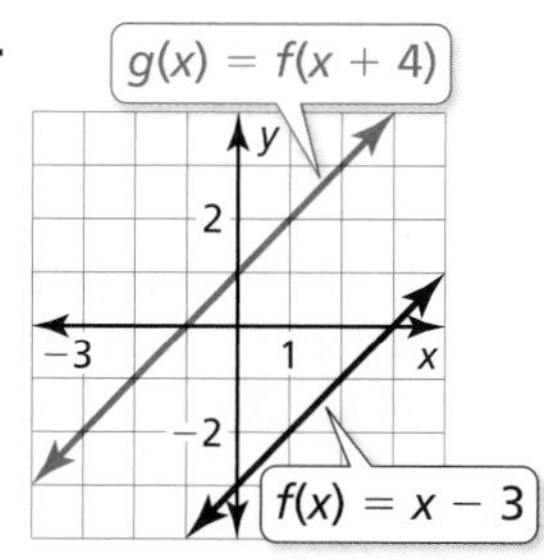

3. $f(x) = \frac{1}{3}x + 3$; $g(x) = f(x) - 3$

4. $f(x) = -3x + 4$; $g(x) = f(x) + 1$

5. $f(x) = -x - 2$; $g(x) = f(x + 5)$

6. $f(x) = \frac{1}{2}x - 5$; $g(x) = f(x - 3)$

7. MODELING REAL LIFE You and your friend start biking from the same location. Your distance (in miles) after t minutes is represented by $d(t) = \frac{1}{5}t$. Your friend starts biking 5 minutes after you. Her distance is represented by $f(t) = d(t - 5)$. Describe the transformation from the graph of d to the graph of f.

8. MODELING REAL LIFE The total cost (in dollars) to bowl n games is represented by $C(n) = 4.5n + 2.5$. The shoe rental price increases \$0.50. The new total cost is represented by $T(n) = C(n) + 0.5$. Describe the transformation from the graph of C to the graph of T.

Bowling: \$4.50 per game
Shoe Rental: \$2.50

In Exercises 9–12, use the graphs of *f* and *h* to describe the transformation from the graph of *f* to the graph of *h*. *Example 2*

9.

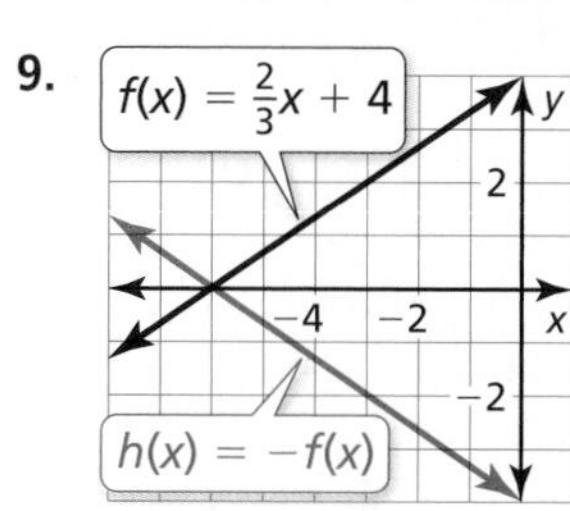

10.

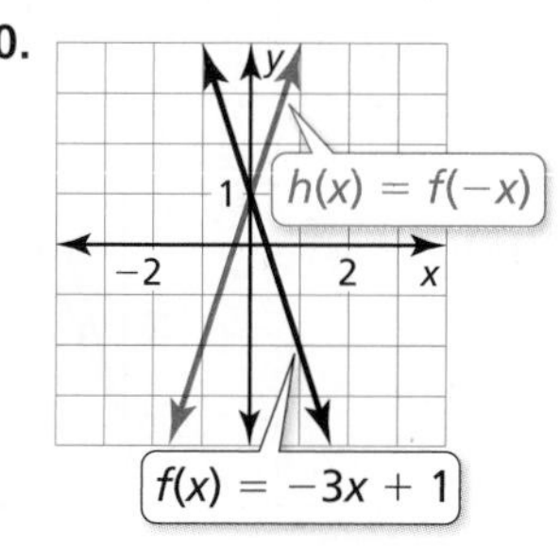

11. $f(x) = -5 - x$; $h(x) = f(-x)$

12. $f(x) = \frac{1}{4}x - 2$; $h(x) = -f(x)$

In Exercises 13–18, use the graphs of *f* and *r* to describe the transformation from the graph of *f* to the graph of *r*. *Example 3*

13.

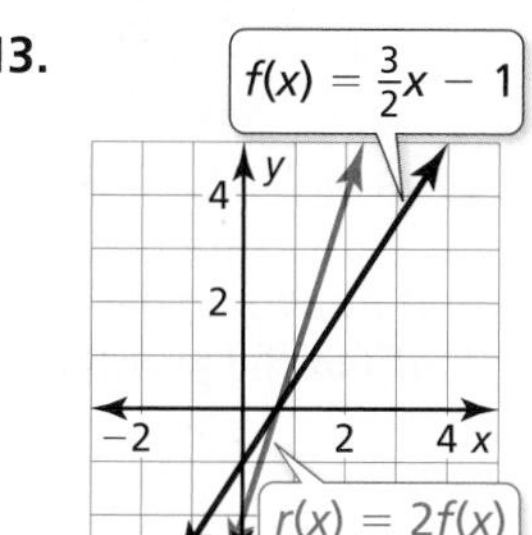

14.

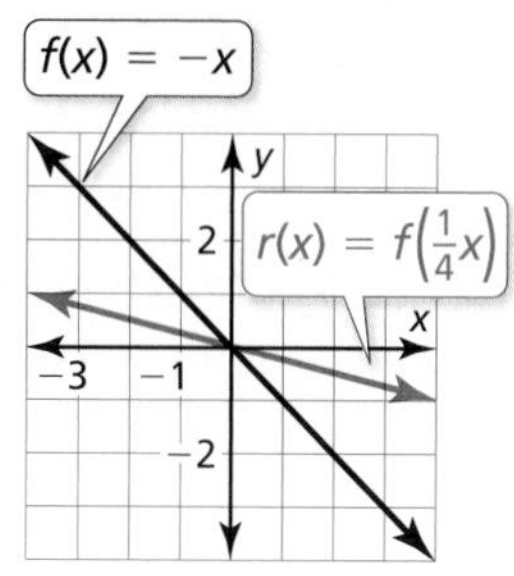

15. $f(x) = -2x - 4$; $r(x) = f\left(\frac{1}{2}x\right)$

16. $f(x) = 3x + 5$; $r(x) = f\left(\frac{1}{3}x\right)$

17. $f(x) = \frac{2}{3}x + 1$; $r(x) = 3f(x)$

18. $f(x) = -\frac{1}{4}x - 2$; $r(x) = 4f(x)$

In Exercises 19–24, use the graphs of *f* and *h* to describe the transformation from the graph of *f* to the graph of *h*. *Example 4*

19.

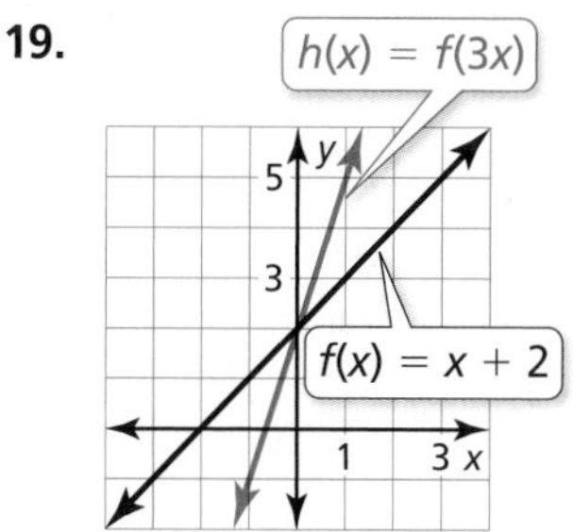

20.

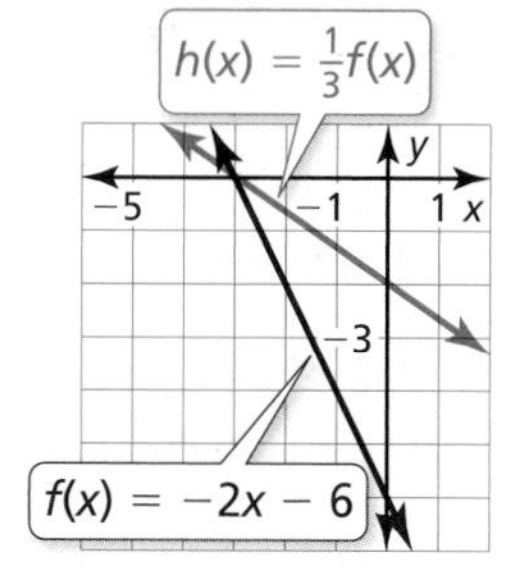

21. $f(x) = 3x - 12$; $h(x) = \frac{1}{6}f(x)$

22. $f(x) = -x + 1$; $h(x) = f(2x)$

23. $f(x) = -2x - 2$; $h(x) = f(5x)$

24. $f(x) = 4x + 8$; $h(x) = \frac{3}{4}f(x)$

25. MODELING REAL LIFE The temperature (in degrees Fahrenheit) x hours after 5 P.M. is represented by $t(x) = -4x + 72$. The temperature x hours after 10 A.M. is represented by $d(x) = 4x + 72$. Describe the transformation from the graph of t to the graph of d.

26. **MODELING REAL LIFE** The cost (in dollars) of a basic music streaming service for m months is represented by $B(m) = 5m$. The cost of the premium service is represented by $P(m) = 10m$. Describe the transformation from the graph of B to the graph of P.

In Exercises 27–32, use the graphs of f and g to describe the transformation from the graph of f to the graph of g.

27. $f(x) = x - 2$; $g(x) = f(x + 4)$

28. $f(x) = -4x + 8$; $g(x) = -f(x)$

29. $f(x) = -2x - 7$; $g(x) = f(x - 2)$

30. $f(x) = 3x + 8$; $g(x) = f\left(\frac{2}{3}x\right)$

31. $f(x) = x - 6$; $g(x) = 6f(x)$

32. $f(x) = -x$; $g(x) = f(x) - 3$

In Exercises 33–36, write a function g in terms of f so that the statement is true.

33. The graph of g is a horizontal translation 2 units right of the graph of f.

34. The graph of g is a reflection in the y-axis of the graph of f.

35. The graph of g is a vertical translation 4 units up of the graph of f.

36. The graph of g is a horizontal shrink by a factor of $\frac{1}{5}$ of the graph of f.

ERROR ANALYSIS In Exercises 37 and 38, describe and correct the error in graphing g.

37.

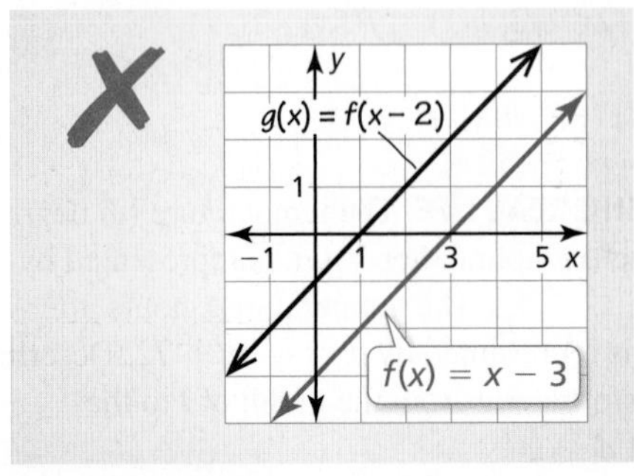

38.

y
4
f(x) = −x + 3
2
−2
1
4 x
−2
g(x) = f(−x)

In Exercises 39–42, graph f and h. Describe the transformations from the graph of f to the graph of h. *Example 5*

39. $f(x) = x$; $h(x) = 4x - 2$

40. $f(x) = x$; $h(x) = -\frac{1}{2}x + 3$

41. $f(x) = 2x$; $h(x) = 6x - 5$

42. $f(x) = 3x$; $h(x) = -3x - 7$

43. **WRITING** How does the value of p in the equation $y = g(x) + p$ affect the graph of $y = g(x)$? How does the value of p in the equation $y = g(x + p)$ affect the graph of $y = g(x)$?

44. **MP STRUCTURE** The graph of $g(x) = a \cdot f(x - b) + c$ is a transformation of the graph of the linear function f. Complete each statement.

a. The graph of g is a vertical ______ of the graph of f when $a = 4$, $b = 0$, and $c = 0$.

b. The graph of g is a vertical translation 1 unit up of the graph of f when $a = 1$, $b = 0$, and $c =$ ____.

c. The graph of g is a reflection in the ______ of the graph of f when $a = -1$, $b = 0$, and $c = 0$.

45. **MODELING REAL LIFE** The cost (in dollars) of a gym membership for m months is represented by the function g. In January, the gym multiplies the monthly fee by a factor of a. The gym then adds a sign-up fee of b dollars. Use the graph to find and interpret the values of a and b. *Example 6*

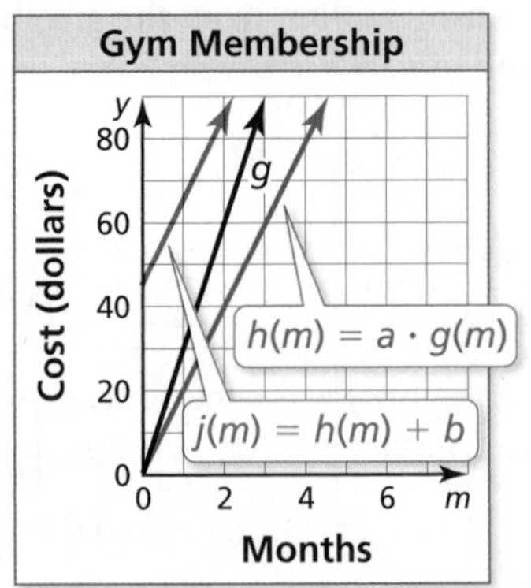

46. MODELING REAL LIFE The function $w(x) = 250x$ represents the amount of money (in dollars) a consumer pays for a car after x months, without a down payment. The function $d(x)$ represents the amount paid for the same car with a down payment.

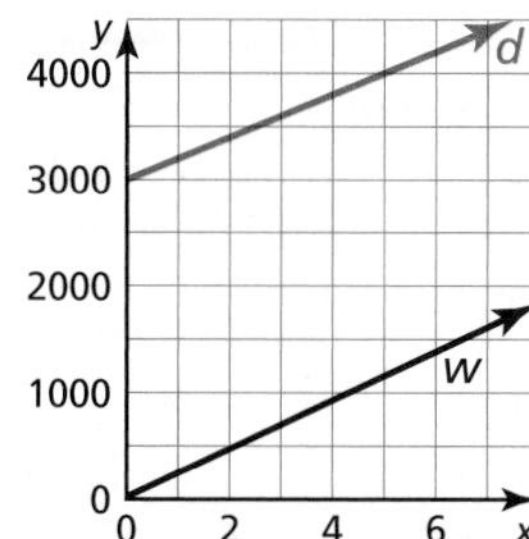

a. Describe the transformations of the graph of w that result in the graph of d.

b. What does 250 represent in the function w?

c. How much is the down payment?

d. The car will be paid in full after 60 months. Find and describe the domain and range of each function in this context.

47. COLLEGE PREP Which of the graphs are related by only a translation? Explain.

Ⓐ 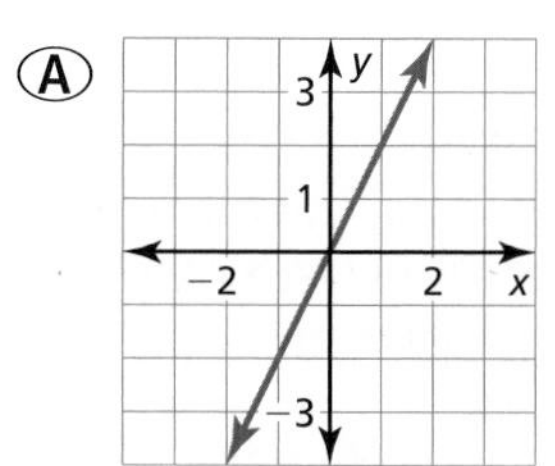 Ⓑ 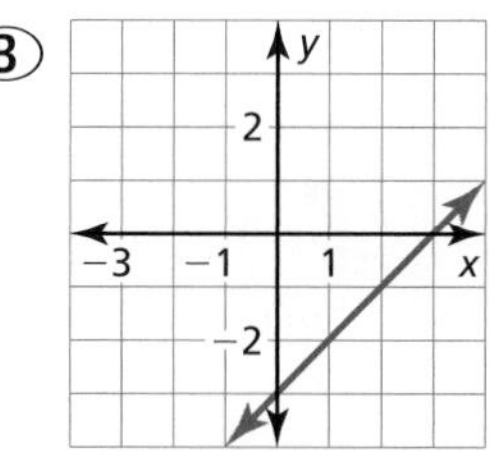

Ⓒ 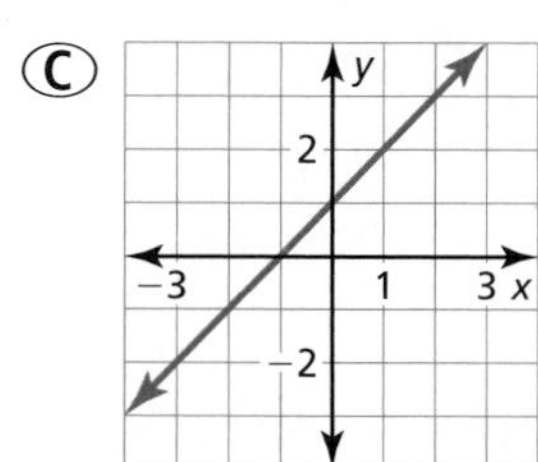 Ⓓ 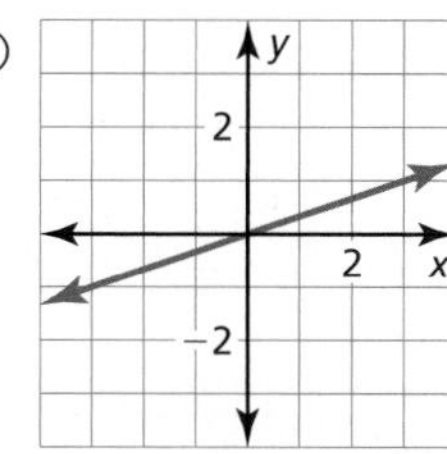

Ⓔ 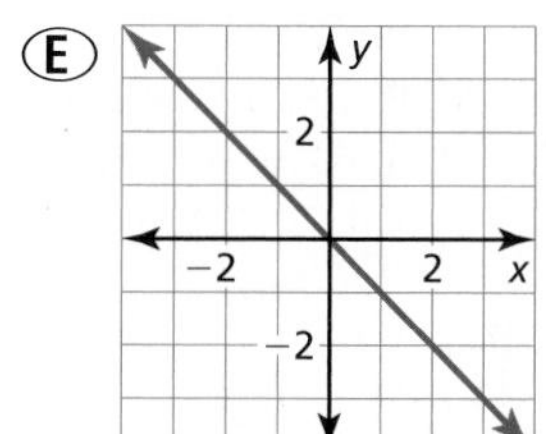 Ⓕ 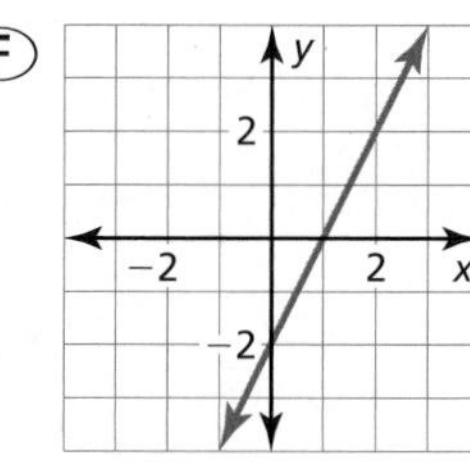

48. MP REASONING The graph of $f(x) = x + 5$ is a vertical translation 5 units up of the graph of $f(x) = x$. How can you obtain the graph of $f(x) = x + 5$ from the graph of $f(x) = x$ using a horizontal translation?

OPEN-ENDED In Exercises 49–52, write a function whose graph passes through the given point and is a transformation of the graph of $f(x) = x$.

49. $(4, 2)$

50. $(-1, 3)$

51. $\left(\frac{3}{2}, \frac{7}{2}\right)$

52. $\left(2, -\frac{5}{2}\right)$

53. ANALYZING RELATIONSHIPS A swimming pool is filled with water by a hose at a rate of 1020 gallons per hour. The amount (in gallons) of water in the pool after t hours is represented by the function $v(t) = 1020t$. How does the graph of v change in each situation?

a. A larger hose is found. Then the pool is filled at a rate of 1360 gallons per hour.

b. Before filling up the pool with a hose, a water truck adds 2000 gallons of water to the pool.

54. HOW DO YOU SEE IT?
Match each function with its graph. Explain.

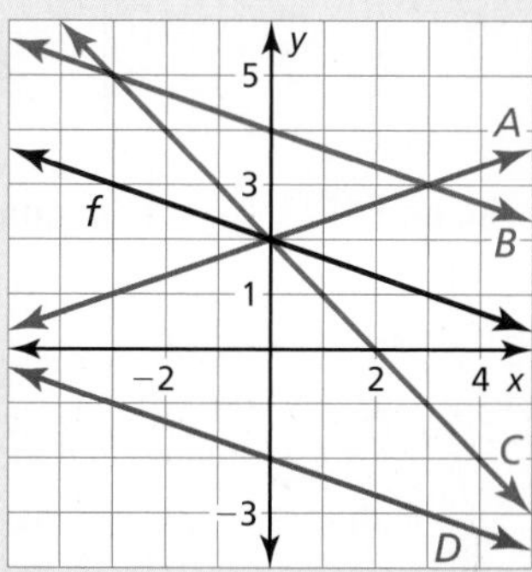

a. $a(x) = f(-x)$

b. $g(x) = f(x) - 4$

c. $h(x) = f(x) + 2$

d. $k(x) = f(3x)$

MP STRUCTURE In Exercises 55–58, find the value of r.

55.

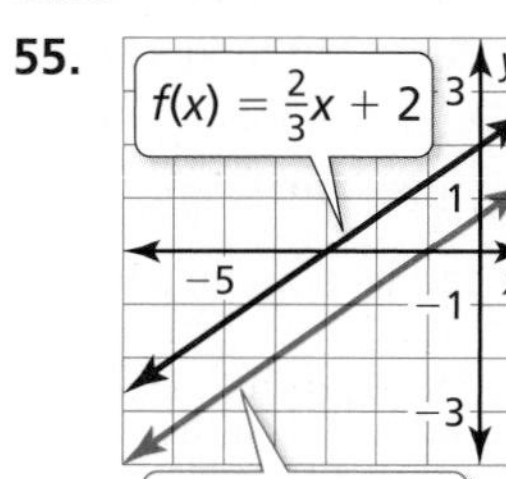

56.

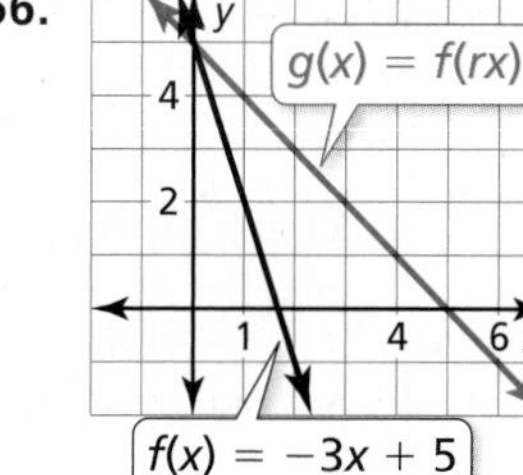

57.

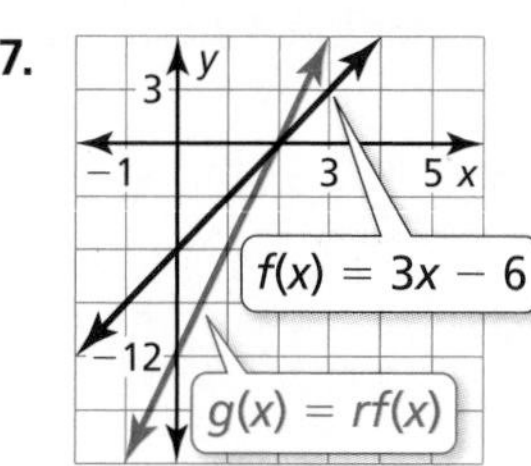

58.

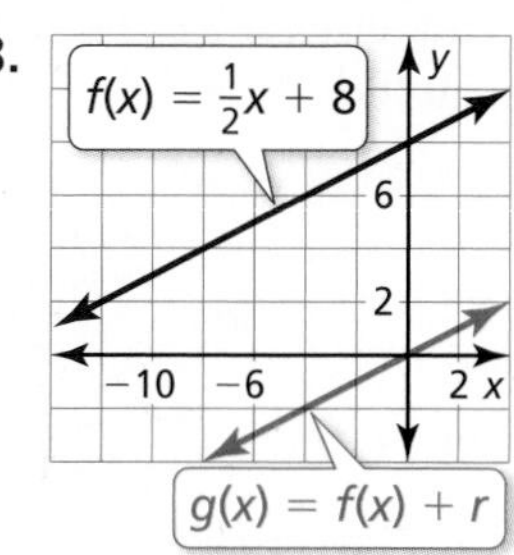

In Exercises 59–62, graph f and g. Write g in terms of f. Describe the transformation from the graph of f to the graph of g.

59. $f(x) = 2x - 5;\ g(x) = 2x - 8$

60. $f(x) = 3x + 9;\ g(x) = 3x + 15$

61. $f(x) = -x - 4;\ g(x) = x - 4$

62. $f(x) = x - 1;\ g(x) = 3x - 3$

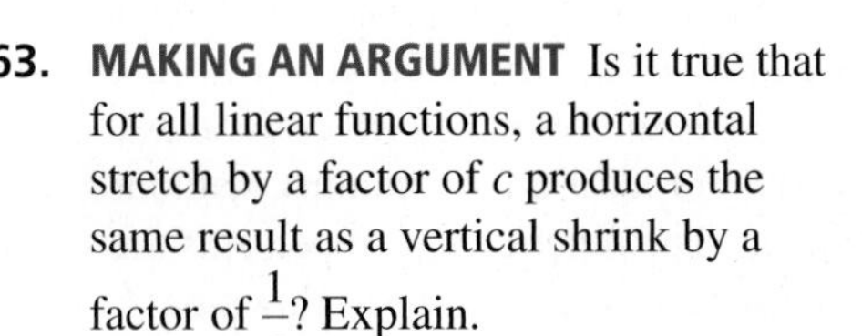

63. MAKING AN ARGUMENT Is it true that for all linear functions, a horizontal stretch by a factor of c produces the same result as a vertical shrink by a factor of $\frac{1}{c}$? Explain.

64. THOUGHT PROVOKING
When is the graph of $y = f(x) + w$ the same as the graph of $y = f(x + w)$ for linear functions? Explain your reasoning.

REVIEW & REFRESH

65. The red figure is similar to the blue figure. Describe a similarity transformation between the figures.

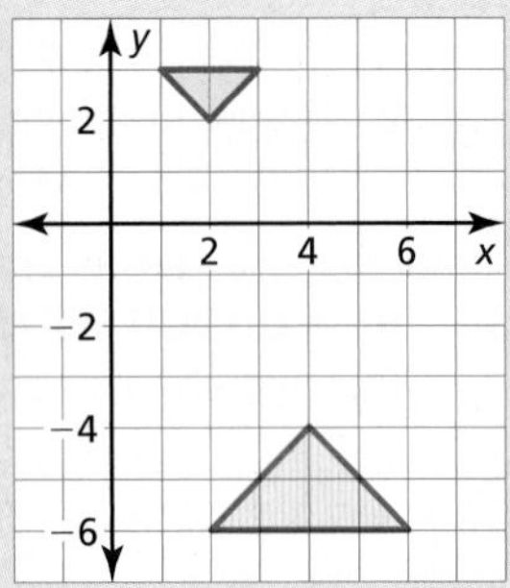

In Exercises 66 and 67, solve the inequality. Graph the solution, if possible.

66. $5|x + 7| < 25$

67. $-2|x + 1| \geq 18$

68. MP REASONING Complete the inequality $-\frac{1}{6}n$ ▭ $\frac{2}{3}$ with $<$, $\leq$, $>$, or $\geq$ so that the solution is $n \leq -4$.

69. Evaluate $g(x) = \frac{1}{4}x - 5$ when $x = 12$ and when $x = -2$.

70. MODELING REAL LIFE An elevator on the top floor of a building begins to descend to the ground floor. The function $h(t) = -8t + 250$ models the situation, where $h(t)$ is the height (in meters) of the elevator t seconds after it begins to descend.

a. Graph the function and find its domain and range.

b. Interpret the terms and coefficient in the equation, and the x-intercept of its graph.

In Exercises 71–74, solve the equation. Check your solution.

71. $2.5b = 10$

72. $\frac{c}{5} + 1 = -2$

73. $14 - 3q = 4q - 14 + q$

74. $|-4r + 6| - 5 = 13$

75. MODELING REAL LIFE The linear function $m = 55 - 8.5b$ represents the amount m (in dollars) of money that you have after buying b books.

a. Find the domain of the function. Is the domain discrete or continuous? Explain.

b. Graph the function using its domain.

In Exercises 76 and 77, graph f and h. Describe the transformations from the graph of f to the graph of h.

76. $f(x) = x;\ h(x) = \frac{1}{3}x + 1$

77. $f(x) = x;\ h(x) = -3x - 4$

78. MP STRUCTURE The graph of the equation $Ax + By = 15$ is shown. Find the values of A and B.

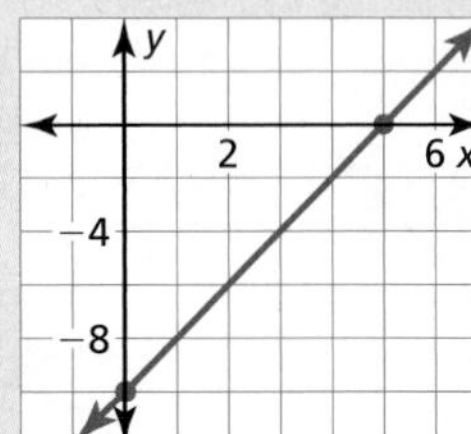

79. Determine whether the relation is a function. Explain.

$(-10, 2), (-8, 3), (-6, 5), (-8, 8), (-10, 6)$

80. Solve the formula for h.

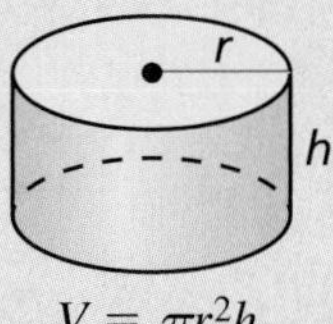

$V = \pi r^2 h$

81. Write an inequality that represents the graph.

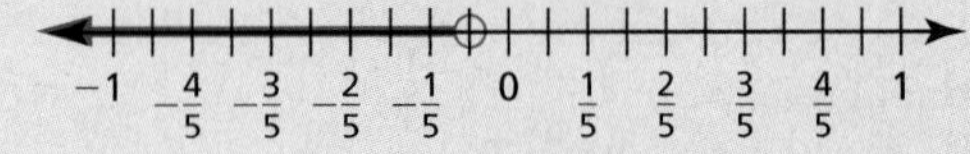

3.8 Graphing Absolute Value Functions

Learning Target Graph absolute value functions.

Success Criteria
- I can graph absolute value functions.
- I can find the domain and range of absolute value functions.
- I can describe transformations of graphs of absolute value functions.

EXPLORE IT! Understanding Graphs of Absolute Value Functions

Work with a partner.

a. Think about the absolute value of a number. What characteristics might you observe in the graph of an *absolute value function*?

b. Graph $y = |x|$. Make several observations about the graph.

c. Let f be the parent absolute value function $f(x) = |x|$. Which of the following functions have a graph with one x-intercept? two x-intercepts? no x-intercept? Explain your reasoning.

$g(x) = f(x) - 1$	$h(x) = f(x - 1)$
$p(x) = -f(x)$	$q(x) = f(x + 1) + 1$

Math Practice

Use Prior Results How can you use what you know about transformations of linear functions to make conclusions about transformations of absolute value functions?

d. Match each absolute value function with its graph. Explain your reasoning. Then use technology to check your answers.

i. $g(x) = -|x - 2|$ **ii.** $g(x) = |x - 2| + 2$

iii. $g(x) = |x - 2| - 2$ **iv.** $g(x) = 2|x - 2|$

A.
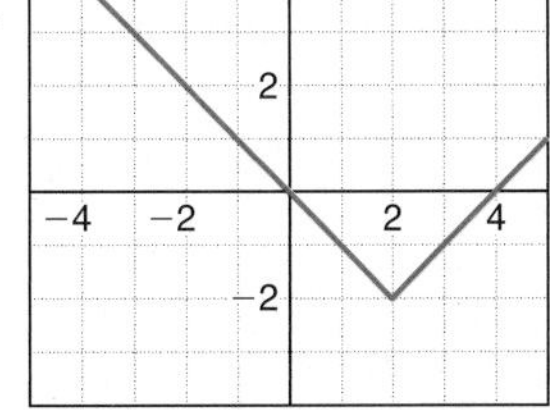

B.
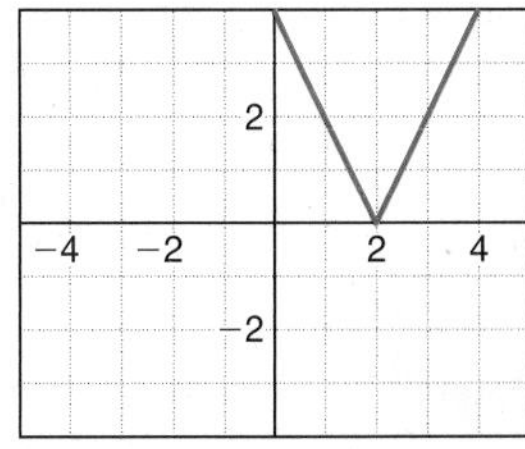

C.
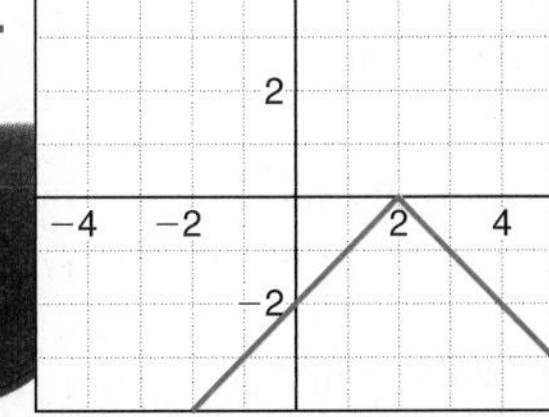

D.
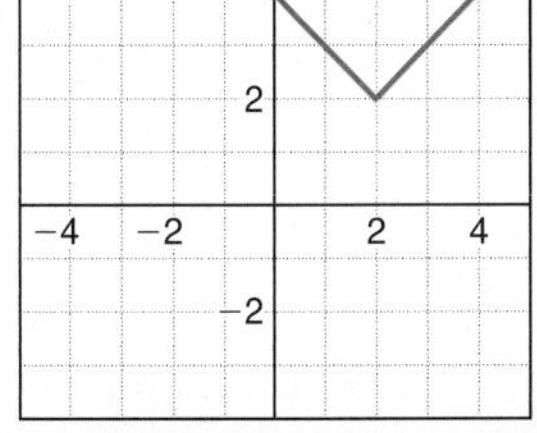

Translating Graphs of Absolute Value Functions

Vocabulary

absolute value function, *p. 168*
vertex, *p. 168*
vertex form, *p. 170*

WORDS AND MATH

In geometry, a *vertex* is the point where the sides meet for an angle, polygon, or solid.

KEY IDEA

Absolute Value Function

An **absolute value function** is a function that contains an absolute value expression. The parent absolute value function is $f(x) = |x|$. The graph of $f(x) = |x|$ is V-shaped and symmetric about the y-axis. The **vertex** is the point where the graph changes direction. The vertex of the graph of $f(x) = |x|$ is $(0, 0)$.

The domain of $f(x) = |x|$ is all real numbers. The range is $y \geq 0$.

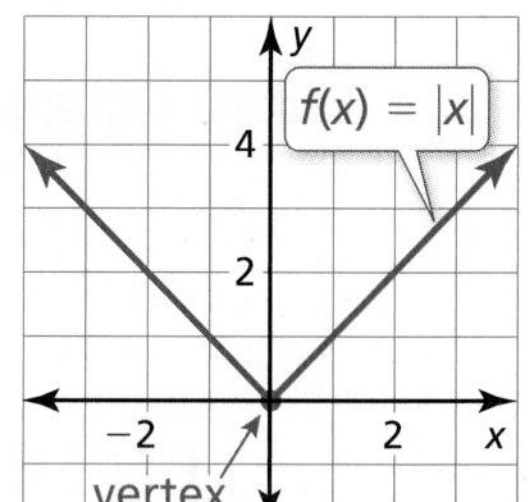

The graphs of all other absolute value functions are transformations of the graph of the parent function $f(x) = |x|$. The transformations presented in the previous section also apply to absolute value functions.

EXAMPLE 1 **Graphing $g(x) = |x| + k$ and $g(x) = |x - h|$**

Graph each function. Compare each graph to the graph of $f(x) = |x|$. Find the domain and range.

a. $g(x) = |x| + 3$

b. $m(x) = |x - 2|$

SOLUTION

a. Step 1 Make a table of values.

x	−2	−1	0	1	2
$g(x)$	5	4	3	4	5

Step 2 Plot the ordered pairs.

Step 3 Draw the graph.

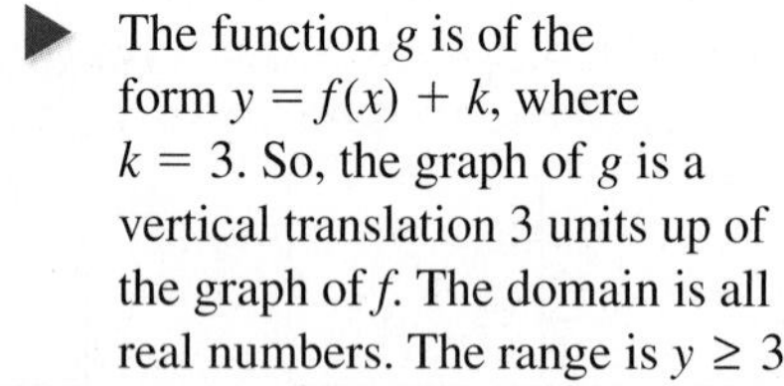

▶ The function g is of the form $y = f(x) + k$, where $k = 3$. So, the graph of g is a vertical translation 3 units up of the graph of f. The domain is all real numbers. The range is $y \geq 3$.

b. Step 1 Make a table of values.

x	0	1	2	3	4
$m(x)$	2	1	0	1	2

Step 2 Plot the ordered pairs.

Step 3 Draw the graph.

▶ The function m is of the form $y = f(x - h)$, where $h = 2$. So, the graph of m is a horizontal translation 2 units right of the graph of f. The domain is all real numbers. The range is $y \geq 0$.

SELF-ASSESSMENT

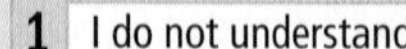

1 I do not understand. 2 I can do it with help. 3 I can do it on my own. 4 I can teach someone else.

Graph the function. Compare the graph to the graph of $f(x) = |x|$. Find the domain and range.

1. $h(x) = |x| - 1$
2. $n(x) = |x + 4|$
3. $m(x) = \left|x - \frac{3}{2}\right|$
4. **WRITING** How are the graphs of absolute value functions and linear functions alike? How are they different?
5. **MP REASONING** Without graphing, explain how the graph of $g(x) = |x - 2| + 5$ compares to the graph of $f(x) = |x|$.

Sketching, Shrinking, and Reflecting

EXAMPLE 2 **Graphing $g(x) = a|x|$** 

Graph each function. Compare each graph to the graph of $f(x) = |x|$. Find the domain and range.

a. $q(x) = 2|x|$ **b.** $p(x) = -\frac{1}{2}|x|$

SOLUTION

a. Step 1 Make a table of values.

x	-2	-1	0	1	2
q(x)	4	2	0	2	4

STUDY TIP
A vertical stretch of the graph of $f(x) = |x|$ is *narrower* than the graph of $f(x) = |x|$.

Step 2 Plot the ordered pairs.

Step 3 Draw the graph.

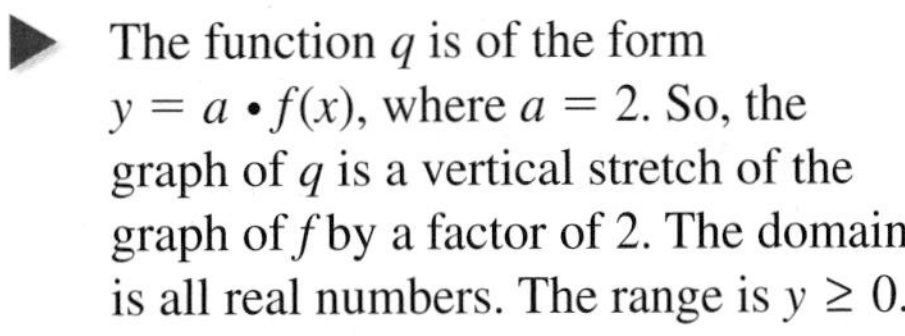

▶ The function q is of the form $y = a \cdot f(x)$, where $a = 2$. So, the graph of q is a vertical stretch of the graph of f by a factor of 2. The domain is all real numbers. The range is $y \geq 0$.

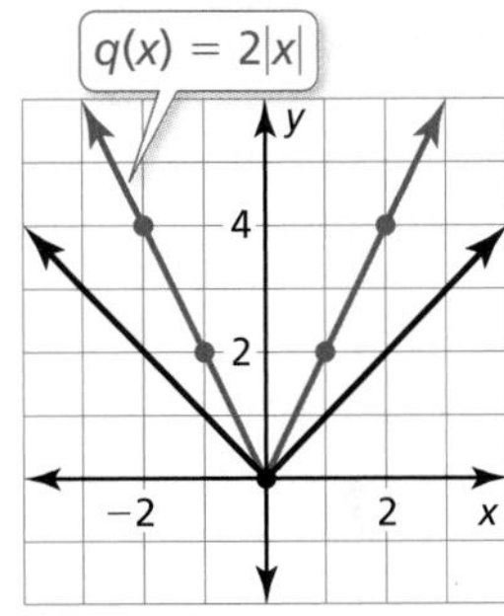

b. Step 1 Make a table of values.

x	-2	-1	0	1	2
p(x)	-1	$-\frac{1}{2}$	0	$-\frac{1}{2}$	-1

STUDY TIP
A vertical shrink of the graph of $f(x) = |x|$ is *wider* than the graph of $f(x) = |x|$.

Step 2 Plot the ordered pairs.

Step 3 Draw the graph.

▶ The function p is of the form $y = -a \cdot f(x)$, where $a = \frac{1}{2}$. So, the graph of p is a vertical shrink of the graph of f by a factor of $\frac{1}{2}$ and a reflection in the x-axis. The domain is all real numbers. The range is $y \leq 0$.

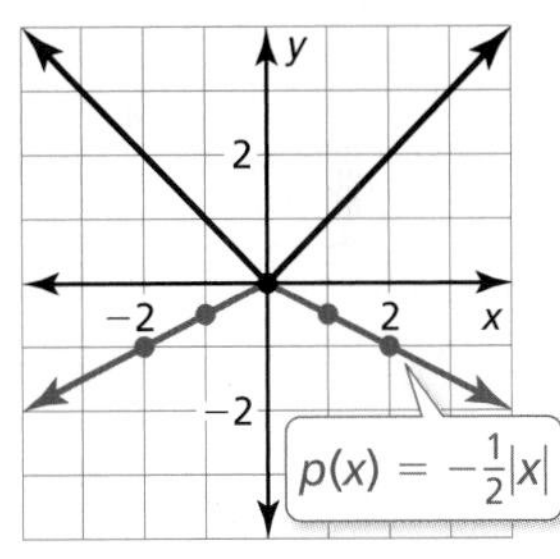

SELF-ASSESSMENT 1 I do not understand. 2 I can do it with help. 3 I can do it on my own. 4 I can teach someone else.

Graph the function. Compare the graph to the graph of $f(x) = |x|$. Find the domain and range.

6. $t(x) = -3|x|$
7. $v(x) = \frac{1}{4}|x|$
8. $w(x) = 2.5|x|$

9. **MP STRUCTURE** How do you know whether the graph of $g(x) = a|x|$ is a vertical stretch or a vertical shrink of the graph of $f(x) = b|x|$?

10. **OPEN-ENDED** Write an absolute value function that is a transformation of the parent absolute value function. Describe the end behavior of the function.

11. **MP USING TOOLS** Write an equation of the absolute value function whose graph is shown. Use technology to verify your equation.

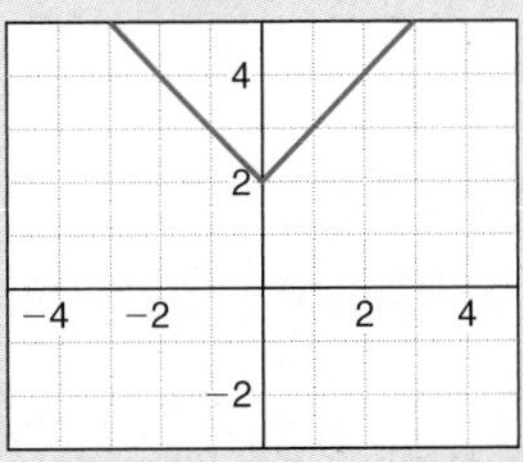

KEY IDEA

Vertex Form of an Absolute Value Function

An absolute value function written in the form $g(x) = a|x - h| + k$, where $a \neq 0$, is in **vertex form**. The vertex of the graph of g is (h, k).

Any absolute value function can be written in vertex form, and its graph is symmetric about the line $x = h$.

EXAMPLE 3 Graphing $f(x) = |x - h| + k$ and $g(x) = f(ax)$

STUDY TIP

The function g is *not* in vertex form because the x variable does not have a coefficient of 1.

Graph $f(x) = |x + 2| - 3$ and $g(x) = |2x + 2| - 3$. Compare the graph of g to the graph of f.

SOLUTION

Step 1 Make a table of values for each function.

x	−4	−3	−2	−1	0	1	2
$f(x)$	−1	−2	−3	−2	−1	0	1

x	−2	−1.5	−1	−0.5	0	0.5	1
$g(x)$	−1	−2	−3	−2	−1	0	1

Step 2 Plot the ordered pairs.

Step 3 Draw the graph of each function. Notice that the vertex of the graph of f is $(-2, -3)$ and the graph is symmetric about $x = -2$.

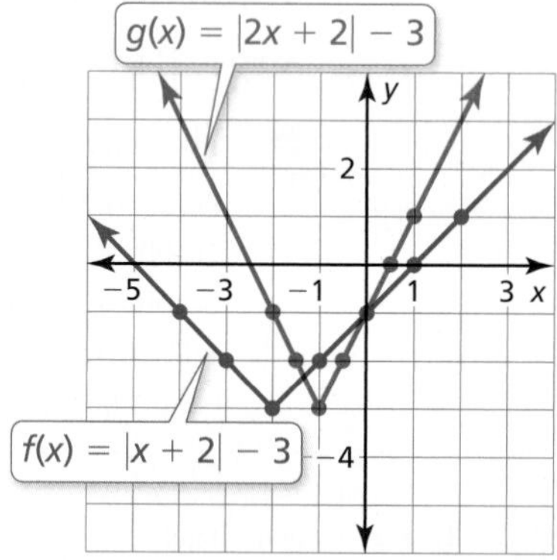

▶ Note that you can rewrite g as $g(x) = f(2x)$, which is of the form $y = f(ax)$, where $a = 2$. So, the graph of g is a horizontal shrink of the graph of f by a factor of $\frac{1}{2}$. The y-intercept is the same for both graphs. The points on the graph of f move halfway closer to the y-axis, resulting in the graph of g. When the input values of f are 2 times the input values of g, the output values of f and g are the same.

SELF-ASSESSMENT 1 I do not understand. 2 I can do it with help. 3 I can do it on my own. 4 I can teach someone else.

Graph and compare the two functions.

12. $f(x) = |x - 1|$; $g(x) = \left|\frac{1}{2}x - 1\right|$

13. $f(x) = |x + 2| + 2$; $g(x) = |-4x + 2| + 2$

Combining Transformations

EXAMPLE 4 **Graphing $g(x) = a|x - h| + k$**

REMEMBER

You can obtain the graph of $y = a \cdot f(x - h) + k$ from the graph of $y = f(x)$ using the steps you learned in the previous section.

Graph $g(x) = -2|x - 1| + 3$. Describe the transformations from the graph of $f(x) = |x|$ to the graph of g.

SOLUTION

Step 1 Translate the graph of f horizontally 1 unit right to get the graph of $t(x) = |x - 1|$.

Step 2 Stretch the graph of t vertically by a factor of 2 to get the graph of $h(x) = 2|x - 1|$.

Step 3 Reflect the graph of h in the x-axis to get the graph of $r(x) = -2|x - 1|$.

Step 4 Translate the graph of r vertically 3 units up to get the graph of $g(x) = -2|x - 1| + 3$.

▶ The graph of g is a horizontal translation 1 unit right, a vertical stretch by a factor of 2, a reflection in the x-axis, and a vertical translation 3 units up of the graph of f.

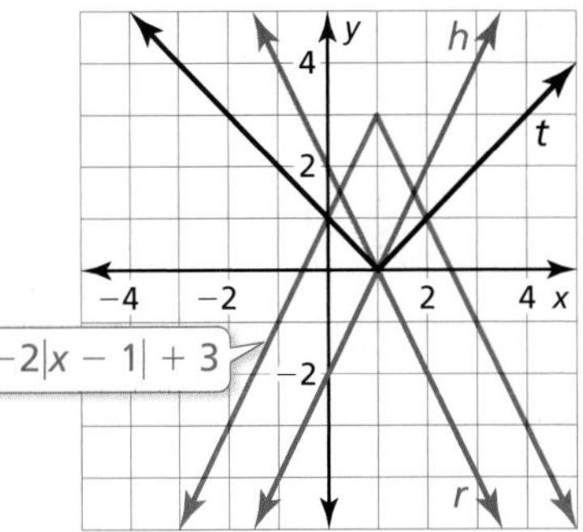

Check Graph the function using symmetry.

Step 1 Identify and plot the vertex.
$(h, k) = (1, 3)$

Step 2 Plot another point on the graph, such as $(2, 1)$. Because the graph is symmetric about the line $x = 1$, you can use symmetry to plot a third point, $(0, 1)$.

Step 3 Draw the graph. ✓

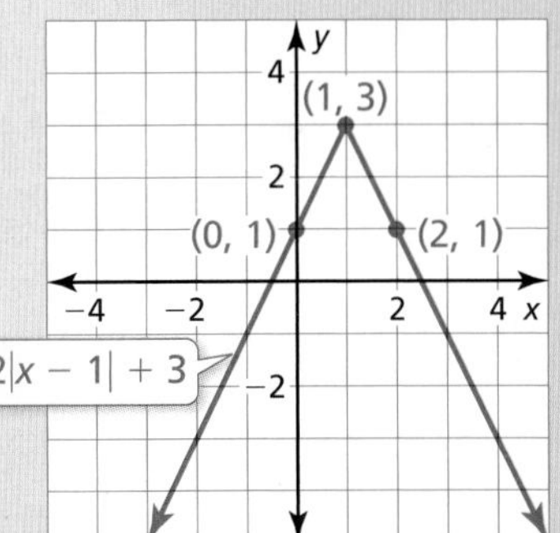

SELF-ASSESSMENT

1 I do not understand. **2** I can do it with help. **3** I can do it on my own. **4** I can teach someone else.

14. Graph $g(x) = \left|-\frac{1}{2}x + 2\right| + 1$. Describe the transformations from the graph of $f(x) = |x|$ to the graph of g.

15. **MP REASONING** The graph of which function has the same y-intercept as the graph of $f(x) = |x - 2| + 5$? Explain.

$g(x) = |3x - 2| + 5$ $\qquad$ $h(x) = 3|x - 2| + 5$

16. **MP STRUCTURE** How do the values of a, h, and k affect the graph of the absolute value function $g(x) = a|x - h| + k$?

3.8 Practice WITH CalcChat® AND CalcView®

In Exercises 1–8, graph the function. Compare the graph to the graph of $f(x) = |x|$. Find the domain and range. *Examples 1 and 2*

1. $d(x) = |x| - 4$
2. $r(x) = |x| + 5$
3. $m(x) = |x + 1|$
4. $v(x) = |x - 3|$
5. $p(x) = \frac{1}{3}|x|$
6. $j(x) = 3|x|$
7. $a(x) = -5|x|$
8. $q(x) = -\frac{3}{2}|x|$

In Exercises 9–12, write an equation that represents the given transformation(s) of the graph of $g(x) = |x|$.

9. vertical translation 7 units down
10. horizontal translation 10 units left
11. vertical shrink by a factor of $\frac{1}{4}$
12. vertical stretch by a factor of 3 and a reflection in the x-axis

In Exercises 13–18, graph and compare the two functions. *Example 3*

13. $f(x) = |x - 4|$; $g(x) = |3x - 4|$
14. $h(x) = |x + 5|$; $t(x) = |2x + 5|$
15. $p(x) = |x + 1| - 2$; $q(x) = \left|\frac{1}{4}x + 1\right| - 2$
16. $w(x) = |x - 3| + 4$; $y(x) = |5x - 3| + 4$
17. $a(x) = |x + 2| + 3$; $b(x) = |-4x + 2| + 3$
18. $u(x) = |x - 1| + 2$; $v(x) = \left|-\frac{1}{2}x - 1\right| + 2$

In Exercises 19–22, compare the graphs. Find the value of h, k, or a.

19.

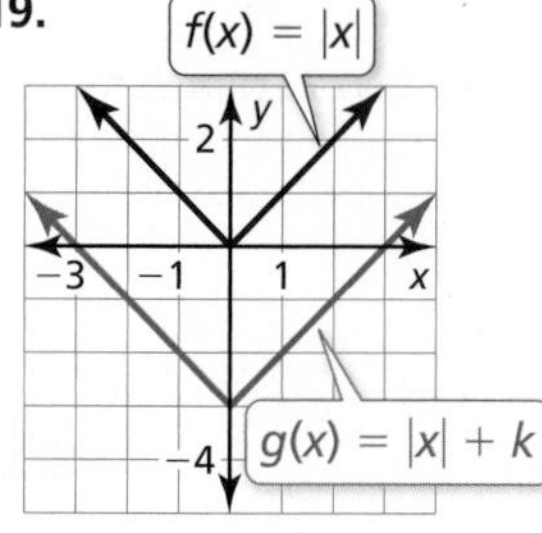

20.

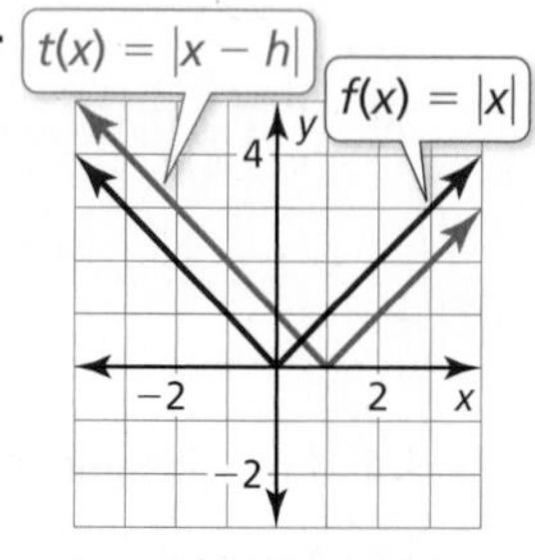

21.

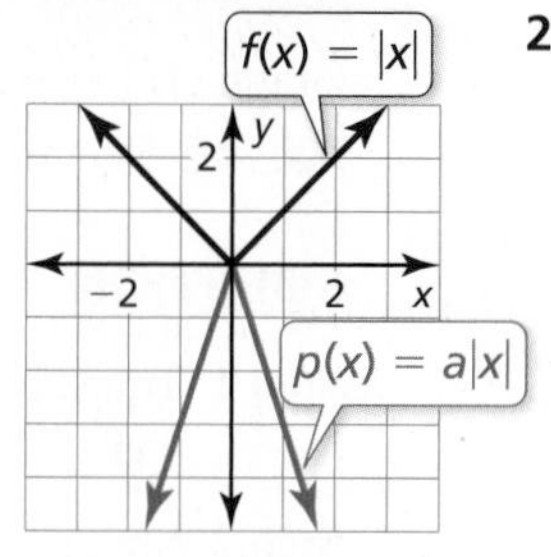

22.

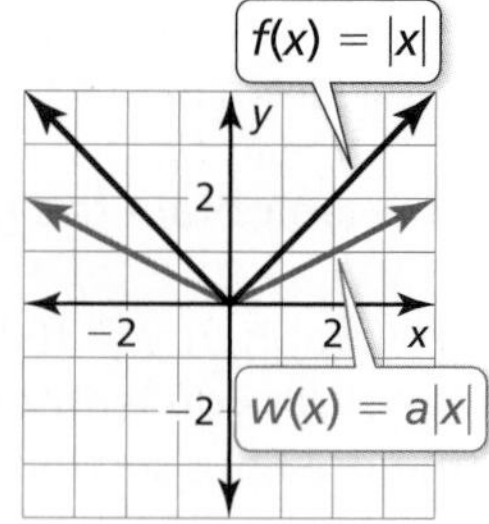

In Exercises 23–30, graph the function. Then describe the transformations from the graph of $f(x) = |x|$ to the graph of the function. *Example 4*

23. $r(x) = |x + 2| - 6$
24. $c(x) = |x + 4| + 4$
25. $d(x) = -|x - 3| + 5$
26. $v(x) = -3|x + 1| + 4$
27. $m(x) = \frac{1}{2}|x + 4| - 1$
28. $s(x) = |2x - 2| - 3$
29. $j(x) = |-x + 1| - 5$
30. $n(x) = \left|-\frac{1}{3}x + 1\right| + 2$

31. **MODELING REAL LIFE** On the pool table shown, you bank the five ball off the side represented by the x-axis. The path of the ball is modeled by the function $p(x) = \frac{4}{3}\left|x - \frac{5}{4}\right|$.

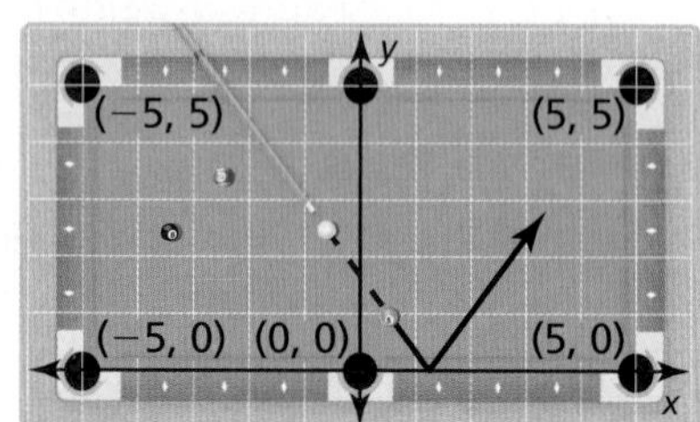

a. At what point does the five ball bank off the side?

b. Do you make the shot? Explain your reasoning.

32. **ERROR ANALYSIS** Describe and correct the error in graphing the function.

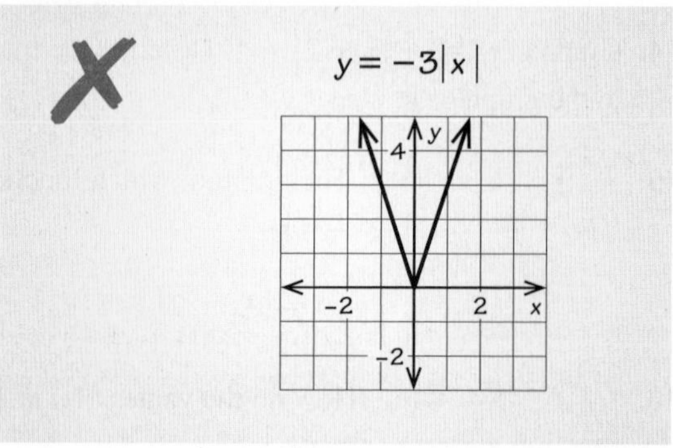

33. **MP REASONING** An absolute value function is positive over its entire domain. How many x-intercepts does the graph of the function have?

34. **MODELING REAL LIFE** A traveler is driving from Nevada to Arizona. The function $d(t) = 60|t - 2.5|$ represents the distance (in miles) the car is from the state line after t hours.

 a. Graph the function and interpret the intercepts.

 b. When is the function decreasing? increasing? Explain what each represents in this context.

 c. A rest stop is 90 miles from the state line. How long will it take the traveler to reach the rest stop? Explain.

35. **MP STRUCTURE** The points $A\left(-\frac{1}{2}, 3\right)$, $B(1, 0)$, and $C(-4, -2)$ lie on the graph of the absolute value function f. Find the coordinates of the points corresponding to A, B, and C on the graph of each function.

 a. $g(x) = f(x) - 5$ b. $h(x) = f(x - 3)$

 c. $j(x) = -f(x)$ d. $k(x) = 4f(x)$

36. **MP STRUCTURE** Explain how the graph of each function compares to the graph of $y = |x|$ for positive and negative values of k, h, and a.

 a. $y = |x| + k$ b. $y = |x - h|$

 c. $y = a|x|$ d. $y = |ax|$

CONNECTING CONCEPTS In Exercises 37 and 38, write an absolute value function whose graph intersects the given graph to form an enclosed square.

37.

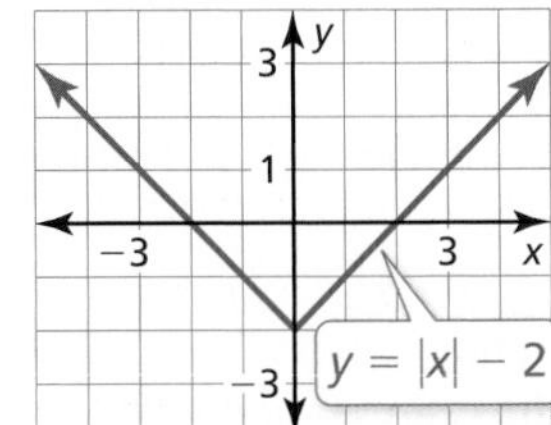

38.

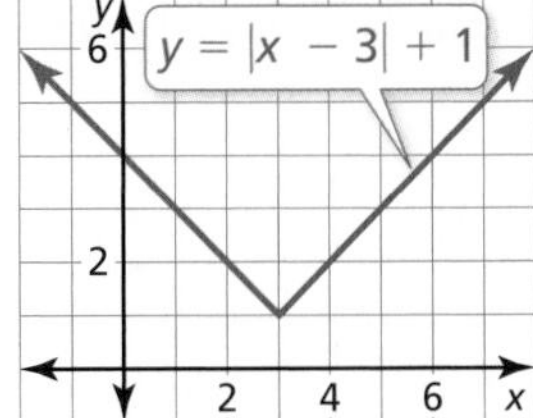

39. **MP REASONING** Is it possible for an absolute value function to always be increasing? decreasing? Explain your reasoning.

40. **HOW DO YOU SEE IT?**
The object of a computer game is to break bricks by deflecting a ball toward them using a paddle. The graph shows the current path of the ball and the location of the last brick.

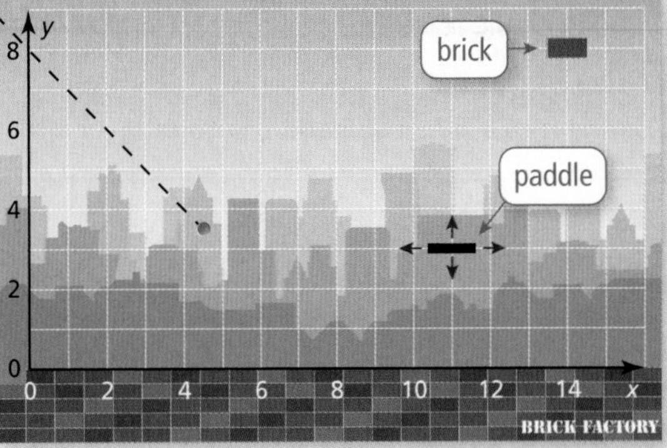

 a. You can move the paddle up, down, left, and right. At what coordinates should you place the paddle to break the last brick? Assume the ball deflects at a right angle.

 b. You move the paddle to the coordinates in part (a), and the ball is deflected. How can you write an absolute value function that describes the path of the ball?

In Exercises 41–44, graph the function. Then rewrite the absolute value function as two linear functions, one that has the domain $x < 0$ and one that has the domain $x \geq 0$.

41. $y = |x|$ 42. $y = |x| - 3$

43. $y = -|x| + 9$ 44. $y = -4|x|$

In Exercises 45–48, sketch a graph of an absolute value function that has the given characteristics. Then write the function represented by your graph.

45. vertex $(3, -4)$, x-intercepts: 1 and 5

46. vertex $\left(-\frac{3}{2}, 3\right)$, x-intercepts: $-\frac{5}{2}$ and $-\frac{1}{2}$

47. vertex $(-6, -1)$, y-intercept: -5

48. x-intercept: -2, y-intercept: $\frac{1}{2}$

49. **COLLEGE PREP** Which of the following functions have the same end behavior?

 Ⓐ $a(x) = 4|x - 2| + 3$

 Ⓑ $b(x) = -\frac{3}{2}|x + 5|$

 Ⓒ $c(x) = |-2x - 6| - 1$

 Ⓓ $d(x) = \left|9 - \frac{1}{2}x\right|$

50. THOUGHT PROVOKING
Graph an absolute value function f that represents the route a wide receiver runs in a football game. Let the x-axis represent distance (in yards) across the field horizontally. Let the y-axis represent distance (in yards) down the field. Limit the domain so the route is realistic.

In Exercises 51–54, graph and compare the two functions.

51. $f(x) = |x - 1| + 2$; $g(x) = 4|x - 1| + 8$

52. $s(x) = |2x - 5| - 6$; $t(x) = \frac{1}{2}|2x - 5| - 3$

53. $v(x) = -2|3x + 1| + 4$; $w(x) = 3|3x + 1| - 6$

54. $c(x) = 4|x + 3| - 1$; $d(x) = -\frac{4}{3}|x + 3| + \frac{1}{3}$

55. MP USING TOOLS Graph $y = 2|x + 2| - 6$ and $y = -2$ in the same coordinate plane. Use the graph to solve the equation $2|x + 2| - 6 = -2$. Use technology to check your solutions.

56. MP REASONING Describe the transformations from the graph of $g(x) = -2|x + 1| + 4$ to the graph of $h(x) = |x|$. Explain your reasoning.

57. MAKING AN ARGUMENT Let p be a positive constant, where the graph of $y = |x| + p$ is a vertical translation in the positive direction of the graph of $y = |x|$. Does this mean that the graph of $y = |x + p|$ is a horizontal translation in the positive direction of the graph of $y = |x|$? Explain.

58. DIG DEEPER Write the vertex of the absolute value function $f(x) = |ax - h| + k$ in terms of a, h, and k.

REVIEW & REFRESH

59. Find the slope of the line.

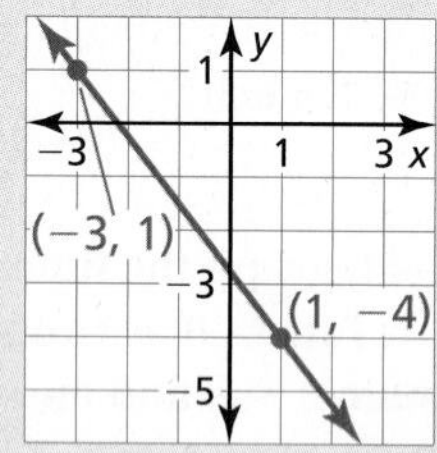

60. Let $f(t)$ be the outside temperature (in degrees Celsius) t hours after 9 A.M. Explain the meaning of each statement.

a. $f(4) = 30$ **b.** $f(m) = 28.9$
c. $f(2) = f(9)$ **d.** $f(6.5) > f(0)$

In Exercises 61–64, solve the inequality. Graph the solution, if possible.

61. $2a - 7 \leq -2$

62. $-3(2p + 4) > -6p - 5$

63. $4(3h + 1.5) \geq 6(2h - 2)$

64. $-4(x + 6) < 2(2x - 9)$

In Exercises 65 and 66, use the graphs of f and g to describe the transformation from the graph of f to the graph of g.

65. $f(x) = -\frac{1}{2}x$; $g(x) = f(x + 2)$

66. $f(x) = 3x - 1$; $g(x) = -f(x)$

67. MODELING REAL LIFE You have \$15 to purchase pecans and walnuts. The equation $12x + 7.5y = 15$ models this situation, where x is the number of pounds of pecans and y is the number of pounds of walnuts.

a. Interpret the terms and coefficients in the equation.

b. Graph the equation. Interpret the intercepts.

In Exercises 68 and 69, solve the equation.

68. $-4|2x - 3| + 12 = -8$

69. $|x + 4| = |5x + 2|$

70. OPEN-ENDED Draw a graph that does *not* represent a function.

71. Convert 160 meters per minute to feet per second. Round your answer to the nearest hundredth.

72. MP STRUCTURE Compare the graphs. Find the values of h and k.

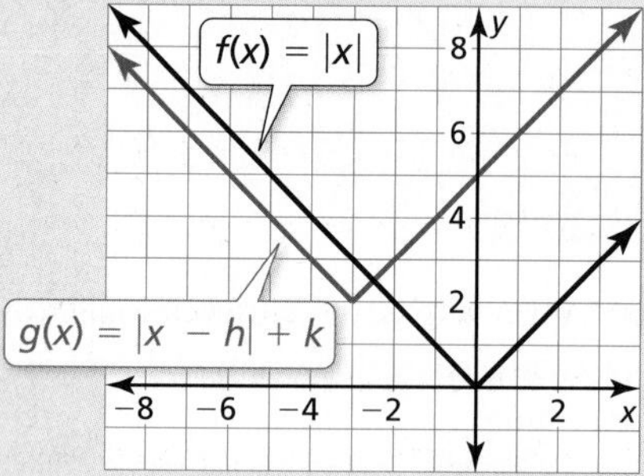

3 Chapter Review WITH CalcChat®

Chapter Learning Target Understand graphing linear functions.

Chapter Success Criteria
- ◆ I can identify the graph of a linear function.
- ◆ I can graph linear functions written in different forms.
- ■ I can describe the characteristics of a function.
- ■ I can explain how a transformation affects the graph of a linear function.

◆ Surface
■ Deep

SELF-ASSESSMENT 1 I do not understand. 2 I can do it with help. 3 I can do it on my own. 4 I can teach someone else.

3.1 Functions *(pp. 111–118)*

Learning Target: Understand the concept of a function.

Vocabulary
relation
function
domain
range
independent variable
dependent variable

Determine whether the relation is a function. Explain.

1. (0, 1), (5, 6), (7, 9), (8, 9)

2.

Input, *x*	Output, *y*
5	11
7	19
9	3

Determine whether the graph represents a function. Then find the domain and range.

3. 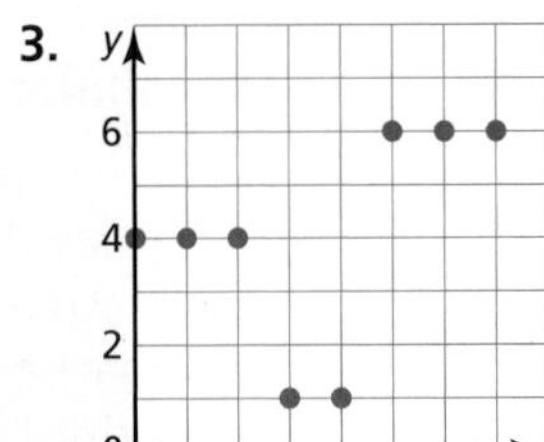

4. 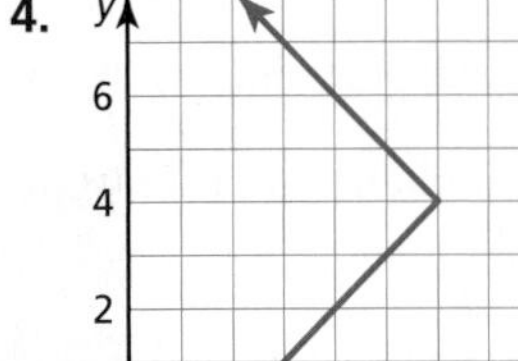

5. 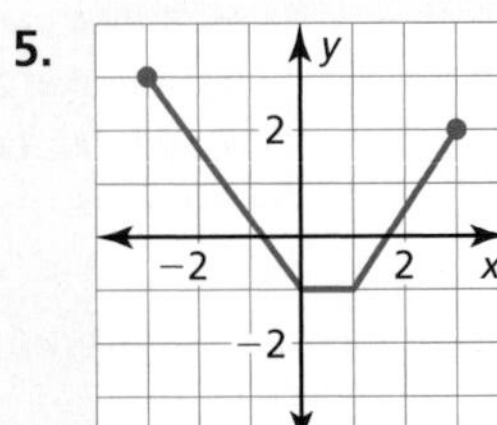

6. 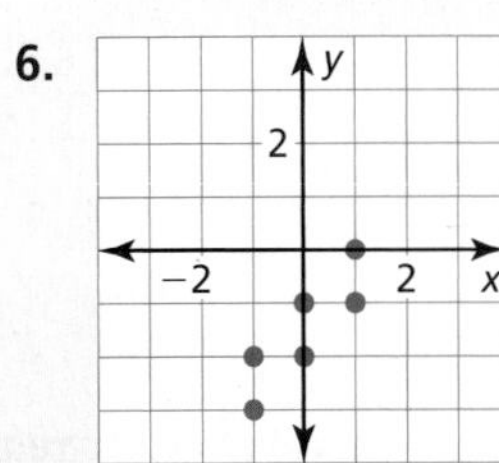

7. You have \$170. You start a part-time job that pays \$8.50 per hour.
   a. Does the situation represent a function? If so, identify the independent and dependent variables.
   b. You work no more than 4 hours. Find the domain and range.

8. Write a relation consisting of five ordered pairs that satisfies the following conditions.
   - The relation is a function.
   - Switching the *x*- and *y*-coordinates of each ordered pair results in a relation that is *not* a function.

GO DIGITAL

3.2 Characteristics of Functions (pp. 119–124)

Learning Target: Describe characteristics of functions.

Vocabulary

x-intercept
y-intercept
increasing
decreasing
end behavior

Approximate when the function is positive, negative, increasing, or decreasing. Then describe the end behavior of the function.

9.

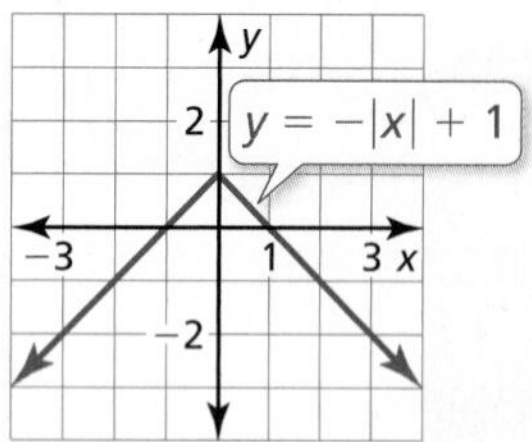

10.

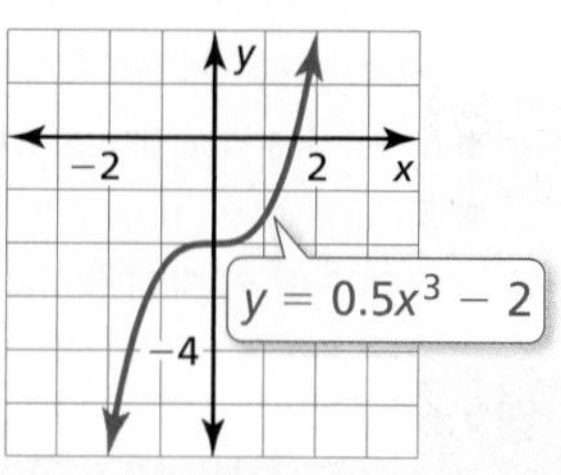

11. A goalie kicks a soccer ball so that it lands about 60 meters away, reaching a maximum height of about 15 meters after traveling a horizontal distance of about 30 meters. The graph shows the path of the second kick. Compare the two kicks.

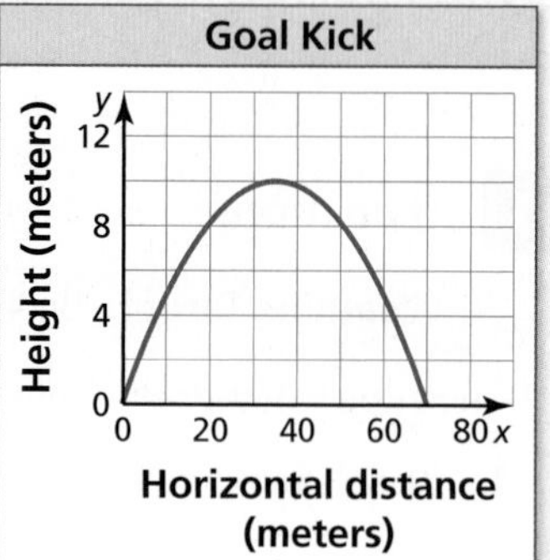

12. Sketch a graph of a function with the given characteristics.

- The x-intercepts are $-\frac{7}{2}$, $-\frac{1}{2}$, and $\frac{5}{2}$.
- The function is increasing when $x < -\frac{3}{2}$, decreasing when $-\frac{3}{2} < x < 1$, and increasing when $x > 1$.

3.3 Linear Functions (pp. 125–134)

Learning Target: Identify and graph linear functions.

Vocabulary

linear equation in two variables
linear function
nonlinear function
solution of a linear equation in two variables
discrete domain
continuous domain

Determine whether the table, graph, or equation represents a *linear* or *nonlinear* function. Explain.

13.

x	2	7	12	17
y	2	−1	−4	−7

14.

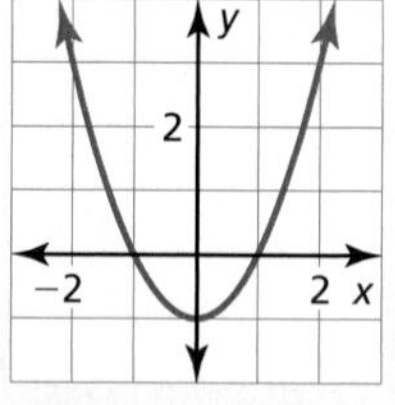

15. $\frac{y}{x+3} = 4$

16. $xy = 9$

Graph the function using its domain. Explain your reasoning.

17.

Games, *x*	1	2	3	4	5
Tokens, *y*	8	6	4	2	0

18.

Time (minutes), *x*	1.5	3.0	4.5
Elevation (feet), *y*	1500	3000	4500

19. The function $y = 60 - 8x$ represents the amount y (in dollars) of money you have after buying x movie tickets. (a) Find the domain of the function. Is the domain *discrete* or *continuous*? Explain. (b) Graph the function using its domain.

3.4 Function Notation (pp. 135–140)

Learning Target: Understand and use function notation.

function notation

Evaluate the function when $x = -3, 0,$ and 5.

20. $f(x) = x + 8$

21. $h(x) = 3x - 9$

22. Let $p(t)$ be the number of people in a stadium t hours after 11:00 A.M. Explain the meaning of each statement.

a. $p(3) = p(5)$

b. $p(6) < p(2.5)$

Find the value of x so that the function has the given value.

23. $k(x) = 7x$; $k(x) = 49$

24. $r(x) = -5x - 1$; $r(x) = 19$

Graph the linear function.

25. $g(x) = -2x - 3$

26. $h(x) = \frac{2}{3}x + 4$

27. The function $d(x) = 1375 - 110x$ represents the distance (in miles) a high-speed train is from its destination after x hours.

a. How far is the train from its destination after 8 hours?

b. How long does the train travel before reaching its destination?

3.5 Graphing Linear Equations in Standard Form (pp. 141–146)

Learning Target: Graph and interpret linear equations written in standard form.

Vocabulary

standard form

Graph the linear equation.

28. $x = 6$

29. $y = \frac{3}{2}$

Use intercepts to graph the linear equation. Label the points corresponding to the intercepts.

30. $2x + 3y = 6$

31. $8x - 4y = 16$

32. $-12x - 3y = 36$

33. $\frac{1}{2}x - y = -2$

34. Graph the equations $x = -2$, $y = 2$, and $-x + y = 2$. Find the area of the enclosed figure.

35. You lose track of how many 2-point baskets and 3-point baskets a team makes in a basketball game. The team misses all the 1-point baskets and still scores 54 points. The equation $2x + 3y = 54$ models the total points scored.

a. What do the terms and coefficients of the equation represent?

b. Can the number of 3-point baskets made be odd? Explain your reasoning.

c. Graph the equation. Interpret the intercepts.

d. Find four possible solutions in the context of the problem.

3.6 Graphing Linear Equations in Slope-Intercept Form (pp. 147–156)

Learning Target: Find the slope of a line and use slope-intercept form.

Vocabulary
slope
rise
run
slope-intercept form
constant function

36. Describe the slope of the line. Then find the slope.

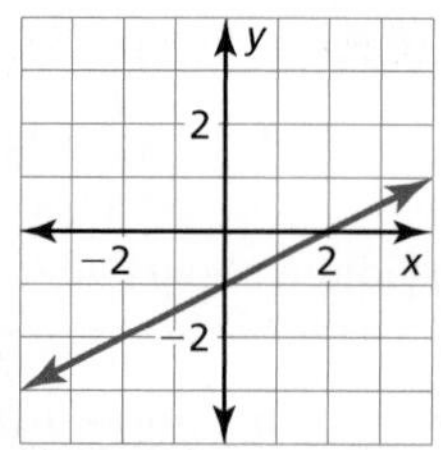

The points represented by the table lie on a line. Find the slope of the line.

37.

x	y
6	9
11	15
16	21
21	27

38.

x	y
3	−5
3	−2
3	5
3	8

39.

x	y
−4	−1.6
−3	−1.6
1	−1.6
9	−1.6

Graph the linear equation. Identify the x-intercept.

40. $y = 2x + 4$

41. $-5x + y = -10$

42. $-\frac{1}{2}x + y = 1$

43. $x + 3y = 9$

44. A linear function h models a relationship in which the dependent variable decreases 2 units for every 3 units the independent variable increases. The value of the function at 0 is 2. Graph h. Identify the slope and the intercepts of the graph.

3.7 Transformations of Linear Functions (pp. 157–166)

Learning Target: Graph transformations of linear functions.

Vocabulary
family of functions
parent function
transformation
translation
reflection
horizontal shrink
horizontal stretch
vertical stretch
vertical shrink

Let $f(x) = 3x + 4$. Graph f and h. Describe the transformation from the graph of f to the graph of h.

45. $h(x) = f(x + 3)$

46. $h(x) = f(x) + 1$

47. $h(x) = f(-x)$

48. $h(x) = -f(x)$

49. $h(x) = 3f(x)$

50. $h(x) = f(6x)$

51. Graph $f(x) = x$ and $g(x) = 5x + 1$. Describe the transformations from the graph of f to the graph of g.

52. Graph $k(x) = x$ and $p(x) = -3x - 2$. Describe the transformations from the graph of k to the graph of p.

53. The function $f(x) = 3x + 47$ represents the temperature (in degrees Fahrenheit) from 6 A.M. to 12 P.M., where x is the number of hours after 6 A.M. The function $h(x) = f(n \cdot x) + p$ represents the temperature (in degrees Fahrenheit) from 12 P.M. to 6 P.M., where x is the number of hours after 12 P.M. At 6 P.M., the temperature is 47°F. Find the values of n and p.

3.8 Graphing Absolute Value Functions (pp. 167–174)

Learning Target: Graph absolute value functions.

Vocabulary

absolute value function
vertex
vertex form

Graph the function. Compare the graph to the graph of $f(x) = |x|$. Find the domain and range.

54. $m(x) = |x| + 6$

55. $p(x) = |x - 4|$

56. $q(x) = 4|x|$

57. $r(x) = -\frac{1}{4}|x|$

Write an equation that represents the given transformation(s) of the graph of $g(x) = |x|$.

58. horizontal translation 9 units right

59. vertical shrink by a factor of $\frac{1}{6}$

60. vertical stretch by a factor of 5 and a reflection in the x-axis

61. Graph $f(x) = |x - 2| + 4$ and $g(x) = |3x - 2| + 4$. Compare the graph of g to the graph of f.

Compare the graphs. Find the value of h or a.

62.

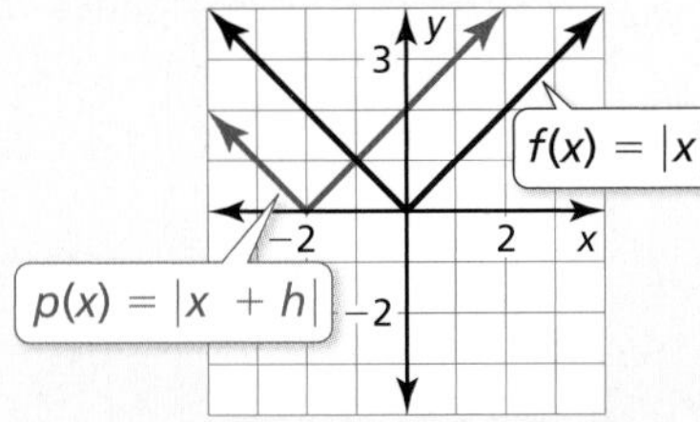

63.

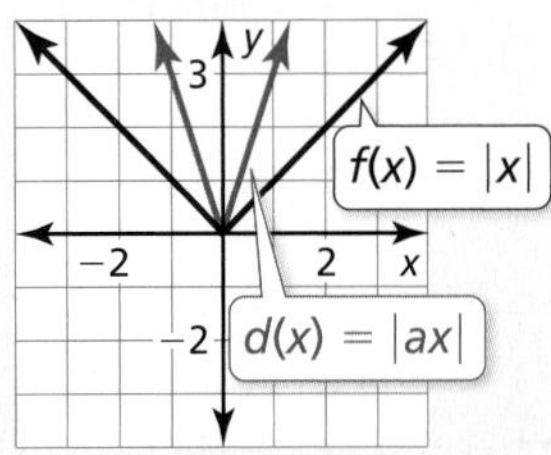

64. Write a function g whose graph is a horizontal shrink by a factor of $\frac{1}{3}$, followed by a translation 4 units right of the graph of f.

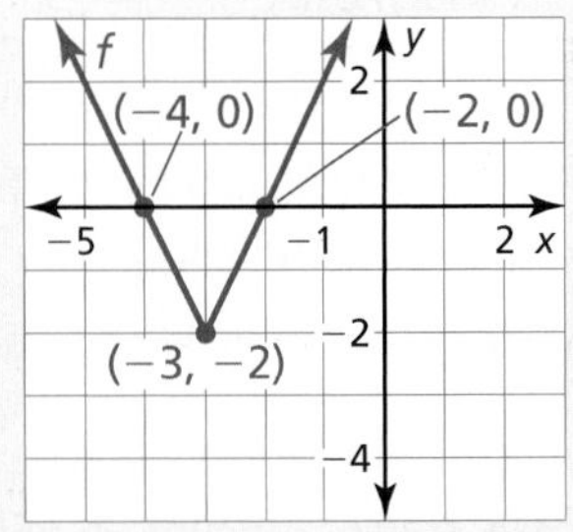

65. Your distance (in miles) from an exit after t hours on a highway is represented by $d(t) = |65t - 13|$.

a. Graph the function and interpret the intercepts.

b. A sign says that after this exit, you will need to travel an additional 52 miles before reaching a second exit. How long does it take to reach the second exit?

Mathematical Practices

Use Appropriate Tools Strategically

Mathematically proficient students use technological tools to explore concepts and solve problems.

1. Describe a situation in this chapter in which you used technology to explore a concept or solve a problem. Which technological tool did you use? Why?

2. You want to analyze the inputs and outputs of $f(x) = 3x + 8$. What technological tool would you use? Describe how you would use the tool that you chose.

3 Practice Test WITH CalcChat®

Determine whether the relation is a function. If the relation is a function, determine whether the function is *linear* or *nonlinear*. Explain.

1.

x	-1	0	1	2
y	6	5	9	14

2. $y = -2x + 3$

3. $x = -2$

Graph the equation and identify the intercept(s). If the equation is linear, find the slope.

4. $2x - 3y = 6$

5. $y = 4.5$

6. $y = \frac{4}{5}x + 3$

7. $y = |x - 1| - 2$

Use the graph of the function shown.

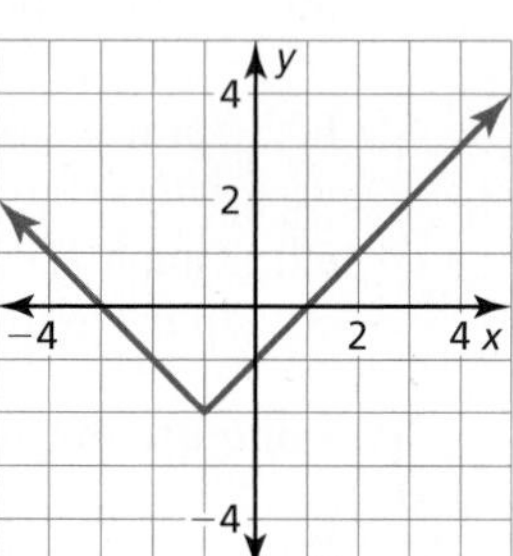

8. Find the domain and range. Is the domain *discrete* or *continuous*? Explain.

9. Approximate when the function is positive, negative, increasing, or decreasing. Then describe the end behavior of the function.

Graph f and g. Describe the transformations from the graph of f to the graph of g.

10. $f(x) = x$; $g(x) = -x + 3$

11. $f(x) = 4x$; $g(x) = 6x - 4$

12. $f(x) = 5x + 8$; $g(x) = -\frac{5}{2}x + 3$

13. $f(x) = |x|$; $g(x) = |2x + 4|$

14. The function $m = 30 - 3r$ represents the amount m (in dollars) of money you have after renting r video games.
   a. Identify the independent and dependent variables.
   b. Find the domain and range of the function. Is the domain *discrete* or *continuous*? Explain.
   c. Graph the function using its domain.

15. A mountain climber is scaling a cliff that is 500 feet above sea level. The graph shows the elevation of the climber over time.
   a. Interpret the slope and the y-intercept.
   b. How long does it take the climber to reach the top of the cliff? Explain.

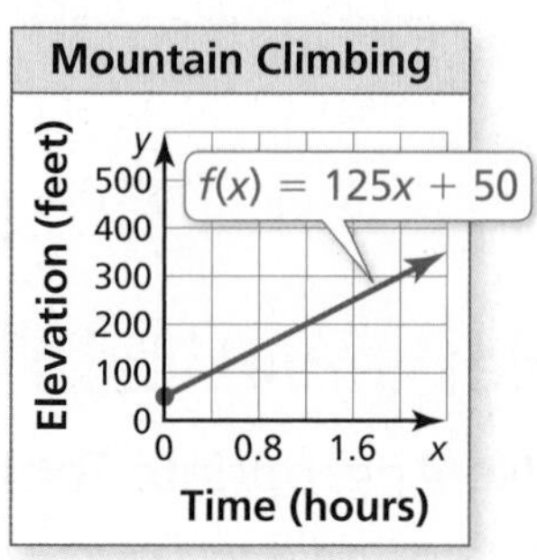

16. Graph the equations $y = 2$, $y = -3$, $y = -\frac{5}{2}x + 12$, and $-5x + 2y = -6$ in the same coordinate plane. What is the area of the enclosed shape?

17. A rock band releases a new single. The number (in thousands) of times the song is downloaded at an online store increases and then decreases as described by the function $n(t) = -2|t - 20| + 40$, where t is time (in weeks).
   a. Identify the independent and dependent variables.
   b. Graph n. Describe the transformations from the graph of $f(t) = |t|$ to the graph of n.

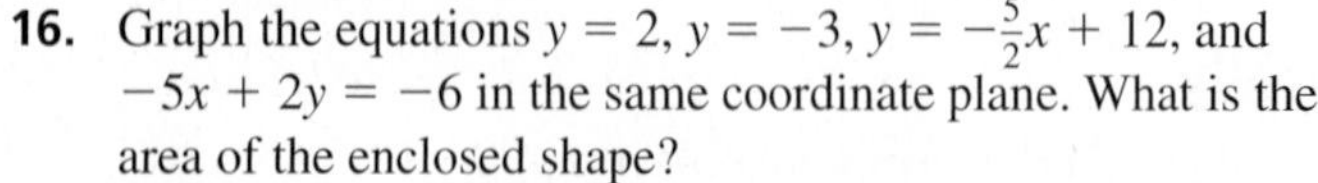

3 Performance Task
Into the Deep!

A 12-liter tank compressed to 200 bar can hold 2400 liters of air, which lasts a beginner scuba diver about 1 hour when diving at a depth of 10 meters.

Scuba tanks come in several sizes and are filled with compressed air. The table shows the capacities of several tanks compressed to a pressure of 200 bar or 300 bar.

		TANK SIZE			
		10 L	**12 L**	**15 L**	**18 L**
COMPRESSION	**200 bar**	2000 L	**2400 L**	3000 L	3600 L
	300 bar	3000 L	3600 L	4500 L	5400 L

Pressure increases 1 atmosphere (atm) for every 10-meter increase in depth.

As pressure doubles, the amount of air that you inhale with each breath also doubles.

1 atm	0 m
2 atm	10 m
3 atm	20 m
4 atm	30 m
5 atm	40 m

The maximum depth for recreational divers is about 40 meters.

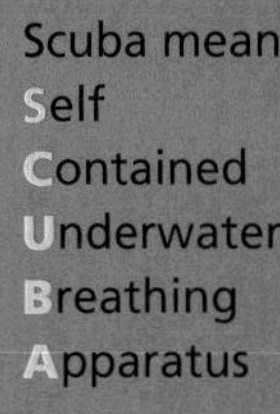

Scuba means:
Self
Contained
Underwater
Breathing
Apparatus

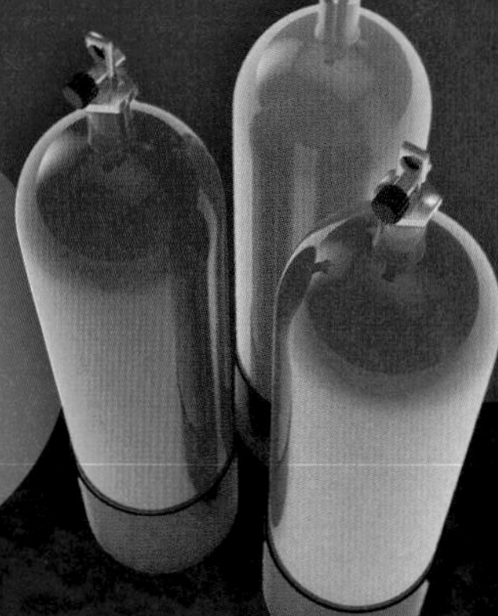

DIVE PLANNING

Plan a dive. Make sure to choose a tank size, a depth that you will dive to, and the amount of time that you will spend underwater. Include a graph of the amount of oxygen you will have remaining over time.

Explain how you can increase the duration of your dive. Describe how to model this change using transformations.

3 College and Career Readiness WITH CalcChat®

Tutorial videos are available for each exercise.

1. You claim you can use the values below to create a table that represents a linear function. Your friend claims he can create a table that represents a nonlinear function. What values can you use for x (the input) and y (the output) to support your claim? What values can your friend use?

	Your claim			
x				
y				

	Friend's claim			
x				
y				

−4   −3   −2   −1   0

1   2   3   4   5

2. A car rental company charges an initial fee of \$42 and a daily fee of \$12. A customer pays a total of \$138. How many days did the customer rent the car?

3. Which of the following numbers is *not* a solution of $6x - 11 \geq 4x - 13$?

Ⓐ −2   Ⓑ −1   Ⓒ 0   Ⓓ 1

4. Which ordered pair is a solution of the equation represented by the graph?

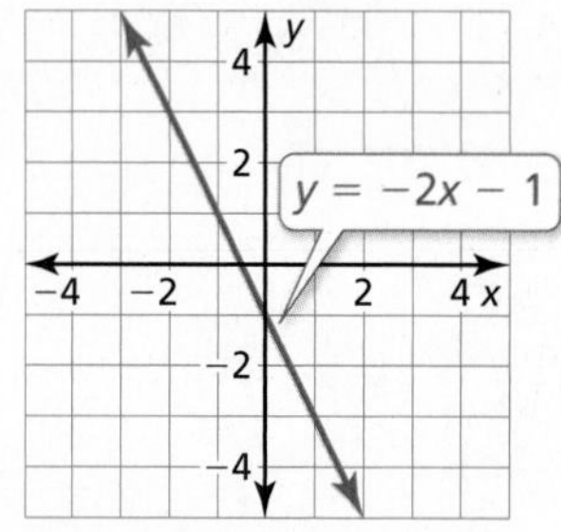

Ⓐ (−1.5, 4)   Ⓑ (−1, 0)   Ⓒ (2, 3)   Ⓓ (0, −1)

5. $18 + 1.5x$ is 8 less than 36.5. What is the value of $4x$?

Ⓐ 4   Ⓑ 7   Ⓒ 28   Ⓓ None of the above

6. Complete the inequality with <, ≤, >, or ≥ so that the solution is represented by the graph.

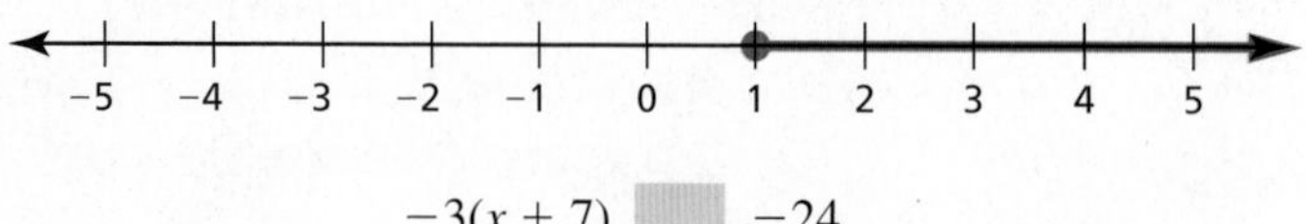

$-3(x + 7)$ ▢ -24

7. You work at a furniture store earning \$8.25 per hour. Does this situation represent a function? If so, find the domain and range.

8. The graph of the function $ax + by = 40$ has an x-intercept of -10 and a y-intercept of 8. What are the values of a and b?

Ⓐ $a = -10, b = 8$ Ⓑ $a = 10, b = -8$

Ⓒ $a = -4, b = 5$ Ⓓ $a = 5, b = -4$

9. Which equations have exactly one solution? Select all that apply.

Ⓐ $2x - 9 = 5x - 33$ Ⓑ $5x - 6 = 10x + 10$

Ⓒ $2(8x - 3) = 4(4x + 7)$ Ⓓ $-7x + 5 = 2(x - 10.1)$

Ⓔ $6(2x + 4) = 4(4x + 10)$ Ⓕ $8(3x + 4) = 2(12x + 16)$

10. The table shows the cost (in dollars) of bologna at a deli. Represent the data in a coordinate plane. Decide whether you should connect the points with a line. Explain your reasoning.

Pounds, x	0.5	1	1.5	2
Cost, y	3	6	9	12

11. The graph of a linear function f passes through the points $(0, 2)$ and $(3, -1)$. The graph of a linear function g passes through the points $(0, -8)$ and $(3, 4)$. Find the value of a so that $g(x) = a \cdot f(x)$.

12. What is the sum of the integer solutions of $2|x - 5| < 16$?

Ⓐ 72 Ⓑ 75 Ⓒ 85 Ⓓ 88

13. The graph of the function f is shown. Which of the following equal 2?

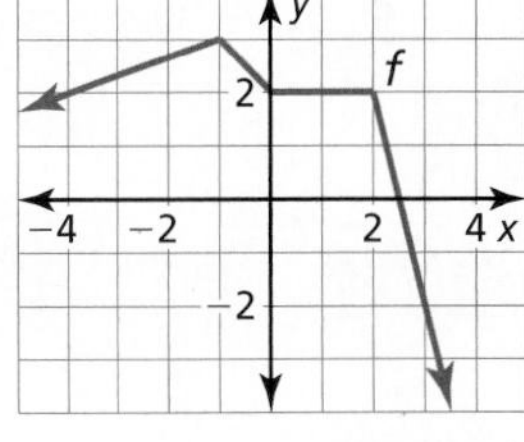

I. $f(-4)$ II. $f\left(\frac{5}{4}\right)$ III. $f(2)$

Ⓐ I only Ⓑ I and III only

Ⓒ II and III only Ⓓ I, II, and III

14. Your bank offers a text alert service that notifies you when your checking account balance drops below a specific amount. You set it up so you are notified when your balance drops below \$700. The balance is currently \$3000. You only use your account for paying your rent (no other deposits or deductions occur). Your rent each month is \$625.

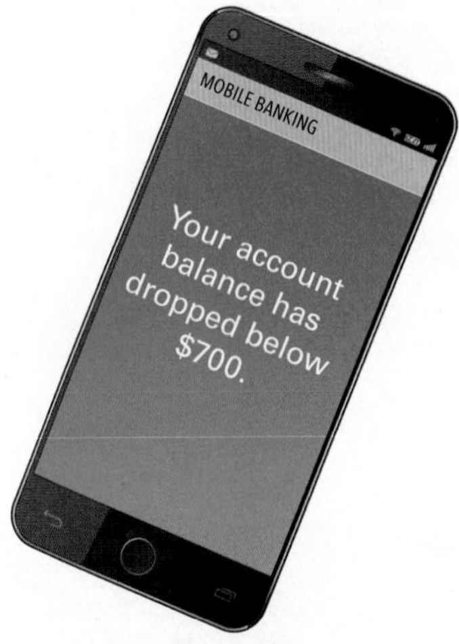

a. What is the maximum number of months you can pay your rent without receiving a text alert? Use an inequality to justify your answer.

b. You start paying rent in June. In what months can you pay your rent without making a deposit?

4 Writing Linear Functions

GO DIGITAL

- **4.1** Writing Equations in Slope-Intercept Form
- **4.2** Writing Equations in Point-Slope Form
- **4.3** Writing Equations of Parallel and Perpendicular Lines
- **4.4** Scatter Plots and Lines of Fit
- **4.5** Analyzing Lines of Fit
- **4.6** Arithmetic Sequences
- **4.7** Piecewise Functions

NATIONAL GEOGRAPHIC EXPLORER

Katey Walter Anthony

Dr. Katey Walter Anthony measures the rate at which the permafrost in Alaskan lakes is thawing, causing a release of methane. Her data feed into mathematical models that predict global warming, which inspire ideas to reduce it. One of the primary ideas for reducing global warming is to implement the use of renewable energy.

- What are the main ways that electricity is generated? Of these, which are classified as *renewable energy*?
- On a wind farm, how much electricity is produced per day by each turbine?
- How many homes does a typical wind turbine power?

STEM

Wind is one example of a renewable energy resource that can provide long-lasting benefits. In the Performance Task, you will write a proposal for a new wind farm in your community, detailing the size, cost, and energy production of the farm.

Renewable Energy

Preparing for Chapter 4

Chapter Learning Target Understand writing linear functions.

Chapter Success Criteria
- ◆ I can determine the slope given ordered pairs, a graph, or a context.
- ◆ I can write the equation of a line in different forms.
- ■ I can interpret scatter plots and analyze lines of fit.
- ■ I can write a function that represents an arithmetic sequence to solve a real-life problem.

◆ Surface
■ Deep

Chapter Vocabulary

Work with a partner. Discuss each of the vocabulary terms.

linear model	correlation	causation
point-slope form	interpolation	piecewise function
scatter plot	extrapolation	step function

Mathematical Practices

Make Sense of Problems and Persevere in Solving Them

Mathematically proficient students try special cases and simpler forms of the original problem in order to gain insight into the solution.

Work with a partner. A wind farm contains 250 wind turbines that produce varying amounts of energy each day.

1. A particular turbine on the wind farm produces 545 kilowatt hours (kWh) of energy every half hour that it runs. The turbine runs for 4 hours and 55 minutes. What is the total amount of energy produced by the turbine?

Your friend solves a simpler form of the problem, as shown.

$$\text{Energy production} \approx \frac{550 \text{ kWh}}{1/2 \text{ h}} \bullet 5 \text{ h}$$

$$= \frac{1100 \text{ kWh}}{1 \cancel{\text{h}}} \bullet 5 \cancel{\text{h}}$$

$$= 5500 \text{ kWh}$$

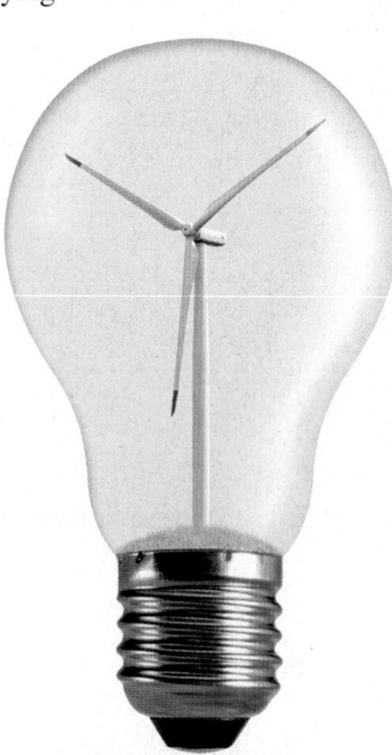

a. Your friend solves the original problem and determines that the turbine produces 5600 kilowatt hours of energy. Without solving, determine whether this solution is reasonable. Explain your reasoning.

b. Solve the original problem. Is your answer reasonable? Explain.

2. The owner of the wind farm wants to know the annual energy output of the entire farm. How could you use a simpler form of the problem to find the solution?

4 Prepare WITH CalcChat®

Using a Coordinate Plane

Example 1 **What ordered pair corresponds to point *A*?**

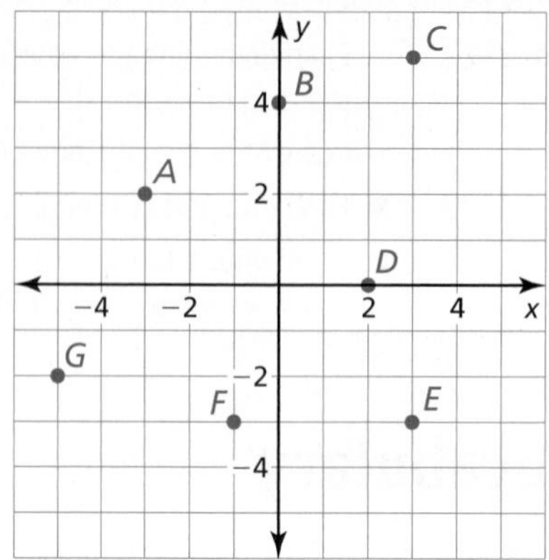

Point A is 3 units to the left of the origin and 2 units up. So, the x-coordinate is -3 and the y-coordinate is 2.

▶ The ordered pair $(-3, 2)$ corresponds to point A.

Use the graph to answer the question.

1. What ordered pair corresponds to point G?

2. What ordered pair corresponds to point D?

3. Which point is located in Quadrant I?

4. Which point is located in Quadrant IV?

Rewriting Equations

Example 2 **Solve the equation $3x - 2y = 8$ for y.**

$3x - 2y = 8$	Write the equation.
$3x - 2y - 3x = 8 - 3x$	Subtraction Property of Equality
$-2y = 8 - 3x$	Simplify.
$\frac{-2y}{-2} = \frac{8 - 3x}{-2}$	Division Property of Equality
$y = -4 + \frac{3}{2}x$	Simplify.

Solve the equation for y.

5. $x - y = 5$

6. $6x + 3y = -1$

7. $0 = 2y - 8x + 10$

8. $-x + 4y - 28 = 0$

9. $2y + 1 - x = 7x$

10. $y - 4 = 3x + 5y$

11. **MP REASONING** Both coordinates of a point (x, y) are multiplied by the same negative number. How does this change the location of the point? (*Hint:* Consider every possible location of the original point.)

4.1 Writing Equations in Slope-Intercept Form

Learning Target Write equations of lines in slope-intercept form.

Success Criteria
- I can find the slope and the y-intercept of a line.
- I can use the slope and the y-intercept to write an equation of a line.
- I can write equations in slope-intercept form to solve real-life problems.

EXPLORE IT! Interpreting a Real-Life Graph

Work with a partner. You find the following graph online.

Landline Phones and Cell Phones in U.S. households

Percent (0–100) vs. Year (2005–2017)

- Working landline phone: (2005, 90), (2017, 43.8)
- Cell phone only: (2005, 7.3), (2017, 52.5)

a. Explain what the graph represents. Make several observations from the graph.

b. Your friend thinks something is wrong with the graph because for a given year, the two percents do not add up to 100%. Is your friend's reasoning valid? Explain.

c. You want to write an equation that represents each line. What do you need to consider to write the equations? What do you need to calculate?

d. Approximate the slope of each line. Interpret each slope in the context of the problem.

e. When do you expect the percent of U.S. households with only cell phone service will exceed 70%? Explain how you made your prediction.

Math Practice

Specify Units
What would you let the independent variable represent in your equations in part (c)? Why?

Writing Equations in Slope-Intercept Form

Vocabulary AZ VOCAB

linear model, *p. 190*

EXAMPLE 1 **Using Slopes and *y*-Intercepts to Write Equations**

Write an equation of each line with the given slope and *y*-intercept.

a. slope $= -3$; *y*-intercept $= \frac{1}{2}$ **b.** slope $= 0$; *y*-intercept $= -2$

SOLUTION

a. $y = mx + b$ Write the slope-intercept form.

$y = -3x + \frac{1}{2}$ Substitute -3 for m and $\frac{1}{2}$ for b.

▶ An equation is $y = -3x + \frac{1}{2}$.

b. $y = mx + b$ Write the slope-intercept form.

$y = 0x + (-2)$ Substitute 0 for m and -2 for b.

$y = -2$ Simplify.

▶ An equation is $y = -2$.

SELF-ASSESSMENT 1 I do not understand. 2 I can do it with help. 3 I can do it on my own. 4 I can teach someone else.

Write an equation of the line with the given slope and *y*-intercept.

1. slope $= 7$; *y*-intercept $= 2$

2. slope $= \frac{1}{3}$; *y*-intercept $= -1$

3. **MP REASONING** Write equations that represent the *x*-axis and the *y*-axis. Are the equations in slope-intercept form? Explain your reasoning.

EXAMPLE 2 **Using Graphs to Write Equations**

Write an equation of each line in slope-intercept form.

a.

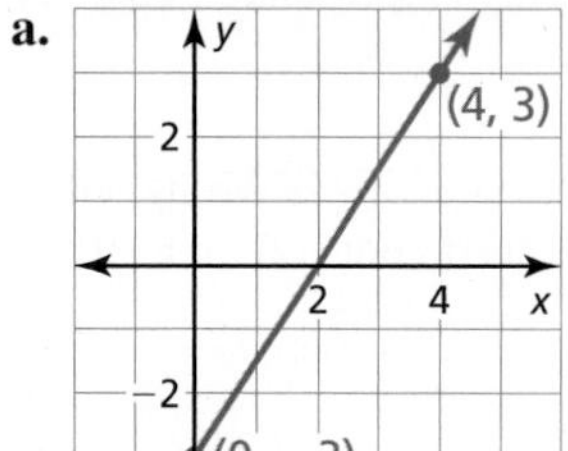

b.

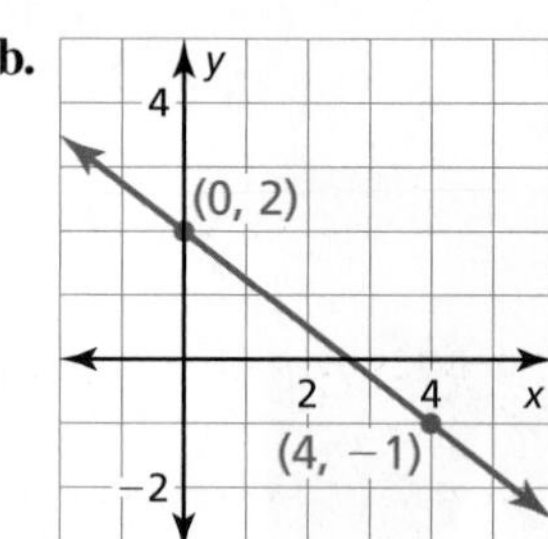

STUDY TIP

You can use any two points on a line to find the slope.

SOLUTION

a. Find the slope and *y*-intercept.

Let $(x_1, y_1) = (0, -3)$ and $(x_2, y_2) = (4, 3)$.

$$m = \frac{y_2 - y_1}{x_2 - x_1}$$

$$= \frac{3 - (-3)}{4 - 0} = \frac{6}{4}, \text{ or } \frac{3}{2}$$

Because the line crosses the *y*-axis at $(0, -3)$, the *y*-intercept is -3.

▶ So, the equation is $y = \frac{3}{2}x - 3$.

b. Find the slope and *y*-intercept.

Let $(x_1, y_1) = (0, 2)$ and $(x_2, y_2) = (4, -1)$.

$$m = \frac{y_2 - y_1}{x_2 - x_1}$$

$$= \frac{-1 - 2}{4 - 0} = \frac{-3}{4}, \text{ or } -\frac{3}{4}$$

Because the line crosses the *y*-axis at $(0, 2)$, the *y*-intercept is 2.

▶ So, the equation is $y = -\frac{3}{4}x + 2$.

STUDY TIP

After writing an equation, check that the given points are solutions of the equation.

EXAMPLE 3 Using Points to Write Equations

Write an equation of the line that passes through each pair of points.

a. $(-3, 5), (0, -1)$

b. $(0, -5.8), (8, -5.8)$

SOLUTION

a. Find the slope and y-intercept.

$$m = \frac{-1 - 5}{0 - (-3)} = \frac{-6}{3} = -2$$

Because the line crosses the y-axis at $(0, -1)$, the y-intercept is -1.

▶ So, an equation is $y = -2x - 1$.

b. Find the slope and y-intercept.

$$m = \frac{-5.8 - (-5.8)}{8 - 0} = \frac{0}{8} = 0$$

Because the line crosses the y-axis at $(0, -5.8)$, the y-intercept is -5.8.

▶ So, an equation is $y = -5.8$.

EXAMPLE 4 Writing a Linear Function

Write a linear function f with the values $f(0) = 10$ and $f(6) = 34$.

REMEMBER

If f is a function and x is in its domain, then $f(x)$ represents the output of f corresponding to the input x.

SOLUTION

Step 1 Interpret the function values. The values $f(0) = 10$ and $f(6) = 34$ indicate that $(0, 10)$ and $(6, 34)$ are on the graph of f.

Step 2 Find the slope of the line that passes through $(0, 10)$ and $(6, 34)$.

$$m = \frac{34 - 10}{6 - 0} = \frac{24}{6} = 4$$

Step 3 Write an equation of the line. Because the line crosses the y-axis at $(0, 10)$, the y-intercept is 10. Use the slope and y-intercept to write an equation of the line.

$y = mx + b$ Write the slope-intercept form.

$y = 4x + 10$ Substitute 4 for m and 10 for b.

▶ A function is $f(x) = 4x + 10$.

SELF-ASSESSMENT

1 I do not understand. 2 I can do it with help. 3 I can do it on my own. 4 I can teach someone else.

4. Write an equation of each line shown at the right in slope-intercept form.

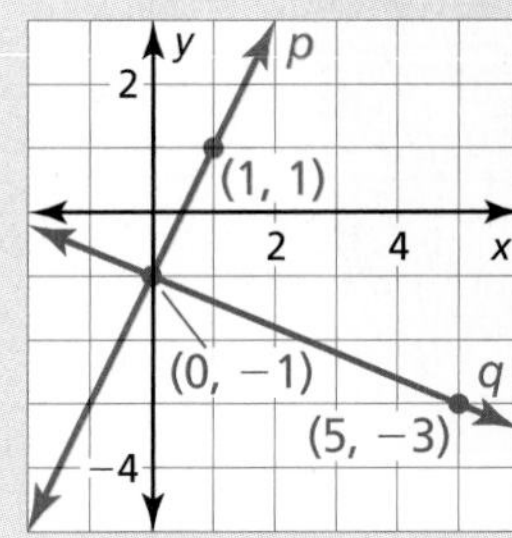

Write an equation of the line that passes through the given points.

5. $(0, -2), (4, 10)$

6. $\left(-\frac{4}{5}, \frac{1}{2}\right), \left(13, \frac{1}{2}\right)$

7. WRITING In Example 3(b), explain how you can write the equation without performing any calculations.

Write a linear function g with the given values.

8. $g(0) = 9, g(8) = 7$

9. $g(-2.5) = -5, g(0) = -4$

10. MP REASONING A function f represents a proportional relationship where $f(1) = \frac{2}{3}$. Write the function.

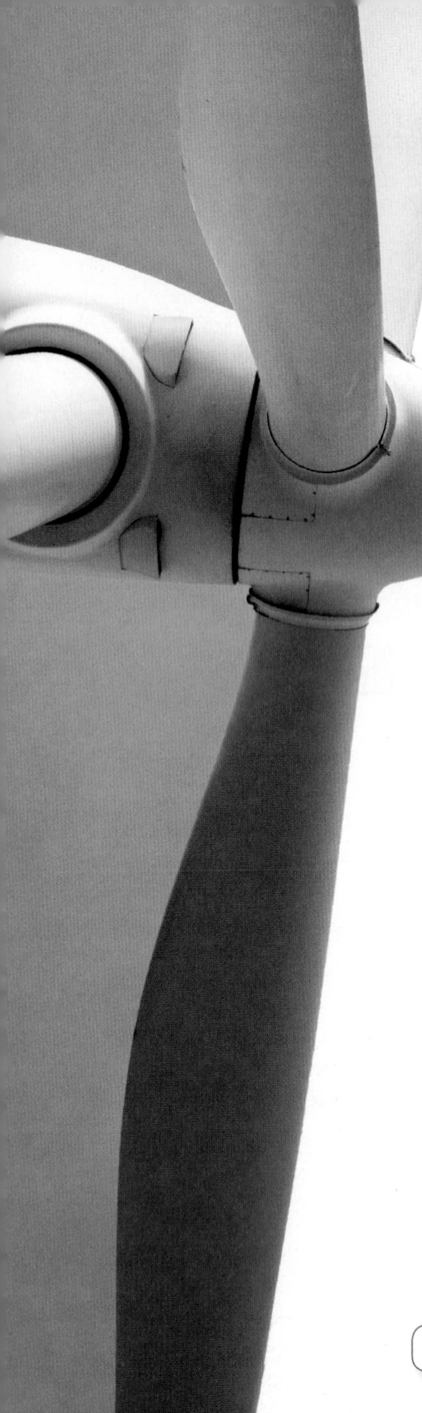

Solving Real-Life Problems

A **linear model** is a linear function that models a real-life situation. When a quantity y changes at a constant rate with respect to a quantity x, you can use the equation $y = mx + b$ to model the relationship. The value of m is the constant rate of change, and the value of b is the initial, or starting, value of y.

EXAMPLE 5 Modeling Real Life

Excluding hydroelectric and solar, renewable energy sources in the U.S. generated 143.4 million megawatt hours of electricity in 2009. This quantity increased at an approximately constant rate and reached 333.0 million megawatt hours by 2017. Estimate the amount of electricity generated from these sources in 2021.

SOLUTION

1. **Understand the Problem** You know the amounts of electricity generated in two distinct years and that it increased at a constant rate. You are asked to estimate the amount generated in a later year.

2. **Make a Plan** Find the initial value and the rate of change. Use these values to write a linear model and estimate the amount generated in 2021.

3. **Solve and Check** Let x represent the number of years since 2009 and let y represent the number of megawatt hours (in millions). Because 2009 corresponds to $x = 0$ and 2017 corresponds to $x = 8$, the linear model representing the situation passes through the points (0, 143.4) and (8, 333).

   Let $(x_1, y_1) = (0, 143.4)$ and $(x_2, y_2) = (8, 333)$. The initial value is the y-intercept b, which is 143.4. The rate of change is the slope m.

$$m = \frac{y_2 - y_1}{x_2 - x_1} = \frac{333 - 143.4}{8 - 0} = \frac{189.6}{8} = 23.7$$

Megawatt hours (millions)	=	Initial value	+	Rate of change	•	Years since 2009
y	=	143.4	+	23.7	•	x

$y = 143.4 + 23.7x$ Write the equation.

2021 corresponds to $x = 12$. → $y = 143.4 + 23.7(12)$ Substitute 12 for x.

$y = 427.8$ Simplify.

▶ The linear model is $y = 23.7x + 143.4$. The model estimates that renewable energy sources generated about 427.8 million megawatt hours in 2021.

Another Way Use the slope to find amounts of electricity generated in later years.

x	2017	2018	2019	2020	2021
y	333.0	356.7	380.4	404.1	427.8

+ 23.7 + 23.7 + 23.7 + 23.7

SELF-ASSESSMENT 1 I do not understand. 2 I can do it with help. 3 I can do it on my own. 4 I can teach someone else.

11. Wind energy in the U.S. generated about 74 million megawatt hours of electricity in 2009. This quantity increased at an approximately constant rate and reached about 254 million megawatt hours by 2017. Estimate how many more megawatt hours were generated from wind in 2020 than in 2016. Explain your reasoning.

4.1 Practice WITH CalcChat® AND CalcView®

In Exercises 1–6, write an equation of the line with the given slope and *y*-intercept. ▶ *Example 1*

1. slope: 2
y-intercept: 9

2. slope: 0
y-intercept: 5

3. slope: -3
y-intercept: 0

4. slope: -7.5
y-intercept: 1.5

5. slope: $\frac{2}{3}$
y-intercept: -8

6. slope: $-\frac{3}{4}$
y-intercept: $-\frac{1}{4}$

In Exercises 7–10, write an equation of the line in slope-intercept form. ▶ *Example 2*

7.

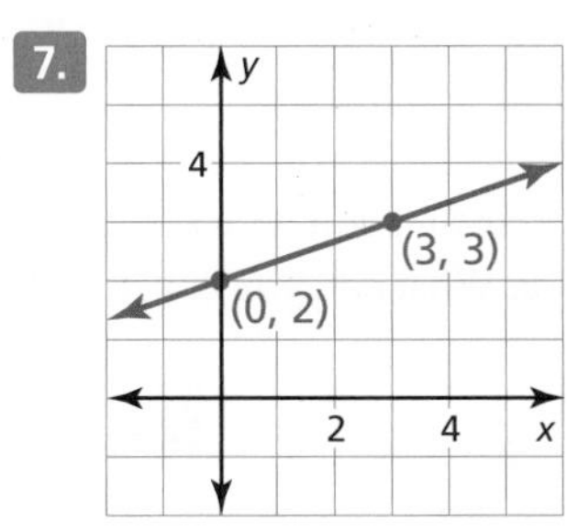

8.

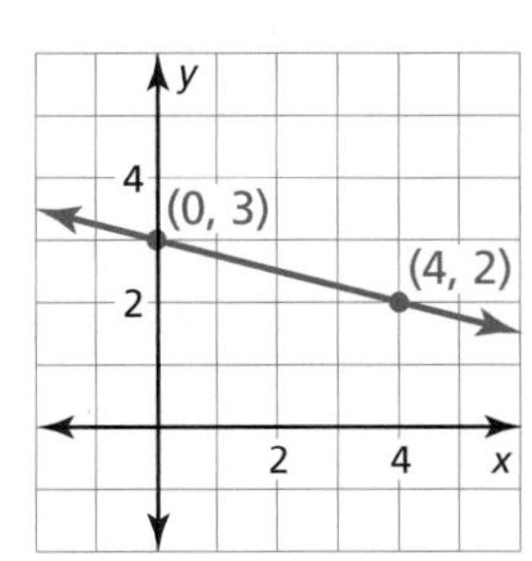

9.

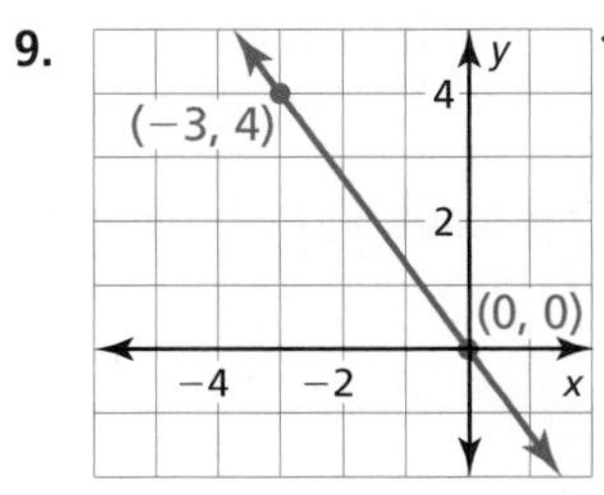

10.

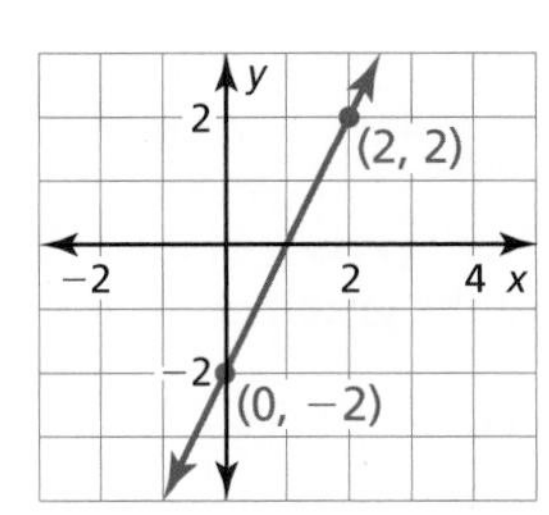

In Exercises 11–16, write an equation of the line that passes through the given points. ▶ *Example 3*

11. (3, 1), (0, 10)

12. (2, 7), (0, -5)

13. (2, -4), (0, -4)

14. (-6, 0), (0, -24)

15. (0, 5.2), (-1.5, 1)

16. $\left(0, \frac{1}{3}\right), \left(-5, \frac{7}{3}\right)$

In Exercises 17–22, write a linear function *f* with the given values. ▶ *Example 4*

17. $f(0) = 2, f(2) = 4$

18. $f(0) = 7, f(3) = 1$

19. $f(4) = -3, f(0) = -2$

20. $f(5) = -1, f(0) = -5$

21. $f\left(-\frac{1}{2}\right) = 1, f(0) = -4$

22. $f(0) = 3.75, f(-6) = 3.75$

In Exercises 23 and 24, write a linear function *f* with the given values.

23.

x	$f(x)$
1	-1
0	1
-1	3

24.

x	$f(x)$
-4	-2
-2	-1
0	0

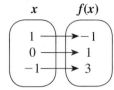

25. ERROR ANALYSIS Describe and correct the error in writing an equation of the line with a slope of 2 and a *y*-intercept of 7.

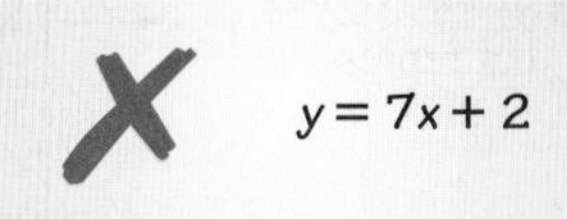

26. ERROR ANALYSIS Describe and correct the error in writing an equation of the line shown.

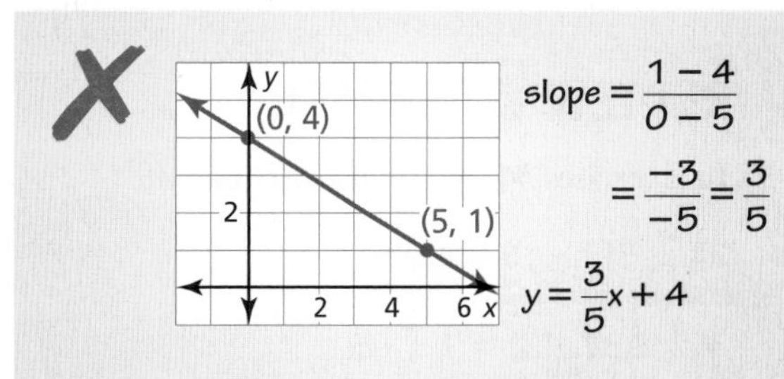

27. MODELING REAL LIFE A public university charged \$9200 for tuition and fees in the 2014–2015 academic year. This cost increased at a constant rate and reached \$10,900 in the 2019–2020 academic year. Estimate the cost of tuition and fees in the 2023–2024 academic year. ▶ *Example 5*

28. MODELING REAL LIFE A recording studio charges musicians an initial fee of \$50 to record an album. Studio time costs an additional \$75 per hour. Is it less expensive to purchase 12 hours of recording time at the studio or a \$795 music software program that you can use to record on your own computer? Use a linear model to justify your answer.

29. **MAKING AN ARGUMENT** Your friend claims that given $f(0)$ and any other value of a linear function f, you can write an equation in slope-intercept form that represents the function. Your cousin disagrees, claiming that the two points could lie on a vertical line. Who is correct? Explain.

30. **THOUGHT PROVOKING** A linear function f has values $f(-9) = -2$ and $f(-3) = -6$. The y-intercept of a linear function g is six greater than the y-intercept of f, and the x-intercept of g is the same as the x-intercept of f. Write equations that represent f and g.

31. **CONNECTING CONCEPTS** Line ℓ is a reflection in the x-axis of line k. Write an equation that represents line k.

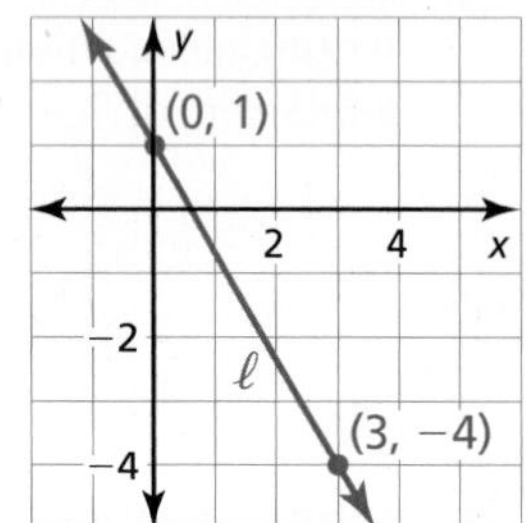

32. **HOW DO YOU SEE IT?** The profits of Company A and Company B x years since 2016 can be modeled by $f(x) = ax + b$ and $g(x) = cx + d$, respectively.

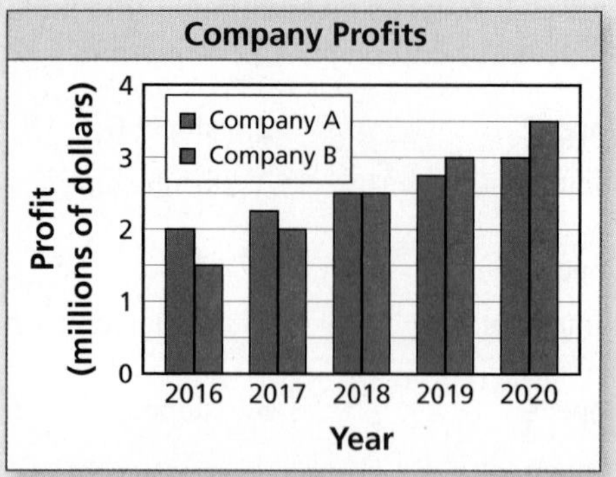

a. Compare the values of b and d. Explain your reasoning.

b. Compare the values of a and c. Explain your reasoning.

33. **DIG DEEPER** Write a linear function with the values $f(0) = b$ and $f(1) = b + m$. What can you conclude?

REVIEW & REFRESH

In Exercises 34–36, solve the equation.

34. $-4y - 10 = 4(y - 3)$

35. $2(3d + 3) = 7 + 6d$

36. $-5(-4 + 2n) = -10(n - 2)$

37. Write an equation of the line in slope-intercept form.

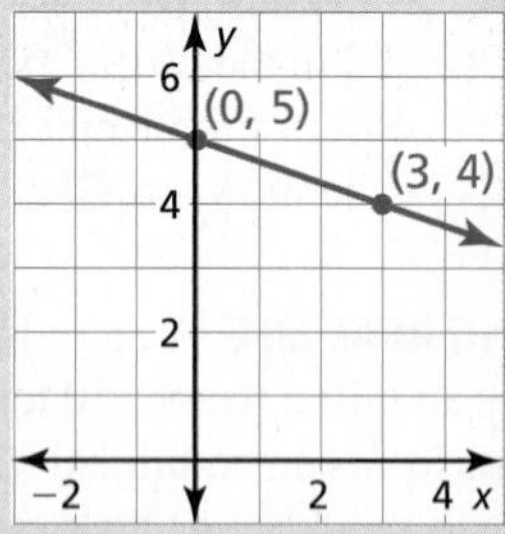

38. Use intercepts to graph the linear equation $-4x + 2y = 16$. Label the points corresponding to the intercepts.

39. Let $g(x) = -\frac{1}{2}|x + 2| - 4$. (a) Describe the transformations from the graph of $f(x) = |x|$ to the graph of g. (b) Graph g.

40. **MP REASONING** What is the least value of $4x - 5$ when $-\frac{1}{5} \leq x - \frac{7}{10}$?

In Exercises 41 and 42, find the slope and y-intercept of the graph of the linear equation.

41. $y = 9.5$

42. $10x + y = -7$

43. Tell whether 18 is a solution of $-13 < 5 - x$.

44. **MODELING REAL LIFE** Your total earnings (in dollars) after working x weeks are represented by the function f. You get a promotion, and your weekly earnings are multiplied by a factor of a. You then get a one-time bonus of k dollars. Use the graph to find and interpret the values of a and k.

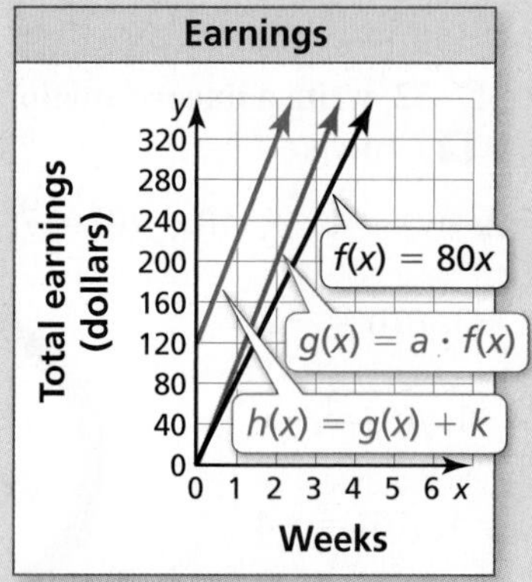

4.2 Writing Equations in Point-Slope Form

Learning Target Write equations of lines in point-slope form.

Success Criteria
- I can use a point on a line and the slope to write an equation of the line.
- I can use any two points to write an equation of a line.
- I can write a linear function using any two function values.

EXPLORE IT! Writing Equations

Work with a partner.

a. For each graph, find the y-intercept of the line that has the given slope and passes through the given point. Then write an equation of the line.

$m = \frac{1}{2}$

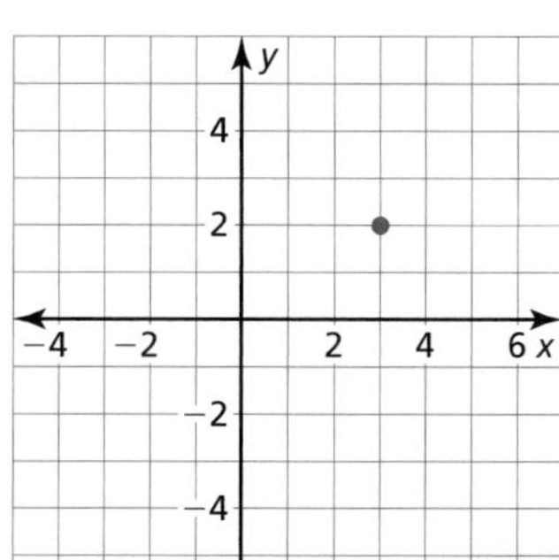

$m = -2$

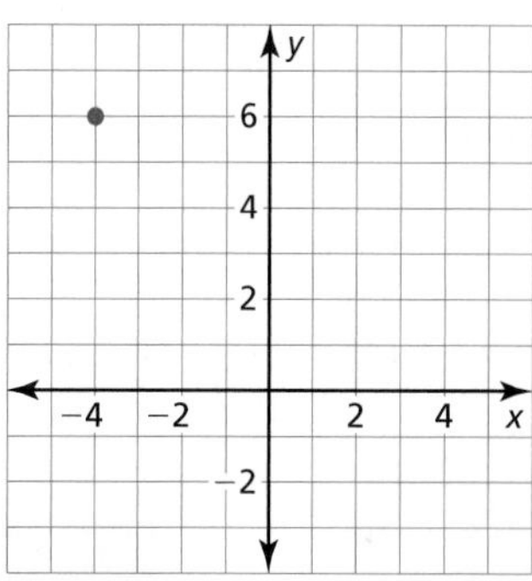

b. The point (x_1, y_1) is a given point on a nonvertical line. The point (x, y) is any other point on the line. Write an equation that represents the slope m. Then solve your equation for $(y - y_1)$. What does the resulting equation represent? Explain your reasoning.

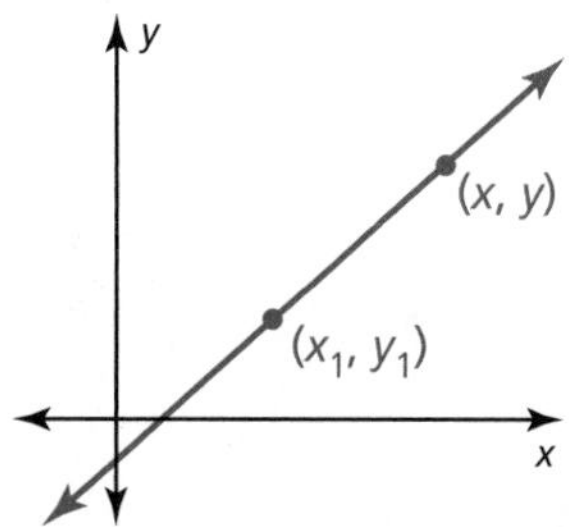

c. Justify your equations in part (a) using the results of part (b). Which method do you prefer? Explain your reasoning.

Math Practice

Find Entry Points
What information do you need in order to write an equation of a line using your equation in part (b)?

Writing Equations of Lines in Point-Slope Form

Vocabulary 

point-slope form, *p. 194*

Given a point on a line and the slope of the line, you can write an equation of the line. Consider the line that passes through (2, 3) and has a slope of $\frac{1}{2}$. Let (x, y) be another point on the line where $x \neq 2$. You can write an equation relating x and y using the slope formula with $(x_1, y_1) = (2, 3)$ and $(x_2, y_2) = (x, y)$.

$m = \dfrac{y_2 - y_1}{x_2 - x_1}$ — Write the slope formula.

$\dfrac{1}{2} = \dfrac{y - 3}{x - 2}$ — Substitute values.

$\dfrac{1}{2}(x - 2) = y - 3$ — Multiply each side by $(x - 2)$.

The equation in *point-slope form* is $y - 3 = \frac{1}{2}(x - 2)$.

KEY IDEA

Point-Slope Form

Words A linear equation written in the form $y - y_1 = m(x - x_1)$ is in **point-slope form**. The line passes through the point (x_1, y_1), and the slope of the line is m.

Algebra $y - y_1 = m(x - x_1)$

slope (points to m); passes through (x_1, y_1)

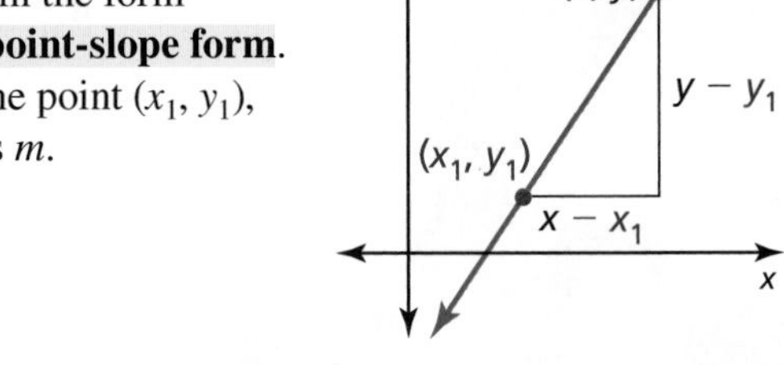

EXAMPLE 1 Using a Slope and a Point to Write an Equation

Write an equation in point-slope form of the line that passes through the point $(-8, 3)$ and has a slope of $\frac{1}{4}$.

SOLUTION

$y - y_1 = m(x - x_1)$ — Write the point-slope form.

$y - 3 = \frac{1}{4}[x - (-8)]$ — Substitute $\frac{1}{4}$ for m, -8 for x_1, and 3 for y_1.

$y - 3 = \frac{1}{4}(x + 8)$ — Simplify.

▶ An equation is $y - 3 = \frac{1}{4}(x + 8)$.

Check

$y - 3 = \frac{1}{4}(x + 8)$

$3 - 3 \stackrel{?}{=} \frac{1}{4}(-8 + 8)$

$0 = 0$ ✓

SELF-ASSESSMENT 1 I do not understand. 2 I can do it with help. 3 I can do it on my own. 4 I can teach someone else.

Write an equation in point-slope form of the line that passes through the given point and has the given slope.

1. $(3, -1)$; $m = -2$
2. $(4, 0)$; $m = -\frac{2}{3}$
3. $(2, 4.5)$; $m = 1.25$
4. $\left(-\frac{2}{5}, \frac{4}{5}\right)$; $m = \frac{3}{4}$
5. **MP STRUCTURE** Without simplifying, identify the slope of the line given by the equation $y - 5 = -2(x + 5)$. Then identify one point on the line.

Writing Equations of Lines Given Two Points

When you are given two points on a line, you can write an equation of the line using the following steps.

Step 1 Find the slope of the line.

Step 2 Use the slope and one of the points to write an equation of the line in point-slope form.

> **ANOTHER WAY**
>
> You can use either of the given points to write an equation of the line.
>
> Use $m = -2$ and $(3, -2)$.
>
> $$y - (-2) = -2(x - 3)$$
> $$y + 2 = -2x + 6$$
> $$y = -2x + 4$$

EXAMPLE 2 Using Two Points to Write an Equation

WATCH

Write an equation in slope-intercept form of the line shown.

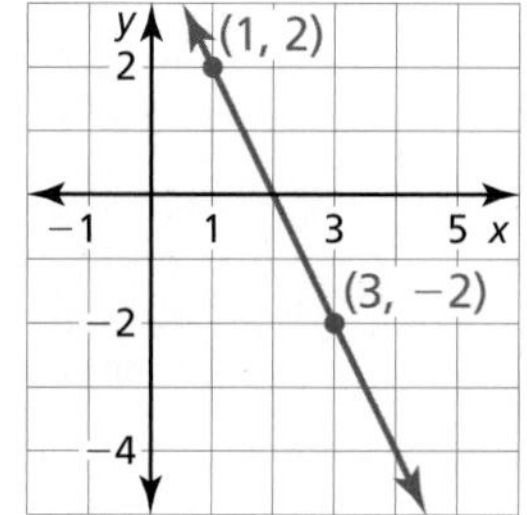

SOLUTION

Step 1 Find the slope of the line.

$$m = \frac{-2 - 2}{3 - 1} = \frac{-4}{2} = -2$$

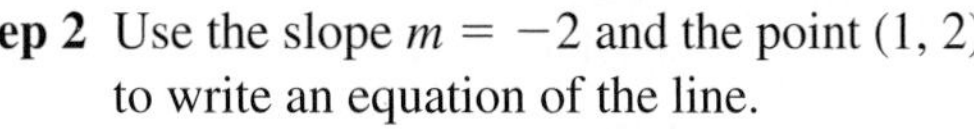

Step 2 Use the slope $m = -2$ and the point $(1, 2)$ to write an equation of the line.

$y - y_1 = m(x - x_1)$	Write the point-slope form.
$y - 2 = -2(x - 1)$	Substitute -2 for m, 1 for x_1, and 2 for y_1.
$y - 2 = -2x + 2$	Distributive Property
$y = -2x + 4$	Write in slope-intercept form.

▶ An equation is $y = -2x + 4$.

EXAMPLE 3 Writing a Linear Function

Write a linear function f with the values $f(4) = -2$ and $f(8) = 4$.

SOLUTION

The function values $f(4) = -2$ and $f(8) = 4$ indicate that $(4, -2)$ and $(8, 4)$ are on the graph of f.

Step 1 Find the slope of the line that passes through $(4, -2)$ and $(8, 4)$.

$$m = \frac{4 - (-2)}{8 - 4} = \frac{6}{4} = 1.5$$

Step 2 Use the slope $m = 1.5$ and the point $(8, 4)$ to write an equation of the line.

$y - y_1 = m(x - x_1)$	Write the point-slope form.
$y - 4 = 1.5(x - 8)$	Substitute 1.5 for m, 8 for x_1, and 4 for y_1.
$y - 4 = 1.5x - 12$	Distributive Property
$y = 1.5x - 8$	Write in slope-intercept form.

▶ A function is $f(x) = 1.5x - 8$.

SELF-ASSESSMENT 1 I do not understand. 2 I can do it with help. 3 I can do it on my own. 4 I can teach someone else.

Write an equation in slope-intercept form of the line that passes through the given points.

6. $(1, 4), (3, 10)$

7. $(-4, -1), (8, -4)$

8. Write a linear function g with the values $g(2) = 3$ and $g(6) = 5$.

Solving Real-Life Problems

GO DIGITAL

EXAMPLE 4 Modeling Real Life

Your student council is ordering customized foam hands to promote school spirit. The table shows the total costs of ordering different numbers of foam hands. Determine the total cost of ordering 150 foam hands.

Number of foam hands	4	6	8	10
Total cost (dollars)	51.40	57.10	62.80	68.50

SOLUTION

1. **Understand the Problem** You know the total costs for four different orders of foam hands. You are asked to determine the total cost of ordering 150 foam hands.
2. **Make a Plan** Find the rate of change for consecutive data pairs in the table. If the rate of change is constant, you can use the point-slope form to write a linear model. Use the model to find the total cost of 150 foam hands.
3. **Solve and Check**

Step 1 Find the rate of change for consecutive data pairs in the table.

$$\frac{57.10 - 51.40}{6 - 4} = 2.85, \quad \frac{62.80 - 57.10}{8 - 6} = 2.85, \quad \frac{68.50 - 62.80}{10 - 8} = 2.85$$

Because the rate of change is constant, the data are linear.

Step 2 Use the constant rate of change (slope) $m = 2.85$ and the data pair (4, 51.40) to write a linear model. Let C represent the total cost (in dollars) and let n represent the number of foam hands.

$C - C_1 = m(n - n_1)$	Write the point-slope form.
$C - 51.40 = 2.85(n - 4)$	Substitute 2.85 for m, 4 for n_1, and 51.40 for C_1.
$C - 51.40 = 2.85n - 11.40$	Distributive Property
$C = 2.85n + 40$	Write in slope-intercept form.

To find the total cost of ordering 150 foam hands, find C when $n = 150$.

$$C = 2.85(150) + 40 = 467.50$$

▶ The total cost of ordering 150 foam hands is $467.50.

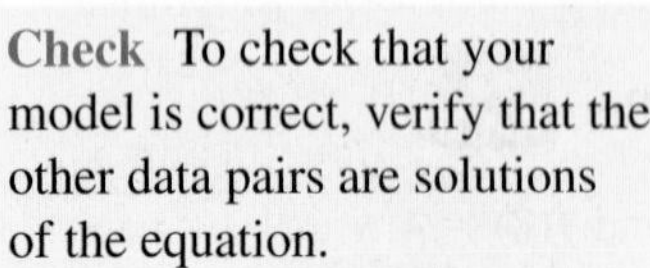

Check To check that your model is correct, verify that the other data pairs are solutions of the equation.

$57.10 = 2.85(6) + 40$ ✓

$62.80 = 2.85(8) + 40$ ✓

$68.50 = 2.85(10) + 40$ ✓

SELF-ASSESSMENT

1 I do not understand. 2 I can do it with help. 3 I can do it on my own. 4 I can teach someone else.

9. A political campaign manager orders bumper stickers online. The company charges a shipping fee in addition to the cost per sticker. Customers who order more than 100 stickers receive a 25% discount on the price of each bumper sticker. The table shows the total costs of ordering different numbers of stickers. What is the total cost of ordering 275 bumper stickers?

Number of stickers	Total cost (dollars)
25	53.25
50	98.25
75	143.25
100	188.25

4.2 Practice WITH CalcChat® AND CalcView®

In Exercises 1–8, write an equation in point-slope form of the line that passes through the given point and has the given slope. *Example 1*

1. $(2, 1);\ m = 2$ **2.** $(3, 5);\ m = -1$

3. $(7, -4);\ m = -6$ **4.** $(-8, -2);\ m = 5$

5. $\left(\frac{5}{6}, 0\right);\ m = -3$ **6.** $\left(0, -\frac{1}{2}\right);\ m = \frac{3}{4}$

7. $(5, -12);\ m = -\frac{2}{5}$ **8.** $(-6, 8.2);\ m = 1.5$

In Exercises 9–12, write an equation in slope-intercept form of the line shown. *Example 2*

9.

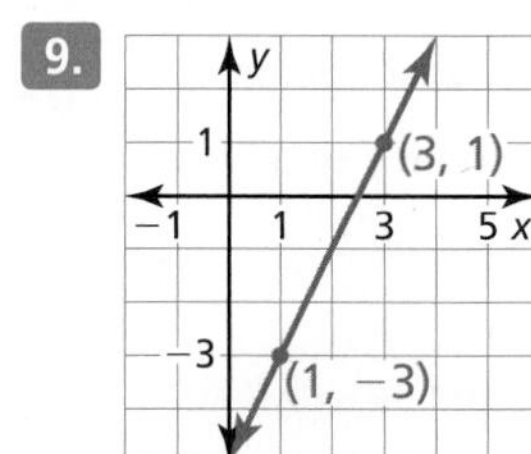

10.

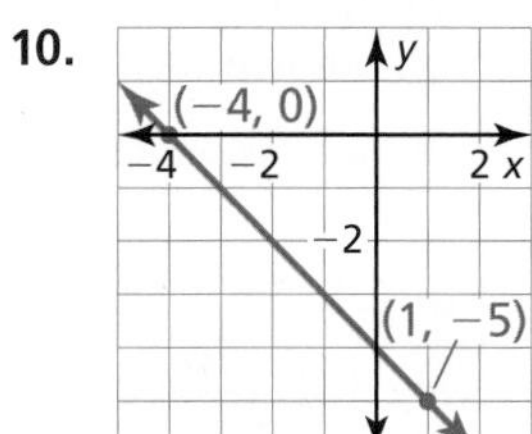

11.

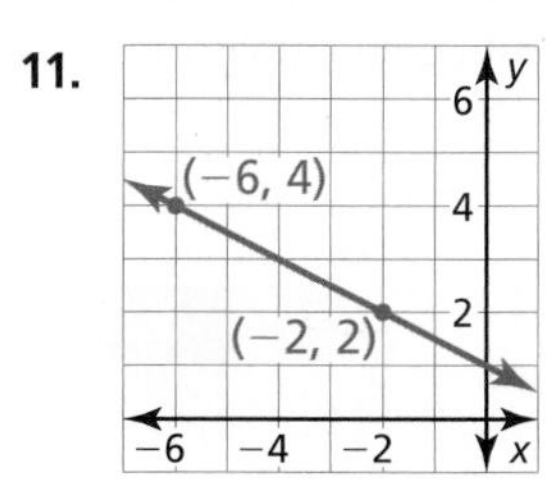

12.

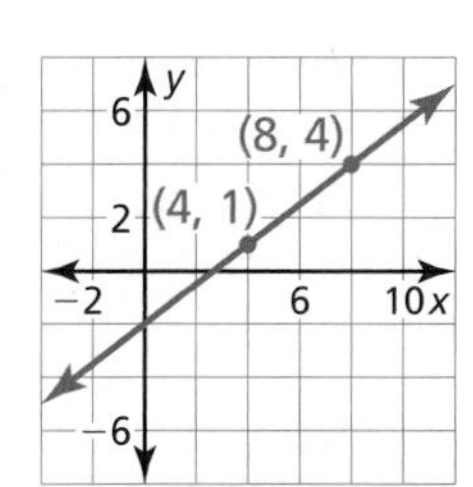

In Exercises 13–18, write an equation in slope-intercept form of the line that passes through the given points.

13. $(7, 2), (2, 12)$ **14.** $(6, -2), (12, 1)$

15. $(1, -9), (-3, -9)$ **16.** $(-5, 19), (5, 13)$

17. $(6, 11), \left(2, \frac{25}{3}\right)$ **18.** $(2, -3), \left(-\frac{1}{2}, \frac{1}{8}\right)$

In Exercises 19–24, write a linear function f with the given values. *Example 3*

19. $f(2) = -2, f(1) = 1$

20. $f(5) = 7, f(-2) = 0$

21. $f(-4) = 2, f(6) = -3$

22. $f(-10) = 4.5, f(-2) = 4.5$

23. $f(-3) = 1, f(13) = 5$

24. $f(-9) = 10, f(-1) = -2$

In Exercises 25 and 26, tell whether the data in the table can be modeled by a linear equation. Explain. If possible, write a linear equation that represents y as a function of x.

25.

x	2	4	6	8	10
y	−1	5	15	29	47

26.

x	0	1	2	4	5
y	1.2	1.4	1.6	2	2.2

27. MODELING REAL LIFE A homeowner charges a processing fee and a daily fee to rent a house. The table shows the total costs of renting the house for different numbers of days. *Example 4*

Days	2	4	6	8
Total cost (dollars)	258	467	676	885

a. Can the situation be modeled by a linear equation? Explain.

b. What is the processing fee? the daily fee?

c. A guest can spend no more than $1200 on the house rental. What is the maximum number of days the guest can rent the house?

28. MODELING REAL LIFE You want to order posters to advertise your band. A company charges $109.95 for the first 100 posters and $65 for each additional 100 posters.

a. Write an equation that represents the total cost (in dollars) of the posters as a function of the number (in hundreds) of posters ordered.

b. Find the total cost of 1000 posters.

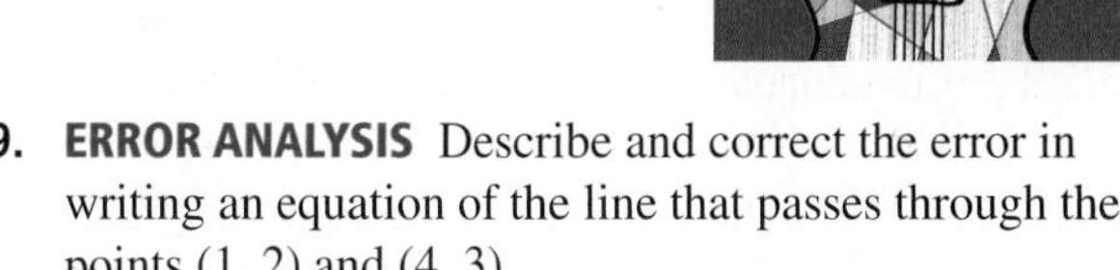

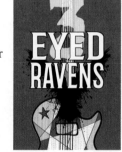

29. ERROR ANALYSIS Describe and correct the error in writing an equation of the line that passes through the points (1, 2) and (4, 3).

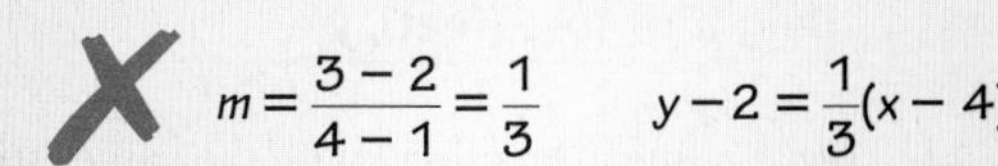

$m = \frac{3-2}{4-1} = \frac{1}{3}$ $\qquad y - 2 = \frac{1}{3}(x - 4)$

30. **MAKING AN ARGUMENT** Your friend says she can write a linear function g with the values $g(4) = -2$ and $g(-1) = -2$. Is your friend correct? Explain.

31. **CONNECTING CONCEPTS** Compare the graph of $y = 2x$ to the graph of $y - 1 = 2(x + 3)$. Make a conjecture about the graphs of $y = mx$ and $y - k = m(x - h)$.

32. **HOW DO YOU SEE IT?**
The graph shows two points that lie on the graph of a linear function.

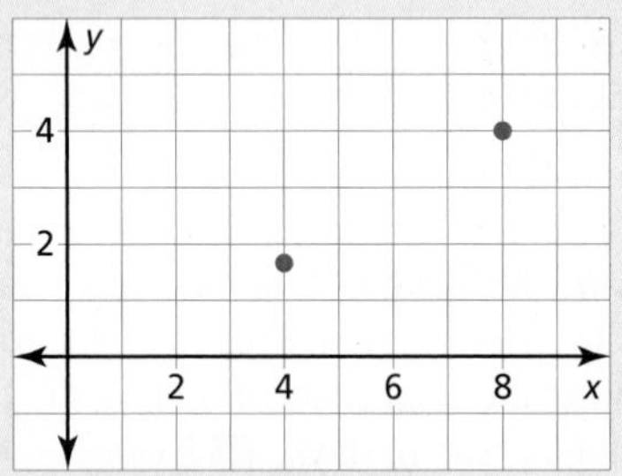

a. Does the y-intercept of the graph of the linear function appear to be positive or negative? Explain.

b. Estimate the coordinates of the two points. How can you use your estimates to confirm your answer in part (a)?

33. **MULTIPLE REPRESENTATIONS** Three bank accounts are opened and then have fixed amounts of money withdrawn each month. The graph shows Account A, the table represents Account B, and the equation $y = -22.5x + 90$ represents Account C, where y represents the amount of money (in dollars) left after x months.

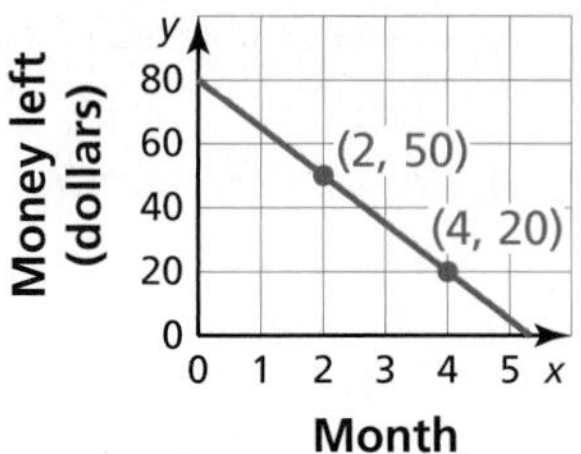

Month, x	Money left, y
1	\$100
2	\$75
3	\$50
4	\$25

a. Which account has the greatest initial value? the least initial value?

b. Which account has the most amount of money withdrawn each month? the least amount?

c. Which account runs out of money first? last?

34. **THOUGHT PROVOKING**
A line passing through $\left(p, \frac{1}{2}\right)$ and $(-8, q)$ has a slope of $\frac{3}{4}$. Find two possible values for each of p and q, and write the corresponding equations of the lines in slope-intercept form.

REVIEW & REFRESH

In Exercises 35–38, write the reciprocal of the number.

35. 5

36. -8

37. $-\frac{2}{7}$

38. $\frac{3}{2}$

39. Write an equation in point-slope form of the line that passes through the point $(-9, 1)$ and has a slope of $\frac{2}{3}$.

40. **WRITING** Compare the graphs of $p(x) = |x - 6|$ and $q(x) = |x| - 6$.

41. Determine whether the domain is *discrete* or *continuous*. Explain.

Input Years, x	1	2	3
Output Height of tree (feet), y	6	9	12

42. Write a linear function f with the values $f(0) = 2$ and $f(5) = -3$.

43. **MODELING REAL LIFE** The total cost (in dollars) to cater an event with p people is represented by $C(p) = 18p + 50$. The set-up fee increases by \$25. The new total cost is represented by $T(p) = C(p) + 25$. Describe the transformation from the graph of C to the graph of T.

44. Solve the inequality $2r + 3 < 7$ *or* $-r + 9 \leq 2$. Graph the solution.

In Exercises 45 and 46, graph the linear equation and identify the intercepts.

45. $4x + 5y = 20$

46. $y = \frac{1}{2}x - 3$

4.3 Writing Equations of Parallel and Perpendicular Lines

Learning Target Recognize and write equations of parallel and perpendicular lines.

Success Criteria
- I can identify parallel and perpendicular lines from their equations.
- I can write equations of parallel lines.
- I can write equations of perpendicular lines.

EXPLORE IT! Recognizing Parallel and Perpendicular Lines

Work with a partner. Consider the graph of the linear function f.

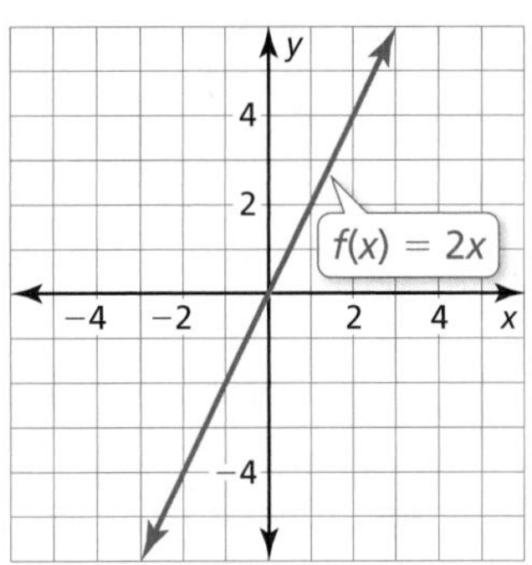

a. Write and graph a function g that is a horizontal or vertical translation of the graph of f. Do the graphs ever intersect? How do you know?

b. Write and graph a function h that is a 90° clockwise rotation of the graph of f. Do the graphs ever intersect? If so, what are the measures of the angles created by the intersection? How do you know?

Two lines in the same plane that never intersect are **parallel lines**. Two lines in the same plane that intersect to form right angles are **perpendicular lines**.

Math Practice

Make Conjectures
Why is it important to consider several examples before making a conjecture?

c. Compare your equations and graphs with other students. Make a conjecture about how you can use equations to determine whether two lines are parallel or perpendicular.

d. Write a linear function that has a different slope than the graph of f. Repeat parts (a) and (b) using this function. Do the results support your conjecture in part (c)?

e. Without graphing, determine whether any of the following are equations of parallel or perpendicular lines. Explain your reasoning.

$3x + 4y = 6$ Equation 1

$3x + 4y = 12$ Equation 2

$4x - 3y = 12$ Equation 3

Identifying and Writing Equations of Parallel Lines

Vocabulary

parallel lines, *p. 200*
perpendicular lines, *p. 201*

READING

The phrase "*A if and only if B*" is a way of writing two conditional statements at once. It means that if *A* is true, then *B* is true. It also means that if *B* is true, then *A* is true.

KEY IDEA

Parallel Lines and Slopes

Two lines in the same plane that never intersect are **parallel lines**. Two distinct nonvertical lines are parallel if and only if they have the same slope.

All distinct vertical lines are parallel.

EXAMPLE 1 Identifying Parallel Lines

Determine which of the lines are parallel.

SOLUTION

Find the slope of each line.

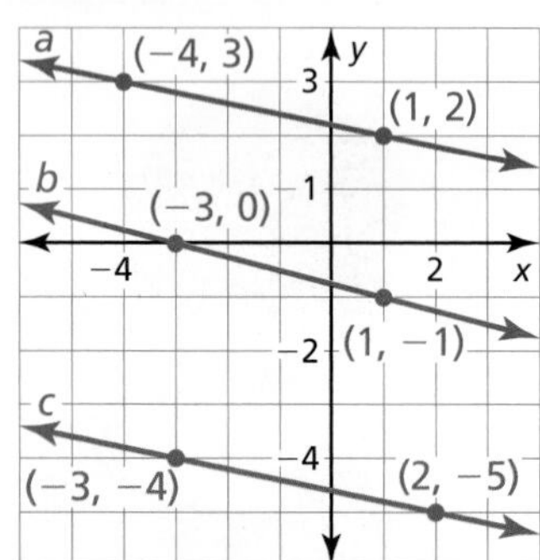

Line a: $m = \dfrac{2 - 3}{1 - (-4)} = -\dfrac{1}{5}$

Line b: $m = \dfrac{-1 - 0}{1 - (-3)} = -\dfrac{1}{4}$

Line c: $m = \dfrac{-5 - (-4)}{2 - (-3)} = -\dfrac{1}{5}$

▶ Lines a and c have the same slope, so they are parallel.

EXAMPLE 2 Writing an Equation of a Parallel Line

Write an equation of the line that passes through $(5, -4)$ and is parallel to the line $y = 2x + 3$.

SOLUTION

Step 1 Find the slope of the parallel line. The graph of the given equation has a slope of 2. So, the parallel line that passes through $(5, -4)$ also has a slope of 2.

Step 2 Use the slope-intercept form to find the y-intercept of the parallel line.

$y = mx + b$	Write the slope-intercept form.
$-4 = 2(5) + b$	Substitute 2 for m, 5 for x, and -4 for y.
$-14 = b$	Solve for b.

▶ Using $m = 2$ and $b = -14$, an equation of the parallel line is $y = 2x - 14$.

SELF-ASSESSMENT

1 I do not understand. 2 I can do it with help. 3 I can do it on my own. 4 I can teach someone else.

1. Line a passes through $(-5, 3)$ and $(-6, -1)$. Line b passes through $(3, -2)$ and $(2, -7)$. Are the lines parallel? Explain.

Write an equation of the line that passes through the given point and is parallel to the given line.

2. $(0, -3)$; $y = -2x - 5$

3. $(-4, 2)$; $y = \frac{1}{4}x + 1$

4. $(1, 3.5)$; $y = 15$

5. MP **REASONING** Let f, g, and h be linear functions. The graph of g is a vertical translation of the graph of f, and the graph of h is a vertical stretch of the graph of f. Are any of the graphs of the functions parallel? Explain your reasoning.

Identifying and Writing Equations of Perpendicular Lines

STUDY TIP

The product of a nonzero number m and its negative reciprocal is -1.

$$m\left(-\frac{1}{m}\right) = -1$$

KEY IDEA

Perpendicular Lines and Slopes

Two lines in the same plane that intersect to form right angles are **perpendicular lines**. Nonvertical lines are perpendicular if and only if their slopes are negative reciprocals.

Vertical lines are perpendicular to horizontal lines.

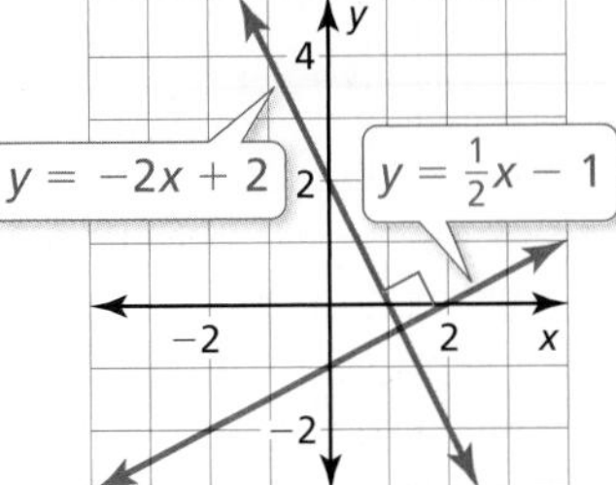

EXAMPLE 3 Identifying Parallel and Perpendicular Lines

Determine which of the lines, if any, are parallel or perpendicular.

Line a: $y = 4x + 2$ Line b: $x + 4y = 3$ Line c: $-8y - 2x = 16$

SOLUTION

Write the equations in slope-intercept form. Then compare the slopes.

Line a: $y = 4x + 2$ Line b: $y = -\frac{1}{4}x + \frac{3}{4}$ Line c: $y = -\frac{1}{4}x - 2$

▶ Lines b and c have slopes of $-\frac{1}{4}$, so they are parallel. Line a has a slope of 4, the negative reciprocal of $-\frac{1}{4}$, so it is perpendicular to lines b and c.

EXAMPLE 4 Writing an Equation of a Perpendicular Line

Write an equation of the line that passes through $(-3, 1)$ and is perpendicular to the line $y = \frac{1}{2}x + 3$.

SOLUTION

Step 1 Find the slope of the perpendicular line. The graph of the given equation has a slope of $\frac{1}{2}$. Because the slopes of perpendicular lines are negative reciprocals, the slope of the perpendicular line that passes through $(-3, 1)$ is -2.

Step 2 Use the slope $m = -2$ and the point-slope form to write an equation of the perpendicular line that passes through $(-3, 1)$.

$y - y_1 = m(x - x_1)$ Write the point-slope form.

$y - 1 = -2[x - (-3)]$ Substitute -2 for m, -3 for x_1, and 1 for y_1.

$y - 1 = -2x - 6$ Simplify.

$y = -2x - 5$ Write in slope-intercept form.

▶ An equation of the perpendicular line is $y = -2x - 5$.

SELF-ASSESSMENT 1 I do not understand. 2 I can do it with help. 3 I can do it on my own. 4 I can teach someone else.

6. Determine which of the lines, if any, are parallel or perpendicular. Explain.

   Line a: $2x + 6y = -3$ Line b: $y = 3x - 8$ Line c: $-6y + 18x = 9$

7. Write an equation of the line that passes through $(-3, 5)$ and is perpendicular to the line $y = -3x - 1$.

Writing Equations for Real-Life Problems

EXAMPLE 5 **Modeling Real Life**

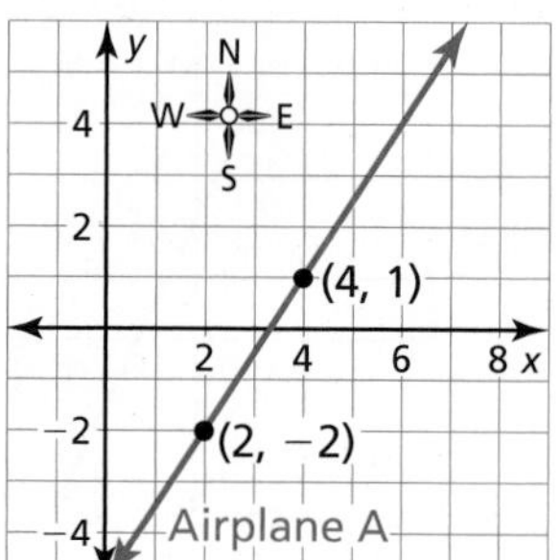

The planned path of Airplane A is shown in the graph. Each grid square represents 1 square mile. Airplane B will fly along a path parallel to Airplane A, passing through the point (14, 4). Airplane C will fly along a path perpendicular to each of these paths, passing through the point (7, −1). An air traffic controller is in charge of the region represented by the fourth quadrant. Do any of the paths intersect in the air traffic controller's region?

SOLUTION

Use the slope of the path of Airplane A to write equations that represent the paths of Airplanes B and C. Then graph the equations to determine whether any paths intersect in the air traffic controller's region, the fourth quadrant.

Airplane A Find the slope of the path of Airplane A. The line passes through the points (2, −2) and (4, 1). So, the slope is $m = \frac{1 - (-2)}{4 - 2} = \frac{3}{2}$.

Airplane B
Because the paths of Airplanes A and B are parallel, the slopes of their graphs are the same.

Use the slope $m = \frac{3}{2}$ and the point (14, 4) to write an equation.

$$y - y_1 = m(x - x_1)$$
$$y - 4 = \tfrac{3}{2}(x - 4)$$
$$y - 4 = \tfrac{3}{2}x - 21$$
$$y = \tfrac{3}{2}x - 17$$

Airplane C
Because the paths of Airplanes A and C are perpendicular, the slopes of their graphs are negative reciprocals. So, the slope of the path of Airplane C is $-\frac{2}{3}$.

Use the slope $m = -\frac{2}{3}$ and the point (7, −1) to write an equation.

$$y - y_1 = m(x - x_1)$$
$$y - (-1) = -\tfrac{2}{3}(x - 7)$$
$$y + 1 = -\tfrac{2}{3}x + \tfrac{14}{3}$$
$$y = -\tfrac{2}{3}x + \tfrac{11}{3}$$

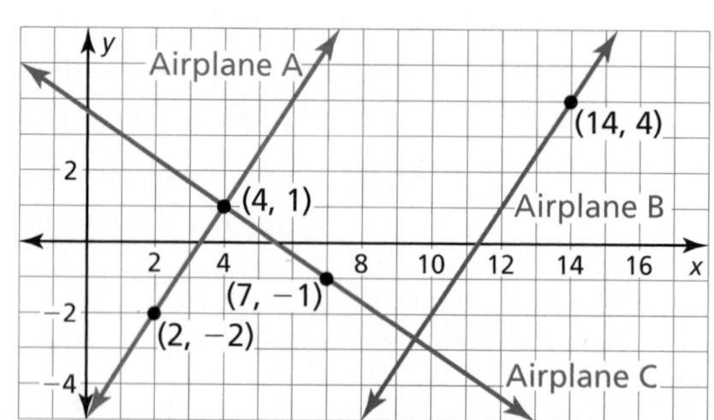

▶ The graph shows that the paths of Airplanes B and C intersect in the air traffic controller's region.

SELF-ASSESSMENT 1 I do not understand. 2 I can do it with help. 3 I can do it on my own. 4 I can teach someone else.

8. In Example 5, the pilot of Airplane C submits a new flight plan, which indicates a path that is a translation of the original path. Do any of the paths intersect in the air traffic controller's region when the translation is (a) 3 miles north or (b) 3 miles west? Explain your reasoning.

4.3 Practice WITH CalcChat® AND CalcView®

In Exercises 1–6, determine which of the lines, if any, are parallel. Explain. *Example 1*

1. 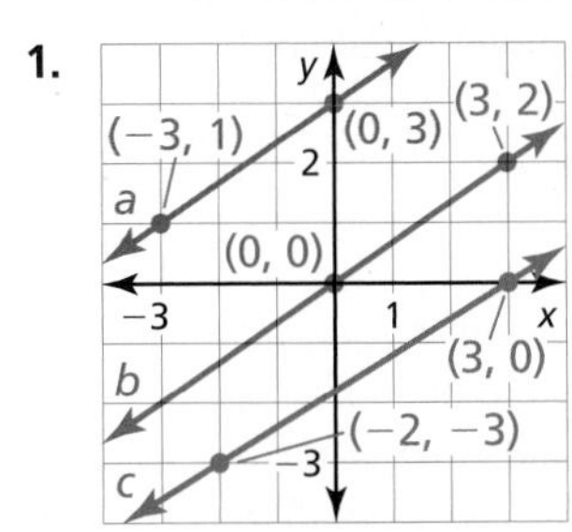

2. 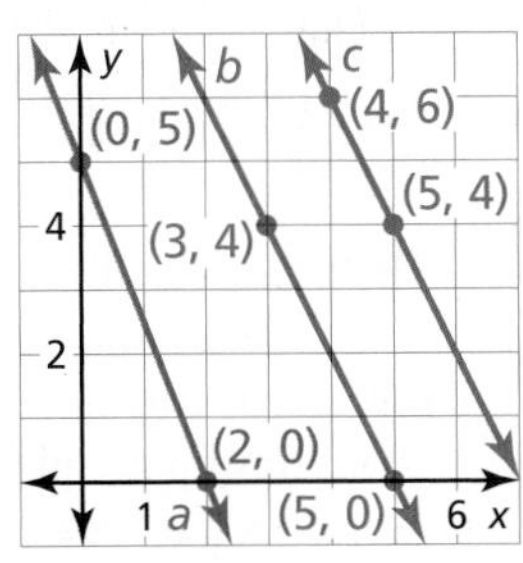

3. Line a passes through $(-1, -2)$ and $(1, 0)$.
Line b passes through $(4, 2)$ and $(2, -2)$.
Line c passes through $(0, 2)$ and $(-1, 1)$.

4. Line a passes through $(-1, 3)$ and $(1, 9)$.
Line b passes through $(-2, 12)$ and $(-1, 14)$.
Line c passes through $(3, 8.5)$ and $(6, 10.5)$.

5. Line a: $4y + x = 8$
Line b: $2y + x = 4$
Line c: $2y = -3x + 6$

6. Line a: $3y - x = 6$
Line b: $3y = x + 18$
Line c: $3y - 2x = 9$

In Exercises 7–10, write an equation of the line that passes through the given point and is parallel to the given line. *Example 2*

7. $(-1, 3)$; $y = -3x + 2$

8. $(1, 2)$; $y = -5x + 4$

9. $(6, 4)$; $3y - x = -12$

10. $(2, -5)$; $2y = 3x + 10$

In Exercises 11–16, determine which of the lines, if any, are parallel or perpendicular. Explain. *Example 3*

11. 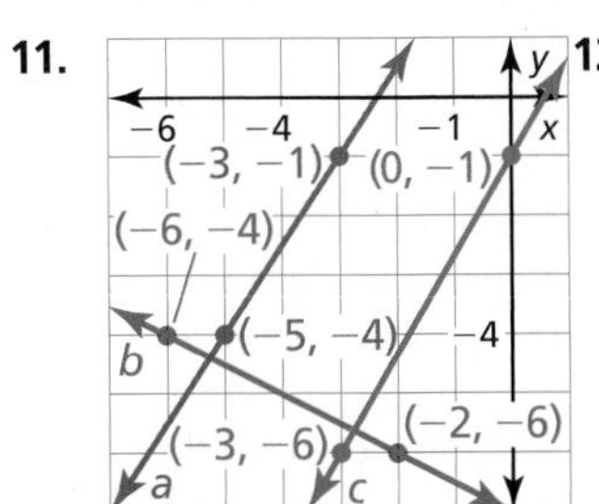

12. 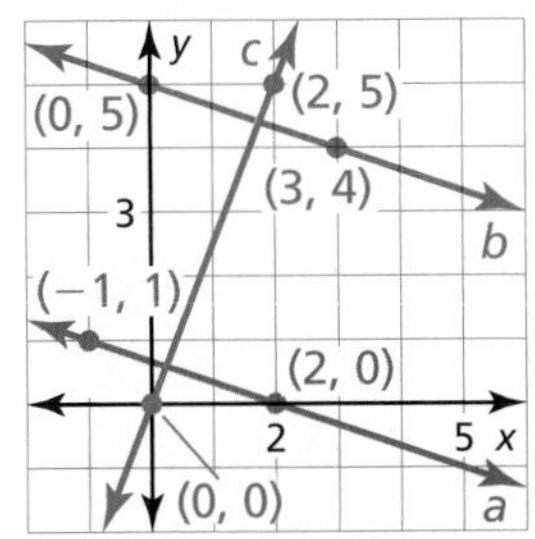

13. Line a passes through $(-2, 1)$ and $(0, 3)$.
Line b passes through $(4, 1)$ and $(6, 4)$.
Line c passes through $(1, 3)$ and $(4, 1)$.

14. Line a passes through $(2, 10)$ and $(4, 13)$.
Line b passes through $(4, 9)$ and $(6, 12)$.
Line c passes through $(2, 10)$ and $(4, 9)$.

15. Line a: $4x - 3y = 2$
Line b: $y = \frac{4}{3}x + 2$
Line c: $4y + 3x = 4$

16. Line a: $y = 6x - 2$
Line b: $6y = -x$
Line c: $y + 6x = 1$

In Exercises 17–20, write an equation of the line that passes through the given point and is perpendicular to the given line. *Example 4*

17. $(7, 10)$; $y = -\frac{1}{5}x - 9$

18. $(-4, -1)$; $y = \frac{4}{3}x + 6$

19. $(-3, 3)$; $2y = 8x - 6$

20. $(8, 1)$; $2y + 4x = 12$

21. **MODELING REAL LIFE** A city water department is proposing the construction of a new water pipe. The new pipe will be perpendicular to the existing pipe shown, passing through the point $(1, 0)$. The two pipes will be connected at their intersection. At what point will the two pipes intersect? *Example 5*

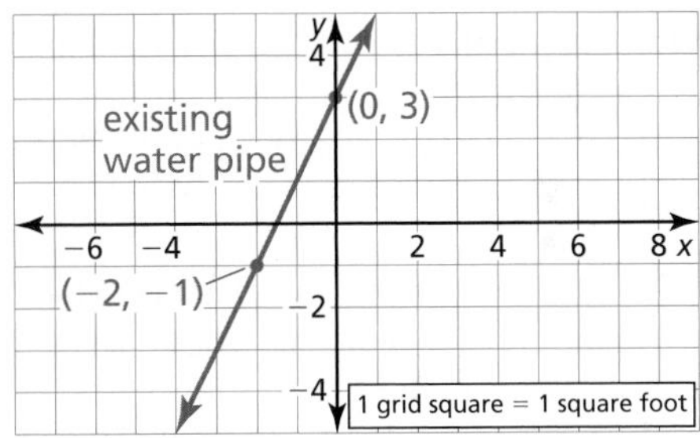

22. **MODELING REAL LIFE** A parks and recreation department wants to construct a new bike path that is parallel to the railroad tracks and does not intersect the trees shown. Will the department be able to build the path so that it passes through the parking area at the point $(4, 5)$? Justify your answer.

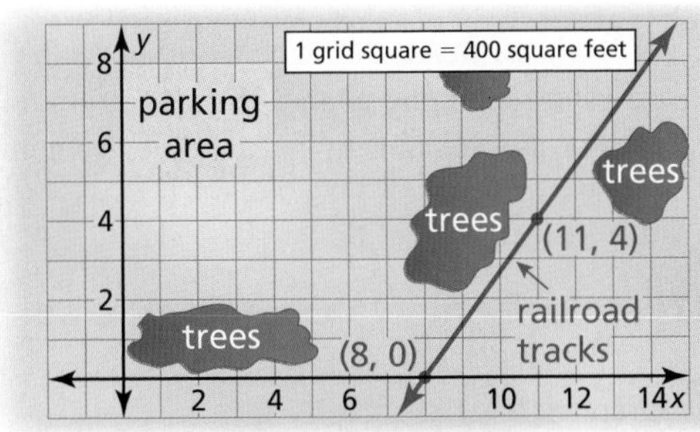

23. **ERROR ANALYSIS** Describe and correct the error in writing an equation of the line that passes through $(4, -5)$ and is perpendicular to the line $y = \frac{1}{3}x + 5$.

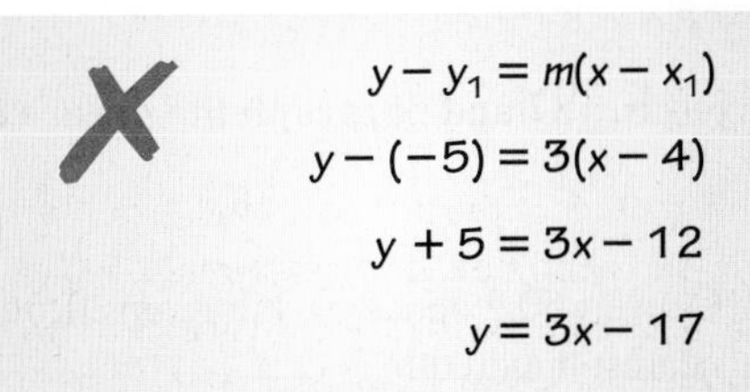

24. HOW DO YOU SEE IT?
A softball academy charges students an initial registration fee plus a monthly fee. The graph shows the total amounts paid by two students over a 4-month period. The lines are parallel. Did one of the students pay a greater registration fee? a greater monthly fee? Explain.

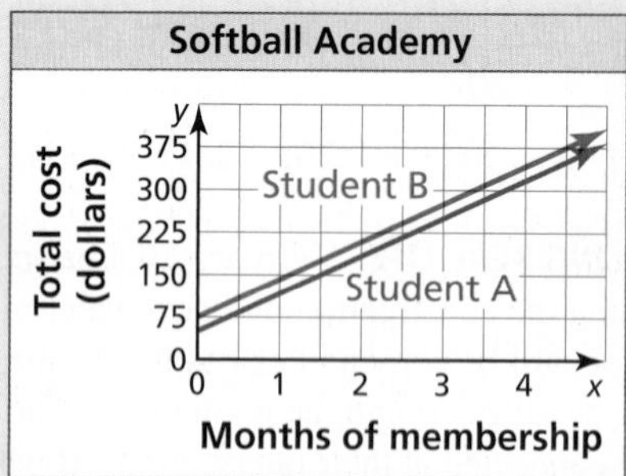

MP REASONING In Exercises 27–29, determine whether the statement is *always*, *sometimes*, or *never* true. Explain your reasoning.

27. Two lines with positive slopes are perpendicular.

28. A vertical line is parallel to the y-axis.

29. Two lines with the same y-intercept are perpendicular.

30. THOUGHT PROVOKING
You are designing a new logo for your math club. Your teacher asks you to include at least one pair of parallel lines and at least one pair of perpendicular lines. Sketch your logo in a coordinate plane. Write the equations of the parallel and perpendicular lines.

25. CONNECTING CONCEPTS The vertices of a quadrilateral are $A(2, 2)$, $B(6, 4)$, $C(8, 10)$, and $D(4, 8)$. Is quadrilateral $ABCD$ a parallelogram? a rectangle? Explain.

26. MP REASONING Lines a and b are perpendicular. Lines b and c are perpendicular. The slope of line a is m. What are the slopes of lines b and c? What can you conclude?

31. MAKING AN ARGUMENT
A hockey puck leaves the blade of a hockey stick, bounces off a wall, and travels in a new direction, as shown. Your friend claims the path of the puck forms a right angle. Is your friend correct? Explain.

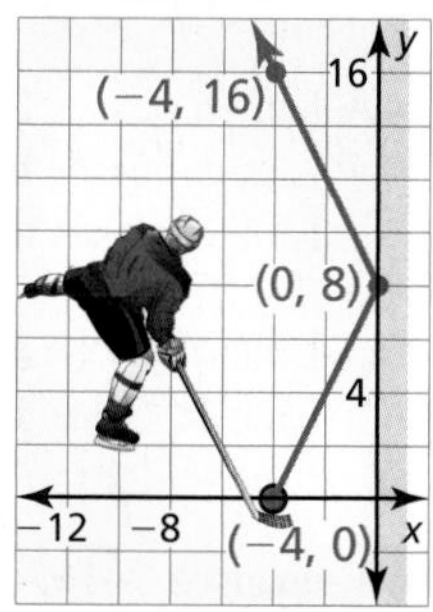

REVIEW & REFRESH

32. Determine whether the relation is a function. Explain.

$$(-1, 6), (1, 4), (-1, 2), (1, 6), (-1, 5)$$

33. MODELING REAL LIFE The table shows the amounts of water remaining in a water tank as it drains. How much water remains in the tank after 30 minutes?

Time (minutes)	8	10	12	14	16
Water (gallons)	155	150	145	140	135

34. Graph $x > \frac{3}{4}$.

In Exercises 35 and 36, graph the function. Compare the graph to the graph of $f(x) = |x|$. Find the domain and range.

35. $g(x) = |x| + 7$ **36.** $h(x) = -4|x|$

In Exercises 37 and 38, graph the linear equation.

37. $x = 6$ **38.** $y = -\frac{3}{2}$

39. Convert 50.2 ounces to kilograms. Round to the nearest hundredth.

WATCH

40. Write an equation of the line that passes through (4, 3) and is (a) parallel and (b) perpendicular to the line shown.

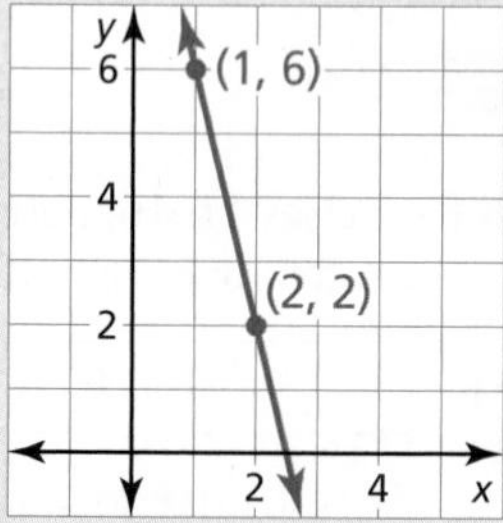

41. Write an equation of the line that passes through the points $(0, -4.5)$ and $(-3, 0.9)$.

42. MP STRUCTURE For what value of a are the graphs of $6y = -2x + 4$ and $2y = ax - 5$ parallel? perpendicular?

43. Find the surface area of the regular pyramid.

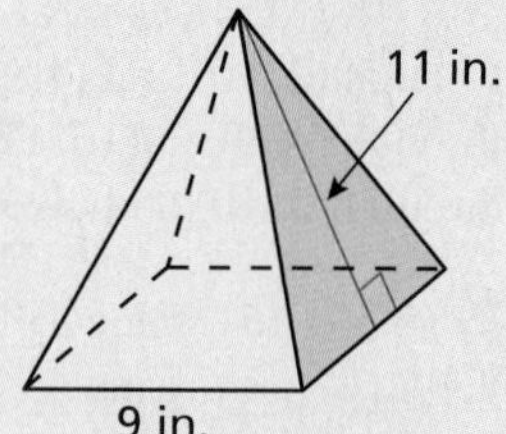

4.4 Scatter Plots and Lines of Fit

Learning Target Use scatter plots and lines of fit to describe relationships between data.

Success Criteria
- I can read and interpret scatter plots.
- I can identify correlations between data.
- I can write and interpret an equation of a line of fit.

EXPLORE IT! Examining Scatter Plots

Work with a partner. A survey was taken of 179 married couples. Each person was asked his or her age. The graph shows the results.

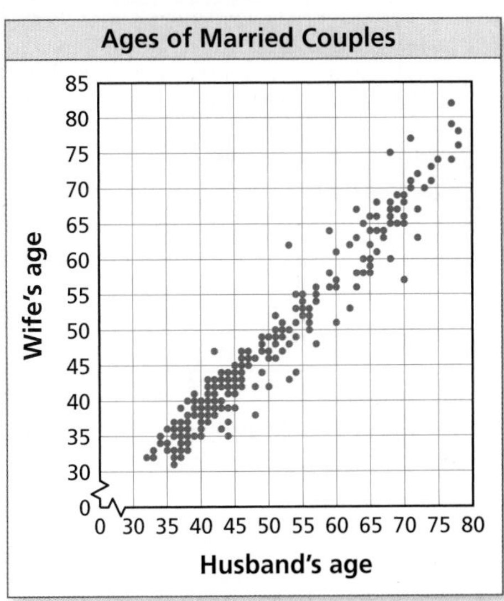

Math Practice

Explain the Meaning
How do you use the parts of the graph to help you make observations?

a. Make several observations about the data in the graph. What do the data show? What might be some reasons for the patterns in the data?

b. Is the relationship positive or negative? Describe what that means in this context.

c. Do the data have a linear relationship? If so, explain how you can use a linear equation to represent the data.

d. The graph at the right shows the median ages of American men and women at their first marriage for selected years from 1960 to 2015. Make several observations about the data in the graph. Why do you think the ages are increasing over time?

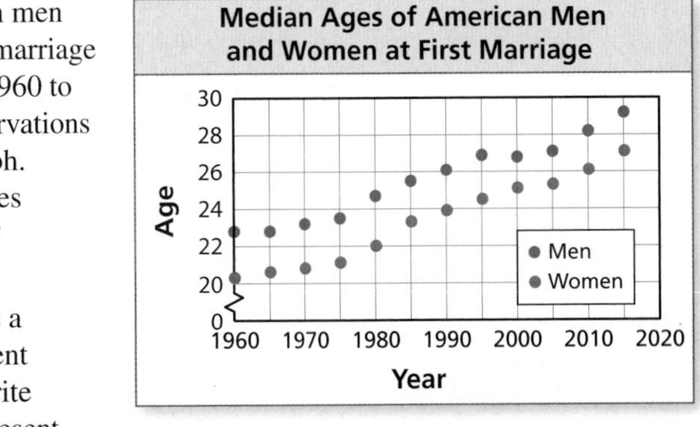

e. Explain how you can use a linear equation to represent each set of data. Then write each equation. Let x represent the number of years since 1960. Explain the method you used.

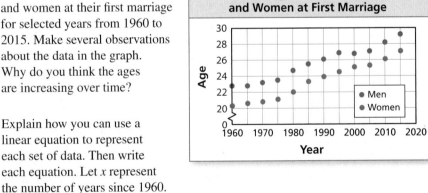

f. Find the y-intercept of the graph of each equation in part (e). Interpret its meaning.

g. Explain how you can use your equation from part (e) to predict when the median age of American women at their first marriage will be 30.

Interpreting Scatter Plots

Vocabulary 

scatter plot, *p. 206*
correlation, *p. 207*
line of fit, *p. 208*

KEY IDEA

Scatter Plot

A **scatter plot** is a graph that shows the relationship between two data sets. The two data sets are graphed as ordered pairs in a coordinate plane. Scatter plots can show trends in the data.

EXAMPLE 1 Interpreting a Scatter Plot

The scatter plot shows the amounts x (in grams) of sugar and the numbers y of calories in 10 smoothies.

a. How many calories are in the smoothie that contains 56 grams of sugar?

b. How many grams of sugar are in the smoothie that contains 320 calories?

c. What tends to happen to the number of calories as the number of grams of sugar increases?

SOLUTION

a. Draw a horizontal line from the point that has an x-value of 56. It intersects the y-axis at 270.

▶ So, the smoothie has 270 calories.

b. Draw a vertical line from the point that has a y-value of 320. It intersects the x-axis at 70.

▶ So, the smoothie has 70 grams of sugar.

c. Looking at the graph, the plotted points go up from left to right.

▶ So, as the number of grams of sugar increases, the number of calories increases.

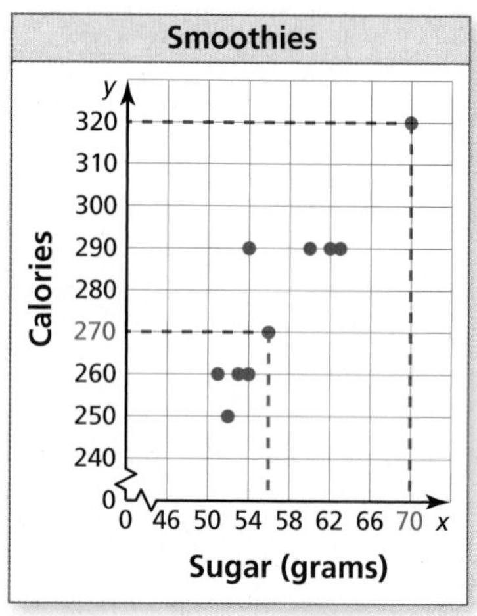

SELF-ASSESSMENT

1 I do not understand. 2 I can do it with help. 3 I can do it on my own. 4 I can teach someone else.

1. How many calories are in the smoothie that contains 51 grams of sugar?
2. How many grams of sugar are in the smoothie that contains 250 calories?
3. Another point, (55, 280), is plotted on the graph. Explain the meaning of this point.
4. **WRITING** Do you think it is possible for a smoothie to be represented by a point on the y-axis? on the x-axis? Explain your reasoning.
5. **MP REASONING** From the graph, find the number of smoothies for each description. Explain your reasoning.

   a. smoothies with at least 270 calories

   b. smoothies with less than 50 grams of sugar

   c. smoothies with more than 275 calories and less than 62 grams of sugar

Identifying Correlations between Data Sets

A **correlation** is a relationship between data sets. You can use a scatter plot to describe the correlation between data.

STUDY TIP

You can think of a positive linear correlation as having a positive slope and a negative linear correlation as having a negative slope.

Positive Linear Correlation

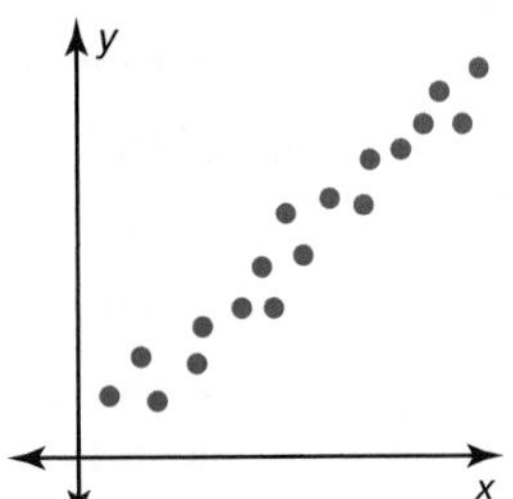

The points lie close to a line. As x increases, y increases.

Negative Linear Correlation

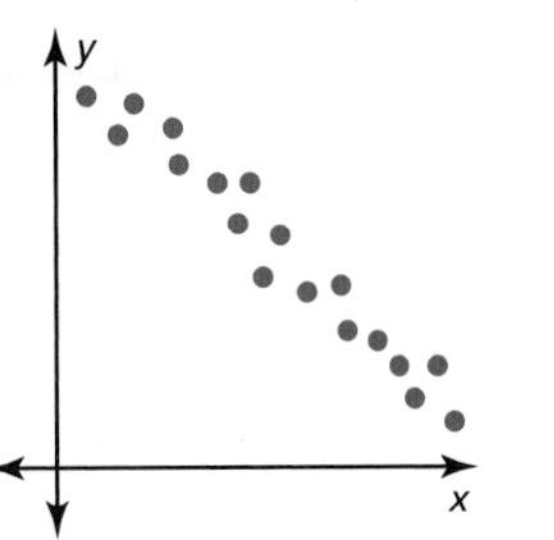

The points lie close to a line. As x increases, y decreases.

No Correlation

The points show no pattern.

EXAMPLE 2 Identifying Correlations

Describe the relationship between the data in each scatter plot.

a. age and vehicles owned

b. temperature and coat sales at a store

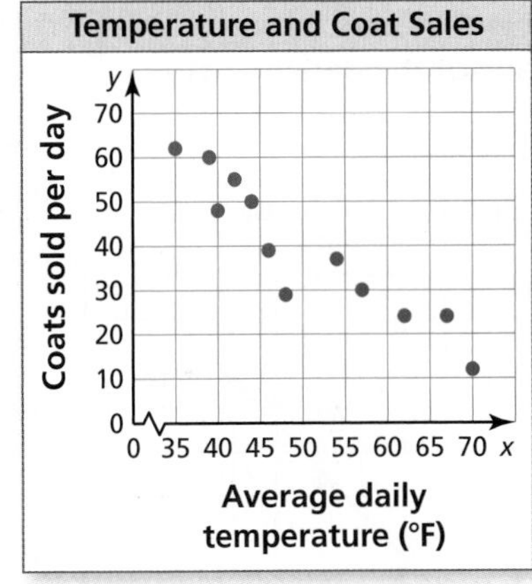

SOLUTION

a. The points show no pattern. The number of vehicles owned does not depend on a person's age. So, the scatter plot shows no correlation.

b. The points appear to lie close to a line with a negative slope. As the average temperature increases, the number of coats sold decreases. So, the scatter plot shows a negative linear correlation.

SELF-ASSESSMENT

1 I do not understand. 2 I can do it with help. 3 I can do it on my own. 4 I can teach someone else.

Make a scatter plot of the data. Then describe the relationship between the data.

6.

Temperature (°F), x	82	78	68	87	75	71	92	84
Attendees (thousands), y	4.5	4.0	1.7	5.5	3.8	2.9	4.7	5.3

7.

Age of a car (years), x	1	2	3	4	5	6	7	8
Value (thousands), y	\$24	\$21	\$19	\$18	\$15	\$12	\$8	\$7

8. OPEN-ENDED Give an example of a real-life data set that has no correlation.

Using Lines of Fit to Model Data

When data show a positive or negative linear correlation, you can model the *trend* in the data using a line of fit. A **line of fit** is a line drawn on a scatter plot that is close to most of the data points.

STUDY TIP
A line of fit is also called a *trend line.*

KEY IDEA

Using a Line of Fit to Model Data

Step 1 Make a scatter plot of the data.

Step 2 Decide whether the data can be modeled by a line.

Step 3 Draw a line that appears to fit the data closely. There should be about as many points above the line as below it.

Step 4 Write an equation using two points on the line. The points do not have to represent actual data pairs, but they must lie on the line of fit.

EXAMPLE 3 Finding a Line of Fit

Math Practice
Use a Graph
A line of fit does not need to pass through any of the data points.

The table shows the total numbers y (in millions) of subscribers to a video-sharing website x years since 2010. Write an equation that models the total number of subscribers as a function of the number of years since 2010. Interpret the slope and y-intercept of the line of fit.

Year, x	Subscribers (millions), y
0	9
1	21
2	26
3	33
4	43
5	53
6	71
7	76
8	89

SOLUTION

Step 1 Make a scatter plot of the data.

Step 2 Decide whether the data can be modeled by a line. Because the scatter plot shows a positive linear correlation, you can fit a line to the data.

Step 3 Draw a line that appears to fit the data closely. Try to have as many points above the line as below it. One possibility is shown.

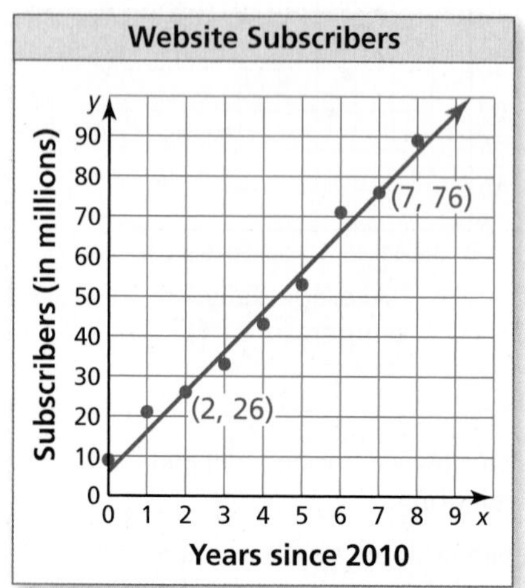

Step 4 Write an equation using two points on the line. The line passes through (2, 26) and (7, 76). The slope of the line is $m = \dfrac{76 - 26}{7 - 2} = 10$.

Use the slope $m = 10$ and the point (2, 26) to write an equation of the line.

$y - y_1 = m(x - x_1)$ Write the point-slope form.

$y - 26 = 10(x - 2)$ Substitute 10 for m, 2 for x_1, and 26 for y_1.

$y = 10x + 6$ Solve for y.

▶ An equation of a line of fit is $y = 10x + 6$. The slope is 10 and the y-intercept is 6. So, in 2010 there were about 6 million subscribers, and the number of subscribers increased by about 10 million each year.

SELF-ASSESSMENT 1 I do not understand. 2 I can do it with help. 3 I can do it on my own. 4 I can teach someone else.

9. The table shows the gross revenue y (in millions of dollars) for a movie each week for x weeks since its release. Write an equation that models the gross revenue as a function of the number of weeks since its release. Interpret the slope and intercepts of the line of fit.

Week, x	1	2	3	4	5	6	7	8
Gross revenue (millions), y	\$135	\$110	\$77	\$65	\$34	\$21	\$14	\$8

4.4 Practice WITH CalcChat® AND CalcView®

1. **INTERPRETING A SCATTER PLOT** The scatter plot shows the amounts x (in gigabytes) of random-access memory (RAM) and the prices y (in dollars) of 10 laptops. *Example 1*

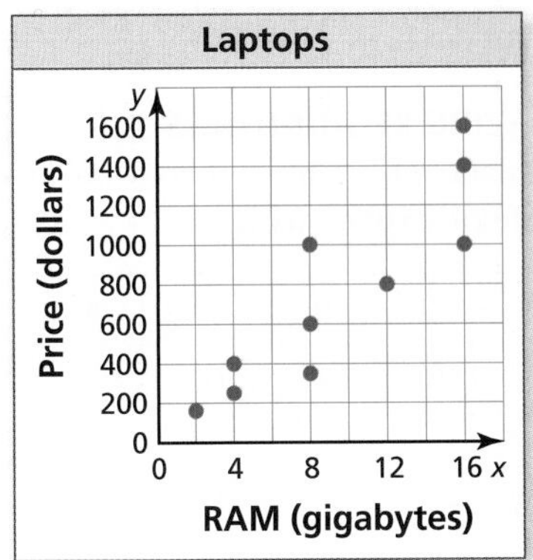

a. What is the price of the laptop with a RAM of 12 gigabytes?

b. What is the RAM of the \$1400 laptop?

c. What tends to happen to the price as the RAM increases?

2. **INTERPRETING A SCATTER PLOT** The scatter plot shows the earned run averages and the winning percentages of eight pitchers on a baseball team.

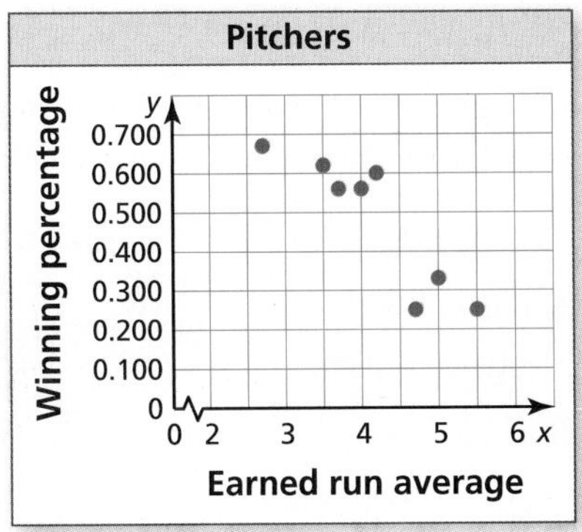

a. What is the winning percentage of the pitcher with an earned run average of 4.20?

b. What is the earned run average of the pitcher with a winning percentage of 0.333?

c. What tends to happen to the winning percentage as the earned run average increases?

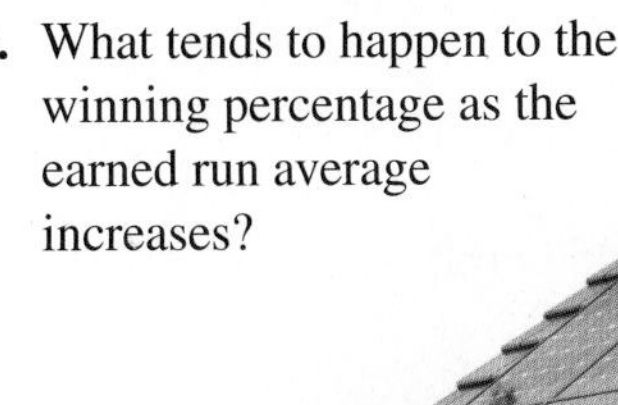

In Exercises 3–6, describe the relationship between the data in the scatter plot. *Example 2*

3.

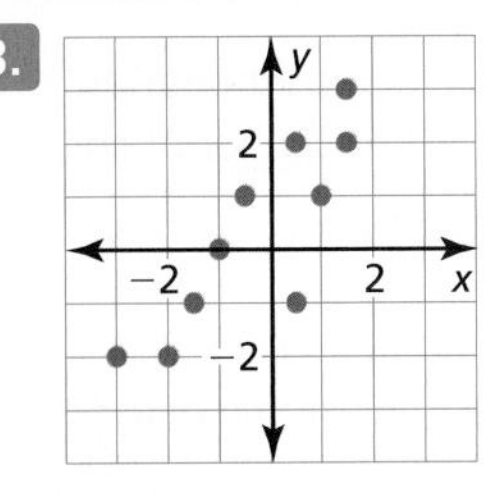

4.

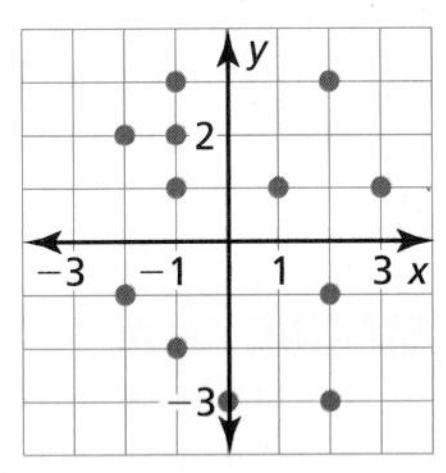

5.

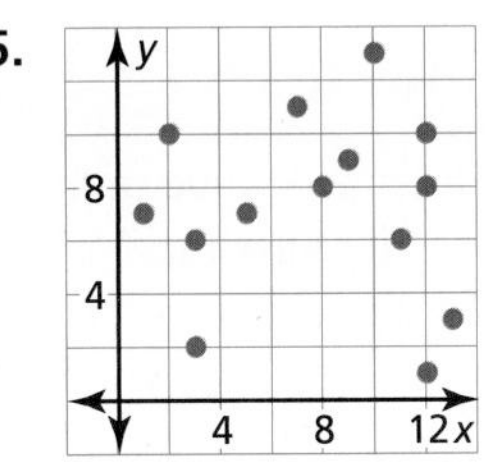

6.

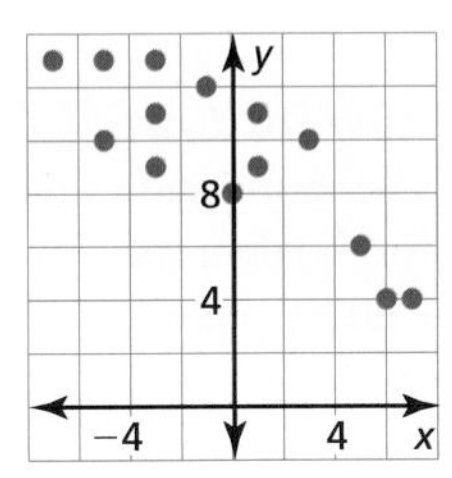

In Exercises 7 and 8, make a scatter plot of the data. Then describe the relationship between the data.

7.

x	3.1	2.2	2.5	3.7	3.9	1.5	2.7	2.0
y	1	0	1	2	0	2	3	2

8.

x	3	4	5	6	7	8	9	10
y	67	67	50	33	25	21	19	4

9. **MODELING REAL LIFE** The table shows the total amounts y (in thousands of dollars) of money a homeowner saves on electric bills x years after installing solar panels. *Example 3*

x	0	5	10	15	20	25
y	-12	-5.2	3.8	10.5	20	28.4

a. Write an equation that models the total amount of money saved as a function of the number of years after the solar panels were installed.

b. Interpret the slope and y-intercept of the line of fit.

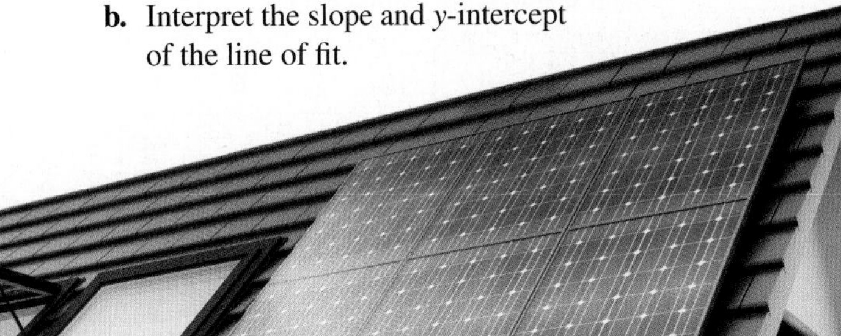

10. MODELING REAL LIFE The table shows the amounts of storage left y (in gigabytes) on a music playing device when there are x songs on the device.

x	0	242	519	698	825	1009
y	16	14.8	14.1	13.5	12.7	11.6

a. Write an equation that models the amount of storage left as a function of the number of songs.

b. Interpret the slope and y-intercept of the line of fit.

11. MAKING AN ARGUMENT Your friend says that a line of fit must pass through at least one of the data points. Is your friend correct? Explain.

12. HOW DO YOU SEE IT?
The graph shows part of a data set and a line of fit for the data set. Four data points are missing. Choose possible coordinates for these data points.

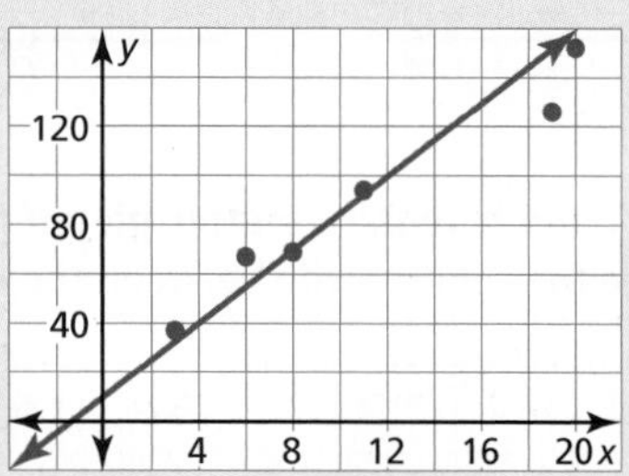

13. MP CHOOSE TOOLS Measure the heights and arm spans of five people.

GO DIGITAL

a. Make a scatter plot using the data you collected. Then draw a line of fit for the data.

b. Interpret the terms and coefficient in the equation of the line of fit.

14. WRITING When is data best displayed in a scatter plot, rather than another type of display, such as a bar graph or circle graph?

15. ANALYZING RELATIONSHIPS Is it possible to fit a line to the data in the tables? If so, write an equation of the line. If not, explain why.

x	−12	−9	−7	−4	−3	−1
y	150	76	50	15	10	1

x	2	5	6	7	9	15
y	5	22	37	52	90	226

16. THOUGHT PROVOKING
Describe a situation in which a line is a good fit for a set of data, but the data do *not* show a positive or a negative linear correlation.

REVIEW & REFRESH

17. MP REASONING A data set has no correlation. Does it make sense to find a line of fit for the data? Explain.

18. Write an equation of the line that passes through the given point and is (a) parallel and (b) perpendicular to the given line.

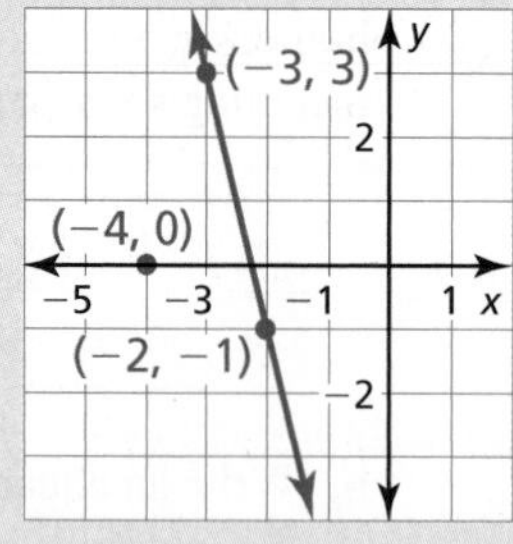

19. Make a scatter plot of the data. Then describe the relationship between the data.

x	14	12	10	8	6	4	2
y	4	1	0	−1	−2	−4	−5

In Exercises 20 and 21, graph the function. Compare the graph to the graph of $f(x) = |x - 6|$.

20. $h(x) = |x - 6| + 2$ **21.** $g(x) = |x - 1|$

22. MODELING REAL LIFE The costs for setting up and maintaining a website at two different website hosting companies are shown. You have \$620. At which company can you set up and maintain a website for the greatest amount of time? Explain.

Company A	Company B
Set-up fee: **\$48** Maintenance fee: **\$44** per month	NO SET-UP FEE!!! Maintenance fee: \$62 per month

23. Tell whether the data can be modeled by a linear equation. Explain. If possible, write a linear equation that represents y as a function of x.

x	−3	−1	1	3	5
y	16	11.5	7	2.5	−2

24. Solve $P = 2\ell + 2w$ for w.

25. What percent of 45 is 18?

4.5 Analyzing Lines of Fit

Learning Target Analyze lines of fit and find lines of best fit.

Success Criteria
- I can use residuals to determine how well lines of fit model data.
- I can use technology to find lines of best fit.
- I can distinguish between correlation and causation.

EXPLORE IT! Comparing Lines of Fit

Work with a partner. Consider the scatter plots shown below.

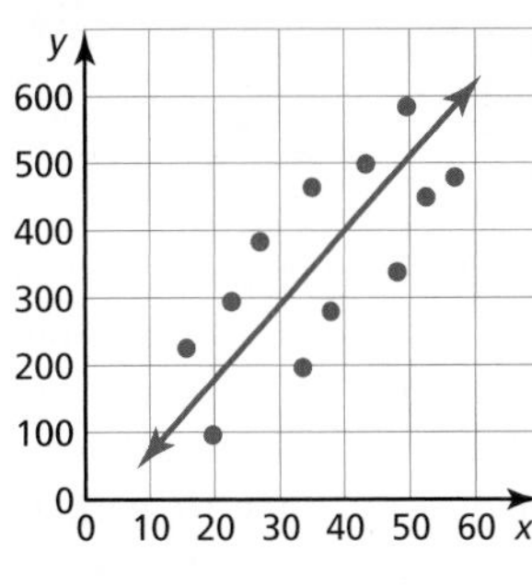
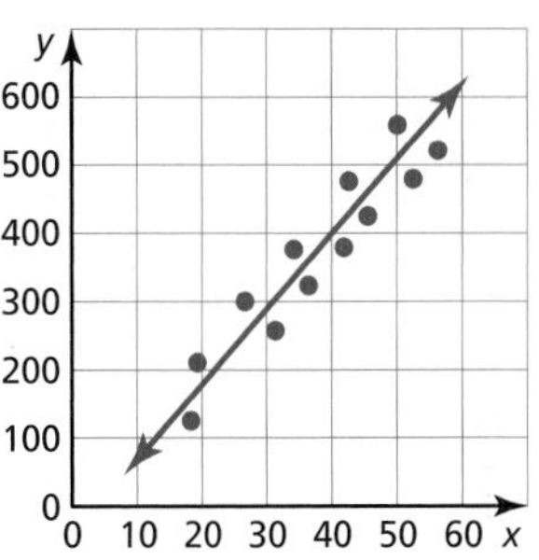
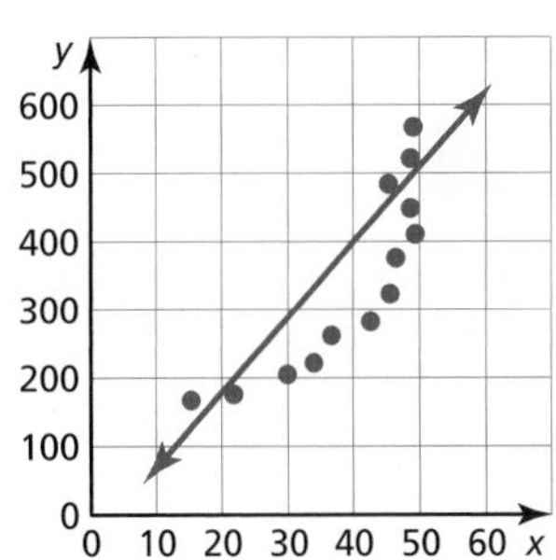
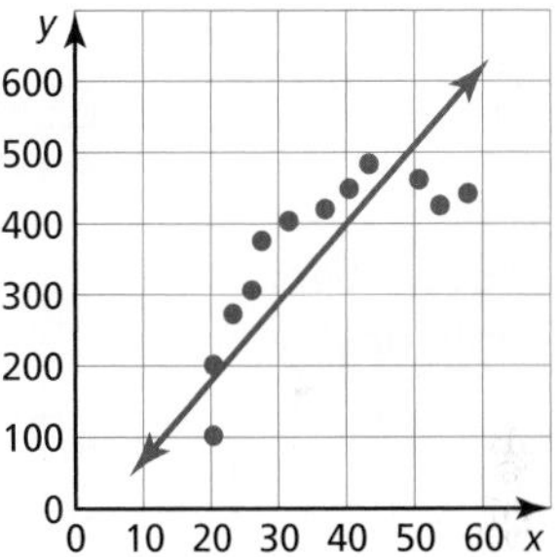

Math Practice

Construct Arguments
What are some characteristics of a line of fit that might make it more reliable than other lines of fit?

a. Make several observations about each scatter plot. Is each line shown a good fit for the data? Explain your reasoning.

b. What makes one line a better fit than another line?

c. How would you define a *line of best fit*? How can you *analytically* find a line of best fit for a data set?

The data set below gives the temperatures x (in degrees Fahrenheit) and numbers y of people at a beach.

(68, 105), (70, 210), (73, 290), (76, 240), (80, 300), (81, 385),
(86, 380), (90, 490), (92, 430), (95, 570), (97, 510), (99, 560)

d. MP **CHOOSE TOOLS** Make a scatter plot of the data. Then write an equation that models the data. Compare your equation with those of other classmates.

e. Choose an equation from part (d) that you think best represents the data. Do you think this equation is the equation of the line of best fit? Explain.

f. How can you predict the number of people who will be at the beach if the temperature is expected to reach 85°F? Explain.

Analyzing Residuals

One way to determine how well a line of fit models a data set is to analyze *residuals*.

Vocabulary 

residual, *p. 212*
linear regression, *p. 213*
line of best fit, *p. 213*
correlation coefficient, *p. 213*
interpolation, *p. 215*
extrapolation, *p. 215*
causation, *p. 215*

KEY IDEA

Residuals

A **residual** is the difference of the y-value of a data point and the corresponding y-value found using the line of fit. A residual can be positive, negative, or zero.

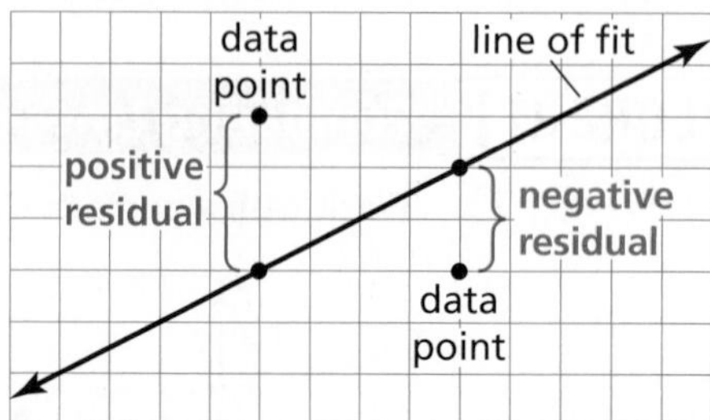

A scatter plot of the residuals shows how well a model fits a data set. If the model is a good fit, then the absolute values of the residuals are relatively small, and the residual points will be more or less evenly dispersed about the horizontal axis. If the model is not a good fit, then the residual points will form some type of pattern that suggests the data are not linear. Wildly scattered residual points suggest that the data might have no correlation.

EXAMPLE 1 Using Residuals 

Year, x	Subscribers (millions), y
0	9
1	21
2	26
3	33
4	43
5	53
6	71
7	76
8	89

In Example 3 in Section 4.4, the equation $y = 10x + 6$ models the data in the table shown. Is the model a good fit?

SOLUTION

Step 1 Calculate the residuals and organize your results in a table.

Step 2 Use the points (x, residual) to make a scatter plot.

x	y	y-Value from model	Residual
0	9	6	$9 - 6 = 3$
1	21	16	$21 - 16 = 5$
2	26	26	$26 - 26 = 0$
3	33	36	$33 - 36 = -3$
4	43	46	$43 - 46 = -3$
5	53	56	$53 - 56 = -3$
6	71	66	$71 - 66 = 5$
7	76	76	$76 - 76 = 0$
8	89	86	$89 - 86 = 3$

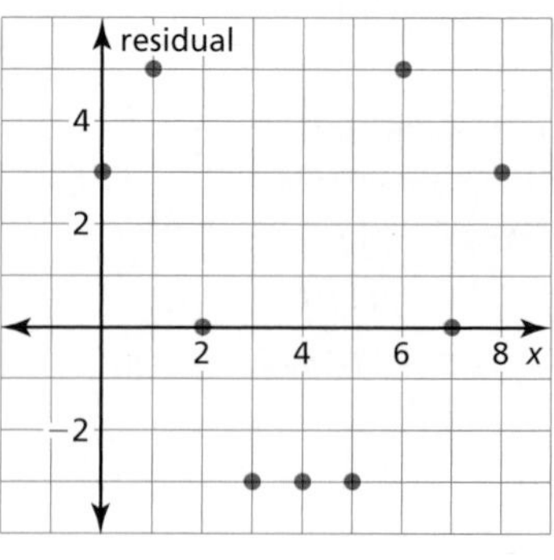

The absolute values of the residuals are relatively small, and the points are more or less evenly dispersed about the horizontal axis.

▶ So, the equation $y = 10x + 6$ is a good fit.

EXAMPLE 2 Using Residuals

Age, x	Salary, y
35	42
37	44
41	47
43	50
45	52
47	51
53	49
55	45

The table shows the ages x and salaries y (in thousands of dollars) of eight employees at a company. The equation $y = 0.2x + 38$ models the data. Is the model a good fit?

SOLUTION

Step 1 Calculate the residuals and organize your results in a table.

Step 2 Use the points (x, residual) to make a scatter plot.

x	y	y-Value from model	Residual
35	42	45.0	$42 - 45.0 = -3.0$
37	44	45.4	$44 - 45.4 = -1.4$
41	47	46.2	$47 - 46.2 = 0.8$
43	50	46.6	$50 - 46.6 = 3.4$
45	52	47.0	$52 - 47.0 = 5.0$
47	51	47.4	$51 - 47.4 = 3.6$
53	49	48.6	$49 - 48.6 = 0.4$
55	45	49.0	$45 - 49.0 = -4.0$

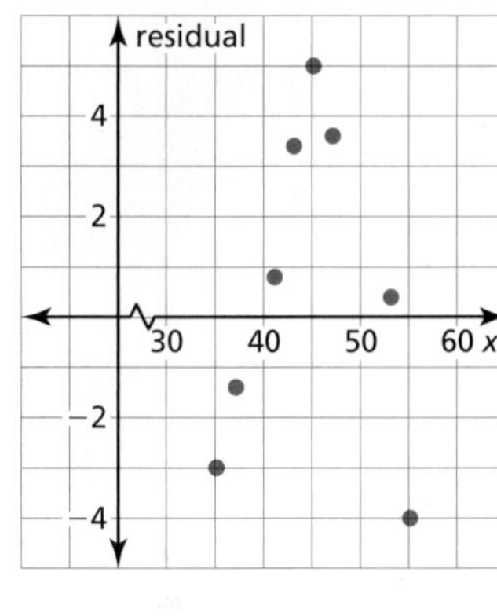

The residual points form a ∩-shaped pattern, which suggests the data are not linear.

▶ So, the equation $y = 0.2x + 38$ does not model the data well.

SELF-ASSESSMENT

1 I do not understand. 2 I can do it with help. 3 I can do it on my own. 4 I can teach someone else.

1. The table shows the attendances y (in thousands) at an amusement park from 2010 to 2020, where $x = 0$ represents the year 2010. The equation $y = -9.2x + 850$ models the data. Is the model a good fit? Explain your reasoning.

Year, x	0	1	2	3	4	5	6	7	8	9	10
Attendance, y	850	845	828	798	800	792	785	781	775	760	760

2. WRITING Describe when a residual is positive, negative, and zero.

3. MP STRUCTURE Explain how you can use residuals to determine how well a line of fit models a data set.

Finding Lines of Best Fit

You can use technology to perform a method called **linear regression** to find a precise line of fit called a **line of best fit**. This line best models a set of data. Technology will often give a value r, called the **correlation coefficient**. This value tells whether the correlation is positive or negative and how closely the equation models the data. Values of r range from -1 to 1. When r is close to 1 or -1, there is a strong correlation between the variables. As r gets closer to 0, the correlation becomes weaker.

STUDY TIP

You know how to use two points to find an equation of a line of fit. When finding an equation of the line of best fit, every point in the data set is used.

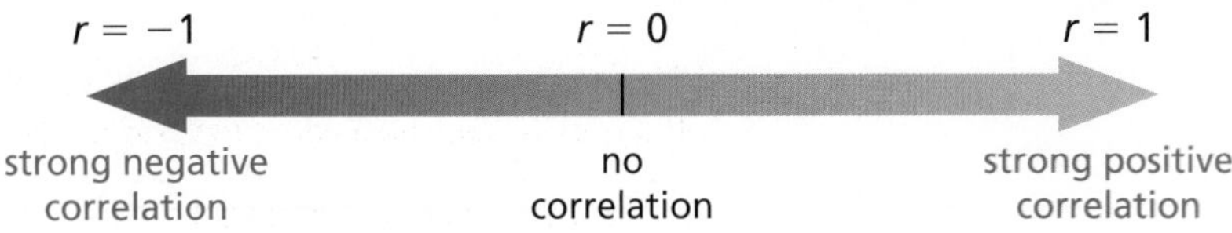

Finding a Line of Best Fit Using Technology

The table shows the durations x (in minutes) of several eruptions of the geyser Old Faithful and the times y (in minutes) until the next eruption. (a) Use technology to find an equation of the line of best fit. Then graph the equation with the data. (b) Identify and interpret the correlation coefficient. (c) Interpret the slope and y-intercept of the line of best fit.

Duration, *x*	2.0	3.7	4.2	1.9	3.1	2.5	4.4	3.9
Time, *y*	60	83	84	58	72	62	85	85

SOLUTION

a. Step 1 Enter the data from the table into a technology table.

x	y
2.0	60
3.7	83
4.2	84
1.9	58
3.1	72
2.5	62
4.4	85
3.9	85

Step 2 Use *linear regression*. The values in the equation can be rounded to obtain $y = 12.0x + 35$.

$y = mx + b$

PARAMETERS

$m = 11.9901$ (slope) $b = 35.1068$ (y-intercept)

STATISTICS

$r^2 = 0.9579$

$r = 0.9787$ (correlation coefficient)

Step 3 Graph the equation $y = 12.0x + 35$ with the data.

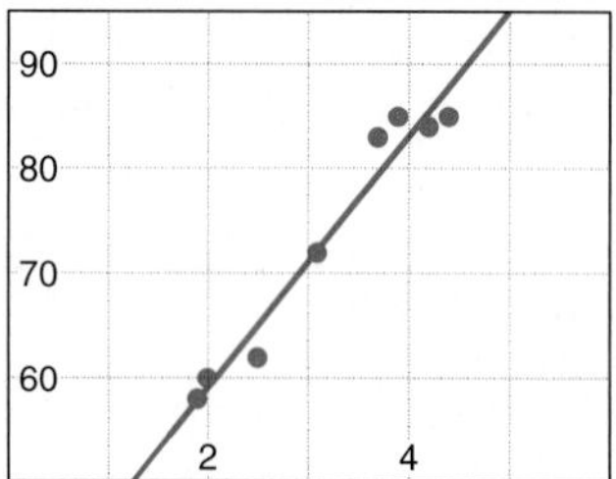

Math Practice

Analyze Givens

How can you determine appropriate scales for your graph?

b. The correlation coefficient is about 0.979. This means that the relationship between the durations and the times until the next eruption has a strong positive correlation and the equation closely models the data, as shown in the graph.

c. The slope of the line is about 12. This means the time until the next eruption increases by about 12 minutes for each minute the duration increases. The y-intercept is about 35, but it has no meaning in this context because the duration cannot be 0 minutes.

SELF-ASSESSMENT

1 I do not understand. **2** I can do it with help. **3** I can do it on my own. **4** I can teach someone else.

4. Use the data in Exercise 1 on the previous page. (a) Use technology to find an equation of the line of best fit. Then graph the equation with the data. (b) Identify and interpret the correlation coefficient. (c) Interpret the slope and y-intercept of the line of best fit.

5. WHICH ONE DOESN'T BELONG? Which correlation coefficient does *not* belong with the other three? Explain your reasoning.

$r = -0.98$ $r = 0.96$ $r = -0.09$ $r = 0.97$

GO DIGITAL

WORDS AND MATH

How can the prefixes *inter-* and *extra-* help you remember the meanings of *interpolation* and *extrapolation*?

Using a graph or its equation to *approximate* a value between two known values is called **interpolation**. Using a graph or its equation to *predict* a value outside the range of known values is called **extrapolation**. In general, the farther removed a value is from the known values, the less confidence you can have in the accuracy of the prediction.

EXAMPLE 4 Interpolating and Extrapolating Data

WATCH

Refer to Example 3. Use the equation of the line of best fit. (a) Approximate the time until the next eruption after an eruption lasting $3\frac{1}{2}$ minutes. (b) Predict the time until the next eruption after an eruption lasting 5.0 minutes.

SOLUTION

a. $y = 12.0x + 35$ Write the equation.

$= 12.0\left(3\frac{1}{2}\right) + 35$ Substitute $3\frac{1}{2}$ for x.

$= 77$ Evaluate.

▶ The next eruption will occur about 77 minutes after an eruption lasting $3\frac{1}{2}$ minutes.

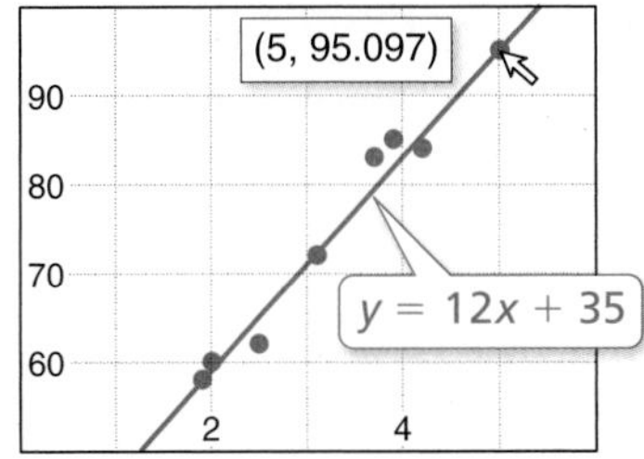

b. Use technology to graph the equation and find the value of y when $x \approx 5.0$.

▶ The next eruption will occur about 95 minutes after an eruption lasting 5.0 minutes.

Correlation and Causation

When a change in one variable causes a change in another variable, it is called **causation.** Causation produces a strong correlation between the two variables. The converse is *not* true. In other words, correlation does not imply causation.

EXAMPLE 5 Identifying Correlation and Causation

WATCH

READING

A causal relationship exists when one variable *causes* a change in another variable.

Tell whether a correlation is likely in the situation. If so, tell whether there is a causal relationship. Explain your reasoning.

a. time spent exercising and the number of calories burned

▶ There is a positive correlation and a causal relationship because the more time you spend exercising, the more calories you burn.

b. the number of banks and the population of a city

▶ There may be a positive correlation but no causal relationship. Building more banks will not cause the population to increase.

SELF-ASSESSMENT 1 I do not understand. 2 I can do it with help. 3 I can do it on my own. 4 I can teach someone else.

6. Refer to Exercise 4 on the previous page. Predict the attendance at the amusement park in 2023.

7. MP **REASONING** Why do you think extrapolating a value to make a prediction is likely to result in a less accurate prediction than interpolating a value to find an estimate?

8. Is there a correlation between time spent playing video games and grade point average? If so, is there a causal relationship? Explain your reasoning.

9. **WRITING** In your own words, explain why correlation does not imply causation.

4.5 Practice WITH CalcChat® AND CalcView®

In Exercises 1–4, use residuals to determine whether the model is a good fit for the data in the table. Explain.
Examples 1 and 2

1. $y = 4x - 5$

x	−4	−3	−2	−1	0	1	2	3	4
y	−18	−13	−10	−7	−2	0	6	10	15

2. $y = 6x + 4$

x	1.5	3	4.5	6	7.5	9	10.5	12	13.5
y	14	23	29	42	48	62	63	75	88

3. $y = -1.3x + 1$

x	−8	−6	−4	−2	0	2	4	6	8
y	9	10	5	8	−1	1	−4	−12	−7

4. $y = -0.5x - 2$

x	4	6	8	10	12	14	16	18	20
y	−1	−3	−6	−8	−10	−10	−10	−9	−9

5. **ANALYZING RESIDUALS** The table shows the growth y (in inches) of an elk's antlers during week x. The equation $y = -0.7x + 6.8$ models the data. Is the model a good fit? Explain.

Week, x	Growth, y
1	6.0
2	5.5
3	4.7
4	3.9
5	3.3

6. **ANALYZING RESIDUALS** The table shows the approximate numbers y (in thousands) of movie tickets sold from January to June for a theater. In the table, $x = 1$ represents January. The equation $y = 1.3x + 27$ models the data. Is the model a good fit? Explain.

Month, x	1	2	3	4	5	6
Ticket sales, y	27	28	36	28	32	35

In Exercises 7 and 8, use technology to find an equation of the line of best fit for the data. Identify and interpret the correlation coefficient.

7.

x	−15	−10	−5	0	5	10	15	20
y	−4	2	7	16	22	30	37	43

8.

x	5.4	6.8	7.2	8.6	9.0	10.4	11.8
y	12	−2	8	3	−1	−4	6

9. **MODELING REAL LIFE** The table shows the numbers y of people who volunteer at an animal shelter on day x.
Example 3

Day, x	1	2	3	4	5	6	7	8
People, y	9	5	13	11	10	11	19	12

a. Use technology to find an equation of the line of best fit. Then plot the data and graph the equation in the same viewing window.

b. Identify and interpret the correlation coefficient.

c. Interpret the slope and y-intercept of the line of best fit.

10. **MODELING REAL LIFE** The table shows the total numbers y of people who reported an earthquake x minutes after it ended.

Minutes, x	People, y
1	12
2	97
3	408
4	915
5	1420
6	1786
7	2092

a. Use technology to find an equation of the line of best fit. Then plot the data and graph the equation in the same viewing window.

b. Identify and interpret the correlation coefficient.

c. Interpret the slope and y-intercept of the line of best fit.

GO DIGITAL

11. MODELING REAL LIFE The table shows the mileages x (in thousands of miles) and the selling prices y (in thousands of dollars) of several used automobiles of the same year and model. *Example 4*

Mileage, x	22	14	18	30	8	24
Price, y	16	17	17	14	18	15

a. Use technology to find an equation of the line of best fit.

b. Identify and interpret the correlation coefficient.

c. Interpret the slope and y-intercept of the line of best fit.

d. Approximate the price of an automobile with 25,000 miles.

e. Predict the price of an automobile with 6000 miles.

12. MODELING REAL LIFE The table shows the grade point averages y of several students and the numbers x of hours they spend watching television each week.

Hours, x	GPA, y
5	3.4
3	3.5
12	2.7
20	2.1
15	2.8
8	3.0
4	3.7

a. Use technology to find an equation of the line of best fit.

b. Identify and interpret the correlation coefficient.

c. Interpret the slope and y-intercept of the line of best fit.

d. Approximate the GPA of a student who watches 14 hours of television each week.

e. Predict the GPA of a student who watches 1 hour of television each week.

13. ERROR ANALYSIS Describe and correct the error in interpreting the technology display.

$y = mx + b$
PARAMETERS
$m = -4.47$ $b = 23.16$
STATISTICS
$r^2 = 0.9989$
$r = -0.9995$

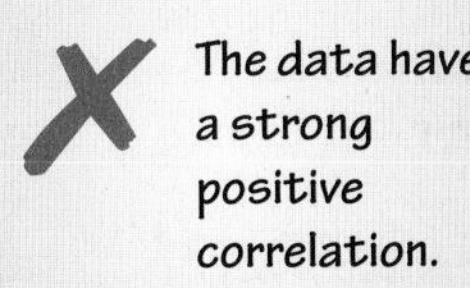
The data have a strong positive correlation.

14. USING MODELS Refer to Exercise 10.

a. Predict the total numbers of people who reported an earthquake 9 minutes and 15 minutes after it ended.

b. The table shows the actual data. Describe the accuracy of your extrapolations in part (a).

Minutes, x	People, y
9	2750
15	3203

In Exercises 15–18, tell whether a correlation is likely in the situation. If so, tell whether there is a causal relationship. Explain your reasoning. *Example 5*

15. time spent talking on a cell phone and the remaining battery life

16. the height of a building and the number of steps inside

17. the number of hats you own and the size of your head

18. the weight of a dog and the length of its tail

19. OPEN-ENDED Describe a data set that has a strong correlation but does not have a causal relationship.

20. HOW DO YOU SEE IT?
Match each graph with its correlation coefficient. Explain your reasoning.

a.
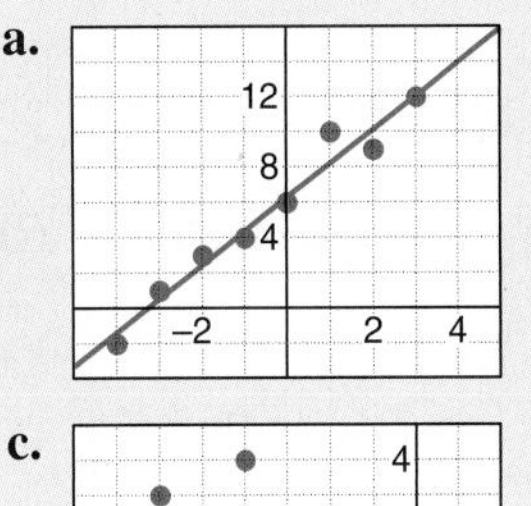

b.
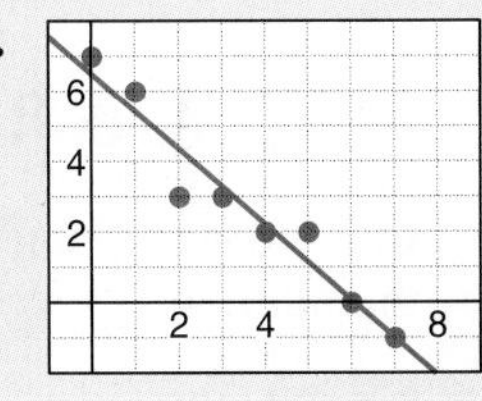

c.
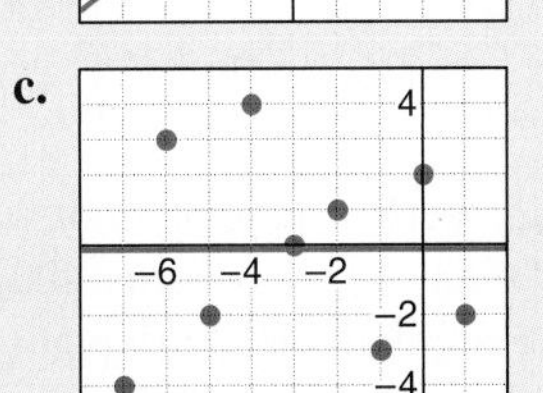

d.
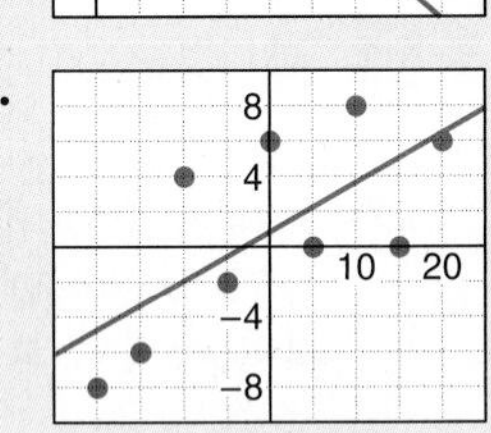

A. $r = 0$ B. $r = 0.98$

C. $r = -0.97$ D. $r = 0.69$

21. COMPARING METHODS The table shows the number y (in billions) of text messages sent each year in a five-year period, where $x = 1$ represents the first year in the five-year period.

Year, x	1	2	3	4	5
Text messages (billions), y	241	601	1360	1806	2206

a. Use technology to find an equation of the line of best fit. Identify and interpret the correlation coefficient.

b. Is there a causal relationship? Explain.

c. Calculate the residuals. Then make a scatter plot of the residuals and interpret the results.

d. Compare the methods you used in parts (a) and (c) to determine whether the model is a good fit. Which method do you prefer? Explain.

22. **ABSTRACT REASONING** A data set consists of the number x of people at Park A and the number y of people at Park B recorded daily for 1 week. Sketch a possible graph of the data set. Describe the relationship shown in the graph and give a possible correlation coefficient. Determine whether there is a causal relationship. Explain.

23. **MAKING AN ARGUMENT** Your friend uses technology to find the line of best fit, $y = 1.7x$, for the data in the table. He says the model is a good fit because the correlation coefficient is about 0.95. Your cousin makes a scatter plot of the data and says the model is *not* a good fit because the data do not appear to be linear. Who is correct? Explain.

x	1.0	0.8	1.5	0.5	5.0	1.2	0.75
y	1.25	1.5	1.0	0.8	8.5	2.0	2.5

24. **THOUGHT PROVOKING** The time line shows the amounts of electricity (in millions of megawatt hours) generated by nuclear power in the United States from 2010 to 2017.

GO DIGITAL

U.S. Nuclear Power Generation

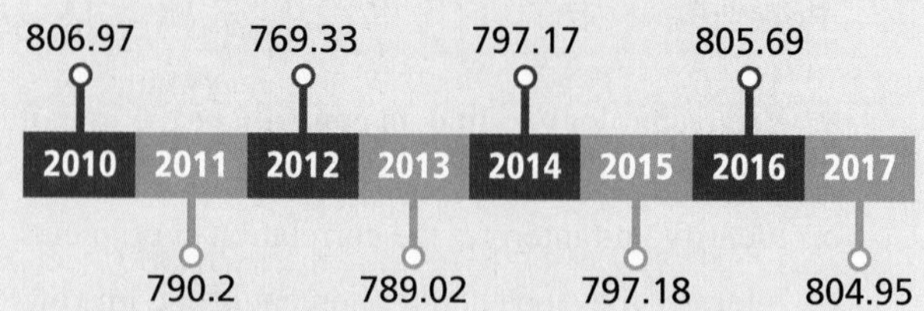

a. Analyze the data. Is a linear model a good fit? Explain.

b. Estimate the amount of electricity generated by nuclear power in 2021. Explain your method.

REVIEW & REFRESH

WATCH

In Exercises 25 and 26, solve the inequality. Graph the solution.

25. $20 \geq \frac{4}{5}w$

26. $-9y < 24$

27. Is there a correlation between the outdoor temperature and the number of reported illnesses? If so, is there a causal relationship? Explain your reasoning.

28. **MODELING REAL LIFE** You buy two tickets to an escape room using a coupon for \$5 off your entire purchase. You pay a total of \$48.15, which includes 7% sales tax. What is the original price of one ticket?

29. Determine whether the table represents a *linear* or *nonlinear* function. Explain.

x	2	4	6	8
y	13	8	3	−2

30. Write an equation of the line with a slope of $\frac{1}{2}$ and a y-intercept of −7.

31. Describe the relationship between the data in the scatter plot.

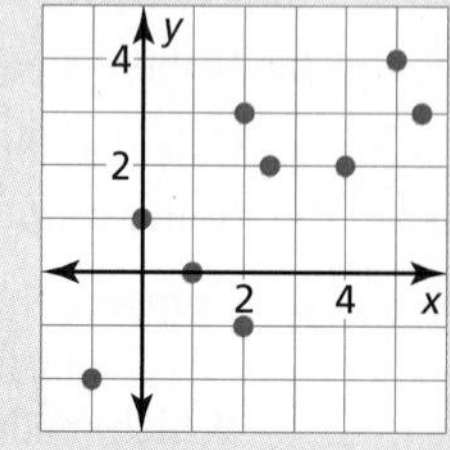

32. **WRITING** Compare interpolation and extrapolation.

33. Write an equation in slope-intercept form of the line shown.

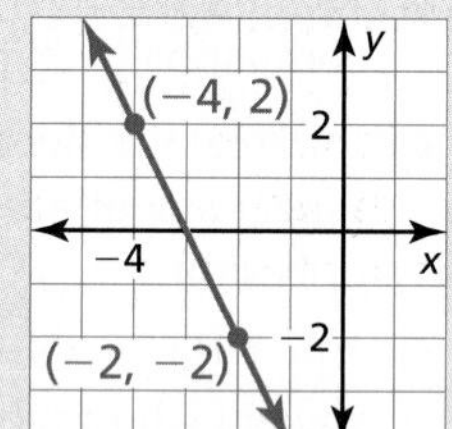

34. Determine which of the lines, if any, are parallel or perpendicular. Explain.

Line a passes through (−2, 2) and (2, 1).

Line b passes through (1, −8) and (3, 0).

Line c passes through (−4, −3) and (0, −2).

In Exercises 35 and 36, solve the equation. Check your solutions.

35. $|-3d| = 15$

36. $|b - 8| = |b + \frac{1}{4}|$

In Exercises 37 and 38, use technology to find an equation of the line of best fit for the data. Identify and interpret the correlation coefficient.

37.

x	0	1	2	3	4	5	6	7
y	−8	−5	−2	−1	−1	2	5	8

38.

x	−4	−2	0	2	4	6	8	10
y	17	7	8	1	5	−2	2	−8

4.6 Arithmetic Sequences

Learning Target Understand the concept of arithmetic sequences.

Success Criteria
- I can write the terms of arithmetic sequences.
- I can graph arithmetic sequences.
- I can identify arithmetic sequences.
- I can write arithmetic sequences as functions.

EXPLORE IT! Describing Patterns Involving Squares

Work with a partner. Use the figures below.

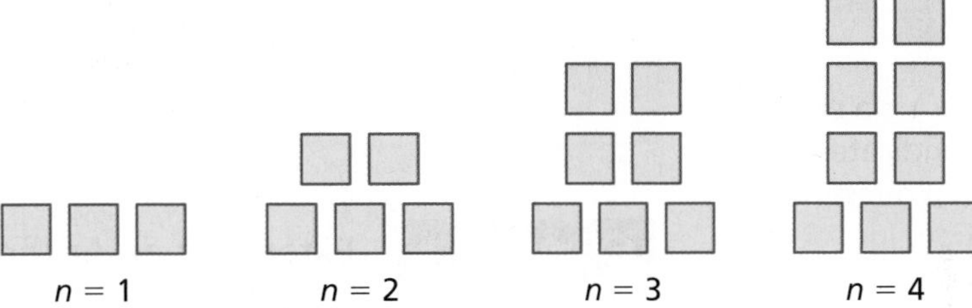

Math Practice

Analyze Givens

Be sure you can identify the important quantities in a problem. What do you think n represents in this situation?

a. Complete the table. What do you notice?

n	1	2	3	4
Number of squares, q_n	3			
Number of sides, s_n	12			

b. Graph the data in the table. What do you notice?

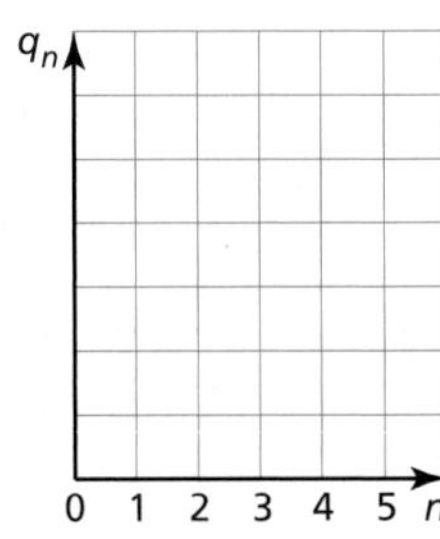

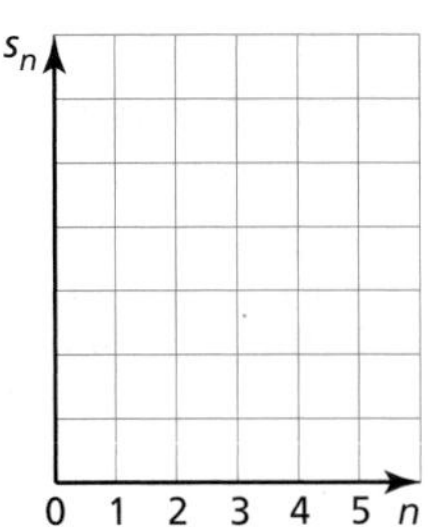

c. Can you write an equation that represents each graph? Explain.

d. How can you extend the patterns to find the number of squares or the number of sides for greater values of n? Explain your reasoning.

e. Find the number of squares and the number of sides when $n = 20$.

Writing the Terms of Arithmetic Sequences

Vocabulary

sequence, *p. 220*
term, *p. 220*
arithmetic sequence, *p. 220*
common difference, *p. 220*

A **sequence** is an ordered list of numbers. Each number in a sequence is called a **term**. Each term a_n has a specific position n in the sequence.

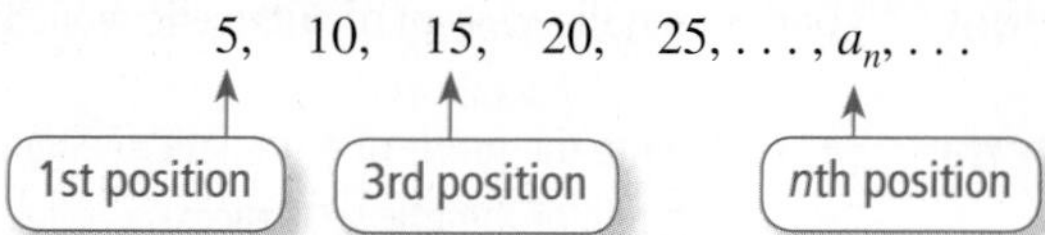

KEY IDEA

Arithmetic Sequence

In an **arithmetic sequence**, the difference between each pair of consecutive terms is the same. This difference is called the **common difference**. Each term is found by adding the common difference to the previous term.

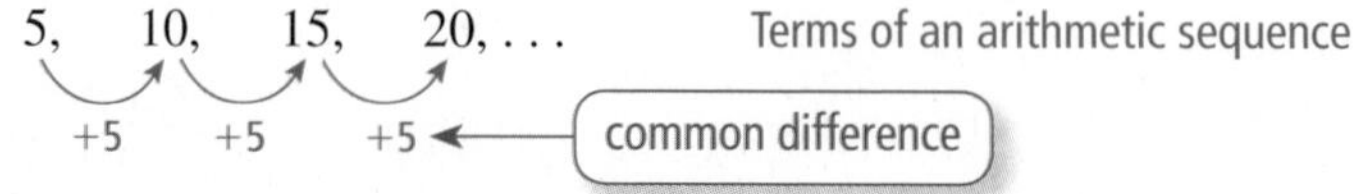

READING

An ellipsis (. . .) is a series of dots that indicates an intentional omission of information. In mathematics, the . . . notation means "and so forth." The ellipsis indicates that there are more terms in the sequence that are not shown.

EXAMPLE 1 Extending an Arithmetic Sequence

Write the next three terms of the arithmetic sequence.

$-7, -14, -21, -28, \ldots$

SOLUTION

Use a table to organize the terms and find the pattern.

Position	1	2	3	4
Term	−7	−14	−21	−28

+(−7) +(−7) +(−7)

Each term is 7 less than the previous term. So, the common difference is −7.

Add −7 to a term to find the next term.

Position	1	2	3	4	5	6	7
Term	−7	−14	−21	−28	−35	−42	−49

+(−7) +(−7) +(−7)

▶ The next three terms are −35, −42, and −49.

SELF-ASSESSMENT 1 I do not understand. 2 I can do it with help. 3 I can do it on my own. 4 I can teach someone else.

1. **WRITING** Explain how to find the common difference of an arithmetic sequence.
2. **OPEN-ENDED** Give an example of an arithmetic sequence. Then give an example of a sequence that is not arithmetic but has the same first term as the arithmetic sequence you wrote.

Write the next three terms of the arithmetic sequence.

3. $-12, 0, 12, 24, \ldots$
4. $0.2, 0.6, 1, 1.4, \ldots$
5. $4, 3\frac{3}{4}, 3\frac{1}{2}, 3\frac{1}{4}, \ldots$

Graphing Arithmetic Sequences

To graph a sequence, let a term's position number n in the sequence be the x-value. The term a_n is the corresponding y-value. Plot the ordered pairs (n, a_n).

GO DIGITAL

EXAMPLE 2 Graphing an Arithmetic Sequence

Graph the arithmetic sequence 4, 8, 12, 16, ... What do you notice?

SOLUTION

Make a table. Then plot the ordered pairs (n, a_n).

Position, n	Term, a_n
1	4
2	8
3	12
4	16

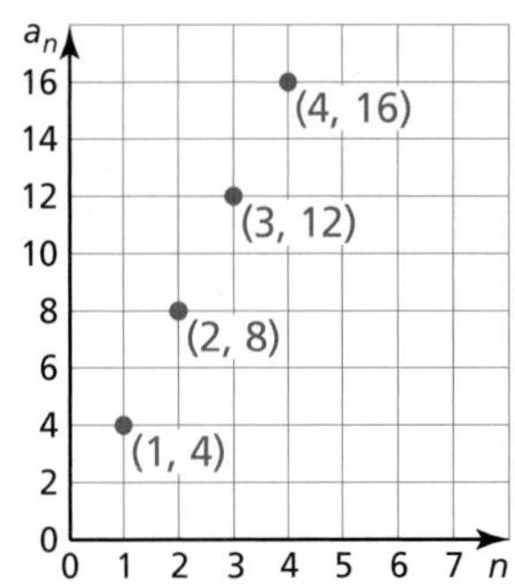

The points lie on a line.

EXAMPLE 3 Identifying an Arithmetic Sequence from a Graph

Does the graph represent an arithmetic sequence? Explain.

SOLUTION

Make a table to organize the ordered pairs. Then determine whether there is a common difference.

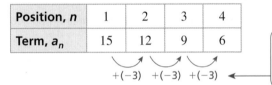

Position, n	1	2	3	4
Term, a_n	15	12	9	6

$+(-3)$ $+(-3)$ $+(-3)$

Each term is 3 less than the previous term. So, the common difference is -3.

Consecutive terms have a common difference of -3. So, the graph represents the arithmetic sequence 15, 12, 9, 6, ...

SELF-ASSESSMENT

1 I do not understand. 2 I can do it with help. 3 I can do it on my own. 4 I can teach someone else.

Graph the arithmetic sequence. What do you notice?

6. 3, 12, 21, 30, . . .

7. 4, 2, 0, -2, . . .

8. 1, 0.8, 0.6, 0.4, . . .

Determine whether the graph represents an arithmetic sequence. Explain.

9.

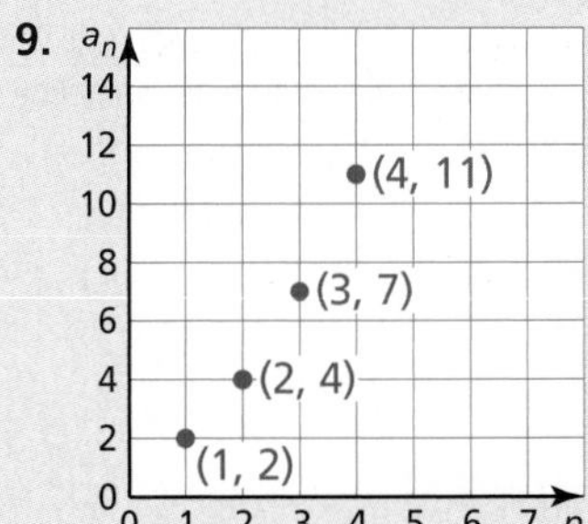

10.

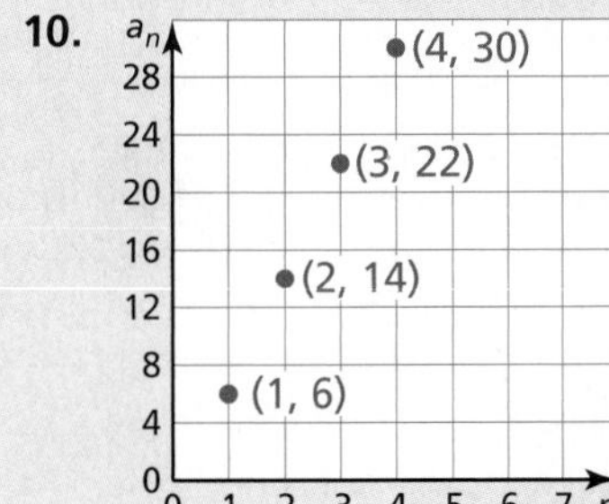

11.

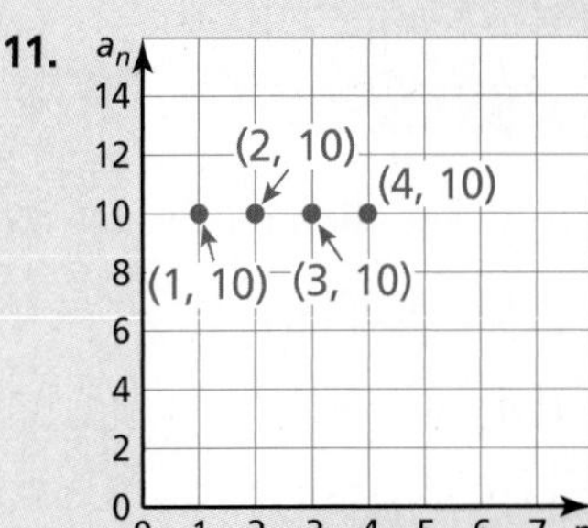

Writing Arithmetic Sequences as Functions

Because consecutive terms of an arithmetic sequence have a common difference, the sequence has a constant rate of change. So, the points represented by any arithmetic sequence lie on a line. You can use the first term and the common difference to write a linear function that describes an arithmetic sequence. For example, let $a_1 = 4$ and $d = 3$.

Position, n	Term, a_n	Written using a_1 and d	Numbers
1	first term, a_1	a_1	4
2	second term, a_2	$a_1 + d$	$4 + 3 = 7$
3	third term, a_3	$a_1 + 2d$	$4 + 2(3) = 10$
4	fourth term, a_4	$a_1 + 3d$	$4 + 3(3) = 13$
⋮	⋮	⋮	⋮
n	nth term, a_n	$a_1 + (n - 1)d$	$4 + (n - 1)(3)$

ANOTHER WAY

An *arithmetic sequence* is a linear function whose domain is the set of positive integers. You can think of d as the slope and $(1, a_1)$ as a point on the graph of the function. An equation in point-slope form of the function is

$$a_n - a_1 = d(n - 1).$$

This equation can be rewritten as

$$a_n = a_1 + (n - 1)d.$$

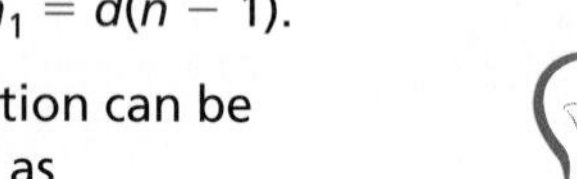

KEY IDEA

Equation for an Arithmetic Sequence

Let a_n be the nth term of an arithmetic sequence with first term a_1 and common difference d. The nth term is given by $a_n = a_1 + (n - 1)d$.

EXAMPLE 4 Finding the *n*th Term of an Arithmetic Sequence

Write an equation for the nth term of the arithmetic sequence 55, 40, 25, 10, ... Then find a_{16}.

STUDY TIP

Notice that the equation in Example 4 is of the form $y = mx + b$, where y is replaced by a_n and x is replaced by n.

SOLUTION

The first term is 55, and the common difference is -15.

$a_n = a_1 + (n - 1)d$ — Equation for an arithmetic sequence

$a_n = 55 + (n - 1)(-15)$ — Substitute 55 for a_1 and -15 for d.

$a_n = -15n + 70$ — Simplify.

Use the equation to find the 16th term.

$a_n = -15n + 70$ — Write the equation.

$a_{16} = -15(16) + 70$ — Substitute 16 for n.

$= -170$ — Simplify.

▶ The 16th term of the arithmetic sequence is -170.

SELF-ASSESSMENT 1 I do not understand. 2 I can do it with help. 3 I can do it on my own. 4 I can teach someone else.

Write an equation for the nth term of the arithmetic sequence. Then find a_{25}.

12. 8, 16, 24, 32, . . .

13. 1, 0, -1, -2, . . .

14. 4, $5\frac{1}{2}$, 7, $8\frac{1}{2}$, . . .

You can rewrite the equation for an arithmetic sequence with first term a_1 and common difference d in function notation by replacing a_n with $f(n)$.

$$f(n) = a_1 + (n - 1)d$$

The domain of the function is the set of positive integers.

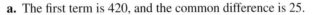

EXAMPLE 5 Modeling Real Life

Winter

heating system

heat exchanger and pump

heat transferred to pipe from ground during winter

Online bidding for a geothermal heat pump increases by \$25 for each bid after the \$420 initial bid.

a. Write a function that represents the arithmetic sequence. Then graph the function.

b. The winning bid is \$1520. How many bids were there?

SOLUTION

a. The first term is 420, and the common difference is 25.

$f(n) = a_1 + (n - 1)d$	Function for an arithmetic sequence
$f(n) = 420 + (n - 1)25$	Substitute 420 for a_1 and 25 for d.
$f(n) = 25n + 395$	Simplify.

▶ The function $f(n) = 25n + 395$ represents the arithmetic sequence.

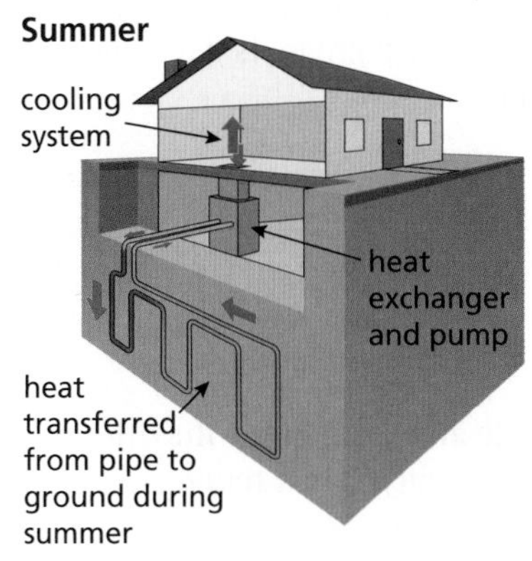

Make a table. Then plot the ordered pairs $(n, f(n))$.

Bid number, n	Bid amount, $f(n)$
1	\$420
2	\$445
3	\$470
4	\$495

Online Bidding

Bid amount (dollars): $f(n)$ 0, 400, 425, 450, 475, 500, 525

Points: (1, 420), (2, 445), (3, 470), (4, 495)

Bid number: 0 1 2 3 4 5 6 n

b. Use the function to find the value of n for which $f(n) = 1520$.

$f(n) = 25n + 395$	Write the function.
$1520 = 25n + 395$	Substitute 1520 for $f(n)$.
$1125 = 25n$	Subtract 395 from each side.
$45 = n$	Solve for n.

▶ There were 45 bids.

Check

$f(n) = 25n + 395$

$1520 \stackrel{?}{=} 25(45) + 395$

$1520 \stackrel{?}{=} 1125 + 395$

$1520 = 1520$ ✓

SELF-ASSESSMENT

1 I do not understand. 2 I can do it with help. 3 I can do it on my own. 4 I can teach someone else.

15. A carnival charges \$1.50 for each game after you pay a \$10 entry fee.

a. Write a function that represents the arithmetic sequence. Then graph the function.

b. You have \$35. How many games can you play?

Games	Total cost
1	\$11.50
2	\$13.00
3	\$14.50
4	\$16.00

16. WHAT IF? In Example 5, online bidding increases by about 10% for each bid after the \$420 initial bid. Can this situation be represented by an arithmetic sequence? Explain.

4.6 Practice WITH CalcChat® AND CalcView®

In Exercises 1 and 2, write the next three terms of the arithmetic sequence.

1. First term: 2
   Common difference: 13

2. First term: 18
   Common difference: −6

In Exercises 3–6, find the common difference of the arithmetic sequence.

3. 13, 18, 23, 28, . . .

4. 175, 150, 125, 100, . . .

5. $4, 3\frac{2}{3}, 3\frac{1}{3}, 3, \ldots$

6. 6.5, 5, 3.5, 2, . . .

In Exercises 7–12, write the next three terms of the arithmetic sequence. *Example 1*

7. 19, 22, 25, 28, . . .

8. 1, 12, 23, 34, . . .

9. 16, 21, 26, 31, . . .

10. 60, 30, 0, −30, . . .

11. 1.3, 1, 0.7, 0.4, . . .

12. $\frac{5}{6}, \frac{2}{3}, \frac{1}{2}, \frac{1}{3}, \ldots$

In Exercises 13–18, graph the arithmetic sequence. *Example 2*

13. 4, 12, 20, 28, . . .

14. −15, 0, 15, 30, . . .

15. −1, −3, −5, −7, . . .

16. 2, 19, 36, 53, . . .

17. $0, 4\frac{1}{2}, 9, 13\frac{1}{2}, \ldots$

18. 6, 5.25, 4.5, 3.75, . . .

In Exercises 19–22, determine whether the graph represents an arithmetic sequence. Explain. *Example 3*

19. 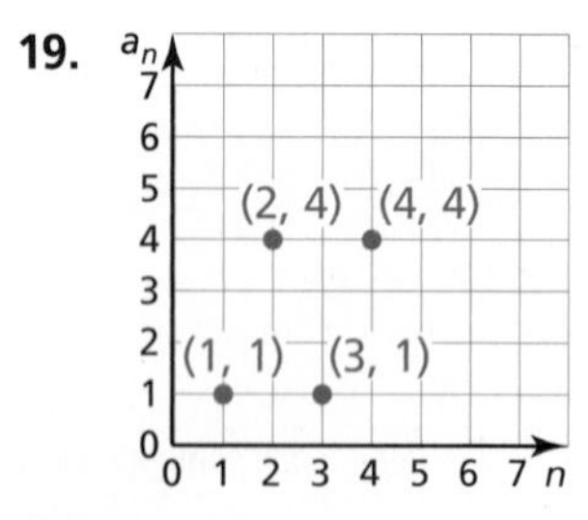

20. 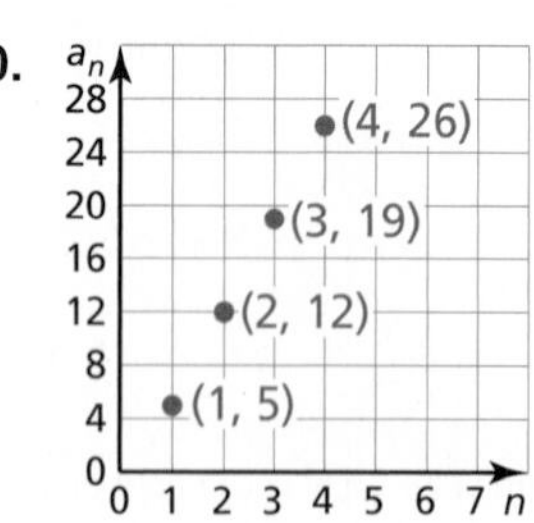

21. 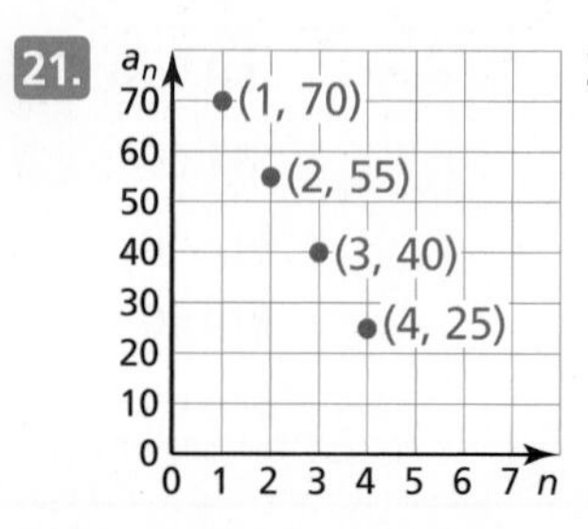

22. 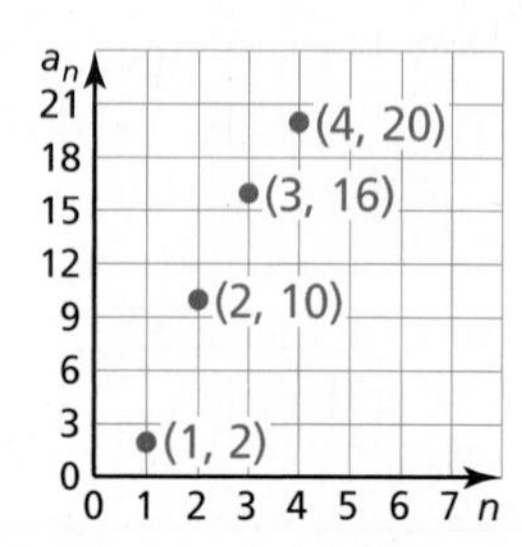

In Exercises 23–26, determine whether the sequence is arithmetic. If so, find the common difference.

23. 13, 26, 39, 52, . . .

24. 5, 9, 14, 20, . . .

25. 48, 24, 12, 6, . . .

26. 87, 81, 75, 69, . . .

27. **MP PATTERNS** Write a sequence that represents the number of smiley faces in each group. Is the sequence arithmetic? Explain.

28. **MP PATTERNS** Write a sequence that represents the number of cubes in each group. Is the sequence arithmetic? Explain.

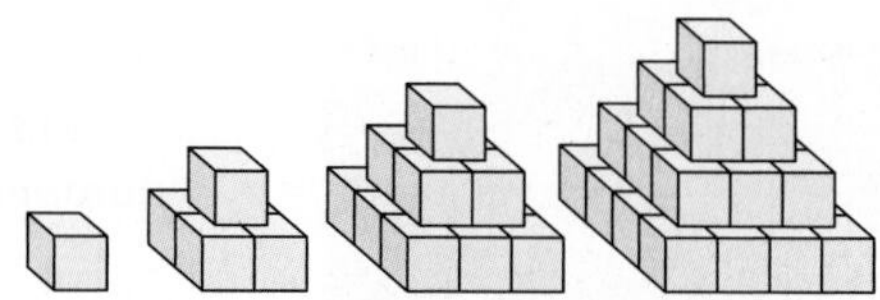

In Exercises 29–34, write an equation for the *n*th term of the arithmetic sequence. Then find a_{10}. *Example 4*

29. −5, −4, −3, −2, . . .

30. −6, −9, −12, −15, . . .

31. $\frac{1}{2}, 1, 1\frac{1}{2}, 2, \ldots$

32. 100, 110, 120, 130, . . .

33. 10, 0, −10, −20, . . .

34. $\frac{3}{7}, \frac{4}{7}, \frac{5}{7}, \frac{6}{7}, \ldots$

35. **ERROR ANALYSIS** Describe and correct the error in finding the common difference of the arithmetic sequence.

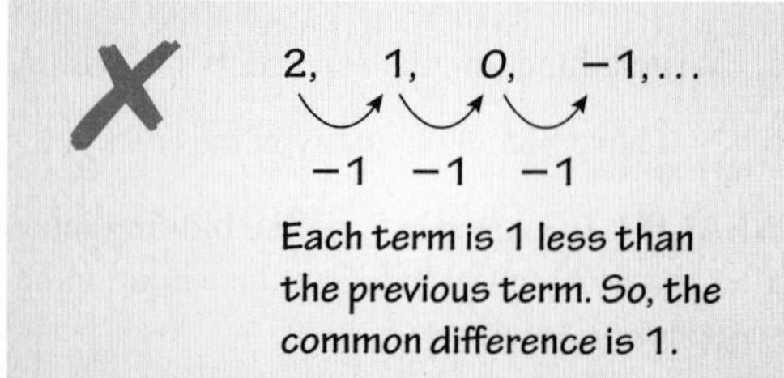

2, 1, 0, −1, . . .
−1 −1 −1
Each term is 1 less than the previous term. So, the common difference is 1.

36. ERROR ANALYSIS Describe and correct the error in writing an equation for the nth term of the arithmetic sequence.

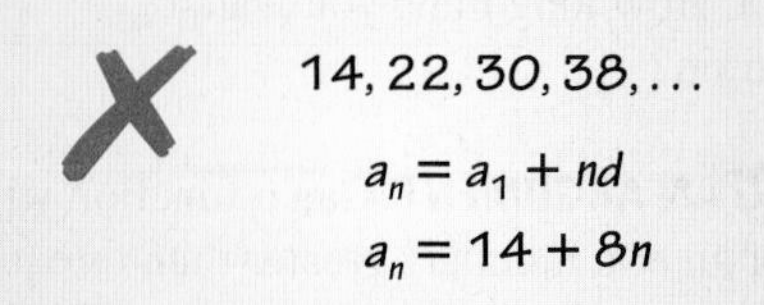

37. MP NUMBER SENSE The fifth term of an arithmetic sequence is 21. The common difference of the sequence is 1.5 times the first term. Graph the sequence.

38. MP NUMBER SENSE The fourth term of an arithmetic sequence is 20. The common difference of the sequence is $-\frac{1}{5}$ times the first term. Graph the sequence.

39. MODELING REAL LIFE The total number of babies born in a country each minute after midnight on January 1st can be estimated by the arithmetic sequence shown in the table. *Example 5*

Minutes after midnight January 1st	1	2	3	4
Total babies born	5	10	15	20

a. Write a function that represents the sequence. Then graph the function.

b. Estimate how many minutes after midnight on January 1st it takes for 100 babies to be born.

40. MODELING REAL LIFE The gross revenue from a musical each week after opening night can be approximated by the arithmetic sequence shown in the table.

Week	1	2	3	4
Gross revenue (millions of dollars)	2.6	2.4	2.2	2.0

a. Write a function that represents the sequence. Then graph the function.

b. In what week does the musical earn $1.6 million?

41. COLLEGE PREP Which function represents the sequence 5, 1.5, −2, −5.5, . . .?

Ⓐ $f(n) = -3.5n + 5$ Ⓑ $g(n) = -3.5n + 8.5$

Ⓒ $h(n) = 3.5n + 1.5$ Ⓓ $k(n) = 5n - 8.5$

42. OPEN-ENDED Write the first four terms of two different arithmetic sequences with a common difference of −3. Write an equation for the nth term of each sequence.

MP REPEATED REASONING In Exercises 43 and 44, a sequence represents the figures. (a) Draw the next three figures represented by the sequence and (b) describe the figure represented by the 20th number in the sequence.

43.

44.

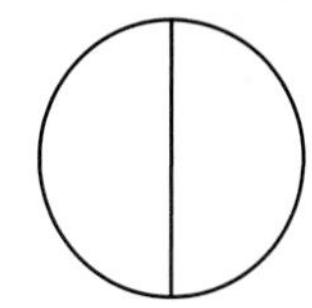
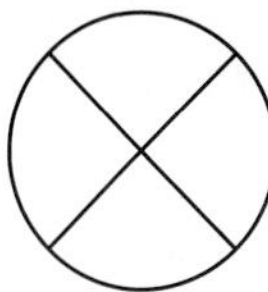
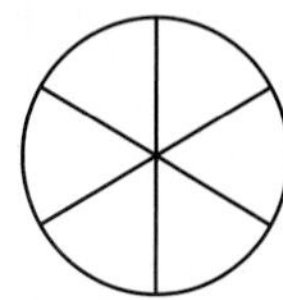

45. CRITICAL THINKING Your friend says that the figures shown cannot be represented by an arithmetic sequence. Describe a sequence that supports your friend's claim. Then describe a sequence that does *not* support your friend's claim.

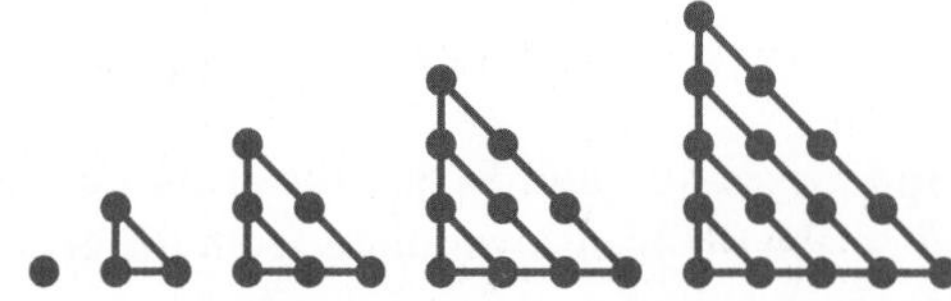

46. HOW DO YOU SEE IT?
The bar graph shows the costs of advertising in a magazine.

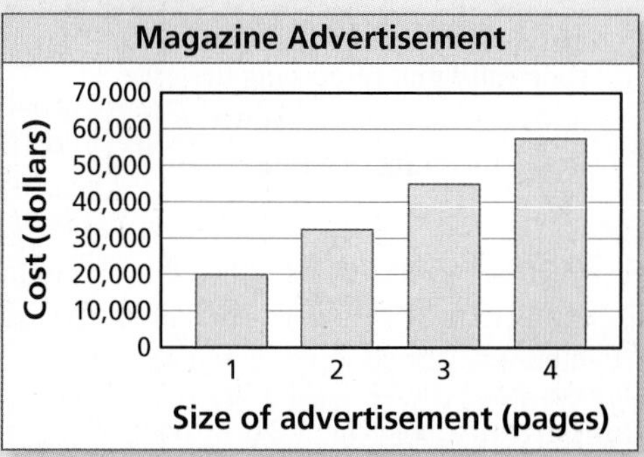

a. Does the graph represent an arithmetic sequence? Explain.

b. Explain how you would estimate the cost of a six-page advertisement in the magazine.

47. **MP REPEATED REASONING** Firewood is stacked in a pile. The bottom row has 20 logs, and the top row has 14 logs. Each row has one more log than the row above it. How many logs are in the pile?

48. **THOUGHT PROVOKING**
Write a function that you can use to find the increase in area from one square to the next as the side length increases by 1 inch. Explain your reasoning. Then find the increase in area from the 10th square to the 11th square.

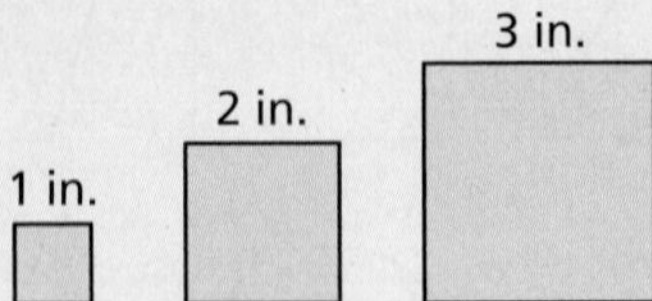

49. **MP PROBLEM SOLVING** A train stops at a station every 12 minutes starting at 6:00 A.M. You arrive at the station at 7:29 A.M. How long must you wait for the train?

50. **MAKING AN ARGUMENT** Can a function with a range of all real numbers greater than or equal to zero represent an arithmetic sequence? Explain your reasoning.

51. 

Let x be a constant. Determine whether each sequence is an arithmetic sequence. Explain.

a. $x + 6, 3x + 6, 5x + 6, 7x + 6, \ldots$

b. $x + 1, 3x + 1, 9x + 1, 27x + 1, \ldots$

WATCH

REVIEW & REFRESH

52. Determine which of the lines, if any, are parallel or perpendicular. Explain.

Line a: $-x + 3y = 9$

Line b: $y = \frac{1}{3}x - 2$

Line c: $12 = 3x + y$

In Exercises 53 and 54, use the graphs of f and g to describe the transformations from the graph of f to the graph of g.

53. $f(x) = -2x + 7$; $g(x) = -10x + 5$

54. $f(x) = -\frac{3}{4}x + 6$; $g(x) = \frac{3}{4}x - 3$

55. **MP REASONING** Write a function f that represents the arithmetic sequence shown in the mapping diagram.

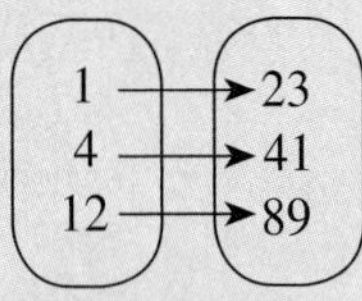

56. **MODELING REAL LIFE** The table shows the temperatures x (in degrees Fahrenheit) and the numbers y of shoppers at a mall.

Temperature, x	53	76	64	61	78	58
Number of shoppers, y	422	331	384	390	326	409

a. Approximate the number of shoppers when the temperature is 70°F.

b. Predict the number of shoppers when the temperature is 85°F.

In Exercises 57–60, classify the number as *rational* or *irrational*. Explain your reasoning.

57. $\frac{9}{13}$ **58.** $\sqrt{7}$

59. $-\sqrt{49}$ **60.** 2π

61. The scatter plot shows the low temperature x (in degrees Fahrenheit) and the high temperature y (in degrees Fahrenheit) each day for 10 days in a city.

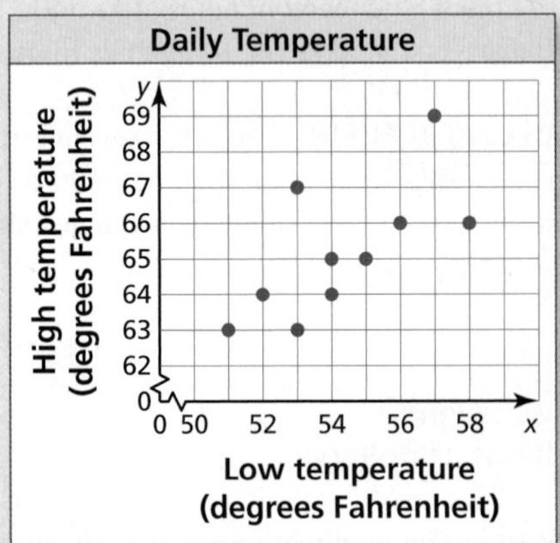

a. What was the high temperature on the day when the low temperature was 55°F?

b. What was the low temperature on the day when the high temperature was 67°F?

In Exercises 62 and 63, determine whether the sequence is arithmetic. If so, find the common difference.

62. $27, 9, 3, 1, \ldots$ **63.** $-14, -9, -4, 1, \ldots$

4.7 Piecewise Functions

Learning Target Graph and write piecewise functions.

Success Criteria
- I can evaluate piecewise functions.
- I can graph piecewise functions.
- I can write piecewise functions.

EXPLORE IT! Interpreting a Graph

Work with a partner. At the beginning of the day on Monday, your friend has $300 in her digital wallet. She sends and receives the following electronic payments through Sunday.

- $50 payment received on Wednesday
- $150 payment sent on Thursday
- $100 payment received on Saturday

She graphs the balance of her account during the week as shown.

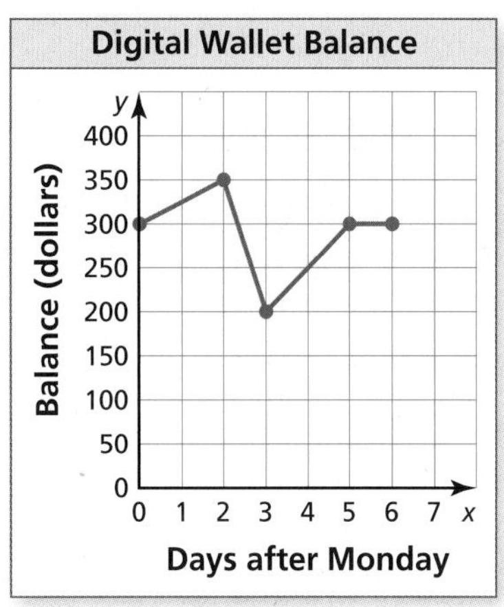

a. Does the graph represent y as a function of x? Explain your reasoning.

b. According to the graph, what is your friend's balance when $x = 2$? when $x = 4$? Do these values match what you expect given the list of payments sent and received?

c. Does the graph accurately show how the account balance changes during the week? Explain your reasoning.

d. Create a graph that more accurately shows how the account balance changes during the week.

Math Practice

Simplify a Situation
How can finding the balance on each day of the week help you create a more accurate graph?

Evaluating Piecewise Functions

Vocabulary 

piecewise function, *p. 228*
step function, *p. 230*

KEY IDEA

Piecewise Function

A **piecewise function** is a function defined by two or more equations. Each "piece" of the function applies to a different part of its domain. An example is shown below.

$$f(x) = \begin{cases} x - 2, & \text{if } x \le 0 \\ 2x + 1, & \text{if } x > 0 \end{cases}$$

- The expression $x - 2$ represents the value of f when x is less than or equal to 0.
- The expression $2x + 1$ represents the value of f when x is greater than 0.

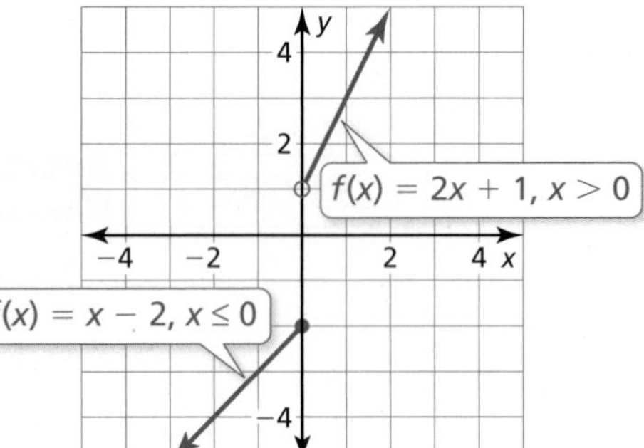

EXAMPLE 1 Evaluating a Piecewise Function

Evaluate $f(x) = \begin{cases} 3x + 1, & \text{if } x < 2 \\ x - 5, & \text{if } x \ge 2 \end{cases}$ when (a) $x = 2$ and (b) $x = -\frac{1}{3}$.

SOLUTION

a. Because $x = 2$ and $2 \ge 2$, use the second equation.

$f(x) = x - 5$	Write the second equation.
$f(2) = 2 - 5$	Substitute 2 for x.
$f(2) = -3$	Subtract.

▶ The value of f is -3 when $x = 2$.

b. Because $x = -\frac{1}{3}$ and $-\frac{1}{3} < 2$, use the first equation.

$f(x) = 3x + 1$	Write the first equation.
$f\left(-\frac{1}{3}\right) = 3\left(-\frac{1}{3}\right) + 1$	Substitute $-\frac{1}{3}$ for x.
$f\left(-\frac{1}{3}\right) = 0$	Simplify.

▶ The value of f is 0 when $x = -\frac{1}{3}$.

SELF-ASSESSMENT

1 I do not understand. 2 I can do it with help. 3 I can do it on my own. 4 I can teach someone else.

Evaluate the function when $x = -8, -2, 0, \frac{7}{2}$, and 5.

1. $h(x) = \begin{cases} -3x, & \text{if } x < 0 \\ 2x + 7, & \text{if } x \ge 0 \end{cases}$

2. $f(x) = \begin{cases} 3, & \text{if } x < -2 \\ x + 2, & \text{if } -2 \le x \le 5 \\ 4x, & \text{if } x > 5 \end{cases}$

3. **MP REASONING** When evaluating a piecewise function, can two different inputs have the same output? Explain your reasoning.

Graphing and Writing Piecewise Functions

EXAMPLE 2 Graphing a Piecewise Function

Graph $y = \begin{cases} -x - 4, & \text{if } x < 0 \\ x, & \text{if } x \geq 0 \end{cases}$. Find the domain and range.

SOLUTION

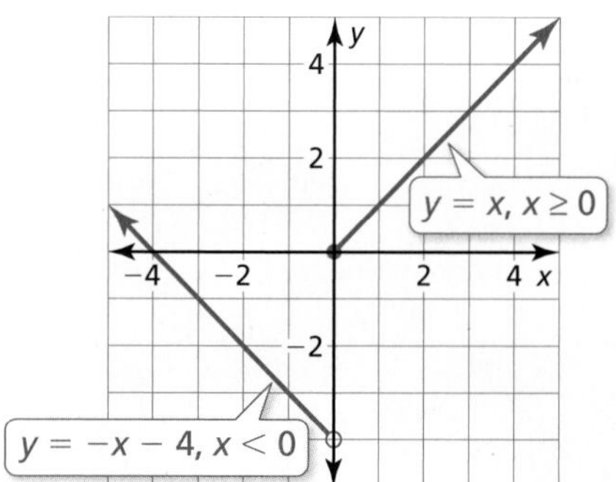

Step 1 Graph $y = -x - 4$ for $x < 0$. Because 0 is not included in the domain for this equation, use an open circle at $(0, -4)$.

Step 2 Graph $y = x$ for $x \geq 0$. Because 0 is included in the domain for this equation, use a closed circle at $(0, 0)$.

▶ The domain is all real numbers. The range is $y > -4$.

EXAMPLE 3 Writing a Piecewise Function

Write a piecewise function represented by the graph.

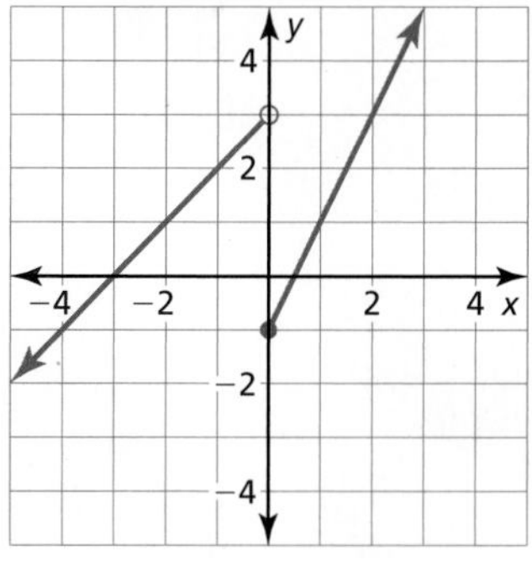

SOLUTION

Each "piece" of the function is linear.

Left Piece When $x < 0$, the graph is the line represented by $y = x + 3$.

Right Piece When $x \geq 0$, the graph is the line represented by $y = 2x - 1$.

▶ So, a piecewise function represented by the graph is

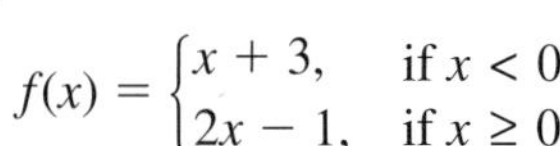

$$f(x) = \begin{cases} x + 3, & \text{if } x < 0 \\ 2x - 1, & \text{if } x \geq 0 \end{cases}.$$

SELF-ASSESSMENT

1 I do not understand. 2 I can do it with help. 3 I can do it on my own. 4 I can teach someone else.

Graph the function. Find the domain and range.

4. $y = \begin{cases} x + 1, & \text{if } x \leq 0 \\ -x, & \text{if } x > 0 \end{cases}$

5. $y = \begin{cases} x - 2, & \text{if } x < -1 \\ 4x, & \text{if } x \geq -1 \end{cases}$

Write a piecewise function represented by the graph.

6. 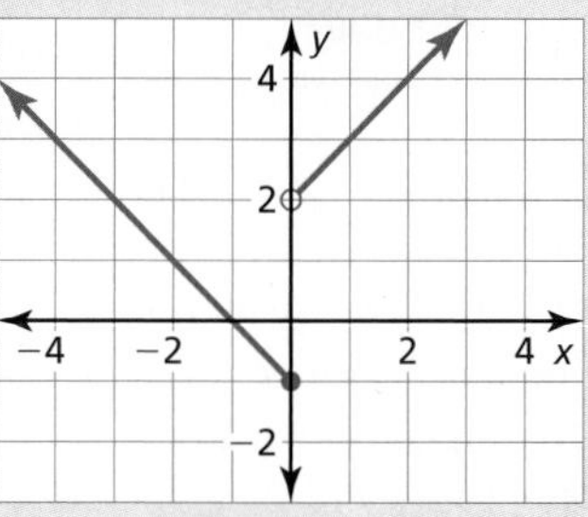

7. 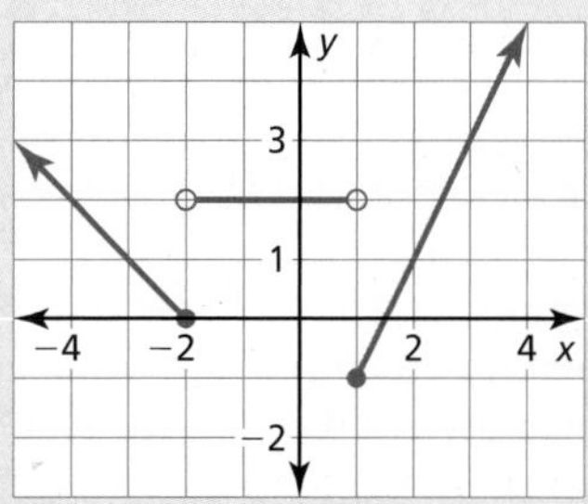

8. **OPEN-ENDED** Write a piecewise function that is positive over its entire domain.

Graphing and Writing Step Functions

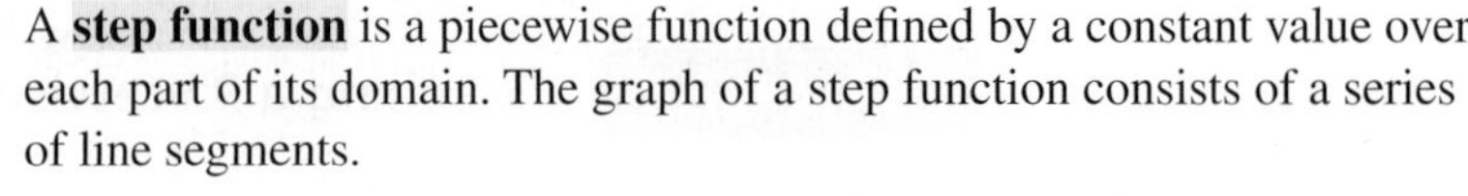

A **step function** is a piecewise function defined by a constant value over each part of its domain. The graph of a step function consists of a series of line segments.

WORDS AND MATH

How does the graph of a step function relate to your understanding of the word *step*?

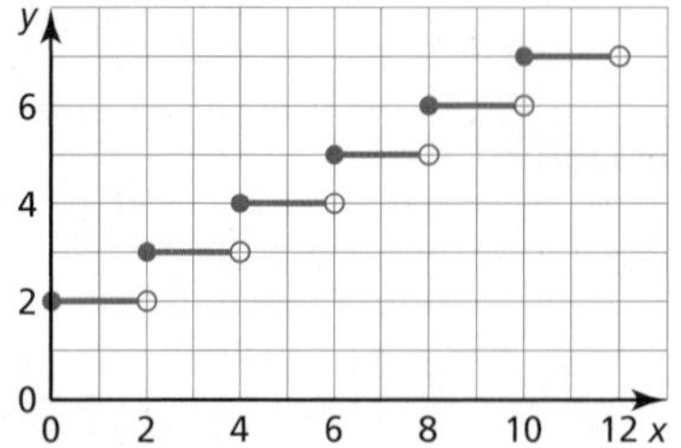

$$f(x) = \begin{cases} 2, & \text{if } 0 \le x < 2 \\ 3, & \text{if } 2 \le x < 4 \\ 4, & \text{if } 4 \le x < 6 \\ 5, & \text{if } 6 \le x < 8 \\ 6, & \text{if } 8 \le x < 10 \\ 7, & \text{if } 10 \le x < 12 \end{cases}$$

EXAMPLE 4 Modeling Real Life

You rent a karaoke machine for 5 days. The rental company charges \$50 for the first day and \$25 for each additional day or any portion of a day. Write and graph a step function that represents the relationship between the number x of days and the total cost y (in dollars) of renting the karaoke machine.

SOLUTION

Step 1 Use a table to organize the information.

Number of days	Total cost (dollars)
$0 < x \le 1$	50
$1 < x \le 2$	75
$2 < x \le 3$	100
$3 < x \le 4$	125
$4 < x \le 5$	150

Step 2 Write the step function.

$$f(x) = \begin{cases} 50, & \text{if } 0 < x \le 1 \\ 75, & \text{if } 1 < x \le 2 \\ 100, & \text{if } 2 < x \le 3 \\ 125, & \text{if } 3 < x \le 4 \\ 150, & \text{if } 4 < x \le 5 \end{cases}$$

Step 3 Graph the step function.

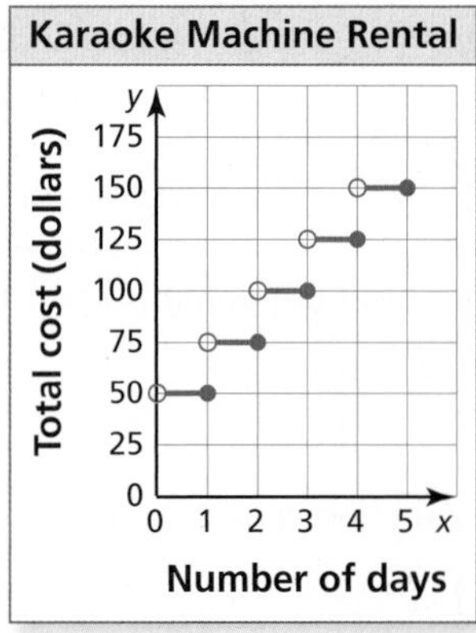

SELF-ASSESSMENT 1 I do not understand. 2 I can do it with help. 3 I can do it on my own. 4 I can teach someone else.

9. A landscaper rents a wood chipper for 4 days. The rental company charges \$100 for the first day and \$50 for each additional day or any portion of a day. Write and graph a step function that represents the relationship between the number x of days and the total cost y (in dollars) of renting the chipper.

10. **MP REASONING** Is it possible to perform a vertical translation on a step function f? a horizontal translation? If so, how would the equation that represents f change?

Writing Absolute Value Functions

The absolute value function $f(x) = |x|$ can be written as a piecewise function.

$$f(x) = \begin{cases} -x, & \text{if } x < 0 \\ x, & \text{if } x \geq 0 \end{cases}$$

Similarly, the vertex form of an absolute value function $g(x) = a|x - h| + k$ can be written as a piecewise function.

$$g(x) = \begin{cases} a[-(x - h)] + k, & \text{if } x - h < 0 \\ a(x - h) + k, & \text{if } x - h \geq 0 \end{cases}$$

REMEMBER

The vertex form of an absolute value function is $g(x) = a|x - h| + k$, where $a \neq 0$. The vertex of the graph of g is (h, k).

EXAMPLE 5 Modeling Real Life

In holography, light from a laser beam is split into two beams, a reference beam and an object beam. Light from the object beam reflects off an object and is recombined with the reference beam to form images on film that can be used to create three-dimensional images.

a. Write an absolute value function that represents the path of the reference beam.

b. Write the function in part (a) as a piecewise function.

SOLUTION

a. The vertex of the path of the reference beam is (5, 8). So, the function has the form $g(x) = a|x - 5| + 8$. Substitute the coordinates of the point (0, 0) into the equation and solve for a.

$g(x) = a\|x - 5\| + 8$	Vertex form of the function
$0 = a\|0 - 5\| + 8$	Substitute 0 for x and 0 for $g(x)$.
$-1.6 = a$	Solve for a.

▶ So, the function $g(x) = -1.6|x - 5| + 8$ represents the path of the reference beam.

b. Write $g(x) = -1.6|x - 5| + 8$ as a piecewise function.

$$g(x) = \begin{cases} -1.6[-(x - 5)] + 8, & \text{if } x - 5 < 0 \\ -1.6(x - 5) + 8, & \text{if } x - 5 \geq 0 \end{cases}$$

Simplify each expression, and solve the inequalities.

▶ So, a piecewise function for $g(x) = -1.6|x - 5| + 8$ is

$$g(x) = \begin{cases} 1.6x, & \text{if } x < 5 \\ -1.6x + 16, & \text{if } x \geq 5 \end{cases}.$$

STUDY TIP

Recall that the graph of an absolute value function is symmetric about the line $x = h$. So, it makes sense that the piecewise function "splits" at $x = 5$.

SELF-ASSESSMENT

1 I do not understand. 2 I can do it with help. 3 I can do it on my own. 4 I can teach someone else.

11. WHAT IF? In Example 5, the reference beam originates at (3, 0) and reflects off a mirror at (5, 4).

a. Write an absolute value function that represents the path of the reference beam.

b. Write the function in part (a) as a piecewise function.

12. WRITING Write a piecewise function represented by the graph. Then describe a real-life situation that can be modeled by the graph.

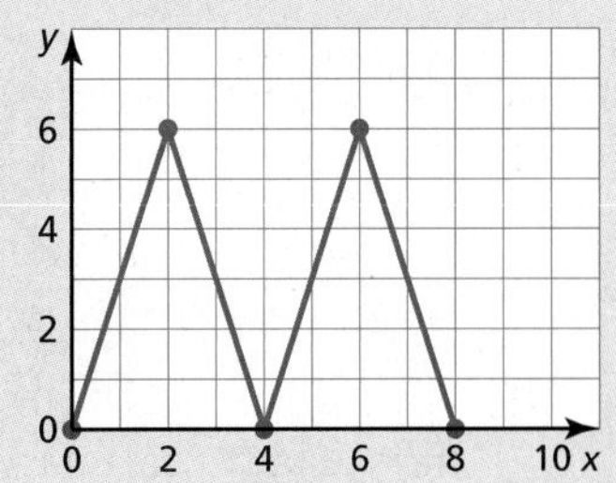

4.7 Practice WITH CalcChat® AND CalcView®

In Exercises 1 and 2, evaluate the function when $x = -4, -2, -1, \frac{1}{2}$, and 2. ▶ *Example 1*

1. $f(x) = \begin{cases} 5x - 1, & \text{if } x \le -2 \\ x + 3, & \text{if } x > -2 \end{cases}$

2. $g(x) = \begin{cases} -x + 4, & \text{if } x < -1 \\ 3, & \text{if } -1 \le x < 2 \\ 2x - 5, & \text{if } x \ge 2 \end{cases}$

In Exercises 3–8, graph the function. Find the domain and range. ▶ *Example 2*

3. $y = \begin{cases} -x, & \text{if } x < 2 \\ x - 6, & \text{if } x \ge 2 \end{cases}$

4. $y = \begin{cases} 2x, & \text{if } x \le -3 \\ -2x, & \text{if } x > -3 \end{cases}$

5. $y = \begin{cases} -3x - 2, & \text{if } x \le -1 \\ x + 2, & \text{if } x > -1 \end{cases}$

6. $y = \begin{cases} x + 8, & \text{if } x < 4 \\ 4x - 4, & \text{if } x \ge 4 \end{cases}$

7. $y = \begin{cases} 1, & \text{if } x < -3 \\ x - 1, & \text{if } -3 \le x \le 3 \\ -\frac{5}{3}x + 4, & \text{if } x > 3 \end{cases}$

8. $y = \begin{cases} 2x + 1, & \text{if } x \le -1 \\ -x + 2, & \text{if } -1 < x < 2 \\ -3.5, & \text{if } x \ge 2 \end{cases}$

9. MODELING REAL LIFE On a trip, the total distance (in miles) you travel in x hours is represented by the piecewise function

$$d(x) = \begin{cases} 55x, & \text{if } 0 \le x \le 2 \\ 65x - 20, & \text{if } 2 < x \le 5 \end{cases}.$$

How far do you travel in 4 hours?

10. ERROR ANALYSIS Describe and correct the error in graphing

$$y = \begin{cases} x + 6, & \text{if } x \le -2 \\ 1, & \text{if } x > -2 \end{cases}.$$

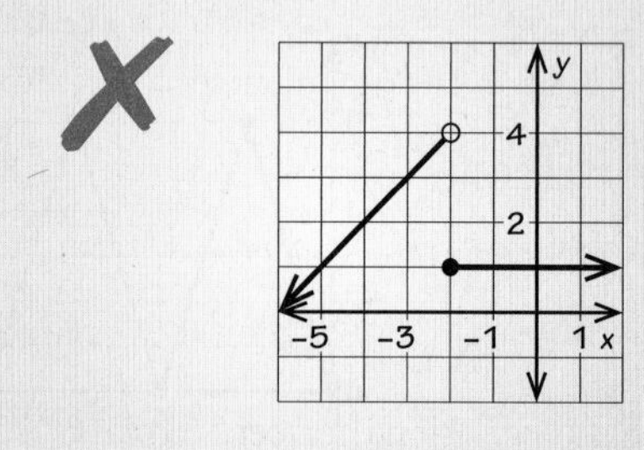

In Exercises 11–16, write a piecewise function represented by the graph. ▶ *Example 3*

11.

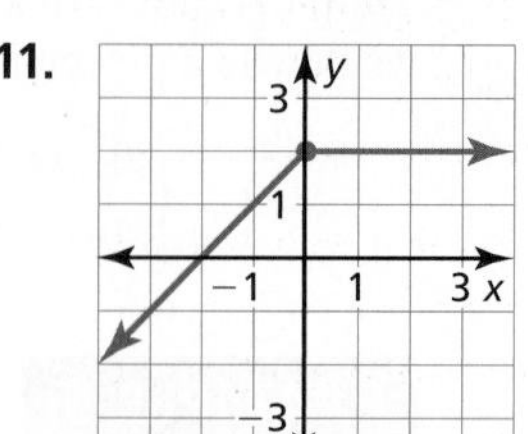

12.

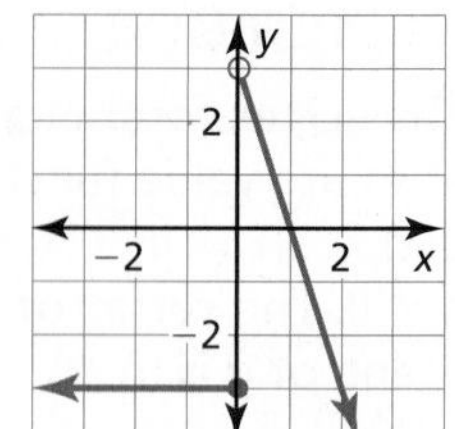

13.

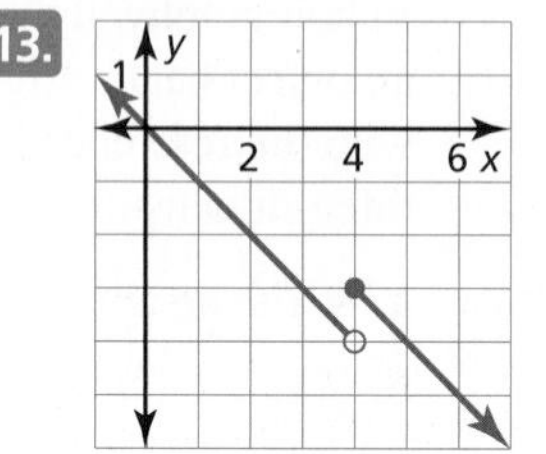

14.

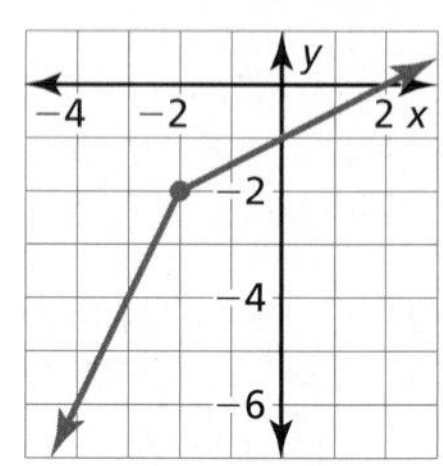

15.

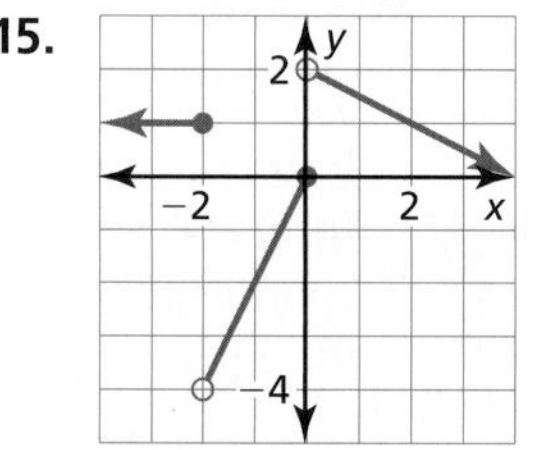

16.

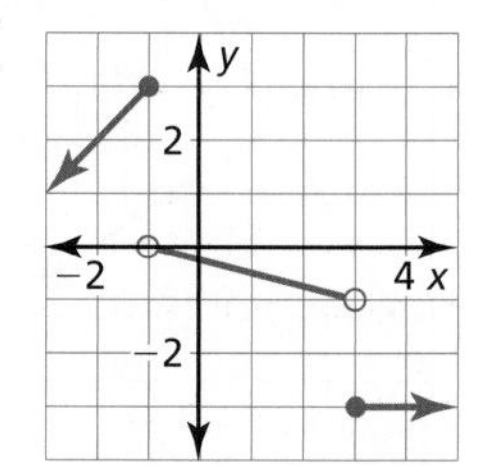

17. WRITING When you graph the solutions of a piecewise function and a linear function, how do the graphs differ?

18. MODELING REAL LIFE Write a piecewise function that represents the total cost y (in dollars) of ordering x custom shirts. Then determine the total cost of ordering 26 shirts.

Custom Shirts
0–24 shirts
$17.00 per shirt
25–49 shirts
$15.80 per shirt
50+ shirts
$14.00 per shirt
plus a $20 processing fee on all orders

In Exercises 19 and 20, graph the step function. Find the domain and range.

19. $f(x) = \begin{cases} 3, & \text{if } 0 \le x < 2 \\ 4, & \text{if } 2 \le x < 4 \\ 5, & \text{if } 4 \le x < 6 \\ 6, & \text{if } 6 \le x < 8 \end{cases}$

20. $f(x) = \begin{cases} -\frac{5}{2}, & \text{if } -6 \le x < -5 \\ -1, & \text{if } -5 \le x < -3 \\ 0, & \text{if } -3 \le x < -2 \\ 1, & \text{if } -2 \le x < 0 \end{cases}$

21. MODELING REAL LIFE A state issues tickets for speeding on an interstate highway as follows.

- no more than 10 miles per hour over: \$40
- more than 10 miles per hour to no more than 20 miles per hour over: \$70
- more than 20 miles per hour to no more than 30 miles per hour over: \$120
- more than 30 miles per hour over: \$200

Write and graph a step function that represents the relationship between the number x of miles per hour over the speed limit and the cost y (in dollars) of the speeding ticket. *Example 4*

22. MODELING REAL LIFE A parking garage charges \$4 per hour or any portion of an hour, up to a daily maximum of \$15.

a. Write and graph a step function that represents the relationship between the number x of hours a car is parked in the garage and the total cost y (in dollars) of parking in the garage for up to 1 day.

b. Is x a function of y? Explain your reasoning.

In Exercises 23–28, write the absolute value function as a piecewise function.

23. $y = |x| + 1$

24. $y = |x - 2|$

25. $y = 4|x - 1|$

26. $y = -3|x + 6|$

27. $y = -|x - 3| + 2$

28. $y = 7.5|x + 1| - 5$

29. MODELING REAL LIFE You are sitting on a boat on a lake. You can get a sunburn from the sunlight that hits you directly and also from the sunlight that reflects off the water. *Example 5*

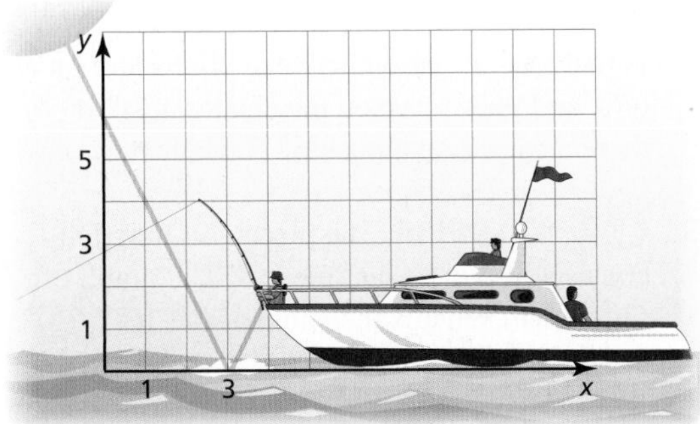

a. Write an absolute value function that represents the path of the sunlight that reflects off the water.

b. Write the function in part (a) as a piecewise function.

30. MODELING REAL LIFE You are trying to make a hole in one on the miniature golf green.

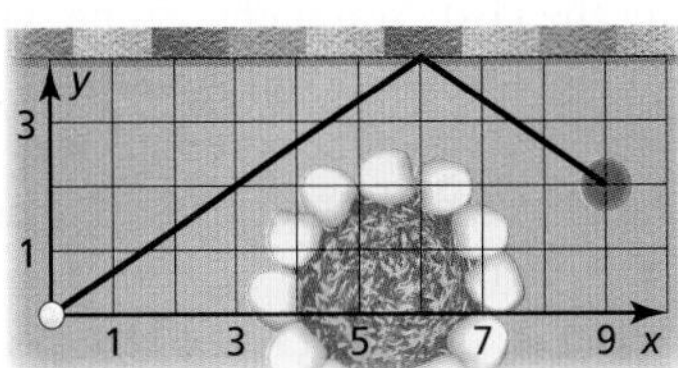

a. Write an absolute value function that represents the path of the golf ball.

b. Write the function in part (a) as a piecewise function.

31. COLLEGE PREP Which of the following are true about $f(x) = \begin{cases} 2x + 8, & \text{if } x < -3 \\ -\frac{2}{3}x, & \text{if } x \geq -3 \end{cases}$? Select all that apply.

Ⓐ The y-intercept of the graph is 8.

Ⓑ The function is increasing when $x < -3$ and decreasing when $x > -3$.

Ⓒ The function is negative when $x < -4$, positive when $-4 < x < 0$, and negative when $x > 0$.

Ⓓ $f\left(-\frac{7}{2}\right) = f\left(-\frac{3}{2}\right)$

32. HOW DO YOU SEE IT? The graph of a piecewise function f is shown. What is the value of $f(1)$? Which is greater, $f(4)$ or $f(4.1)$?

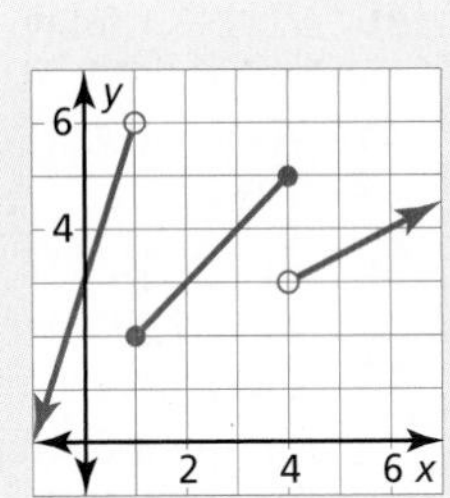

33. CRITICAL THINKING Describe how the graph of each piecewise function changes when < is replaced with ≤ and ≥ is replaced with >. Do the domain and range change? Explain.

a. $f(x) = \begin{cases} x + 2, & \text{if } x < 2 \\ -x - 1, & \text{if } x \geq 2 \end{cases}$

b. $f(x) = \begin{cases} \frac{1}{2}x + \frac{3}{2}, & \text{if } x < 1 \\ -x + 3, & \text{if } x \geq 1 \end{cases}$

34. MP STRUCTURE Graph $y = \begin{cases} -x + 2, & \text{if } x \leq -2 \\ |x|, & \text{if } x > -2 \end{cases}$.

Find the domain and range.

35. MAKING AN ARGUMENT Your friend says that $y = \begin{cases} 2x - 2, & \text{if } x \leq 3 \\ -3, & \text{if } x \geq 3 \end{cases}$ represents a piecewise function. Is your friend correct? Explain.

36. **MULTIPLE REPRESENTATIONS** You purchase a new cell phone that costs \$250. You select a payment plan where you initially pay \$10, and then pay \$10 every month for the next 24 months. So far, you have paid \$60. Two graphs that model this situation are shown. Explain how each graph represents the situation. Then describe an advantage and disadvantage of each representation.

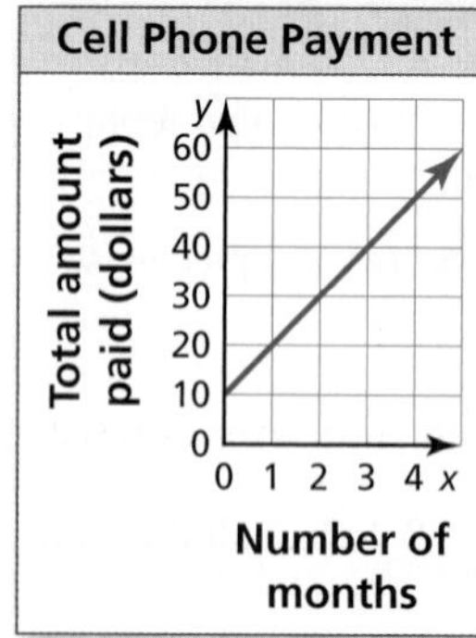

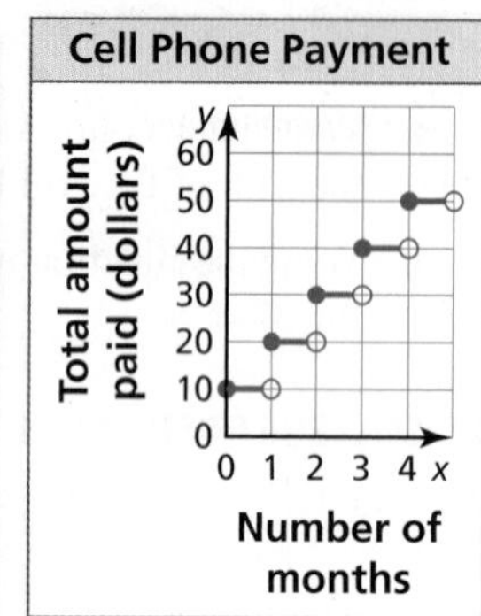

37. **PERFORMANCE TASK** You are the manager of a store. During a sale, you offer customers different discounts based on the total amounts they spend. Write and graph a step function that represents your discount policy. Then create an advertisement explaining your discount policy to customers.

38. **THOUGHT PROVOKING** The output y of the *greatest integer function* is the greatest integer less than or equal to the input value x. This function is written as $f(x) = [\![x]\!]$. Graph the function for $-4 \leq x < 4$. Is it a piecewise function? a step function? Explain.

39. **DIG DEEPER** During a 9-hour snowstorm, it snows at a rate of 1 inch per hour for the first 2 hours, 2 inches per hour for the next 6 hours, and 1 inch per hour for the final hour. Write and graph a piecewise function that represents the snow accumulation during the storm. What is the total accumulation?

REVIEW & REFRESH

In Exercises 40–42, graph f and h. Describe the transformations from the graph of f to the graph of h.

40. $f(x) = x$; $h(x) = 4x + 3$

41. $f(x) = x$; $h(x) = -x - 8$

42. $f(x) = x$; $h(x) = -\frac{1}{2}x + 5$

43. Describe the relationship between the data in the scatter plot.

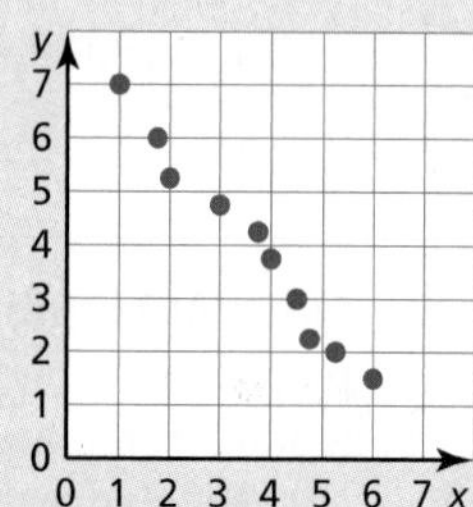

In Exercises 44 and 45, solve the equation.

44. $7.5 + x = 15.5$

45. $-5(x - 4) - 12 = 23$

46. **MP NUMBER SENSE** The sixth term of an arithmetic sequence is 8. The common difference of the sequence is $-\frac{1}{3}$ times the first term. Graph the sequence.

47. The points represented by the table lie on a line. Find the slope of the line.

x	4	4	4	4
y	−6	−3	0	3

48. **MODELING REAL LIFE** There must be 2 chaperones for every 25 students at a school dance. How many chaperones are needed for 200 students?

49. Graph $y = \begin{cases} -\frac{1}{4}x, & \text{if } x \leq -4 \\ 2x + 3, & \text{if } x > -4 \end{cases}$. Find the domain and range.

In Exercises 50 and 51, write a linear function f with the given values.

50. $f(-2) = 5$, $f(6) = -3$

51. $f(0) = -4$, $f(10) = -12$

52. Is there a correlation between your score on a math quiz and your score on the chapter test? If so, is there a causal relationship? Explain your reasoning.

53. **MP REASONING** The piecewise function f consists of two linear "pieces." The graph of f is shown. What is the value of $f(-10)$? $f(8)$?

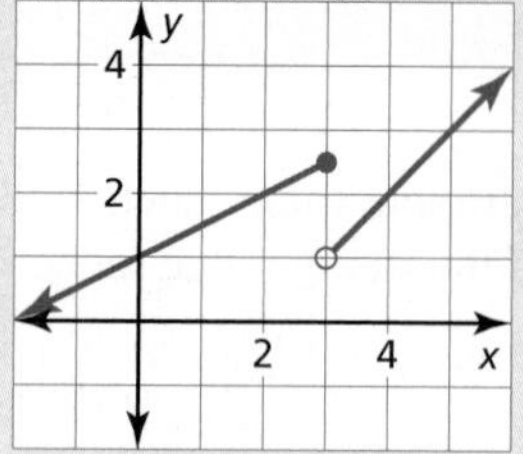

4 Chapter Review WITH CalcChat®

Chapter Learning Target Understand writing linear functions.

Chapter Success Criteria
- ◆ I can determine the slope given ordered pairs, a graph, or a context.
- ◆ I can write the equation of a line in different forms.
- ■ I can interpret scatter plots and analyze lines of fit.
- ■ I can write a function that represents an arithmetic sequence to solve a real-life problem.

◆ Surface
■ Deep

SELF-ASSESSMENT 1 I do not understand. 2 I can do it with help. 3 I can do it on my own. 4 I can teach someone else.

4.1 Writing Equations in Slope-Intercept Form (pp. 187–192)

Learning Target: Write equations of lines in slope-intercept form.

Vocabulary

linear model

Write an equation of the line in slope-intercept form.

1.
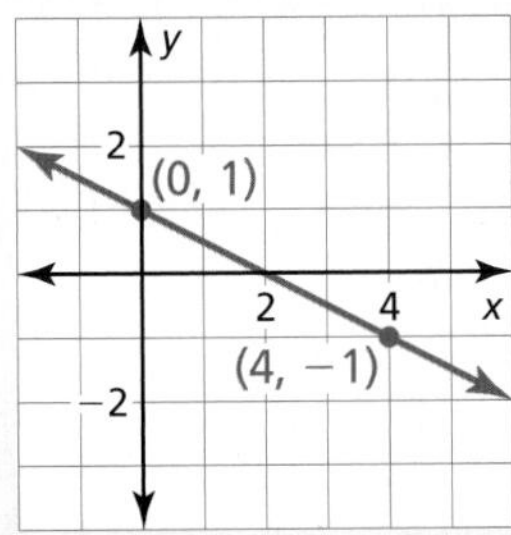

2.
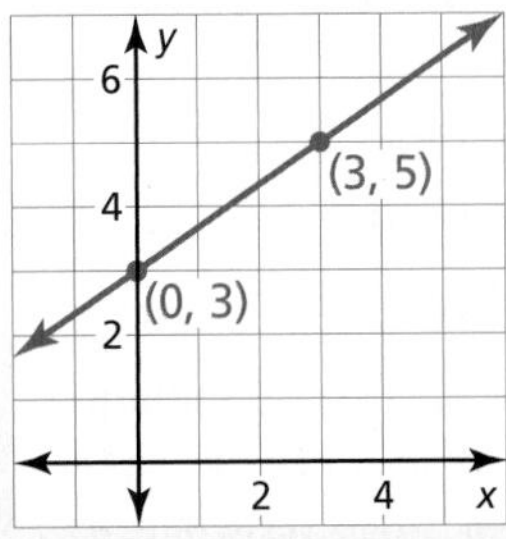

3. A landlord charged $865 per month to rent an apartment in 2010. The rent increased at a constant rate and reached $1065 per month in 2018. Estimate the monthly rent in 2021.

4.2 Writing Equations in Point-Slope Form (pp. 193–198)

Learning Target: Write equations of lines in point-slope form.

Vocabulary AZ VOCAB
point-slope form

4. Write an equation in point-slope form of the line that passes through the point (4, 7) and has a slope of -1.

Write a linear function *f* with the given values.

5. $f(10) = 5, f(2) = -3$
6. $f(3) = -4, f(5) = -4$
7. $f(6) = 8, f(9) = 3$

8. Write $Ax + By = C$ in point-slope form, where A and B are nonzero constants.

9. You are ordering party hats for New Year's Eve. The table shows the total costs of ordering different numbers of party hats. Determine the total cost of ordering 25 party hats.

Number of party hats	3	6	9	12
Total cost (dollars)	2.67	5.34	8.01	10.68

4.3 Writing Equations of Parallel and Perpendicular Lines (pp. 199–204) WATCH

Learning Target: Recognize and write equations of parallel and perpendicular lines.

Vocabulary 

parallel lines
perpendicular lines

Determine which of the lines, if any, are parallel or perpendicular. Explain.

10. Line a passes through (0, 4) and (4, 3).
Line b passes through (0, 1) and (4, 0).
Line c passes through (2, 0) and (4, 4).

11. Line a: $2x - 7y = 14$
Line b: $y = \frac{7}{2}x - 8$
Line c: $2x + 7y = -21$

12. Write an equation of the line that passes through (1, 5) and is parallel to the line $y = -4x + 2$.

13. Write an equation of the line that passes through (2, −3) and is perpendicular to the line $y = -2x - 3$.

4.4 Scatter Plots and Lines of Fit (pp. 205–210) 

Learning Target: Use scatter plots and lines of fit to describe relationships between data.

The scatter plot shows the roasting times y (in hours) and weights x (in pounds) of seven turkeys.

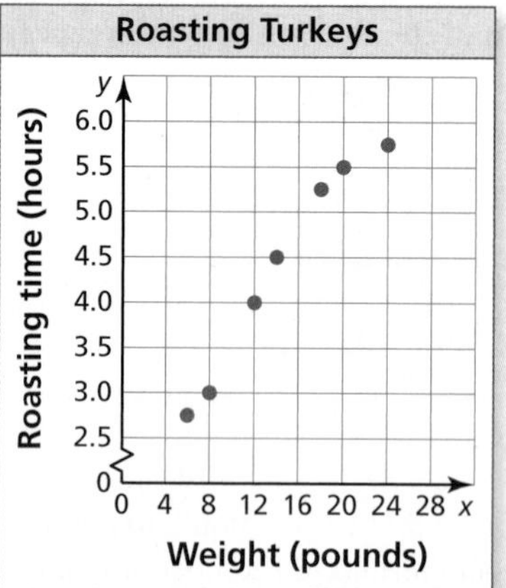

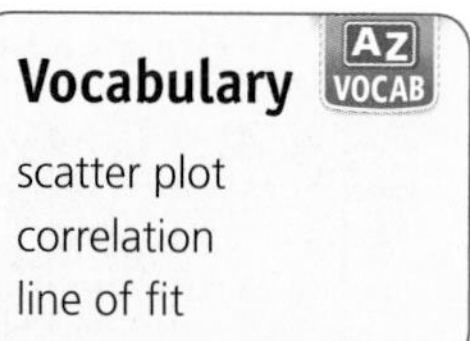

14. What is the roasting time for a 12-pound turkey?

15. Describe the relationship between the data.

16. The table shows the salary caps y (in millions of dollars) in the NBA x years since the beginning of the season in 2013. Write an equation that models the salary cap as a function of time. Interpret the slope and y-intercept of the line of fit.

Year, x	0	1	2	3	4
Salary cap (millions of dollars), y	58.68	63.07	70.00	91.14	99.09

4.5 Analyzing Lines of Fit (pp. 211–218) 

Learning Target: Analyze lines of fit and find lines of best fit.

Vocabulary 

residual
linear regression
line of best fit
correlation coefficient
interpolation
extrapolation
causation

17. The table shows the heights x (in inches) and shoe sizes y of several students.

Height, x	64	62	70	63	72	68	66	74	68	59
Shoe size, y	9	7	12	8	13	9.5	9	13.5	10	6.5

a. Find an equation of the line of best fit. Identify and interpret the correlation coefficient.

b. Make a scatter plot of the residuals to verify that the model is a good fit.

c. Is there a causal relationship in the data? Explain.

4.6 Arithmetic Sequences (pp. 219–226)

Learning Target: Understand the concept of arithmetic sequences.

Vocabulary

sequence
term
arithmetic sequence
common difference

Write an equation for the nth term of the arithmetic sequence. Then find a_{30}.

18. 6, 12, 18, 24, . . .

19. $-9, -6, -3, 0, \ldots$

20. Does the graph shown represent an arithmetic sequence? Explain.

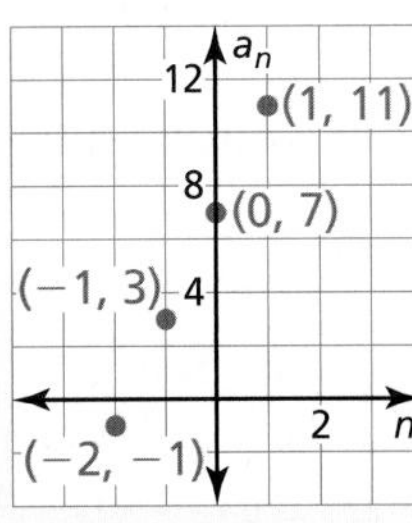
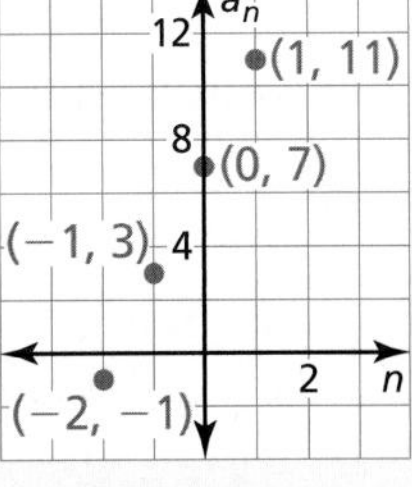

21. In chemistry, water is called H_2O because each molecule of water has two hydrogen atoms and one oxygen atom. Describe the pattern shown below. Use the pattern to determine the total number of atoms in 23 molecules.

$n = 1$ 

$n = 2$ 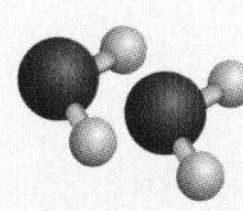

$n = 3$ 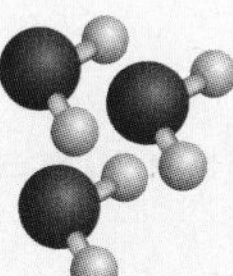

$n = 4$ 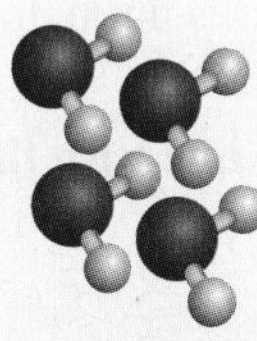

$n = 5$ 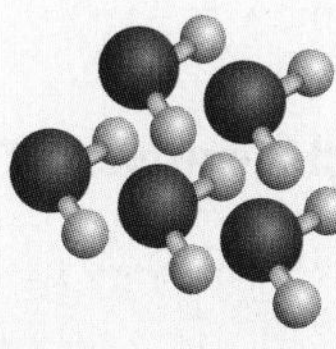

4.7 Piecewise Functions (pp. 227–234)

WATCH

Learning Target: Graph and write piecewise functions.

Vocabulary

piecewise function
step function

22. Evaluate $y = \begin{cases} \frac{3}{2}x + 3, & \text{if } x \leq 0 \\ -2x, & \text{if } x > 0 \end{cases}$ when (a) $x = 0$ and (b) $x = 5$.

Graph the function. Find the domain and range.

23. $y = \begin{cases} x + 6, & \text{if } x \leq 0 \\ -3x, & \text{if } x > 0 \end{cases}$

24. $y = \begin{cases} 4x + 2, & \text{if } x < -4 \\ 2x - 6, & \text{if } x \geq -4 \end{cases}$

Write the absolute value function as a piecewise function.

25. $y = |x| + 15$

26. $y = 4|x + 5|$

27. $y = 2|x + 2| - 3$

28. You are organizing a school fair and rent a popcorn machine for 3 days. The rental company charges $65 for the first day and $35 for each additional day or any portion of a day. Write and graph a step function that represents the relationship between the number x of days and the total cost y (in dollars) of renting the popcorn machine.

Mathematical Practices

Make Sense of Problems and Persevere in Solving Them

Mathematically proficient students try special cases and simpler forms of the original problem in order to gain insight into the solution.

1. In Exercise 36 on page 234, which graph represents a simpler form of the original problem? What insight can you gain from the simpler form?

2. The function shown represents the total cost y (in dollars) of ordering x ornaments. Your friend says that the total cost is always greater when you order more ornaments. How can you test special cases to evaluate your friend's claim?

$$y = \begin{cases} 3x + 5, & \text{if } 0 < x \leq 10 \\ 2.7x + 5, & \text{if } 10 < x \leq 20 \\ 2.5x + 5, & \text{if } x > 20 \end{cases}$$

4 Practice Test WITH CalcChat®

1. Graph $y = \begin{cases} 2x + 4, & \text{if } x \leq -1 \\ \frac{1}{3}x - 1, & \text{if } x > -1 \end{cases}$. Find the domain and range.

Write an equation in slope-intercept form of the line with the given characteristics.

2. slope $= \frac{2}{5}$; y-intercept $= -7$

3. passes through $(0, 6)$ and $(3, -3)$

4. parallel to the line $y = 3x - 1$; passes through $(-2, -8)$

5. perpendicular to the line $y = \frac{1}{4}x - 9$; passes through $(1, 1)$

Write an equation in point-slope form of the line with the given characteristics.

6. slope $= 10$; passes through $(6, 2)$

7. passes through $(-3, 2)$ and $(6, -1)$

8. Write a linear function f with the values $f(0) = 6$ and $f(7) = 27$.

9. Let a, b, c, and d be constants. Determine which of the lines, if any, are parallel or perpendicular. Explain.

   Line 1: $y - c = ax$

   Line 2: $ay = -x - b$

   Line 3: $ax + y = d$

10. The first row of an auditorium has 42 seats. Each row after the first has three more seats than the row before it.

    a. Find the number of seats in Row 25.

    b. Which row has 90 seats?

11. The graph of f is a line that passes through the points $(-7, 11)$ and $(3, 5)$. Write an equation of a line that is a horizontal shrink by a factor of $\frac{1}{2}$, followed by a horizontal translation 3 units right of the graph of f.

12. The table shows the amounts x (in dollars) spent on advertising for a festival and the attendances y of the festival for several years.

    a. Find an equation of the line of best fit. Interpret the slope and y-intercept.

    b. What would you expect a scatter plot of the residuals to look like? Explain your reasoning.

    c. Is there a causal relationship in the data? Explain.

    d. Predict the attendance when the advertising cost is \$8900.

Advertising (dollars), x	Yearly attendance, y
500	400
1000	550
1500	550
2000	800
2500	650
3000	800
3500	1050
4000	1100

13. Write a piecewise function defined by three equations that has a domain of all real numbers and a range of $-3 < y \leq 1$.

4 Performance Task
This One's a Breeze!

The capacity of a wind turbine is the maximum amount of power it can generate. Most wind farms have turbines with capacities of 2 to 3 megawatts (MW), which is equivalent to 2000 to 3000 kilowatts (kW).

In optimal conditions, the actual amount of power generated by a wind turbine is typically about 35% of its capacity.

In the United States, installing commercial wind turbines costs about $1.65 million per megawatt.

The average American household uses about 10,400 kilowatt hours (kWh) of energy each year.

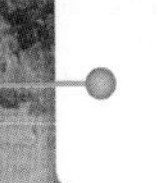

Wind turbines require about $\frac{3}{4}$ acre of land per megawatt of power.

Kern County, California has over 4500 wind turbines.

DESIGN A WIND FARM

Write a proposal to government officials for a new wind farm in your county. Choose the amount of land that will be occupied by your farm and the power of the turbines. Use functions and graphs to show the cost of the turbines and the total power generated. Relate the energy output of the wind farm to the amount of energy used in a typical household.

Energy (kWh) = Power (kW) × Time (h)

4 College and Career Readiness WITH CalcChat®

Tutorial videos are available for each exercise.

1. Which function represents the arithmetic sequence shown in the graph?

Ⓐ $f(n) = 21 + 3n$

Ⓑ $f(n) = 18 - 3n$

Ⓒ $f(n) = 27 - 3n$

Ⓓ $f(n) = 24 - 3n$

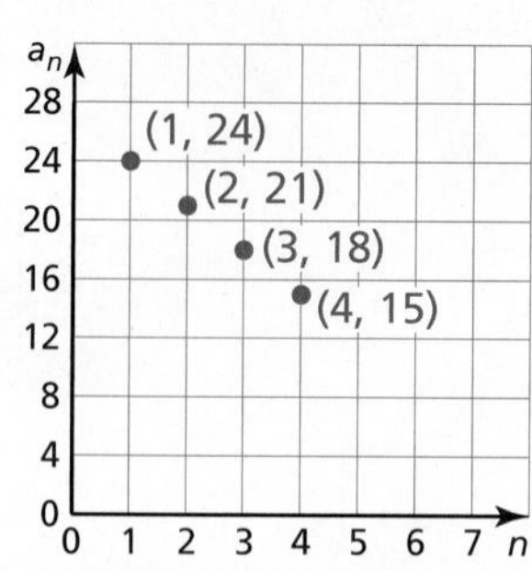

2. Consider the function $f(x) = x - 1$. Select each function shown in the graph.

Ⓐ $f(x + 2)$

Ⓑ $f(3x)$

Ⓒ $f(x) + 4$

Ⓓ $f(-x)$

Ⓔ $3f(x)$

Ⓕ $-f(x)$

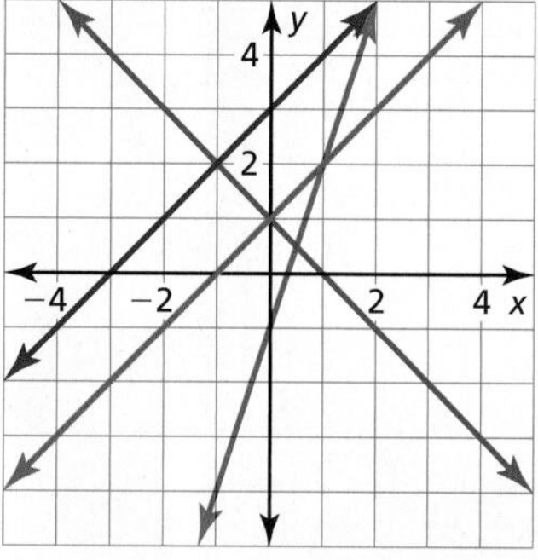

3. Which equation is equivalent to $\frac{3}{4}x - \frac{5}{2}y = -2x$?

Ⓐ $y = \frac{1}{2}x$

Ⓑ $3x - \frac{5}{2}y = -8x$

Ⓒ $\frac{3}{4}x = -2x - \frac{5}{2}y$

Ⓓ $y = \frac{11}{10}x$

4. You download a digital soccer game for \$2.50. You can add new players for \$1.50 each to upgrade your team. The total cost c is a function of the number n of new players that you add.

a. Is the domain discrete or continuous? Explain.

b. Graph the function using its domain.

5. Find the domain and range of the function represented by the graph.

Ⓐ The domain is -2, 1, and -1.
The range is -1, 0, 1, and 2.

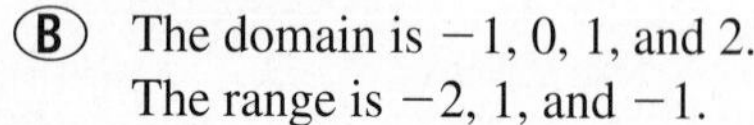

Ⓑ The domain is -1, 0, 1, and 2.
The range is -2, 1, and -1.

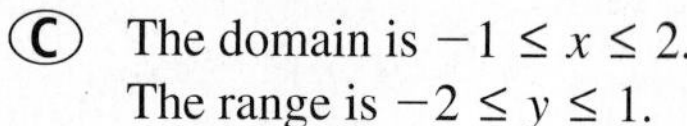

Ⓒ The domain is $-1 \leq x \leq 2$.
The range is $-2 \leq y \leq 1$.

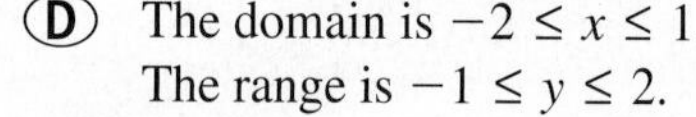

Ⓓ The domain is $-2 \leq x \leq 1$.
The range is $-1 \leq y \leq 2$.

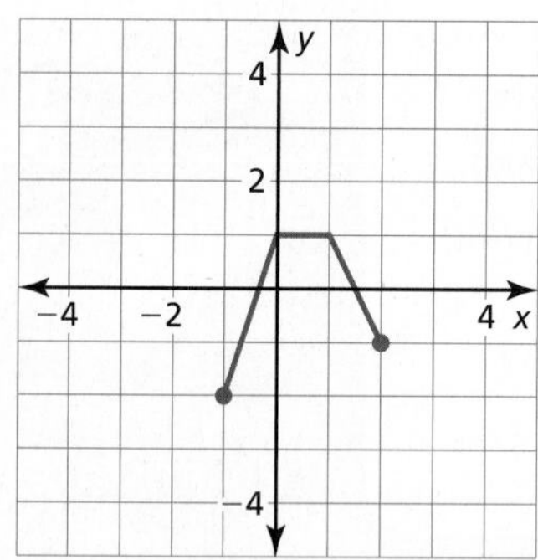

6. Complete the piecewise function with $-$, $+$, $<$, $\leq$, $>$, or $\geq$ so that the function is represented by the graph.

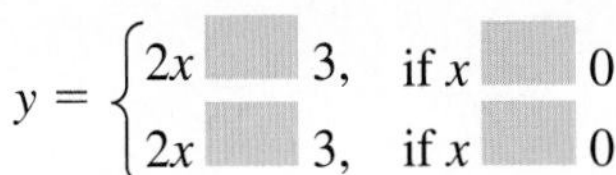

$$y = \begin{cases} 2x \; \square \; 3, & \text{if } x \; \square \; 0 \\ 2x \; \square \; 3, & \text{if } x \; \square \; 0 \end{cases}$$

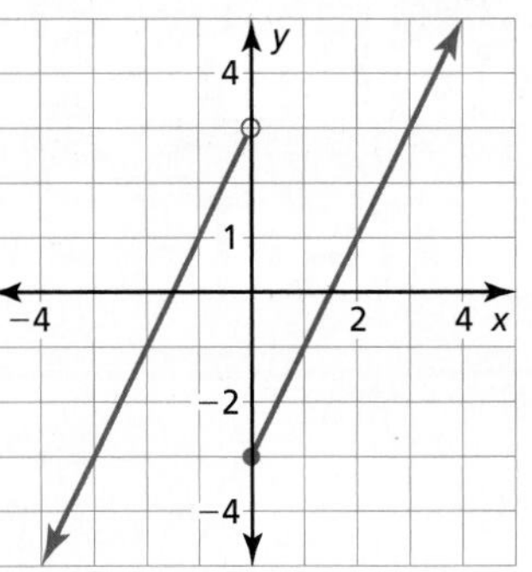

7. Find values for m and b so that the graph of $y = mx + b$ passes through the points (6, 1) and $(-2, -3)$.

Ⓐ $m = \frac{1}{2}, b = -2$

Ⓑ $m = \frac{1}{2}, b = 2$

Ⓒ $m = -\frac{1}{2}, b = 4$

Ⓓ $m = -\frac{1}{2}, b = -4$

8. For a function f, $y \to -\infty$ as $x \to -\infty$, $y \to -\infty$ as $x \to +\infty$, and the graph has x-intercepts of -2.5 and 1. Which graph could represent the function?

Ⓐ

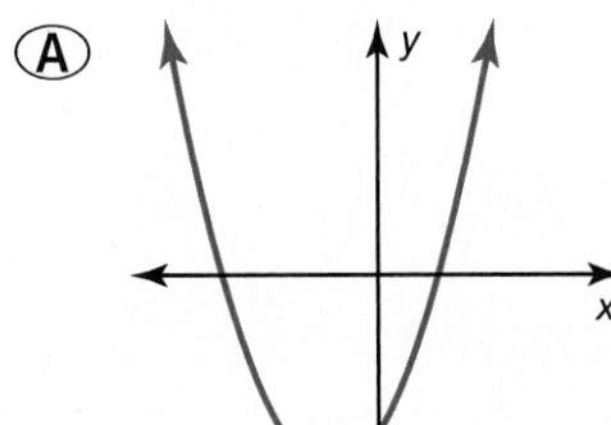

Ⓑ

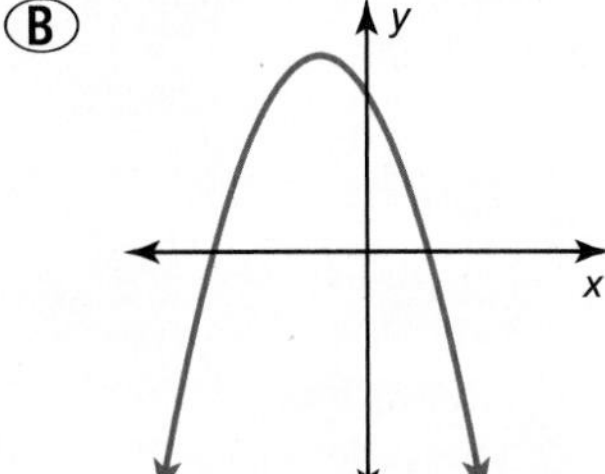

Ⓒ

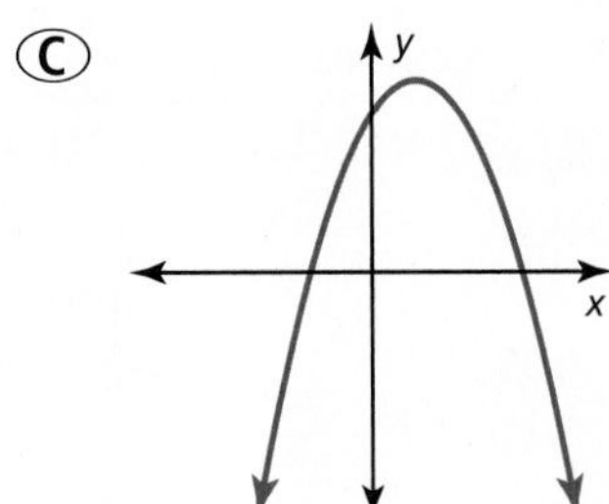

Ⓓ

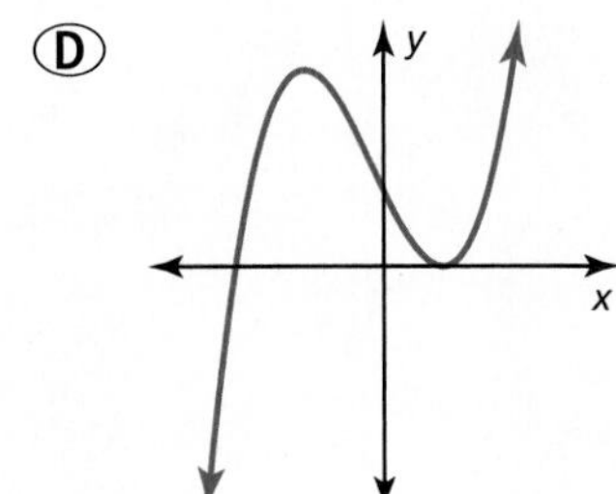

9. The table shows the daily high temperatures x (in degrees Fahrenheit) and the numbers y of frozen fruit bars sold on eight randomly selected days. The equation $y = 3x - 50$ models the data.

Temperature (°F), x	54	60	68	72	78	84	92	98
Frozen fruit bars, y	40	120	180	260	280	260	220	180

a. Select the points that appear on a scatter plot of the residuals.

(92, −6)	(78, 96)	(60, −10)	(84, 58)	(98, −64)
(72, 94)	(54, −72)	(96, 78)	(60, 10)	(68, 26)

b. Determine whether the model is a good fit for the data. Explain your reasoning.

5 Solving Systems of Linear Equations

NATIONAL GEOGRAPHIC EXPLORER

Corey J. Jaskolski

Corey Jaskolski is an engineer with degrees in physics and mathematics. He led a team that developed the world's first pressure-tolerant lithium-polymer battery pack used by underwater vehicles. The battery can withstand the crushing pressure of deep-ocean deployments without needing to be protected inside a pressure vessel.

- What is the deepest that a human has been outside of an underwater vehicle? inside an underwater vehicle?
- What is the pressure of sea water at a depth of 1000 feet? 2000 feet? 3000 feet? 4000 feet? Graph your results. Is pressure a linear function of depth?

STEM

The deepest location on Earth, the Challenger Deep, is located in the Pacific Ocean. In the Performance Task, you will plan an expedition to the Challenger Deep, including a dive schedule and goals that you hope to accomplish.

Deep Ocean Exploration

Preparing for Chapter 5

Chapter Learning Target Understand solving systems of linear equations.

Chapter Success Criteria

- ◆ I can identify a system of linear equations.
- ◆ I can describe different methods for solving systems of linear equations.
- ■ I can analyze systems of linear equations and decide what solution method is most efficient.
- ■ I can predict whether a system of linear equations has one solution, no solution, or infinitely many solutions.

◆ Surface
■ Deep

Chapter Vocabulary

Work with a partner. Discuss each of the vocabulary terms.

system of linear equations
linear inequality in two variables
half-planes
system of linear inequalities

Mathematical Practices

Use Appropriate Tools Strategically

Mathematically proficient students use technological tools to explore and deepen their understanding of concepts.

Work with a partner. A dive center earns \$9550 by selling tickets for deep-sea dives to tourists. The dive center sells a total of 14 tickets: x Basic Adventure tickets and y Extreme Adventure tickets.

1. Write two equations to represent this situation. Explain your reasoning.
2. Use technology to graph both equations. Explain how you determined an appropriate viewing window for this situation.
3. Use technology to find the point of intersection of the graphs of the equations. Explain your method.
4. Interpret the point of intersection.

5 Prepare WITH CalcChat®

Graphing Linear Functions

Example 1 **Graph $3 + y = \frac{1}{2}x$.**

Step 1 Rewrite the equation in slope-intercept form.

$$y = \frac{1}{2}x - 3$$

Step 2 Find the slope and the y-intercept.

$$m = \frac{1}{2} \text{ and } b = -3$$

Step 3 The y-intercept is -3. So, plot $(0, -3)$.

Step 4 Use the slope to find another point on the line.

$$\text{slope} = \frac{\text{rise}}{\text{run}} = \frac{1}{2}$$

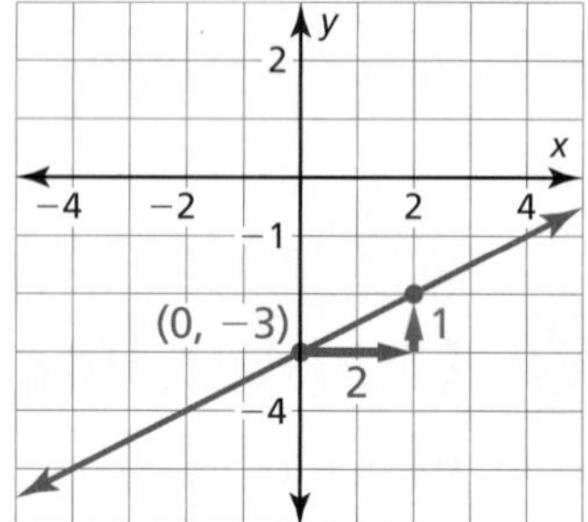

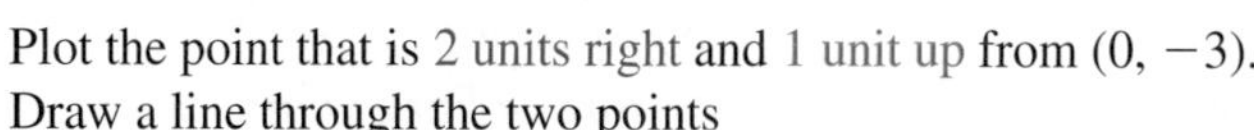

Plot the point that is 2 units right and 1 unit up from $(0, -3)$.
Draw a line through the two points

Graph the equation.

1. $y + 4 = x$ **2.** $6x - y = -1$ **3.** $4x + 5y = 20$ **4.** $-2y + 12 = -3x$

Solving and Graphing Linear Inequalities

Example 2 **Solve $2x - 17 \le 8x - 5$. Graph the solution.**

$2x - 17 \le 8x - 5$	Write the inequality.
$\underline{+5} \quad \underline{+5}$	Addition Property of Inequality
$2x - 12 \le 8x$	Simplify.
$\underline{-2x} \quad \underline{-2x}$	Subtraction Property of Inequality
$-12 \le 6x$	Simplify.
$\frac{-12}{6} \le \frac{6x}{6}$	Division Property of Inequality
$-2 \le x$	Simplify.

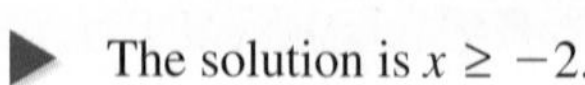

▶ The solution is $x \ge -2$.

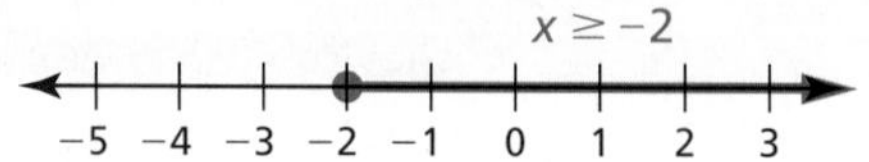

Solve the inequality. Graph the solution.

5. $m + 4 > 9$ **6.** $24 \le -6t$ **7.** $2a - 5 \le 13$

8. $-1.25z + 1 < -14$ **9.** $4k - 16 < \frac{1}{2}k + 5$ **10.** $7w + 9 \ge 2w - 3$

11. MP **REASONING** The graphs of the linear functions g and h have different slopes. The value of both functions when $x = a$ is b. When you graph g and h in the same coordinate plane, what happens at the point (a, b)?

5.1 Solving Systems of Linear Equations by Graphing

Learning Target Solve linear systems by graphing.

Success Criteria
- I can determine whether an ordered pair is a solution of a system.
- I can graph a linear system.
- I can approximate the solution of a linear system using a graph.

EXPLORE IT! Using a System of Linear Equations

Work with a partner. You have a bag of dimes and quarters. You put the coins in a coin-counting machine and see the following display.

a. You want to know how many dimes and how many quarters you had. Do you have enough information to find these quantities? Explain your reasoning.

b. Your friend tries to find the numbers of dimes and quarters by creating the table shown. Did your friend find the solution? If not, find the solution.

Dimes	80	60	50	40	43
Quarters	6	26	36	46	46
Total value (dollars)	9.50	12.50	14.00	15.50	15.80

Math Practice

Maintain Oversight
Describe your friend's approach to creating the table. What mistake did your friend make?

c. Write an equation in two variables that represents the number of coins you had. Then write an equation in two variables that represents the total value of the coins you had.

d. MP **CHOOSE TOOLS** In the same coordinate plane, graph your equations from part (c). How can you use the graph to find the numbers of dimes and quarters you had? Explain.

Systems of Linear Equations

Vocabulary 

system of linear equations, *p. 246*
solution of a system of linear equations, *p. 246*

A **system of linear equations** is a set of two or more linear equations in the same variables. An example is shown.

$x + y = 7$ Equation 1

$2x - 3y = -11$ Equation 2

A **solution of a system of linear equations** in two variables is an ordered pair that is a solution of each equation in the system.

EXAMPLE 1 Checking Solutions 

Tell whether the ordered pair is a solution of the system of linear equations.

a. (2, 5); $x + y = 7$ Equation 1; $2x - 3y = -11$ Equation 2

b. (−2, 0); $y = -2x - 4$ Equation 1; $y = x + 4$ Equation 2

SOLUTION

a. Substitute 2 for x and 5 for y in each equation.

Equation 1	Equation 2
$x + y = 7$	$2x - 3y = -11$
$2 + 5 \stackrel{?}{=} 7$	$2(2) - 3(5) \stackrel{?}{=} -11$
$7 = 7$ ✓	$-11 = -11$ ✓

READING
A system of linear equations is also called a *linear system*.

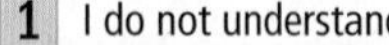

▶ Because the ordered pair (2, 5) is a solution of each equation, it is a solution of the linear system.

b. Substitute −2 for x and 0 for y in each equation.

Equation 1	Equation 2
$y = -2x - 4$	$y = x + 4$
$0 \stackrel{?}{=} -2(-2) - 4$	$0 \stackrel{?}{=} -2 + 4$
$0 = 0$ ✓	$0 \neq 2$ ✗

▶ The ordered pair (−2, 0) is a solution of the first equation, but it is not a solution of the second equation. So, (−2, 0) is *not* a solution of the linear system.

SELF-ASSESSMENT

1 I do not understand. 2 I can do it with help. 3 I can do it on my own. 4 I can teach someone else.

Tell whether the ordered pair is a solution of the system of linear equations.

1. (0, 0); $2x + y = 0$, $-x + 2y = 5$
2. (1, 4); $y = 3x + 1$, $y = -x + 5$
3. (4, −10); $y = -2.5x$, $3x + y = 2$
4. (−2, −0.5); $y + x = -3$, $x = 2y - 1$
5. **MP REASONING** One equation in a linear system is $\frac{1}{2}x + y = 1$. Is it possible for the system to have a solution of (0, 0)? (100, −49)? Explain your reasoning.
6. **OPEN-ENDED** Write a system of linear equations that has a solution of (−1, −3).

Solving Systems of Linear Equations by Graphing

A solution of a system of linear equations is a point of intersection of the graphs of the equations.

KEY IDEA

Solving a System of Linear Equations by Graphing

Step 1 Graph each equation in the same coordinate plane.

Step 2 Estimate the point of intersection.

Step 3 Check the point from Step 2 by substituting for x and y in each equation of the original system.

EXAMPLE 2 Solving a System of Linear Equations by Graphing

Solve the system by graphing.

$y = -2x + 5$ Equation 1

$y = 4x - 1$ Equation 2

SOLUTION

Step 1 Graph each equation.

Step 2 Estimate the point of intersection. The graphs appear to intersect at (1, 3).

Step 3 Check that (1, 3) is a solution of each equation.

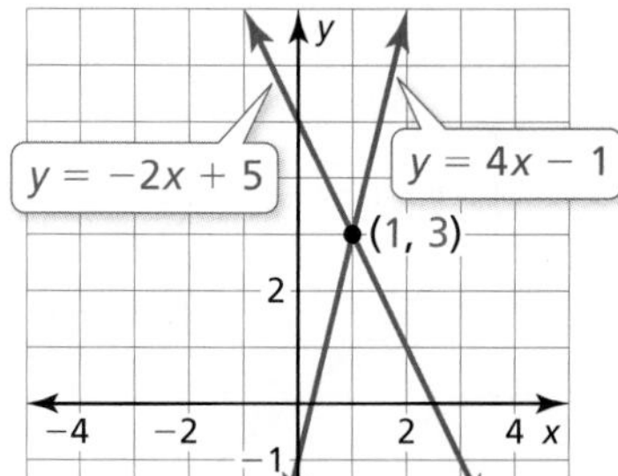

Equation 1	Equation 2
$y = -2x + 5$	$y = 4x - 1$
$3 \stackrel{?}{=} -2(1) + 5$	$3 \stackrel{?}{=} 4(1) - 1$
$3 = 3$ ✓	$3 = 3$ ✓

▶ The solution is (1, 3).

STUDY TIP

Always check that the estimated intersection point is a solution of each equation in the system.

Another Way Use technology to solve the system.

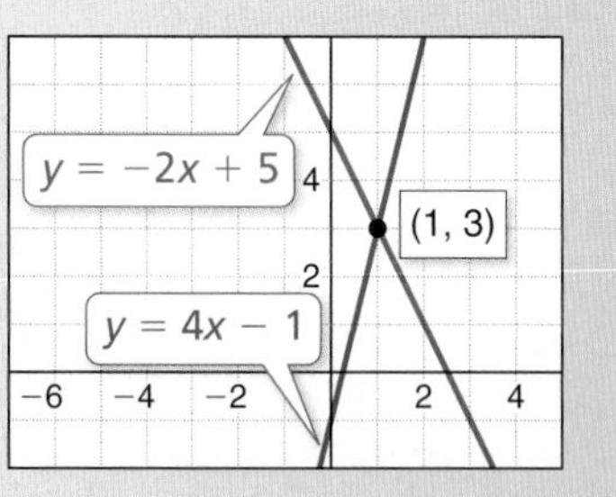

SELF-ASSESSMENT 1 I do not understand. 2 I can do it with help. 3 I can do it on my own. 4 I can teach someone else.

Solve the system by graphing.

7. $y = x - 2$
$y = -x + 4$

8. $y = \frac{1}{2}x + 3$
$y = -\frac{3}{2}x - 5$

9. $2x + y = -6$
$3x - 0.5y = -7$

10. OPEN-ENDED Draw a graph that represents a system of three linear equations with a solution of $(0, -2)$.

Solving Real-Life Problems

Modeling Real Life

A roofing contractor buys 15 bundles of shingles and 8 rolls of roofing paper for \$640. In a second purchase, the contractor buys 8 bundles of shingles and 2 rolls of roofing paper for \$296. Find the price per bundle of shingles and the price per roll of roofing paper.

SOLUTION

1. **Understand the Problem** You know the total price of each purchase and how many of each item were purchased. You are asked to find the price of each item.
2. **Make a Plan** Use a verbal model to write a system that represents the problem. Then solve the system.
3. **Solve and Check**

Verbal Model

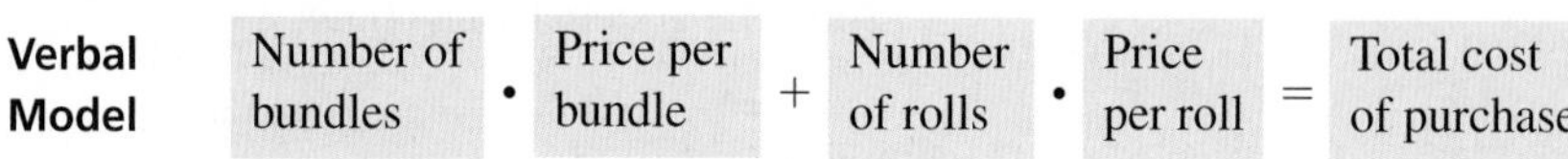

Number of bundles
•
Price per bundle
+
Number of rolls
•
Price per roll
=
Total cost of purchase

Variables Let x be the price (in dollars) per bundle and let y be the price (in dollars) per roll.

System $15x + 8y = 640$ Equation 1 (first purchase)

$8x + 2y = 296$ Equation 2 (second purchase)

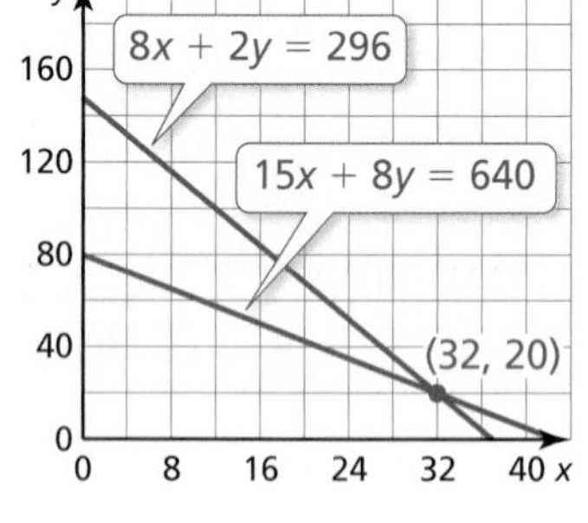

Graph each equation. Note that only the first quadrant is shown because x and y must be positive.

The graphs appear to intersect at (32, 20). Check that (32, 20) is a solution of each equation.

Equation 1	Equation 2
$15x + 8y = 640$	$8x + 2y = 296$
$15(32) + 8(20) \stackrel{?}{=} 640$	$8(32) + 2(20) \stackrel{?}{=} 296$
$640 = 640$ ✓	$296 = 296$ ✓

▶ The solution is (32, 20). So, the price per bundle of shingles is \$32, and the price per roll of roofing paper is \$20.

Another Way Assume the contractor buys 4 times the amounts in the second purchase, so that each purchase contains 8 rolls of roofing paper. The 32 bundles and 8 rolls would cost \$1184. The extra 17 bundles of shingles cost \$1184 − \$640 = \$544. So, the price for shingles is \$544 ÷ 17 bundles = \$32 per bundle.

SELF-ASSESSMENT

1 I do not understand. 2 I can do it with help. 3 I can do it on my own. 4 I can teach someone else.

11. You have a total of 18 science and history questions for homework. You have six more science questions than history questions. How many questions do you have in each subject?

12. You order 3 strings of white LED lights and 2 strings of colored LED lights for \$66. In a second order, you buy one string of each type for \$27.

    a. Which type of LED light is more expensive?

    b. Which type of LED light do you spend more money buying? How much more?

5.1 Practice WITH CalcChat® AND CalcView®

In Exercises 1–6, tell whether the ordered pair is a solution of the system of linear equations.
Example 1

1. $(2, 6)$; $x + y = 8$, $3x - y = 0$

2. $(8, 2)$; $x - y = 6$, $2x - 10y = 4$

3. $(-1, 3)$; $y = -7x - 4$, $y = 8x + 5$

4. $(5, -6)$; $6x + 3y = 12$, $4x + y = 14$

5. $\left(\frac{1}{2}, -2\right)$; $6x + 5y = -7$, $2x - 4y = -8$

6. $(-2.5, -4)$; $y = 6x + 11$, $2x + y = -9$

In Exercises 7 and 8, use the graph to solve the system. Check your solution.

7. $x - y = 4$
$4x + y = 1$

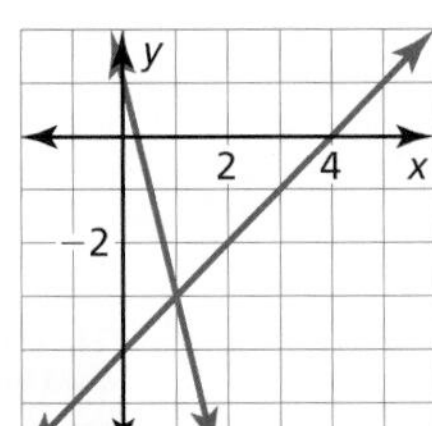

8. $6y + 3x = 18$
$-x + 4y = 24$

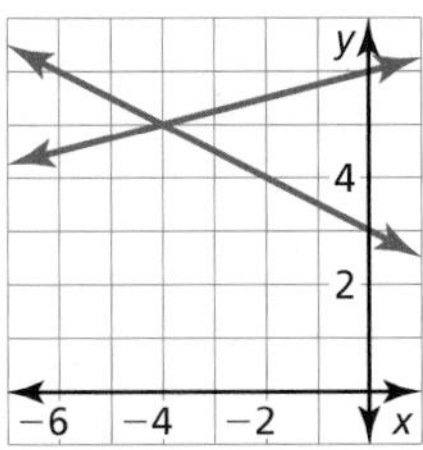

In Exercises 9–16, solve the system by graphing.
Example 2

9. $y = -x + 7$
$y = x + 1$

10. $y = -x + 4$
$y = 2x - 8$

11. $y = \frac{1}{3}x + 2$
$y = \frac{2}{3}x + 5$

12. $y = \frac{3}{4}x - 4$
$y = -\frac{1}{2}x + 11$

13. $9x + 3y = -3$
$2x - y = -4$

14. $3y - 9x = 9$
$x + 3y = -6$

15. $4x - 4y = 22$
$y = -5.5$

16. $x - 2y = -\frac{1}{2}$
$-4x - 8y = 2$

MP USING TOOLS In Exercises 17–20, use technology to solve the system.

17. $0.2x + 0.4y = 4$
$-0.6x + 0.6y = -3$

18. $-1.6x - 3.2y = -24$
$2.6x + 2.6y = 26$

19. $-7x + 6y = 0$
$0.5x + y = 2$

20. $4x - y = 1.5$
$2x + y = 1.5$

21. ERROR ANALYSIS Describe and correct the error in solving the linear system.

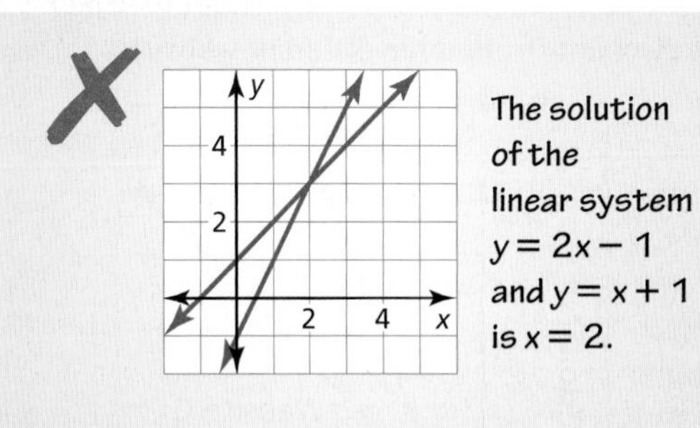

The solution of the linear system y = 2x − 1 and y = x + 1 is x = 2.

22. COLLEGE PREP You make a total of 16 two-point and three-point shots in a basketball game. You score a total of 35 points. Which system can be used to find the number p of two-point shots and the number q of three-point shots you make? Explain your reasoning.

Ⓐ $p + q = 35$, $2p + 3q = 16$

Ⓑ $p + q = 16$, $2p + 3q = 35$

Ⓒ $p + q = 16$, $3p + 2q = 35$

Ⓓ $p + q = 35$, $16p + 16q = 35$

23. MODELING REAL LIFE You have 40 minutes to exercise at the gym, and you want to burn a total of 300 calories using both machines. How much time should you spend on each machine? *Example 3*

Elliptical Trainer — 8 calories per minute

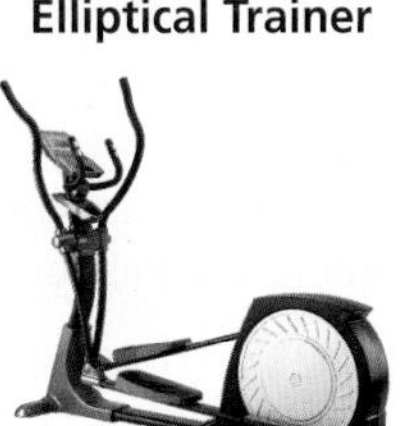

Stationary Bike — 6 calories per minute

24. MODELING REAL LIFE You collect \$234 selling small and large smoothies. You sell a total of 46 smoothies. How many of each size did you sell?

25. CONNECTING CONCEPTS Angle X and angle Y are complementary angles. The measure of angle Y is 6 less than twice the measure of angle X. What is the measure of each angle?

26. HOW DO YOU SEE IT?
The graph shows the total costs of ordering x key chains from three different websites.

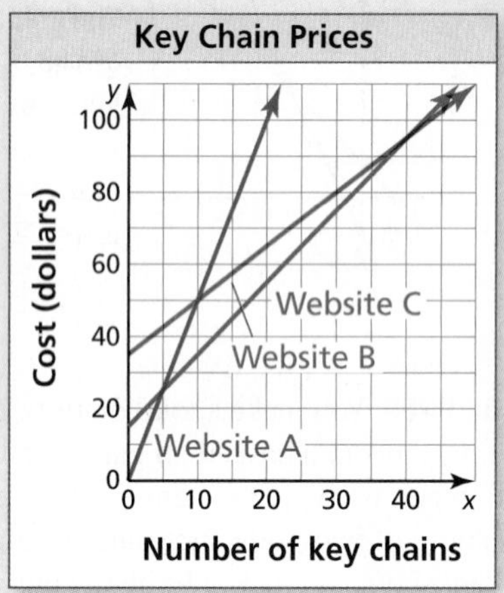

a. For what numbers of key chains are the costs the same at two different websites? Explain.

b. How do your answers in part (a) relate to systems of linear equations?

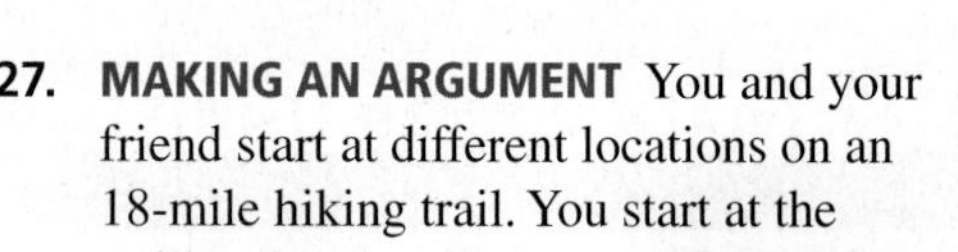

27. MAKING AN ARGUMENT You and your friend start at different locations on an 18-mile hiking trail. You start at the trailhead and walk 4.5 miles per hour. Your friend starts 1.5 miles from the trailhead and walks 3 miles per hour.

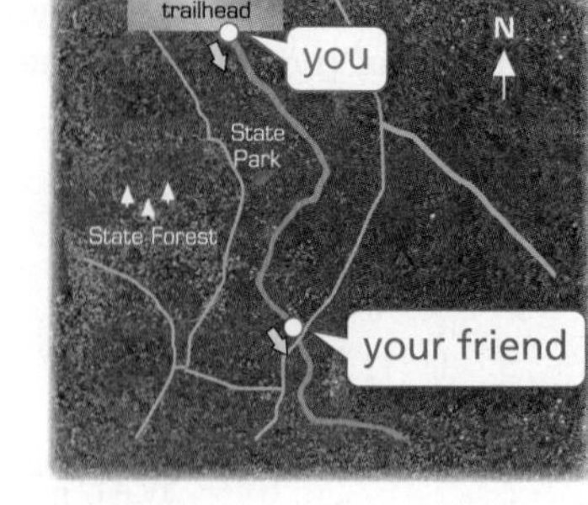

a. Your friend says that you will be at the same location on the trail after one hour of hiking. Is your friend correct? Explain.

b. Who will reach the end of the trail first? How much longer will it take the other person to reach the end of the trail? Explain.

28. THOUGHT PROVOKING
Without graphing, use slopes and intercepts to determine which quadrant contains the solution of the system below. Explain your reasoning.

$$5x + 13y = 72$$
$$4x + 7y = 65$$

REVIEW & REFRESH

WATCH

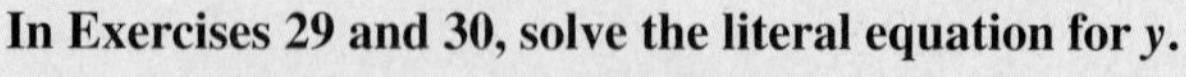

In Exercises 29 and 30, solve the literal equation for y.

29. $9x + 18 = 6y - 3x$ **30.** $\frac{3}{4}x + \frac{1}{4}y = 5$

31. MULTIPLE REPRESENTATIONS The graph of a linear function passes through the point $(12, -5)$ and has a slope of $\frac{2}{5}$. Represent this function in two other forms.

In Exercises 32–35, solve the equation.

32. $n + 6 = 11$ **33.** $\frac{r}{3} = -4$

34. $2p - 7 = 9$ **35.** $\frac{k + 1}{8} = 3$

36. Determine whether the graph represents an arithmetic sequence. Explain.

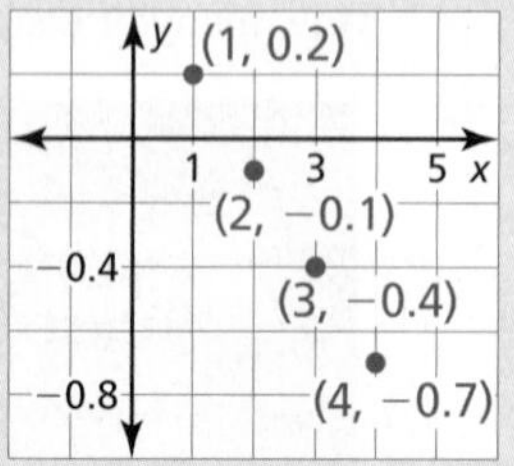

37. Solve the system $x - 4y = -4$ and $-3x - 4y = 12$ by graphing.

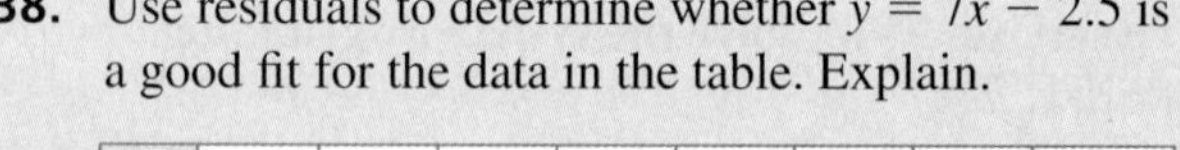

38. Use residuals to determine whether $y = 7x - 2.5$ is a good fit for the data in the table. Explain.

x	0.5	1.0	1.5	2.0	2.5	3.0	3.5	4.0
y	2.5	5	7	14	15	17	21	27.5

39. Estimate the intercepts of the graph of the function.

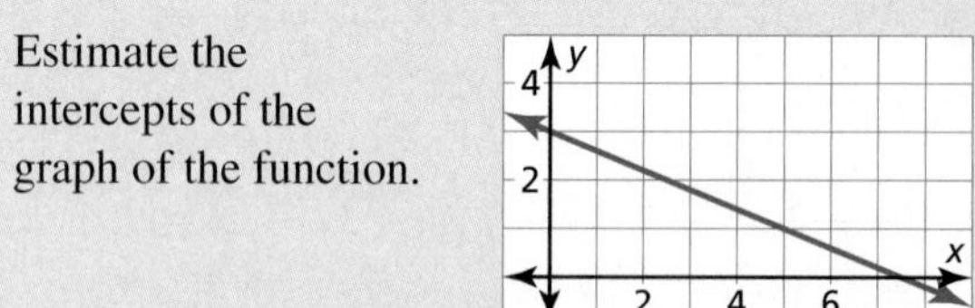

40. MODELING REAL LIFE A dumpster rental fee is \$350 for the first week and \$10 for each additional day or any portion of a day. Write and graph a step function that represents the cost y (in dollars) to rent the dumpster for x days.

41. Write an equation in slope intercept form of the line that passes through $(-4, 5)$ and $(4, -1)$.

42. Solve $-4(3n + 8) \leq 6(-2n - 5)$.

5.2 Solving Systems of Linear Equations by Substitution

Learning Target Solve linear systems by substitution.

Success Criteria

- I can solve a system of linear equations by substitution.
- I can solve a linear equation in two variables for either variable.
- I can solve real-life problems using substitution.

EXPLORE IT! Solving Systems of Linear Equations

Math Practice

Compare Arguments How can understanding different solution methods help you solve systems of linear equations?

Work with a partner.

a. Two students are solving the linear system below. The first portions of their solutions are shown. Justify each solution step and describe their methods. Are the methods valid? Explain.

$x - 6y = -11$ Equation 1

$3x + y = 5$ Equation 2

Student 1

$x - 6y = -11$	Equation 1
$x - 6(-3x + 5) = -11$	__________
$x + 18x - 30 = -11$	__________
$19x - 30 = -11$	__________
$19x = 19$	__________
$x = 1$	__________

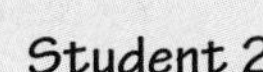

Student 2

$3x + y = 5$	Equation 2
$3(6y - 11) + y = 5$	__________
$18y - 33 + y = 5$	__________
$19y - 33 = 5$	__________
$19y = 38$	__________
$y = 2$	__________

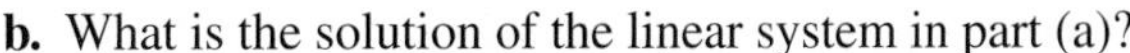

b. What is the solution of the linear system in part (a)?

c. Explain how to solve a linear system using one of the methods above. Then choose one of the methods to solve each system. Check your solutions.

i. $x + 2y = -7$
$2x - y = -9$

ii. $x - 2y = -6$
$2x + y = -2$

iii. $3x - y = -6$
$4x + 5y = 11$

Solving Linear Systems by Substitution

Another way to solve a system of linear equations is to use substitution to obtain an equation in one variable.

KEY IDEA

Solving a System of Linear Equations by Substitution

Step 1 Solve one of the equations for one of the variables or terms.

Step 2 Substitute the expression from Step 1 into the other equation and solve for the other variable.

Step 3 Substitute the value from Step 2 into one of the original equations and solve to find the value of the other variable.

WORDS AND MATH

When someone makes a substitution, they replace one thing with another. When you solve a system of linear equations by substitution, you make two substitutions.

EXAMPLE 1 Solving a System of Linear Equations by Substitution

Solve the system by substitution.

$y = -2x - 9$ Equation 1

$6x - 5y = -19$ Equation 2

SOLUTION

Step 1 Equation 1 is already solved for y.

Step 2 Substitute $-2x - 9$ for y in Equation 2 to obtain an equation in one variable, x. Then solve the equation to find the value of x.

$6x - 5y = -19$	Equation 2
$6x - 5(-2x - 9) = -19$	Substitute $-2x - 9$ for y.
$6x + 10x + 45 = -19$	Distributive Property
$16x + 45 = -19$	Combine like terms.
$16x = -64$	Subtract 45 from each side.
$x = -4$	Divide each side by 16.

Step 3 Substitute -4 for x in Equation 1 and solve for y.

$y = -2x - 9$	Equation 1
$= -2(-4) - 9$	Substitute -4 for x.
$= 8 - 9$	Multiply.
$= -1$	Subtract.

▶ The solution is $(-4, -1)$.

Check

Equation 1

$y = -2x - 9$

$-1 \stackrel{?}{=} -2(-4) - 9$

$-1 = -1$ ✓

Equation 2

$6x - 5y = -19$

$6(-4) - 5(-1) \stackrel{?}{=} -19$

$-19 = -19$ ✓

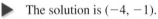

SELF-ASSESSMENT 1 I do not understand. 2 I can do it with help. 3 I can do it on my own. 4 I can teach someone else.

1. **WRITING** Explain how you can use two equations in a system of linear equations to find the value of one of the variables.

Solve the system by substitution. Check your solution.

2. $y = 3x + 14$
   $y = -4x$

3. $3x + 2y = 0$
   $y = \frac{1}{2}x - 1$

4. $x = 6y - 7$
   $4x + y = -3$

EXAMPLE 2 Solving a System of Linear Equations by Substitution

Solve the system by substitution.

$3x = y + 8$ Equation 1

$3x + 2y = -1$ Equation 2

SOLUTION

ANOTHER WAY

You can also begin by solving Equation 1 for *y*, then substituting $3x - 8$ for *y* in Equation 2 and solving to find the value of *x*.

Step 1 Notice that both equations have a term of $3x$, and Equation 1 is already solved for $3x$.

Step 2 Substitute $y + 8$ for $3x$ in Equation 2 and solve to find the value of *y*.

$3x + 2y = -1$ Equation 2

$y + 8 + 2y = -1$ Substitute $y + 8$ for $3x$.

$3y + 8 = -1$ Combine like terms.

$3y = -9$ Subtract 8 from each side.

$y = -3$ Divide each side by 3.

Step 3 Substitute -3 for *y* in Equation 1 and solve for *x*.

$3x = y + 8$ Equation 1

$3x = -3 + 8$ Substitute -3 for *y*.

$3x = 5$ Add.

$x = \frac{5}{3}$ Divide each side by 3.

▶ The solution is $\left(\frac{5}{3}, -3\right)$.

Algebraic Check

Equation 1

$3x = y + 8$

$3\left(\frac{5}{3}\right) \stackrel{?}{=} -3 + 8$

$5 = 5$ ✓

Equation 2

$3x + 2y = -1$

$3\left(\frac{5}{3}\right) + 2(-3) \stackrel{?}{=} -1$

$-1 = -1$ ✓

Graphical Check

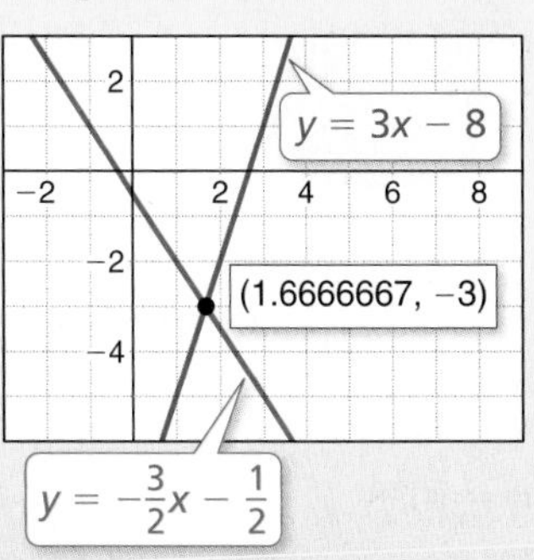

SELF-ASSESSMENT

1 I do not understand. 2 I can do it with help. 3 I can do it on my own. 4 I can teach someone else.

5. **MP STRUCTURE** A system has two equations that are both written in slope-intercept form. Which method would you use to solve this system, graphing or substitution? Explain your reasoning.

Solve the system by substitution. Check your solution.

6. $4x + 5y = 7$
   $5y = 2x + 19$

7. $2x = 4y - 5$
   $2x - 3y = 1$

8. $x - 2y = 7$
   $3x - 2y = 3$

9. $-x + y = -4.5$
   $4x - y = 16.5$

Solving Real-Life Problems

GO DIGITAL

EXAMPLE 3 Modeling Real Life

WATCH

A comedy club earns \$1088 from an opening night performance and \$1183 from a second performance. On opening night, the club sells 68 adult tickets and 136 student tickets. For the second performance, the club sells 79 adult tickets and 140 student tickets. What is the price of each type of ticket?

SOLUTION

1. **Understand the Problem** You know the amounts earned for each performance, and the total numbers of adult and student tickets sold for each. You are asked to find the price of each type of ticket.
2. **Make a Plan** Use a verbal model to write a system that represents the problem. Then solve the system.
3. **Solve and Check**

Verbal Model Number of adult tickets • Adult ticket price + Number of student tickets • Student ticket price = Total amount earned

Variables Let x be the price (in dollars) of an adult ticket and let y be the price (in dollars) of a student ticket.

System
$68x + 136y = 1088$ Equation 1 (first performance)
$79x + 140y = 1183$ Equation 2 (second performance)

Step 1 Solve for y in Equation 1.

$68x + 136y = 1088$ Equation 1
$y = 8 - \frac{1}{2}x$ Solve for y.

Step 2 Substitute $8 - \frac{1}{2}x$ for y in Equation 2 and solve for x.

$79x + 140y = 1183$ Equation 2
$79x + 140\left(8 - \frac{1}{2}x\right) = 1183$ Substitute $8 - \frac{1}{2}x$ for y.
$79x + 1120 - 70x = 1183$ Distributive Property
$x = 7$ Solve for x.

Step 3 Substitute 7 for x in Equation 1 and solve for y.

$68x + 136y = 1088$ Equation 1
$68(7) + 136y = 1088$ Substitute 7 for x.
$y = 4.5$ Solve for y.

▶ The solution is (7, 4.5). So, an adult ticket costs \$7 and a student ticket costs \$4.50.

Check

Equation 1
$68(7) + 136(4.5) \stackrel{?}{=} 1088$
$1088 = 1088$ ✓

Equation 2
$79(7) + 140(4.5) \stackrel{?}{=} 1183$
$1183 = 1183$ ✓

SELF-ASSESSMENT
1 I do not understand. 2 I can do it with help. 3 I can do it on my own. 4 I can teach someone else.

10. **MP REASONING** You are selling tickets at a dance. Individual tickets cost \$6 and 2 tickets for a couple cost \$10. After the dance, you count \$1075 and 195 tickets. Your friend finds \$1 near your table and asks if it belongs with the ticket money. Do you think it does? How many couples bought tickets for the dance? Explain your reasoning.

5.2 Practice WITH CalcChat® AND CalcView®

In Exercises 1–6, describe how you would obtain an equation in one variable to solve the system by substitution.

1. $x + 4y = 30$
   $x = 2y$

2. $y = -8x + 2$
   $2x + y = -10$

3. $12y = x - 15$
   $-3x + 12y = 3$

4. $5x + 3y = 11$
   $5x = y + 5$

5. $x - y = -3$
   $4x + 3y = -5$

6. $3x + 5y = 25$
   $x - 2y = -6$

In Exercises 7–16, solve the system by substitution. Check your solution. *Examples 1 and 2*

7. $x = 17 - 4y$
   $y = x - 2$

8. $6x - 9 = y$
   $y = -3x$

9. $x = 16 - 4y$
   $3x + 4y = 8$

10. $-5x + 3y = 51$
    $y = 10x - 8$

11. $-5x + 6y = -11$
    $6y = x + 5$

12. $8x = 5y + 24$
    $-9y = 40 - 8x$

13. $2x - 3y = -9$
    $x - 5y = -29$

14. $2x - y = 23$
    $x + 4y = -20$

15. $\frac{1}{3}x + y = -1$
    $\frac{1}{3}x + 8y = 13$

16. $5x + 2y = 9$
    $-0.5x - y = 7.5$

17. **ERROR ANALYSIS** Describe and correct the error in solving the linear system $2y = 3x + 4$ and $7x - 2y = 12$.

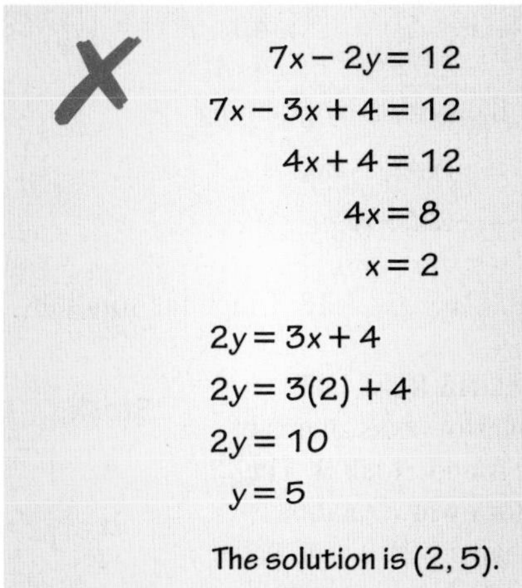

18. **ERROR ANALYSIS** Describe and correct the error in solving for one of the variables in the linear system $8x + 2y = -12$ and $5x - y = 4$.

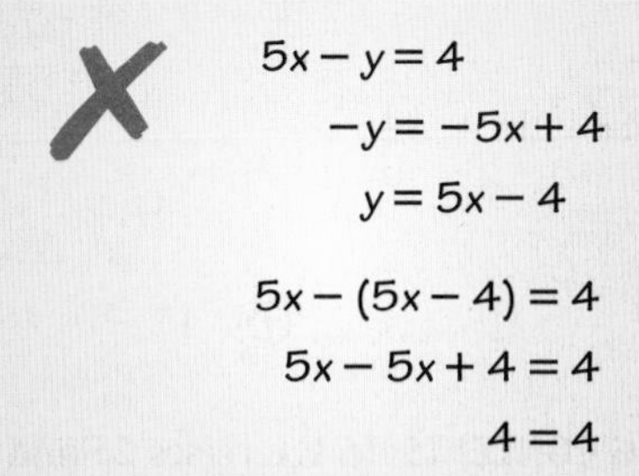

19. **MODELING REAL LIFE** A test is worth 100 points. Each problem is worth either 2 points or 5 points. The number of 5-point problems is 22 less than the number of 2-point problems. How many problems of each type are on the test? *Example 3*

20. **MODELING REAL LIFE** A group spends \$277.50 to rent a total of 15 tubes. How many of each type of tube does the group rent?

RIVER
TUBING
1 Person Tube: $12.50 2 Person Tube: $20

21. **OPEN-ENDED** Write a linear system that has the ordered pair $(15, -25)$ as its solution. Then solve the system by substitution to justify your answer.

22. **HOW DO YOU SEE IT?** The graphs of two linear equations are shown.

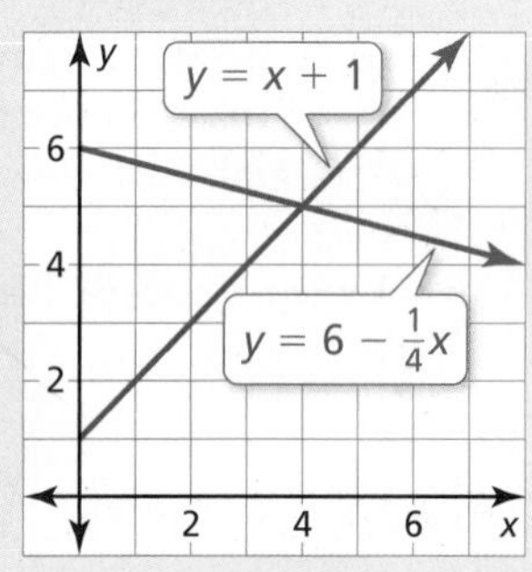

    a. At what point do the lines appear to intersect?

    b. Can you solve a system of linear equations by substitution to check your answer in part (a)? Explain.

GO DIGITAL

23. MAKING AN ARGUMENT To solve the system $-7x - 2y = 21$ and $-7x = 42 - y$ by substitution, you begin by solving for y in the second equation. Your friend says that this step is not necessary. Is your friend correct? Explain.

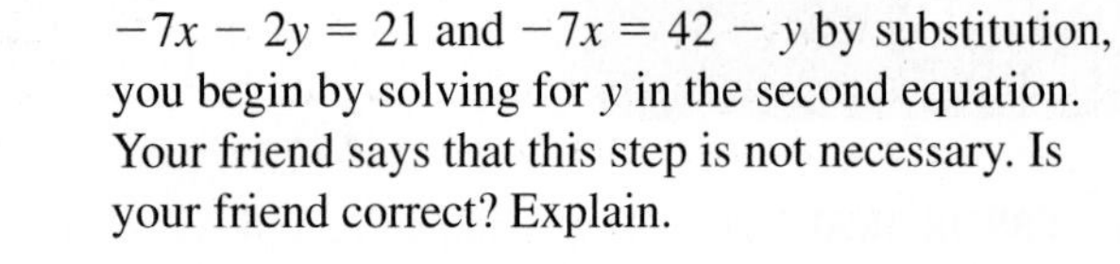

24. COLLEGE PREP For the system shown, what is the value of $y - x$?

$$x + \frac{3}{4}y = -14$$
$$-4x + 3y = -16$$

Ⓐ -17　　Ⓑ -7

Ⓒ 7　　Ⓓ 17

CONNECTING CONCEPTS In Exercises 25 and 26, find the values of x and y.

25. $x + 2 = 3y$

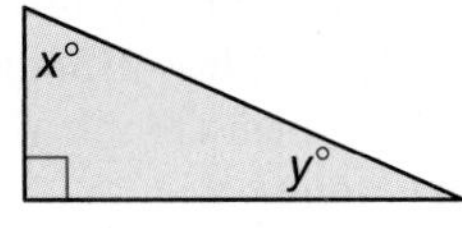

26. $-2x + y = -35$

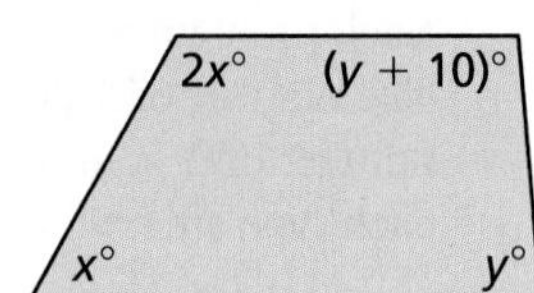

27. MP REASONING Find the values of a and b so that the solution of the linear system is $(-9, 1)$.

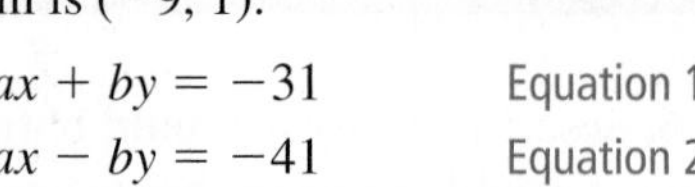

$ax + by = -31$　　Equation 1
$ax - by = -41$　　Equation 2

28. THOUGHT PROVOKING
Write a system of linear equations in which $(3, -5)$ is a solution of Equation 1 but not a solution of Equation 2, and $(-1, 7)$ is the solution of the system. Then solve the system by substitution to verify that $(-1, 7)$ is the solution.

29. MP NUMBER SENSE The sum of the digits of a two-digit number is 11. When the digits are reversed, the number increases by 27. Find the original number.

30. DIG DEEPER You withdraw \$375 from your bank account. You receive a stack of 24 bills consisting of \$5, \$10, and \$20 bills. The number of \$5 bills is one-half the number of \$10 bills. How many of each type of bill do you receive?

REVIEW & REFRESH

In Exercises 31–33, find the sum or difference.

31. $(x - 4) + (2x - 7)$　　**32.** $(6d + 2) - (3d - 3)$

33. $2(5v + 6) - 6(-9v + 2)$

34. Solve the system by substitution.

$$x - 8y = 7$$
$$5x + 6y = 12$$

35. The theoretical probability of drawing a red marble from a bag is $\frac{2}{5}$. The bag contains 60 marbles.

a. How many red marbles are in the bag?

b. A marble is drawn from the bag and replaced 80 times. How many times do you expect a red marble to be drawn?

36. Write a piecewise function represented by the graph.

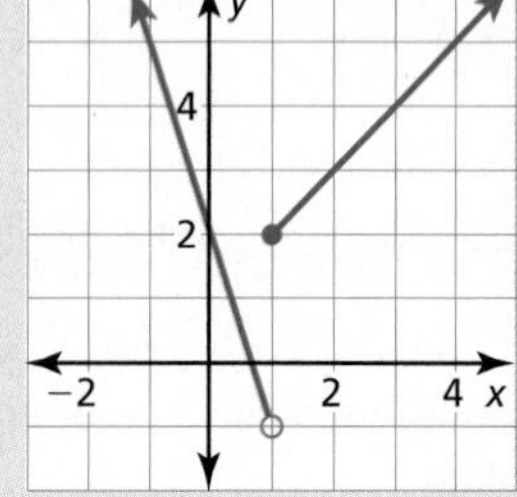

37. MP REASONING Find the value of a so that the line that passes through $(-5, a)$ and $(1, -10)$ has a slope of $-\frac{4}{3}$.

38. Write an equation for the nth term of the arithmetic sequence shown. Then find a_{15}.

$$-14, -5, 4, 13, \ldots$$

In Exercises 39 and 40, graph the function. Compare the graph to the graph of $f(x) = |x|$. Find the domain and range.

39. $g(x) = |x + 5|$　　**40.** $p(x) = |x| - 8$

41. Solve the system by graphing.

$$y = \frac{2}{3}x + 4$$
$$y = -2x - 4$$

42. Solve $3|2x - 7| > 18$. Graph the solution.

43. MODELING REAL LIFE
An investor owns shares of Stock A and Stock B. The investor owns a total of 200 shares with a total value of \$4000. How many shares of each stock does the investor own?

Stock	Price
A	\$9.50
B	\$27.00

5.3 Solving Systems of Linear Equations by Elimination

Learning Target Solve linear systems by elimination.

Success Criteria
- I can add or subtract linear equations.
- I can solve a system of linear equations by elimination.
- I can explain why the elimination method produces a valid solution.
- I can solve real-life problems using elimination.

EXPLORE IT! Solving Systems of Linear Equations

Work with a partner. You, your friend, and your cousin buy drinks and sandwiches at a food truck. Each drink has the same price and each sandwich has the same price.

- You purchase a drink and a sandwich for \$4.50.
- Your cousin purchases a drink and three sandwiches for \$10.50.

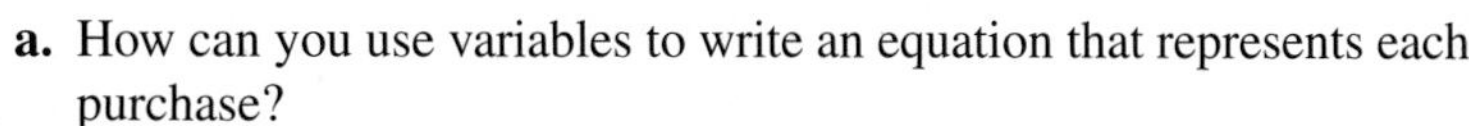

a. How can you use variables to write an equation that represents each purchase?

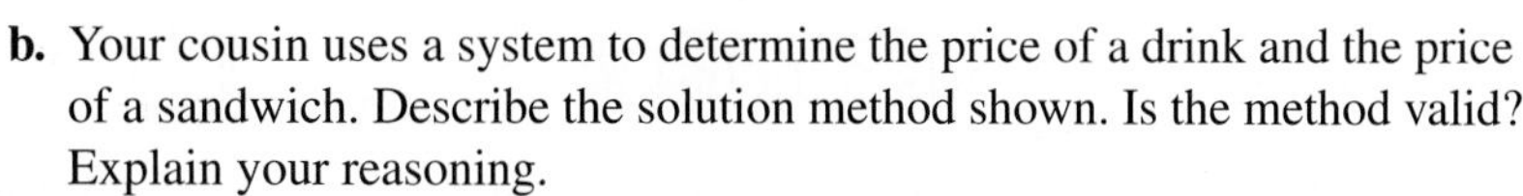

b. Your cousin uses a system to determine the price of a drink and the price of a sandwich. Describe the solution method shown. Is the method valid? Explain your reasoning.

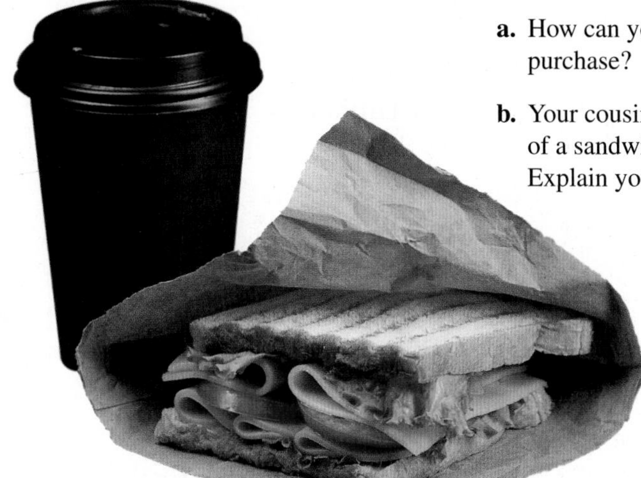

$x + 3y = 10.50$ Your cousin
$x + y = 4.50$ You
$2y = 6$

So, $y = 3$ and each sandwich is \$3.
Each drink is \$4.50 − \$3 = \$1.50.

c. Your friend purchases two drinks and four sandwiches for \$15.00 and writes the system below to check the answer in part (b). What can you do to one or both equations so that you can use an approach similar to the approach in part (b)? Solve the system.

$2x + 4y = 15.00$ Your friend
$x + y = 4.50$ You

Math Practice

Make a Plan
How can you use the coefficients of the variable terms to decide on a strategy for solving the system in part (c)?

d. Explain how to solve a system of linear equations algebraically without using substitution.

Solving Linear Systems by Elimination

KEY IDEA

Solving a System of Linear Equations by Elimination

Step 1 Multiply, if necessary, one or both equations by a constant so at least one pair of like terms has the same or opposite coefficients.

Step 2 Add or subtract the equations to eliminate one of the variables.

Step 3 Solve the resulting equation.

Step 4 Substitute the value from Step 3 into one of the original equations and solve for the other variable.

WORDS AND MATH

Elimination is the process of removing something. When you solve a system of linear equations by elimination, you add or subtract equations to remove one of the variables.

When at least one pair of like terms in a linear system has the same or opposite coefficients, you can add or subtract the equations to *eliminate* one of the variables. Then use the resulting equation to solve the system.

System 1

$a = b$ Equation 1

$c = d$ Equation 2

System 2

$a + c = b + d$ Equation 3

$c = d$ Equation 2

To justify this approach, consider System 1. In this system, a and c are algebraic expressions, and b and d are constants. You can rewrite Equation 1 as Equation 3 by adding c on the left and d on the right by the Addition Property of Equality. You can rewrite Equation 3 as Equation 1 by subtracting c on the left and d on the right by the Subtraction Property of Equality. Because you can rewrite either system as the other, System 1 and System 2 have the same solution.

EXAMPLE 1 Solving a System of Linear Equations by Elimination

Solve the system by elimination.

$3x + 2y = 4$ Equation 1

$3x - 2y = -4$ Equation 2

SOLUTION

Step 1 Because the coefficients of the x-terms are the same, you do not need to multiply either equation by a constant.

Step 2 Subtract the equations to eliminate the x-terms.

$$\begin{aligned} 3x + 2y &= 4 && \text{Equation 1} \\ 3x - 2y &= -4 && \text{Equation 2} \\ \hline 4y &= 8 && \text{Subtract the equations.} \end{aligned}$$

Step 3 Solve for y.

$$\begin{aligned} 4y &= 8 && \text{Resulting equation from Step 2} \\ y &= 2 && \text{Divide each side by 4.} \end{aligned}$$

Step 4 Substitute 2 for y in one of the original equations and solve for x.

$$\begin{aligned} 3x + 2y &= 4 && \text{Equation 1} \\ 3x + 2(2) &= 4 && \text{Substitute 2 for } y. \\ 3x &= 0 && \text{Simplify.} \\ x &= 0 && \text{Divide each side by 3.} \end{aligned}$$

▶ The solution is (0, 2).

ANOTHER WAY

Because the coefficients of the y-terms are opposites, you can add the equations to eliminate the y-terms.

$$\begin{aligned} 3x + 2y &= 4 \\ 3x - 2y &= -4 \\ \hline 6x &= 0 \end{aligned}$$

Check

Equation 1

$3(0) + 2(2) \stackrel{?}{=} 4$

$4 = 4$ ✓

Equation 2

$3(0) - 2(2) \stackrel{?}{=} -4$

$-4 = -4$ ✓

EXAMPLE 2 Solving a System of Linear Equations by Elimination

Solve the system by elimination.

$-10x + 3y = 1$ Equation 1

$-5x - 6y = 23$ Equation 2

ANOTHER WAY

To use subtraction to eliminate one of the variables, multiply Equation 2 by 2 and subtract the equations.

$$\begin{aligned} -10x + 3y &= 1 \\ -10x - 12y &= 46 \\ \hline 15y &= -45 \end{aligned}$$

SOLUTION

Step 1 Notice that no pairs of like terms have the same or opposite coefficients. One way to solve by elimination is to multiply Equation 2 by -2 so that the coefficients of the x-terms are opposites.

$-10x + 3y = 1$ → $-10x + 3y = 1$ Equation 1

$-5x - 6y = 23$  $10x + 12y = -46$ Revised Equation 2

Step 2 Add the equations to eliminate the x-terms.

$-10x + 3y = 1$ Equation 1

$10x + 12y = -46$ Revised Equation 2

$15y = -45$ Add the equations.

Step 3 Solve for y.

$15y = -45$ Resulting equation from Step 2

$y = -3$ Divide each side by 15.

Step 4 Substitute -3 for y in one of the original equations and solve for x.

$-5x - 6y = 23$ Equation 2

$-5x - 6(-3) = 23$ Substitute -3 for y.

$-5x + 18 = 23$ Multiply.

$-5x = 5$ Subtract 18 from each side.

$x = -1$ Divide each side by -5.

▶ The solution is $(-1, -3)$.

Check

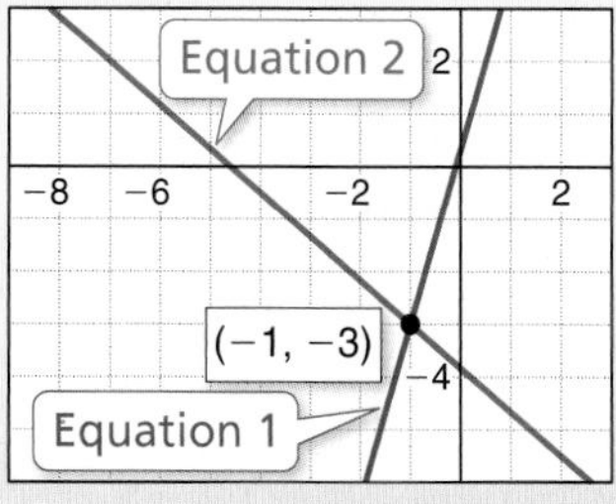

SELF-ASSESSMENT

1 I do not understand. 2 I can do it with help. 3 I can do it on my own. 4 I can teach someone else.

Solve the system by elimination. Check your solution.

1. $2x + y = -4$
   $x + y = 9$
2. $3x + 2y = 7$
   $-3x + 4y = 5$
3. $4x - 3y = 15$
   $-3y - 4x = 6$
4. **MP STRUCTURE** In the system at the right, for what value of a can you eliminate a variable by adding the equations? For what value of b can you eliminate a variable by subtracting the equations?

   $\frac{1}{2}x + ay = -15$ Equation 1

   $bx - \frac{7}{5}y = 1$ Equation 2

Solve the system by elimination. Check your solution.

5. $x - 3y = 24$
   $3x + y = 12$
6. $x + 4y = 22$
   $4x + y = 13$
7. $-5x + \frac{1}{2}y = 3$
   $4x - 2y = -8$
8. **MP REASONING** Your friend says that replacing one equation in a system with the sum of that equation and a multiple of the other produces a system with the same solution. Use properties of equality to show that your friend is correct.

GO DIGITAL

Solving Real-Life Problems

EXAMPLE 3 Modeling Real Life

A business with two locations buys seven large delivery vans and five small delivery vans. Location A receives five large vans and two small vans for a total cost of \$235,000. Location B receives two large vans and three small vans for a total cost of \$160,000. What is the cost of each type of van?

SOLUTION

Use a verbal model to write and solve a linear system that represents the problem.

Verbal Model Number of large vans $\cdot$ Cost of large van $+$ Number of small vans $\cdot$ Cost of small van $=$ Total cost of vans

Variables Let x be the cost (in dollars) of a large van and let y be the cost (in dollars) of a small van.

System $5x + 2y = 235{,}000$ Equation 1

$2x + 3y = 160{,}000$ Equation 2

Step 1 One way to find the cost of each type of van is to first eliminate the y-terms and solve for x. Multiply Equation 1 by 3 and Equation 2 by 2.

$5x + 2y = 235{,}000$ **Multiply by 3.** → $15x + 6y = 705{,}000$ Revised Equation 1

$2x + 3y = 160{,}000$ **Multiply by 2.** → $4x + 6y = 320{,}000$ Revised Equation 2

Step 2 Subtract the equations to obtain $11x = 385{,}000$.

Step 3 Solving the equation $11x = 385{,}000$ gives $x = 35{,}000$.

Step 4 Substitute 35,000 for x in one of the original equations and solve for y.

$5(35{,}000) + 2y = 235{,}000$ Substitute 35,000 for x in Equation 1.

$y = 30{,}000$ Solve for y.

▶ The solution is (35,000, 30,000). So, a large van costs \$35,000 and a small van costs \$30,000.

STUDY TIP

In Example 3, both equations are multiplied by a constant so that the coefficients of the y-terms are the same.

SELF-ASSESSMENT

1 I do not understand. 2 I can do it with help. 3 I can do it on my own. 4 I can teach someone else.

9. **WHAT IF?** The total cost of the vans for Location A is \$228,500. The total cost for Location B is \$153,000. What is the cost of each type of van?

CONCEPT SUMMARY

Methods for Solving Linear Systems

Method	When to Use
Graphing *(Lesson 5.1)*	To estimate solutions
Substitution *(Lesson 5.2)*	When one of the variable terms in one of the equations has a coefficient of 1 or −1
Elimination *(Lesson 5.3)*	When at least one pair of like terms has the same or opposite coefficients
Elimination (Multiply First) *(Lesson 5.3)*	When one of the variables cannot be eliminated by adding or subtracting the equations

5.3 Practice WITH CalcChat® AND CalcView®

In Exercises 1–8, solve the system by elimination. Check your solution. *Example 1*

1. $x + 2y = 13$
$-x + y = 5$

2. $9x + y = 2$
$-4x - y = -17$

3. $5x + 6y = 50$
$x - 6y = -26$

4. $-x + y = 4$
$x + 3y = 4$

5. $-3x - 5y = -7$
$-4x + 5y = 14$

6. $1.5x - 9y = -21$
$-1.5x - 3y = 9$

7. $-y - 10 = 6x$
$5x + y = -10$

8. $3x - 30 = y$
$7y - 6 = 3x$

In Exercises 9–16, solve the system by elimination. Check your solution. *Example 2*

9. $x + y = 2$
$2x + 7y = 9$

10. $8x - 5y = 11$
$4x - 3y = 5$

11. $11x - 20y = 28$
$3x + 4y = 36$

12. $10x - 9y = 46$
$-2x + 3y = 10$

13. $4x - 3y = 8$
$5x - 2y = -11$

14. $-2x - 5y = 9$
$3x + 11y = 4$

15. $9x + 2y = 39$
$6x + 13y = -9$

16. $12x - 7y = -2$
$8x + 11y = 30$

17. MODELING REAL LIFE A service center charges a fee of x dollars for an oil change plus y dollars per quart of oil used. Customer A receives 5 quarts of oil and pays a total of \$37.45. Customer B receives 7 quarts of oil and pays a total of \$46.45. Find the fee and cost per quart of oil. *Example 3*

18. MODELING REAL LIFE A music website charges x dollars for individual songs and y dollars for entire albums. Person A pays \$25.92 to download 6 individual songs and 2 albums. Person B pays \$33.93 to download 4 individual songs and 3 albums. How much does the website charge to download a song? an entire album?

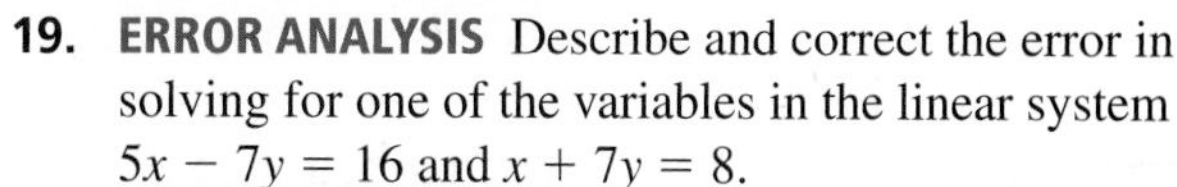

19. ERROR ANALYSIS Describe and correct the error in solving for one of the variables in the linear system $5x - 7y = 16$ and $x + 7y = 8$.

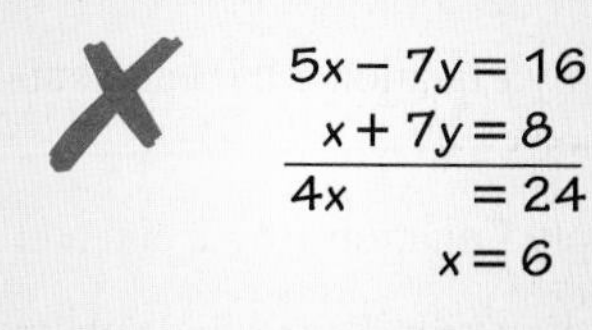

20. WRITING For what values of a can you solve the linear system $ax + 3y = 2$ and $4x + 5y = 6$ by elimination without multiplying first? Explain.

In Exercises 21–26, solve the system using any method. Explain your choice of method.

21. $3x + 2y = 4$
$2y = 8 - 5x$

22. $-6y + 2 = -4x$
$y - 2 = x$

23. $y - x = 2$
$y = -\frac{1}{4}x + 7$

24. $3x + y = \frac{1}{3}$
$2x - 3y = \frac{8}{3}$

25. $0.3x - 0.2y = -2.1$
$0.6x + 1.3y = 0.9$

26. $\frac{1}{3}x + \frac{2}{3}y = 2$
$\frac{1}{2}x - \frac{1}{4}y = -\frac{3}{4}$

27. OPEN-ENDED Write a linear system for which you can add *or* subtract to eliminate a variable.

28. HOW DO YOU SEE IT?
The circle graph shows the results of a survey in which 50 students were asked about their favorite meal.

Favorite Meal
Dinner 25
Lunch
Breakfast

a. Estimate the numbers of students who chose breakfast and lunch.

b. The number of students who chose lunch is 5 more than the number of students who chose breakfast. Write a linear system that represents the numbers of students who chose breakfast and lunch.

c. Explain how you can solve the linear system in part (b) to check your answers in part (a).

29. **COLLEGE PREP** Which of the following approaches result in an equation in one variable? Select all that apply. Explain your reasoning.

$3x + y = 7$ Equation 1
$-x - 2y = 16$ Equation 2

Ⓐ Add the equations.

Ⓑ Multiply Equation 2 by 3 and subtract the equations.

Ⓒ Multiply Equation 1 by 2 and add the equations.

Ⓓ Solve Equation 1 for y and substitute the result in Equation 2.

30. **MAKING AN ARGUMENT** Your friend says that any system of equations that can be solved by elimination can be solved by substitution in an equal or fewer number of steps. Is your friend correct? Explain.

31. **MP PROBLEM SOLVING** You use bottles of 100% fruit juice and 20% fruit juice to make fruit punch for a party. How many quarts of each type of juice should you mix to make 6 quarts of 80% fruit juice?

32. **MP PROBLEM SOLVING** A motorboat takes 40 minutes to travel 20 miles downstream. The return trip takes 60 minutes. For both trips, the boat travels through the water at a constant speed. What is the speed of the current?

GO DIGITAL

33. **CRITICAL THINKING** Refer to the discussion of System 1 and System 2 on page 258. Without solving, explain why the systems shown have the same solution.

System 1		System 2	
$3x - 2y = 8$	Equation 1	$5x = 20$	Equation 3
$x + y = 6$	Equation 2	$x + y = 6$	Equation 2

34. **THOUGHT PROVOKING**
There are three integers. The sums of each distinct pair of integers are -13, -4, and 3. What is the greatest integer?

35. **DIG DEEPER** Solve the system of equations for x, y, and z. Explain your steps.

$x + 7y + 3z = 29$ Equation 1
$3z + x - 2y = -7$ Equation 2
$5y = 10 - 2x$ Equation 3

REVIEW & REFRESH

WATCH

In Exercises 36 and 37, solve the equation.

36. $5d - 8 = 1 + 5d$ 37. $9 + 4t = 12 - 4t$

38. **WRITING** Explain how to solve the system shown by elimination.

$2x - 3y = -4$ Equation 1
$-5x + 9y = 7$ Equation 2

39. Write an equation of the line that passes through $(-5, -2)$ and is (a) parallel and (b) perpendicular to $y = \frac{2}{3}x + 1$.

In Exercises 40 and 41, solve the system by elimination. Check your solution.

40. $2x - y = 14$
$-3x + y = -6$

41. $x + 3y = -6$
$3x - 4y = 8$

42. Determine whether the graph represents a function. Explain.

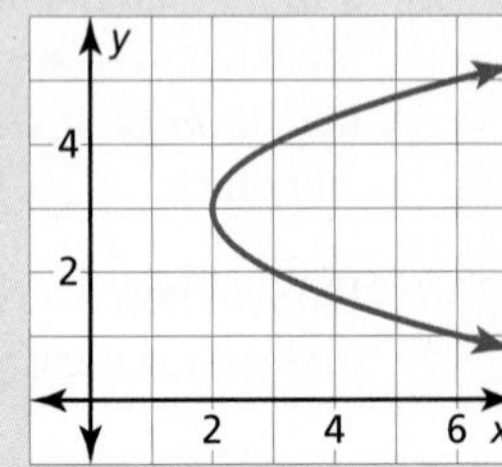

43. Tell whether $(-2, 3)$ is a solution of the system $y = \frac{1}{2}x + 4$ and $3x - y = 6$.

44. Graph $y = \begin{cases} -x + 3, & \text{if } x \leq 2 \\ 2x - 2, & \text{if } x > 2 \end{cases}$. Describe the domain and range.

45. **MP LOGIC** Find the value of each symbol in the system.

★ − ■ = −5 Equation 1
★ + ★ = 11 − ■ Equation 2

46. Evaluate the function $d(x) = -2x + 9$ when $x = 5$.

In Exercises 47–52, solve the inequality. Graph the solution.

47. $c + 15 \leq -7$ 48. $9 > -6y$

49. $8 - 3z < 5z - 16$ 50. $|7d + 23| \geq -10$

51. $-1 < \frac{1}{2}(g - 8) < 9$ 52. $0 \geq r + 1$ *or* $\frac{2}{3}r \geq 4$

53. Graph $f(x) = |x - 4| + 2$. Compare the graph to the graph of $g(x) = |x + 1| + 3$.

5.4 Solving Special Systems of Linear Equations

Learning Target Solve linear systems with different numbers of solutions.

Success Criteria
- I can determine the number of solutions of a system.
- I can solve a system of linear equations with any number of solutions.

EXPLORE IT! Solving Linear Systems

Work with a partner. You invest \$30 on equipment to make skateboards. The materials for each skateboard cost \$20. You have three plans for how to sell the skateboards.

Plan #1: Sell each skateboard for \$20.

Plan #2: Sell each skateboard for \$25.

Plan #3: Sell the first skateboard for \$50 to make up for your initial costs, and then sell every other skateboard for \$20.

a. Match each plan with one of the following systems. Explain your reasoning.

System 1: $y = 20x + 30$ Equation 1 (cost)
$y = 25x$ Equation 2 (revenue)

System 2: $y = 20x + 30$ Equation 1 (cost)
$y = 20x + 30$ Equation 2 (revenue)

System 3: $y = 20x + 30$ Equation 1 (cost)
$y = 20x + 50$ Equation 2 (revenue)

System 4: $y = 20x + 30$ Equation 1 (cost)
$y = 20x$ Equation 2 (revenue)

b. What does the solution of each system represent?

c. Solve the system for each plan by graphing. Then solve the systems algebraically. What do you notice?

d. Which plan makes the most sense? Explain your reasoning.

e. Explain how you can use slopes and y-intercepts to determine the number of solutions of a system.

Math Practice

Analyze Relationships
For the system that has one solution, what does the vertical distance between the lines represent to the left of the intersection point? to the right?

The Numbers of Solutions of Linear Systems

KEY IDEA

Solutions of Systems of Linear Equations

A system of linear equations can have *one solution*, *no solution*, or *infinitely many solutions*.

One solution

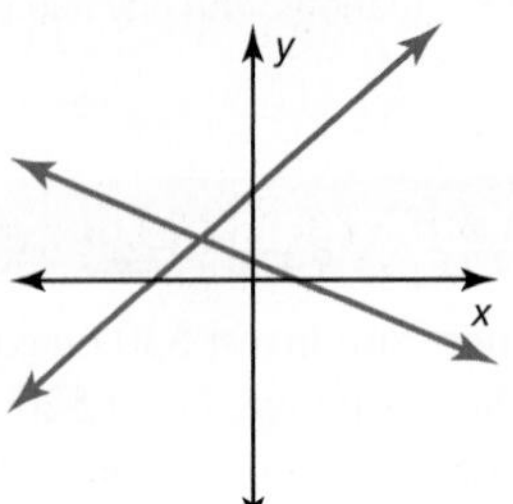

The lines intersect.
- different slopes

No solution

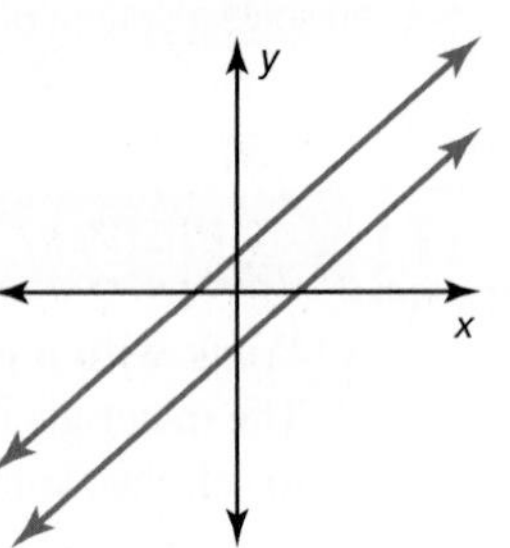

The lines are parallel.
- same slope
- different y-intercepts

Infinitely many solutions

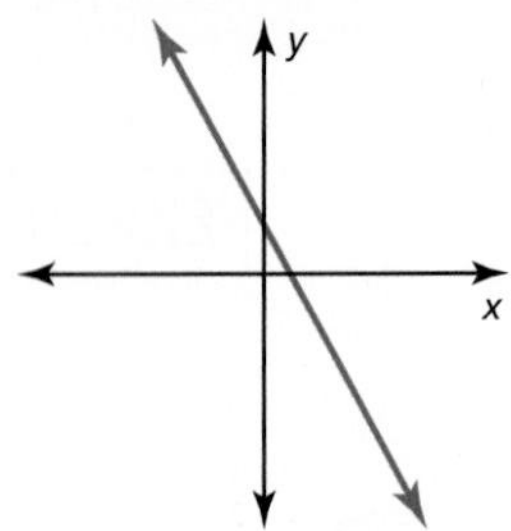

The lines are the same.
- same slope
- same y-intercept

STUDY TIP

A linear system with no solution is called an *inconsistent system*.

A linear system with infinitely many solutions is called a *consistent dependent system*.

EXAMPLE 1 Solving a System: No Solution

Solve the system using any method.

$y = 2x + 1$ Equation 1

$y = 2x - 5$ Equation 2

SOLUTION

Method 1 Solve by graphing.

Graph each equation.

The lines have the same slope, 2, and different y-intercepts, 1 and -5. So, the lines are parallel.

Because parallel lines do not intersect, there is no point that is a solution of both equations.

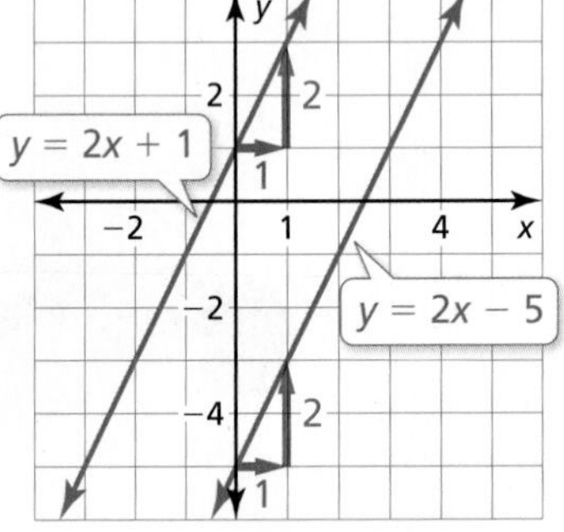

▶ So, the system has no solution.

ANOTHER WAY

You can solve some linear systems by inspection. In Example 1, notice you can rewrite the system as

$-2x + y = 1$

$-2x + y = -5.$

This system has no solution because $-2x + y$ cannot be equal to both 1 and -5.

Method 2 Because the equations are solved for y, another way to solve is by substitution.

Substitute $2x - 5$ for y in Equation 1.

$y = 2x + 1$ Equation 1

$2x - 5 = 2x + 1$ Substitute $2x - 5$ for y.

$-5 = 1$  Subtract $2x$ from each side.

▶ The equation $-5 = 1$ is never true. So, the system has no solution.

EXAMPLE 2 Solving a System: Infinitely Many Solutions

Solve the system using any method.

$-2x + y = 3$ Equation 1

$-4x + 2y = 6$ Equation 2

SOLUTION

Method 1 Solve by graphing.

Graph each equation.

The lines have the same slope, 2, and the same y-intercept, 3. So, the lines are the same.

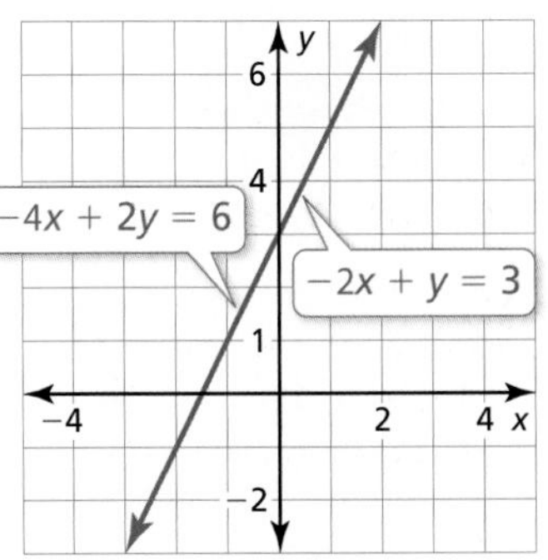

▶ Because the lines are the same, the system has infinitely many solutions. The solutions are all the points on the line $-2x + y = 3$.

Method 2 Another way to solve is by elimination. Multiply Equation 1 by -2 so that the coefficients of the x-terms are opposites.

Step 1 Multiply Equation 1 by -2.

$-2x + y = 3$	**Multiply by −2.**	$4x - 2y = -6$	Revised Equation 1
$-4x + 2y = 6$		$-4x + 2y = 6$	Equation 2

Step 2 Add the equations.

$4x - 2y = -6$ Revised Equation 1

$-4x + 2y = 6$ Equation 2

$0 = 0$ Add the equations.

▶ The equation $0 = 0$ is always true. So, the system has infinitely many solutions. The solutions are all the points on the line $-2x + y = 3$.

SELF-ASSESSMENT

1 I do not understand. 2 I can do it with help. 3 I can do it on my own. 4 I can teach someone else.

Solve the system. Explain your choice of method.

1. $x + y = 3$
$2x + 2y = 6$

2. $y = -x + 3$
$2x + 2y = 4$

3. $5x + y = 4$
$x + 6y = 9.5$

4. $y = -10x + 2$
$10x + y = 10$

5. $\frac{5}{2}x + y = -10$
$\frac{5}{2}x = -10 - y$

6. $x + y = 3$
$x + 2y = 4$

7. **MP REASONING** Is it possible for a system of linear equations to have exactly two solutions? Explain.

8. **MP STRUCTURE** For what value(s) of a does the system have no solution? infinitely many solutions? Is it possible for the system to have exactly one solution?

$3x - 9y = a$ Equation 1

$-x + 3y = 2$ Equation 2

Solving Real-Life Problems

Modeling Real Life

You buy 1 bag of dog food and 2 bags of treats online for a total of \$48. A few weeks later, you buy 2 bags of the same dog food and 4 bags of the same treats for a total of \$96. Find the price of each bag of food and each bag of treats.

SOLUTION

1. **Understand the Problem** You know the numbers of bags of dog food and treats you buy in two separate purchases as well as the total cost of each purchase. You are asked to find the price of each bag of food and each bag of treats.
2. **Make a Plan** Use a verbal model to write a system that represents the problem. Then solve the system.
3. **Solve and Check**

Verbal Model Number of bags of food • Cost of bag of food + Number of bags of treats • Cost of bag of treats = Total cost

Variables Let x be the cost (in dollars) of a bag of food and let y be the cost (in dollars) of a bag of treats.

System
$x + 2y = 48$ Equation 1
$2x + 4y = 96$ Equation 2

One way to find the costs per bag is to first eliminate the x-terms and solve for y. Multiply Equation 1 by 2 and subtract the equations.

$x + 2y = 48$ **Multiply by 2.** $2x + 4y = 96$ Revised Equation 1
$2x + 4y = 96$ $\qquad 2x + 4y = 96$ Equation 2
$0 = 0$ Subtract the equations.

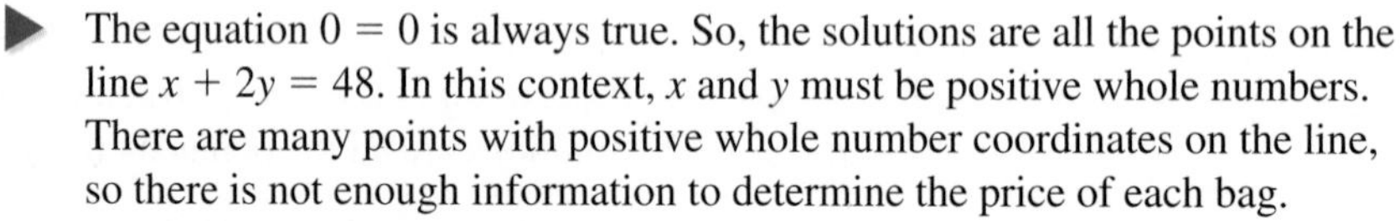

▶ The equation $0 = 0$ is always true. So, the solutions are all the points on the line $x + 2y = 48$. In this context, x and y must be positive whole numbers. There are many points with positive whole number coordinates on the line, so there is not enough information to determine the price of each bag.

Look Back Find ordered pairs (x, y) that are solutions of Equation 1. You should find that they are also solutions of Equation 2.

Equation 1: Let $x = 30$.
$30 + 2y = 48$
$y = 9$
Equation 2: Test (30, 9).
$2(30) + 4(9) \stackrel{?}{=} 96$
$96 = 96$ ✓

Equation 1: Let $x = 40$.
$40 + 2y = 48$
$y = 4$
Equation 2: Test (40, 4).
$2(40) + 4(4) \stackrel{?}{=} 96$
$96 = 96$ ✓

1 I do not understand. 2 I can do it with help. 3 I can do it on my own. 4 I can teach someone else.

9. **WHAT IF?** In Example 3, you purchase 2 bags of the same dog food and 1 bag of the same treats for a total of \$81. Do you now have enough information to find the prices? If so, find the prices and explain why this new information is sufficient to do so. If not, explain why not.

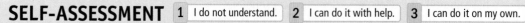

5.4 Practice WITH CalcChat® AND CalcView®

In Exercises 1–10, solve the system. Explain your choice of method. *Examples 1 and 2*

1. $y = -2x - 4$
$y = 2x - 4$

2. $y = -6x - 8$
$y = -6x + 8$

3. $3x - y = 6$
$-3x + y = -6$

4. $-x + 2y = 7$
$x - 2y = 7$

5. $4x + 4y = -8$
$-2x - 2y = 4$

6. $15x - 5y = -20$
$-3x + y = 4$

7. $9x - 15y = 24$
$6x - 10y = -16$

8. $3x - 2y = -5$
$4x + 5y = 47$

9. $\frac{4}{3}y = 3x - 14$
$3x + \frac{4}{3}y = -10$

10. $-\frac{1}{4}x + 3y = 6$
$-2x + 24y = 48$

In Exercises 11–16, use only the slopes and *y*-intercepts of the graphs of the equations to determine the number of solutions of the system. Explain your reasoning.

11. $y = 7x + 13$
$-21x + 3y = 39$

12. $y = -6x - 3$
$12x + 2y = -6$

13. $4x + 3y = 27$
$4x - 3y = -27$

14. $-7x + 7y = 1$
$2x - 2y = -18$

15. $-18x + 6y = 24$
$3x - y = -2$

16. $2x - 2y = 16$
$3x - 6y = 30$

ERROR ANALYSIS In Exercises 17 and 18, describe and correct the error in determining the number of solutions of the system.

17.

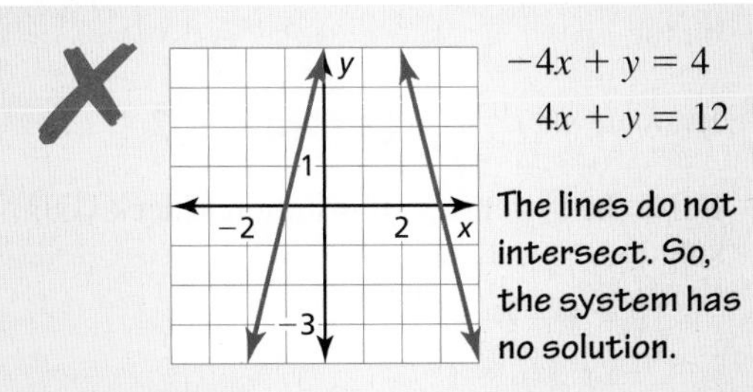

y
x
1
−2
2
−3
$-4x + y = 4$
$4x + y = 12$
The lines do not intersect. So, the system has no solution.

18.

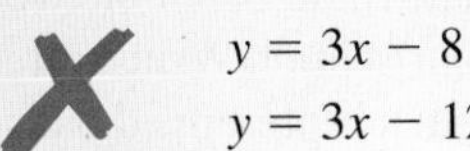

$y = 3x - 8$
$y = 3x - 12$
The lines have the same slope. So, the system has infinitely many solutions.

19. MODELING REAL LIFE A small bag of trail mix contains 3 cups of dried fruit and 4 cups of almonds. A large bag contains $4\frac{1}{2}$ cups of dried fruit and 6 cups of almonds. Find the price of 1 cup of dried fruit and 1 cup of almonds. *Example 3*

$9 $6

20. MODELING REAL LIFE In a canoe race, the distance *y* (in miles) that Team A travels in *x* hours is represented by $y = 6x$. Team B travels 6 miles per hour and is 2.25 miles ahead of Team A. The teams continue traveling at their current rates for the remainder of the race. Will Team A catch up to Team B? Use a system to justify your answer.

21. MP PROBLEM SOLVING A train travels from New York City to Washington, D.C., and then back to New York City. The table shows the numbers of tickets purchased for each leg of the trip. The cost per ticket is the same for each leg of the trip. Is there enough information to determine the cost of one coach ticket? Explain.

Destination	Coach tickets	Business class tickets	Money collected (dollars)
Washington, D.C.	150	80	22,860
New York City	170	100	27,280

22. MAKING AN ARGUMENT One admission to an ice skating rink costs *x* dollars, and renting a pair of ice skates costs *y* dollars. Your friend says she can determine the exact cost of one admission and one skate rental. Is your friend correct? Explain.

Lake Erie Ice Rink	
Order No.	240796
3	Admissions
2	Skate Rentals
Total	$ 38.00

Lake Erie Ice Rink	
Order No.	240797
15	Admissions
10	Skate Rentals
Total	$ 190.00

23. **MP REASONING** In a system of linear equations, one equation has a slope of 2 and the other equation has a slope of $-\frac{1}{3}$. How many solutions does the system have? Explain.

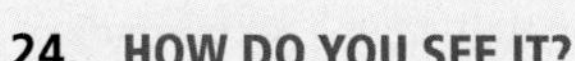

24. HOW DO YOU SEE IT?
The graphs of three linear equations are shown.

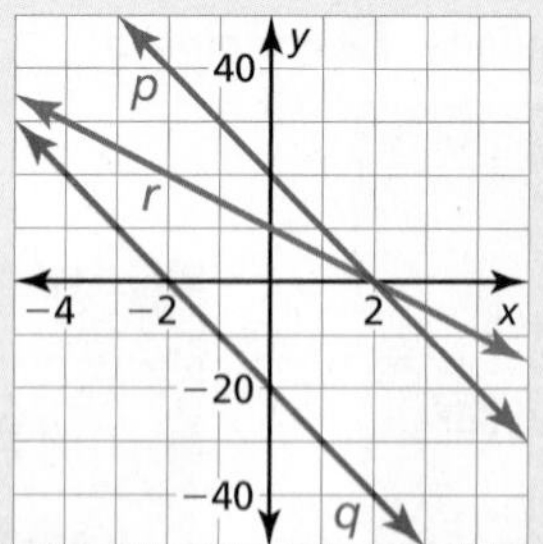

a. Name a pair of lines whose equations form a system that has one solution.

b. Name a pair of lines whose equations form a system that has no solution.

25. **MP STRUCTURE** Write a system that contains $3x - 8y = 7$ and has (a) one solution, (b) no solution, and (c) infinitely many solutions.

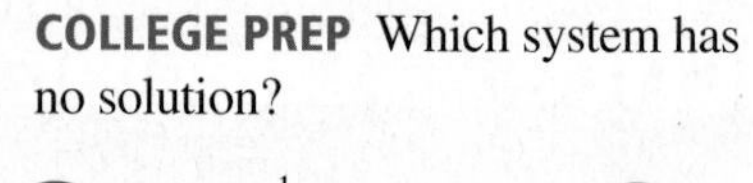

26. **COLLEGE PREP** Which system has no solution?

Ⓐ $y = -\frac{1}{5}x + 2$
$y = -\frac{3}{5}x + 2$

Ⓑ $y = -\frac{3}{5}x + 5$
$-\frac{3}{5}x + y = 6$

Ⓒ $-3x - 5y = -15$
$12x + 20y = 60$

Ⓓ $-\frac{3}{5}x = y - 4$
$-6x - 10y = 40$

27. **ABSTRACT REASONING** Consider the system $y = ax + 4$ and $y = bx - 2$, where a and b are real numbers. Determine whether each statement is *always*, *sometimes*, or *never* true. Explain your reasoning.

a. The system has infinitely many solutions.

b. The system has no solution.

c. When $a > b$, the system has one solution.

28. THOUGHT PROVOKING
Write a system of three linear equations in two variables so that any two of the equations form a system that has exactly one solution, but the entire system has no solution.

REVIEW & REFRESH

29. Use the graph to solve the system. Check your solution.

$y = \frac{1}{2}x - 1$
$y = 4x + 6$

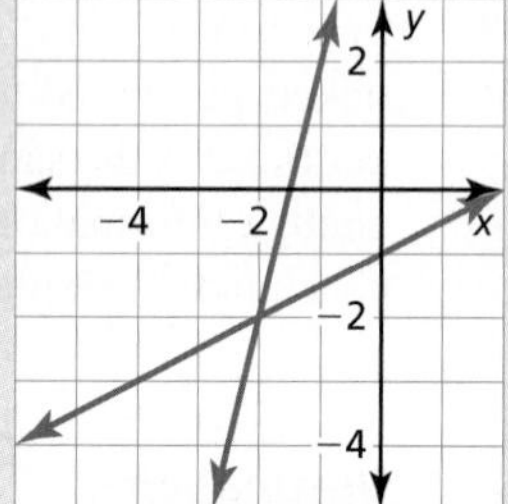

In Exercises 30 and 31, solve the equation. Check your solutions.

30. $|3x - 45| = 12x$

31. $|2x + 1| = |3x - 11|$

32. Solve the system by elimination. Check your solution.

$x + 3y = 1$
$5x + 6y = 14$

33. Solve the literal equation $y = 7x + 5xz - 8$ for x.

In Exercises 34 and 35, determine whether the equation represents a *linear* or *nonlinear* function. Explain.

34. $y = \dfrac{3}{x} + 7$

35. $y = 9x - \sqrt{16}$

In Exercises 36 and 37, use only the slopes and *y*-intercepts of the graphs of the equations to determine the number of solutions of the system. Explain your reasoning.

36. $y = -4x + 11$
$4x + y = -11$

37. $2x - 3y = -15$
$-\frac{2}{3}x + y = 5$

38. **MP STRUCTURE** Without simplifying, identify the slope of the line given by the equation $y + 10 = -\frac{1}{4}(x - 8)$. Then identify one point on the line.

39. Evaluate $g(x) = 3 - \frac{5}{6}x$ when $x = 12$.

40. Solve the system by substitution. Check your solution.

$y = x - 4$
$-2x + y = 18$

41. **MODELING REAL LIFE** The graph shows the distances d (in feet) that would break the women's long jump record at your school. Write and interpret an inequality that represents the distances.

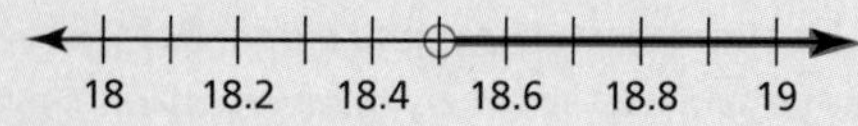

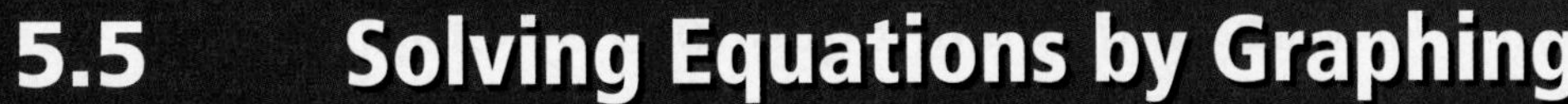

5.5 Solving Equations by Graphing

Learning Target Solve equations by graphing.

Success Criteria
- I can solve a linear equation by graphing.
- I can solve an absolute value equation by graphing.
- I can explain why the x-coordinate of a point where $y = f(x)$ and $y = g(x)$ intersect is a solution of $f(x) = g(x)$.

EXPLORE IT! Solving a Real-Life Problem

Work with a partner. Two autonomous underwater vehicles (AUVs) are mapping the ocean floor. One begins an ascent to the surface while the other begins a descent from the surface. The graph shows the depth of each AUV over time.

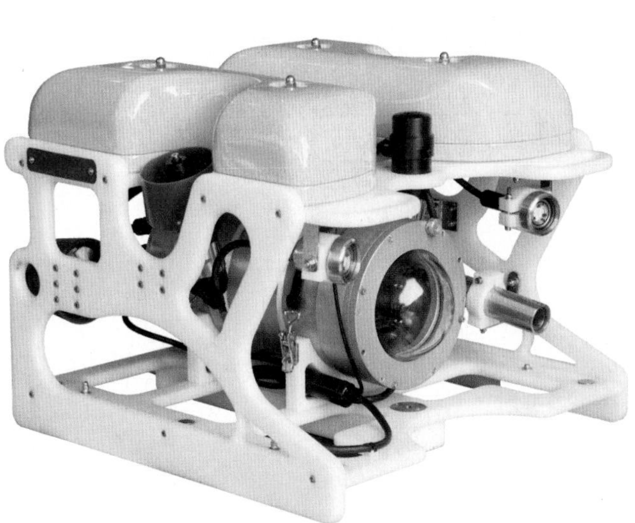

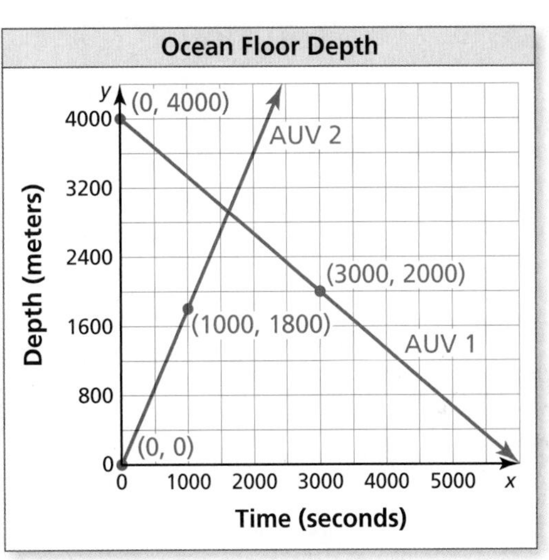

a. In the graph, does the line with a positive slope indicate the AUV is ascending or descending? Why?

b. Approximate the intersection point and explain what it represents.

c. What does each expression below represent in this situation? Explain your reasoning.

Expression 1: $-\frac{2}{3}x + 4000$

Expression 2: $\frac{9}{5}x$

d. What does the solution of $-\frac{2}{3}x + 4000 = \frac{9}{5}x$ represent? Solve the equation.

e. How can you find the solution of an equation in one variable using a graph? Explain why your method works.

> **Math Practice**
>
> **Label Axes**
>
> How does determining the number scales for the axes of the graph affect the approximation of the intersection point?

Solving Linear Equations by Graphing

KEY IDEA

Solving Equations by Graphing

Step 1 To solve the equation $f(x) = g(x)$, first write functions to represent each side of the equation.

$$f(x) = g(x)$$

$y = f(x)$ → $f(x)$; $g(x)$ ← $y = g(x)$

Step 2 Graph the functions. The x-value of an intersection point of the graphs of the functions is a solution of the equation $f(x) = g(x)$.

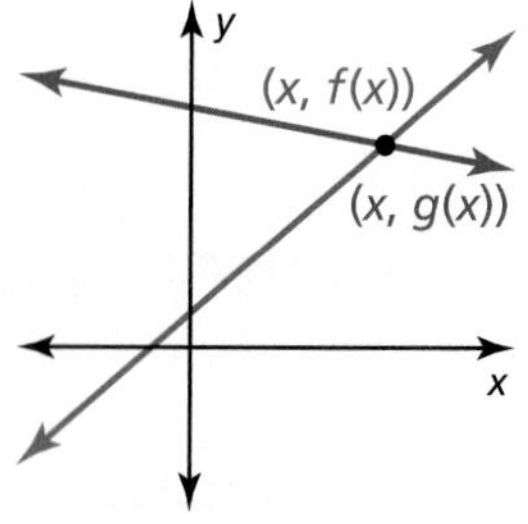

STUDY TIP

You can think of this as solving the system of equations

$y = f(x)$

$y = g(x)$

by graphing.

EXAMPLE 1 Solving a Linear Equation by Graphing

Solve $-x + 1 = 2x - 5$ by graphing. Check your solution.

SOLUTION

Step 1 Write functions to represent each side of the original equation.

$$-x + 1 = 2x - 5$$

$y = -x + 1$ → $-x + 1$; $2x - 5$ ← $y = 2x - 5$

Step 2 Graph the functions and find the intersection point.

The graphs intersect at $(2, -1)$.

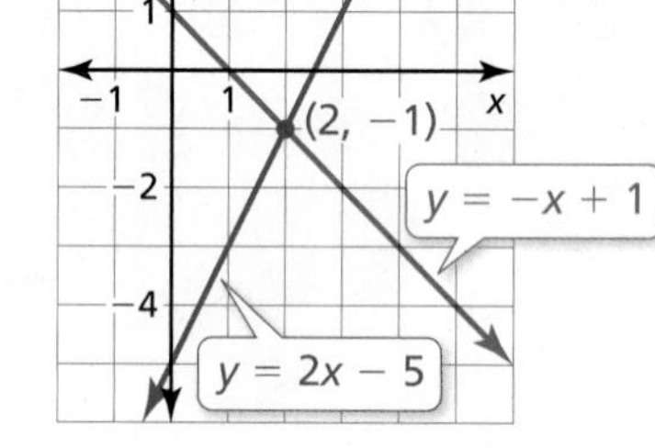

Check

$-x + 1 = 2x - 5$

$-(2) + 1 \stackrel{?}{=} 2(2) - 5$

$-1 = -1$ ✓

▶ So, the solution of the equation is $x = 2$.

SELF-ASSESSMENT

1 I do not understand. 2 I can do it with help. 3 I can do it on my own. 4 I can teach someone else.

Solve the equation by graphing. Check your solution.

1. $\frac{1}{2}x - 3 = 2x$
2. $-4 + 9x = -3x + 2$
3. $-3x - 2.5 = x - 2.5$

4. **WRITING** Explain why the x-coordinates of the points where the graphs of the equations $y = f(x)$ and $y = g(x)$ intersect are the solutions of the equation $f(x) = g(x)$.

5. **DIFFERENT WORDS, SAME QUESTION** Which is different? Find "both" answers.

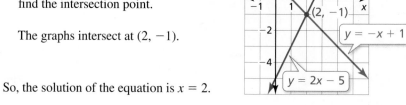

What is the solution of $x + 1 = 2x - 2$?	When are the values of $x + 1$ and $2x - 2$ equal?
At what point do the graphs of $y = x + 1$ and $y = 2x - 2$ intersect?	What is the x-value of the intersection point of the graphs of $y = x + 1$ and $y = 2x - 2$?

Solving Absolute Value Equations by Graphing

EXAMPLE 2 Solving an Absolute Value Equation by Graphing 

Solve $|x + 1| = |2x - 4|$ by graphing. Check your solution.

SOLUTION

ANOTHER WAY

You can also write the two related linear equations for the absolute value equation, and solve each by graphing.

$x + 1 = 2x - 4$

$x + 1 = -(2x - 4)$

Step 1 Write functions to represent each side of the original equation.

$$|x + 1| = |2x - 4|$$

$y = |x + 1|$ $y = |2x - 4|$

Step 2 Graph the functions and find the intersection points.

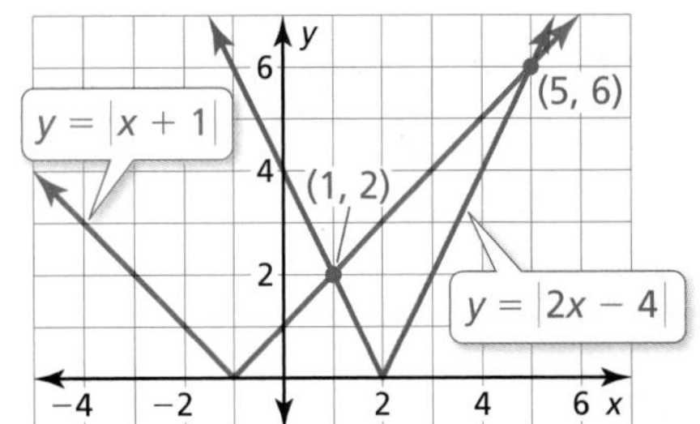

The graphs intersect at (1, 2) and (5, 6).

▶ So, the solutions of the equation are $x = 1$ and $x = 5$.

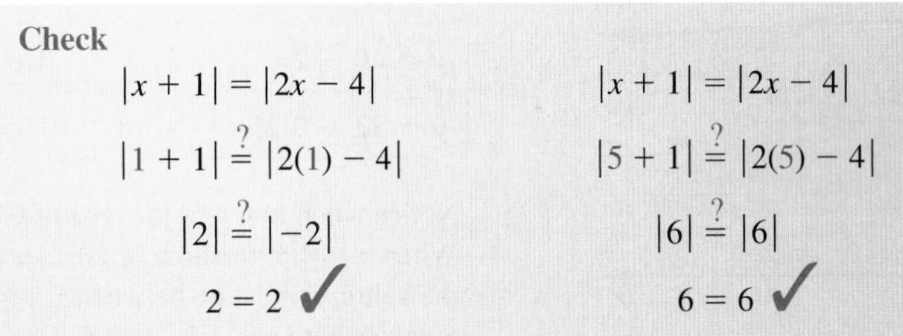

Check

$\lvert x + 1\rvert = \lvert 2x - 4\rvert$	$\lvert x + 1\rvert = \lvert 2x - 4\rvert$
$\lvert 1 + 1\rvert \stackrel{?}{=} \lvert 2(1) - 4\rvert$	$\lvert 5 + 1\rvert \stackrel{?}{=} \lvert 2(5) - 4\rvert$
$\lvert 2\rvert \stackrel{?}{=} \lvert -2\rvert$	$\lvert 6\rvert \stackrel{?}{=} \lvert 6\rvert$
$2 = 2$ ✓	$6 = 6$ ✓

SELF-ASSESSMENT 1 I do not understand. 2 I can do it with help. 3 I can do it on my own. 4 I can teach someone else.

Solve the equation by graphing. Check your solutions.

6. $|2x + 2| = |x - 2|$

7. $|x - 6| = |-x + 4|$

8. $|5 - x| = |3x - 15|$

9. **MP REASONING** The graphs of the equations $y = |x| - 1$ and $y = 3$ intersect at the points $(-4, 3)$ and $(4, 3)$. Without solving, find the solutions of the equation $|x| - 1 = 3$. Explain your reasoning.

10. **MP REASONING** Consider the graphs shown.

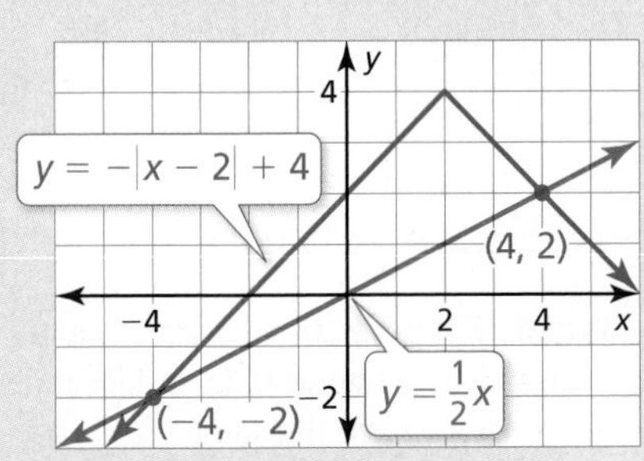

   a. Write an equation in one variable with solutions that are the x-coordinates of the intersection points of the graphs.

   b. Given an equation with an absolute value expression on one side and a linear expression on the other side, how many solutions can the equation have? Explain your reasoning.

Solving Real-Life Problems

EXAMPLE 3 Modeling Real Life

You are studying two glaciers. In 2020, Glacier A had an area of about 40 square miles and Glacier B had an area of about 32 square miles. You estimate that Glacier A will melt at a rate of 2 square miles per decade and Glacier B will melt at a rate of 0.25 square mile per decade. In what year will the areas of the glaciers be the same?

SOLUTION

Step 1 Use a verbal model to write an equation that represents the problem. Let x be the number of decades after 2020. Then write functions to represent each side of the equation.

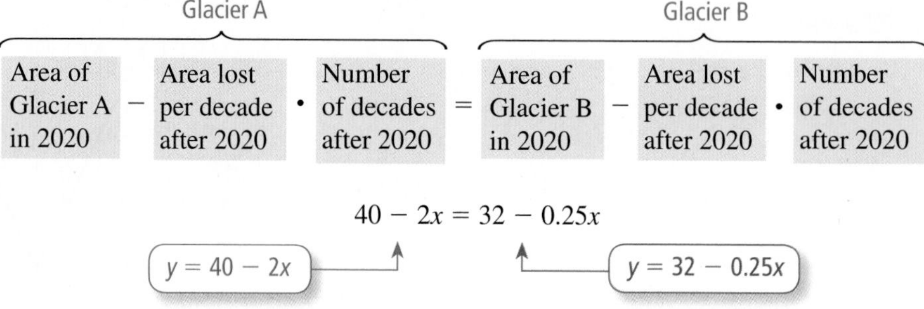

Glacier A
Glacier B
Area of Glacier A in 2020
−
Area lost per decade after 2020
•
Number of decades after 2020
=
Area of Glacier B in 2020
−
Area lost per decade after 2020
•
Number of decades after 2020

$$40 - 2x = 32 - 0.25x$$

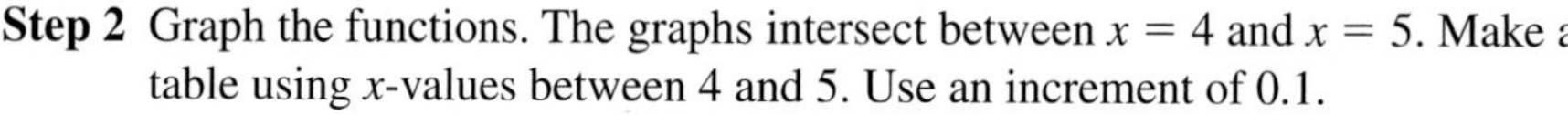

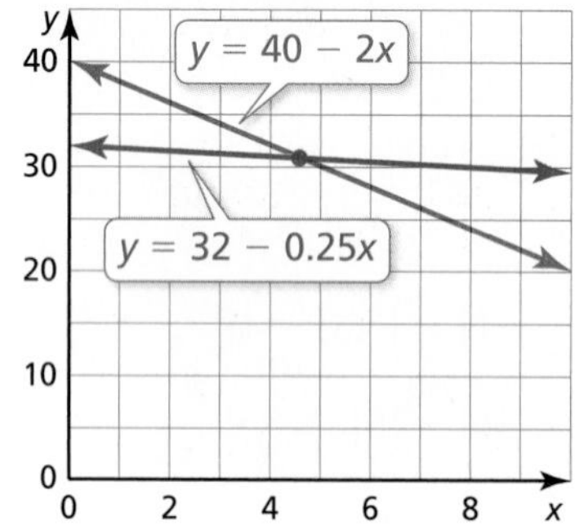

Step 2 Graph the functions. The graphs intersect between $x = 4$ and $x = 5$. Make a table using x-values between 4 and 5. Use an increment of 0.1.

x	4.1	4.2	4.3	4.4	4.5	4.6	4.7
$y = 40 - 2x$	31.8	31.6	31.4	31.2	31	30.8	30.6
$y = 32 - 0.25x$	30.98	30.95	30.93	30.9	30.88	30.85	30.83

Notice when $x = 4.5$, the area of Glacier A is greater than the area of Glacier B. When $x = 4.6$, the area of Glacier A is less than the area of Glacier B. So, the solution must be between $x = 4.5$ and $x = 4.6$. Make another table using x-values between 4.5 and 4.6. Use an increment of 0.01.

x	4.51	4.52	4.53	4.54	4.55	4.56	4.57	4.58
$y = 40 - 2x$	30.98	30.96	30.94	30.92	30.9	30.88	30.86	30.84
$y = 32 - 0.25x$	30.87	30.87	30.87	30.87	30.86	30.86	30.86	30.86

When $x = 4.57$, the corresponding y-values are about the same. So, the graphs intersect at about (4.57, 30.86).

▶ So, the areas of the glaciers will be the same after about 4.57 decades, or around the year 2066.

SELF-ASSESSMENT

1 I do not understand. 2 I can do it with help. 3 I can do it on my own. 4 I can teach someone else.

11. WHAT IF? In 2020, Glacier C had an area of about 30 square miles. You estimate that it will melt at a rate of 0.45 square mile per decade. In what year will the areas of Glacier A and Glacier C be the same?

5.5 Practice WITH CalcChat® AND CalcView®

GO DIGITAL

In Exercises 1 and 2, use the graph to solve the equation. Check your solution.

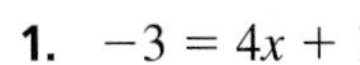

1. $-3 = 4x + 1$

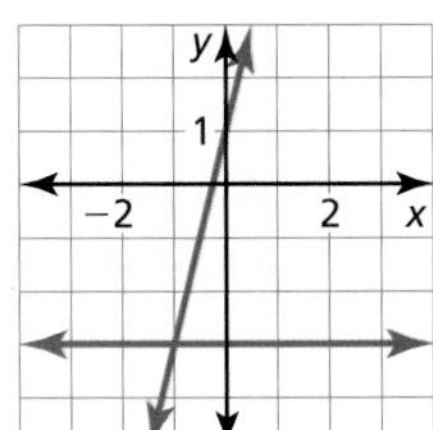

2. $-\frac{3}{2}x - 2 = -4x + 3$

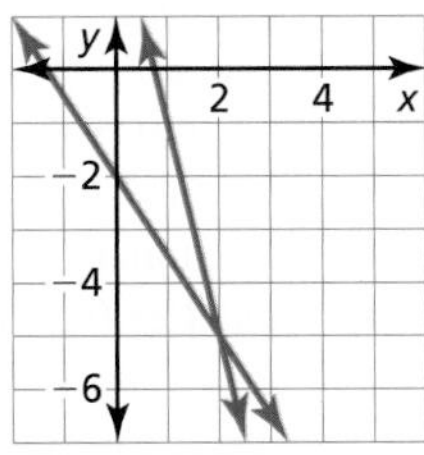

In Exercises 3–10, solve the equation by graphing. Check your solution. *Example 1*

3. $x + 4 = -x$

4. $-2x + 6 = 5x - 1$

5. $\frac{1}{2}x - 2 = 9 - 5x$

6. $-5 + \frac{1}{4}x = 3x + 6$

7. $5x - 7 = 2(x + 1)$

8. $-6(x + 4) = -3x - 6$

9. $\frac{4}{5}x + \frac{7}{5} = 3x - 3$

10. $-x + 2.5 = 2x - 0.5$

In Exercises 11–14, solve the equation by graphing. Determine whether the equation has *one solution*, *no solution*, or *infinitely many solutions*.

11. $-2x - 3 = 2(x - 2)$

12. $-4(2 - x) = 4x - 8$

13. $\frac{1}{2}(8x + 3) = 4x + \frac{3}{2}$

14. $-x - 5 = -\frac{1}{3}(3x + 5)$

In Exercises 15–26, solve the equation by graphing. Check your solutions. *Example 2*

15. $|2x| = |x + 3|$

16. $|2x - 6| = |x|$

17. $|-x + 4| = |2x - 2|$

18. $|2x + 5| = |-2x + 1|$

19. $|2x - 3| = x + 3$

20. $|x + 1| = -4x + 6$

21. $|2x + 6| = 4$

22. $|-3x + 9| + 2 = 1$

23. $|x - 3| = 2|x|$

24. $4|x + 2| = |2x + 7|$

25. $\left|-\frac{2}{3}x + 1\right| = \left|\frac{2}{3}x + 5\right|$

26. $|-3x + 1.5| = |x + 1.5|$

27. MP **STRUCTURE** Use the graph to solve $|2x + 4| = |x - 1|$. Check your solutions.

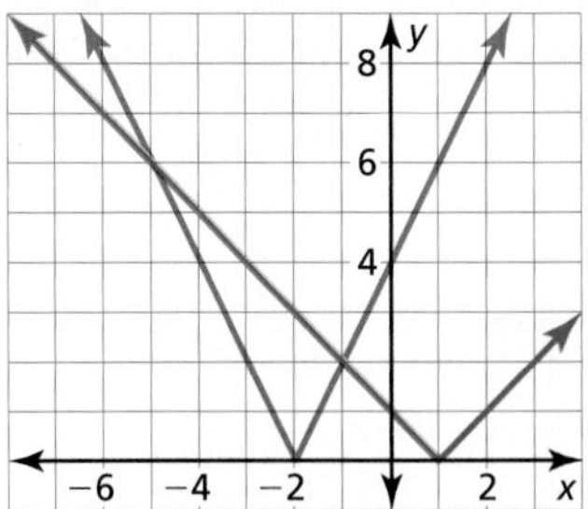

28. **ERROR ANALYSIS** Describe and correct the error in solving $-\frac{1}{3}x + 2 = \frac{2}{3}x + 5$ by graphing.

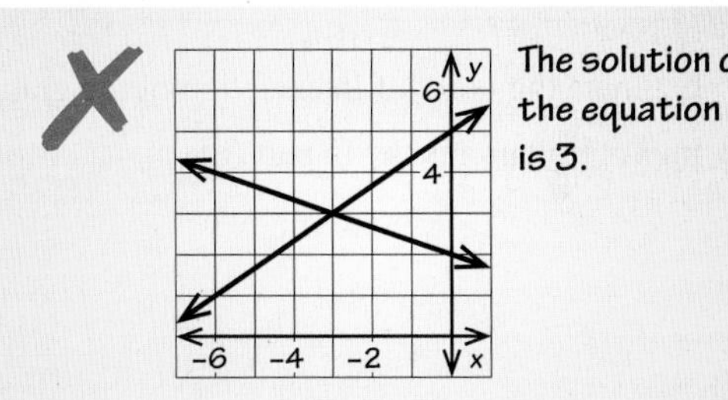

The solution of the equation is 3.

MP **USING TOOLS** **In Exercises 29 and 30, use technology to solve the equation.**

29. $0.7x + 0.5 = -0.2x - 1.3$

30. $2.1x + 0.6 = -1.4x + 6.9$

31. **MODELING REAL LIFE** There are about 34 million gallons of water in Reservoir A and about 38 million gallons in Reservoir B. During a drought, Reservoir A loses about 0.8 million gallons per month and Reservoir B loses about 1.1 million gallons per month. After how many months will the reservoirs contain the same amount of water? *Example 3*

32. **MODELING REAL LIFE** Your dog is 16 years old in dog years. Your cat is 28 years old in cat years. For every human year, your dog ages by 7 dog years and your cat ages by 4 cat years. In how many human years will both pets be the same age in their respective types of years?

33. MAKING AN ARGUMENT The graphs of $y = -x + 4$ and $y = 2x - 8$ intersect at (4, 0). Your friend says the solution of the equation $-x + 4 = 2x - 8$ is (4, 0). Is your friend correct? Explain.

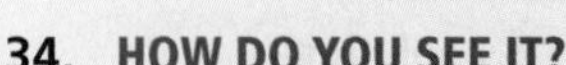

34. HOW DO YOU SEE IT?

The graph shows the total revenue and expenses of a company x years after it opens for business.

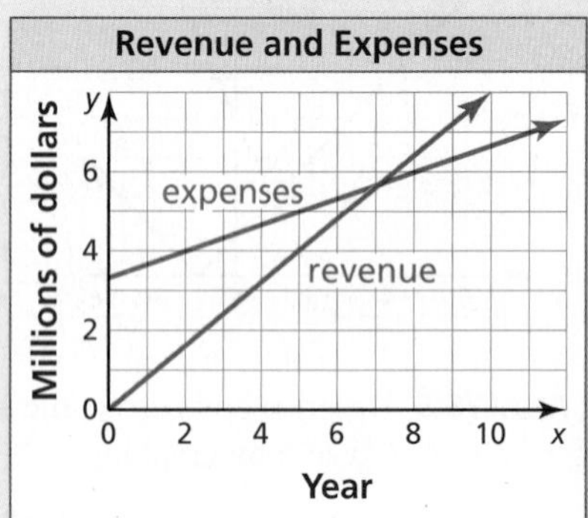

a. Estimate the point of intersection of the graphs.

b. Interpret your answer in part (a).

35. OPEN-ENDED Find values for m and b so that the solution of $mx + b = -2x - 1$ is $x = -3$.

36. ABSTRACT REASONING Determine the sign of the solution of $ax + b = cx + d$ in each situation. Justify your reasoning with a graph.

a. $0 < b < d$ and $a < c$ **b.** $d < b < 0$ and $a < c$

37. DIG DEEPER You and your friend race across a field to a fence and back. Your friend has a 50-meter head start. The equations shown represent you and your friend's distances d (in meters) from the fence t seconds after the race begins.

You: $d = |-5t + 100|$

Your friend: $d = \left|-\frac{10}{3}t + 50\right|$

a. How long does it take you to catch up to your friend?

b. Who finishes the race first? How much sooner does this person finish? Explain.

38. THOUGHT PROVOKING

Explain how you can use a graph to solve $\frac{1}{2}x + 4 \le -\frac{1}{4}x + 1$.

REVIEW & REFRESH

WATCH

In Exercises 39 and 40, use the graphs of f and g to describe the transformation from the graph of f to the graph of g.

39. $f(x) = x - 5$; $g(x) = f(x) + 2$

40. $f(x) = \frac{1}{2}x - 2$; $g(x) = f(x - 1)$

41. OPEN-ENDED Give an example of a real-life data set that shows a negative correlation.

42. Use the graph to solve $|x - 4| = |3x|$. Check your solutions.

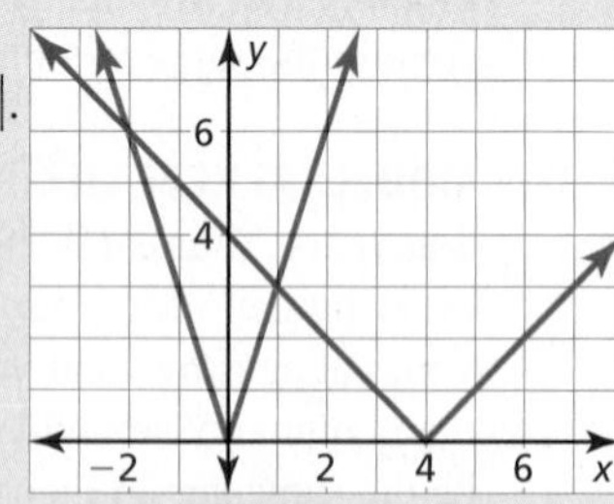

43. Tell whether $n = -5$ is a solution of the inequality $14 \ge -2n + 4$.

In Exercises 44 and 45, graph the inequality.

44. $n \ge 9$ **45.** $c < -6$

46. MODELING REAL LIFE You sell small and large candles at a craft fair. You collect \$144 selling a total of 28 candles. How many of each type of candle did you sell?

In Exercises 47–50, solve the system using any method. Explain your choice of method.

47. $y = -x + 8$
$6x - 2y = 16$

48. $-3x - 3y = 4$
$1.5x + 1.5y = -2$

49. $2x + 5y = -9$
$-2x - y = 17$

50. $y = \frac{3}{2}x + 1$
$y = -\frac{1}{4}x + 8$

51. Solve $3x - 1 = -x + 7$ by graphing. Check your solution.

52. Write an equation in point-slope form of the line that passes through $(9, -2)$ and has a slope of $-\frac{2}{3}$.

53. Determine whether the equation $y = 2x(x - 5)$ represents a *linear* or *nonlinear* function. Explain.

5.6 Graphing Linear Inequalities in Two Variables

Learning Target Graph linear inequalities in two variables.

Success Criteria
- I can determine whether an ordered pair is a solution of a linear inequality in two variables.
- I can graph linear inequalities in two variables.
- I can interpret solutions of a linear inequality in two variables in a real-life situation.

EXPLORE IT! Graphing a Linear Inequality in Two Variables

Work with a partner. You have \$60 to spend on sand and gravel to make a pen for your dog.

a. Use an inequality to represent the situation.

Math Practice

Interpret a Solution What is the meaning of each solution (x, y) in this situation?

b. Identify several solutions (x, y) of the inequality. Plot your solutions in the coordinate plane.

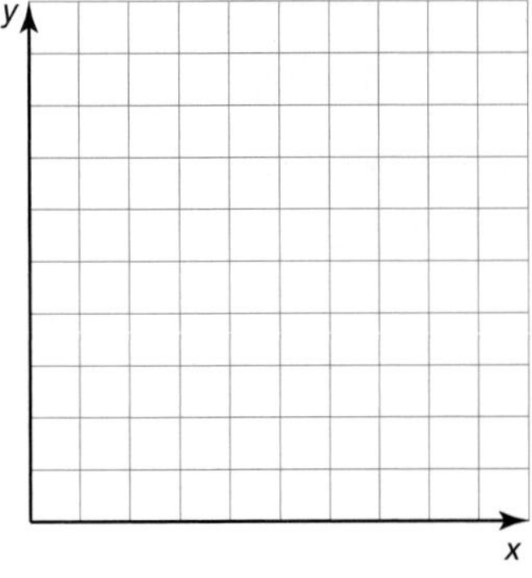

c. Graph every possible solution of the inequality in the coordinate plane. Explain your method.

d. Use technology to graph the inequality. Compare the result with your graph in part (b).

e. Use technology to graph each inequality.

i. $y < x + 1.5$ **ii.** $y \geq \frac{1}{4}x - 3$

iii. $x + y > 7$ **iv.** $4x + 2y \leq 9$

f. Explain how to graph a linear inequality in two variables without using technology.

Linear Inequalities

Vocabulary 

linear inequality in two variables, *p. 276*
solution of a linear inequality in two variables, *p. 276*
graph of a linear inequality, *p. 276*
half-planes, *p. 276*

A **linear inequality in two variables**, x and y, can be written in one of the following forms where a, b, and c are real numbers.

$ax + by < c \qquad ax + by \leq c$

$ax + by > c \qquad ax + by \geq c$

A **solution of a linear inequality in two variables** is an ordered pair (x, y) that makes the inequality true.

EXAMPLE 1 Checking Solutions 

Tell whether the ordered pair is a solution of the inequality.

a. $2x + y < -3$; $(-1, 9)$ **b.** $x - 3y \geq 8$; $(2, -2)$

SOLUTION

a. $2x + y < -3$ Write the inequality.

$2(-1) + 9 \overset{?}{<} -3$ Substitute -1 for x and 9 for y.

$7 \not< -3$ ✗ Simplify. 7 is *not* less than -3.

▶ So, $(-1, 9)$ is *not* a solution of the inequality.

b. $x - 3y \geq 8$ Write the inequality.

$2 - 3(-2) \overset{?}{\geq} 8$ Substitute 2 for x and -2 for y.

$8 \geq 8$ ✓ Simplify. 8 is equal to 8.

▶ So, $(2, -2)$ is a solution of the inequality.

SELF-ASSESSMENT 1 I do not understand. 2 I can do it with help. 3 I can do it on my own. 4 I can teach someone else.

Tell whether the ordered pair is a solution of the inequality.

1. $x + y > 0$; $(-2, 2)$

2. $4x - y \geq 5$; $(0, 0)$

3. $5x - 2y \leq -1$; $(-4, -1)$

4. $-2x - 3y < 15$; $(5.5, -7)$

Graphing Linear Inequalities in Two Variables

The **graph of a linear inequality** in two variables shows all the solutions of the inequality in a coordinate plane. A dashed boundary line means that points on the line are *not* solutions. A solid boundary line means that points on the line are solutions.

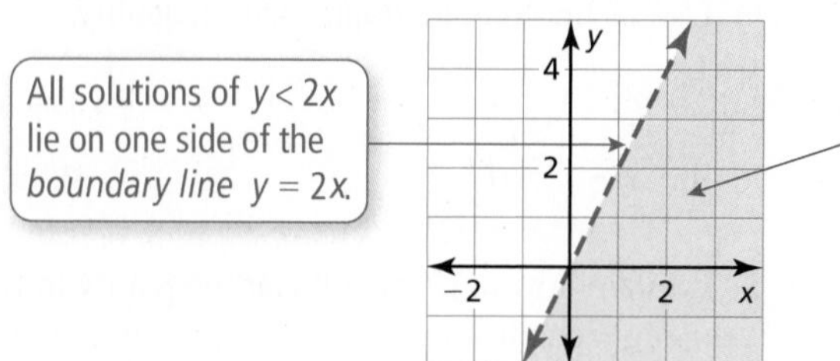

All solutions of $y < 2x$ lie on one side of the boundary line $y = 2x$.
y
4
2
−2
2
x
The boundary line divides the coordinate plane into two **half-planes**. The shaded half-plane is the graph of $y < 2x$.

KEY IDEA

Graphing a Linear Inequality in Two Variables

Step 1 Graph the boundary line for the inequality. Use a dashed line for < or >. Use a solid line for ≤ or ≥.

Step 2 Test a point that is not on the boundary line to determine whether it is a solution of the inequality.

Step 3 When the test point is a solution, shade the half-plane that contains the point. When the test point is *not* a solution, shade the half-plane that does *not* contain the point.

EXAMPLE 2 Graphing a Linear Inequality in Two Variables

Graph $y \leq 2$ in a coordinate plane.

SOLUTION

Step 1 Graph $y = 2$. Use a solid line because the inequality symbol is ≤.

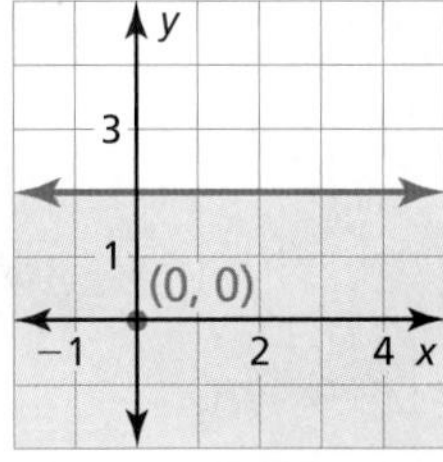

Step 2 Test (0, 0).

$y \leq 2$ Write the inequality.

$0 \leq 2$ ✓ Substitute.

Step 3 Because (0, 0) is a solution, shade the half-plane that contains (0, 0).

STUDY TIP

It is often convenient to use the origin as a test point. However, you must choose a different test point when the origin is on the boundary line.

EXAMPLE 3 Graphing a Linear Inequality in Two Variables

Graph $-x + 2y > 2$ in a coordinate plane.

SOLUTION

Step 1 Graph $-x + 2y = 2$, or $y = \frac{1}{2}x + 1$. Use a dashed line because the inequality symbol is >.

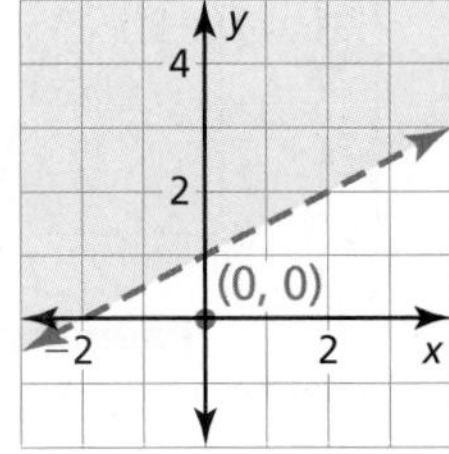

Step 2 Test (0, 0).

$-x + 2y > 2$ Write the inequality.

$-(0) + 2(0) \overset{?}{>} 2$ Substitute.

$0 \not> 2$ ✗ Simplify.

Step 3 Because (0, 0) is *not* a solution, shade the half-plane that does *not* contain (0, 0).

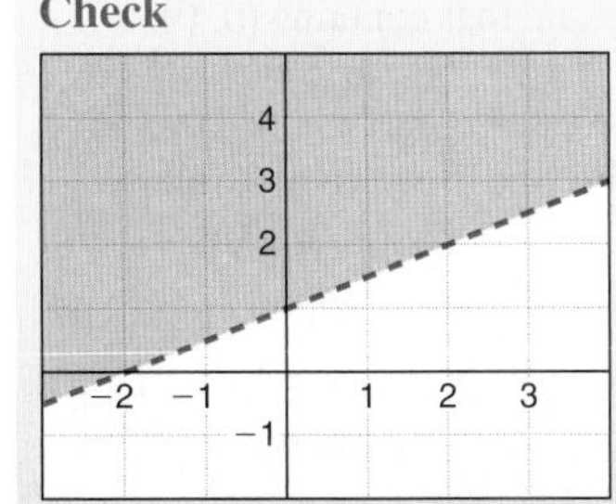

SELF-ASSESSMENT

1 I do not understand. 2 I can do it with help. 3 I can do it on my own. 4 I can teach someone else.

Graph the inequality in a coordinate plane.

5. $y > -1$

6. $x \leq -4$

7. $x + y \leq -4$

8. $x - 2y < 0$

9. $x \leq 0.75y - 3$

10. $\frac{3}{4} \geq -2x + \frac{1}{2}y$

11. WRITING When determining which half-plane to shade in the graph of an inequality in two variables, why is it important to test a point that is not on the boundary line?

Solving Real-Life Problems

EXAMPLE 4 **Modeling Real Life**

You can spend at most \$10 on grapes and apples for a fruit salad. Grapes cost \$2.50 per pound, and apples cost \$1 per pound. Write and graph an inequality that represents the amounts of grapes and apples you can buy. Identify and interpret two solutions of the inequality.

SOLUTION

1. **Understand the Problem** You know the most that you can spend and the prices per pound for grapes and apples. You are asked to write and graph an inequality and then identify and interpret two solutions.
2. **Make a Plan** Use a verbal model to write an inequality that represents the problem. Then graph the inequality. Use the graph to identify two solutions. Then interpret the solutions.
3. **Solve and Check**

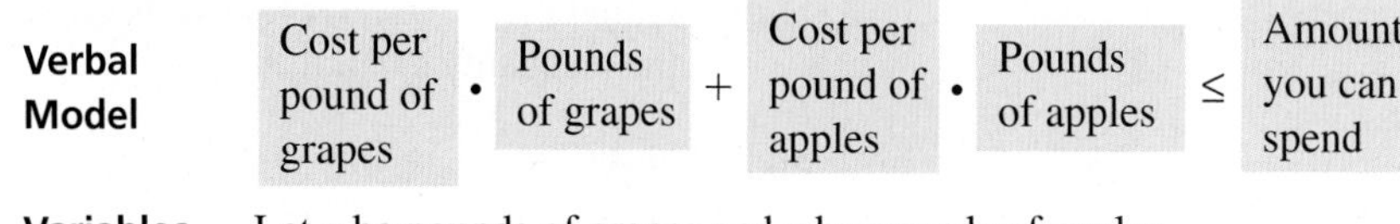

Verbal Model Cost per pound of grapes • Pounds of grapes + Cost per pound of apples • Pounds of apples ≤ Amount you can spend

Variables Let x be pounds of grapes and y be pounds of apples.

Inequality $2.50 \cdot x + 1 \cdot y \leq 10$

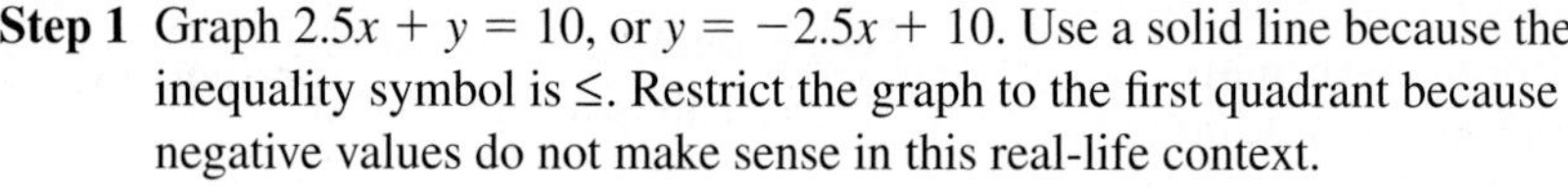

Step 1 Graph $2.5x + y = 10$, or $y = -2.5x + 10$. Use a solid line because the inequality symbol is ≤. Restrict the graph to the first quadrant because negative values do not make sense in this real-life context.

Fruit Salad

Pounds of apples (y: 0–10); Pounds of grapes (x: 0–6); points (1, 6) and (2, 5)

Step 2 Test (0, 0).

$$2.5x + y \leq 10 \quad \text{Write the inequality.}$$

$$2.5(0) + 0 \overset{?}{\leq} 10 \quad \text{Substitute.}$$

$$0 \leq 10 \checkmark \quad \text{Simplify.}$$

Step 3 Because (0, 0) is a solution, shade the half-plane that contains (0, 0).

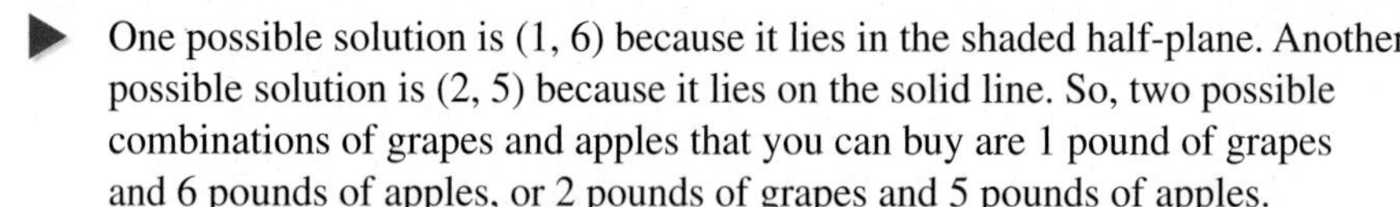

▶ One possible solution is (1, 6) because it lies in the shaded half-plane. Another possible solution is (2, 5) because it lies on the solid line. So, two possible combinations of grapes and apples that you can buy are 1 pound of grapes and 6 pounds of apples, or 2 pounds of grapes and 5 pounds of apples.

Check Check your solutions by substituting them into the original inequality.

$$2.5x + y \leq 10 \qquad 2.5x + y \leq 10$$

$$2.5(1) + 6 \overset{?}{\leq} 10 \qquad 2.5(2) + 5 \overset{?}{\leq} 10$$

$$8.5 \leq 10 \checkmark \qquad 10 \leq 10 \checkmark$$

SELF-ASSESSMENT

1 I do not understand. 2 I can do it with help. 3 I can do it on my own. 4 I can teach someone else.

12. **MODELING REAL LIFE** You can spend at most \$12 on red peppers and tomatoes for salsa. Red peppers cost \$4 per pound, and tomatoes cost \$3 per pound. Write and graph an inequality that represents the amounts of red peppers and tomatoes you can buy. Identify and interpret two solutions of the inequality.

5.6 Practice WITH CalcChat® AND CalcView®

In Exercises 1–8, tell whether the ordered pair is a solution of the inequality. ▶ *Example 1*

1. $x + y < 7$; $(2, 3)$

2. $x - y \le 0$; $(5, 4)$

3. $x + 3y \ge -2$; $(-9, 1)$

4. $8x + y > -6$; $(-1, 2)$

5. $-6x + 4y \le 6$; $(-3, -3)$

6. $3x - 5y \ge 0.5$; $(-1.5, -1)$

7. $-x - 6y > 12$; $\left(-8, -\frac{2}{3}\right)$

8. $-4x + \frac{1}{2}y < -3$; $\left(\frac{1}{4}, -5\right)$

In Exercises 9–14, tell whether the ordered pair is a solution of the inequality whose graph is shown.

9. $(0, -1)$

10. $(-1, 3)$

11. $(1, 4)$

12. $(0, 0)$

13. $(3, 3)$

14. $\left(2, 1\frac{1}{2}\right)$

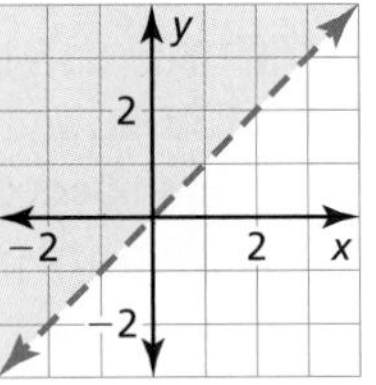

In Exercises 15–20, graph the inequality in a coordinate plane. ▶ *Example 2*

15. $y \le 5$

16. $y > 6$

17. $x < 2$

18. $x \ge -3$

19. $y > -3\frac{1}{2}$

20. $x < 7.5$

In Exercises 21–28, graph the inequality in a coordinate plane. ▶ *Example 3*

21. $y > -2x - 4$

22. $y \ge -x - 1$

23. $-4x + y < -7$

24. $3x - y \ge 5$

25. $5x - 2y \le 6$

26. $-x + 4y > -12$

27. $-4.5y \ge 27x$

28. $\frac{4}{3}x + y < 0$

ERROR ANALYSIS In Exercises 29 and 30, describe and correct the error in graphing the inequality.

29. $y < -x + 1$

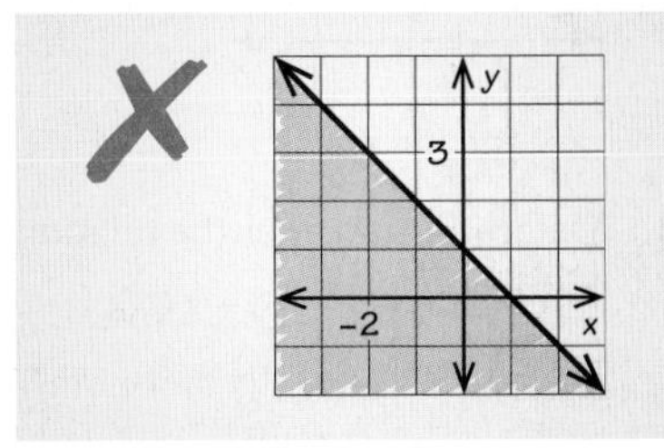

30. $y \le 3x - 2$

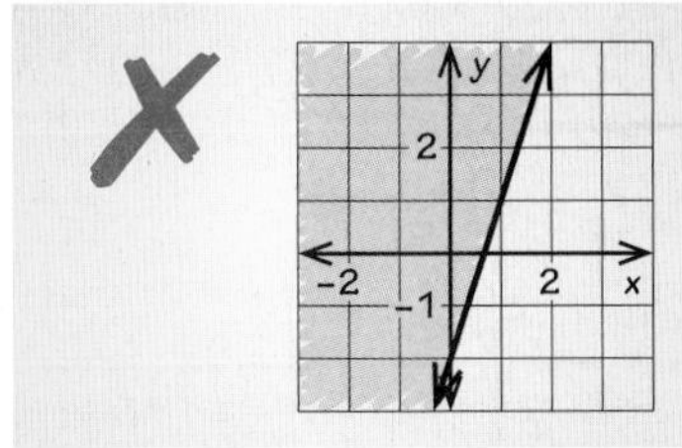

31. MODELING REAL LIFE A carpenter has at most \$250 to spend on lumber. The inequality $8x + 12y \le 250$ represents the numbers x of 2-by-8 boards and the numbers y of 4-by-4 boards the carpenter can buy. Can the carpenter buy twelve 2-by-8 boards and fourteen 4-by-4 boards? Explain.

32. MODELING REAL LIFE The inequality $3x + 2y \ge 93$ represents the numbers x of multiple-choice questions and the numbers y of matching questions you can answer correctly to receive an A on a test. You answer 20 multiple-choice questions and 18 matching questions correctly. Do you receive an A on the test? Explain.

In Exercises 33 and 34, write an inequality that represents the graph.

33.

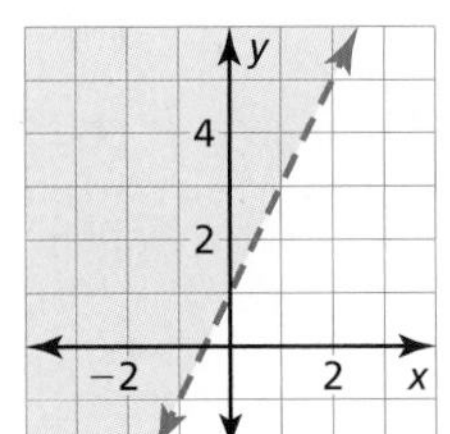

34.

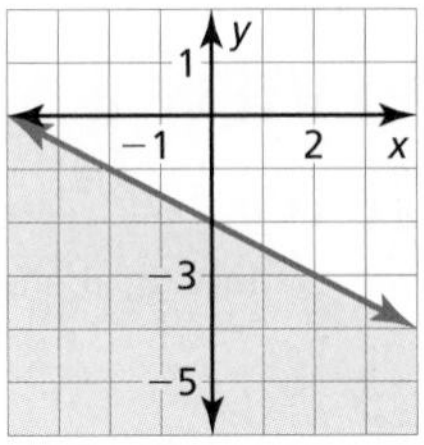

35. MODELING REAL LIFE You have at most \$25 to spend on in-app purchases for a game. Sets of extra lives cost \$1 each, and bags of gold cost \$5 each. Write and graph an inequality that represents the numbers of each item you can buy. Identify and interpret two solutions of the inequality. ▶ *Example 4*

36. MODELING REAL LIFE The total ticket sales from a school play must be at least \$1500 to cover the expenses of producing the play. Write and graph an inequality that represents how many adult and student tickets the club must sell. Identify and interpret two solutions of the inequality.

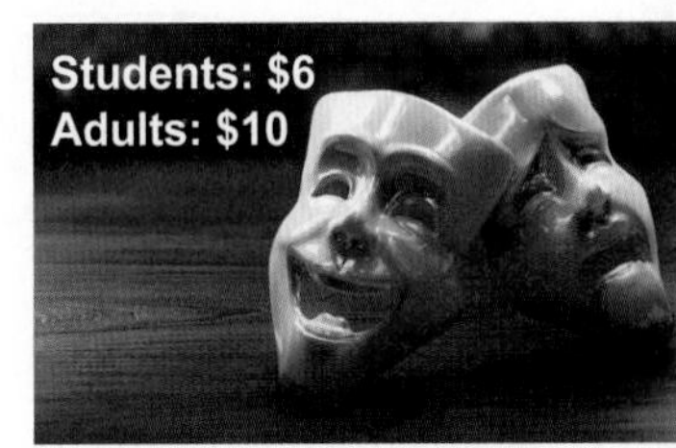

37. MP STRUCTURE Complete the inequality $y \;\square\; mx + b$, where $b > 0$, so that the graph of the inequality has a dashed boundary line and $(0, 0)$ is a solution.

38. HOW DO YOU SEE IT?
Match each inequality with its graph.

a. $3x - 2y \leq 6$ **b.** $3x - 2y < 6$

c. $3x - 2y > 6$ **d.** $3x - 2y \geq 6$

A. 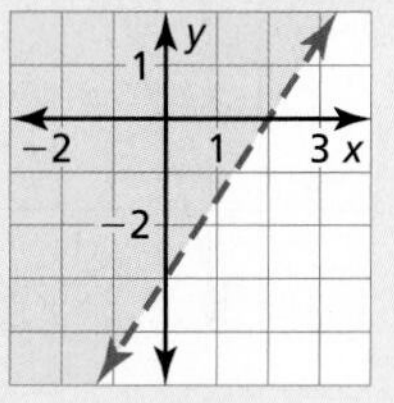

B. 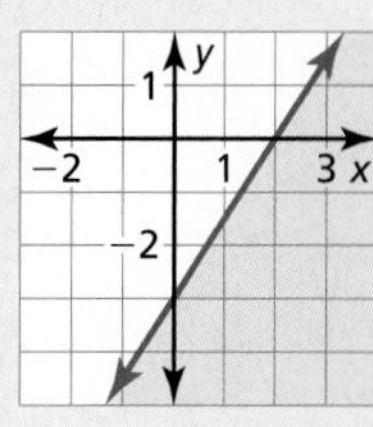

C. 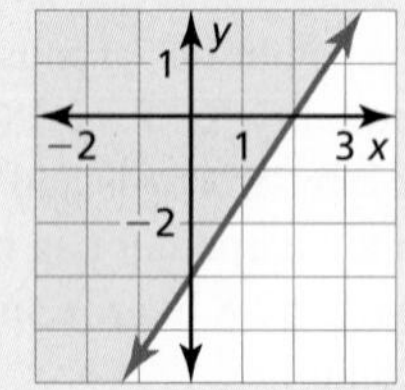

D. 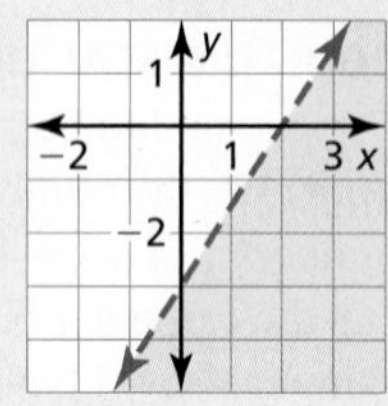

39. MAKING AN ARGUMENT Your friend says you cannot use (0, 0) as the test point when graphing an inequality whose boundary line represents a proportional relationship. Is your friend correct? Explain.

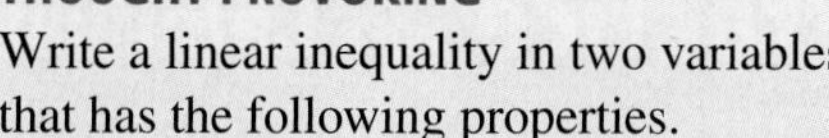

40. THOUGHT PROVOKING
Write a linear inequality in two variables that has the following properties.

- (0, 0), (0, −1), and (0, 1) are *not* solutions.
- (1, 1), (3, −1), and (−1, 3) are solutions.

CRITICAL THINKING In Exercises 41 and 42, write and graph an inequality whose graph is described by the given information.

41. • (2, 5) and (−3, −5) lie on the boundary line.
• (6, 5) and (−2, −3) are solutions.

42. • (−7, −16) and (1, 8) lie on the boundary line.
• (−7, 0) and (3, 14) are *not* solutions.

43. **DIG DEEPER** Two large boxes and three small boxes weigh 270 pounds. One large box and four small boxes weigh 235 pounds.

a. The weight limit on an elevator is 2000 pounds. Write and graph an inequality that represents the numbers of large and small boxes a 200-pound delivery person can take on the elevator.

b. Explain why some solutions of the inequality may not be practical in real life.

REVIEW & REFRESH

WATCH

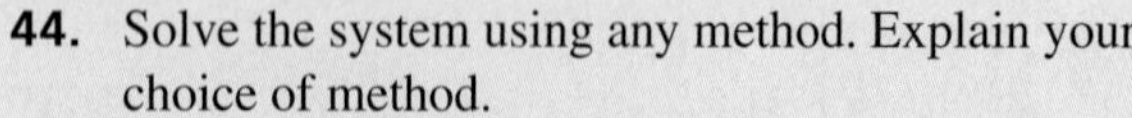

44. Solve the system using any method. Explain your choice of method.

$$y = \frac{4}{5}x - 2$$
$$-8x + 10y = -20$$

45. Approximate when the function is positive, negative, increasing, or decreasing. Then describe the end behavior of the function.

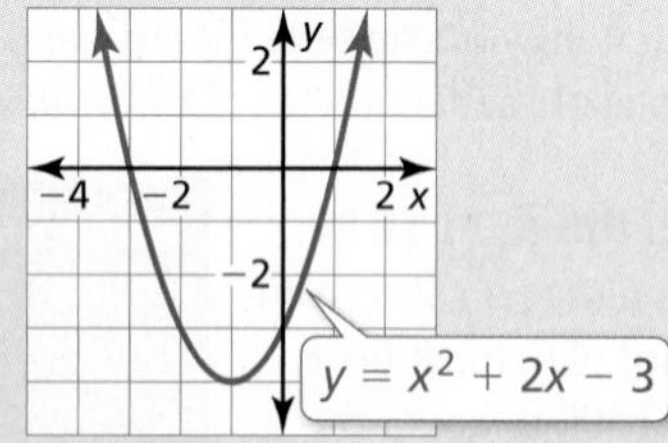

46. Graph $x - 5y > -10$ in a coordinate plane.

In Exercises 47 and 48, write the next three terms of the arithmetic sequence.

47. $-5, -8, -11, -14, -17, \ldots$

48. $-\frac{3}{2}, -\frac{1}{2}, \frac{1}{2}, \frac{3}{2}, \frac{5}{2}, \ldots$

49. WRITING For what values of b can you solve the linear system $7x + 3y = -1$ and $9x + by = -15$ by elimination without multiplying first? Explain.

50. Write 3.26×10^7 in standard form.

In Exercises 51 and 52, solve the equation by graphing. Check your solution(s).

51. $\frac{1}{3}x - 4 = -3x + 6$ **52.** $|x + 5| = |2x + 1|$

In Exercises 53 and 54, write an inequality that represents the graph.

53. 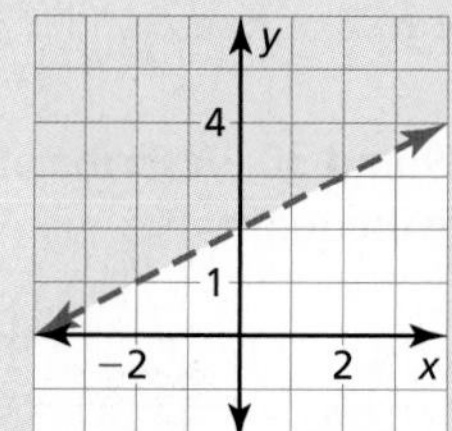

54. 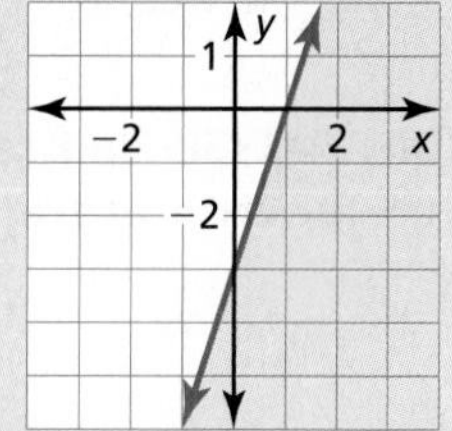

55. Determine whether the relation is a function. Explain.

(−5, 2), (−7, 4), (−3, 0), (−4, 3), (−5, 4)

5.7 Systems of Linear Inequalities

Learning Target Graph and write systems of linear inequalities.

Success Criteria

- I can determine whether an ordered pair is a solution of a system of linear inequalities.
- I can graph systems of linear inequalities.
- I can write systems of linear inequalities from a graph.
- I can solve real-life problems using systems of linear inequalities.

EXPLORE IT! Writing Systems of Linear Inequalities

Work with a partner.

a. Write two linear equations: one with a positive slope and a nonzero y-intercept, and one with a negative slope and a nonzero y-intercept. Graph the equations in the same coordinate plane.

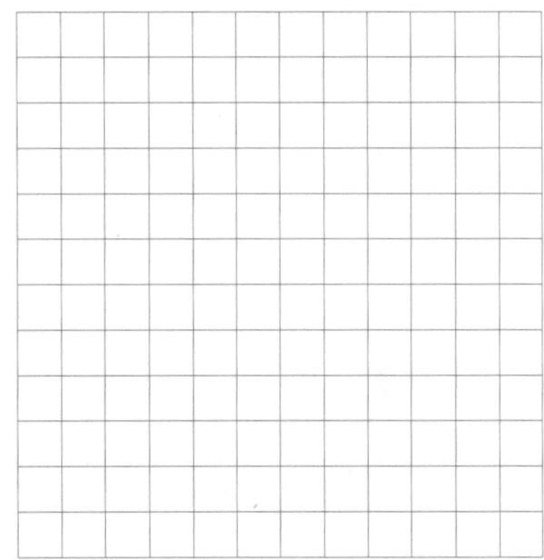

b. How many regions are formed by the graphs of the equations? Shade and label each region a different color.

c. How can you represent a region algebraically? Use your method to represent each region in part (b).

d. Use your method to represent the shaded region of each graph algebraically.

i.

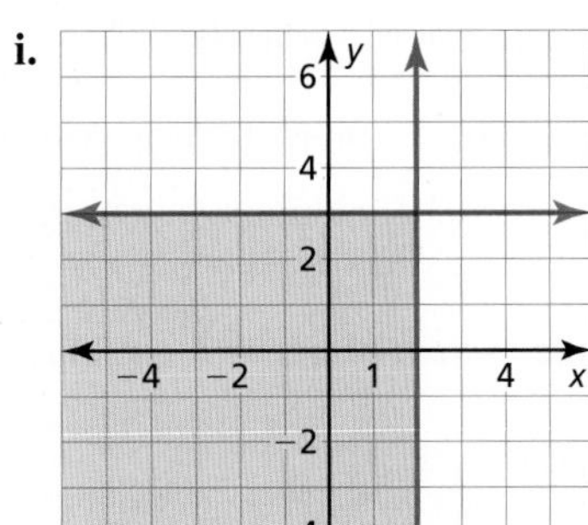

ii.

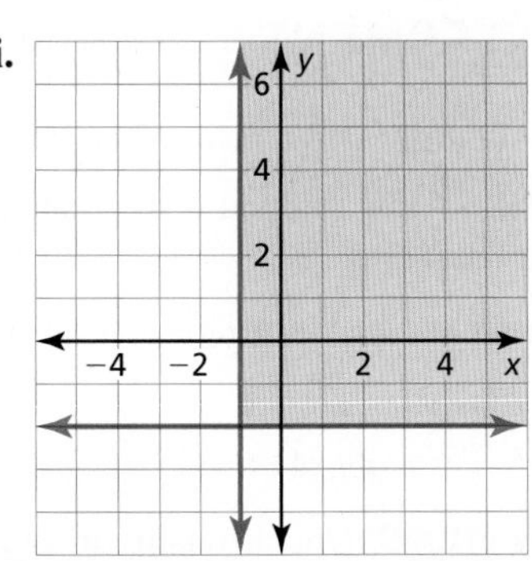

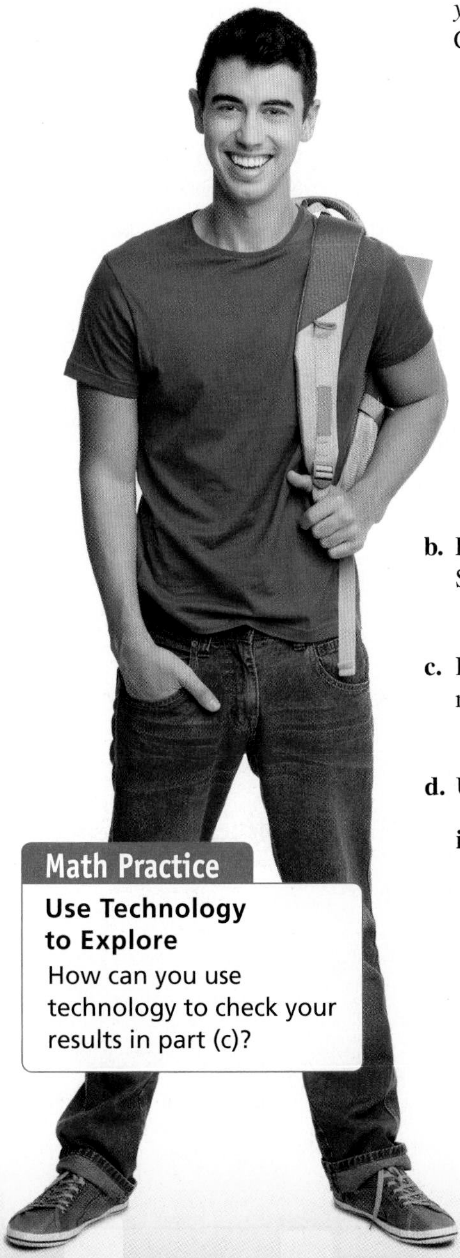

Math Practice

Use Technology to Explore

How can you use technology to check your results in part (c)?

Systems of Linear Inequalities

Vocabulary 

system of linear inequalities, *p. 282*
solution of a system of linear inequalities, *p. 282*
graph of a system of linear inequalities, *p. 283*

A **system of linear inequalities** is a set of two or more linear inequalities in the same variables. An example is shown below.

$y < x + 2$ Inequality 1
$y \geq 2x - 1$ Inequality 2

A **solution of a system of linear inequalities** in two variables is an ordered pair that is a solution of each inequality in the system.

EXAMPLE 1 Checking Solutions 

Tell whether each ordered pair is a solution of the system of linear inequalities.

$y < 2x$ Inequality 1
$y \geq x + 1$ Inequality 2

a. (3, 5) **b.** (−2, 0)

SOLUTION

a. Substitute 3 for x and 5 for y in each inequality.

Inequality 1	Inequality 2
$y < 2x$	$y \geq x + 1$
$5 \overset{?}{<} 2(3)$	$5 \overset{?}{\geq} 3 + 1$
$5 < 6$ ✓	$5 \geq 4$ ✓

▶ Because the ordered pair (3, 5) is a solution of each inequality, it is a solution of the system.

b. Substitute −2 for x and 0 for y in each inequality.

Inequality 1	Inequality 2
$y < 2x$	$y \geq x + 1$
$0 \overset{?}{<} 2(-2)$	$0 \overset{?}{\geq} -2 + 1$
$0 \not< -4$ ✗	$0 \geq -1$ ✓

▶ Because (−2, 0) is not a solution of each inequality, it is *not* a solution of the system.

SELF-ASSESSMENT

1 I do not understand. 2 I can do it with help. 3 I can do it on my own. 4 I can teach someone else.

1. **VOCABULARY** How many linear inequalities are in a system of linear inequalities?
2. **WRITING** How can you verify that an ordered pair is a solution of a system of linear inequalities?

Tell whether the ordered pair is a solution of the system of linear inequalities.

3. $(-1, 5)$; $y < 5$, $y > x - 4$
4. $(1, 4)$; $y \geq 3x + 1$, $y > x - 1$
5. $\left(0, -\frac{5}{2}\right)$; $y > \frac{1}{2}x - 8$, $y < 6 - x$
6. **OPEN-ENDED** One inequality in a system is $y \geq 2x + 3$. Write another possible inequality in the system so that $(-2, 6)$ is a solution of the system.

Graphing Systems of Linear Inequalities

The **graph of a system of linear inequalities** is the graph of all the solutions of the system.

KEY IDEA

Graphing a System of Linear Inequalities

Graph each inequality in the same coordinate plane. Then find the intersection of the half-planes that are solutions of the inequalities. This intersection is the graph of the system.

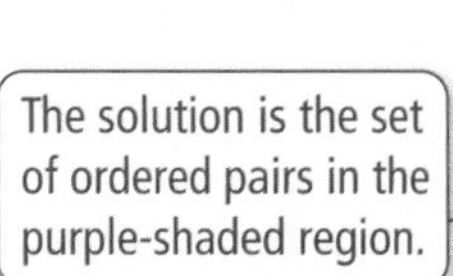

The solution is the set of ordered pairs in the purple-shaded region.

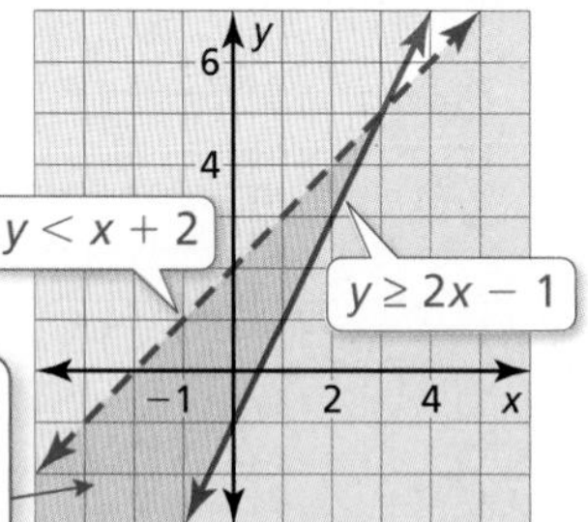

EXAMPLE 2 Graphing a System of Linear Inequalities

Graph the system. Identify a solution.

$y \leq 3$ Inequality 1

$y > x + 2$ Inequality 2

SOLUTION

Graph each inequality. Then find the intersection of the half-planes.

▶ One solution is $(-3, 1)$.

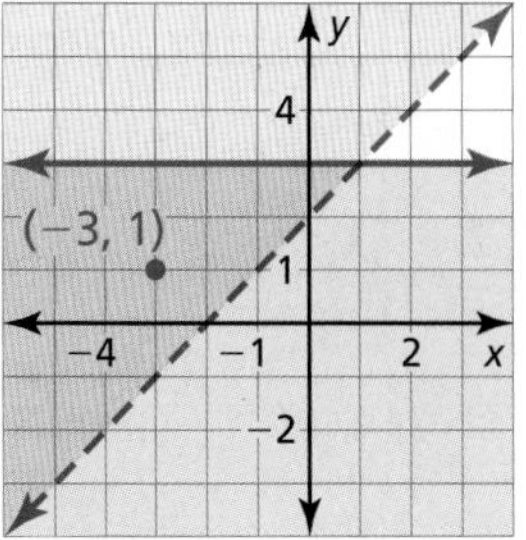

Check

Verify that $(-3, 1)$ is a solution of each inequality.

Inequality 1	Inequality 2
$y \leq 3$	$y > x + 2$
$1 \leq 3$ ✓	$1 \overset{?}{>} -3 + 2$
	$1 > -1$ ✓

EXAMPLE 3 Graphing a System of Linear Inequalities: No Solution

Graph the system.

$2x + y < -1$ Inequality 1

$2x + y > 3$ Inequality 2

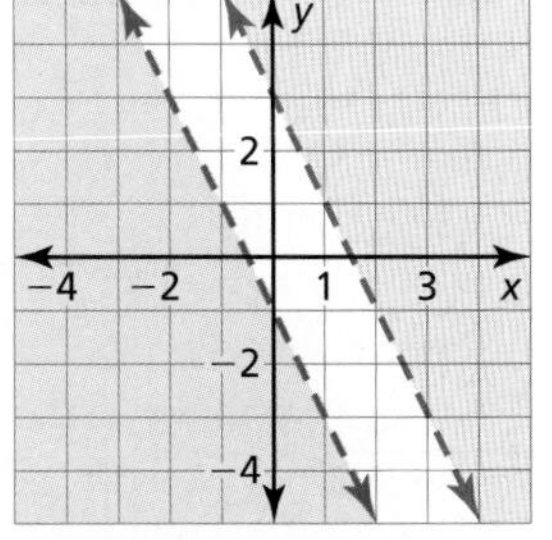

SOLUTION

Graph each inequality. Then find the intersection of the half-planes. Notice that the lines are parallel, and the half-planes do not intersect.

▶ So, the system has no solution.

SELF-ASSESSMENT 1 I do not understand. 2 I can do it with help. 3 I can do it on my own. 4 I can teach someone else.

Graph the system. Identify a solution, if possible.

7. $y \geq -x + 4$
$x + y \leq 0$

8. $y > 2x - 3$
$y \geq \frac{1}{2}x + 1$

9. $-2x + y < 4$
$2x + y > 4$

Writing Systems of Linear Inequalities

EXAMPLE 4 Writing a System of Linear Inequalities

Write a system of linear inequalities represented by the graph.

SOLUTION

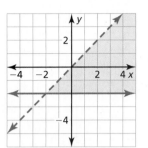

Inequality 1 The horizontal boundary line passes through $(0, -2)$. So, an equation of the line is $y = -2$. The shaded region is *above* the *solid* boundary line, so the inequality is $y \geq -2$.

Inequality 2 The slope of the other boundary line is 1, and the y-intercept is 0. So, an equation of the line is $y = x$. The shaded region is *below* the *dashed* boundary line, so the inequality is $y < x$.

▶ The system of linear inequalities represented by the graph is

$y \geq -2$ Inequality 1

$y < x$. Inequality 2

EXAMPLE 5 Writing a System of Linear Inequalities

Write a system of linear inequalities represented by the graph.

SOLUTION

Inequality 1 The vertical boundary line passes through $(3, 0)$. So, an equation of the line is $x = 3$. The shaded region is to the *left* of the *solid* boundary line, so the inequality is $x \leq 3$.

Inequality 2 The slope of the other boundary line is $\frac{2}{3}$, and the y-intercept is -1. So, an equation of the line is $y = \frac{2}{3}x - 1$. The shaded region is *above* the *dashed* boundary line, so the inequality is $y > \frac{2}{3}x - 1$.

▶ The system of linear inequalities represented by the graph is

$x \leq 3$ Inequality 1

$y > \frac{2}{3}x - 1$. Inequality 2

SELF-ASSESSMENT

1 I do not understand. 2 I can do it with help. 3 I can do it on my own. 4 I can teach someone else.

Write a system of linear inequalities represented by the graph.

10.

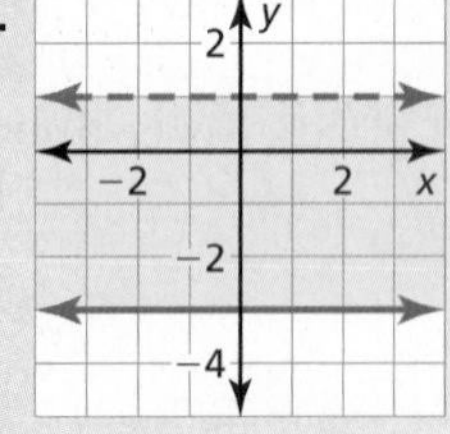

11.

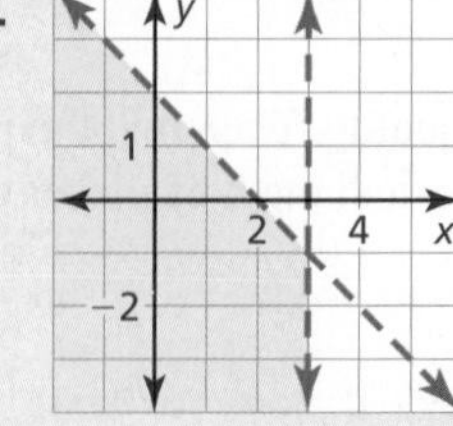

12.

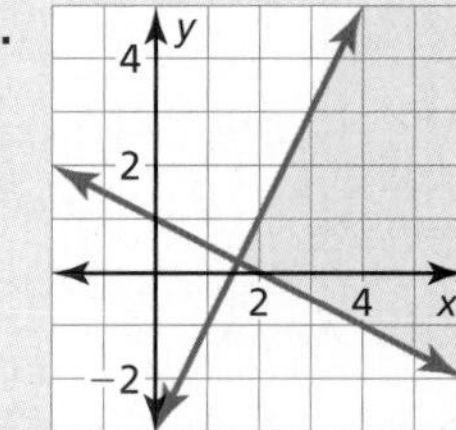

13. OPEN-ENDED Write a system of linear inequalities whose graph can be represented by a rectangular region.

14. MP REASONING Is it possible to write a system of three linear inequalities that has no solution? If so, give an example. If not, explain why not.

Solving Real-Life Problems

EXAMPLE 6 **Modeling Real Life** 

A company is loading recliners and sofas onto a trailer that has a volume of about 3800 cubic feet. Each recliner takes up about 40 cubic feet and each sofa takes up about 80 cubic feet. The company wants the shipment to have at least 30 recliners and more than 25 sofas. Write and graph a system that represents the situation. Give one example of the numbers of recliners and sofas the company can have in the shipment.

SOLUTION

1. **Understand the Problem** You know the volume of the trailer and the volume of each recliner and sofa. You also know how many recliners and sofas the company wants in the shipment. You are asked to give an example of the numbers of recliners and sofas the company can have in the shipment.

2. **Make a Plan** Use the given information to write a system of linear inequalities. Then graph the system and identify and interpret an ordered pair in the solution region.

3. **Solve and Check** Let r be the number of recliners and let s be the number of sofas in the shipment.

$40r + 80s \le 3800$	at most 3800 cubic feet is available in the shipment
$r \ge 30$	at least 30 recliners in the shipment
$s > 25$	more than 25 sofas in the shipment

Graph the system.

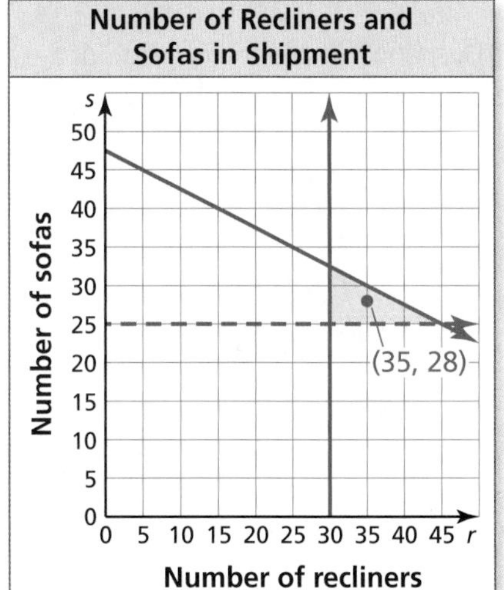

One ordered pair in the solution region is (35, 28).

▶ So, the company can have 35 recliners and 28 sofas in the shipment.

Check Check your solution by substituting it into the inequalities in the system.

$40r + 80s \le 3800$ $\qquad r \ge 30$ $\qquad s > 25$

$40(35) + 80(28) \overset{?}{\le} 3800$ $\qquad 35 \ge 30$ ✓ $\qquad 28 > 25$ ✓

$3640 \le 3800$ ✓

SELF-ASSESSMENT 1 I do not understand. 2 I can do it with help. 3 I can do it on my own. 4 I can teach someone else.

15. Identify and interpret another ordered pair in the solution region in Example 6.

16. You have at most 8 hours to spend at the mall and at the beach. You want to spend more than 2 hours at the mall and more than 4 hours at the beach.

a. Write and graph a system that represents the situation. Give one example of the amount of time you can spend at each location.

b. You want to spend at least 45 more minutes at the mall. How does this change the system in part (a)? Is your example still valid? Explain.

5.7 Practice WITH CalcChat® AND CalcView®

In Exercises 1–4, tell whether the ordered pair is a solution of the system of linear inequalities. *Example 1*

1. $(-5, 2)$; $y < 4$, $y > x + 3$

2. $(1, -1)$; $y > -2$, $y > x - 5$

3. $(0, 0)$; $y \le x + 7$, $y \ge 2x + 3$

4. $(4, -3)$; $y \le -x + 1$, $y \le 5x - 2$

In Exercises 5–8, tell whether the ordered pair is a solution of the system of linear inequalities.

5. $(-4, 3)$

6. $(-3, -1)$

7. $(-2, 0)$

8. $(1, 0.5)$

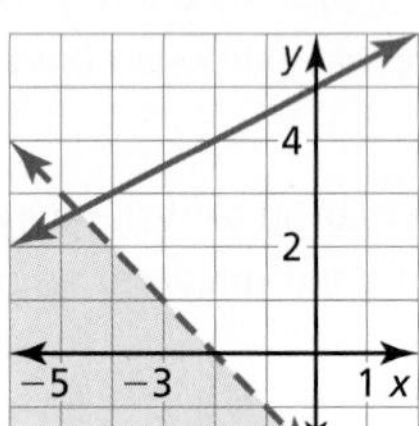

In Exercises 9–18, graph the system. Identify a solution, if possible. *Examples 2 and 3*

9. $y > -3$
$y \ge 5x$

10. $y < -1$
$x > 4$

11. $y < -2$
$y > 2$

12. $y < x - 1$
$y \ge x + 1$

13. $y \ge -5$
$y - 1 < 3x$

14. $x + y > 4$
$y \ge \frac{3}{2}x - 9$

15. $x + y > 1$
$-x - y < -3$

16. $2x + y \le 5$
$y + 2 \ge -2x$

17. $x < 3.5$
$y > 1$
$y \ge -x + 1$

18. $\frac{3}{4}x + y \le 3$
$\frac{3}{4}x - y \ge 1$
$y > -1\frac{1}{2}$

In Exercises 19–24, write a system of linear inequalities represented by the graph. *Examples 4 and 5*

19.

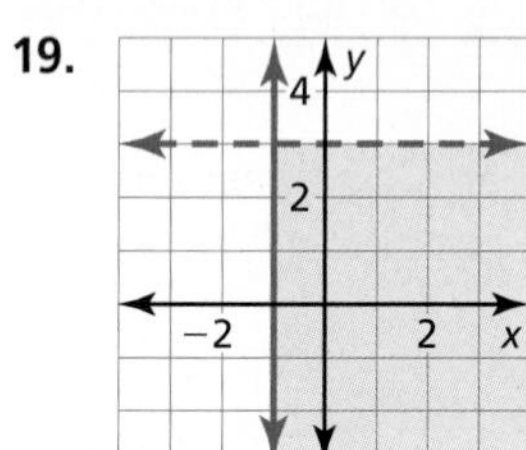

20.

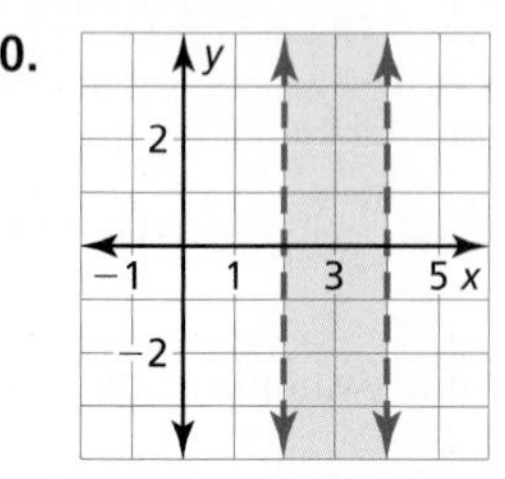

21.

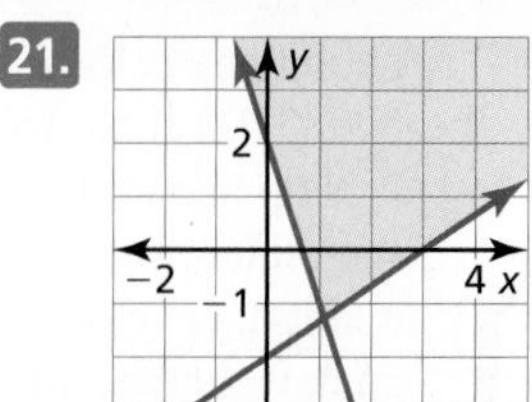

22.

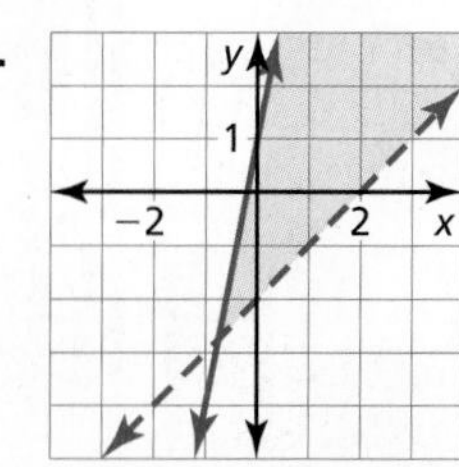

23.

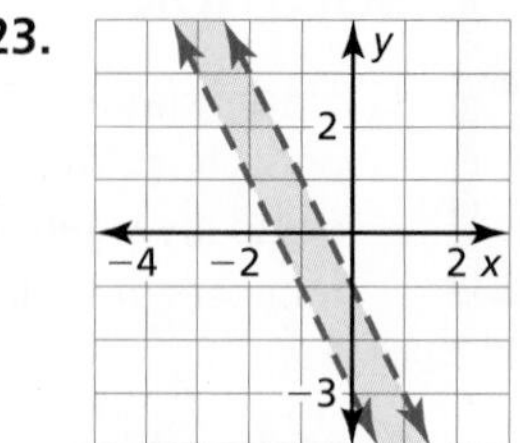

24.

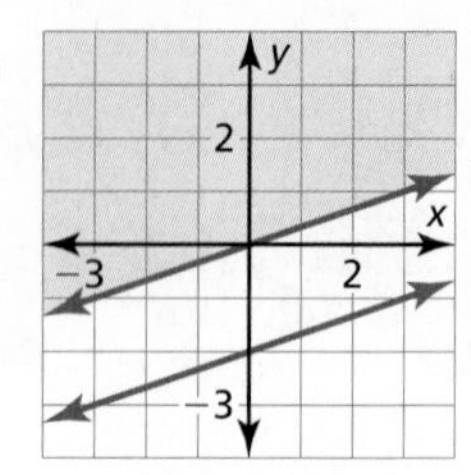

25. ERROR ANALYSIS Describe and correct the error in graphing the system $y \le 3x + 4$ and $y > \frac{1}{2}x + 2$.

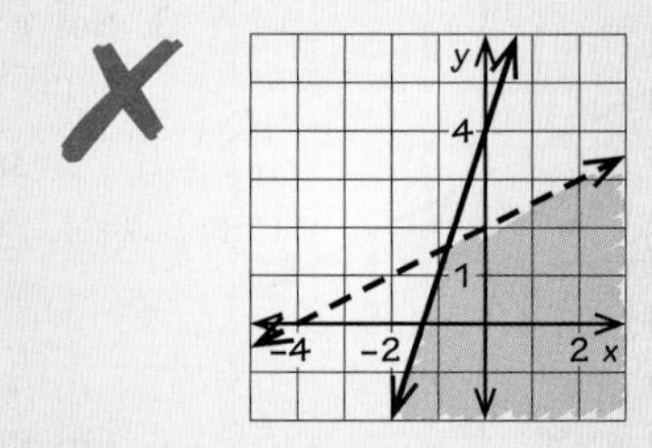

26. COLLEGE PREP Which of the following systems is represented by the graph?

Ⓐ $y \le -\frac{1}{2}x - 2$
$y > 4x + 1$

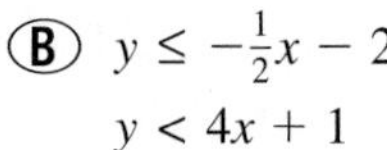

Ⓑ $y \le -\frac{1}{2}x - 2$
$y < 4x + 1$

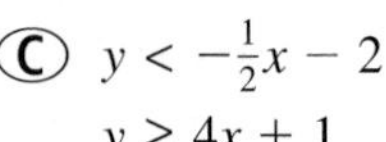

Ⓒ $y < -\frac{1}{2}x - 2$
$y \ge 4x + 1$

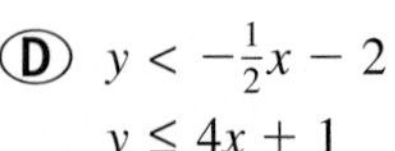

Ⓓ $y < -\frac{1}{2}x - 2$
$y \le 4x + 1$

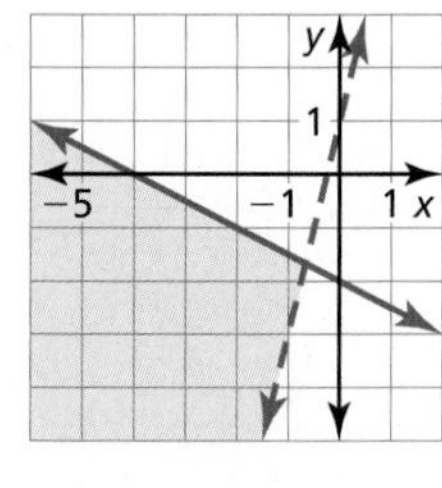

27. MODELING REAL LIFE A group of scientists have at most 7 hours to spend on an expedition to one of the deepest areas of the ocean. They expect the total travel time to be more than 3 hours and want to spend at least $2\frac{1}{2}$ hours exploring. Write and graph a system that represents the situation. Give one example of the amount of time they can spend on each part of the expedition. *Example 6*

28. MODELING REAL LIFE You earn \$10 per hour working at a grocery store and must work there at least 8 hours per week. You also teach music lessons for \$15 per hour. Between the two jobs, you need to earn at least \$120 per week and work no more than 20 hours per week. Write and graph a system that represents the situation. Give one example of the number of hours you can work at each job.

29. MODELING REAL LIFE You are fishing for surfperch and rockfish. The graph shows limits on the numbers of fish you are allowed to catch per day.

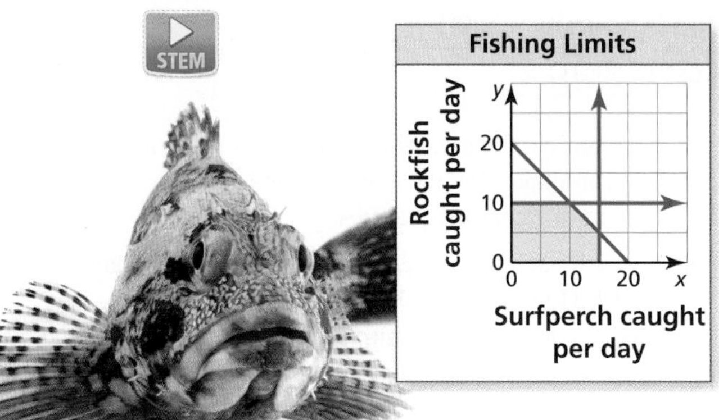

Rockfish

a. Write and interpret a system of linear inequalities that represents the situation.

b. Can you catch 11 surfperch and 9 rockfish in 1 day? Explain.

30. MP REASONING Describe the graph of the system shown.

$x - y \leq 4$
$x - y \geq 4$

31. MP PROBLEM SOLVING Your cousin plans to spend less than half of her monthly \$2000 paycheck on housing and savings. She wants to spend at least 10% of her paycheck on savings and at most 30% of it on housing. Give one example of the amount of money your cousin can spend on savings and housing. Justify your answer using a system of linear inequalities.

32. MP PROBLEM SOLVING A travel club can spend at most 10 nights in two cities on a trip. The club needs to reserve four rooms each night and wants to spend no more than \$4200 on hotels and fuel. The estimated fuel cost is \$200. Can the club spend 3 nights in City A and 6 nights in City B? 7 nights in City A and 3 nights in City B? Justify your answers using a system of linear inequalities.

Nightly Hotel Rates	
City A hotel	City B hotel
\$85 per room	\$130 per room

33. CONNECTING CONCEPTS The vertices of a shaded rectangle are $(-1, 1)$, $(6, 1)$, $(6, -3)$, and $(-1, -3)$.

a. Write a system of linear inequalities with a graph that can be represented by the shaded rectangle.

b. Find the area of the rectangle.

34. CONNECTING CONCEPTS The vertices of a shaded triangle are $(2, 5)$, $(6, -3)$, and $(-2, -3)$.

a. Write a system of linear inequalities with a graph that can be represented by the shaded triangle.

b. Find the area of the triangle.

35. MP STRUCTURE Write a system of linear inequalities that has the same solutions as $|y| < x$, where $x > 0$. Graph the system.

36. HOW DO YOU SEE IT?
The graphs of two linear equations are shown.

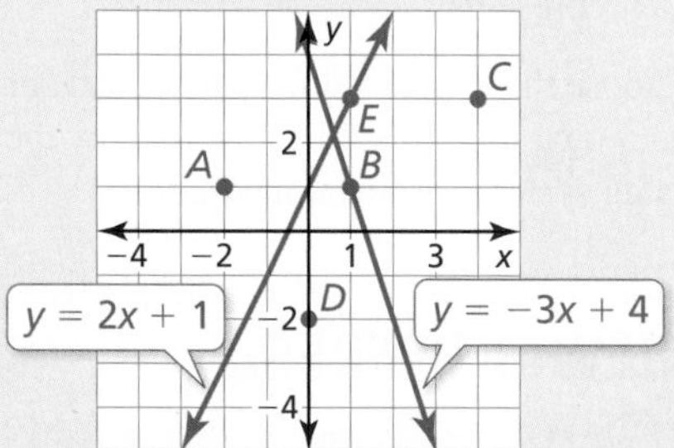

Replace the equal signs with inequality symbols to create a system of linear inequalities that has points *C* and *E* as solutions, but not points *A*, *B*, and *D*. Explain your reasoning.

$y \; \square \; -3x + 4$

$y \; \square \; 2x + 1$

37. MAKING AN ARGUMENT Your friend says that a system of linear inequalities in which the boundary lines are parallel must have no solution. Is your friend correct? Explain.

38. CRITICAL THINKING Is it possible for the solution set of a system of linear inequalities to be all points in the coordinate plane? Explain your reasoning.

OPEN-ENDED In Exercises 39–41, write a system of linear inequalities with the given characteristic.

39. All solutions are in Quadrant I.

40. All solutions have one positive coordinate and one negative coordinate.

41. There are no solutions.

42. OPEN-ENDED One inequality in a system is $-4x + 2y > 6$. Write another possible inequality in the system so that the system has no solution.

43. PERFORMANCE TASK The table shows three systems.

System A	System B	System C
$y \ge x$ $y \le x + 4$ $y \ge -2$ $y \le 6$	$y > x + 4$ $x \ge -6$ $y \le 6$	$y < x$ $x \le 6$ $y \ge -2$

a. Graph each system in the same coordinate plane. Color the solutions of System A yellow, the solutions of System B green, and the solutions of System C red. Erase all other shading.

b. The directions in part (a) produce the flag of a country. Determine which country the flag represents.

c. Choose the flag of a different country, or design your own flag. Describe how to draw the flag using systems of linear inequalities.

44. THOUGHT PROVOKING Write a system of linear inequalities that has exactly one solution.

45. DIG DEEPER You make necklaces and key chains to sell at a craft fair. The table shows the amounts of time and money it takes to make a necklace and a key chain, and the amounts of time and money you have available for making them.

	Necklace	Key chain	Available
Time (hours)	0.5	0.25	20
Cost (dollars)	2	3	120

a. Give three examples of the number of each item you can make. Justify your answers using a system of linear inequalities.

b. You sell each necklace for \$10 and each key chain for \$8. How many necklaces and key chains should you sell to maximize your revenue? What is the maximum revenue? (*Hint:* The maximum revenue occurs at one of the vertices of the graph of the system in part (a).)

REVIEW & REFRESH

WATCH

46. Graph $-\frac{3}{4}x - y < 6$ in a coordinate plane.

In Exercises 47 and 48, write the product as a power.

47. $(-13) \cdot (-13) \cdot (-13)$

48. $x \cdot x \cdot x \cdot x \cdot x \cdot x$

49. Write a system of linear inequalities represented by the graph.

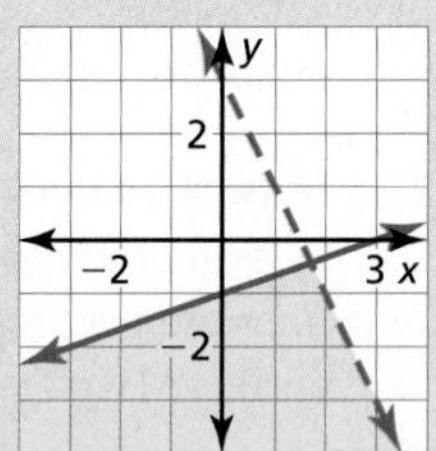

50. Write an equation of the line with a slope of $-\frac{1}{4}$ and a y-intercept of -1.

In Exercises 51 and 52, solve the equation.

51. $\frac{2}{3}(x - 6) = 4$

52. $6x - 7 = -2x - 9$

In Exercises 53 and 54, solve the system using any method. Explain your choice of method.

53. $5x + 10y = 8$
$3x + 6y = 4$

54. $-11x + 2y = 12$
$y = 4x + 3$

55. MODELING REAL LIFE Slitsnails are large mollusks that live in deep waters. They have been found in the range of elevations shown. Write and graph a compound inequality that represents this range.

56. Solve $x + 5 = -2x - 4$ by graphing. Check your solution.

57. OPEN-ENDED Write an absolute value equation that has exactly one solution.

58. Use intercepts to graph the equation $-3x + 6y = 24$. Label the points corresponding to the intercepts.

59. Make a scatter plot of the data. Then describe the relationship between the data.

x	4	8	1	9	3	6	2	5
y	−2	0	−5	−1	−5	−2	−7	−4

60. Graph $g(x) = |x - 3| + 1$. Compare the graph to the graph of $f(x) = |x - 3|$.

5 Chapter Review WITH CalcChat®

Chapter Learning Target Understand solving systems of linear equations.

Chapter Success Criteria

- ◆ I can identify a system of linear equations.
- ◆ I can describe different methods for solving systems of linear equations.
- ■ I can analyze systems of linear equations and decide what solution method is most efficient.
- ■ I can predict whether a system of linear equations has one solution, no solution, or infinitely many solutions.

◆ Surface
■ Deep

SELF-ASSESSMENT 1 I do not understand. 2 I can do it with help. 3 I can do it on my own. 4 I can teach someone else.

5.1 Solving Systems of Linear Equations by Graphing (pp. 245–250)

Learning Target: Solve linear systems by graphing.

Vocabulary
system of linear equations
solution of a system of linear equations

Solve the system by graphing.

1. $y = -3x + 1$
   $y = x - 7$

2. $y = -4x + 3$
   $4x - 2y = 6$

3. $5x + 5y = 15$
   $2x - 2y = 10$

4. $-\frac{2}{3}x + y = 2$
   $y + 8 = 4x$

5. Write a system of linear equations in two variables that has a solution of $(4.2, -2.5)$. Use a graph to justify your answer.

6. The graphs of two equations in a linear system have the same x-intercept. One equation in the system is $\frac{1}{5}x + 4y = a$. What is the solution of the system?

7. You plant a spruce tree that grows 4 inches per year and a hemlock tree that grows 6 inches per year. The initial heights of the trees are shown. After how many years will the trees be the same height?

5.2 Solving Systems of Linear Equations by Substitution (pp. 251–256)

Learning Target: Solve linear systems by substitution.

Solve the system by substitution. Check your solution.

8. $3x + y = -9$
   $y = 5x + 7$

9. $x + 4y = 6$
   $x - y = 1$

10. $2x + 3y = 4$
    $y + 3x = 6$

11. You spend \$20 total on tubes of paint and disposable brushes for an art project. Tubes of paint cost \$4.00 each and brushes cost \$0.50 each. You purchase twice as many brushes as tubes of paint. How many brushes and tubes of paint do you purchase?

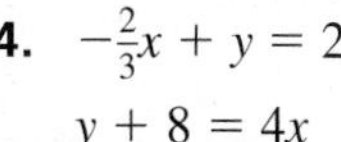

5.3 Solving Systems of Linear Equations by Elimination (pp. 257–262)

Learning Target: Solve linear system by elimination.

Solve the system by elimination. Check your solution.

12. $9x - 2y = 34$
$5x + 2y = -6$

13. $x + 6y = 28$
$2x - 3y = -19$

14. $8x - 6y = -3$
$6x - 5y = -1$

15. In a football game, all of the home team's points are from 7-point touchdowns and 3-point field goals. The team scores six times. Find the numbers of touchdowns and field goals that the home team scores.

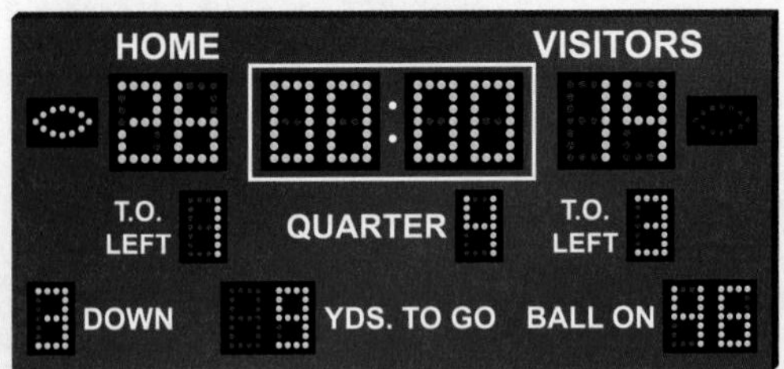

5.4 Solving Special Systems of Linear Equations (pp. 263–268)

Learning Target: Solve linear systems with different numbers of solutions.

Use the graph to determine whether the system has *no solution*, *one solution*, or *infinitely many solutions*. Justify your answer algebraically.

16.

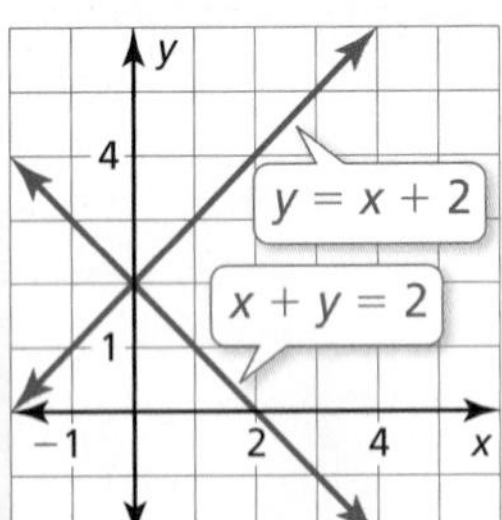

17.

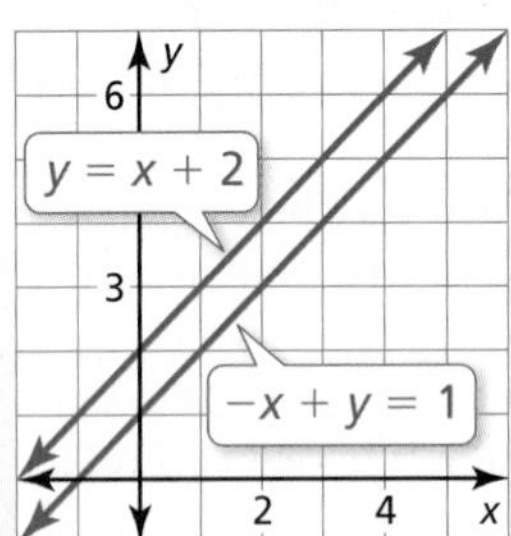

18.

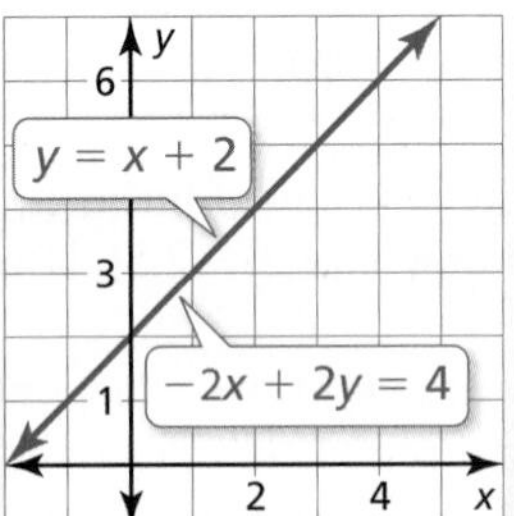

Solve the system using any method. Explain your choice of method.

19. $x = y + 2$
$-3x + 3y = 6$

20. $0.25x - 6y = -6$
$-5x + 10y = 10$

21. $-4x + 4y = 32$
$3x + 24 = 3y$

5.5 Solving Equations by Graphing (pp. 269–274)

Learning Target: Solve equations by graphing.

Solve the equation by graphing. Check your solution(s).

22. $\frac{1}{3}x + 5 = -2x - 2$

23. $|x + 1| = |-x - 9|$

24. $|2x - 8| = |x + 5|$

25. In 2020, Forest A had an area of about 4000 acres and Forest B had an area of about 3600 acres. Researchers expect deforestation to cause the area of Forest A to decrease at a rate of 105 acres per decade and the area of Forest B to decrease at a rate of 30 acres per decade. In what year do they expect the areas of the forests be the same?

5.6 Graphing Linear Inequalities in Two Variables (pp. 275–280)

Learning Target: Graph linear inequalities in two variables.

Vocabulary

linear inequality in two variables
solution of a linear inequality in two variables
graph of a linear inequality
half-planes

Graph the inequality in a coordinate plane.

26. $y > -4$ **27.** $-9x + 3y \geq 3$ **28.** $5x + 10y < 40$

Write an inequality that represents the graph.

29.

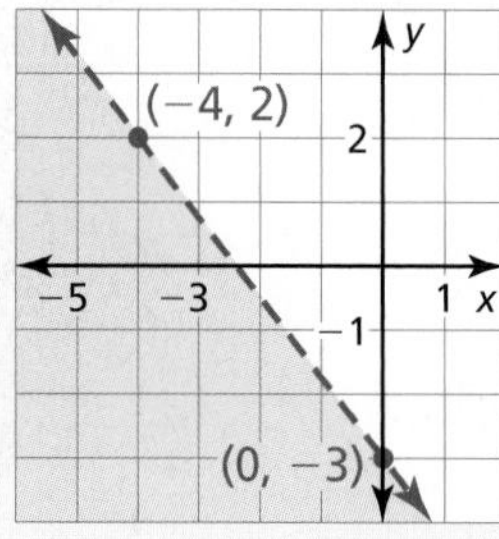

30.

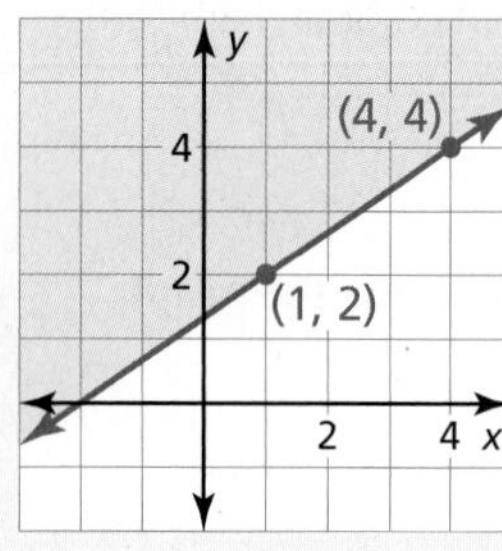

5.7 Systems of Linear Inequalities (pp. 281–288)

Learning Target: Graph and write systems of linear inequalities.

Vocabulary

system of linear inequalities
solution of a system of linear inequalities
graph of a system of linear inequalities

Graph the system.

31. $y \leq x - 3$
$y \geq x + 1$

32. $y > -2x + 3$
$y \geq \frac{1}{4}x - 1$

33. $x + 3y > 6$
$2x + y < 7$

Match the system of linear inequalities with its graph, where *a* and *b* are positive numbers. Explain your reasoning.

34. $y \leq ax + b$
$y > ax - b$

35. $y \geq ax + b$
$y < ax - b$

36. $y < ax + b$
$y \geq ax - b$

A.

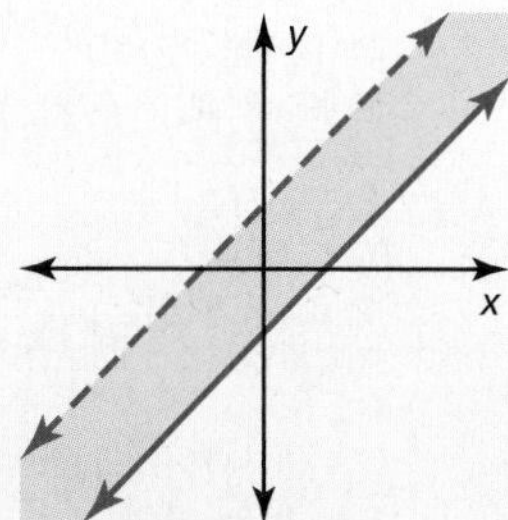

B.

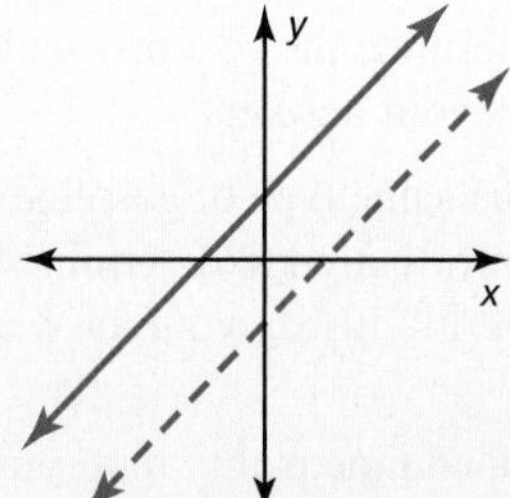

C.

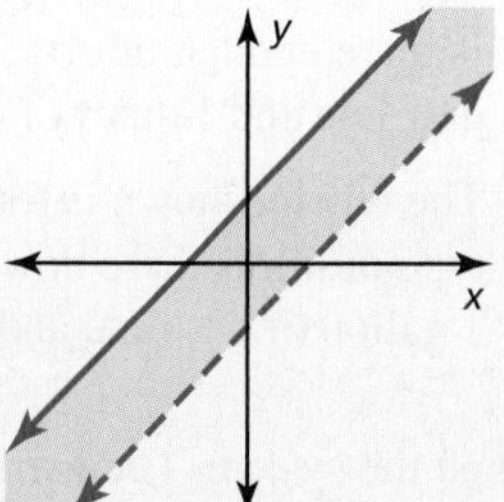

Mathematical Practices

Use Appropriate Tools Strategically

Mathematically proficient students use technological tools to explore and deepen their understanding of concepts.

1. Describe a situation in this chapter where you used technology to explore a mathematical concept.

2. When is it most helpful to use technology to solve a linear system? Explain your reasoning.

5 Practice Test WITH CalcChat®

Solve the system using any method. Explain your choice of method.

1. $8x + 3y = -9$
   $-8x + y = 29$

2. $\frac{1}{2}x + y = -6$
   $y = \frac{3}{5}x + 5$

3. $y = 4x + 4$
   $-8x + 2y = 8$

4. $x = y - 11$
   $x - 3y = 1$

5. $6x - 4y = 9$
   $9x - 6y = 15$

6. $y = 5x - 7$
   $-4x + y = -1$

Write an inequality that represents the graph.

7.

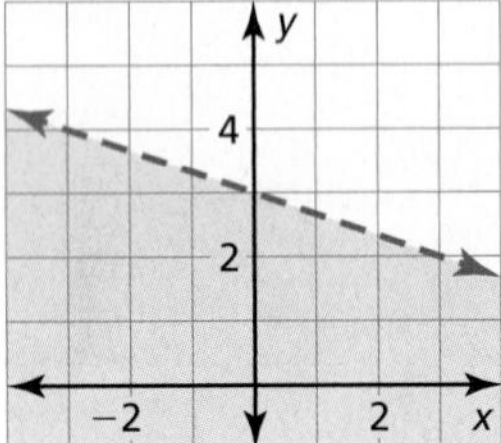

8.

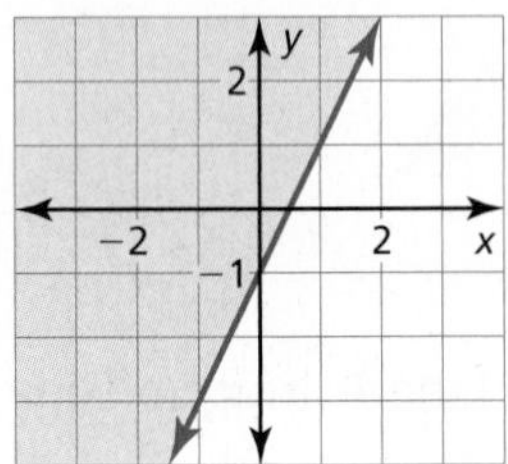

Graph the system. Identify a solution, if possible.

9. $y > \frac{1}{2}x + 4$
   $2y \leq x + 4$

10. $x + y < 1$
    $5x + y > 4$

11. $y \geq -\frac{2}{3}x + 1$
    $-3x + y > -2$

12. Solve $|2x - 8| = |x - 7|$ by graphing. Check your solutions.

13. You pay \$45.50 for 10 gallons of gasoline and 2 quarts of oil at a gas station. Your friend pays \$22.75 for 5 gallons of the same type of gasoline and 1 quart of the same type of oil.

    a. Is there enough information to determine the cost of 1 gallon of gasoline and 1 quart of oil? Justify your answer.

    b. The receipt shown is for buying the same type of gasoline and same type of oil. Is there now enough information to determine the cost of 1 gallon of gasoline and 1 quart of oil? Justify your answer.

RECEIPT
DATE 11/12/20 16:25
PUMP # 03
PRODUCT: REGUNL
GALLONS: 8.00
2 QUARTS OIL
TOTAL: $38.40
THANK YOU
HAVE A NICE DAY

14. Graph the system. Then write a compound inequality represented by the graph. Explain your reasoning.

    $y \geq 2x + 1$
    $5x > y - 3$

15. You have at most \$60 to spend on trophies and medals to give as prizes for a contest.

    a. Write and graph an inequality that represents the numbers of trophies and medals you can buy. Identify and interpret a solution of the inequality.

    b. You want to purchase at least 6 items. Write and graph a system that represents the situation. How many of each item can you buy?

5 Performance Task
A Challenging Descent

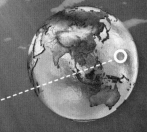

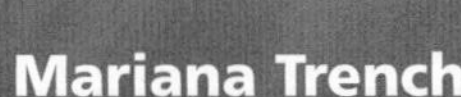

Mariana Trench

The Mariana Trench in the Pacific Ocean is home to the deepest location on Earth, the **Challenger Deep**.

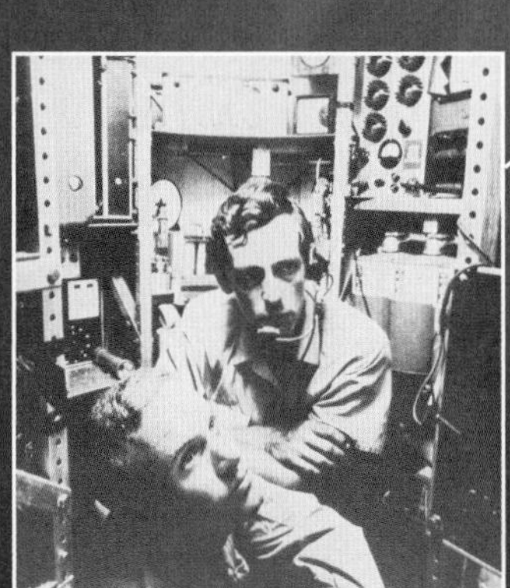

January 23, 1960

Aboard the bathyscaphe Trieste, Jacques Piccard and Don Walsh became the first people to explore the Challenger Deep. The expedition lasted 8 hours and 22 minutes, with only 20 minutes on the ocean floor.

March 26, 2012

Film director James Cameron piloted the Deepsea Challenger on the second manned dive to the Challenger Deep. The expedition lasted 6 hours and 40 minutes, with 2 hours and 34 minutes on the ocean floor.

Submersibles can ascend more rapidly than they can descend because of the buoyancy of the air inside a submersible's *ballasts*. For Piccard and Walsh, the descent took about 1.5 times as long as the ascent. For Cameron, the descent took about 1.75 times as long as the ascent.

PLAN AN EXPEDITION

You pilot a manned dive to the Challenger Deep. Use the ascent times and the descent times for the 1960 and 2012 expeditions to write a plan for your dive, including:

- *how long you will spend descending*
- *how long you will spend on the ocean floor*
- *how long you will spend ascending*
- *goals you hope to accomplish.*

Dive schedules must be flexible to allow for unexpected circumstances. Determine the maximum total amount of time for your expedition and the minimum and maximum amounts of time you want to spend on the ocean floor. Use a graph to show the amounts of time that you can spend on the ocean floor and the amounts of time that you can spend traveling.

5 College and Career Readiness WITH CalcChat®

Tutorial videos are available for each exercise.

1. Which equation is represented by the graph?

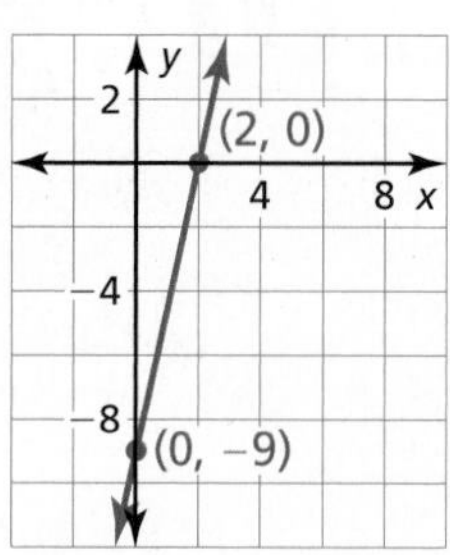

Ⓐ $9x - 2y = -18$

Ⓑ $-9x - 2y = 18$

Ⓒ $9x + 2y = 18$

Ⓓ $-9x + 2y = -18$

2. A company rents out 6-, 8-, 12-, and 16-passenger vans. The function $C(x) = 100 + 5x$ represents the cost C (in dollars) of renting an x-passenger van for a day. Which numbers are in the range of the function? Select all that apply.

Ⓐ 130 Ⓑ 140

Ⓒ 150 Ⓓ 160

Ⓔ 170 Ⓕ 180

Ⓖ 190 Ⓗ 200

3. Complete the system of linear inequalities with <, ≤, >, or ≥ so that the graph represents the system.

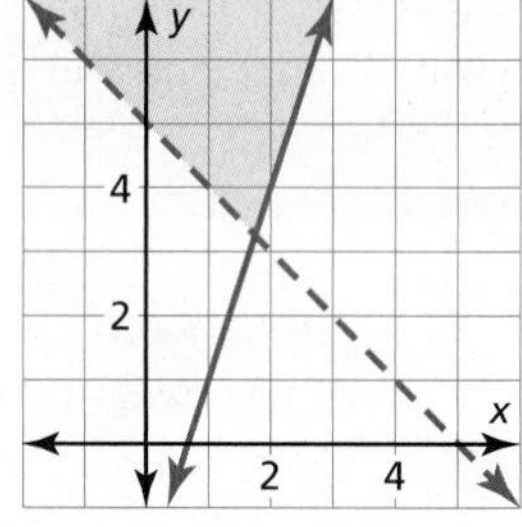

y ▭ $3x - 2$

y ▭ $-x + 5$

4. Which of the following describes the transformations from the graph of f to the graph of g?

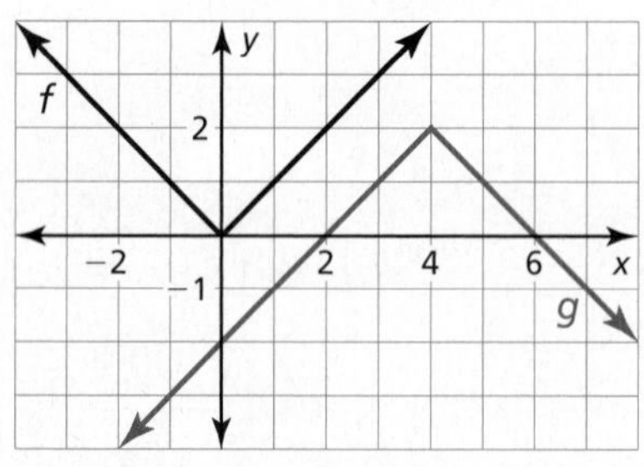

Ⓐ a reflection in the x-axis, followed by a translation 2 units up and 4 units right

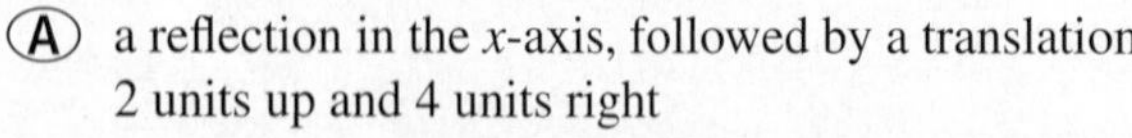

Ⓑ a reflection in the x-axis, followed by a translation 2 units up and 4 units left

Ⓒ a translation 2 units up and 4 units right followed by a reflection in the x-axis

Ⓓ a reflection in the y-axis, followed by a translation 2 units up and 4 units right

5. Which two equations form a system of linear equations that has no solution?

$y = 3x + 2$ $y = \frac{1}{3}x + 2$ $y = 2x + 3$ $y = 3x + \frac{1}{2}$

6. Find values of a so that each statement is true for the equation $ax - 8 = 4 - x$.

a. When $a =$ ▢, the solution is $x = -2$.

b. When $a =$ ▢, the solution is $x = 12$.

c. When $a =$ ▢, the solution is $x = 3$.

7. Which inequality is represented by the graph?

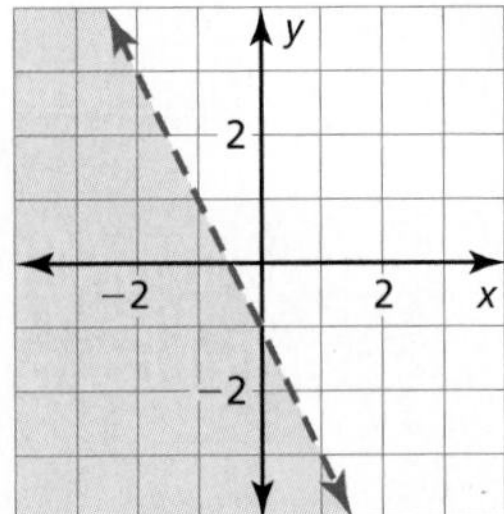

Ⓐ $y + 2x \leq -1$

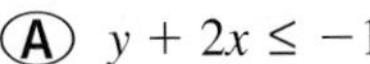

Ⓑ $y + 1 < -2x$

Ⓒ $-2x < y + 1$

Ⓓ $-2x - y \leq 1$

8. Which of the systems are equivalent?

$4x - 5y = 3$	$4x - 5y = 3$	$4x - 5y = 3$	$12x - 15y = 9$
$2x + 15y = -1$	$-4x - 30y = 2$	$4x + 30y = -1$	$2x + 15y = -1$

9. The value of x is greater than 9. Write a compound inequality that represents the perimeter P (in feet) of the triangle. Explain your reasoning.

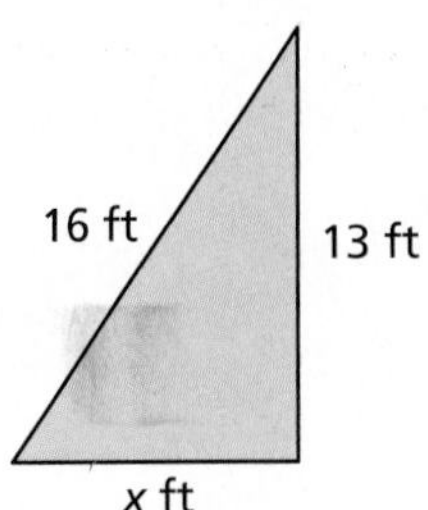

10. Which is the graph of $f(x) = \begin{cases} 2x + 3, & \text{if } x < 1 \\ -x + 1, & \text{if } x \geq 1 \end{cases}$?

Ⓐ

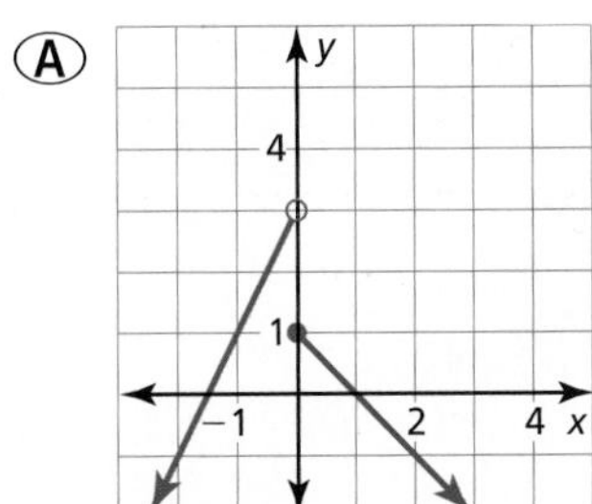

Ⓑ

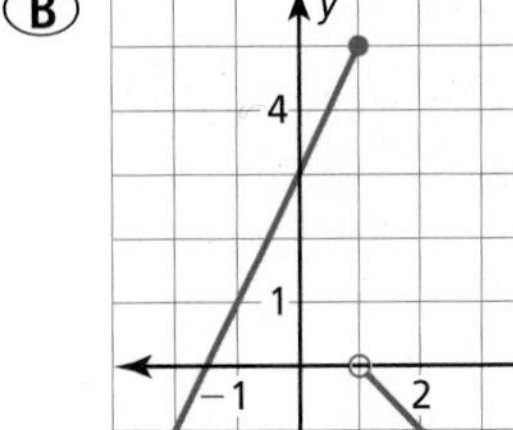

Ⓒ

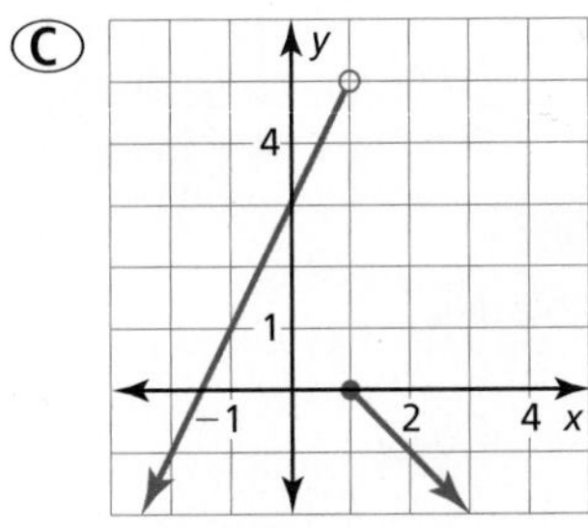

Ⓓ

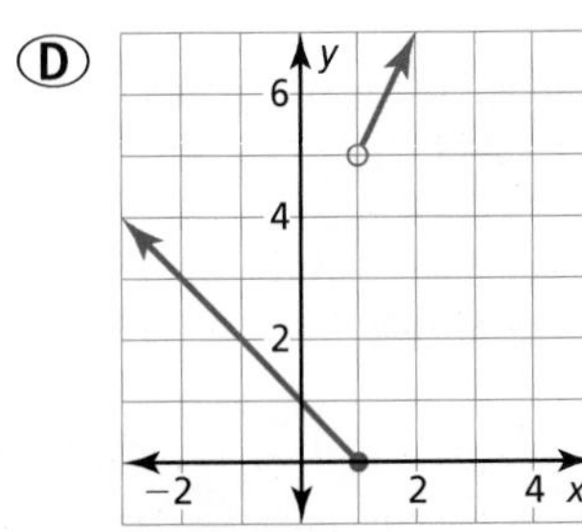

6 Exponential Functions and Sequences

NATIONAL GEOGRAPHIC EXPLORER

Nathan D. Wolfe

Dr. Nathan Wolfe works to create an early warning system that can forecast and contain new plagues before they sicken millions of people. Nathan compares the system to compounding interest. "As you go further out in time, you save more and more lives. If you compound a chronic pandemic over decades, you begin to see the enormous impact viral forecasting could have."

- A bacterial culture increases by 20 percent each day. Is this an example of linear growth? Explain.
- A bacterial culture increases by 30 percent each week. Graph the results over a period of 6 weeks.
- Compare bacterial and viral growth to compound interest.

STEM

The number of people infected by a virus can grow more and more quickly if immediate action is not taken. In the Performance Task, you will write a report for a health organization, forecasting the spread of an Ebola epidemic and recommending steps that can be taken to slow its spread.

Bacterial and Viral Growth

Preparing for Chapter 6

Chapter Learning Target Understand exponential functions and sequences.

Chapter Success Criteria

- ◆ I can identify and use properties of exponents.
- ◆ I can describe exponential functions.
- ■ I can analyze data, a graph, or a context to determine whether it represents exponential growth or decay.
- ■ I can model using an exponential function or a geometric sequence.

◆ Surface
■ Deep

Chapter Vocabulary

Work with a partner. Discuss each of the vocabulary terms.

exponential function
exponential growth
exponential decay
exponential equation

Mathematical Practices

Look for and Make Use of Structure

Mathematically proficient students look closely to discern a pattern or structure.

Work with a partner. The volumes of seven chambers of a chambered nautilus are shown.

1. Use a graph to estimate the volume of Chamber 10.
2. Relate the volume of each chamber to the volume of the previous chamber. What do you notice?
3. Was your estimate for the volume of Chamber 10 reasonable? Explain.
4. Write an expression that represents the volume of the *n*th chamber. Explain your reasoning.

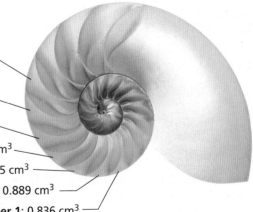

Chamber 7: 1.207 cm^3
Chamber 6: 1.135 cm^3
Chamber 5: 1.068 cm^3
Chamber 4: 1.005 cm^3
Chamber 3: 0.945 cm^3
Chamber 2: 0.889 cm^3
Chamber 1: 0.836 cm^3

6 Prepare WITH CalcChat®

Using Order of Operations

Example 1 **Evaluate $10^2 \div (30 \div 3) - 4(3 - 9) + 5^1$.**

1. Perform operations in grouping symbols. $10^2 \div (30 \div 3) - 4(3 - 9) + 5^1 = 10^2 \div 10 - 4(-6) + 5^1$
2. Evaluate numbers with exponents. $= 100 \div 10 - 4(-6) + 5$
3. Multiply and divide from left to right. $= 10 + 24 + 5$
4. Add and subtract from left to right. $= 39$

Evaluate the expression.

1. $12\left(\frac{14}{2}\right) - 3^3 + 15 - 9^2$ **2.** $5^2 \cdot 8 \div 2^2 + 20 \cdot 3 - 4$ **3.** $-\frac{3}{8} + 16 \times \left(\frac{1}{4}\right)^2 + (14 - 2^4)$

Finding Square Roots

WATCH

Example 2 **Find $-\sqrt{81}$.**

▶ $-\sqrt{81}$ represents the negative square root. Because $9^2 = 81$, $-\sqrt{81} = -\sqrt{9^2} = -9$.

Find the square root(s).

4. $\sqrt{64}$ **5.** $-\sqrt{4}$ **6.** $-\sqrt{\frac{25}{49}}$ **7.** $\pm\sqrt{121}$

Writing Equations for Arithmetic Sequences

Example 3 **Write an equation for the *n*th term of the arithmetic sequence 5, 15, 25, 35, ...**

The first term is 5, and the common difference is 10.

$a_n = a_1 + (n - 1)d$ Equation for an arithmetic sequence

$a_n = 5 + (n - 1)(10)$ Substitute 5 for a_1 and 10 for d.

$a_n = 10n - 5$ Simplify.

Write an equation for the *n*th term of the arithmetic sequence.

8. 12, 14, 16, 18, . . . **9.** 6, 3, 0, −3, . . . **10.** 9, 7.25, 5.5, 3.75, . . .

11. MP **NUMBER SENSE** Recall that a perfect square is a number with integers as its square roots. Is the product of two perfect squares always a perfect square? Is the quotient of two perfect squares always a perfect square? Explain your reasoning.

6.1 Properties of Exponents

Learning Target Write equivalent expressions involving powers.

Success Criteria

- I can explain the meanings of zero and negative exponents.
- I can evaluate and simplify expressions involving zero and negative exponents.
- I can simplify expressions using properties of exponents.

EXPLORE IT! Writing Rules for Properties of Exponents

Work with a partner. Choose several values for the variables to find a pattern. Then write a general rule.

REMEMBER

Notice that you are using *inductive reasoning* to write your rules. While it does not provide certainty that your rule is true, it provides evidence that it may be true.

a. What happens when you multiply two powers with the same base? Write the product of the two powers as a single power. $a^m \cdot a^n =$

b. What happens when you divide two powers with the same base? Write the quotient of the two powers as a single power. $\frac{a^m}{a^n} =$

c. What happens when you find a power of a power? Write the expression as a single power. $(a^m)^n =$

d. What happens when you find a power of a product? Write the expression as the product of two powers. $(ab)^m =$

e. What happens when you find a power of a quotient? Write the expression as the quotient of two powers. $\left(\frac{a}{b}\right)^m =$

f. What happens when an exponent is 0? $a^0 =$

g. What happens when an exponent is negative? Write the expression in a form that contains only positive exponents. $a^{-n} =$

Math Practice

Look for Structure

How can you use what you know about a^0 and $\frac{a^m}{a^n}$ to justify your answer in part (g)?

Using Zero and Negative Exponents

KEY IDEAS

Zero Exponent

Words For any nonzero number a, $a^0 = 1$. The power 0^0 is undefined.

Numbers $4^0 = 1$

Algebra $a^0 = 1$, where $a \neq 0$

Negative Exponents

Words For any integer n and any nonzero number a, a^{-n} is the reciprocal of a^n.

Numbers $4^{-2} = \frac{1}{4^2}$

Algebra $a^{-n} = \frac{1}{a^n}$, where $a \neq 0$

EXAMPLE 1 Using Zero and Negative Exponents

Evaluate each expression.

a. 6.7^0

b. $(-2)^{-4}$

SOLUTION

a. $6.7^0 = 1$ — Definition of zero exponent

b. $(-2)^{-4} = \frac{1}{(-2)^4}$ — Definition of negative exponent

$= \frac{1}{16}$ — Simplify.

EXAMPLE 2 Simplifying an Expression

Simplify the expression $\frac{4x^0}{y^{-3}}$. Write your answer using only positive exponents.

SOLUTION

$\frac{4x^0}{y^{-3}} = 4x^0y^3$ — Definition of negative exponent

$= 4y^3$ — Definition of zero exponent

SELF-ASSESSMENT

1 I do not understand. 2 I can do it with help. 3 I can do it on my own. 4 I can teach someone else.

Evaluate the expression.

1. $(-9)^0$
2. 3^{-3}
3. $\frac{10^{-3}}{10^0}$
4. $\frac{-5^0}{2^{-2}}$
5. **MP REASONING** Your friend claims that $\frac{1}{a^{-n}} = a^n$. Is your friend correct? Explain your reasoning.

Simplify the expression. Write your answer using only positive exponents.

6. m^{-3}
7. $\frac{w}{4^{-2}}$
8. $\frac{3^{-2}x^{-5}}{y^0}$
9. $\frac{8^{-2}p^0}{q^{-3}r^5}$

Using Properties of Exponents

KEY IDEAS

Product of Powers Property

Let a be a real number, and let m and n be integers.

Words To multiply powers with the same base, add their exponents.

Numbers $4^6 \cdot 4^3 = 4^{6+3} = 4^9$ **Algebra** $a^m \cdot a^n = a^{m+n}$

REMEMBER

The expression 4^6 is called a *power*. The *base*, 4, is used as a factor 6 times because the *exponent* is 6.

Quotient of Powers Property

Let a be a nonzero real number, and let m and n be integers.

Words To divide powers with the same base, subtract their exponents.

Numbers $\frac{4^6}{4^3} = 4^{6-3} = 4^3$ **Algebra** $\frac{a^m}{a^n} = a^{m-n}$, where $a \neq 0$

Power of a Power Property

Let a be a real number, and let m and n be integers.

Words To find a power of a power, multiply the exponents.

Numbers $(4^6)^3 = 4^{6 \cdot 3} = 4^{18}$ **Algebra** $(a^m)^n = a^{mn}$

EXAMPLE 3 Using Properties of Exponents

Simplify each expression. Write your answer using only positive exponents.

a. $3^2 \cdot 3^6$ **b.** $\frac{(-4)^2}{(-4)^7}$ **c.** $(z^4)^{-3}$

SOLUTION

a. $3^2 \cdot 3^6 = 3^{2+6}$ Product of Powers Property

$= 3^8$ Simplify.

b. $\frac{(-4)^2}{(-4)^7} = (-4)^{2-7}$ Quotient of Powers Property

$= (-4)^{-5}$ Simplify.

$= \frac{1}{(-4)^5}$ Definition of negative exponent

c. $(z^4)^{-3} = z^{4 \cdot (-3)}$ Power of a Power Property

$= z^{-12}$ Simplify.

$= \frac{1}{z^{12}}$ Definition of negative exponent

SELF-ASSESSMENT 1 I do not understand. 2 I can do it with help. 3 I can do it on my own. 4 I can teach someone else.

Simplify the expression. Write your answer using only positive exponents.

10. $10^4 \cdot 10^{-6}$ **11.** $\frac{-5^8}{-5^4}$ **12.** $\frac{y^6}{y^7}$ **13.** $(w^{12})^5$

14. DIFFERENT WORDS, SAME QUESTION Which is different? Find "both" answers.

Simplify $3^3 \cdot 3^6$. Simplify 3^{3+6}. Simplify $3^{6 \cdot 3}$. Simplify $3^6 \cdot 3^3$.

KEY IDEAS

Power of a Product Property

Let a and b be real numbers, and let m be an integer.

Words To find a power of a product, find the power of each factor and multiply.

Numbers $(3 \cdot 2)^5 = 3^5 \cdot 2^5$ **Algebra** $(ab)^m = a^m b^m$

Power of a Quotient Property

Let a and b be real numbers with $b \neq 0$, and let m be an integer.

Words To find the power of a quotient, find the power of the numerator and the power of the denominator and divide.

Numbers $\left(\frac{3}{2}\right)^5 = \frac{3^5}{2^5}$ **Algebra** $\left(\frac{a}{b}\right)^m = \frac{a^m}{b^m}$, where $b \neq 0$

EXAMPLE 4 Using Properties of Exponents

Simplify each expression. Write your answer using only positive exponents.

a. $(-1.5y)^2$ **b.** $\left(\frac{a}{-10}\right)^3$ **c.** $\left(\frac{3d}{2}\right)^4$ **d.** $\left(\frac{2x}{3}\right)^{-5}$

SOLUTION

a. $(-1.5y)^2 = (-1.5)^2 \cdot y^2$ Power of a Product Property

$= 2.25y^2$ Simplify.

b. $\left(\frac{a}{-10}\right)^3 = \frac{a^3}{(-10)^3}$ Power of a Quotient Property

$= -\frac{a^3}{1000}$ Simplify.

c. $\left(\frac{3d}{2}\right)^4 = \frac{(3d)^4}{2^4}$ Power of a Quotient Property

$= \frac{3^4d^4}{2^4}$ Power of a Product Property

$= \frac{81d^4}{16}$ Simplify.

d. $\left(\frac{2x}{3}\right)^{-5} = \frac{(2x)^{-5}}{3^{-5}}$ Power of a Quotient Property

$= \frac{3^5}{(2x)^5}$ Definition of negative exponent

$= \frac{3^5}{2^5x^5}$ Power of a Product Property

$= \frac{243}{32x^5}$ Simplify.

ANOTHER WAY

Because the exponent is negative, you could find the reciprocal of the base first. Then simplify.

$$\left(\frac{2x}{3}\right)^{-5} = \left(\frac{3}{2x}\right)^5 = \frac{243}{32x^5}$$

SELF-ASSESSMENT

1 I do not understand. 2 I can do it with help. 3 I can do it on my own. 4 I can teach someone else.

Simplify the expression. Write your answer using only positive exponents.

15. $(10y)^{-3}$ **16.** $\left(-\frac{4}{n}\right)^5$ **17.** $\left(\frac{1}{2k^2}\right)^5$ **18.** $\left(\frac{6c}{7}\right)^{-2}$

19. MP **REASONING** Which definitions or properties would you use to simplify $(4^8 \cdot 4^{-4})^{-2}$? Explain.

Solving Real-Life Problems

Volume = ?

$2\pi r^3$	$\pi h^3 2^{-2}$	$\pi h 4^{-1}$
$\frac{\pi h^2}{4}$	$\frac{\pi h^3}{4}$	$\frac{\pi h^3}{2}$

EXAMPLE 5 Simplifying a Real-Life Expression

Which of the expressions shown represent the volume of the cylindrical can, where r is the radius and h is the height?

SOLUTION

$V = \pi r^2 h$ — Formula for the volume of a cylinder

$= \pi\left(\frac{h}{2}\right)^2(h)$ — Substitute $\frac{h}{2}$ for r.

$= \pi\left(\frac{h^2}{2^2}\right)(h)$ — Power of a Quotient Property

$= \frac{\pi h^3}{4}$ — Simplify.

Any expression equivalent to $\frac{\pi h^3}{4}$ represents the volume of the cylinder.

- You can use the properties of exponents to write $\pi h^3 2^{-2}$ as $\frac{\pi h^3}{4}$.
- Note $h = 2r$. When you substitute $2r$ for h in $\frac{\pi h^3}{4}$, you can write $\frac{\pi(2r)^3}{4}$ as $2\pi r^3$.
- None of the other expressions are equivalent to $\frac{\pi h^3}{4}$.

▶ The expressions $2\pi r^3$, $\pi h^3 2^{-2}$, and $\frac{\pi h^3}{4}$ represent the volume of the cylinder.

REMEMBER

A number is written in scientific notation when it is of the form $a \times 10^b$, where $1 \le a < 10$ and b is an integer.

EXAMPLE 6 Modeling Real Life

A jellyfish emits about 1.25×10^8 particles of light, or photons, in 6.25×10^{-4} second. How many photons does the jellyfish emit each second? Write your answer in scientific notation and in standard form.

SOLUTION

Divide to find the unit rate in photons per second.

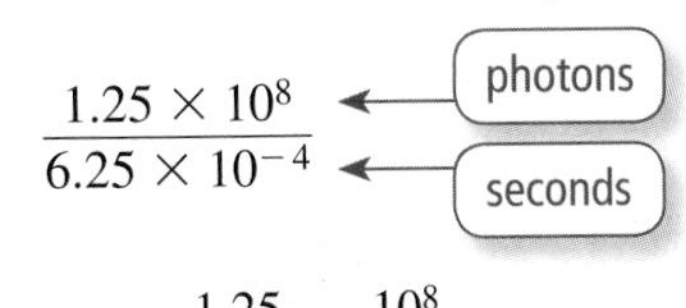

$\frac{1.25 \times 10^8}{6.25 \times 10^{-4}}$ — Divide the number of photons by the number of seconds.

$= \frac{1.25}{6.25} \times \frac{10^8}{10^{-4}}$ — Rewrite.

$= 0.2 \times 10^{12}$ — Simplify.

$= 2 \times 10^{11}$ — Write in scientific notation.

▶ The jellyfish emits 2×10^{11}, or 200,000,000,000 photons per second.

SELF-ASSESSMENT 1 I do not understand. 2 I can do it with help. 3 I can do it on my own. 4 I can teach someone else.

20. Write an expression in terms of h that represents the area of a base of the cylindrical can in Example 5.

21. It takes the Sun about 2.3×10^8 years to orbit the center of the Milky Way. It takes the Moon about 7.5×10^{-2} year to orbit Earth. About how many times does the Moon orbit Earth while the Sun completes one orbit around the center of the Milky Way? Write your answer in scientific notation.

6.1 Practice WITH CalcChat® AND CalcView®

In Exercises 1–8, evaluate the expression. *Example 1*

1. $(-7)^0$
2. 4^0
3. 5^{-4}
4. $(-2)^{-5}$
5. $\frac{2^{-6}}{4^0}$
6. $\frac{5^{-1}}{-9^0}$
7. $\frac{-3^{-3}}{6^{-2}}$
8. $\frac{(-8)^{-2}}{3^{-4}}$

In Exercises 9–18, simplify the expression. Write your answer using only positive exponents. *Example 2*

9. x^{-7}
10. y^0
11. $9x^0y^{-3}$
12. $15c^{-8}d^0$
13. $\frac{2^{-2}m^{-3}}{n^0}$
14. $\frac{10^0r^{-11}s}{3^2}$
15. $\frac{4^{-3}a^0}{b^{-7}}$
16. $\frac{p^{-8}}{7^{-2}q^{-9}}$
17. $\frac{2^2y^{-6}}{8^{-1}z^0x^{-7}}$
18. $\frac{13x^{-5}y^0}{5^{-3}z^{-10}}$

In Exercises 19–28, simplify the expression. Write your answer using only positive exponents. *Example 3*

19. $\frac{5^6}{5^2}$
20. $\frac{(-6)^8}{(-6)^5}$
21. $(-9)^2 \cdot (-9)^2$
22. $4^{-5} \cdot 4^5$
23. $(p^6)^4$
24. $(s^{-5})^3$
25. $6^{-10} \cdot 6^5$
26. $-7 \cdot (-7)^{-4}$
27. $\frac{x^5}{x^4} \cdot x$
28. $\frac{z^8 \cdot z^2}{z^5}$

29. **MODELING REAL LIFE** A microscope magnifies an object 10^5 times. The length of an object is 10^{-7} meter. What is its magnified length?

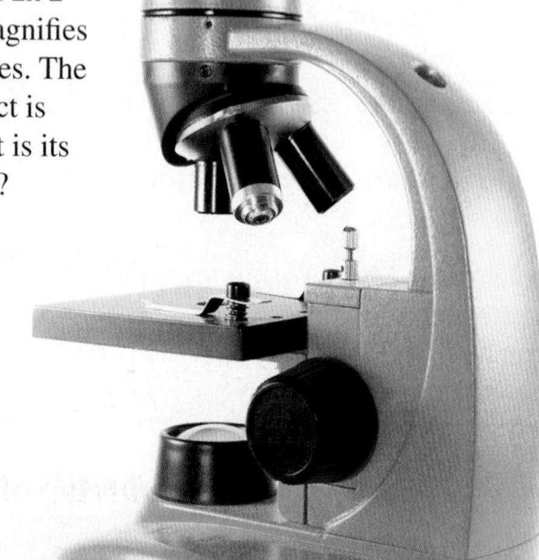

30. **MODELING REAL LIFE** A seed from an orchid has a mass of 10^{-6} gram. The mass of a seed from a double coconut palm is 10^{10} times the mass of the seed from the orchid. What is the mass of the seed from the double coconut palm in kilograms? ($1 \text{ kg} = 10^3 \text{ g}$)

ERROR ANALYSIS In Exercises 31 and 32, describe and correct the error in simplifying the expression.

31.

✗ $2^4 \cdot 2^5 = (2 \cdot 2)^{4+5}$
$= 4^9$

32.

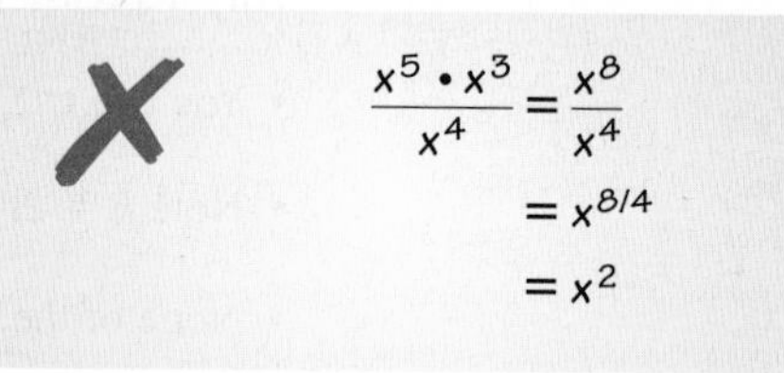

In Exercises 33–40, simplify the expression. Write your answer using only positive exponents. *Example 4*

33. $(-5z)^3$
34. $(4x)^{-4}$
35. $\left(\frac{6}{n}\right)^{-2}$
36. $\left(\frac{-t}{3}\right)^2$
37. $(3s^8)^{-5}$
38. $(-8p^3)^3$
39. $\left(-\frac{w^3}{9}\right)^{-2}$
40. $\left(\frac{1}{2r^6}\right)^{-6}$

41. **COLLEGE PREP** Which of the expressions represent the volume of the square prism, where s is the side length of the base and h is the height of the prism? Select all that apply. *Example 5*

Ⓐ $\frac{h^3}{16}$

Ⓑ $\frac{h^3}{4}$

Ⓒ $\frac{4^{-2}}{h^{-3}}$

Ⓓ $(2^{-2})^2h^3$

Ⓔ $16s^3$

Ⓕ $4s^3$

h

$\frac{h}{4}$

42. **COLLEGE PREP** Which of the expressions represent the volume of the square pyramid, where s is the side length of the base and h is the height of the pyramid? Select all that apply.

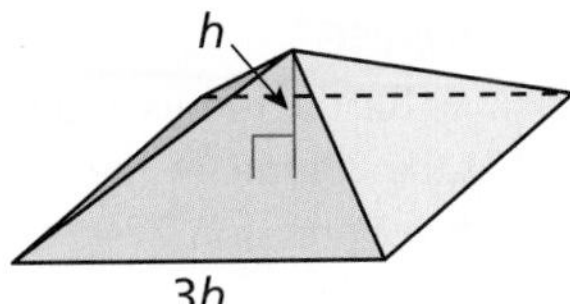

Ⓐ h^3 Ⓑ $3h^3$

Ⓒ $\frac{1}{3^{-1}h^{-3}}$ Ⓓ $\frac{1}{3h^{-3}}$

Ⓔ $\left(\frac{3}{s}\right)^{-3}$ Ⓕ $\frac{s^3}{9}$

In Exercises 43–46, simplify the expression. Write your answer using only positive exponents.

43. $\left(\frac{2x^{-2}y^3}{3xy^{-4}}\right)^4$

44. $\left(\frac{4s^5t^{-7}}{-2s^{-2}t^4}\right)^3$

45. $\left(\frac{3m^{-5}n^2}{4m^{-2}n^0}\right)^2 \cdot \left(\frac{mn^4}{9n}\right)^2$

46. $\left(\frac{3x^3y^0}{x^{-2}}\right)^4 \cdot \left(\frac{y^2x^{-4}}{5xy^{-8}}\right)^3$

In Exercises 47–50, evaluate the expression. Write your answer in scientific notation and in standard form.

47. $(3 \times 10^2)(1.5 \times 10^{-5})$

48. $(6.1 \times 10^{-3})(8 \times 10^9)$

49. $\frac{(6.4 \times 10^7)}{(1.6 \times 10^5)}$

50. $\frac{(3.9 \times 10^{-5})}{(7.8 \times 10^{-8})}$

51. **MODELING REAL LIFE** The human body produces about 4.8×10^6 red blood cells in 4×10^{-2} minute. How many red blood cells does the body produce each minute? Write your answer in scientific notation and in standard form. *Example 6*

52. **MODELING REAL LIFE** The speed of light is approximately 3×10^5 kilometers per second. How long does it take sunlight to reach Jupiter? Write your answer in scientific notation and in standard form.

Average Distance: 7.8×10^8 kilometers

53. **MP NUMBER SENSE** Without evaluating, order $(7 \cdot 7)^5$, $(7 \cdot 7)^{-8}$, and $(7 \cdot 7)^0$ from least to greatest. Explain your reasoning.

54. **MP STRUCTURE** Without evaluating, rewrite $\frac{3^{10} \cdot 27^9}{9^{12}}$ as a single power with base 3.

55. **MP PROBLEM SOLVING** A byte is a unit used to measure a computer's memory. The table shows the numbers of bytes in several units of measure.

Unit	kilobyte	megabyte	gigabyte	terabyte
Number of bytes	2^{10}	2^{20}	2^{30}	2^{40}

a. How many kilobytes are in 1 terabyte? Write your answer as a power.

b. How many megabytes are in 16 gigabytes? Write your answer as a power.

c. Another unit used to measure a computer's memory is a bit. There are 8 bits in a byte. How can you convert the number of bytes in each unit of measure given in the table to bits? Can you still use a base of 2? Explain.

56. **MP STRUCTURE** The probability of rolling a 6 on a number cube is $\frac{1}{6}$. The probability of rolling a 6 twice in a row is $\left(\frac{1}{6}\right)^2 = \frac{1}{36}$.

a. Write an expression that represents the probability of rolling a 6 n times in a row.

b. What is the probability of rolling a 6 four times in a row?

c. What is the probability of flipping heads on a coin five times in a row? Explain.

In Exercises 57–60, rewrite the expression as a power of a product.

57. $8a^3b^3$

58. $16r^2s^2$

59. $64w^{18}z^{12}$

60. $81x^4y^8$

61. **MP STRUCTURE** Find the value of each missing exponent.

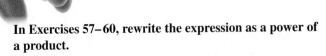

$$\left(\frac{p^5q^7r^2}{p^{-2}qr^6}\right)^{\blacksquare} = \frac{r^{12}}{p^{21}q^{\blacksquare}}$$

62. HOW DO YOU SEE IT?
The shaded part of Figure n represents the portion of a piece of paper visible after folding the paper in half n times.

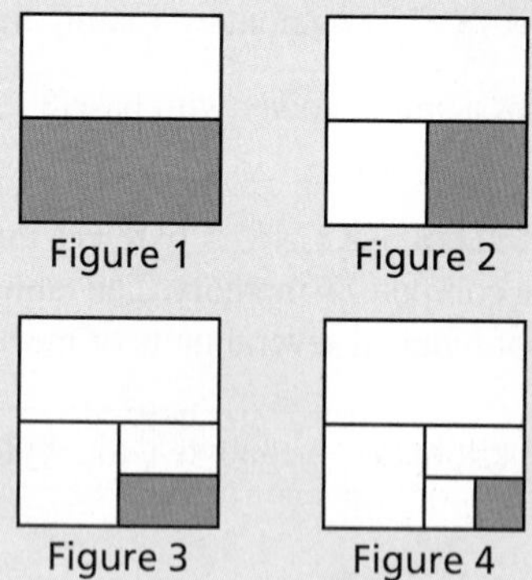

a. What fraction of the original piece of paper is each shaded part?

b. Rewrite each fraction from part (a) in the form 2^x.

63. OPEN-ENDED Write an expression that simplifies to x^3y^2 using at least three different properties of exponents. Identify the properties used.

64. THOUGHT PROVOKING
Write expressions for the radius and the height of a cone so that the volume of the cone can be represented by the expression $27\pi x^8$.

65.  Find x and y when

$$\frac{b^x}{b^y} = b^9 \text{ and } \frac{b^x \cdot b^2}{b^{3y}} = b^{13}.$$

Explain how you found your answer.

66. ABSTRACT REASONING Compare the values of a^n and a^{-n} when $n < 0$, when $n = 0$, and when $n > 0$ for (a) $a > 1$ and (b) $0 < a < 1$. Explain your reasoning.

REVIEW & REFRESH

WATCH

In Exercises 67–70, classify the real number in as many ways as possible.

67. 12

68. $\frac{65}{9}$

69. $\frac{\pi}{4}$

70. $-\frac{15}{3}$

71. Graph $x < -2\frac{1}{2}$ in a coordinate plane.

72. Determine which of the lines, if any, are parallel or perpendicular. Explain.

Line a passes through $(0, 1)$ and $(6, -3)$.
Line b passes through $(-3, 0)$ and $(3, -2)$.
Line c passes through $(-4, -2)$ and $(2, 7)$.

73. Simplify $\left(\frac{2x^0}{4x^{-2}y^4}\right)^2$. Write your answer using only positive exponents.

74. Line ℓ is a reflection in the y-axis of line k. Write an equation that represents line k in slope-intercept form.

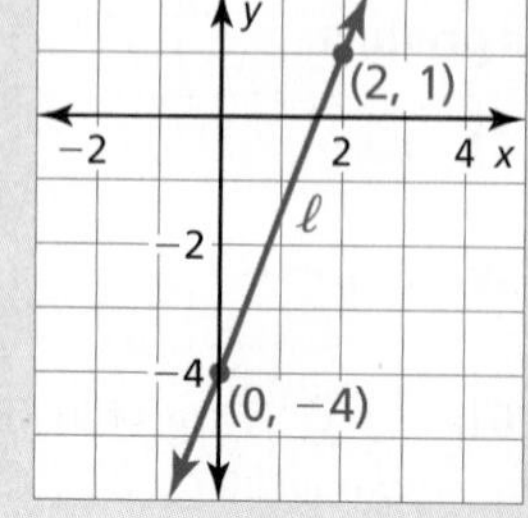

75. Solve $|x - 2| = \frac{1}{3}x + 2$ by graphing. Check your solutions.

In Exercises 76–79, find the square root(s).

76. $\sqrt{25}$

77. $-\sqrt{100}$

78. $\pm\sqrt{\frac{1}{64}}$

79. $-\sqrt{1.44}$

80. MP STRUCTURE For what value(s) of a does the system have no solution? infinitely many solutions?

$$4x - y = -3$$
$$-20x + 5y = a$$

81. MODELING REAL LIFE You can spend at most \$21 on fruit. Blueberries cost \$4 per pound, and strawberries cost \$3 per pound. You need at least 3 pounds of fruit to make muffins. Write and graph a system that represents the situation. How many pounds of each fruit can you buy?

82. The table shows the high temperatures in a city over a 10-day period. Find the mean, median, mode, and range of the temperatures.

Temperatures (degrees Fahrenheit)				
51	54	49	48	56
58	62	57	54	61

6.2 Radicals and Rational Exponents

Learning Target Write and evaluate an *n*th root of a number.

Success Criteria
- I can find *n*th roots.
- I can evaluate expressions with rational exponents.
- I can solve real-life problems involving rational exponents.

EXPLORE IT! Evaluating Rational Exponents

Work with a partner. In the previous section, you worked with integer exponents. Exponents can be any rational number. Assume that the properties of integer exponents hold true for all rational exponents.

Math Practice

Use Prior Results Which property of exponents did you use to evaluate the expressions in part (a)?

a. Evaluate each expression.

  i. $(3^{1/2})^2$
  ii. $(5^{1/3})^3$
  iii. $(10^{1/4})^4$

b. In part (a), $3^{1/2}$ is a number whose square is 3, $5^{1/3}$ is a number whose cube is 5, and $10^{1/4}$ is a number whose fourth power is 10. How else can you write these numbers?

c. What is another way you can write $a^{1/n}$, where n is an integer greater than 1 and a is a real number?

d. Write the side length of the square cover glass with the given area two different ways.

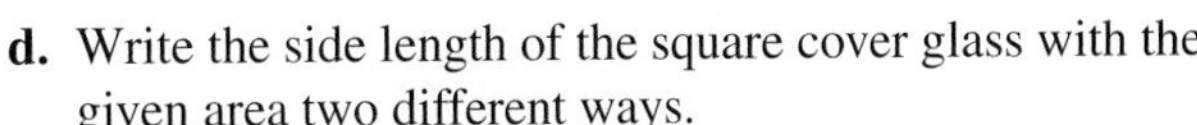

Area ≈ 480 mm²

e. Write the edge length of the ice cube with the given volume two different ways.

Volume ≈ 11 cm³

Finding *n*th Roots

Vocabulary

*n*th root of *a*, *p. 308*
radical, *p. 308*
index of a radical, *p. 308*

You can extend the concept of a square root to other types of roots. For example, 2 is a cube root of 8 because $2^3 = 8$, and 3 is a fourth root of 81 because $3^4 = 81$. In general, for an integer n greater than 1, if $b^n = a$, then b is an ***n*th root of *a***. An nth root of a is written as $\sqrt[n]{a}$, where the expression $\sqrt[n]{a}$ is called a **radical** and n is the **index** of the radical.

You can also write an nth root of a as a power of a. If you assume the Power of a Power Property applies to rational exponents, then the following is true.

$$(a^{1/2})^2 = a^{(1/2) \cdot 2} = a^1 = a$$
$$(a^{1/3})^3 = a^{(1/3) \cdot 3} = a^1 = a$$
$$(a^{1/4})^4 = a^{(1/4) \cdot 4} = a^1 = a$$

Because $a^{1/2}$ is a number whose square is a, you can write $\sqrt{a} = a^{1/2}$. Similarly, $\sqrt[3]{a} = a^{1/3}$ and $\sqrt[4]{a} = a^{1/4}$. In general, $\sqrt[n]{a} = a^{1/n}$ for any integer n greater than 1.

KEY IDEA

Real *n*th Roots of *a*

Let n be an integer greater than 1, and let a be a real number.

- If n is odd, then a has one real nth root: $\sqrt[n]{a} = a^{1/n}$
- If n is even and $a > 0$, then a has two real nth roots: $\pm\sqrt[n]{a} = \pm a^{1/n}$
- If n is even and $a = 0$, then a has one real nth root: $\sqrt[n]{0} = 0$
- If n is even and $a < 0$, then a has no real nth roots.

READING

$\pm\sqrt[n]{a}$ represents both the positive and negative *n*th roots of *a*.

The nth roots of a number may be real numbers or *imaginary numbers*. You will study imaginary numbers in a future course.

EXAMPLE 1 **Finding *n*th Roots**

Find the indicated real nth root(s) of a.

a. $n = 3, a = -27$ **b.** $n = 4, a = 16$

SOLUTION

a. The index $n = 3$ is odd, so -27 has one real cube root. Because $(-3)^3 = -27$, the cube root of -27 is

$$\sqrt[3]{-27} = -3, \text{ or } (-27)^{1/3} = -3.$$

b. The index $n = 4$ is even, and $a > 0$. So, 16 has two real fourth roots. Because $2^4 = 16$ and $(-2)^4 = 16$, the fourth roots of 16 are

$$\pm\sqrt[4]{16} = \pm 2, \text{ or } \pm 16^{1/4} = \pm 2.$$

SELF-ASSESSMENT 1 I do not understand. 2 I can do it with help. 3 I can do it on my own. 4 I can teach someone else.

1. **MP STRUCTURE** What does the exponent $\frac{1}{5}$ mean in the expression $64^{1/5}$?

Find the indicated real *n*th root(s) of *a*.

2. $n = 2, a = 400$
3. $n = 3, a = -125$
4. $n = 6, a = 64$
5. **MP REASONING** Write two different expressions involving rational exponents that are equivalent to $\sqrt{5}$.

Evaluating Expressions with Rational Exponents

Recall that the radical $\sqrt{a}$ indicates the positive square root of a. Similarly, an nth root of a, $\sqrt[n]{a}$, with an *even* index indicates the positive nth root of a.

EXAMPLE 2 Evaluating *n*th Root Expressions

Evaluate each expression.

a. $\sqrt[3]{-8}$ **b.** $-\sqrt[3]{8}$ **c.** $16^{1/4}$ **d.** $(-16)^{1/4}$

SOLUTION

a. $\sqrt[3]{-8} = \sqrt[3]{(-2) \cdot (-2) \cdot (-2)}$ Rewrite the expression showing factors.

$= -2$ Evaluate the cube root.

b. $-\sqrt[3]{8} = -\left(\sqrt[3]{2 \cdot 2 \cdot 2}\right)$ Rewrite the expression showing factors.

$= -(2)$ Evaluate the cube root.

$= -2$ Simplify.

c. $16^{1/4} = \sqrt[4]{16}$ Rewrite the expression in radical form.

$= \sqrt[4]{2 \cdot 2 \cdot 2 \cdot 2}$ Rewrite the expression showing factors.

$= 2$ Evaluate the fourth root.

d. $(-16)^{1/4}$ is not a real number because there is no real number that can be multiplied by itself four times to produce -16.

KEY IDEA

Rational Exponents

Let $a^{1/n}$ be an nth root of a, and let m be a positive integer.

Algebra $a^{m/n} = a^{(1/n) \cdot m} = (a^{1/n})^m = \left(\sqrt[n]{a}\right)^m$ or $a^{m/n} = a^{m \cdot (1/n)} = (a^m)^{1/n} = \sqrt[n]{a^m}$

Numbers $27^{2/3} = 27^{(1/3) \cdot 2} = (27^{1/3})^2 = \left(\sqrt[3]{27}\right)^2$ or $27^{2/3} = 27^{2 \cdot (1/3)} = (27^2)^{1/3} = \sqrt[3]{27^2}$

EXAMPLE 3 Evaluating Expressions with Rational Exponents

Evaluate (a) $16^{3/4}$ and (b) $27^{4/3}$.

SOLUTION

a. $16^{3/4} = (16^{1/4})^3$ Rewrite exponent.

$= 2^3$ Evaluate the *n*th root.

$= 8$ Evaluate the power.

b. $27^{4/3} = (27^{1/3})^4$

$= 3^4$

$= 81$

SELF-ASSESSMENT

1 I do not understand. 2 I can do it with help. 3 I can do it on my own. 4 I can teach someone else.

Evaluate the expression.

6. $\sqrt[3]{-512}$ **7.** $(-64)^{2/3}$ **8.** $9^{5/2}$ **9.** $256^{3/4}$

10. WHICH ONE DOESN'T BELONG? The value of which expression does *not* belong with the other three? Explain your reasoning.

$\left(\sqrt[3]{343}\right)^2$ $343^{2/3}$ 7^2 $\left(\sqrt[2]{343}\right)^3$

Volume = 113 cubic feet

GO DIGITAL

Solving Real-Life Problems

EXAMPLE 4 **Modeling Real Life** 

The radius r of a sphere is given by the equation $r = \left(\frac{3V}{4\pi}\right)^{1/3}$, where V is the volume of the sphere. Find the radius of the beach ball to the nearest foot. Use 3.14 for π.

SOLUTION

1. **Understand the Problem** You know the equation that represents the radius of a sphere in terms of its volume. You are asked to find the radius for a given volume.
2. **Make a Plan** Substitute the given volume into the equation. Then evaluate to find the radius.
3. **Solve and Check**

$$r = \left(\frac{3V}{4\pi}\right)^{1/3}$$ Write the equation.

$$= \left(\frac{3(113)}{4(3.14)}\right)^{1/3}$$ Substitute 113 for V and 3.14 for π.

$$= \left(\frac{339}{12.56}\right)^{1/3}$$ Multiply.

$$\approx 3$$ Use technology.

▶ The radius of the beach ball is about 3 feet.

Check Reasonableness
To check that your answer is reasonable, compare the size of the ball to the size of the person. The ball appears to be slightly taller. So, a radius of 3 feet, or a diameter of 6 feet, seems reasonable for the beach ball.

EXAMPLE 5 **Modeling Real Life**  

To calculate the annual inflation rate r (in decimal form) of an item that increases in value from P to F over a period of n years, you can use the equation $r = \left(\frac{F}{P}\right)^{1/n} - 1$. Find the annual inflation rate of a house that increases in value from \$200,000 to \$235,000 over a period of 5 years. Round your answer to the nearest tenth of a percent.

SOLUTION

$$r = \left(\frac{F}{P}\right)^{1/n} - 1$$ Write the equation.

$$= \left(\frac{235{,}000}{200{,}000}\right)^{1/5} - 1$$ Substitute 235,000 for F, 200,000 for P, and 5 for n.

$$= 1.175^{1/5} - 1$$ Divide.

$$\approx 0.03278$$ Use technology.

▶ The annual inflation rate is about 3.3%.

REMEMBER
To write a decimal as a percent, multiply by 100, which moves the decimal point two places to the right. Then add a percent symbol.

SELF-ASSESSMENT 1 I do not understand. 2 I can do it with help. 3 I can do it on my own. 4 I can teach someone else.

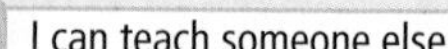

11. The volume of a beach ball is 17,000 cubic inches. How much greater is the radius of the beach ball in Example 4? Use 3.14 for π.
12. The average tuition cost of a 4-year college increases from \$20,125 to \$25,900 over a period of 6 years. The average tuition cost of a 2-year college increases from \$8540 to \$10,950 over the same period. Which has a greater annual inflation rate? Explain.

6.2 Practice WITH CalcChat® AND CalcView®

In Exercises 1 and 2, rewrite the expression in rational exponent form.

1. $\sqrt{10}$
2. $\sqrt[5]{34}$

In Exercises 3 and 4, rewrite the expression in radical form.

3. $15^{1/3}$
4. $140^{1/8}$

In Exercises 5–8, find the indicated real *n*th root(s) of *a*. *Example 1*

5. $n = 2, a = 36$
6. $n = 4, a = 81$
7. $n = 3, a = 1000$
8. $n = 9, a = -512$

MP STRUCTURE In Exercises 9 and 10, find the dimensions of the cube. Check your answer.

9. Volume = 64 in.^{3}

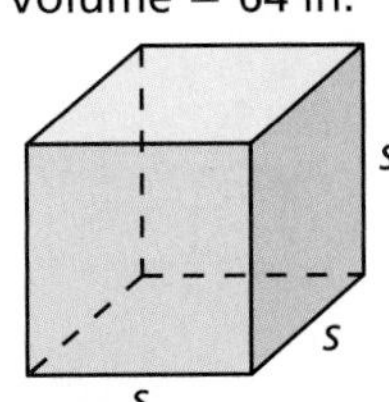

10. Volume = 216 cm^3

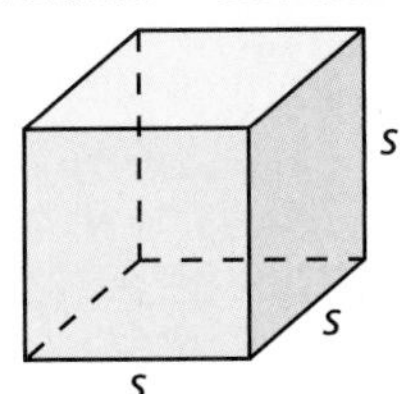

In Exercises 11–16, evaluate the expression. *Example 2*

11. $\sqrt[4]{256}$
12. $\sqrt[3]{-216}$
13. $\sqrt[3]{-343}$
14. $-\sqrt[5]{1024}$
15. $128^{1/7}$
16. $(-64)^{1/2}$

In Exercises 17 and 18, rewrite the expression in rational exponent form.

17. $(\sqrt[5]{8})^4$
18. $\sqrt[5]{-21^6}$

In Exercises 19 and 20, rewrite the expression in radical form.

19. $(-4)^{2/7}$
20. $9^{5/2}$

In Exercises 21–26, evaluate the expression. *Example 3*

21. $32^{3/5}$
22. $125^{2/3}$
23. $(-36)^{3/2}$
24. $(-243)^{2/5}$
25. $(-128)^{5/7}$
26. $343^{4/3}$

27. **ERROR ANALYSIS** Describe and correct the error in rewriting the expression in rational exponent form.

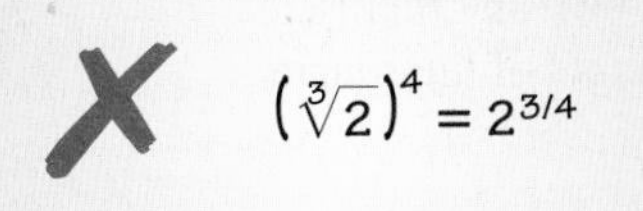

28. **ERROR ANALYSIS** Describe and correct the error in evaluating the expression.

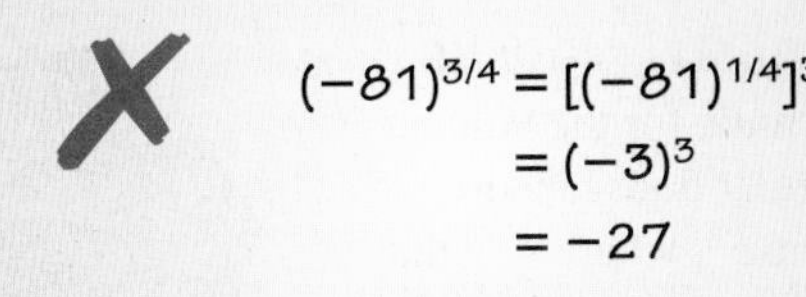

In Exercises 29–32, evaluate the expression.

29. $\left(\frac{1}{1000}\right)^{1/3}$
30. $\left(\frac{1}{64}\right)^{1/6}$
31. $27^{-2/3}$
32. $9^{-5/2}$

33. **MODELING REAL LIFE** The radius r of a cone is given by the equation $r = \left(\frac{3V}{\pi h}\right)^{1/2}$, where V is the volume of the cone and h is the height of the cone. Find the radius, to the nearest inch, of a paper cup that has a volume of 5 cubic inches and a height of 4 inches. Use 3.14 for π. *Example 4*

34. **MODELING REAL LIFE** The volume of a sphere is given by the equation $V = \frac{1}{6\sqrt{\pi}}S^{3/2}$, where S is the surface area of the sphere. Find the volume of a water walking ball, to the nearest cubic meter, that has a surface area of 60 square meters. Use 3.14 for π.

In Exercises 35 and 36, use the formula $r = \left(\frac{F}{P}\right)^{1/n} - 1$ to find the annual inflation rate to the nearest tenth of a percent. *Example 5*

35. A farm increases in value from \$800,000 to \$1,100,000 over a period of 6 years.

36. The cost of a movie ticket increases from \$6.75 to \$9.00 over a period of 10 years.

37. **COMPARING METHODS** You are using mental math to evaluate the expression $16^{5/4}$. Should you evaluate

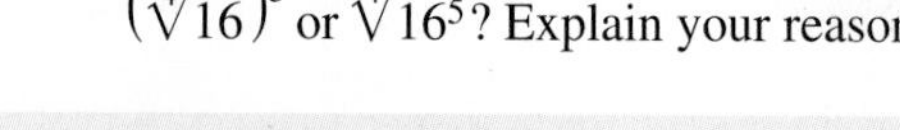

$(\sqrt[4]{16})^5$ or $\sqrt[4]{16^5}$? Explain your reasoning.

38. **HOW DO YOU SEE IT?**
Write an expression in rational exponent form that represents the side length of the square.

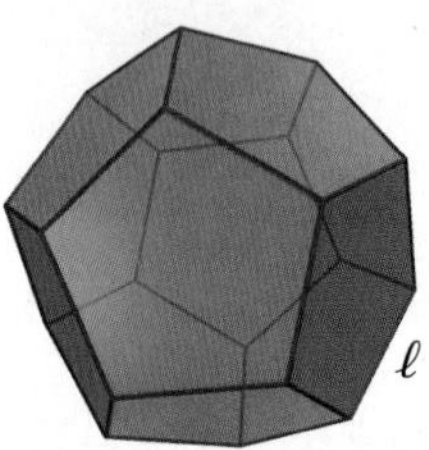

39. **WRITING** Explain how extending the properties of integer exponents to rational exponents allows you to express radicals in terms of rational exponents.

40. **MP PROBLEM SOLVING**
The formula for the volume of a regular dodecahedron is $V \approx 7.66\ell^3$, where ℓ is the length of an edge. The volume of the dodecahedron is 20 cubic feet. Estimate the edge length.

ℓ

In Exercises 41–44, simplify the expression.

41. $(y^{1/6})^3 \cdot \sqrt{x}$

42. $(y \cdot y^{1/3})^{3/2}$

43. $x \cdot \sqrt[3]{y^6} + y^2 \cdot \sqrt[3]{x^3}$

44. $(x^{1/3} \cdot y^{1/2})^9 \cdot \sqrt{y}$

45. **MP REASONING** For what values of x is $x = x^{1/5}$?

46. **THOUGHT PROVOKING**
To find the arithmetic mean of n numbers, divide the sum of the numbers by n. To find the geometric mean of n numbers $a_1, a_2, a_3, \ldots, a_n$, take the nth root of the product of the numbers.

$$\text{geometric mean} = \sqrt[n]{a_1 \cdot a_2 \cdot a_3 \cdot \ldots \cdot a_n}$$

Compare the arithmetic mean to the geometric mean of n numbers.

47. **MAKING AN ARGUMENT** Your friend says that for a real number a and an integer $n > 1$, the value of $\sqrt[n]{a}$ is always positive and the value of $-\sqrt[n]{a}$ is always negative. Is your friend correct? Explain.

ABSTRACT REASONING In Exercises 48–53, let x be a nonnegative real number. Determine whether the statement is *always*, *sometimes*, or *never* true. Justify your answer.

48. $(x^{1/3})^3 = x$

49. $x^{1/3} = x^{-3}$

50. $x^{1/3} = \sqrt[3]{x}$

51. $x^{1/3} = x^3$

52. $\dfrac{x^{2/3}}{x^{1/3}} = \sqrt[3]{x}$

53. $x = x^{1/3} \cdot x^3$

REVIEW & REFRESH

54. Evaluate the function $w(x) = -5x - 1$ when $x = -3, 0,$ and $\frac{4}{5}$.

55. Graph the system $y \geq -\frac{1}{2}x - 3$ and $-x + y < 1$.

In Exercises 56 and 57, solve the system. Explain your choice of method.

56. $y = \frac{1}{3}x - 6$
$y = -2x + 1$

57. $2x - 3y = -5$
$5x + 2y = 16$

58. **MODELING REAL LIFE** The table shows the earnings y (in dollars) of a food server who works x hours.

x	0	1	2	3	4	5	6
y	0	18	40	62	77	85	113

a. Write an equation that models the server's earnings as a function of the number of hours the server works.

b. Interpret the slope and y-intercept of the line of fit.

In Exercises 59 and 60, simplify the expression. Write your answer using only positive exponents.

59. $\dfrac{6^{-2}}{6^4}$

60. $(3z^8)^2$

61. Graph the equations $x = 5$, $x = 2$, $y = -2$, and $y = 1$. Find the area of the enclosed shape formed by the lines.

62. Write a piecewise function represented by the graph.

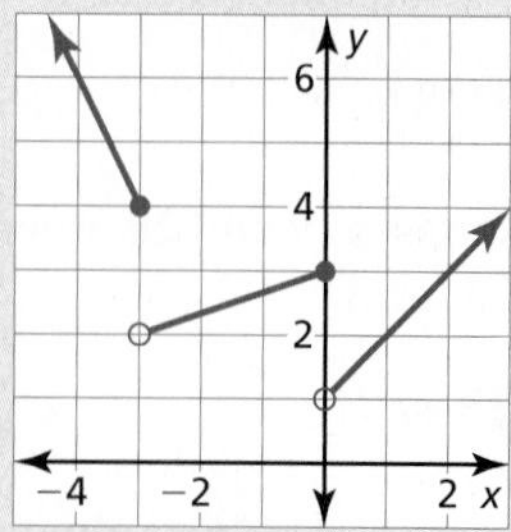

In Exercises 63 and 64, evaluate the expression.

63. $\sqrt[3]{-729}$

64. $256^{3/4}$

65. Tell whether $(-4, 9)$ is a solution of $6x - y \leq 13$.

6.3 Exponential Functions

Learning Target Graph and write exponential functions.

Success Criteria

- I can identify an exponential function.
- I can evaluate and graph an exponential function.
- I can write exponential functions.
- I can model real-life problems using exponential functions.

EXPLORE IT! Understanding Exponential Functions

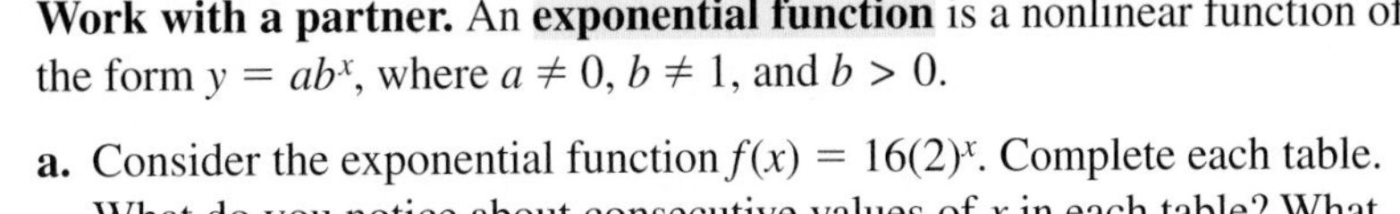

Work with a partner. An **exponential function** is a nonlinear function of the form $y = ab^x$, where $a \neq 0$, $b \neq 1$, and $b > 0$.

a. Consider the exponential function $f(x) = 16(2)^x$. Complete each table. What do you notice about consecutive values of x in each table? What do you notice about consecutive values of $f(x)$?

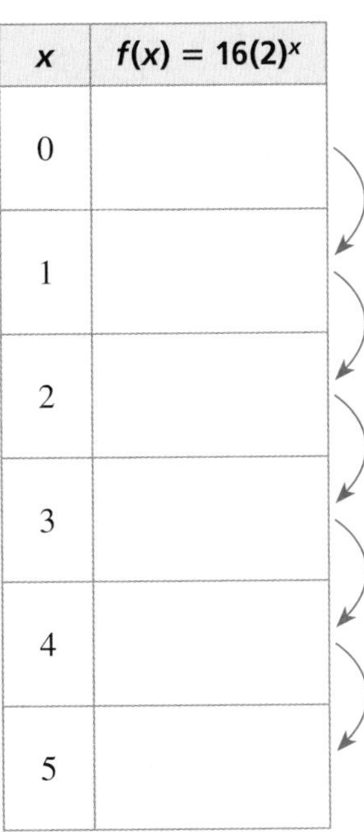
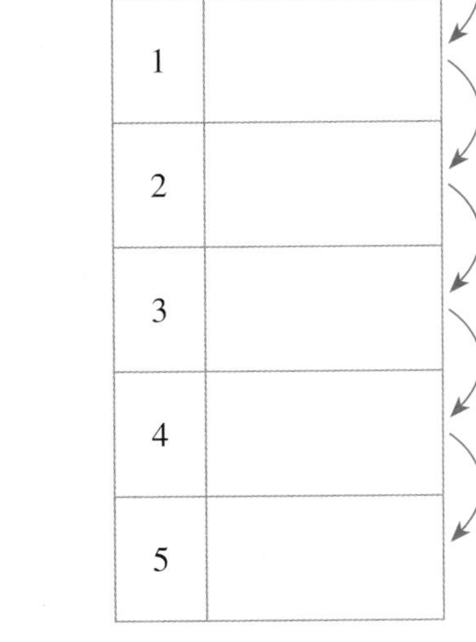

x	$f(x) = 16(2)^x$
0	
1	
2	
3	
4	
5	

x	$f(x) = 16(2)^x$
0	
2	
4	
6	
8	
10	

b. Repeat part (a) for the exponential function $g(x) = 16\left(\frac{1}{2}\right)^x$. Do you think the statement below is true for *any* exponential function? Explain your reasoning.

"As the independent variable x changes by a constant amount, the dependent variable y is multiplied by a constant factor."

c. Let f be an exponential function. Show that when a particular x-value, n, increases by a constant c, the following value is always the same no matter the value of n.

$$\frac{f(n + c)}{f(n)}$$

d. Sketch the graphs of the functions given in parts (a) and (b). How are the graphs similar? How are they different?

Math Practice

Justify Conclusions
What properties did you use in your justification in part (c)? Is the statement true for any exponential function?

GO DIGITAL

Identifying and Evaluating Exponential Functions

Vocabulary 

exponential function, *p. 314*
asymptote, *p. 315*

An **exponential function** is a nonlinear function of the form $y = ab^x$, where $a \neq 0$, $b \neq 1$, and $b > 0$. As the independent variable x changes by a constant amount, the dependent variable y is multiplied by a constant factor, which means consecutive y-values form equivalent ratios.

EXAMPLE 1 Identifying Functions

WATCH

Does each table represent a *linear* or an *exponential* function? Explain.

a.

x	0	1	2	3
y	2	4	6	8

b.

x	0	1	2	3
y	4	8	16	32

SOLUTION

a.

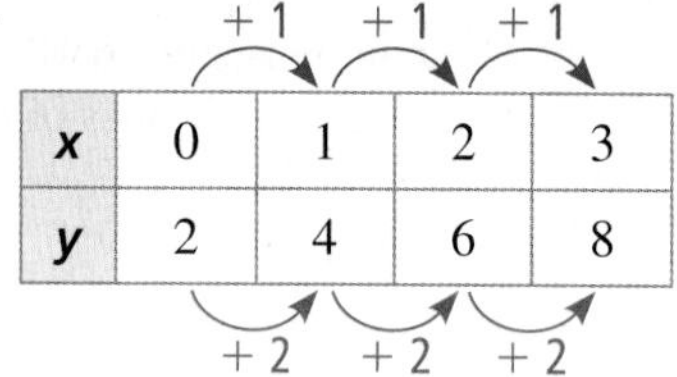

x	0	1	2	3
y	2	4	6	8

▶ As x increases by 1, y increases by 2. The rate of change is constant. So, the function is linear.

b.

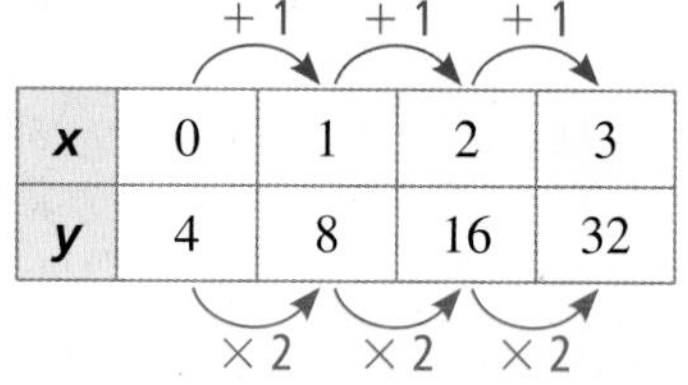

x	0	1	2	3
y	4	8	16	32

▶ As x increases by 1, y is multiplied by 2. So, the function is exponential.

STUDY TIP

In Example 1(b), consecutive y-values form equivalent ratios.

$\frac{8}{4} = 2,\ \frac{16}{8} = 2,\ \frac{32}{16} = 2$

EXAMPLE 2 Evaluating Exponential Functions

Evaluate each function for the given value of x.

a. $y = -2(5)^x$; $x = 3$

b. $y = 3(0.5)^x$; $x = -2$

SOLUTION

a.

$y = -2(5)^x$	Write the function.
$= -2(5)^3$	Substitute for x.
$= -2(125)$	Evaluate the power.
$= -250$	Multiply.

b.

$y = 3(0.5)^x$
$= 3(0.5)^{-2}$
$= 3(4)$
$= 12$

SELF-ASSESSMENT

1 I do not understand. 2 I can do it with help. 3 I can do it on my own. 4 I can teach someone else.

Does the table represent a *linear* or an *exponential* function? Explain.

1.

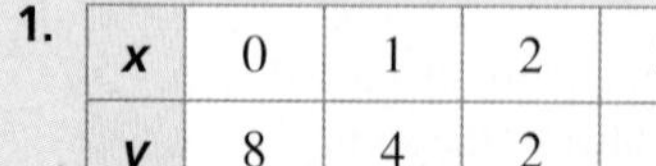

x	0	1	2	3
y	8	4	2	1

2.

x	−4	0	4	8
y	1	0	−1	−2

Evaluate the function when $x = -2$, 0, and $\frac{1}{2}$.

3. $y = 2(9)^x$

4. $y = 1.5(2)^x$

5. $y = -3\left(\frac{1}{4}\right)^x$

6. MP **REASONING** For each function in Example 2, what happens to the y-values as $x \to +\infty$? as $x \to -\infty$? Explain.

Graphing Exponential Functions

The graph of a function $y = ab^x$ is a vertical stretch or shrink by a factor of $|a|$ of the graph of the parent function $y = b^x$. When $a < 0$, the graph is also reflected in the x-axis. The y-intercept of the graph of $y = ab^x$ is a.

KEY IDEA

$y = ab^x$, where $b > 1$

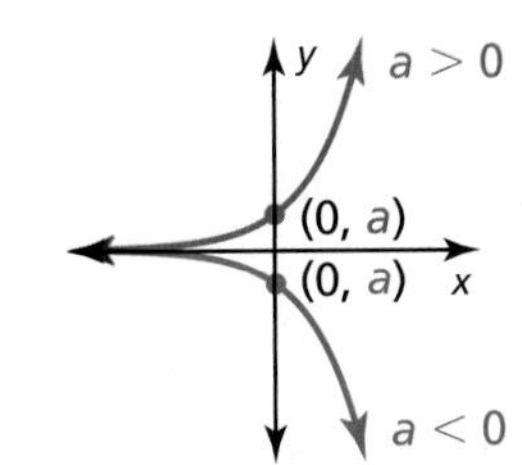

An **asymptote** is a line that a graph approaches more and more closely. The x-axis is an asymptote of the graph of $y = ab^x$.

$y = ab^x$, where $0 < b < 1$

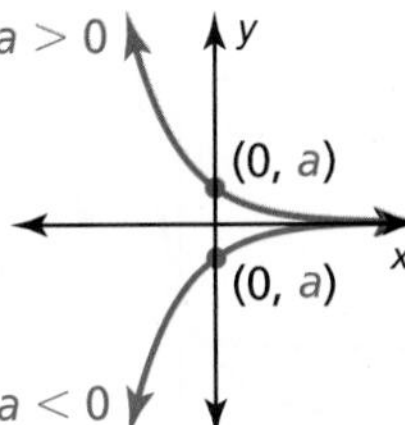

EXAMPLE 3 **Graphing $y = ab^x$**

Graph each function. Compare the graph to the graph of the parent function. Identify the y-intercepts and asymptotes of the graphs. Find the domain and range of f.

a. $f(x) = 4(2)^x$ **b.** $f(x) = -\left(\frac{1}{2}\right)^x$

SOLUTION

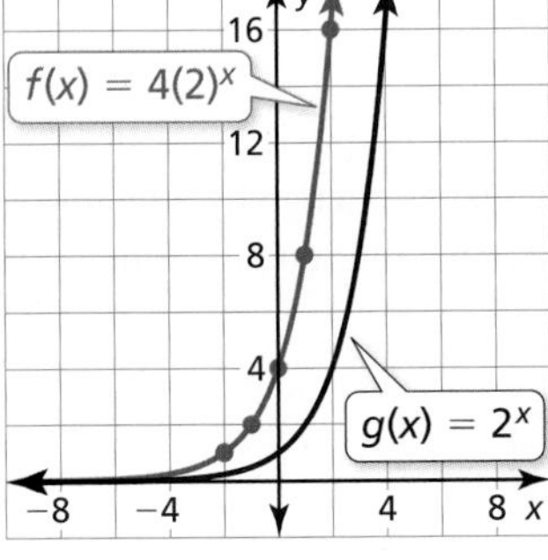

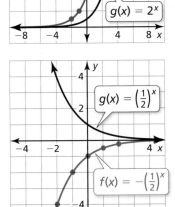

a. Step 1 Make a table of values.

Step 2 Plot the ordered pairs.

Step 3 Draw a smooth curve through the points.

x	−2	−1	0	1	2
f(x)	1	2	4	8	16

▶ The parent function is $g(x) = 2^x$. The graph of f is a vertical stretch by a factor of 4 of the graph of g. The y-intercept of the graph of f, 4, is greater than the y-intercept of the graph of g, 1. The x-axis is an asymptote of both the graphs of f and g. From the graph of f, you can see that the domain is all real numbers and the range is $y > 0$.

b. Step 1 Make a table of values.

Step 2 Plot the ordered pairs.

Step 3 Draw a smooth curve through the points.

x	−2	−1	0	1	2
f(x)	−4	−2	−1	$-\frac{1}{2}$	$-\frac{1}{4}$

▶ The parent function is $g(x) = \left(\frac{1}{2}\right)^x$. The graph of f is a reflection in the x-axis of the graph of g. The y-intercept of the graph of f, −1, is less than the y-intercept of the graph of g, 1. The x-axis is an asymptote of both the graphs of f and g. From the graph of f, you can see that the domain is all real numbers and the range is $y < 0$.

SELF-ASSESSMENT 1 I do not understand. 2 I can do it with help. 3 I can do it on my own. 4 I can teach someone else.

Graph the function. Compare the graph to the graph of the parent function. Identify the y-intercepts and asymptotes of the graphs. Find the domain and range of f.

7. $f(x) = -3^x$ **8.** $f(x) = -2(4)^x$ **9.** $f(x) = 2\left(\frac{1}{4}\right)^x$

10. OPEN-ENDED Sketch an increasing exponential function whose graph has a y-intercept of 2.

To graph a function of the form $y = ab^{x-h} + k$, begin by graphing $y = ab^x$. Then translate the graph horizontally h units and vertically k units.

EXAMPLE 4 Graphing $y = ab^{x-h} + k$

Graph $y = 4(2)^{x-3} + 2$. Identify the asymptote. Find the domain and range.

SOLUTION

Step 1 Graph $y = 4(2)^x$. This is the same function that is in Example 3, which passes through (0, 4) and (1, 8).

Step 2 Translate the graph 3 units right and 2 units up. The graph passes through (3, 6) and (4, 10).

Notice that the graph approaches the line $y = 2$ but does not intersect it.

▶ So, the graph has an asymptote at $y = 2$. From the graph, you can see that the domain is all real numbers and the range is $y > 2$.

SELF-ASSESSMENT

1 I do not understand. 2 I can do it with help. 3 I can do it on my own. 4 I can teach someone else.

Graph the function. Identify the asymptote. Find the domain and range.

11. $f(x) = (0.25)^x + 3$ **12.** $y = 2^{x-1} - 4$ **13.** $y = -2(3)^{x+2} - 1$

14. MP **REASONING** Explain why the graph of an exponential function is not a line.

Solving Real-Life Problems

For an exponential function of the form $y = ab^x$, the y-values change by a factor of b as x increases by 1. You can use this fact to write an exponential function when you know the y-intercept, a.

EXAMPLE 5 Modeling Real Life

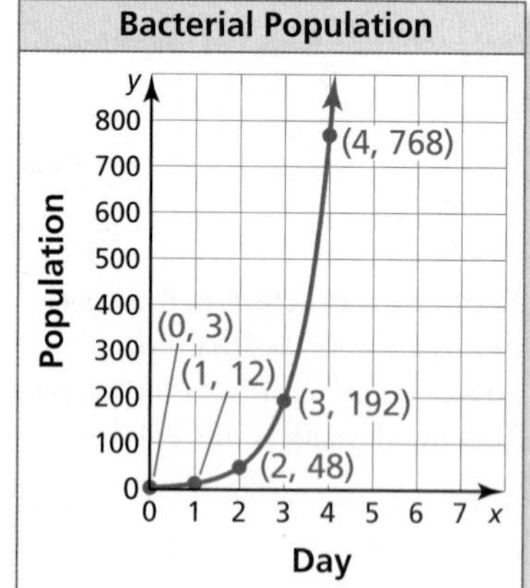

The graph represents a bacterial population y after x days. Find the population after 12 hours and after 5 days.

SOLUTION

One way to find the populations is to write and evaluate the function represented by the graph.

Use the graph to make a table of values.

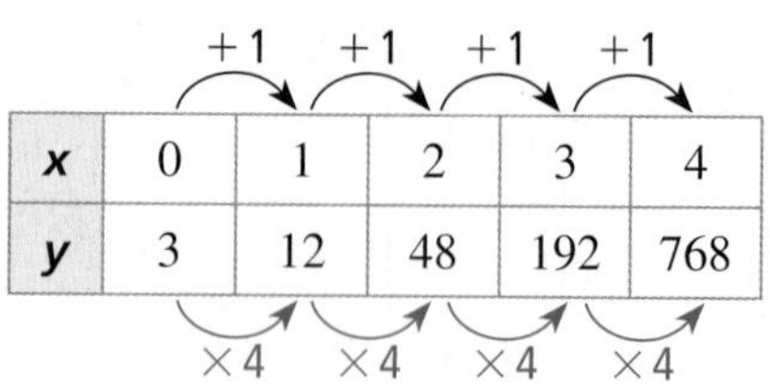

x	0	1	2	3	4
y	3	12	48	192	768

The y-intercept is 3. The y-values increase by a factor of 4 as x increases by 1. So, the population can be modeled by $y = 3(4)^x$.

Population after 12 hours		***Population after 5 days***
$y = 3(4)^x$	Write the function.	$y = 3(4)^x$
$= 3(4)^{1/2}$	Substitute for x.	$= 3(4)^5$
$= 3(2)$	Evaluate the power.	$= 3(1024)$
$= 6$	Multiply.	$= 3072$

12 hours $= \frac{1}{2}$ day

▶ There are 6 bacteria after 12 hours and 3072 bacteria after 5 days.

You have used *linear regression* to find an equation of the line of best fit. Similarly, you can use *exponential regression* to find an exponential function that best fits a data set.

EXAMPLE 6 Modeling Real Life

Time, x	Temperature, y
0	175
1	156
2	142
3	127
4	113
5	101
6	94
7	84
8	75

The table shows the temperatures y (in degrees Fahrenheit) of coffee x minutes after pouring a cup. Use technology to find a function that fits the data. Predict the temperature of the coffee 10 minutes after it is poured.

SOLUTION

Step 1 Enter the data from the table into a technology table and make a scatter plot of the data.

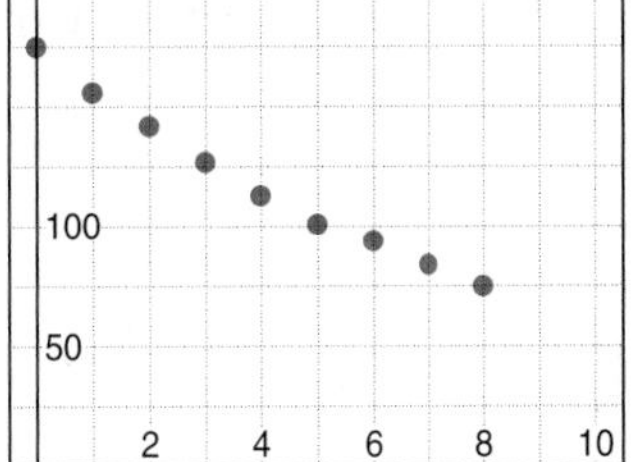

x	y
0	175
1	156
2	142
3	127
4	113
5	101
6	94

It appears that the data can be modeled by an exponential function.

Step 2 Use *exponential regression*. The values in the equation can be rounded to obtain $y = 174(0.9)^x$. Plot the data and graph the equation to check that the function is reasonable.

$y = ab^x$

PARAMETERS

$a = 173.952$ $b = 0.900318$

STATISTICS

$r^2 = 0.9987$

$r = -0.9994$

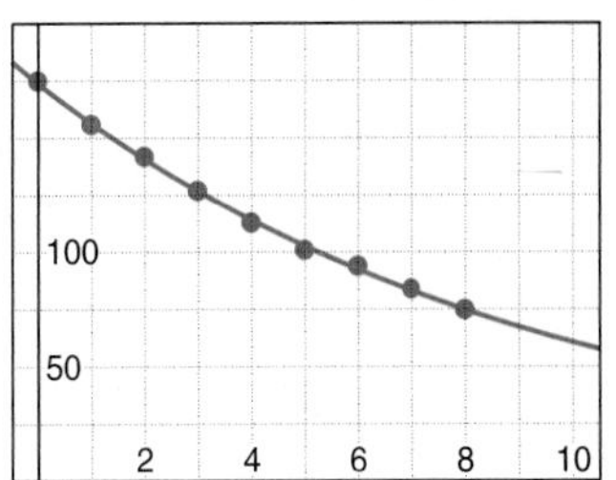

▶ After 10 minutes, the temperature of the coffee will be about $y = 174(0.9)^{10} \approx 60.7$ degrees Fahrenheit.

SELF-ASSESSMENT

1 I do not understand. 2 I can do it with help. 3 I can do it on my own. 4 I can teach someone else.

15. A bacterial population y after x days can be represented by an exponential function whose graph passes through (0, 100) and (1, 200). Find the population after 6 days. Does this bacterial population grow faster than the bacterial population in Example 5? Explain your reasoning.

16. The table shows the per capita U.S. bottled water consumption y (in gallons) x years after 2010. Use technology to find a function that fits the data. Estimate the bottled water consumption in 2022.

Years after 2010, x	0	1	2	3	4	5	6	7
Consumption, y	28.3	29.2	30.9	32.2	34.3	36.7	39.6	42.1

17. MP **REASONING** In Example 6, identify and interpret the correlation coefficient and the y-intercept.

6.3 Practice WITH CalcChat® AND CalcView®

In Exercises 1–6, determine whether the equation represents an exponential function. Explain.

1. $y = 4(7)^x$
2. $y = -6x$
3. $y = 2x^3$
4. $y = -3^x$
5. $y = 9(-5)^x$
6. $y = \frac{1}{2}(1)^x$

In Exercises 7–10, determine whether the table represents a *linear* or an *exponential* function. Explain. *Example 1*

7.

x	y
1	−2
2	0
3	2
4	4

8.

x	y
1	6
2	12
3	24
4	48

9.

x	−1	0	1	2	3
y	0.25	1	4	16	64

10.

x	−3	0	3	6	9
y	10	1	−8	−17	−26

In Exercises 11–16, evaluate the function for the given value of *x*. *Example 2*

11. $y = 3^x$; $x = 2$
12. $f(x) = 3(2)^x$; $x = -1$
13. $y = -4(5)^x$; $x = 2$
14. $f(x) = 0.5^x$; $x = -3$
15. $f(x) = \frac{1}{3}(6)^x$; $x = 3$
16. $y = \frac{1}{4}(4)^x$; $x = \frac{3}{2}$

In Exercises 17–22, graph the function. Compare the graph to the graph of the parent function. Identify the *y*-intercepts and asymptotes of the graphs. Find the domain and range of *f*. *Example 3*

17. $f(x) = -4^x$
18. $f(x) = -2(7)^x$
19. $f(x) = 3(0.5)^x$
20. $f(x) = 6\left(\frac{1}{3}\right)^x$
21. $f(x) = \frac{1}{2}(8)^x$
22. $f(x) = \frac{3}{2}(0.25)^x$

In Exercises 23–28, graph the function. Identify the asymptote. Find the domain and range. *Example 4*

23. $f(x) = 3^x - 1$
24. $f(x) = 4^{x+3}$
25. $y = 5^{x-2} + 7$
26. $y = -\left(\frac{1}{2}\right)^{x+1} - 3$
27. $y = -8(0.75)^{x+2} - 2$
28. $f(x) = 3(6)^{x-1} - 5$

In Exercises 29–32, compare the graphs. Find the value of *h*, *k*, or *a*.

29.

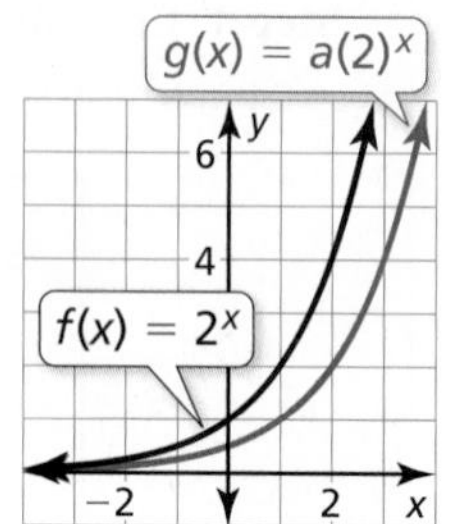

30.

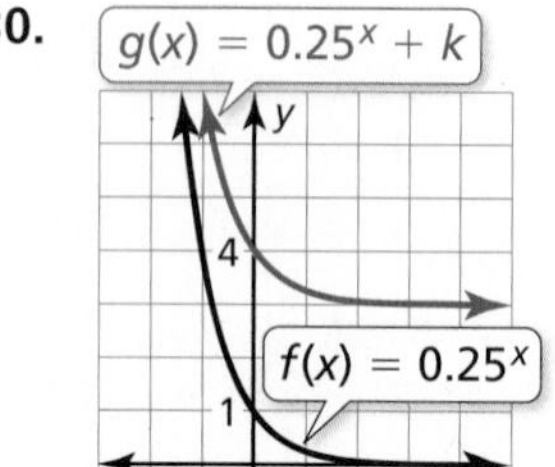

31.

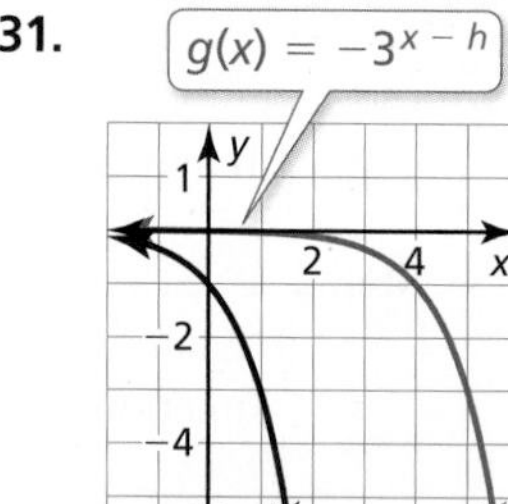

32.

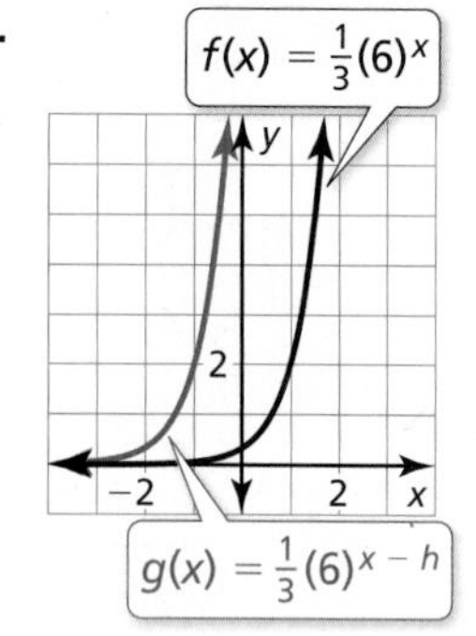

33. **ERROR ANALYSIS** Describe and correct the error in finding the domain and range of *g*.

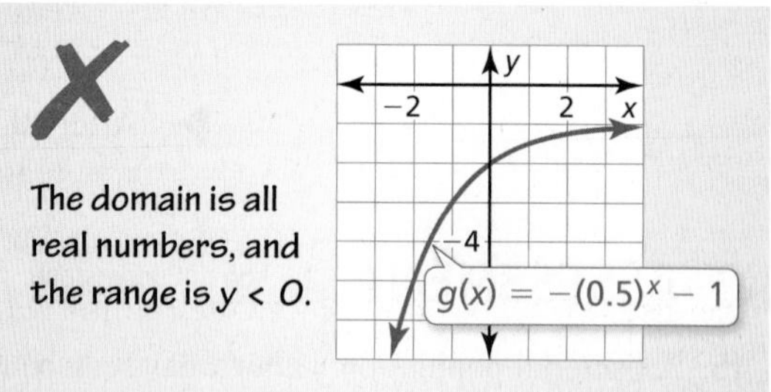

34. **MP REASONING** Determine whether each situation can be represented by a *linear* or an *exponential* function.

a. A checking account receives a $500 deposit each month.

b. The number of people infected by a virus triples each week.

c. An unpaid credit card balance accrues 1.75% interest each month.

d. A radio station chooses two new game contestants each day.

35. **MODELING REAL LIFE** The graph represents the number y of computers infected by a virus after x hours. Find the number of computers infected after 90 minutes and after 6 hours. *Example 5*

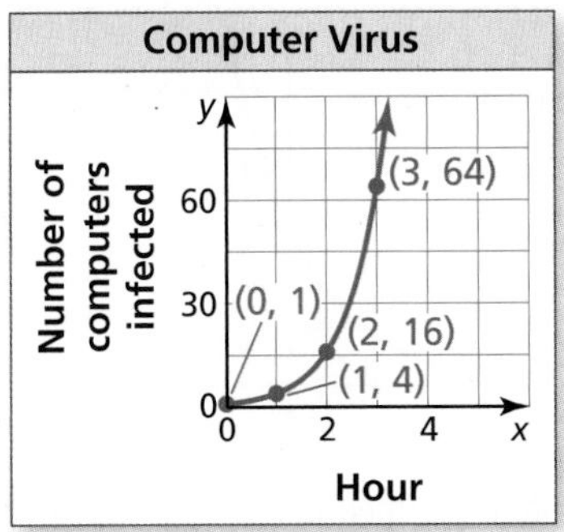

36. **MODELING REAL LIFE** The graph represents the value y of a boat after x years. Find the value of the boat after 2 years and after 8 years.

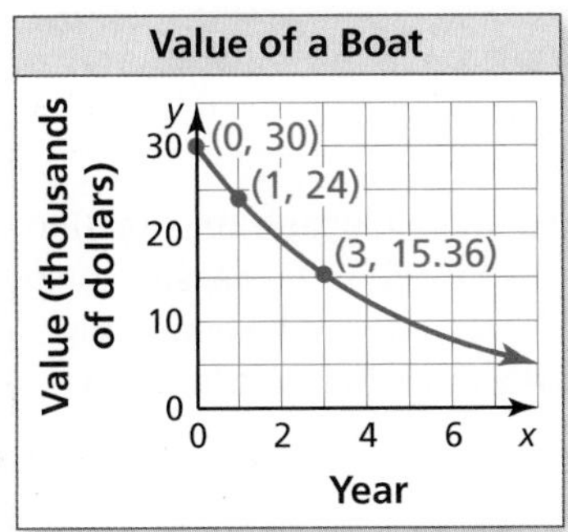

37. MP **REASONING** Explain why a is the y-intercept of the graph of $y = ab^x$.

38. MP **STRUCTURE** Does the table represent a *linear function*, an *exponential function*, or *neither*? Explain.

x	0	1	3	6
y	2	10	50	250

In Exercises 39–42, graph the function. Approximate when the function is increasing or decreasing. Then describe the end behavior of the function.

39. $f(x) = \left(\frac{1}{2}\right)^x - 3$

40. $g(x) = 3(1.5)^x$

41. $c(x) = -2(4)^{x-1} + 4$

42. $d(x) = -\left(\frac{3}{4}\right)^x - 6$

43. **MODELING REAL LIFE** The table shows the numbers y of views an online video receives after being online for x days. Use technology to find a function that fits the data. Predict the number of views the video receives after being online for 7 days. *Example 6*

Day, x	0	1	2	3	4	5
Views, y	12	68	613	3996	27,810	205,017

44. **MODELING REAL LIFE** The table shows the coyote populations y in a national park after t decades. Use technology to find a function that fits the data. Predict the coyote population after 60 years.

Decade, t	0	1	2	3	4
Population, y	15	26	41	72	123

45. **WRITING** Compare the graph of $f(x) = -2^x$ to the graph of $g(x) = -2^x - 3$. How are the y-intercept, domain, and range affected by the translation?

46. **HOW DO YOU SEE IT?**
The exponential function $y = V(x)$ represents the projected value of a stock x weeks after a corporation loses an important legal battle. The graph of the function is shown.

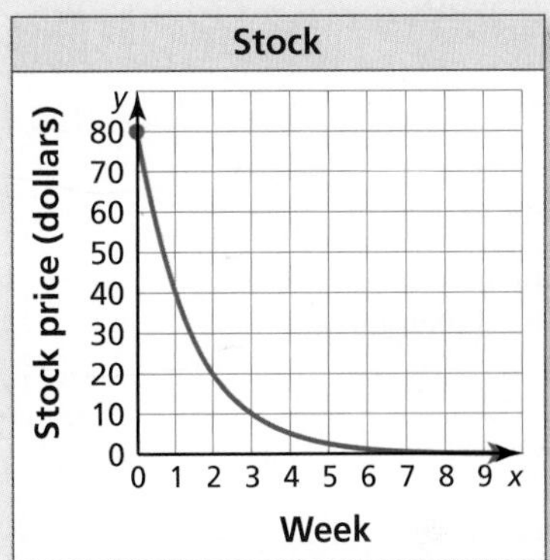

a. After how many weeks will the stock be worth \$20?

b. Describe the change in the stock price from Week 1 to Week 3.

47. **OPEN-ENDED** Write a function whose graph is a horizontal translation of the graph of $h(x) = 4^x$.

48. MP **STRUCTURE** The graph of g is a translation 4 units up and 3 units right of the graph of $f(x) = 5^x$. Write an equation that represents g.

49. MP **STRUCTURE** The graph represents the exponential function f. Find $f(7)$.

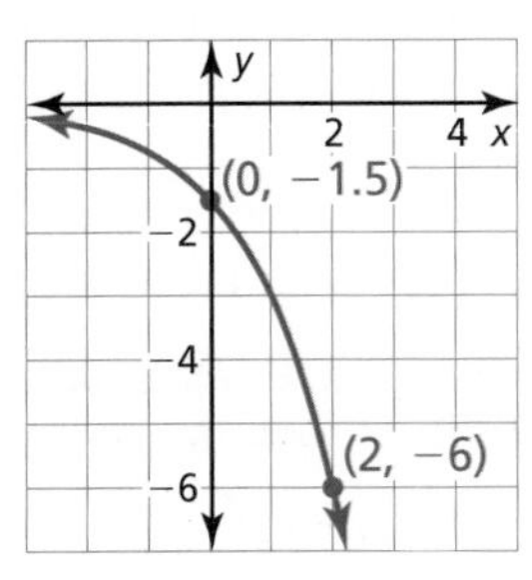

GO DIGITAL

50. MAKING AN ARGUMENT Your friend says that the y-intercept of the graph of $y = -4\left(\frac{1}{2}\right)^{x-1} + 3$ is -4. Is your friend correct? Explain.

51. MP REASONING Is an exponential function always increasing or always decreasing over its entire domain? Explain.

52. THOUGHT PROVOKING
Write an exponential function f so that the slope of a line from the point $(0, f(0))$ to the point $(2, f(2))$ is equal to 12.

53. MP PROBLEM SOLVING A function g models a relationship in which the dependent variable is multiplied by 4 for every 2 units the independent variable increases. The value of the function at 0 is 5. Write an equation that represents g.

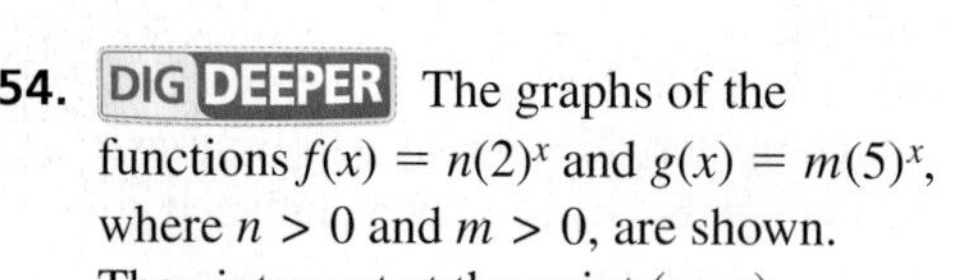

54. DIG DEEPER The graphs of the functions $f(x) = n(2)^x$ and $g(x) = m(5)^x$, where $n > 0$ and $m > 0$, are shown. They intersect at the point (p, q).

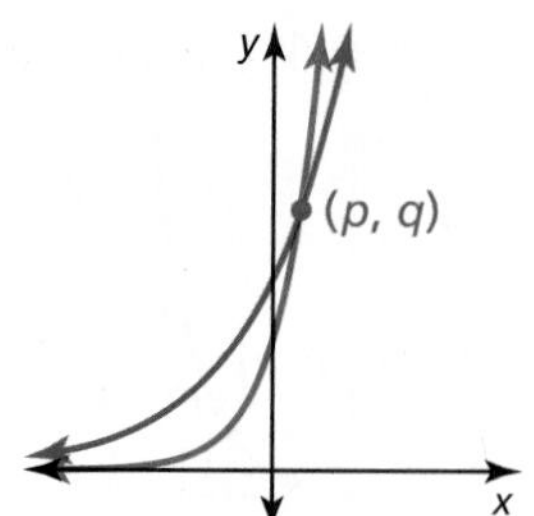

a. Complete the inequality n ▭ m. Explain your reasoning.

b. Determine the value of the ratio of $f(p + 2)$ to $g(p + 2)$. Justify your answer.

REVIEW & REFRESH

In Exercises 55 and 56, write the percent as a decimal.

55. 4%

56. 128%

57. Write a system of linear inequalities represented by the graph.

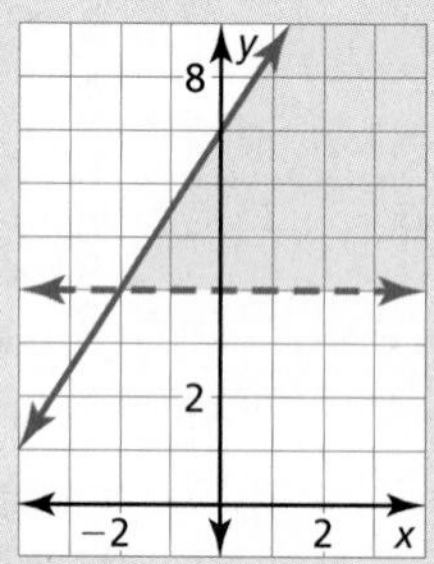

In Exercises 58 and 59, use the graphs of f and g to describe the transformation from the graph of f to the graph of g.

58. $f(x) = -x + 1;\ g(x) = f(x) - 4$

59. $f(x) = \frac{1}{2}x - 3;\ g(x) = f(x + 2)$

60. Write an equation in slope-intercept form of the line that passes through $(-4, 9)$ and $(16, -6)$.

In Exercises 61 and 62, evaluate the expression.

61. $\left(\frac{1}{32}\right)^{1/5}$

62. $(-27)^{5/3}$

63. Write an inequality that represents the graph.

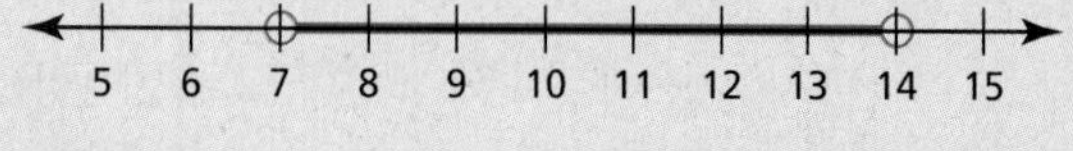

In Exercises 64 and 65, graph the function. Compare the graph to the graph of the parent function. Identify the y-intercepts and asymptotes of the graphs. Find the domain and range of f.

64. $f(x) = -3^{x+1}$

65. $f(x) = -\frac{1}{2}(4)^{x+2} + 7$

66. Tell whether $(8, -1)$ is a solution of $-\frac{1}{2}x + 3y > -1$.

67. MODELING REAL LIFE There are 430 people in a wave pool. Write an inequality that represents how many more people can enter the pool.

HOURS
Monday – Friday: 10 A.M. – 6 P.M.
Saturday – Sunday: 10 A.M. – 7 P.M.
Maximum Capacity: 600

68. Evaluate $f(x) = \begin{cases} -\frac{3}{4}x + 2, & \text{if } x < 4 \\ \frac{3}{2}x - 1, & \text{if } x \geq 4 \end{cases}$ when (a) $x = 4$ and (b) $x = -8$.

69. WRITING Describe the effect of a on the graph of $y = a \cdot 2^x$ when a is positive and when a is negative.

In Exercises 70 and 71, simplify the expression. Write your answer using only positive exponents.

70. $\left(\dfrac{-5d^4}{9d^0}\right)^3$

71. $\left(\dfrac{4x^{-1}y^3}{-8x^2y^2}\right)^4$

6.4 Exponential Growth and Decay

Learning Target Write and graph exponential growth and decay functions.

Success Criteria
- I can determine whether data represent exponential growth or exponential decay.
- I can write exponential growth functions and exponential decay functions.
- I can solve real-life problems using exponential growth and decay functions.

EXPLORE IT! Modeling with Exponential Functions

Math Practice

Communicate Precisely In your own words, define *exponential growth* and *exponential decay*.

Work with a partner. Decide whether each real-life scenario represents *exponential growth*, *exponential decay*, or *neither*. Explain your reasoning.

a. It is estimated that, in 1782, there were about 100,000 nesting pairs of bald eagles in the United States. By the 1960s, this number had dropped to about 500 nesting pairs. In 1967, the bald eagle was declared an endangered species in the United States. With protection, the nesting pair population began to increase. Finally, in 2007, the bald eagle was removed from the list of endangered and threatened species.

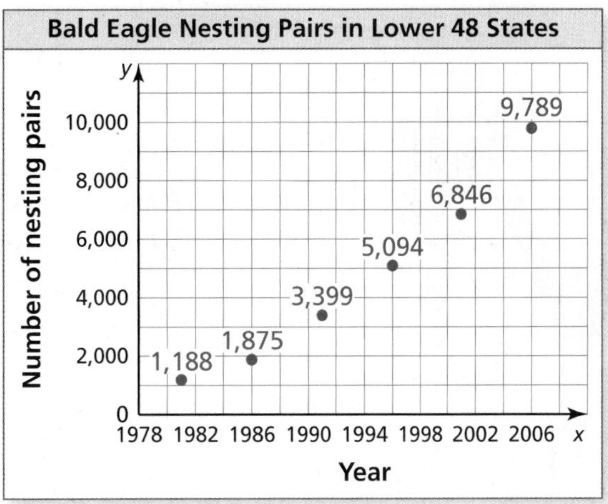

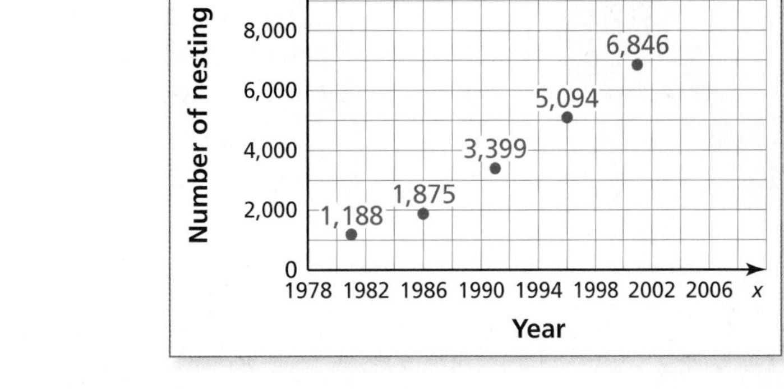

b. The table shows the battery power y (as a percent) of an electric car x hours after noon.

x	0	1	2	3	4	5	6
y	100	86	72	56	52	68	96

c. A forensic pathologist was called to estimate the time of death of a person. At midnight, the body temperature was 80.5°F and the room temperature was a constant 60°F. One hour later, the body temperature was 78.5°F. Each hour, the difference of the body temperature and the room temperature changes by the same percent as in the first hour.

d. Your friend automatically deposits a constant amount of her paycheck into a checking account. The balance y (in dollars) of the account after x deposits can be represented by $y = 100x + 350$.

Exponential Growth and Decay Functions

GO DIGITAL

Vocabulary VOCAB

exponential growth, *p. 322*
exponential growth function, *p. 322*
exponential decay, *p. 323*
exponential decay function, *p. 323*
compound interest, *p. 324*

STUDY TIP

In real-life situations involving exponential growth, the independent variable is usually time, t.

Exponential growth occurs when a quantity increases by the same factor over equal intervals.

KEY IDEA

Exponential Growth Functions

An **exponential growth function** has the form $y = ab^x$, where $a > 0$ and $b > 1$. You can write the *growth factor*, b, as the sum of 1 and the *rate of growth*, r.

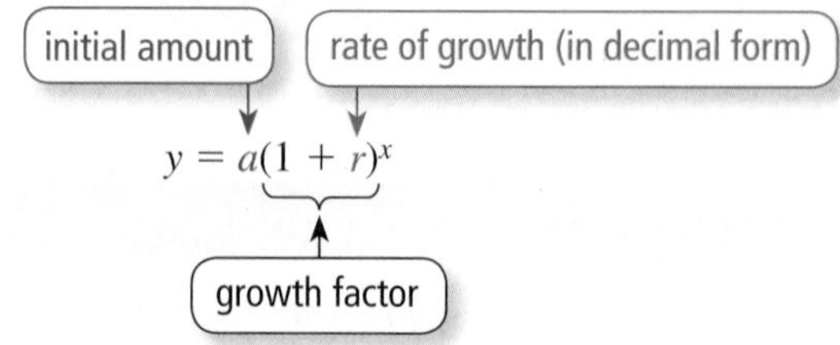

EXAMPLE 1 Using an Exponential Growth Function

The inaugural attendance of an annual music festival is 150,000. The attendance y increases by 8% each year.

a. Write an exponential growth function that represents the attendance after t years.

b. About how many people will attend the festival in the fifth year?

SOLUTION

a. The initial amount is 150,000, and the rate of growth is 8%, or 0.08.

$y = a(1 + r)^t$	Write the exponential growth function.
$= 150{,}000(1 + 0.08)^t$	Substitute 150,000 for *a* and 0.08 for *r*.
$= 150{,}000(1.08)^t$	Add.

▶ The festival attendance can be represented by $y = 150{,}000(1.08)^t$.

b. The value $t = 4$ represents the fifth year because $t = 0$ represents the first year.

$y = 150{,}000(1.08)^t$	Write the exponential growth function.
$= 150{,}000(1.08)^4$	Substitute 4 for *t*.
$\approx 204{,}073$	Use technology.

▶ About 204,000 people will attend the festival in the fifth year.

SELF-ASSESSMENT

1 I do not understand. 2 I can do it with help. 3 I can do it on my own. 4 I can teach someone else.

1. A website has 500,000 members in 2020. The number y of members increases by 15% each year.

a. Write an exponential growth function that represents the website membership t years after 2020.

b. About how many members will there be in 2026?

2. WRITING When does the function $y = ab^x$ represent exponential growth?

Exponential decay occurs when a quantity decreases by the same factor over equal intervals.

KEY IDEA

Exponential Decay Functions

An **exponential decay function** has the form $y = ab^x$, where $a > 0$ and $0 < b < 1$. You can write the *decay factor*, b, as the difference of 1 and the *rate of decay*, r.

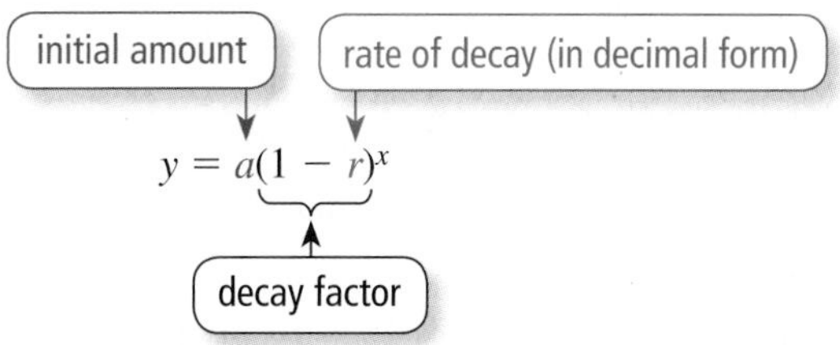

EXAMPLE 2 Identifying Exponential Growth and Decay

Determine whether each table represents an *exponential growth function*, an *exponential decay function*, or *neither*. Explain.

a.

x	0	1	2	3
y	270	90	30	10

b.

x	0	1	2	3
y	5	10	20	40

SOLUTION

a.

+1 +1 +1

x	0	1	2	3
y	270	90	30	10

$\times\frac{1}{3}$ $\times\frac{1}{3}$ $\times\frac{1}{3}$

▶ As x increases by 1, y is multiplied by $\frac{1}{3}$. So, the table represents an exponential decay function.

b.

+1 +1 +1

x	0	1	2	3
y	5	10	20	40

×2 ×2 ×2

▶ As x increases by 1, y is multiplied by 2. So, the table represents an exponential growth function.

SELF-ASSESSMENT

1 I do not understand. 2 I can do it with help. 3 I can do it on my own. 4 I can teach someone else.

Determine whether the table represents an *exponential growth function*, an *exponential decay function*, or *neither*. Explain.

3.

x	0	1	2	3
y	64	16	4	1

4.

x	1	3	5	7
y	4	11	18	25

5. **WHICH ONE DOESN'T BELONG?** Which function does *not* belong with the other three? Explain your reasoning.

$y = 5^x$ $f(x) = 2(4)^x$ $f(x) = 0.3^x$ $y = 5(3)^x$

GO DIGITAL

Interpreting and Rewriting Exponential Functions

EXAMPLE 3 Interpreting Exponential Functions

Determine whether each function represents *exponential growth* or *exponential decay*. Identify the percent rate of change.

a. $y = 5(1.07)^t$

b. $f(t) = 0.2(0.98)^t$

SOLUTION

a. Because $1.07 > 1$, the function represents exponential growth. The growth factor $1 + r$ is equal to 1.07, so you can determine that $r = 0.07$.

▶ So, the function represents exponential growth and the rate of growth is 7%.

b. Because $0 < 0.98 < 1$, the function represents exponential decay. The decay factor $1 - r$ is equal to 0.98, so you can determine that $r = 0.02$.

▶ So, the function represents exponential decay and the rate of decay is 2%.

EXAMPLE 4 Rewriting Exponential Functions

Determine whether each function represents *exponential growth* or *exponential decay*.

a. $y = 100(0.96)^{t/4}$

b. $f(t) = (1.1)^{t-3}$

SOLUTION

a. Use properties of exponents to rewrite the function in the form $y = a(1 \pm r)^t$.

$y = 100(0.96)^{t/4}$	Write the function.
$= 100(0.96^{1/4})^t$	Power of a Power Property
$\approx 100(0.99)^t$	Evaluate the power.

▶ So, the function represents exponential decay.

b. Use properties of exponents to rewrite the function in the form $y = a(1 \pm r)^t$.

$f(t) = (1.1)^{t-3}$	Write the function.
$= \dfrac{(1.1)^t}{(1.1)^3}$	Quotient of Powers Property
$\approx 0.75(1.1)^t$	Evaluate the power and simplify.

▶ So, the function represents exponential growth.

SELF-ASSESSMENT

1 I do not understand. 2 I can do it with help. 3 I can do it on my own. 4 I can teach someone else.

Determine whether the function represents *exponential growth* or *exponential decay*. Identify the percent rate of change.

6. $y = 2(0.92)^t$

7. $f(t) = (1.2)^t$

8. $f(t) = \frac{1}{2}\left(\frac{3}{2}\right)^t$

Determine whether the function represents *exponential growth* or *exponential decay*.

9. $f(t) = 3(1.02)^{10t}$

10. $y = (0.8)^{t-1}$

11. $y = (0.95)^{t+2}$

GO DIGITAL

Solving Real-Life Problems

Exponential growth functions are used in real-life situations involving *compound interest*. Although interest earned is expressed as an *annual* rate, the interest is usually compounded more frequently than once per year. So, the formula $y = a(1 + r)^t$ must be modified for compound interest problems.

KEY IDEA

Compound Interest

Compound interest is the interest earned on the principal *and* on previously earned interest. The balance y of an account earning compound interest is

$$y = P\left(1 + \frac{r}{n}\right)^{nt}.$$

P = principal (initial amount)
r = annual interest rate (in decimal form)
t = time (in years)
n = number of times interest is compounded per year

STUDY TIP

For interest compounded yearly, you can substitute 1 for n in the formula to get $y = P(1 + r)^t$.

EXAMPLE 5 Modeling Real Life

You deposit \$100 in an investment account that earns 6% annual interest compounded monthly. You also have a savings account with a constant balance of \$200.

a. Write a function m that represents the balance (in dollars) of the investment account after t years.

b. Write a function B that represents the total balance of the two accounts after t years. Then find and interpret $B(5)$.

SOLUTION

a. $m(t) = P\left(1 + \frac{r}{n}\right)^{nt}$ — Use the compound interest formula.

$= 100\left(1 + \frac{0.06}{12}\right)^{12t}$ — Substitute 100 for P, 0.06 for r, and 12 for n.

$= 100(1.005)^{12t}$ — Simplify.

Math Practice

View as Components
Notice that the function consists of the product of the principal, 100, and a factor independent of the principal, $(1.005)^{12t}$.

b. The \$200 balance of your savings account can be represented by the constant function $c(t) = 200$. Find the total balance $B(t)$ of the two accounts. Then find $B(5)$.

$$B(t) = m(t) + c(t)$$
$$= 100(1.005)^{12t} + 200$$
$$B(5) = 100(1.005)^{12(5)} + 200 \approx 134.89 + 200 = 334.89$$

▶ So, $B(t) = 100(1.005)^{12t} + 200$. The value $B(5) \approx 334.89$ indicates that the sum of the balances of the two accounts after 5 years is \$334.89.

SELF-ASSESSMENT 1 I do not understand. 2 I can do it with help. 3 I can do it on my own. 4 I can teach someone else.

12. WHAT IF? Repeat Example 5 when the investment account earns 3% annual interest compounded monthly.

13. MP STRUCTURE The function $y = 800\left(1 + \frac{0.02}{12}\right)^{12t}$ represents the balance y (in dollars) of a savings account after t years. What can you determine about the account? Explain.

EXAMPLE 6 Modeling Real Life

The value of a car is \$21,500. It loses 12% of its value every year.

a. Write a function that represents the value y (in dollars) of the car after t years.

b. Find the approximate monthly percent decrease in value.

c. Use the graph of the function to estimate the value of the car after 6 years.

SOLUTION

1. **Understand the Problem** You know the value of a car and the annual percent decrease in value. You are asked to approximate the monthly percent decrease in value and to estimate the value of the car in the future.

2. **Make a Plan** Use the initial value and the annual percent decrease in value to write an exponential decay function. Use the decay factor to approximate the monthly percent decrease. Then use the graph of the original function to estimate the y-value when the t-value is 6.

3. **Solve and Check**

Math Practice

Understand Quantities What are the meanings of the decay factor and the rate of decay in this situation?

a. The initial value is \$21,500, and the rate of decay is 12%, or 0.12.

$y = a(1 - r)^t$	Write the exponential decay function.
$= 21{,}500(1 - 0.12)^t$	Substitute 21,500 for a and 0.12 for r.
$= 21{,}500(0.88)^t$	Simplify.

▶ The value of the car can be represented by $y = 21{,}500(0.88)^t$.

b. Use the fact that $t = \frac{1}{12}(12t)$ and the properties of exponents to rewrite the function in a form that reveals the monthly rate of decay.

$y = 21{,}500(0.88)^t$	Write the original function.
$= 21{,}500(0.88)^{(1/12)(12t)}$	Rewrite the exponent.
$= 21{,}500(0.88^{1/12})^{12t}$	Power of a Power Property
$\approx 21{,}500(0.989)^{12t}$	Evaluate the power.

Use the decay factor $1 - r \approx 0.989$ to find the rate of decay $r \approx 0.011$.

▶ So, the monthly percent decrease is about 1.1%.

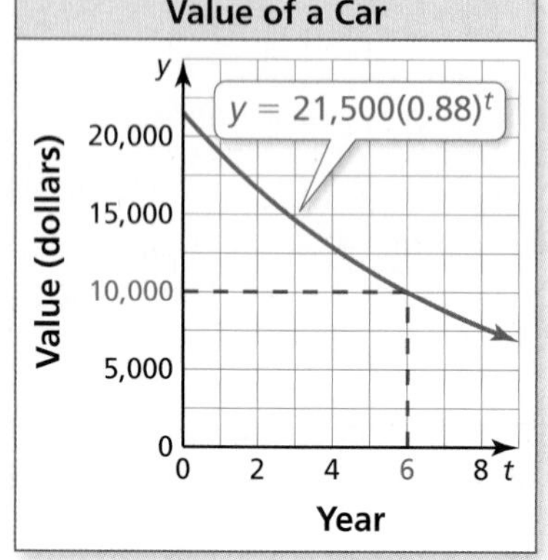

c. From the graph, you can see that the y-value is about 10,000 when $t = 6$.

▶ So, the value of the car is about \$10,000 after 6 years.

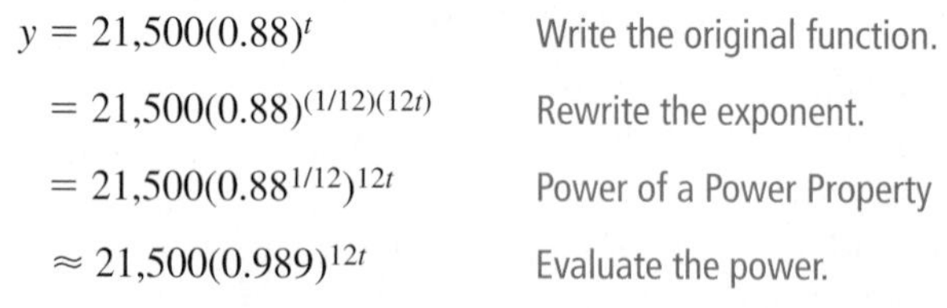

Check Reasonableness When you evaluate $y = 21{,}500(0.88)^t$ for $t = 6$, you get about \$9985. So, \$10,000 is a reasonable estimate.

SELF-ASSESSMENT

1 I do not understand. 2 I can do it with help. 3 I can do it on my own. 4 I can teach someone else.

14. WHAT IF? The car loses 9% of its value every year.

a. Write a function that represents the value y (in dollars) of the car after t years.

b. Find the approximate monthly percent decrease in value.

c. Use the graph of the function to estimate the value of the car after 12 years.

15. MP REASONING In Example 6, when you multiply the monthly percent decrease by the number of months in a year, the result is greater than the yearly percent decrease. Does this make sense? Explain your reasoning.

In Exercises 1–8, identify the initial amount a and the rate of growth r (as a percent) of the exponential function. Evaluate the function when $t = 5$. Round your answer to the nearest tenth.

1. $y = 350(1 + 0.75)^t$
2. $y = 10(1 + 0.4)^t$
3. $y = 25(1.2)^t$
4. $y = 12(1.05)^t$
5. $f(t) = 1500(1.074)^t$
6. $h(t) = 175(1.028)^t$
7. $g(t) = 6.72(2)^t$
8. $p(t) = 1.8^t$

In Exercises 9–12, write a function that represents the situation.

9. Sales of \$10,000 increase by 65% each year.
10. Your starting annual salary of \$35,000 increases by 4% each year.
11. A population of 210,000 increases by 12.5% each year.
12. An item costs \$4.50, and its price increases by 3.5% each year.

13. **MODELING REAL LIFE** The population of Brookfield increases by 2% annually. The sign shown is from the year 2010. ▶ *Example 1*

    a. Write an exponential growth function that represents the population t years after 2010.

    b. What will the population be in 2030?

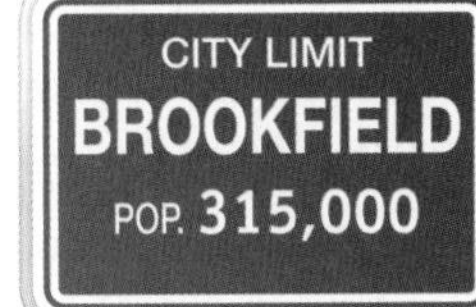

14. **MODELING REAL LIFE** A young channel catfish weighs about 0.1 pound. During the next 8 weeks, its weight increases by about 23% each week.

    a. Write an exponential growth function that represents the weight of the catfish after t weeks during the 8-week period.

    b. About how much does the catfish weigh after 4 weeks?

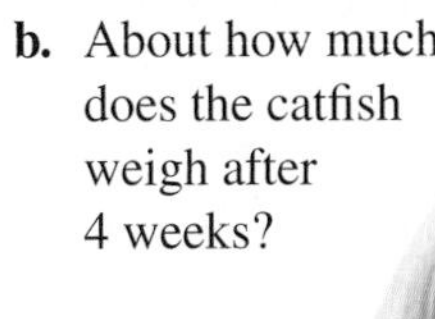

In Exercises 15–22, identify the initial amount a and the rate of decay r (as a percent) of the exponential function. Evaluate the function when $t = 3$. Round your answer to the nearest tenth.

15. $y = 575(1 - 0.6)^t$
16. $y = 8(1 - 0.15)^t$
17. $g(t) = 240(0.75)^t$
18. $f(t) = 475(0.5)^t$
19. $w(t) = 700(0.995)^t$
20. $h(t) = 1250(0.865)^t$
21. $y = \left(\frac{7}{8}\right)^t$
22. $y = 0.5\left(\frac{3}{4}\right)^t$

In Exercises 23–26, write a function that represents the situation.

23. A college enrollment of 100,000 decreases by 2% each year.
24. A \$900 sound system decreases in value by 9% each year.
25. A stock valued at \$100 decreases in value by 9.5% each year.
26. A company profit of \$20,000 decreases by 13.4% each year.

27. **ERROR ANALYSIS** The growth rate of a bacterial culture is 150% each hour. Initially, there are 10 bacteria. Describe and correct the error in finding the number of bacteria in the culture after 8 hours.

$b(t) = 10(1.5)^t$

$b(8) = 10(1.5)^8 \approx 256.3$

After 8 hours, there are about 256 bacteria in the culture.

28. **ERROR ANALYSIS** You purchase a car in 2020 for \$25,000. The value of the car decreases by 14% annually. Describe and correct the error in finding the value of the car in 2025.

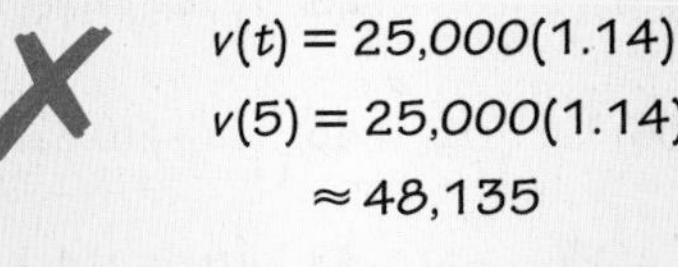

$v(t) = 25{,}000(1.14)^t$

$v(5) = 25{,}000(1.14)^5$

$\approx 48{,}135$

The value of the car in 2025 is about \$48,000.

In Exercises 29–34, determine whether the table represents an *exponential growth function*, an *exponential decay function*, or *neither*. Explain. *Example 2*

29.

x	y
−1	50
0	10
1	2
2	0.4

30.

x	y
0	32
1	28
2	24
3	20

31.

x	y
0	35
1	29
2	23
3	17

32.

x	y
1	17
2	51
3	153
4	459

33.

x	y
5	2
10	8
15	32
20	128
25	512

34.

x	y
3	432
5	72
7	12
9	2
11	$\frac{1}{3}$

In Exercises 35–42, determine whether the function represents *exponential growth* or *exponential decay*. Identify the percent rate of change. *Example 3*

35. $y = 4(0.8)^t$

36. $y = 15(1.1)^t$

37. $y = 30(0.95)^t$

38. $y = 5(1.08)^t$

39. $r(t) = 0.4(1.06)^t$

40. $s(t) = 0.65(0.48)^t$

41. $g(t) = 2\left(\frac{5}{4}\right)^t$

42. $m(t) = \left(\frac{4}{5}\right)^t$

In Exercises 43–50, rewrite the function to determine whether it represents *exponential growth* or *exponential decay*. *Example 4*

43. $y = (0.9)^{t-4}$

44. $y = (1.4)^{t+8}$

45. $y = 2(1.06)^{9t}$

46. $y = 5(0.82)^{t/5}$

47. $x(t) = (1.45)^{t/2}$

48. $f(t) = 0.4(1.16)^{t-1}$

49. $b(t) = 4(0.55)^{t+3}$

50. $r(t) = (0.88)^{4t}$

In Exercises 51 and 52, sketch a graph of an exponential function that has the given characteristics.

51. y-intercept: 3; asymptote: x-axis; decreasing over its entire domain

52. y-intercept: -2; end behavior: $y \to -3$ as $x \to -\infty$ and $y \to +\infty$ as $x \to +\infty$

In Exercises 53–56, write a function that represents the balance y (in dollars) after t years.

53. \$2000 deposit that earns 5% annual interest compounded quarterly

54. \$1400 deposit that earns 10% annual interest compounded semiannually

55. \$6200 deposit that earns 8.4% annual interest compounded monthly

56. \$3500 deposit that earns 9.2% annual interest compounded quarterly

57. MODELING REAL LIFE You deposit \$9000 in a savings account that earns 3.6% annual interest compounded monthly. You also save \$40 per month in a checking account. *Example 5*

a. Write a function s that represents the balance (in dollars) of your savings account after t years.

b. Write a function B that represents the total amount saved after t years. Then find and interpret $B(3)$.

58. MODELING REAL LIFE Your checking account has a constant balance of \$500. Let the function m represent the balance of your savings account after t years. The table shows the total balance of the accounts over time.

a. Write a function B that represents the total balance after t years.

b. Compare the savings account to the account in Exercise 53.

Year, t	Total balance
0	\$2500
1	\$2540
2	\$2580.80
3	\$2622.42
4	\$2664.86
5	\$2708.16

59. MP PROBLEM SOLVING A city has a population of 25,000. The population is expected to increase by 5.5% annually for the next decade. *Example 6*

a. Write a function that represents the population y after t years.

b. Find the approximate monthly percent increase in population.

c. Use the graph of the function to estimate the population after 4 years.

60. **MP PROBLEM SOLVING** Plutonium-238 is a material that generates steady heat due to decay and is used in power systems for some spacecraft. The function $y = a(0.5)^{t/x}$ represents the amount y of a substance remaining after t years, where a is the initial amount and x is the length of the half-life (in years).

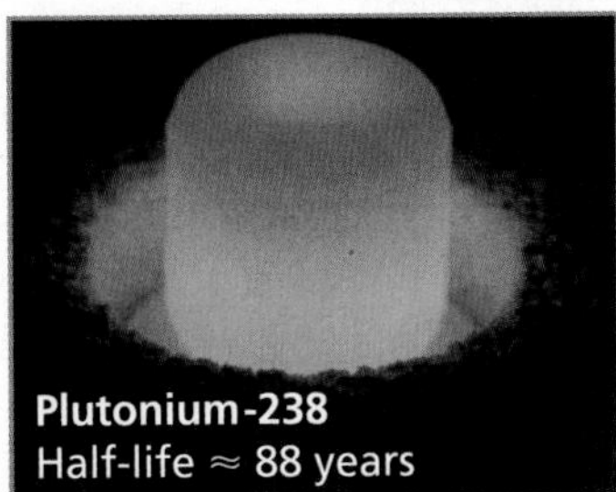

a. A scientist is studying a 3-gram sample. Write a function that represents the amount y of plutonium-238 remaining after t years.

b. What is the yearly percent decrease of plutonium-238?

c. Use the graph of the function to estimate the amount remaining after 12 years.

61. **COMPARING FUNCTIONS** Each of the three functions describe the amount y of ibuprofen (in milligrams) in a person's bloodstream t hours after taking the dosage.

$y \approx 800(0.71)^t$

$y \approx 800(0.9943)^{60t}$

$y \approx 800(0.843)^{2t}$

a. Show that these expressions are approximately equivalent.

b. Describe the information given by each of the functions.

62. **COMPARING FUNCTIONS** The graphs of f and g are shown.

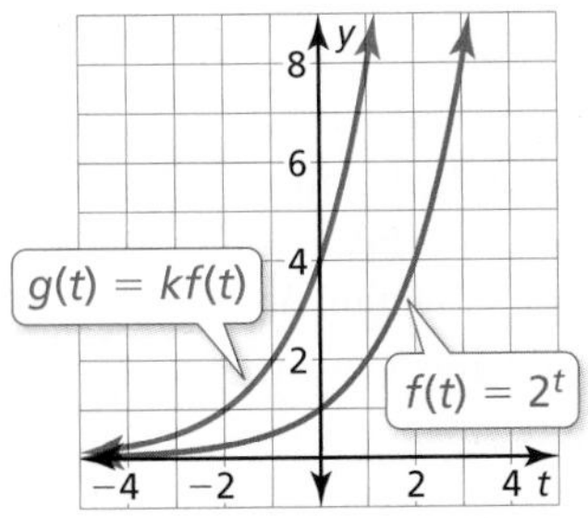

a. Explain why f is an exponential growth function. Identify the rate of growth.

b. Describe the transformation from the graph of f to the graph of g. Determine the value of k.

c. The graph of g is the same as the graph of $h(t) = f(t + r)$. Find the value of r.

63. **MP NUMBER SENSE** During a flu epidemic, the number of sick people triples every week. What is the growth rate as a percent? Explain your reasoning.

64. **HOW DO YOU SEE IT?**
Match each situation with its graph. Explain your reasoning.

a. A bacterial population doubles each hour.

b. The value of a computer decreases by 18% each year.

c. A deposit earns 11% annual interest compounded yearly.

d. A radioactive element decays 5.5% each year.

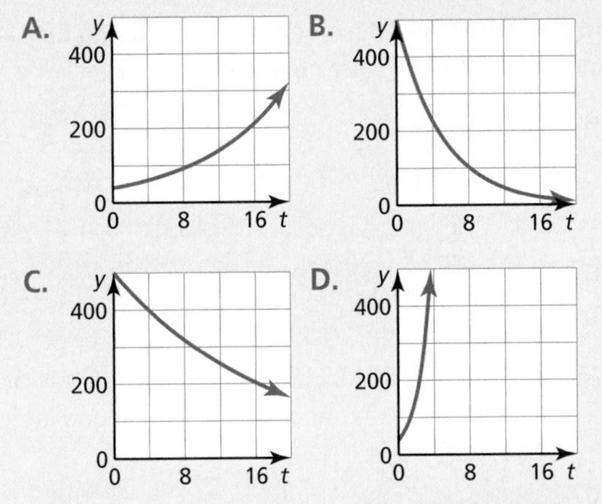

65. **MAKING AN ARGUMENT** A store is having a sale on jeans. On the first day, the prices of the jeans are reduced by 20%. The prices will be reduced another 20% each day until the jeans are sold. Your friend says the jeans will be free on the fifth day. Is your friend correct? Explain.

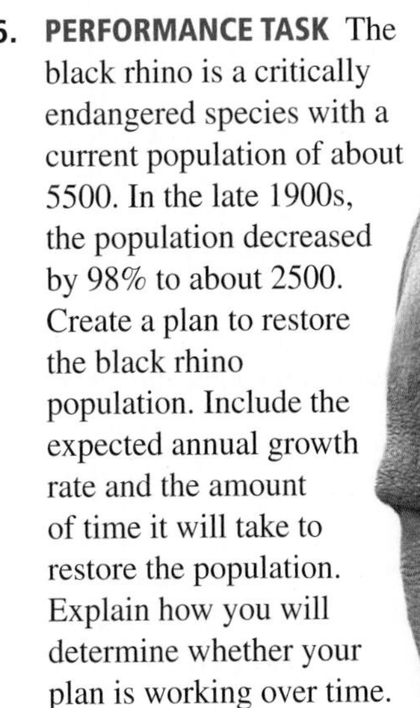

66. **PERFORMANCE TASK** The black rhino is a critically endangered species with a current population of about 5500. In the late 1900s, the population decreased by 98% to about 2500. Create a plan to restore the black rhino population. Include the expected annual growth rate and the amount of time it will take to restore the population. Explain how you will determine whether your plan is working over time.

67. **CONNECTING CONCEPTS** The function shown represents the temperature y (in degrees Celsius) of a body of water, where x is the depth of the water (in hundreds of meters).

$$y = \begin{cases} 13.5, & \text{if } 0 < x \le 2 \\ 18.5(0.76)^x + 2.8, & \text{if } 2 < x \le 15 \end{cases}$$

a. Graph the function. Find the domain and range.

b. Approximate the temperatures of the water (in degrees Fahrenheit) at depths of 100 meters and 1000 meters.

68. **THOUGHT PROVOKING**
Give an example of an equation in the form $y = ab^x$ that does *not* represent an exponential growth function or an exponential decay function. Explain your reasoning.

GO DIGITAL

69. **OPEN-ENDED** Describe two account options into which you can deposit \$1000 and earn compound interest. Write a function that represents the balance of each account after t years. Which account would you rather use? Explain your reasoning.

REVIEW & REFRESH

In Exercises 70–73, solve the system using any method. Explain your choice of method.

70. $y = \frac{1}{2}x - 3$
$y = -\frac{1}{3}x + 2$

71. $4x - 3y = 2$
$-5x + 3y = 2$

72. $2x + y = 7$
$-4x - 2y = 11$

73. $x = 3y - 5$
$2x + y = 4$

74. **MODELING REAL LIFE** The function $f(t) = 5(4)^t$ represents the number of frogs in a pond after t years.

a. Does the function represent *exponential growth* or *exponential decay*? Explain.

b. Graph the function. Find the domain and range.

c. What is the yearly percent change? the approximate monthly percent change?

d. How many frogs are in the pond after 4 years?

75. Describe the relationship between the data in the scatter plot.

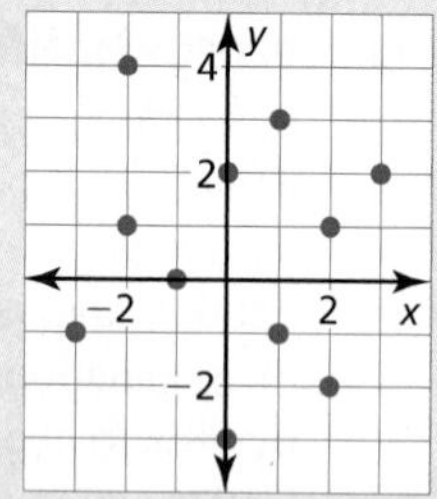

76. **OPEN-ENDED** Complete the inequality so that it has no solution.

$$|3x - 1| + \text{▒} < 7$$

In Exercises 77 and 78, simplify the expression. Write your answer using only positive exponents.

77. $(k^4)^{-3}$

78. $\left(\frac{4r^2}{3s^5}\right)^3$

In Exercises 79 and 80, determine whether the function represents *exponential growth* or *exponential decay*. Identify the percent rate of change.

79. $f(t) = \frac{1}{3}(1.26)^t$

80. $f(t) = 80\left(\frac{3}{5}\right)^t$

In Exercises 81 and 82, write an equation of the line that passes through the given points.

81. $(0, -3), (2, 5)$

82. $(6, -7), (-9, 13)$

83. Determine whether the table represents a *linear* or an *exponential* function. Explain.

x	−3	−1	1	3	5	7
y	15	9	3	−3	−9	−15

In Exercises 84 and 85, find the slope and the y-intercept of the graph of the linear equation.

84. $y = \frac{1}{4}x + 7$

85. $3y = 6x - 12$

In Exercises 86 and 87, evaluate the expression.

86. $\left(\frac{1}{16}\right)^{1/4}$

87. $512^{2/3}$

88. Tell whether the volume of the prism is a *linear* or *nonlinear* function of the missing dimension. Explain.

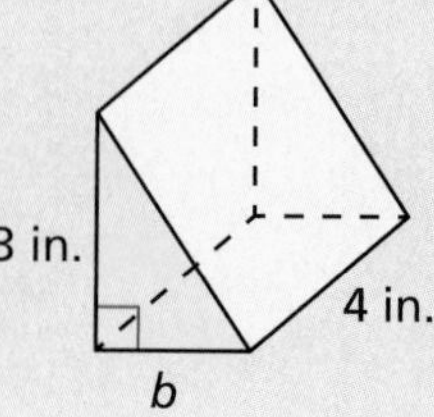

In Exercises 89–92, solve the equation. Check your solution.

89. $8x + 12 = 4x$

90. $5 - t = 7t + 21$

91. $6(r - 2) = 3(2r - 4)$

92. $-4(5v - 2) = -20v$

6.5 Solving Exponential Equations

Learning Target Solve exponential equations.

Success Criteria

- I can solve exponential equations with the same base.
- I can solve exponential equations with unlike bases.
- I can solve exponential equations by graphing.

EXPLORE IT! Solving Exponential Equations

Work with a partner. You open a money market account with \$500. The graph shows the balance y (in dollars) after x years.

Math Practice

Use Equations
What does the equation $500(1.02)^x = 600$ represent in this situation? How can you find the solution?

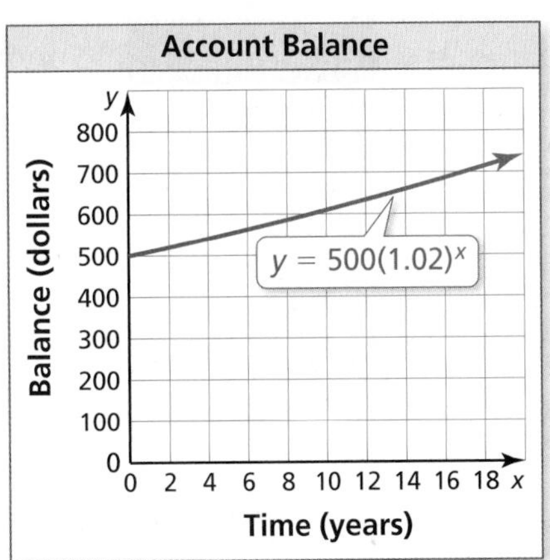

a. **MP CHOOSE TOOLS** Describe several different ways that you can approximate the amount of time until the balance is \$600.

b. You open a savings account with \$450. The balance increases by \$10 each year. Determine whether the balances of the two accounts are ever equal. Explain your method.

c. Suppose the balance of your savings account increases by \$15 each year. Does the balance of your savings account ever equal the balance of your money market account? If so, determine when the balances are equal.

d. The solutions in parts (a)–(c) can be found by writing and solving *exponential equations*. Use technology to solve each exponential equation below. Explain your method.

   i. $2^x = \frac{1}{2}$ ii. $3^{x-1} = 0$

   iii. $2^{x-2} = \frac{3}{2}x - 2$ iv. $4^{x-1} = 2^{x+1}$

e. Can an exponential equation have no solution? more than one solution?

f. Can any of the equations in part (d) be solved algebraically by using properties of exponents? Explain your reasoning.

Solving Exponential Equations with the Same Base

Vocabulary 

exponential equation, *p. 332*

Exponential equations are equations in which variable expressions occur as exponents.

KEY IDEA

Property of Equality for Exponential Equations

Words Two powers with the *same positive base b*, where $b \neq 1$, are equal if and only if their exponents are equal.

Numbers If $2^x = 2^5$, then $x = 5$. If $x = 5$, then $2^x = 2^5$.

Algebra If $b > 0$ and $b \neq 1$, then $b^x = b^y$ if and only if $x = y$.

EXAMPLE 1 Solving Exponential Equations with the Same Base

Solve each equation.

a. $3^{x+1} = 3^5$ **b.** $6 = 6^{2x-3}$ **c.** $10^{3x} = 10^{2x+3}$

SOLUTION

a. $3^{x+1} = 3^5$ Write the equation.

$x + 1 = 5$ Equate the exponents.

$x = 4$ Subtract 1 from each side.

b. $6 = 6^{2x-3}$ Write the equation.

$1 = 2x - 3$ Equate the exponents.

$4 = 2x$ Add 3 to each side.

$2 = x$ Divide each side by 2.

c. $10^{3x} = 10^{2x+3}$ Write the equation.

$3x = 2x + 3$ Equate the exponents.

$x = 3$ Subtract $2x$ from each side.

Check

$10^{3x} = 10^{2x+3}$

$10^{3(3)} \stackrel{?}{=} 10^{2(3)+3}$

$10^9 = 10^9$ ✓

SELF-ASSESSMENT 1 I do not understand. 2 I can do it with help. 3 I can do it on my own. 4 I can teach someone else.

Solve the equation. Check your solution.

1. $2^{2x} = 2^6$ **2.** $5^{2x} = 5^{x+1}$ **3.** $7^{3x+5} = 7^{x+1}$

4. WHICH ONE DOESN'T BELONG? Which equation does *not* belong with the other three? Explain your reasoning.

$2^{x+3} = 2^6$ $5^{3x+8} = 5^{2x}$ $3^4 = x + 3^2$ $2^{x-7} = 2^7$

5. MP **REASONING** Explain why b cannot equal 1 in the Property of Equality for Exponential Equations.

Solving Exponential Equations with Unlike Bases

To solve some exponential equations, you can first rewrite each side of the equation using the same base.

EXAMPLE 2 **Solving Exponential Equations with Unlike Bases**

Solve (a) $5^x = 125$, (b) $4^x = 2^{x-3}$, and (c) $9^{x+2} = 27^x$.

SOLUTION

a. $5^x = 125$ — Write the equation.

$5^x = 5^3$ — Rewrite 125 as 5^3.

$x = 3$ — Equate the exponents.

b. $4^x = 2^{x-3}$ — Write the equation.

$(2^2)^x = 2^{x-3}$ — Rewrite.

$2^{2x} = 2^{x-3}$ — Power of a Power Property

$2x = x - 3$ — Equate the exponents.

$x = -3$ — Simplify.

Check

$4^x = 2^{x-3}$

$4^{-3} \stackrel{?}{=} 2^{-3-3}$

$\frac{1}{64} = \frac{1}{64}$ ✓

c. $9^{x+2} = 27^x$

$(3^2)^{x+2} = (3^3)^x$

$3^{2x+4} = 3^{3x}$

$2x + 4 = 3x$

$4 = x$

EXAMPLE 3 **Solving Exponential Equations When $0 < b < 1$**

Solve (a) $\left(\frac{1}{2}\right)^x = 4$ and (b) $4^{x+1} = \frac{1}{64}$.

SOLUTION

a. $\left(\frac{1}{2}\right)^x = 4$ — Write the equation.

$(2^{-1})^x = 2^2$ — Rewrite $\frac{1}{2}$ as 2^{-1} and 4 as 2^2.

$2^{-x} = 2^2$ — Power of a Power Property

$-x = 2$ — Equate the exponents.

$x = -2$ — Divide each side by -1.

b. $4^{x+1} = \frac{1}{64}$ — Write the equation.

$4^{x+1} = \frac{1}{4^3}$ — Rewrite 64 as 4^3.

$4^{x+1} = 4^{-3}$ — Definition of negative exponent

$x + 1 = -3$ — Equate the exponents.

$x = -4$ — Subtract 1 from each side.

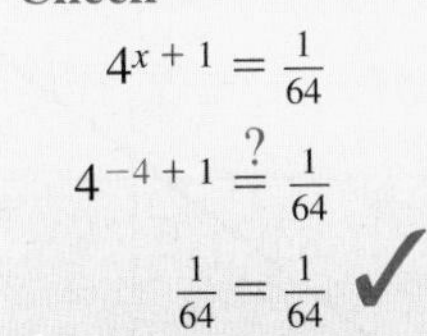

Check

$4^{x+1} = \frac{1}{64}$

$4^{-4+1} \stackrel{?}{=} \frac{1}{64}$

$\frac{1}{64} = \frac{1}{64}$ ✓

SELF-ASSESSMENT 1 I do not understand. 2 I can do it with help. 3 I can do it on my own. 4 I can teach someone else.

Solve the equation. Check your solution.

6. $4^x = 256$

7. $9^{2x} = 3^{x-6}$

8. $4^{3x} = 8^{x+1}$

9. $\left(\frac{1}{3}\right)^{x-1} = 27$

Solving Exponential Equations by Graphing

Sometimes, it is difficult or impossible to rewrite each side of an exponential equation using the same base. You can solve these types of equations by graphing each side and finding the point(s) of intersection. Exponential equations can have no solution, one solution, or more than one solution.

EXAMPLE 4 Solving Exponential Equations by Graphing

Solve (a) $2.4^{x-1} = 5.76$ and (b) $3^{x+2} = x + 1$.

SOLUTION

a. Step 1 Write a function to represent each side of the original equation.

$$y = 2.4^{x-1}$$
$$y = 5.76$$

Step 2 Use technology to graph the functions in a viewing window that shows where the graphs could intersect.

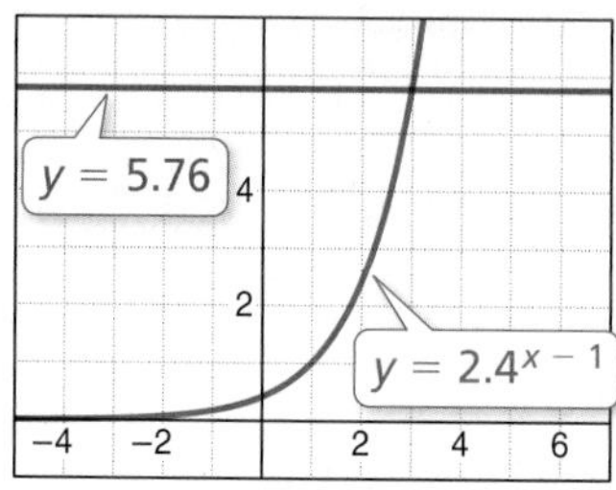

ANOTHER WAY

It may be difficult to recognize, but knowing that $24^2 = 576$ helps you reason that $2.4^2 = 5.76$. This can be used to solve part (a) algebraically.

$$2.4^{x-1} = 5.76$$
$$2.4^{x-1} = 2.4^2$$
$$x - 1 = 2$$
$$x = 3$$

Step 3 Find the point of intersection. The graphs intersect at (3, 5.76).

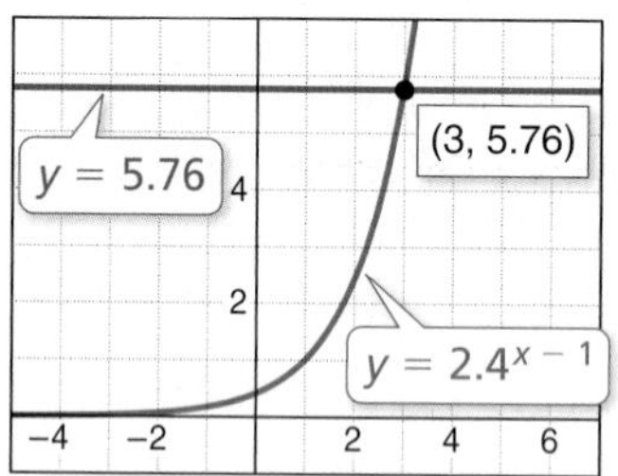

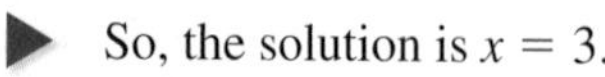

▶ So, the solution is $x = 3$.

b. Step 1 Write a function to represent each side of the original equation.

$$y = 3^{x+2}$$
$$y = x + 1$$

Step 2 Use technology to graph the functions in a viewing window that shows where the graphs could intersect.

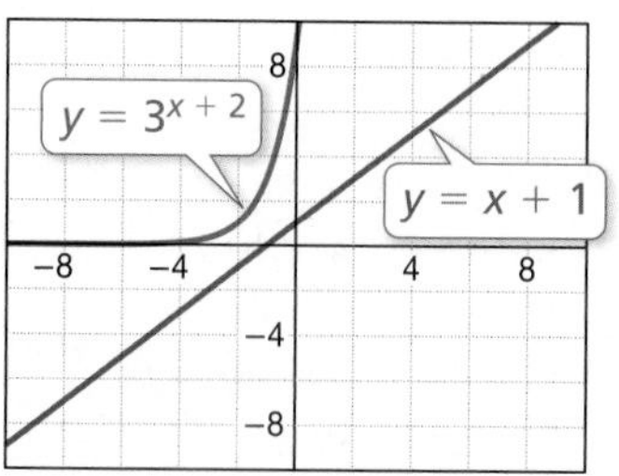

▶ The graphs do not intersect. So, the equation has no solution.

SELF-ASSESSMENT 1 I do not understand. 2 I can do it with help. 3 I can do it on my own. 4 I can teach someone else.

Solve the equation.

10. $3.1^{x+2} = 9.61$

11. $4^{x-3} = 3x - 8$

12. $\left(\frac{1}{4}\right)^x = -2x - 3$

13. MP **PRECISION** In Example 4(a), explain why the solution is not (3, 5.76).

6.5 Practice WITH CalcChat® AND CalcView®

In Exercises 1–10, solve the equation. Check your solution. ▶ *Examples 1 and 2*

1. $4^{5x} = 4^{10}$
2. $7^{x-4} = 7^8$
3. $3^{9x} = 3^{7x+8}$
4. $2^{4x} = 2^{x+9}$
5. $2^x = 64$
6. $3^x = 243$
7. $7^{x-5} = 49^x$
8. $216^x = 6^{x+10}$
9. $64^{2x+4} = 16^{5x}$
10. $27^x = 81^{x+1}$

In Exercises 11–16, solve the equation. Check your solution. ▶ *Example 3*

11. $\left(\frac{1}{5}\right)^x = 125$
12. $\left(\frac{1}{4}\right)^x = 256$
13. $\frac{1}{128} = 2^{5x+3}$
14. $3^{4x-9} = \frac{1}{243}$
15. $36^{-3x+3} = \left(\frac{1}{216}\right)^{x+1}$
16. $\left(\frac{1}{27}\right)^{4-x} = 9^{2x-1}$

ERROR ANALYSIS **In Exercises 17 and 18, describe and correct the error in solving the exponential equation.**

17.

$$5^{3x+2} = 25^{x-8}$$
$$3x + 2 = x - 8$$
$$x = -5$$

18.

$$\left(\frac{1}{8}\right)^{5x} = 32^{x+8}$$
$$(2^3)^{5x} = (2^5)^{x+8}$$
$$2^{15x} = 2^{5x+40}$$
$$15x = 5x + 40$$
$$x = 4$$

In Exercises 19 and 20, use the graph to solve the equation.

19. $2.1^{x-4} = 4.41$

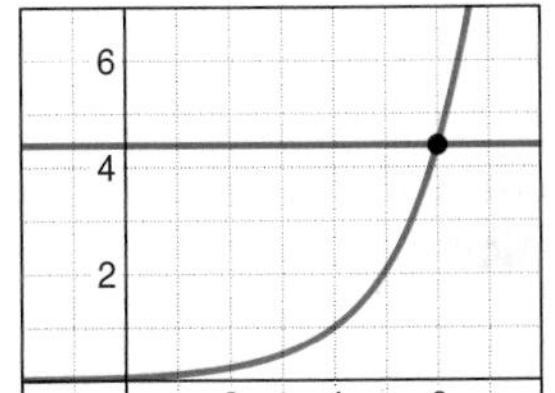

20. $4^{x+2} = -x + 3$

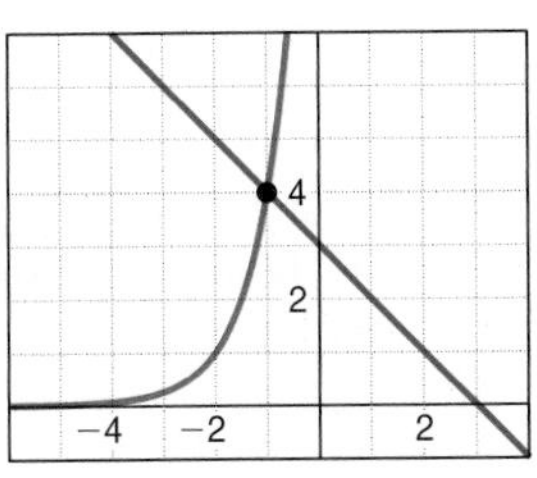

In Exercises 21–30, solve the equation. ▶ *Example 4*

21. $0.25^{x+2} = 16$
22. $1.9^{x-4} = 3.61$
23. $2^{x+3} = 3x + 8$
24. $4x - 3 = 5^{x-1}$
25. $\frac{4}{3}x - 1 = \left(\frac{1}{3}\right)^{2x-1}$
26. $2^{-x+1} = \frac{19 - 15x}{4}$
27. $5^x = -4^{-x+4}$
28. $7^{x-2} = 2^{-x}$
29. $2^{-x-3} = 3^{x+1}$
30. $5^{-2x+3} = -6^{x+5}$

In Exercises 31–34, solve the equation by using the Property of Equality for Exponential Equations.

31. $30 \cdot 5^{x+3} = 150$
32. $12 \cdot 2^{x-7} = 24$
33. $4(3)^{-2x-4} = 36$
34. $2(4)^{2x+1} = 128$

35. **MODELING REAL LIFE** A population of 50 mice is expected to double each year. The number y of mice in the population after x years is represented by $y = 50(2)^x$. After how many years will there be 800 mice in the population?

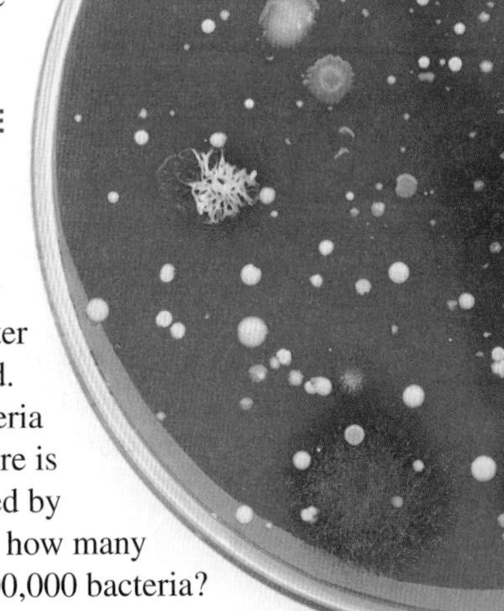

36. **MODELING REAL LIFE** A bacterial culture quadruples in size every hour. You begin observing the number of bacteria 3 hours after the culture is prepared. The amount y of bacteria x hours after the culture is prepared is represented by $y = 192(4)^{x-3}$. After how many hours will there be 200,000 bacteria?

In Exercises 37–40, solve the equation.

37. $3^{3x+6} = 27^{x+2}$
38. $3^{4x+3} = 81^x$
39. $4^{x+3} = 2^{2(x+1)}$
40. $5^{8(x-1)} = 625^{2x-2}$

41. **MP NUMBER SENSE** Explain how you can use mental math to solve the equation $8^{x-4} = 1$.

42. **MP PROBLEM SOLVING** There are a total of 128 teams at the start of a citywide 3-on-3 basketball tournament. Half the teams are eliminated after each round. Write and solve an exponential equation to determine after which round there are 16 teams left.

43. **MP PROBLEM SOLVING** You deposit \$500 in a savings account that earns 6% annual interest compounded yearly. After how many years will the balance of the account be \$750?

44. **HOW DO YOU SEE IT?**
The graph shows the annual attendances at two different events over time.

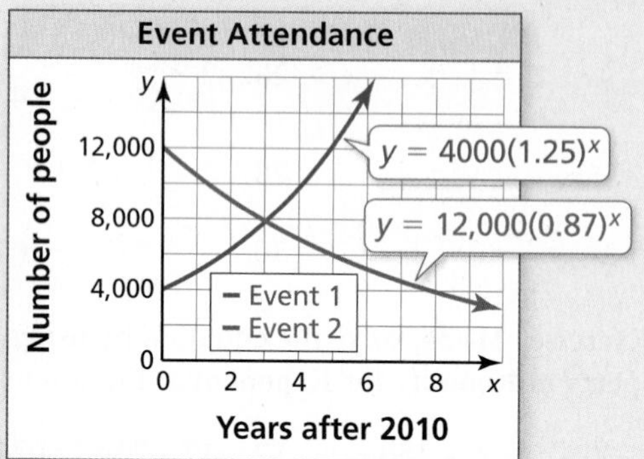

a. Estimate when the events had about the same attendance.

b. Explain how you can verify your answer in part (a).

45. **COLLEGE PREP** What is the value of y when $9^{x+3} = 9^{y-1}$ and $8^{x+4} = 64^{2x+5}$?

Ⓐ -2 Ⓑ -1 Ⓒ 2 Ⓓ 3

46. **THOUGHT PROVOKING**
Write a function g so that the equation $2^{x-1} = g(x)$ has exactly three solutions.

MP STRUCTURE In Exercises 47–52, solve the equation.

47. $8^{x-2} = \sqrt{8}$

48. $\sqrt{5} = 5^{x+4}$

49. $\left(\sqrt[5]{7}\right)^x = 7^{2x+3}$

50. $12^{2x-1} = \left(\sqrt[4]{12}\right)^x$

51. $\left(\sqrt[3]{6}\right)^{2x} = \left(\sqrt{6}\right)^{x+6}$

52. $\left(\sqrt[5]{3}\right)^{5x-10} = \left(\sqrt[8]{3}\right)^{4x}$

53. **MAKING AN ARGUMENT** Consider the equation $\left(\frac{1}{a}\right)^x = b$, where $a > 1$ and $b > 1$. Your friend says the value of x will always be negative. Is your friend correct? Explain.

54. **DIG DEEPER** Solve the equation without graphing.

$$3^x + 3^{x+1} + 3^{x+4} = 61{,}965$$

REVIEW & REFRESH

WATCH

In Exercises 55 and 56, determine whether the sequence is arithmetic. If so, find the common difference.

55. $-20, -26, -32, -38, \ldots$

56. $9, 18, 36, 72, \ldots$

57. Determine whether the table represents an *exponential growth function*, an *exponential decay function*, or *neither*. Explain.

x	0	1	2	3
y	7	21	63	189

In Exercises 58 and 59, solve the inequality. Graph the solution, if possible.

58. $3(2n - 1) < 6n - 4$

59. $|5t + 1| - 10 \le -6$

In Exercises 60 and 61, solve the equation. Check your solution.

60. $11^{x-2} = 11^{2x-7}$

61. $9^{x+3} = \left(\frac{1}{81}\right)^x$

62. Graph $y = 6(2)^{x-4} - 1$. Identify the asymptote. Find the domain and range.

63. Determine whether the graph represents a function. Explain.

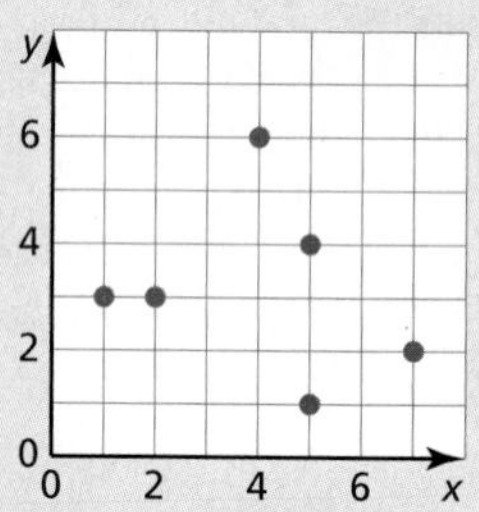

64. **MP REASONING** You are stopped in a line of traffic that is about 1.5 miles long. Estimate the number of vehicles in the line. Explain your reasoning.

65. Rewrite $\left(\sqrt[6]{70}\right)^5$ in rational exponent form.

In Exercises 66 and 67, write an equation in slope-intercept form of the line that passes through the given points.

66. $(1, 7), (3, -3)$

67. $(0, -10), (8, -4)$

68. **MP STRUCTURE** Complete the equation so that it has infinitely many solutions.

$$7x - 20 + 8x = -5(\;\square\;x + \;\square\;)$$

6.6 Geometric Sequences

Learning Target Identify, extend, and graph geometric sequences.

Success Criteria
- I can determine whether a sequence is arithmetic, geometric, or neither.
- I can write and graph the terms of geometric sequences.
- I can write geometric sequences as functions.

EXPLORE IT! Describing a Pattern

Work with a partner. See the figures below. The branch is 4 units long when $n = 1$. When $n = 2$, the new branches are each 2 units long. When $n = 3$, the new branches are each 1 unit long, and so on.

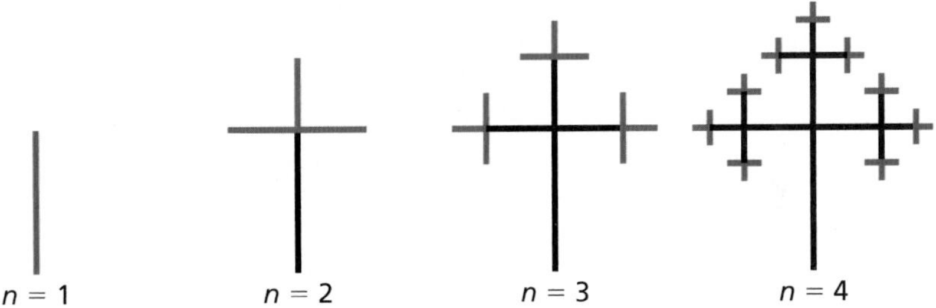

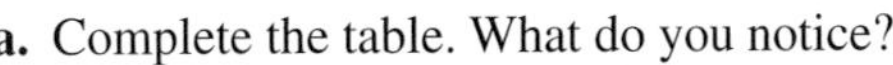

Math Practice

Use Prior Results
How are the graphs in part (b) related to the graphs of exponential growth and decay functions?

a. Complete the table. What do you notice?

n	1	2	3	4
Number of new branches added, a_n	1			
Length of a new branch added, b_n	4			

b. Graph the data in the table. How do the graphs compare to the graphs of arithmetic sequences? Explain.

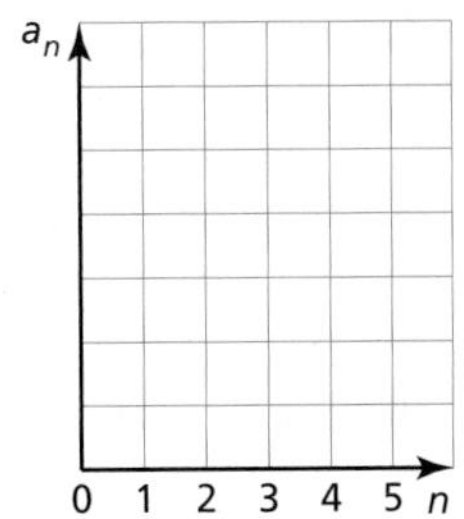

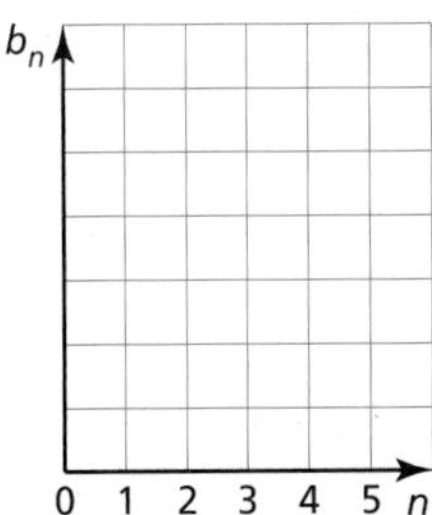

c. Can you write an equation that represents each graph? Explain.

d. How can you extend the patterns to find the number of new branches added or the length of a new branch added for greater values of n? Explain your reasoning.

e. Find the number of new branches added and the length of a new branch added when $n = 8$.

f. Complete a table similar to part (a) for each of the following. Write any observations you make from your table.

i. height of the tree **ii.** total length of new branches

Identifying Geometric Sequences

Vocabulary 

geometric sequence, *p. 338*
common ratio, *p. 338*

KEY IDEA

Geometric Sequence

In a **geometric sequence**, the ratio between each pair of consecutive terms is the same. This ratio is called the **common ratio**. Each term is found by multiplying the previous term by the common ratio.

1, 5, 25, 125, . . . Terms of a geometric sequence

×5 ×5 ×5 ← common ratio

READING

Although $\frac{a}{b}$ is the value of the ratio $a:b$, you can simply refer to $\frac{a}{b}$ as the ratio.

EXAMPLE 1 Identifying Geometric Sequences

Determine whether each sequence is *arithmetic*, *geometric*, or *neither*. Explain your reasoning.

a. 120, 60, 30, 15, . . .

b. 2, 6, 11, 17, . . .

SOLUTION

a. Find the ratio between each pair of consecutive terms.

120 60 30 15

$\frac{60}{120} = \frac{1}{2}$ $\frac{30}{60} = \frac{1}{2}$ $\frac{15}{30} = \frac{1}{2}$

The ratios are the same. The common ratio is $\frac{1}{2}$.

▶ So, the sequence is geometric.

b. Find the ratio between each pair of consecutive terms.

2 6 11 17

$\frac{6}{2} = 3$ $\frac{11}{6} = 1\frac{5}{6}$ $\frac{17}{11} = 1\frac{6}{11}$

There is no common ratio, so the sequence is *not* geometric.

Find the difference between each pair of consecutive terms.

2 6 11 17

$6 - 2 = 4$ $11 - 6 = 5$ $17 - 11 = 6$

There is no common difference, so the sequence is *not* arithmetic.

▶ So, the sequence is *neither* geometric nor arithmetic.

SELF-ASSESSMENT

1 I do not understand. 2 I can do it with help. 3 I can do it on my own. 4 I can teach someone else.

Determine whether the sequence is *arithmetic*, *geometric*, or *neither*. Explain your reasoning.

1. 5, 1, −3, −7, . . .

2. 1024, 128, 16, 2, . . .

3. 2, 6, 10, 16, . . .

4. WRITING Compare the two sequences.

2, 4, 6, 8, 10, . . . 2, 4, 8, 16, 32, . . .

5. MP **REASONING** Does the sequence in Example 1(a) eventually reach 0? Explain your reasoning.

6. OPEN-ENDED Write a geometric sequence with a first term of 3 and a fourth term that is between 40 and 50. Describe the pattern.

Extending and Graphing Geometric Sequences

EXAMPLE 2 Extending Geometric Sequences

Write the next three terms of each geometric sequence.

a. 3, 6, 12, 24, . . .

b. 64, −16, 4, −1, . . .

SOLUTION

Use tables to organize the terms and extend each sequence.

a.

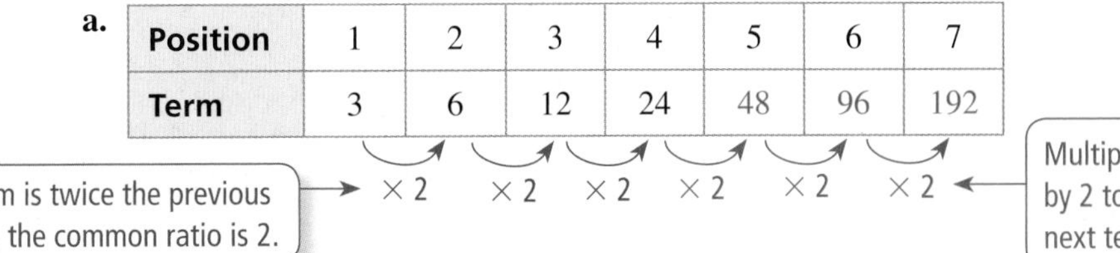

Position	1	2	3	4	5	6	7
Term	3	6	12	24	48	96	192

Each term is twice the previous term. So, the common ratio is 2.

Multiply a term by 2 to find the next term.

▶ The next three terms are 48, 96, and 192.

Math Practice

Look for Patterns
What do the signs of the terms of a geometric sequence tell you about the common ratio?

b.

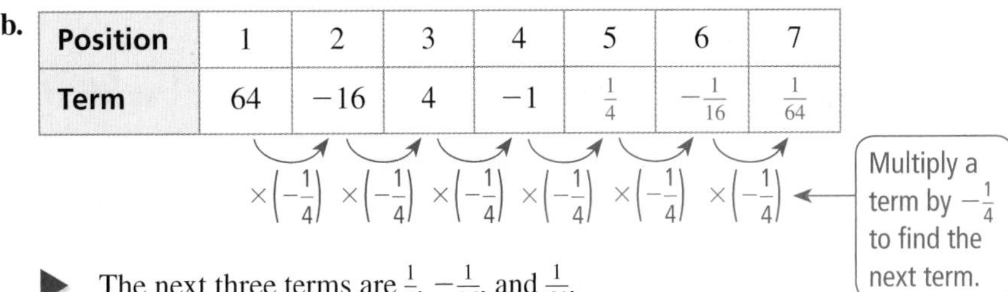

Position	1	2	3	4	5	6	7
Term	64	−16	4	−1	$\frac{1}{4}$	$-\frac{1}{16}$	$\frac{1}{64}$

Multiply a term by $-\frac{1}{4}$ to find the next term.

▶ The next three terms are $\frac{1}{4}$, $-\frac{1}{16}$, and $\frac{1}{64}$.

EXAMPLE 3 Graphing a Geometric Sequence

WATCH

Graph the geometric sequence 32, 16, 8, 4, 2, ... What do you notice?

SOLUTION

Make a table. Then plot the ordered pairs (n, a_n).

Position, n	1	2	3	4	5
Term, a_n	32	16	8	4	2

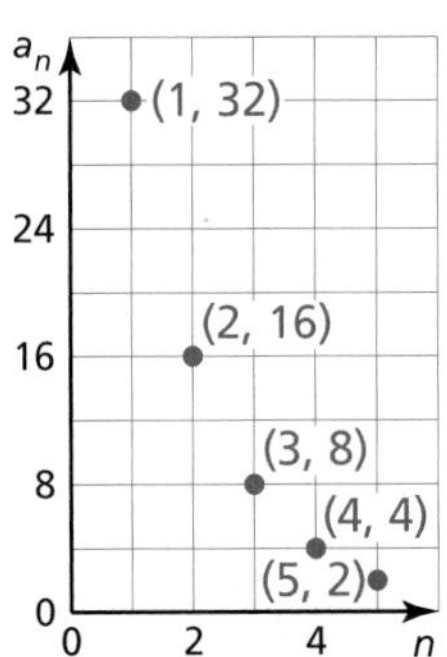

STUDY TIP
The points of any geometric sequence with a *positive* common ratio lie on an exponential curve.

▶ The points lie on an exponential curve.

SELF-ASSESSMENT

1 I do not understand. 2 I can do it with help. 3 I can do it on my own. 4 I can teach someone else.

7. **MP REASONING** Explain why the points of a geometric sequence lie on an exponential curve only when the common ratio is positive.

Write the next three terms of the geometric sequence. Then graph the sequence.

8. 1, 4, 16, 64, . . .

9. 2500, 500, 100, 20, . . .

10. 80, −40, 20, −10, . . .

11. −2, 4, −8, 16, . . .

12. $\frac{7}{25}$, $\frac{7}{5}$, 7, 35, . . .

13. $\frac{3}{4}$, $-\frac{3}{2}$, 3, −6, . . .

Writing Geometric Sequences as Functions

GO DIGITAL

Because consecutive terms of a geometric sequence have a common ratio, you can use the first term a_1 and the common ratio r to write an exponential function that describes a geometric sequence. For example, let $a_1 = 1$ and $r = 5$.

Position, n	Term, a_n	Written using a_1 and r	Numbers
1	first term, a_1	a_1	1
2	second term, a_2	a_1r	$1 \cdot 5 = 5$
3	third term, a_3	a_1r^2	$1 \cdot 5^2 = 25$
4	fourth term, a_4	a_1r^3	$1 \cdot 5^3 = 125$
⋮	⋮	⋮	⋮
n	nth term, a_n	a_1r^{n-1}	$1 \cdot 5^{n-1}$

KEY IDEA

Equation for a Geometric Sequence

Let a_n be the nth term of a geometric sequence with first term a_1 and common ratio r. The nth term is given by

$$a_n = a_1r^{n-1}.$$

STUDY TIP

Notice that the equation $a_n = a_1r^{n-1}$ is of the form $y = ab^x$.

EXAMPLE 4 Finding the nth Term of a Geometric Sequence

Write an equation for the nth term of the geometric sequence 2, 12, 72, 432, ... Then find a_{10}.

WATCH

SOLUTION

The first term is 2, and the common ratio is 6.

$a_n = a_1r^{n-1}$ Equation for a geometric sequence

$a_n = 2(6)^{n-1}$ Substitute 2 for a_1 and 6 for r.

Use the equation to find the 10th term.

$a_n = 2(6)^{n-1}$ Write the equation.

$a_{10} = 2(6)^{10-1}$ Substitute 10 for n.

$= 20{,}155{,}392$ Simplify.

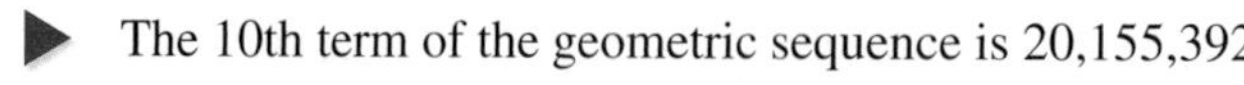
▶ The 10th term of the geometric sequence is 20,155,392.

SELF-ASSESSMENT 1 I do not understand. 2 I can do it with help. 3 I can do it on my own. 4 I can teach someone else.

14. MP **STRUCTURE** What information do you need to find the nth term of a geometric sequence?

Write an equation for the nth term of the geometric sequence. Then find a_7.

15. 1, −5, 25, −125, . . .

16. 13, 26, 52, 104, . . .

17. 432, 72, 12, 2, . . .

18. 4, 10, 25, 62.5, . . .

19. 0.2, −1.4, 9.8, −68.6, . . .

20. $-\frac{1}{4}$, −1, −4, −16, . . .

21. OPEN-ENDED Write a geometric sequence with first term 6, and $a_2 < a_1 < a_3$.

GO DIGITAL

You can rewrite the equation for a geometric sequence with first term a_1 and common ratio r in function notation by replacing a_n with $f(n)$.

$$f(n) = a_1 r^{n-1}$$

The domain of the function is the set of positive integers.

EXAMPLE 5 Modeling Real Life

WATCH

Clicking the *zoom-out* button on a mapping website doubles the side length of the square map. After how many clicks on the *zoom-out* button is the side length of the map 640 miles?

Zoom-out clicks	1	2	3
Map side length (miles)	5	10	20

SOLUTION

1. **Understand the Problem** You know that the side length of the square map doubles after each click on the *zoom-out* button. So, the side lengths of the map represent the terms of a geometric sequence. You need to find the number of clicks it takes for the side length of the map to be 640 miles.
2. **Make a Plan** Begin by writing a function f for the nth term of the geometric sequence. Then find the value of n for which $f(n) = 640$.
3. **Solve and Check** The first term is 5, and the common ratio is 2.

$f(n) = a_1 r^{n-1}$ Function for a geometric sequence

$f(n) = 5(2)^{n-1}$ Substitute 5 for a_1 and 2 for r.

The function $f(n) = 5(2)^{n-1}$ represents the geometric sequence. Use this function to find the value of n for which $f(n) = 640$. So, use each side of the equation $640 = 5(2)^{n-1}$ to write a function.

$y = 5(2)^{n-1}$

$y = 640$

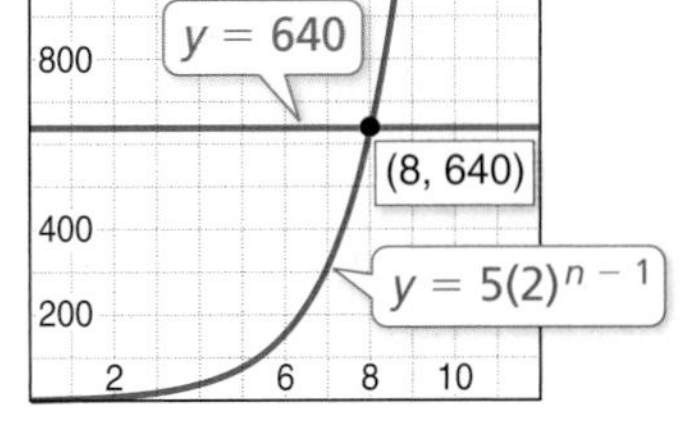

Then use technology to graph the functions and find the point of intersection. The point of intersection is (8, 640).

▶ So, after eight clicks, the side length of the map is 640 miles.

Another Method Find the value of n for which $f(n) = 640$ algebraically.

$640 = 5(2)^{n-1}$ Write the equation.

$128 = (2)^{n-1}$ Divide each side by 5.

$2^7 = (2)^{n-1}$ Rewrite 128 as 2^7.

$7 = n - 1$ Equate the exponents.

$8 = n$ ✓ Add 1 to each side.

SELF-ASSESSMENT

1 I do not understand. 2 I can do it with help. 3 I can do it on my own. 4 I can teach someone else.

22. **WHAT IF?** After how many clicks on the *zoom-out* button is the side length of the map 2560 miles?
23. **MP STRUCTURE** The sequence 86, 86, 86, 86, . . . represents the temperature (in degrees Fahrenheit) of a swimming pool over time. Is this sequence arithmetic? Is it geometric? Explain your reasoning. What can you conclude?

6.6 Practice WITH CalcChat® AND CalcView®

In Exercises 1–6, find the common ratio of the geometric sequence.

1. 4, 12, 36, 108, . . .
2. 36, 6, 1, $\frac{1}{6}$, . . .
3. $\frac{3}{8}$, −3, 24, −192, . . .
4. 0.1, 1, 10, 100, . . .
5. 128, 96, 72, 54, . . .
6. −162, 54, −18, 6, . . .

In Exercises 7–12, determine whether the sequence is *arithmetic*, *geometric*, or *neither*. Explain your reasoning. *Example 1*

7. −8, 0, 8, 16, . . .
8. −1, 4, −7, 10, . . .
9. 9, 14, 20, 27, . . .
10. $\frac{3}{49}$, $\frac{3}{7}$, 3, 21, . . .
11. 192, 24, 3, $\frac{3}{8}$, . . .
12. −25, −18, −11, −4, . . .

In Exercises 13–16, determine whether the graph represents an *arithmetic sequence*, a *geometric sequence*, or *neither*. Explain your reasoning.

13.

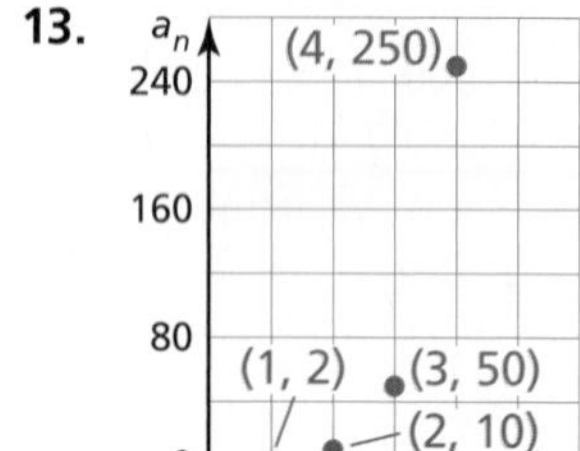

14.

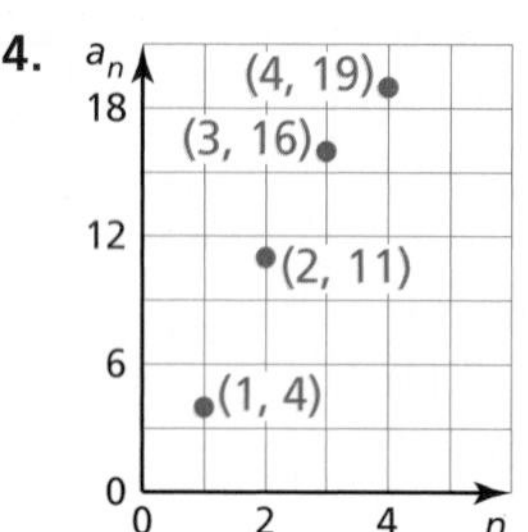

15.

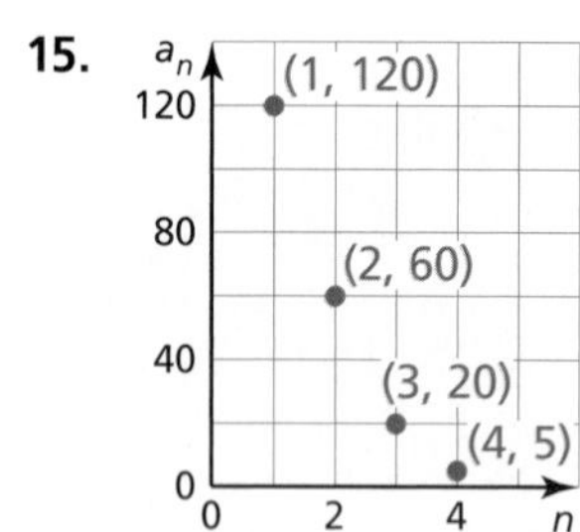

16.

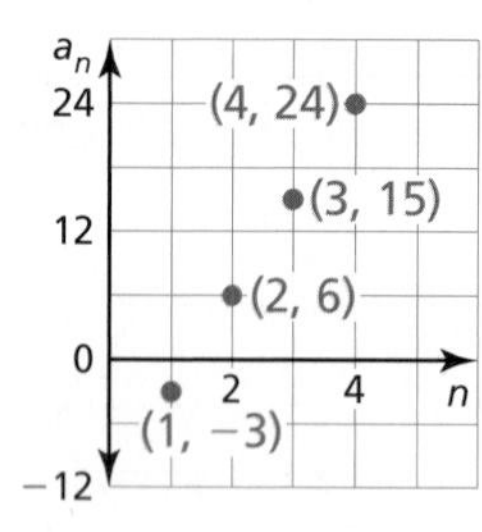

In Exercises 17–22, write the next three terms of the geometric sequence. Then graph the sequence. *Examples 2 and 3*

17. 5, 20, 80, 320, . . .
18. −3, 12, −48, 192, . . .
19. 81, −27, 9, −3, . . .
20. −375, −75, −15, −3, . . .
21. 32, 8, 2, $\frac{1}{2}$, . . .
22. $\frac{16}{9}$, $\frac{8}{3}$, 4, 6, . . .

In Exercises 23–30, write an equation for the *n*th term of the geometric sequence. Then find a_6. *Example 4*

23. 2, 8, 32, 128, . . .
24. 0.6, −3, 15, −75, . . .
25. $-\frac{1}{8}$, $-\frac{1}{4}$, $-\frac{1}{2}$, −1, . . .
26. 0.1, 0.9, 8.1, 72.9, . . .

27.

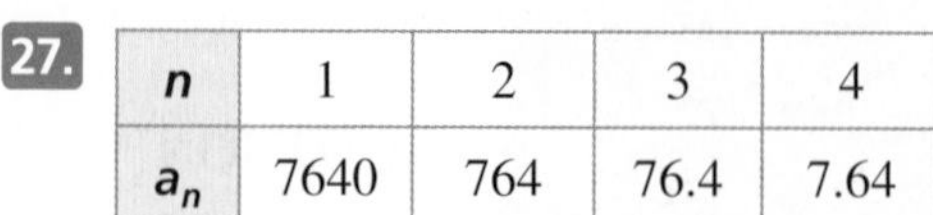

n	1	2	3	4
a_n	7640	764	76.4	7.64

28.

n	1	2	3	4
a_n	−192	48	−12	3

29. 30.

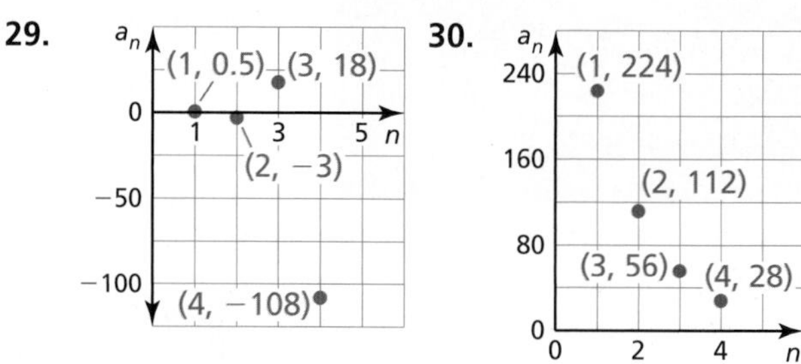

31. **ERROR ANALYSIS** Describe and correct the error in writing the next three terms of the geometric sequence.

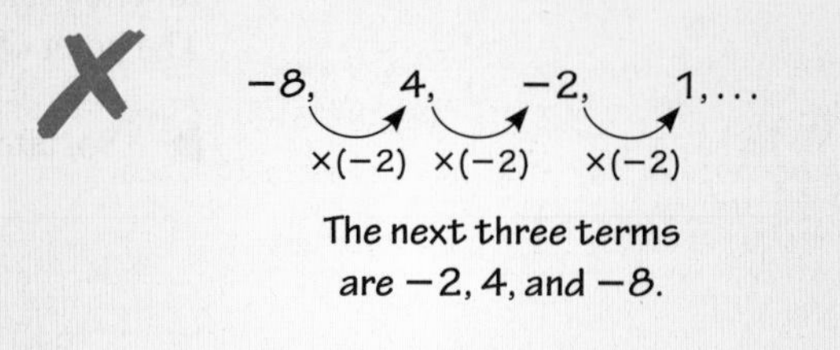

32. **ERROR ANALYSIS** Describe and correct the error in writing an equation for the *n*th term of the geometric sequence.

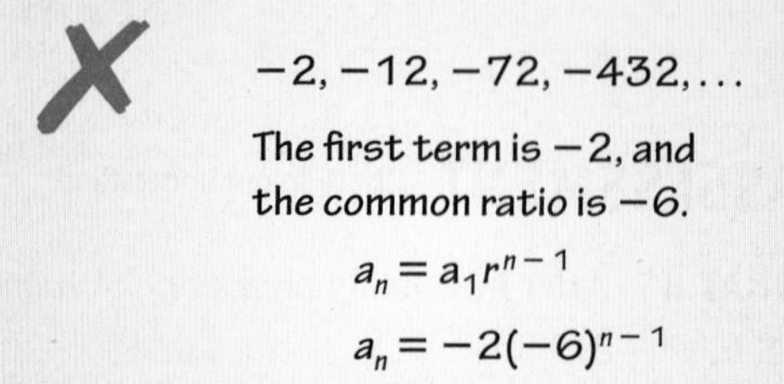

−2, −12, −72, −432, . . .
The first term is −2, and the common ratio is −6.
$a_n = a_1r^{n-1}$
$a_n = -2(-6)^{n-1}$

33. **WRITING** Compare the graphs of arithmetic sequences to the graphs of geometric sequences.

34. MP **REASONING** Does the graph of the geometric sequence represented by $f(n) = 10(4)^{n-1}$ contain the point $\left(\frac{3}{2}, 20\right)$? Explain.

35. **MODELING REAL LIFE** The distance (in millimeters) traveled by a swinging pendulum decreases after each swing, as shown in the table. *Example 5*

Swing	1	2	3
Distance (in millimeters)	625	500	400

a. Write a function that represents the distance the pendulum swings on its *n*th swing.

b. On which swing is the distance 256 millimeters?

36. **MODELING REAL LIFE** You create a post on a social media site and tag six friends. In the second round, each of your friends tags six people. The process continues.

a. Write a function that represents the number of people who are tagged in the *nth* round.

b. In which round will 1296 people be tagged?

MP **REPEATED REASONING** **In Exercises 37 and 38, a sequence represents the figures. Describe the figure represented by the 10th term of the sequence.**

37.

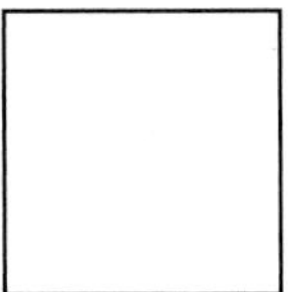 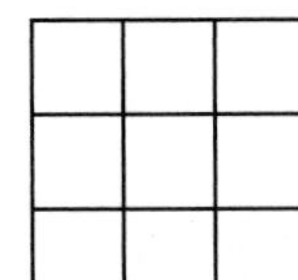 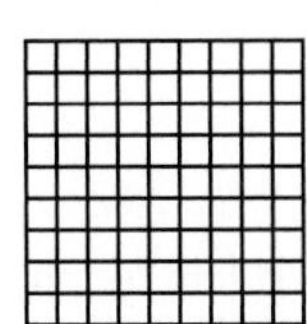

38.

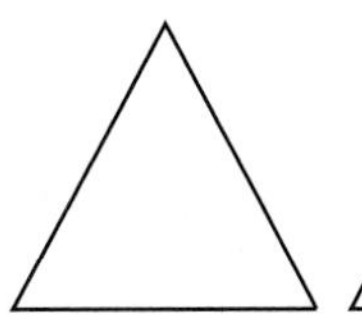 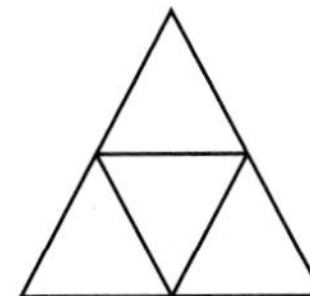 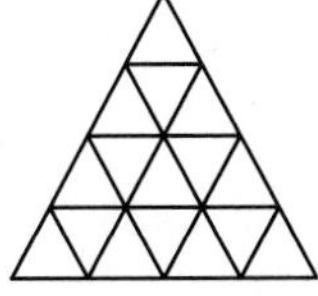

39. **COLLEGE PREP** Which function represents the sequence 90, −30, 10, $-\frac{10}{3}$, . . .?

Ⓐ $f(n) = -\frac{1}{3}(90)^{n-1}$ Ⓑ $f(n) = -90\left(\frac{1}{3}\right)^{n-1}$

Ⓒ $f(n) = 90(-3)^{n-1}$ Ⓓ $f(n) = 90\left(-\frac{1}{3}\right)^{n-1}$

40. **DRAWING CONCLUSIONS** A sheet of paper is about 0.1 millimeter thick.

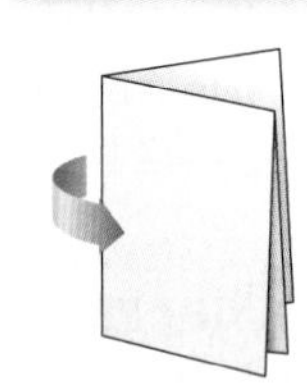

a. How thick will it be when you fold it in half once? twice? three times?

b. Take a piece of paper. What is the greatest number of times you can fold the piece of paper in half? How thick is the result?

c. Do you agree with the statement below? Explain your reasoning.

"If it were possible to fold the paper in half 15 times, it would be taller than you."

41. **MAKING AN ARGUMENT** You are given two consecutive terms of a sequence.

. . . , −8, 0, . . .

Your friend says that the sequence is not geometric. A classmate says that is impossible to know given only two terms. Who is correct? Explain.

42. **HOW DO YOU SEE IT?**
Without performing any calculations, match each equation with its graph. Explain your reasoning.

a. $a_n = 20\left(\frac{4}{3}\right)^{n-1}$ b. $a_n = 20\left(\frac{3}{4}\right)^{n-1}$

c. $a_n = 20\left(-\frac{3}{4}\right)^{n-1}$ d. $a_n = 10\left(\frac{3}{4}\right)^{n-1}$

A.
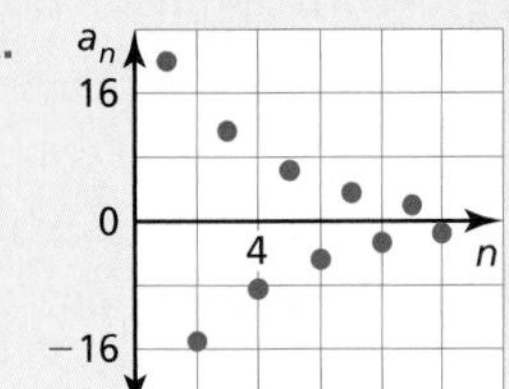

B.
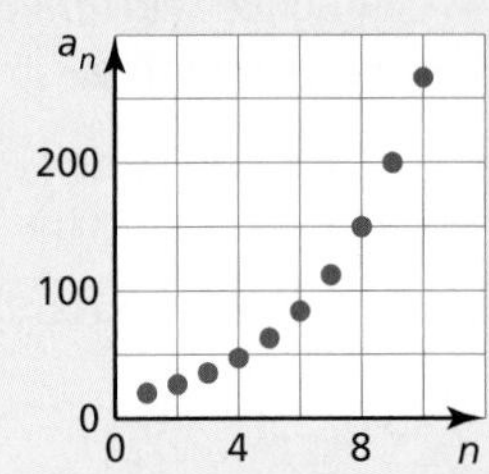

C.
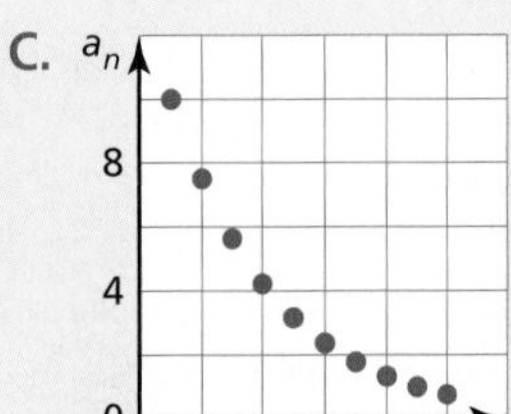

D.
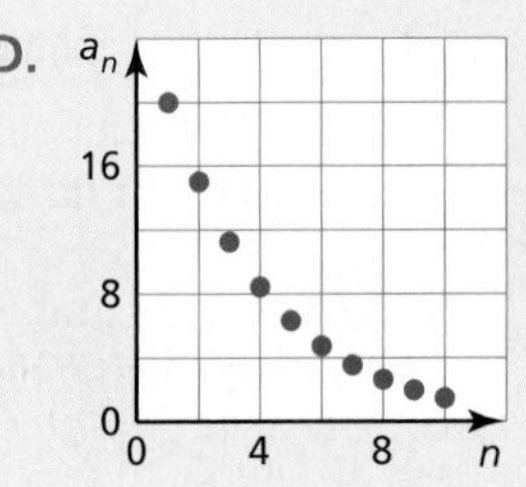

43. MP **REASONING** What is the 9th term of the geometric sequence with $a_3 = 81$ and $r = 3$?

44. MP **STRUCTURE** The sequence is geometric with a positive common ratio. Find the missing terms.

45. DIG DEEPER Consider the two options shown. With which option will you earn more money? How much more? Explain your reasoning.

Option 1	Option 2
Earn \$10 the first hour, \$13 the second hour, \$16 the third hour, and so on for 10 hours.	Earn \$0.01 the first hour, \$0.03 the second hour, \$0.09 the third hour, and so on for 10 hours.

46. **THOUGHT PROVOKING** Find the sum of the terms of the geometric sequence.

$$1, \frac{1}{2}, \frac{1}{4}, \frac{1}{8}, \ldots, \frac{1}{2^{n-1}}, \ldots$$

Explain your reasoning. Write a different geometric sequence that has the same sum.

47. MP **NUMBER SENSE** Write an equation for the nth term of each geometric sequence shown.

n	1	2	3	4
a_n	2	6	18	54

n	1	2	3	4
b_n	1	5	25	125

a. Do the terms $a_1 - b_1, a_2 - b_2, a_3 - b_3, \ldots$ form a geometric sequence? If so, how does the common ratio relate to the common ratios of the sequences above?

b. Do the terms $\frac{a_1}{b_1}, \frac{a_2}{b_2}, \frac{a_3}{b_3}, \ldots$ form a geometric sequence? If so, how does the common ratio relate to the common ratios of the sequences above?

REVIEW & REFRESH

48. Use residuals to determine whether the model is a good fit for the data in the table. Explain.

$y = 3x - 8$

x	0	1	2	3	4	5	6
y	−10	−2	−1	2	1	7	10

In Exercises 49 and 50, determine whether the sequence is *arithmetic*, *geometric*, or *neither*. Explain your reasoning.

49. $18, 12, 8, \frac{16}{3}, \ldots$

50. $-15, -2, 11, 24, \ldots$

In Exercises 51 and 52, graph the equation.

51. $x = -6$

52. $5x - 7y = 35$

53. Write the sentence as an inequality.

The quotient of a number n and 8 is no less than −3.5.

In Exercises 54 and 55, simplify the expression. Write your answer using only positive exponents.

54. $(-3n^5)^4$

55. $\left(\frac{12}{x^3}\right)^{-2}$

56. MP **PRECISION** Are the terms of a geometric sequence independent or dependent? Explain your reasoning.

57. Solve $\frac{3}{2}x - 2 = 3x + 1$ by graphing. Check your solution.

In Exercises 58 and 59, write a function that represents the situation.

58. A \$750 laptop decreases in value by 20% each year.

59. An animal population of 8000 increases by 2.5% each year.

60. Write a system of linear inequalities represented by the graph.

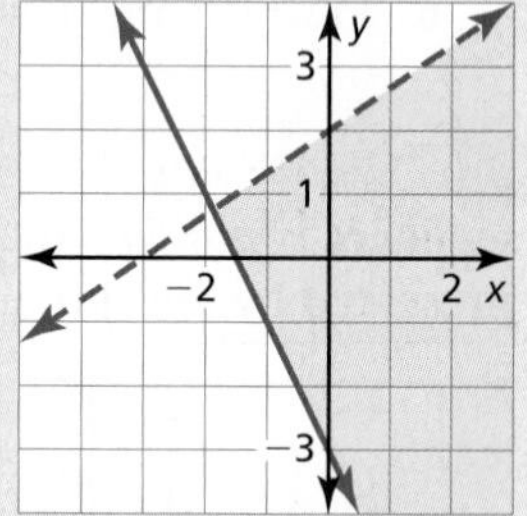

In Exercises 61 and 62, solve the equation. Check your solution.

61. $2^{x-6} = 2^{3x}$

62. $125^{x+1} = 25^{2x+1}$

63. MP **STRUCTURE** The graph of g is a translation 7 units down and 2 units left of the graph of $f(x) = 4^x$. Write an equation that represents g.

64. The points represented by the table lie on a line. Find the slope of the line.

x	−15	−9	−3	3
y	12	7	2	−3

6.7 Recursively Defined Sequences

Learning Target Write terms of recursively defined sequences and write recursive rules for sequences.

Success Criteria
- I can write terms of recursively defined sequences.
- I can write recursive rules for sequences.
- I can translate between recursive rules and explicit rules.

EXPLORE IT! Describing a Pattern

Work with a partner. Consider a hypothetical population of rabbits as shown in the table below. Start with one breeding pair. After each month, each breeding pair produces another breeding pair. The total number of rabbits each month follows the exponential pattern 2, 4, 8, 16, 32, ... Now suppose that in the first month after each pair is born, the pair is too young to reproduce. Each pair produces another pair after it is 2 months old as shown in the diagram below.

Month		Number of pairs
1	**RED** pair is too young to reproduce.	1
	RED pair produces **BLUE** pair.	
	RED pair produces **GREEN** pair.	
	RED pair produces **ORANGE** pair. **BLUE** pair produces **PURPLE** pair.	

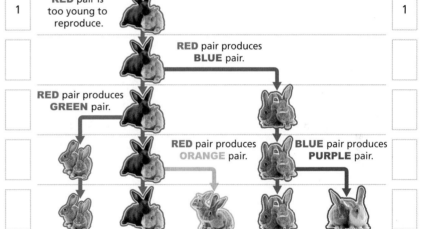

a. Complete the "month" column and "number of pairs" column in the table. Then extend the table for the next month.

b. Describe the pattern shown by the number of pairs.

c. How can you write a rule for this sequence? Explain your reasoning.

d. Construct a table that shows the first 8 terms of the sequence represented by the rule you wrote in part (c). Compare the results with the sequence of the number of pairs in the table above.

e. How is this sequence different from the sequences you have studied so far in this book?

Math Practice

Check Progress
If the terms in your table in part (d) do not match the results in the table above, how can you modify the rule you wrote in part (c)?

Writing Terms of Recursively Defined Sequences

Vocabulary

explicit rule, *p. 346*
recursive rule, *p. 346*

So far in this book, you have defined arithmetic and geometric sequences *explicitly*. An **explicit rule** gives a_n as a function of the term's position number n in the sequence. For example, an explicit rule for the arithmetic sequence 3, 5, 7, 9, . . . is $a_n = 3 + 2(n - 1)$, or $a_n = 2n + 1$.

WORDS AND MATH

The prefix *re-* often indicates repetition.

Now, you will define arithmetic and geometric sequences *recursively*. A **recursive rule** gives the beginning term(s) of a sequence and a *recursive equation* that tells how a_n is related to one or more preceding terms.

KEY IDEAS

Recursive Equation for an Arithmetic Sequence

$a_n = a_{n-1} + d$, where d is the common difference

Recursive Equation for a Geometric Sequence

$a_n = r \cdot a_{n-1}$, where r is the common ratio

Math Practice

Make Sense of Quantities

When working with sequences, be sure you understand which term is represented by an expression such as a_{n-1} or a_{n+2}.

EXAMPLE 1 Writing Terms of Recursively Defined Sequences

Write the first six terms of each sequence. Then graph each sequence.

a. $a_1 = 2, a_n = a_{n-1} + 3$

b. $a_1 = 1, a_n = 3a_{n-1}$

SOLUTION

You are given the first term. Use the recursive equation to find the next five terms.

a. $a_1 = 2$

$a_2 = a_1 + 3 = 2 + 3 = 5$

$a_3 = a_2 + 3 = 5 + 3 = 8$

$a_4 = a_3 + 3 = 8 + 3 = 11$

$a_5 = a_4 + 3 = 11 + 3 = 14$

$a_6 = a_5 + 3 = 14 + 3 = 17$

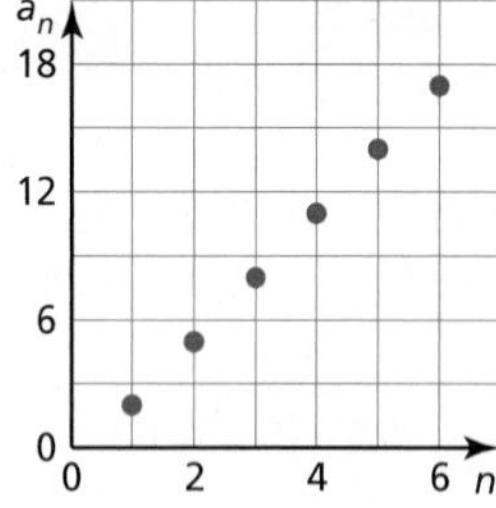

b. $a_1 = 1$

$a_2 = 3a_1 = 3(1) = 3$

$a_3 = 3a_2 = 3(3) = 9$

$a_4 = 3a_3 = 3(9) = 27$

$a_5 = 3a_4 = 3(27) = 81$

$a_6 = 3a_5 = 3(81) = 243$

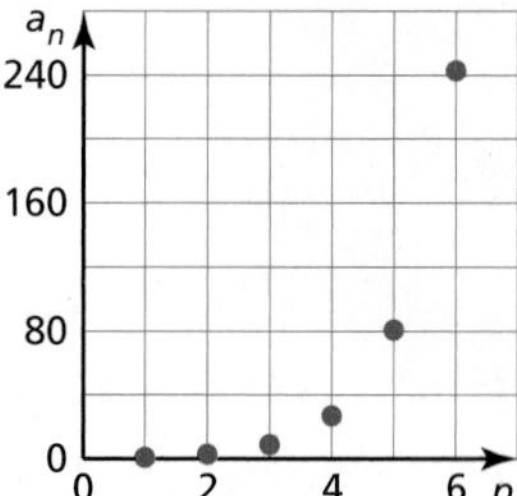

STUDY TIP

A sequence is a discrete function. So, the points on the graph are not connected.

SELF-ASSESSMENT 1 I do not understand. 2 I can do it with help. 3 I can do it on my own. 4 I can teach someone else.

Write the first six terms of the sequence. Then graph the sequence.

1. $a_1 = 0, a_n = a_{n-1} - 8$
2. $a_1 = -7.5, a_n = a_{n-1} + 2.5$
3. $a_1 = -36, a_n = \frac{1}{2}a_{n-1}$
4. $a_1 = 0.7, a_n = 10a_{n-1}$
5. **WRITING** Explain the difference between an explicit rule and a recursive rule.

Writing Recursive Rules

EXAMPLE 2 **Writing Recursive Rules** 

Write a recursive rule for each sequence.

a. $-30, -18, -6, 6, 18, \ldots$

b. $500, 100, 20, 4, 0.8, \ldots$

SOLUTION

Use a table to organize the terms and find the pattern.

a.

Position, n	1	2	3	4	5
Term, a_n	-30	-18	-6	6	18

$+12$ $+12$ $+12$ $+12$

COMMON ERROR

When writing a recursive rule for a sequence, you need to write both the beginning term(s) and the recursive equation.

The sequence is arithmetic, with first term $a_1 = -30$ and common difference $d = 12$.

$a_n = a_{n-1} + d$ Recursive equation for an arithmetic sequence

$a_n = a_{n-1} + 12$ Substitute 12 for d.

▶ So, a recursive rule for the sequence is $a_1 = -30$, $a_n = a_{n-1} + 12$.

b.

Position, n	1	2	3	4	5
Term, a_n	500	100	20	4	0.8

$\times\frac{1}{5}$ $\times\frac{1}{5}$ $\times\frac{1}{5}$ $\times\frac{1}{5}$

The sequence is geometric, with first term $a_1 = 500$ and common ratio $r = \frac{1}{5}$.

$a_n = r \bullet a_{n-1}$ Recursive equation for a geometric sequence

$a_n = \frac{1}{5}a_{n-1}$ Substitute $\frac{1}{5}$ for r.

▶ So, a recursive rule for the sequence is $a_1 = 500$, $a_n = \frac{1}{5}a_{n-1}$.

SELF-ASSESSMENT 1 I do not understand. 2 I can do it with help. 3 I can do it on my own. 4 I can teach someone else.

6. WHICH ONE DOESN'T BELONG? Which rule does *not* belong with the other three? Explain your reasoning.

$a_1 = -1, a_n = 5a_{n-1}$ | $a_n = 6n - 2$ | $a_1 = -3, a_n = a_{n-1} + 1$ | $a_1 = 9, a_n = 4a_{n-1}$

Write a recursive rule for the sequence.

7. $8, 3, -2, -7, -12, \ldots$

8. $1.3, 2.6, 3.9, 5.2, 6.5, \ldots$

9. $4, 20, 100, 500, 2500, \ldots$

10. $128, -32, 8, -2, 0.5, \ldots$

11. Write a recursive rule for the height of the sunflower over time.

1 month: 2 feet

2 months: 3.5 feet

3 months: 5 feet

4 months: 6.5 feet

Translating between Recursive and Explicit Rules

EXAMPLE 3 Translating from Recursive Rules to Explicit Rules

Write an explicit rule for each recursive rule.

a. $a_1 = 25, a_n = a_{n-1} - 10$

b. $a_1 = 19.6, a_n = -0.5a_{n-1}$

SOLUTION

a. The recursive rule represents an arithmetic sequence, with first term $a_1 = 25$ and common difference $d = -10$.

$a_n = a_1 + (n - 1)d$ — Explicit rule for an arithmetic sequence

$a_n = 25 + (n - 1)(-10)$ — Substitute 25 for a_1 and -10 for d.

$a_n = -10n + 35$ — Simplify.

▶ An explicit rule for the sequence is $a_n = -10n + 35$.

b. The recursive rule represents a geometric sequence, with first term $a_1 = 19.6$ and common ratio $r = -0.5$.

$a_n = a_1r^{n-1}$ — Explicit rule for a geometric sequence

$a_n = 19.6(-0.5)^{n-1}$ — Substitute 19.6 for a_1 and -0.5 for r.

▶ An explicit rule for the sequence is $a_n = 19.6(-0.5)^{n-1}$.

EXAMPLE 4 Translating from Explicit Rules to Recursive Rules

Write a recursive rule for each explicit rule.

a. $a_n = -2n + 3$

b. $a_n = -3(2)^{n-1}$

SOLUTION

a. The explicit rule represents an arithmetic sequence, with first term $a_1 = -2(1) + 3 = 1$ and common difference $d = -2$.

$a_n = a_{n-1} + d$ — Recursive equation for an arithmetic sequence

$a_n = a_{n-1} + (-2)$ — Substitute -2 for d.

▶ So, a recursive rule for the sequence is $a_1 = 1, a_n = a_{n-1} - 2$.

b. The explicit rule represents a geometric sequence, with first term $a_1 = -3$ and common ratio $r = 2$.

$a_n = r \cdot a_{n-1}$ — Recursive equation for a geometric sequence

$a_n = 2a_{n-1}$ — Substitute 2 for r.

▶ So, a recursive rule for the sequence is $a_1 = -3, a_n = 2a_{n-1}$.

SELF-ASSESSMENT

1 I do not understand. 2 I can do it with help. 3 I can do it on my own. 4 I can teach someone else.

Write an explicit rule for the recursive rule.

12. $a_1 = -45, a_n = a_{n-1} + 20$

13. $a_1 = 13, a_n = -3a_{n-1}$

Write a recursive rule for the explicit rule.

14. $a_n = -n + 1$

15. $a_n = -2.5(4)^{n-1}$

Writing Recursive Rules for Special Sequences

You can write recursive rules for sequences that are neither arithmetic nor geometric. One way is to look for patterns in the sums of consecutive terms.

EXAMPLE 5 Writing a Recursive Rule for a Special Sequence

Use the sequence shown.

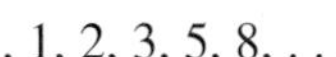

1, 1, 2, 3, 5, 8, . . .

a. Write a recursive rule for the sequence.

b. Write the next three terms of the sequence.

SOLUTION

a. Find the difference and ratio between each pair of consecutive terms.

1 1 2 3

$1 - 1 = 0$ $2 - 1 = 1$ $3 - 2 = 1$

There is no common difference, so the sequence is *not* arithmetic.

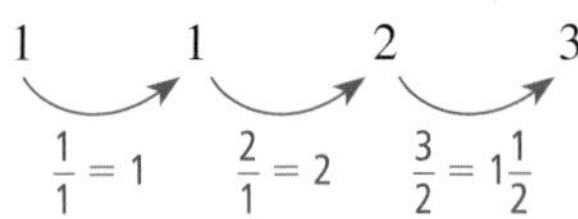

1 1 2 3

$\frac{1}{1} = 1$ $\frac{2}{1} = 2$ $\frac{3}{2} = 1\frac{1}{2}$

There is no common ratio, so the sequence is *not* geometric.

Find the sum of each pair of consecutive terms.

$a_1 + a_2 = 1 + 1 = 2$ 2 is the third term.

$a_2 + a_3 = 1 + 2 = 3$ 3 is the fourth term.

$a_3 + a_4 = 2 + 3 = 5$ 5 is the fifth term.

$a_4 + a_5 = 3 + 5 = 8$ 8 is the sixth term.

Beginning with the third term, each term is the sum of the two previous terms. A recursive equation for the sequence is $a_n = a_{n-2} + a_{n-1}$.

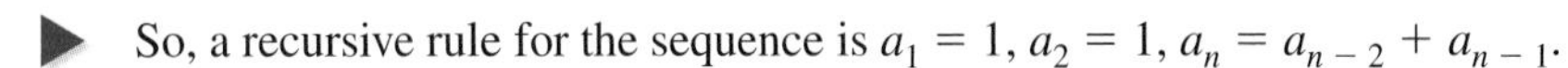

▶ So, a recursive rule for the sequence is $a_1 = 1$, $a_2 = 1$, $a_n = a_{n-2} + a_{n-1}$.

b. Use the recursive equation $a_n = a_{n-2} + a_{n-1}$ to find the next three terms.

$$a_7 = a_5 + a_6 = 5 + 8 = 13 \qquad a_8 = a_6 + a_7 = 8 + 13 = 21 \qquad a_9 = a_7 + a_8 = 13 + 21 = 34$$

▶ The next three terms are 13, 21, and 34.

The sequence in Example 5 is called the *Fibonacci sequence.* This pattern is naturally occurring in many objects, such as flowers.

SELF-ASSESSMENT 1 I do not understand. 2 I can do it with help. 3 I can do it on my own. 4 I can teach someone else.

Write a recursive rule for the sequence. Then write the next three terms of the sequence.

16. 5, 6, 11, 17, 28, . . .

17. −3, −4, −7, −11, −18, . . .

18. 1, 1, 0, −1, −1, 0, 1, 1, . . .

19. 4, 3, 1, 2, −1, 3, −4, . . .

20. Find another example of the pattern given by the Fibonacci sequence occurring in nature.

6.7 Practice WITH CalcChat® AND CalcView®

In Exercises 1–4, determine whether the recursive rule represents an *arithmetic sequence* or a *geometric sequence*.

1. $a_1 = 18, a_n = a_{n-1} + 1$
2. $a_1 = 5, a_n = a_{n-1} - 4$
3. $a_1 = 2, a_n = 7a_{n-1}$
4. $a_1 = 3, a_n = -6a_{n-1}$

In Exercises 5–10, write the first six terms of the sequence. Then graph the sequence. *Example 1*

5. $a_1 = 0, a_n = a_{n-1} + 2$
6. $a_1 = 10, a_n = a_{n-1} - 5$
7. $a_1 = 2, a_n = 3a_{n-1}$
8. $a_1 = 8, a_n = 1.5a_{n-1}$
9. $a_1 = 80, a_n = -\frac{1}{2}a_{n-1}$
10. $a_1 = -7, a_n = -4a_{n-1}$

In Exercises 11–18, write a recursive rule for the sequence. *Example 2*

11.

n	1	2	3	4
a_n	7	16	25	34

12.

n	1	2	3	4
a_n	8	24	72	216

13. 3, 11, 19, 27, 35, . . .
14. 0, −3, −6, −9, −12, . . .
15. 243, 81, 27, 9, 3, . . .
16. 5, −20, 80, −320, 1280, . . .

17.

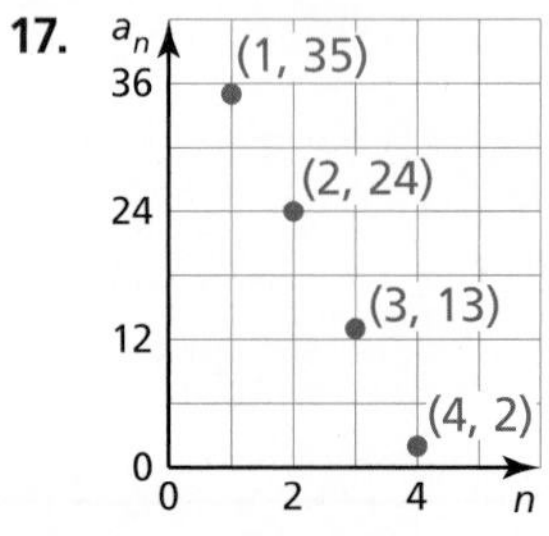

18.

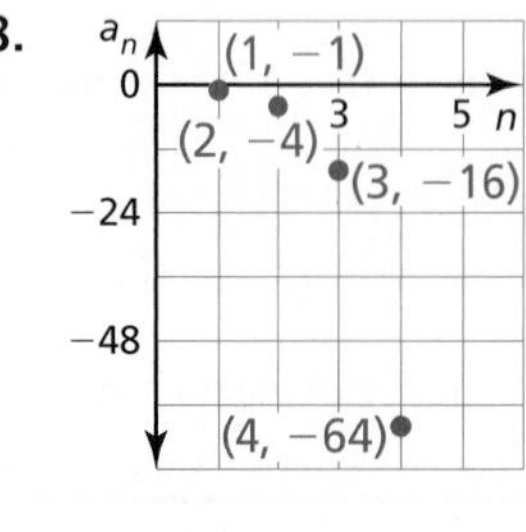

19. **MODELING REAL LIFE** Write a recursive rule that represents the number of bacterial cells over time.

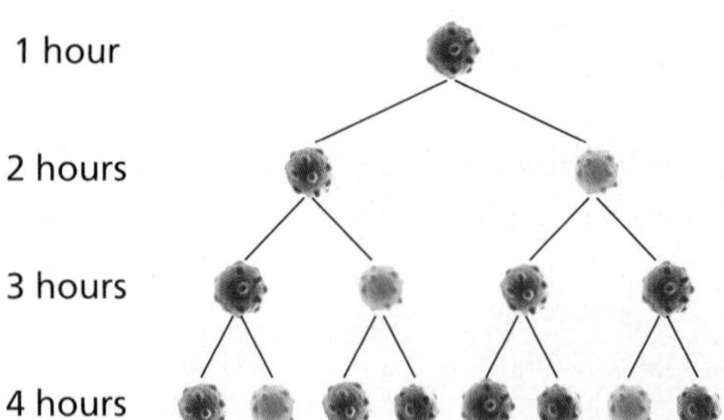

20. **MODELING REAL LIFE** Write a recursive rule that represents the length of the deer antler over time.

Day	Length (inches)
1	$4\frac{1}{2}$
2	$4\frac{3}{4}$
3	5
4	$5\frac{1}{4}$

In Exercises 21–26, write an explicit rule for the recursive rule. *Example 3*

21. $a_1 = -3, a_n = a_{n-1} + 3$
22. $a_1 = 8, a_n = a_{n-1} - 12$
23. $a_1 = -2, a_n = 9a_{n-1}$
24. $a_1 = 5, a_n = -5a_{n-1}$
25. $a_1 = 4, a_n = a_{n-1} + 1.75$
26. $a_1 = 16, a_n = 0.5a_{n-1}$

In Exercises 27–34, write a recursive rule for the explicit rule. *Example 4*

27. $a_n = 8(2)^{n-1}$
28. $a_n = 7(3)^{n-1}$
29. $a_n = 6n - 20$
30. $a_n = -4n + 2$
31. $a_n = 9^{n-1}$
32. $a_n = (-5)^{n-1}$
33. $a_n = -\left(\frac{1}{2}\right)^{n+3}$
34. $a_n = 81\left(\frac{2}{3}\right)^{n-1}$

GO DIGITAL

In Exercises 35–38, graph the first four terms of the sequence with the given description. Write a recursive rule and an explicit rule for the sequence.

35. The first term of a sequence is 5. Each term of the sequence is 15 more than the preceding term.

36. The first term of a sequence is 19. Each term of the sequence is 13 less than the preceding term.

37. The first term of a sequence is 16. Each term of the sequence is half the preceding term.

38. The first term of a sequence is -1. Each term of the sequence is -3 times the preceding term.

In Exercises 39–44, write a recursive rule for the sequence. Then write the next two terms of the sequence. *Example 5*

39. 1, 3, 4, 7, 11, . . .

40. 10, 9, 1, 8, -7, 15, . . .

41. 2, 4, 2, -2, -4, -2, . . .

42. 6, 1, 7, 8, 15, 23, . . .

43.

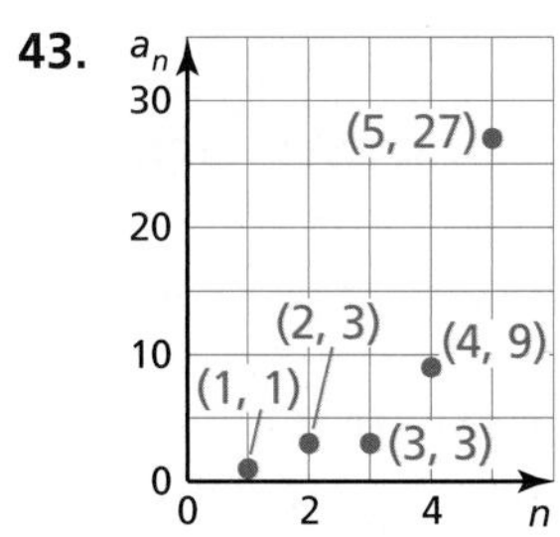

44.

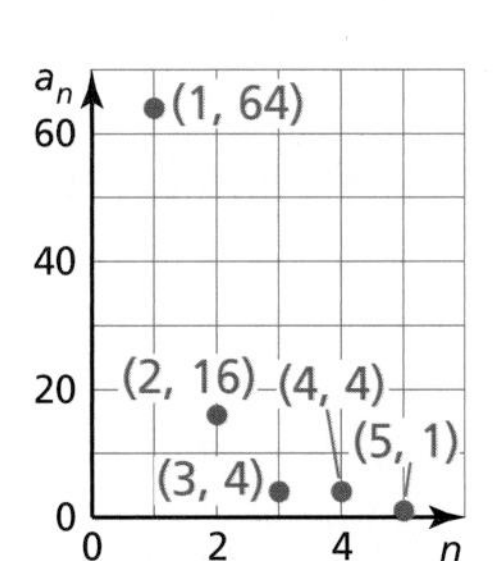

45. ERROR ANALYSIS Describe and correct the error in writing an explicit rule for the recursive rule $a_1 = 6$, $a_n = a_{n-1} - 12$.

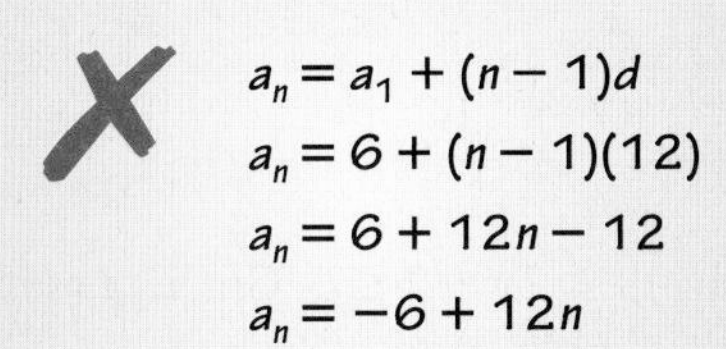

$a_n = a_1 + (n - 1)d$
$a_n = 6 + (n - 1)(12)$
$a_n = 6 + 12n - 12$
$a_n = -6 + 12n$

46. ERROR ANALYSIS Describe and correct the error in writing a recursive rule for the sequence 2, 4, 6, 10, 16, ...

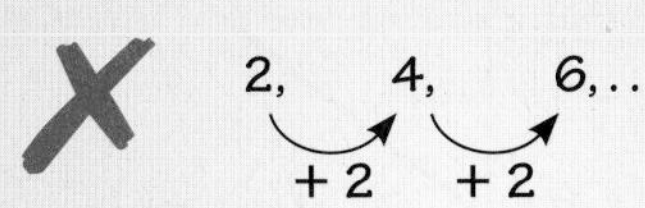

The sequence is arithmetic, with first term $a_1 = 2$ and common difference $d = 2$.

$a_n = a_{n-1} + d$

$a_1 = 2, a_n = a_{n-1} + 2$

In Exercises 47–50, the function *f* represents a sequence. Find the 2nd, 5th, and 10th terms of the sequence.

47. $f(1) = 3,\ f(n) = f(n - 1) + 7$

48. $f(1) = -1,\ f(n) = 6f(n - 1)$

49. $f(1) = 4, f(2) = 5,\ f(n) = f(n - 2) + f(n - 1)$

50. $f(1) = 10, f(2) = 15,\ f(n) = f(n - 1) - f(n - 2)$

51. MP REASONING Write the first 5 terms of the sequence $a_1 = 5$, $a_n = 3a_{n-1} + 4$. Determine whether the sequence is *arithmetic*, *geometric*, or *neither*. Explain your reasoning.

52. MP USING TOOLS You can use a spreadsheet to generate the terms of a sequence.

A2 ▼ = =A1+2

	A	B	C
1	3		
2	5		
3			
4			

a. To generate the terms of the sequence $a_1 = 3$, $a_n = a_{n-1} + 2$, enter the value of a_1, 3, into cell A1. Then enter "=A1+2" into cell A2, as shown. Use the *fill down* feature to generate the first 10 terms of the sequence.

b. Use a spreadsheet to generate the first 10 terms of the sequence $a_1 = 3$, $a_n = 4a_{n-1}$.

c. Use a spreadsheet to generate the first 10 terms of the sequence $a_1 = 4$, $a_2 = 7$, $a_n = a_{n-1} - a_{n-2}$.

53. JUSTIFYING STEPS The explicit rule $a_n = a_1 + (n - 1)d$ defines an arithmetic sequence.

a. Explain why $a_{n-1} = a_1 + [(n - 1) - 1]d$.

b. Justify each step in showing that a recursive equation for the sequence is $a_n = a_{n-1} + d$.

$$a_n = a_1 + (n - 1)d$$
$$= a_1 + [(n - 1) + 0]d$$
$$= a_1 + [(n - 1) - 1 + 1]d$$
$$= a_1 + [((n - 1) - 1) + 1]d$$
$$= a_1 + [(n - 1) - 1]d + d$$
$$= a_{n-1} + d$$

54. HOW DO YOU SEE IT?
Consider Squares 1–6 in the diagram.

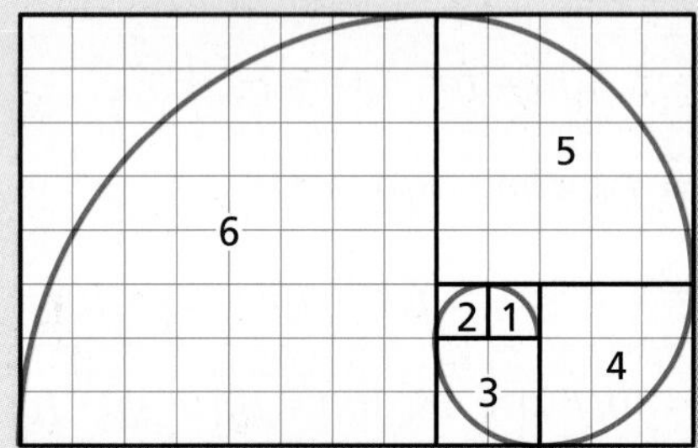

a. Write a sequence in which each term a_n is the side length of square n.

b. What is the name of this sequence? What is the next term of this sequence?

c. Add another square to the diagram and extend the spiral.

55. MAKING AN ARGUMENT Can the sequence $-5, 5, -5, 5, -5, \ldots$ be represented by a recursive rule? Explain.

56. THOUGHT PROVOKING
Part of *Pascal's Triangle* is shown below. Write a recursive rule that gives the mth number in the nth row.

1
1 1
1 2 1
1 3 3 1
1 4 6 4 1
1 5 10 10 5 1

57. DIG DEEPER Write a recursive rule for the sequence.

$3, 7, 15, 31, 63, \ldots$

REVIEW & REFRESH

WATCH

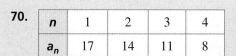

58. Solve the system using any method. Explain your choice of method.

$\frac{1}{5}x - 4y = 3$

$3x - 60y = 45$

In Exercises 59 and 60, determine whether the table represents an *exponential growth function*, an *exponential decay function*, or *neither*. Explain.

59.

x	*y*
2	19
3	13
4	7
5	1

60.

x	*y*
−2	0.1
−1	0.4
0	1.6
1	6.4

61. Write an equation of the line that passes through (6, 1) and is (a) parallel and (b) perpendicular to the line $y = \frac{1}{4}x + 3$.

In Exercises 62–65, solve the equation. Check your solution.

62. $3^{-x-4} = 3^{x+2}$

63. $2^{2x} = 8^{x+1}$

64. $5^{3x+3} = \frac{1}{25}$

65. $2^{x-6} = 13$

66. MP REASONING Can a proportional relationship be represented by an arithmetic sequence? a geometric sequence? Explain your reasoning.

67. Write a linear function f with the values $f(-2) = 0$ and $f(-1) = -3$.

68. Write the next three terms of the sequence. Then graph the sequence.

$\frac{1}{24}, \frac{1}{4}, \frac{3}{2}, 9, \ldots$

In Exercises 69 and 70, write a recursive rule for the sequence.

69.

n	1	2	3	4
a_n	2	8	32	128

70.

n	1	2	3	4
a_n	17	14	11	8

71. Solve $-9 < 2x + 7 \le 5$. Graph the solution.

72. Use the graphs of f and g to describe the transformation from the graph of f to the graph of g.

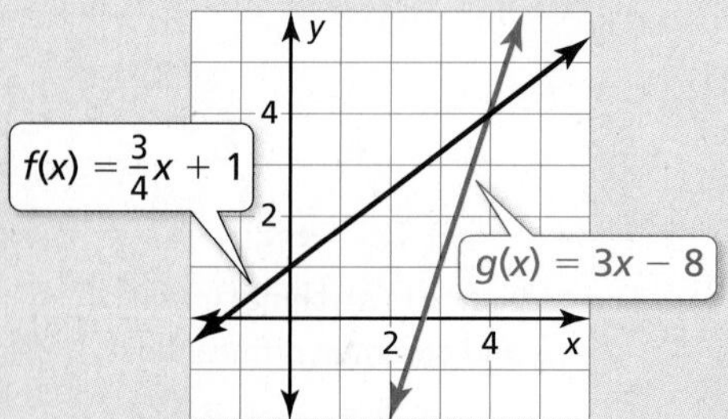

6 Chapter Review WITH CalcChat®

Chapter Learning Target Understand exponential functions and sequences.

Chapter Success Criteria
- ◆ I can identify and use properties of exponents.
- ◆ I can describe exponential functions.
- ■ I can analyze data, a graph, or a context to determine whether it represents exponential growth or decay.
- ■ I can model using an exponential function or a geometric sequence.

◆ Surface
■ Deep

SELF-ASSESSMENT 1 I do not understand. 2 I can do it with help. 3 I can do it on my own. 4 I can teach someone else.

6.1 Properties of Exponents (pp. 299–306)

Learning Target: Write equivalent expressions involving powers.

Simplify the expression. Write your answer using only positive exponents.

1. $y^3 \cdot y^{-5}$ **2.** $\frac{x^4}{x^7}$ **3.** $(x^0y^2)^3$ **4.** $\left(\frac{2x^2}{5y^4}\right)^{-2}$

5. The table shows several units of mass.

Unit of mass	kilogram	hectogram	dekagram	decigram	centigram	milligram	microgram	nanogram
Mass (grams)	10^3	10^2	10^1	10^{-1}	10^{-2}	10^{-3}	10^{-6}	10^{-9}

a. One kilogram is how many times one nanogram? Write your answer using only positive exponents.

b. Which is greater, 10,000 milligrams or 1000 decigrams? Explain your reasoning.

6.2 Radicals and Rational Exponents (pp. 307–312)

Learning Target: Write and evaluate an *n*th root of a number.

Vocabulary
*n*th root of *a*
radical
index of a radical

Evaluate the expression.

6. $\sqrt[3]{8}$ **7.** $\sqrt[5]{-243}$ **8.** $625^{3/4}$ **9.** $(-25)^{1/2}$

10. You can use the equation $A = \left(\frac{HW}{3600}\right)^{1/2}$ to approximate a person's body surface area A (in square meters), where H is height (in centimeters), and W is weight (in kilograms). Approximate the body surface area of a person with a height of 160 centimeters and a weight of 64 kilograms.

11. You store blankets in a cedar chest. What is the volume of the cedar chest?

6.3 Exponential Functions (pp. 313–320)

Learning Target: Graph and write exponential functions.

Vocabulary
exponential function
asymptote

Graph the function. Identify the asymptote. Describe the domain and range.

12. $f(x) = -4\left(\frac{1}{4}\right)^x$ **13.** $f(x) = 3^{x+2}$ **14.** $f(x) = 2^{x-4} - 3$

15. Write and graph an exponential function f represented by the table. Then compare the graph to the graph of the parent function.

x	0	1	2	3
y	2	1	0.5	0.25

16. Write an exponential function with an asymptote of $y = -2$ and a y-intercept of 1.

6.4 Exponential Growth and Decay (pp. 321–330)

Learning Target: Write and graph exponential growth and decay functions.

Vocabulary
exponential growth
exponential growth function
exponential decay
exponential decay function
compound interest

Determine whether the table represents an *exponential growth function*, an *exponential decay function*, or *neither*. Explain.

17.

x	0	1	2	3
y	3	6	12	24

18.

x	1	2	3	4
y	162	108	72	48

Determine whether the function represents *exponential growth* or *exponential decay*. Identify the percent rate of change.

19. $f(t) = 4(1.25)^{t+3}$ **20.** $y = (1.06)^{8t}$ **21.** $f(t) = 6(0.84)^{t-4}$

22. You deposit \$750 in a savings account that earns 5% annual interest compounded quarterly. (a) Write a function that represents the balance y (in dollars) after t years. (b) What is the balance of the account after 4 years?

23. The value of a TV is \$1500. It loses 14% of its value every year. (a) Write a function that represents the value y (in dollars) of the TV after t years. (b) Find the approximate monthly percent decrease in value. (c) Use the graph of the function to estimate the value of the TV after 3 years.

6.5 Solving Exponential Equations (pp. 331–336)

Learning Target: Solve exponential equations.

Vocabulary
exponential equation

Solve the equation. Check your solution.

24. $5^x = 5^{3x-2}$ **25.** $8^{x+4} = 8^{2x-1}$ **26.** $3^{x-2} = 1$

27. $\left(\frac{1}{16}\right)^x = 4^{-2x-3}$ **28.** $\left(\frac{1}{3}\right)^{2x+3} = 5$ **29.** $1.8^{x+5} = 3.24$

30. Consider the equation $p^x = qx + r$, where p, q, and r are real numbers. Determine whether each statement is *always*, *sometimes*, or *never* true. Explain your reasoning.

a. When $p > 0$ and $q < 0$, the equation has no solution.

b. When $p > 0$ and $q > 0$, the equation has more than one solution.

c. When $p > 0$ and $1 < q < r$, the equation has more than one solution.

6.6 Geometric Sequences (pp. 337–344)

Learning Target: Identify, extend, and graph geometric sequences.

Vocabulary
geometric sequence
common ratio

Determine whether the sequence is *arithmetic*, *geometric*, or *neither*. Explain your reasoning. If the sequence is geometric, write the next three terms and graph the sequence.

31. 3, 12, 48, 192, . . .

32. 9, −18, 27, −36, . . .

33. 375, −75, 15, −3, . . .

Write an equation for the *n*th term of the geometric sequence. Then find a_9.

34. 1, 4, 16, 64, . . .

35. 5, −10, 20, −40, . . .

36. 486, 162, 54, 18, . . .

37. For a geometric sequence, $a_5 = 9$ and $a_8 = -243$. Find a_{12}.

38. Each figure in the sequence is composed of equilateral triangles. What is the perimeter of the smallest triangle in the 10th figure of the sequence?

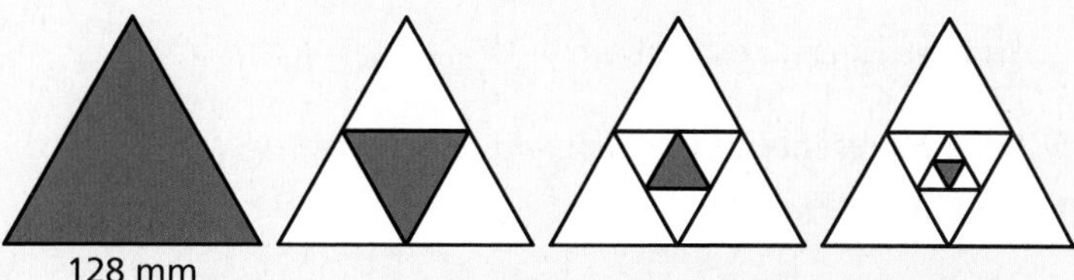

6.7 Recursively Defined Sequences (pp. 345–352)

Learning Target: Write terms of recursively defined sequences and write recursive rules for sequences.

Vocabulary

explicit rule
recursive rule

Write the first six terms of the sequence. Then graph the sequence.

39. $a_1 = 4, a_n = a_{n-1} + 5$

40. $a_1 = 32, a_n = 2\frac{1}{4}a_{n-1}$

Write a recursive rule for the sequence.

41. 3, 8, 13, 18, 23, . . .

42. 3, 6, 12, 24, 48, . . .

43. 7, 6, 13, 19, 32, . . .

44. The first term of a sequence is 8. Each term of the sequence is 5 times the preceding term. Graph the first four terms of the sequence. Write a recursive rule and an explicit rule for the sequence.

Mathematical Practices

Look for and Make Use of Structure

Mathematically proficient students look closely to discern a pattern or structure.

1. In Exercise 54 on page 336, how did you use structure to rewrite the left side of the equation?

2. In Exercise 38 on page 343, describe the pattern shown in the figures. How does identifying the pattern help you write a function for the *n*th term of the geometric sequence?

6 Practice Test WITH CalcChat®

Simplify the expression. Write your answer using only positive exponents.

1. $z^{-2} \cdot z^4$

2. $\dfrac{b^{-5}}{a^0 b^{-8}}$

3. $\left(\dfrac{2c^4}{5}\right)^{-3}$

Evaluate the expression.

4. $-\sqrt[4]{16}$

5. $729^{1/6}$

6. $(-32)^{7/5}$

7. It costs \$850 per month to rent an apartment. The monthly cost increases by 3% each year. Find the monthly cost in 10 years.

8. Write an explicit rule and a recursive rule for the sequence. Then find a_{10}.

n	1	2	3	4
a_n	2187	729	243	81

Solve the equation. Check your solution.

9. $2^x = \dfrac{1}{128}$

10. $256^{x+2} = 16^{3x-1}$

11. Atmospheric pressure P (in atmospheres) can be modeled by $P = (0.99988)^a$, where a is the altitude (in meters).

a. Identify the initial amount, decay factor, and decay rate.

b. Find the atmospheric pressure at an altitude of 5000 feet.

12. Graph $f(x) = 2(6)^{x-5} + 1$. Compare the graph to the graph of the parent function. Identify the y-intercepts and asymptotes of the graphs. Find the domain and range of f.

13. For each equation, determine whether a is *less than*, *greater than*, or *equal to b*. Explain your reasoning.

a. $\dfrac{5^a}{5^b} = 5^{-3}$

b. $9^a \cdot 9^{-b} = 1$

14. You write a function to represent each side of an exponential equation. Write one possible exponential equation so that the graphs of the functions intersect at (1, 3) and (2, 12). Justify your answer.

15. You have \$500 to deposit in a savings account. Which account would you choose? Explain your reasoning. Then explain why someone might choose the other account.

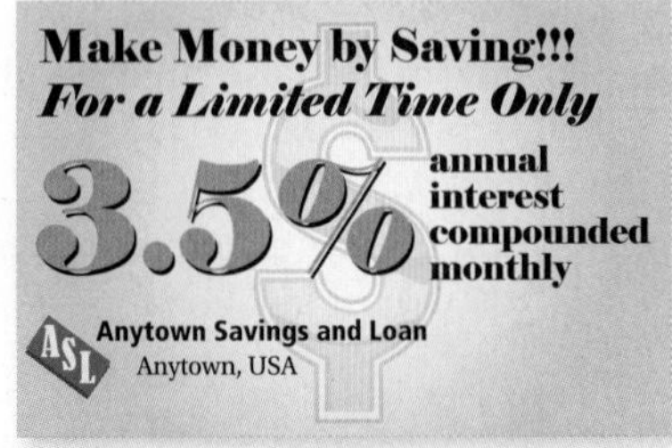

6 Performance Task
Disease Control

GO DIGITAL

AVERAGE REPRODUCTIVE NUMBER:

A measure of how easily a disease spreads

For contagious diseases, a reproductive number of 6 means that each sick person will pass the disease to an average of 6 people.

SERIAL INTERVAL:

A measure of how long it takes an infected person to transmit a disease to the next "round" of people

A serial interval of 9 days means that about 9 days pass from when a person becomes contagious to when the next round of people become contagious.

The serial interval of Ebola is about ***9–15 days***.

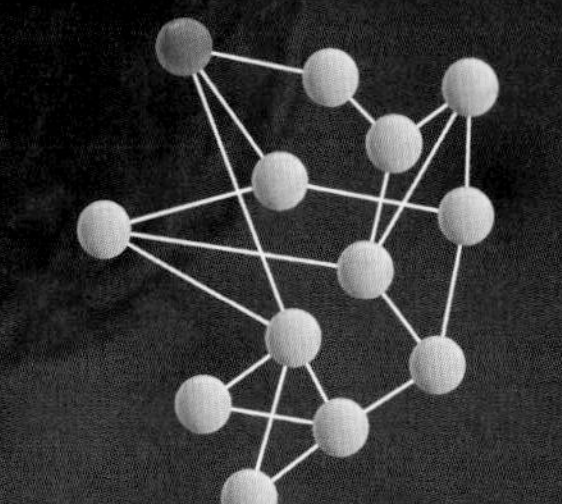

This is you and a network of friends.

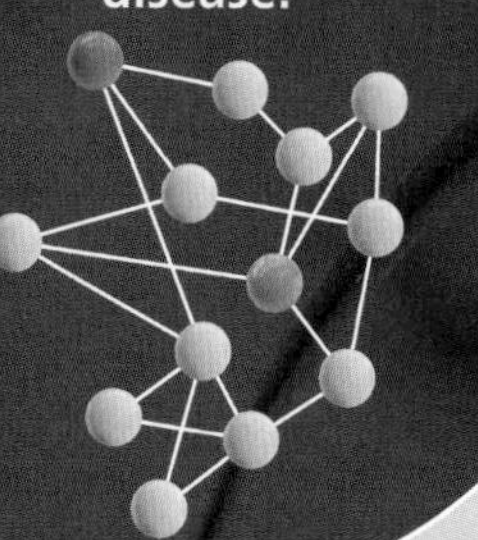

One person in your network contracts a disease.

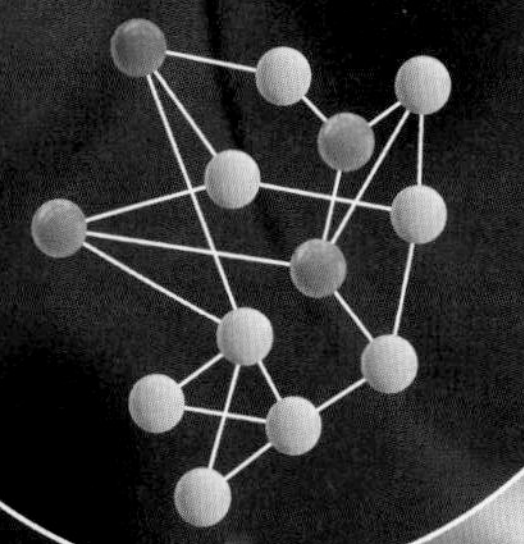

This disease spreads to some friends of the infected person.

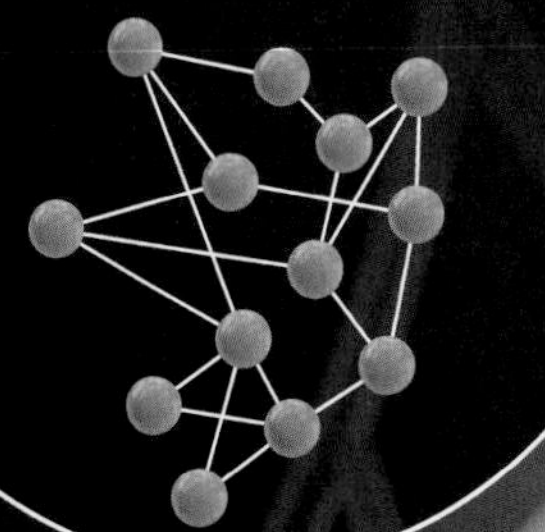

Eventually, the entire network can be infected.

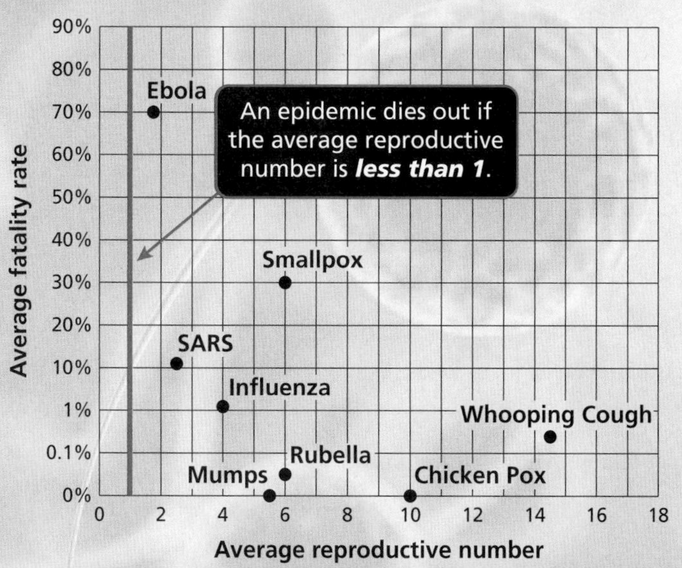

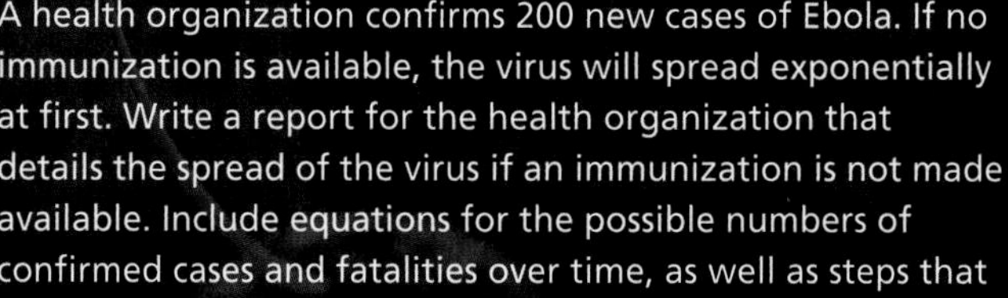

EPIDEMIC!

A health organization confirms 200 new cases of Ebola. If no immunization is available, the virus will spread exponentially at first. Write a report for the health organization that details the spread of the virus if an immunization is not made available. Include equations for the possible numbers of confirmed cases and fatalities over time, as well as steps that can be taken to reduce the reproductive number.

6 College and Career Readiness WITH CalcChat®

Tutorial videos are available for each exercise.

1. Simplify the expression.

$$\frac{x^{5/3} \cdot x^{-1} \cdot x^0}{x^{-2} \cdot \sqrt[3]{x}}$$

Ⓐ 0 Ⓑ $\frac{1}{x}$

Ⓒ $\frac{1}{\sqrt[3]{x}}$ Ⓓ $x^{7/3}$

2. Find the y-intercept of the graph of the function represented by the table.

x	2	4	6	8
y	4.5	11.5	18.5	25.5

3. The second term of a sequence is 7. Each term of the sequence is 10 greater than the preceding term. Write a recursive rule for the sequence.

Ⓐ $a_n = 10n - 13$ Ⓑ $a_1 = 7,\ a_n = a_{n-1} + 10$

Ⓒ $a_1 = -3,\ a_n = a_{n-1} + 10$ Ⓓ $a_1 = \frac{7}{10},\ a_n = 10a_{n-1}$

4. The equation $y = 870 - 14.8t$ represents the height y (in feet) of a hot-air balloon after t minutes. Interpret the slope and the y-intercept of the graph.

Ⓐ The initial height of the hot-air balloon is 870 feet. The slope has no meaning in this context.

Ⓑ The initial height of the hot-air balloon is 870 feet, and it descends 14.8 feet per minute.

Ⓒ The initial height of the hot-air balloon is 870 feet, and it ascends 14.8 feet per minute.

Ⓓ The hot-air balloon descends 14.8 feet per minute. The y-intercept has no meaning in this context.

5. Identify each property used to solve the equation. Select all that apply.

Ⓐ Addition Property of Equality

Ⓑ Subtraction Property of Equality

Ⓒ Multiplication Property of Equality

Ⓓ Division Property of Equality

$$3m + 5 = 4$$
$$3m + 5 - 5 = 4 - 5$$
$$3m = -1$$
$$\frac{3m}{3} = -\frac{1}{3}$$
$$m = -\frac{1}{3}$$

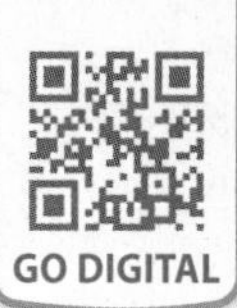

6. Which of the following functions are exponential growth functions?

I. $f(x) = 3\left(\frac{1}{6}\right)^x$ **II.** $f(x) = -2(8)^x$

III. $f(x) = \frac{1}{2}(3)^x$ **IV.** $f(x) = 4(1.6)^{x/10}$

Ⓐ I only Ⓑ II only

Ⓒ III only Ⓓ IV only

Ⓔ II and III only Ⓕ III and IV only

Ⓖ II, III, and IV only Ⓗ I, II, III, and IV

7. Which of the following describes the transformations from the graph of $f(x) = \frac{1}{4}x - 3$ to the graph of g?

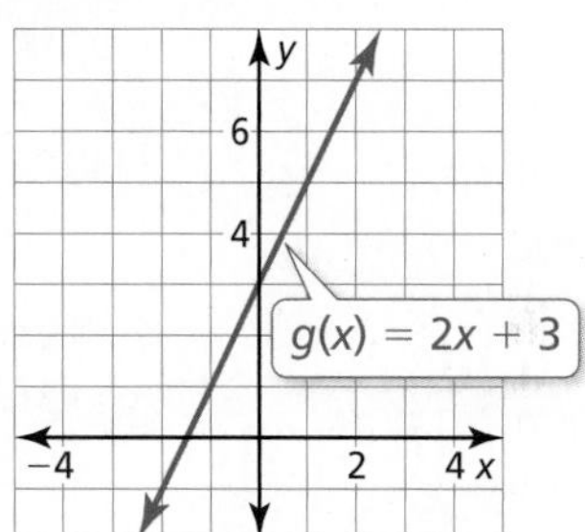

Ⓐ The graph of g is a vertical stretch by a factor of 8, followed by a translation 6 units up of the graph of f.

Ⓑ The graph of g is a horizontal stretch by a factor of 8, followed by a translation 6 units up of the graph of f.

Ⓒ The graph of g is a horizontal shrink by a factor of $\frac{1}{8}$ and a translation 6 units up of the graph of f.

Ⓓ The graph of g is a translation 6 units up, followed by a vertical stretch by a factor of 8 of the graph of f.

8. The graph of the exponential function f is shown. Find $f(-7)$.

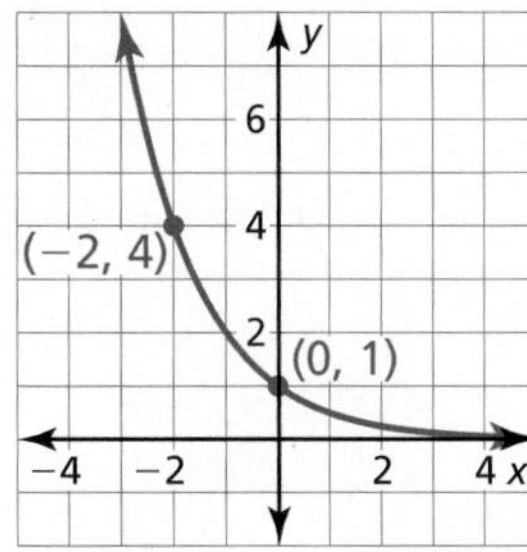

9. Complete the inequality with $<$, $\leq$, $>$, or $\geq$ so that the system has no solution.

Inequality 1 $y - 2x \leq 4$

Inequality 2 $6x - 3y$ ▒ -12

10. Determine which absolute value function has a vertex at $(-6, 6)$.

Ⓐ $y = |x - 6| - 6$ Ⓑ $y = |x + 6| + 6$

Ⓒ $y = |x + 6| - 6$ Ⓓ $y = |x - 6| + 6$

GO DIGITAL

7 Polynomial Equations and Factoring

NATIONAL GEOGRAPHIC EXPLORER

Jedidah Isler

Dr. Jedidah Isler is an award-winning astrophysicist and an advocate for inclusive science, technology, engineering, and mathematics (STEM) education. Her research explores hyperactive black holes at the centers of distant galaxies that create powerful particle jets oriented toward Earth.

- What is a light year? What is the speed of light in miles per hour? Can anything travel faster than light?
- Which star is closest to Earth? How far away is it?
- If you could travel 100 times the speed of light, how long would it take you to travel from Earth to the nearest star?

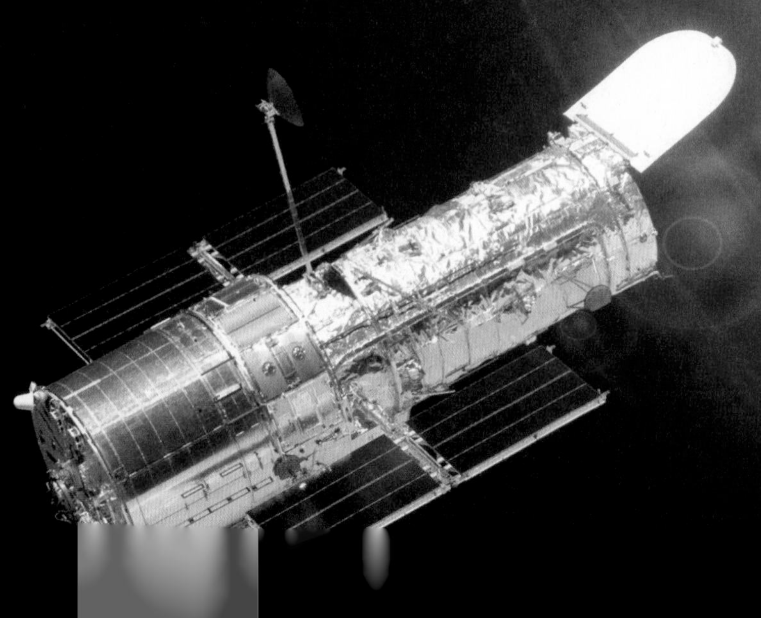

STEM

Astronomers study the effects of gravity to learn about the universe. In the Performance Task, you will create a display that demonstrates how gravity affects objects on each planet in our solar system.

Preparing for Chapter 7

Chapter Learning Target Understand polynomial equations and factoring.

Chapter Success Criteria
- ◆ I can classify polynomials by degree and number of terms.
- ◆ I can add, subtract, multiply, and divide polynomials.
- ■ I can solve polynomial equations.
- ■ I can factor polynomials and use factoring to solve real-life problems.

◆ Surface
■ Deep

Chapter Vocabulary

Work with a partner. Discuss each of the vocabulary terms.

monomial
binomial
trinomial
leading coefficient

Mathematical Practices

Look for and Make Use of Structure

Mathematically proficient students are able to see complicated things as single objects or as being composed of several objects.

Work with a partner. The expression $-16t(t - 13)$ represents the height (in feet) of a model rocket t seconds after it is launched.

1. Complete the table of values for each expression below. What do you notice?

t	0	1	2	3	4	5	6	7
$-16t$								
$t - 13$								

t	8	9	10	11	12	13	14	15
$-16t$								
$t - 13$								

2. Use the completed table to find the values of t that make sense in this context. Explain your reasoning.

3. When can it be helpful to view an expression as a product of individual factors? When can it be helpful to view an expression as a single object?

7 Prepare WITH CalcChat®

Simplifying Algebraic Expressions

Example 1 **Simplify $6x + 5 - 3x - 4$.**

$$6x + 5 - 3x - 4 = 6x - 3x + 5 - 4 \quad \text{Commutative Property of Addition}$$
$$= (6 - 3)x + 5 - 4 \quad \text{Distributive Property}$$
$$= 3x + 1 \quad \text{Simplify.}$$

Example 2 **Simplify $-\frac{1}{2}(10y - 3) + 2y$.**

$$-\tfrac{1}{2}(10y - 3) + 2y = -\tfrac{1}{2}(10y) - \left(-\tfrac{1}{2}\right)(3) + 2y \quad \text{Distributive Property}$$
$$= -5y + \tfrac{3}{2} + 2y \quad \text{Multiply.}$$
$$= -5y + 2y + \tfrac{3}{2} \quad \text{Commutative Property of Addition}$$
$$= (-5 + 2)y + \tfrac{3}{2} \quad \text{Distributive Property}$$
$$= -3y + \tfrac{3}{2} \quad \text{Simplify.}$$

Simplify the expression.

1. $3x - 7 + 2x$

2. $4r + 6 - 9r - 1$

3. $-5t + 3 - t - 4 + 8t$

4. $3(s - 1) + 5$

5. $2m - 7.25(3 - m)$

6. $4(h + 6) - \frac{3}{4}(h - 2)$

Finding the Greatest Common Factor

Example 3 **Find the greatest common factor (GCF) of 42 and 70.**

To find the GCF of two numbers, first write the prime factorization of each number. Then find the product of the common prime factors.

$$42 = 2 \cdot 3 \cdot 7$$
$$70 = 2 \cdot 5 \cdot 7$$

▶ The GCF of 42 and 70 is $2 \cdot 7 = 14$.

Find the greatest common factor.

7. 20, 36

8. 42, 63

9. 54, 81

10. 72, 84

11. 28, 64

12. 30, 77

13. **MP LOGIC** Your friend says that two prime numbers do not have a GCF because the prime factorizations of the numbers do not have any common factors. Is your friend correct? Explain.

7.1 Adding and Subtracting Polynomials

Learning Target Add and subtract polynomials.

Success Criteria
- I can classify polynomials.
- I can add and subtract polynomials.
- I can model real-life situations using sums and differences of polynomials.

A **monomial** is a number, a variable, or the product of a number and one or more variables with whole number exponents. A **polynomial** is a monomial or a sum of monomials.

EXPLORE IT! Adding and Subtracting Polynomials

Work with a partner. You can use algebra tiles to find sums and differences of polynomials.

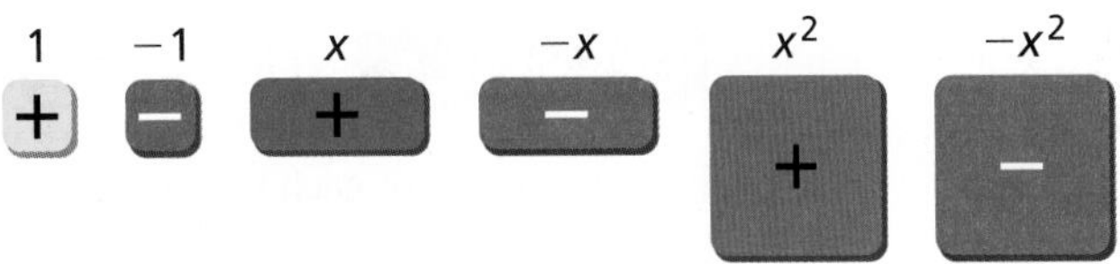

a. Write each expression modeled below. Then use algebra tiles to find each sum or difference.

i.

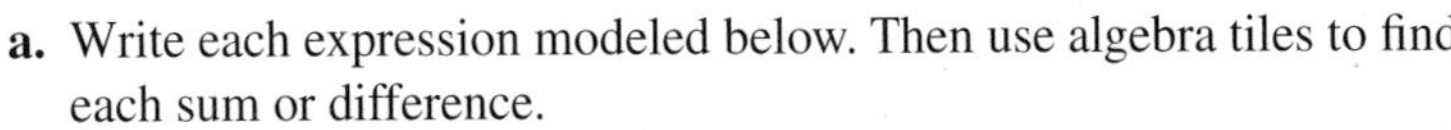

ii.

iii.

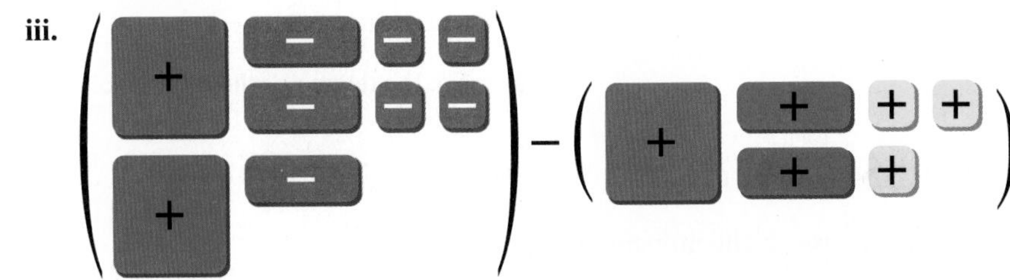

b. Explain how to add and subtract polynomials without using algebra tiles.

c. Write two polynomials of the form $ax^2 + bx + c$, where a, b, and c are rational numbers. Find the sum and difference of the polynomials.

d. Is the sum or difference of two polynomials also a polynomial? Explain your reasoning.

View as Components
When finding a sum or difference of polynomials, why is it useful to view the expression as a sum of monomials?

Finding Degrees of Monomials

Vocabulary

monomial, *p. 364*
degree of a monomial, *p. 364*
polynomial, *p. 365*
binomial, *p. 365*
trinomial, *p. 365*
degree of a polynomial, *p. 365*
standard form, *p. 365*
leading coefficient, *p. 365*
closed, *p. 366*

A **monomial** is a number, a variable, or the product of a number and one or more variables with whole number exponents.

The **degree of a monomial** is the sum of the exponents of the variables in the monomial. The degree of a nonzero constant term is 0. The constant 0 does not have a degree.

Monomial	Degree
10	0
$3x$	1
$\frac{1}{2}ab^2$	$1 + 2 = 3$
$-1.8m^5$	5

Not a monomial	Reason
$5 + x$	A sum is not a monomial.
$\frac{2}{n}$	A monomial cannot have a variable in the denominator.
4^a	A monomial cannot have a variable exponent.
x^{-1}	The variable must have a whole number exponent.

EXAMPLE 1 Finding Degrees of Monomials

Find the degree of each monomial.

a. $5x^2$ **b.** $-\frac{1}{2}xy^3$ **c.** $8x^3y^3$ **d.** -3

SOLUTION

a. The exponent of x is 2.

▶ So, the degree of the monomial is 2.

b. The exponent of x is 1, and the exponent of y is 3.

▶ So, the degree of the monomial is $1 + 3$, or 4.

c. The exponent of x is 3, and the exponent of y is 3.

▶ So, the degree of the monomial is $3 + 3$, or 6.

d. You can rewrite -3 as $-3x^0$.

▶ So, the degree of the monomial is 0.

SELF-ASSESSMENT

1 I do not understand. 2 I can do it with help. 3 I can do it on my own. 4 I can teach someone else.

Find the degree of the monomial.

1. $-3x^4$ **2.** $7c^3d^2$ **3.** $\frac{5}{3}y$ **4.** -20.5

5. WHICH ONE DOESN'T BELONG? Which monomial does *not* belong with the other three? Explain your reasoning.

a^3b^2 a^4b ab^5 a^2b^3

6. **MP REASONING** A monomial contains four variables. What is the least possible degree of the monomial? Explain.

Classifying Polynomials

KEY IDEA

Polynomials

A **polynomial** is a monomial or a sum of monomials. Each monomial is called a *term* of the polynomial. A polynomial with two terms is a **binomial**. A polynomial with three terms is a **trinomial**.

Binomial	Trinomial
$5x + 2$	$x^2 + 5x + 2$

The **degree of a polynomial** is the greatest degree of its terms. A polynomial in one variable is in **standard form** when the exponents of the terms decrease from left to right. When you write a polynomial in standard form, the coefficient of the first term is the **leading coefficient**.

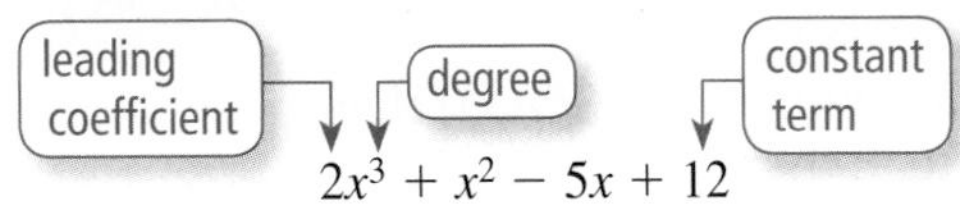

WORDS AND MATH

You may know other words with the prefixes *bi-* and *tri-*, such as *bicycle*, *bidirectional*, *tricycle*, and *triathlon*. A bicycle has two wheels and bidirectional indicates two directions. A tricycle has three wheels and a triathlon is a race composed of three events.

EXAMPLE 2 Writing a Polynomial in Standard Form

Write $15x - x^3 + 3$ in standard form. Identify the degree and leading coefficient of the polynomial.

SOLUTION

Consider the degree of each term of the polynomial.

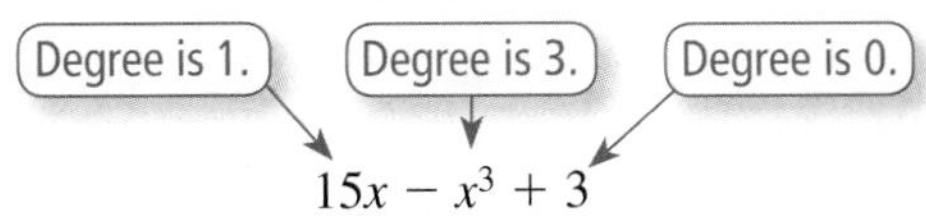

▶ You can write the polynomial in standard form as $-x^3 + 15x + 3$. The greatest degree is 3, so the degree of the polynomial is 3, and the leading coefficient is -1.

EXAMPLE 3 Classifying Polynomials

Write each polynomial in standard form. Identify the degree and classify each polynomial by the number of terms.

a. $-3z^4$ **b.** $4 + 5x^2 - x$ **c.** $8q + q^5$

SOLUTION

Polynomial	Standard Form	Degree	Type of Polynomial
a. $-3z^4$	$-3z^4$	4	monomial
b. $4 + 5x^2 - x$	$5x^2 - x + 4$	2	trinomial
c. $8q + q^5$	$q^5 + 8q$	5	binomial

SELF-ASSESSMENT 1 I do not understand. 2 I can do it with help. 3 I can do it on my own. 4 I can teach someone else.

Write the polynomial in standard form. Identify the degree and leading coefficient of the polynomial. Then classify the polynomial by the number of terms.

7. $4 - 9z$ **8.** $t^2 - t^3 - 10t$ **9.** $2.8x + x^3$

Adding and Subtracting Polynomials

GO DIGITAL

A set of numbers is **closed** under an operation when the operation performed on any two numbers in the set results in a number that is also in the set. For example, the set of integers is closed under addition, subtraction, and multiplication. This means that if a and b are two integers, then $a + b$, $a - b$, and ab are also integers.

The set of polynomials is closed under addition and subtraction. So, the sum or difference of any two polynomials is also a polynomial.

To add polynomials, add like terms. You can use a vertical or a horizontal format.

EXAMPLE 4 Adding Polynomials

> **STUDY TIP**
> When a power of the variable appears in one polynomial but not the other, leave a space in that column, or write the term with a coefficient of 0.

Find the sum.

a. $(2x^3 - 5x^2 + x) + (2x^2 + x^3 - 1)$ **b.** $(3x^2 + x - 6) + (x^2 + 4x + 10)$

SOLUTION

a. Vertical format: Align like terms vertically and add.

$$\begin{array}{r} 2x^3 - 5x^2 + x \\ + \quad x^3 + 2x^2 - 1 \\ \hline 3x^3 - 3x^2 + x - 1 \end{array}$$

▶ The sum is $3x^3 - 3x^2 + x - 1$.

b. Horizontal format: Group like terms and simplify.

$$\begin{aligned}(3x^2 + x - 6) + (x^2 + 4x + 10) &= (3x^2 + x^2) + (x + 4x) + (-6 + 10) \\ &= 4x^2 + 5x + 4\end{aligned}$$

▶ The sum is $4x^2 + 5x + 4$.

To subtract a polynomial, add its opposite. To find the opposite of a polynomial, multiply each of its terms by -1.

EXAMPLE 5 Subtracting Polynomials

Find $(4n^2 + 5) - (-2n^2 + 2n - 4)$.

> **ANOTHER WAY**
> You can also subtract polynomials using a horizontal method.

SOLUTION

Vertical format: Align like terms vertically and subtract.

$$\begin{array}{r} 4n^2 + 5 \\ -\ (-2n^2 + 2n - 4) \\ \hline \end{array} \quad \Rightarrow \quad \begin{array}{r} 4n^2 + 5 \\ +\ 2n^2 - 2n + 4 \\ \hline 6n^2 - 2n + 9 \end{array}$$

▶ The difference is $6n^2 - 2n + 9$.

SELF-ASSESSMENT 1 I do not understand. 2 I can do it with help. 3 I can do it on my own. 4 I can teach someone else.

Find the sum or difference.

10. $(b - 10) + (4b - 3)$

11. $(x^2 - x - 2) + (7x^2 - x)$

12. $(p^2 + p + 3) - (-4p^2 - p + 3)$

13. $\left(-\frac{3}{4}k + 5\right) - \left(\frac{1}{3}k^2 - 6\right)$

Solving Real-Life Problems

EXAMPLE 6 Modeling Real Life

WATCH

A red water balloon is thrown straight down from a height of 200 feet. At the same time, a blue water balloon is dropped from a height of 100 feet. The polynomials represent the heights (in feet) of the balloons after t seconds.

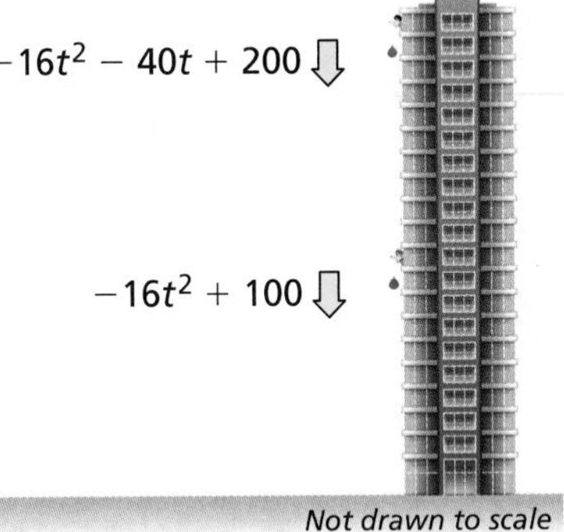

a. Write a polynomial that represents the distance between the water balloons after t seconds.

b. Interpret any coefficients and constants of the polynomial in part (a).

SOLUTION

a. To find the distance between the water balloons after t seconds, subtract the polynomials.

Red Balloon	$-16t^2 - 40t + 200$	➡	$-16t^2 - 40t + 200$
Blue Balloon	$-\ (-16t^2 \qquad + 100)$		$+\ \ 16t^2 \qquad - 100$
			$-40t + 100$

▶ The polynomial $-40t + 100$ represents the distance between the water balloons after t seconds.

b. To find the distance between the water balloons when both begin to fall, let $t = 0$.

$$-40t + 100 = -40(0) + 100 = 100 \text{ feet}$$

So, the constant term 100 represents the distance between the balloons when both begin to fall.

As the value of t increases by 1, the value of $-40t + 100$ decreases by 40. This means that the balloons become 40 feet closer to each other each second. So, -40 represents the amount that the distance between the balloons changes each second.

> **Math Practice**
>
> **Interpret Results**
>
> Notice that each term of the resulting expression has special meaning in the context of the problem. Analyzing the terms helps you understand the problem in greater depth.

SELF-ASSESSMENT

1 I do not understand. 2 I can do it with help. 3 I can do it on my own. 4 I can teach someone else.

14. WHAT IF? The polynomial $-16t^2 - 25t + 200$ represents the height of the red water balloon after t seconds. What is the distance between the balloons when both begin to fall? How does the distance between the balloons change over time?

15. You shoot a basketball to try to knock your friend's shot away from the hoop. The height (in feet) of your friend's basketball t seconds after he shoots is represented by $-16t^2 + 25t + 6.25$. The height (in feet) of your basketball t seconds after you shoot is represented by $-16t^2 + 20t + 5.5$. You and your friend shoot at the same time. Is it possible for the basketballs to collide? Explain.

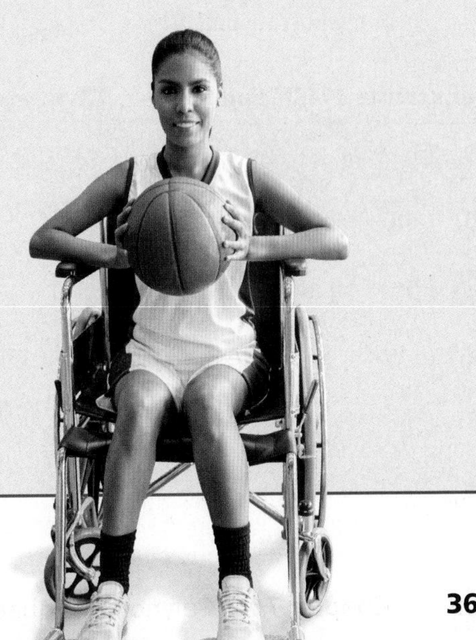

7.1 Practice WITH CalcChat® AND CalcView®

In Exercises 1–8, find the degree of the monomial. *Example 1*

1. $4g$
2. $-\frac{4}{9}$
3. $-1.75k^2$
4. $23x^4$
5. s^8t
6. $8m^2n^4$
7. $9xy^3z^7$
8. $-3q^4rs^6$

In Exercises 9–16, write the polynomial in standard form. Identify the degree and leading coefficient of the polynomial. Then classify the polynomial by the number of terms. *Examples 2 and 3*

9. $3t^8$
10. $\sqrt{7}n^4$
11. $7 + 3p^2$
12. $4w^{11} - w^{12}$
13. $6c^2 + 2c^4 - c$
14. $8d - 2 - 4d^3$
15. $5z + 2z^3 + 3z^4$
16. $\pi r^2 - \frac{5}{7}r^8 + 2r^5$

17. **MP REASONING** The expression $\frac{4}{3}\pi r^3$ represents the volume of a sphere with radius r. Explain why this expression is a monomial. Then identify its degree.

18. **MODELING REAL LIFE** The amount of money you have after investing \$400 for 8 years and \$600 for 6 years at the same interest rate is represented by $400x^8 + 600x^6$, where x is the growth factor.
    a. Classify the polynomial by the number of terms.
    b. Interpret the coefficients and the exponents of the polynomial.

In Exercises 19–26, find the sum. *Example 4*

19. $(5y + 4) + (-2y + 6)$
20. $(-8x - 12) + (9x + 4)$
21. $(2n^2 - 5n - 6) + (-n^2 - 3n + 11)$
22. $(-3p^3 + 5p^2 - 2p) + (-p^3 - 8p^2 - 15p)$
23. $(3g^2 - g) + (3g^2 - 8g + 4)$
24. $(9r^2 + 4r - 7) + (3r^2 - 3r)$
25. $\left(\frac{1}{4}a - a^3 - 3\right) + \left(2a^3 - \frac{1}{2}a^2 + 8\right)$
26. $\left(s^3 - \frac{1}{2}s - 9\right) + \left(2s^2 - \frac{1}{3}s^3 + s\right)$

In Exercises 27–34, find the difference. *Example 5*

27. $(d - 9) - (3d - 1)$
28. $(6x + 9) - (7x + 1)$
29. $(y^2 - 4y + 9) - (3y^2 - 6y - 9)$
30. $(4m^2 - m + 2) - (-3m^2 + 10m + 4)$
31. $(k^3 - 7k + 2) - (k^2 - 12)$
32. $(-r - 10) - (-4r^3 + r^2 + 7r)$
33. $(t^4 - 1.5t^2 + t) - (12 - 9.5t^2 - 7t)$
34. $(4.5d - 6d^3 + 3d^2) - (10d^3 + 7d - 2.5)$

ERROR ANALYSIS In Exercises 35 and 36, describe and correct the error in finding the sum or difference.

35. ✗
$$\begin{aligned}(x^2 + x) - (2x^2 - 3x) &\\ &= (x^2 + x) + (-2x^2 - 3x)\\ &= (x^2 - 2x^2) + (x - 3x)\\ &= -x^2 - 2x\end{aligned}$$

36. ✗
$$\begin{array}{r} x^3 - 4x^2 + 3 \\ + \; -3x^3 + 8x \; - 2 \\ \hline -2x^3 + 4x^2 + 1 \end{array}$$

37. **MODELING REAL LIFE** The cost (in dollars) of making b bracelets is represented by $4 + 5b$. The cost (in dollars) of making b necklaces is represented by $8b + 6$. Write a polynomial that represents how much more it costs to make b necklaces than b bracelets.

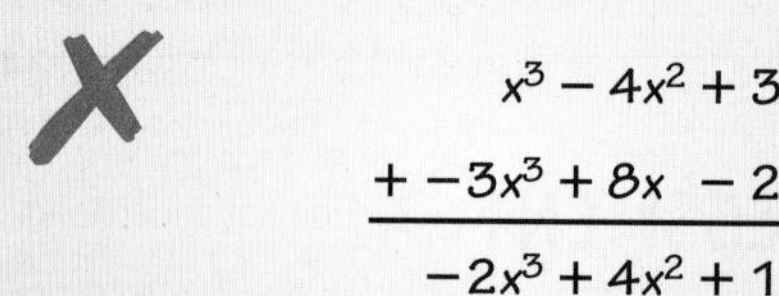

38. MODELING REAL LIFE The number of individual memberships at a fitness center in m months is represented by $142 + 12m$. The number of family memberships at the center in m months is represented by $52 + 6m$. Write a polynomial that represents the total number of memberships at the fitness center.

In Exercises 39–42, find the sum or difference.

39. $(2s^2 - 5st - t^2) - (s^2 + 7st - t^2)$

40. $(a^2 - 3ab + 2b^2) + (-4a^2 + 5ab - b^2)$

41. $(c^2 - 6d^2) + (c^2 - 2cd + 2d^2)$

42. $(-x^2 + 9xy) - (x^2 + 6xy - 8y^2)$

43. MODELING REAL LIFE A water rocket is launched straight into the air from a height of 6 feet with an initial velocity of 60 feet per second. At the same time, a second water rocket is launched straight into the air from the ground with an initial velocity of 50 feet per second. The polynomials $-16t^2 + 60t + 6$ and $-16t^2 + 50t$ represent the heights (in feet) of the rockets after t seconds. *Example 6*

a. Write a polynomial that represents the distance between the heights of the rockets after t seconds.

b. Interpret any coefficients and constants of the polynomial in part (a).

44. MODELING REAL LIFE During a 7-year period, the amounts (in millions of dollars) spent each year on buying new vehicles N and used vehicles U by United States residents are modeled by the equations

$$N = -0.028t^3 + 0.06t^2 + 0.1t + 17$$

$$U = -0.38t^2 + 1.5t + 42$$

where $t = 1$ represents the first year in the 7-year period.

a. Write a polynomial that represents the total amount spent each year on buying new and used vehicles in the 7-year period.

b. How much is spent on buying new and used vehicles in the fifth year?

45. WRITING Explain how you know that the set of polynomials is closed under addition and subtraction.

46. COLLEGE PREP Which of the following expressions is *not* a polynomial?

(A) $a^3 + 4a$ (B) $x^2 - 8^x$

(C) $b - 2^{-1}$ (D) $-\frac{\pi}{3} + 6y^8z$

MP REASONING In Exercises 47–50, complete the statement with *always*, *sometimes*, or *never*. Explain your reasoning.

47. The terms of a polynomial are ________ monomials.

48. The difference of two trinomials is ________ a trinomial.

49. A binomial is ________ a polynomial of degree 2.

50. The sum of two polynomials is ________ a polynomial.

51. CONNECTING CONCEPTS Write the polynomial in standard form that represents the perimeter of the quadrilateral.

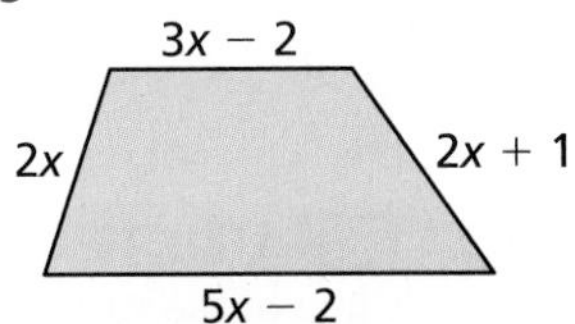

52. HOW DO YOU SEE IT? The right side of the equation of each line is a polynomial.

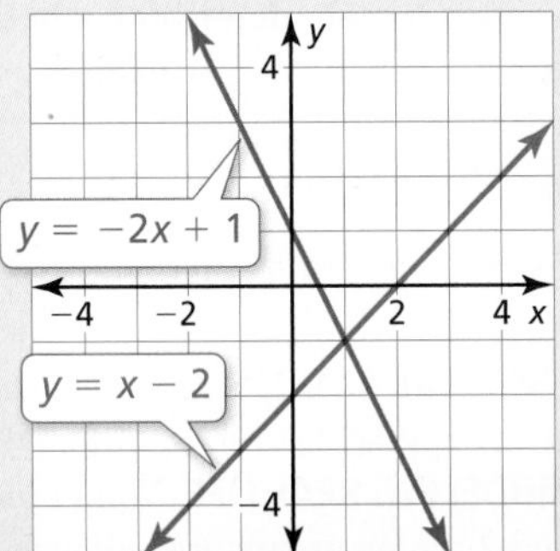

a. The absolute value of the difference of the two polynomials represents the vertical distance between points on the lines with the same x-value. Write this expression.

b. When does the expression in part (a) equal 0? How does this value relate to the graph?

53. MAKING AN ARGUMENT Does the order in which you add polynomials matter? Justify your answer.

54. **DIG DEEPER** You drop a ball from a height of 98 feet. At the same time, your friend throws a ball upward. The polynomials represent the heights (in feet) of the balls after t seconds. Write an expression that represents the distance between your ball and your friend's ball after t seconds. Find the distance between the balls after 2.25 seconds.

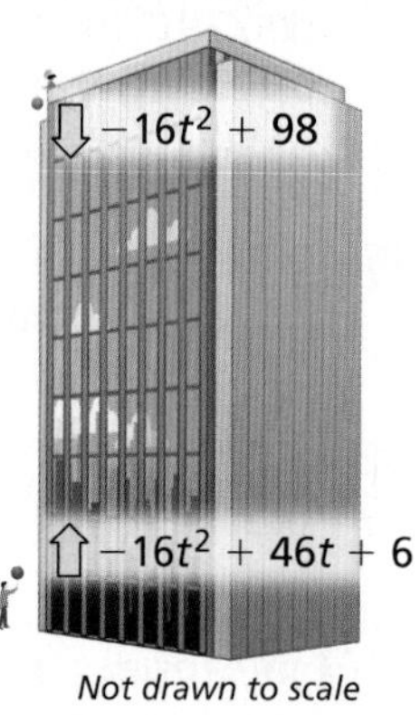

Not drawn to scale

55. **MP PRECISION** Determine whether the set of negative integers is closed under addition, subtraction, and multiplication. Explain.

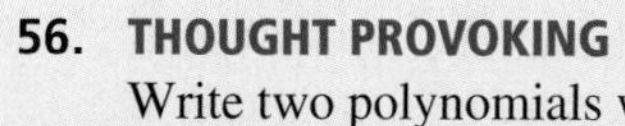

56. **THOUGHT PROVOKING** Write two polynomials whose sum is x^2 and whose difference is 1.

57. **ABSTRACT REASONING** A polynomial $h(x)$ for which $h(x) \geq 0$ for all real numbers x is called a *nonnegative* polynomial.

   a. Determine which of the following polynomials are nonnegative.

   $x^2 + 1$ $\quad$ x^3 $\quad$ $x^3 + x^2$ $\quad$ $ax + b$

   b. Can a nonnegative polynomial have any negative coefficients? Explain.

   c. Is it possible for all of the coefficients of a nonnegative polynomial to be negative? Explain.

REVIEW & REFRESH

WATCH

In Exercises 58–61, solve the equation. Check your solution.

58. $4^{x+2} = 4^{3x-2}$

59. $2^x = 128$

60. $3^{4x+6} = 9^x$

61. $5^{6x} = \frac{1}{125}$

62. **MP STRUCTURE** Find the value of the variable. Then find the angle measures of the triangle.

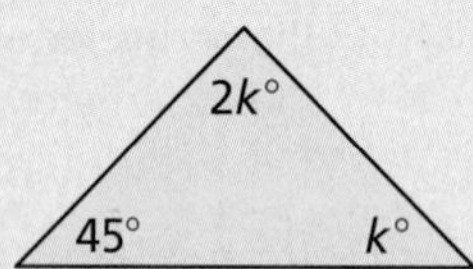

Sum of angle measures: 180°

In Exercises 63–66, determine whether the sequence is *arithmetic*, *geometric*, or *neither*.

63. $-3, 9, -27, 81, \ldots$

64. $2, 3, 5, 8, \ldots$

65. 25, 22.5, 20, 17.5

66. 1880, 940, 470, 235, ...

67. **MODELING REAL LIFE** You order a cell phone case and 2 screen protectors online for a total of \$18.95. Your friend orders 2 cell phone cases and 5 screen protectors at the same unit prices for a total of \$41.40. What is the cost of each cell phone case? each screen protector?

In Exercises 68–71, find the sum or difference.

68. $(-4x^2 + x - 12) + (2x^3 + 3x^2 - 4)$

69. $(3y^3 + 5y + 8) - (y^3 - 4y^2 + 3y)$

70. $(b^4 + 1 - 2b^2) + (-2b + 3b^2 + 3)$

71. $(-d + 6d^3 + 4d^2) - (12 - 4d + 5d^2)$

72. Tell whether the data in the table can be modeled by a linear equation. Explain. If possible, write a linear equation that represents y as a function of x.

x	10	8	6	4	2
y	−5	−2	1	4	7

In Exercises 73 and 74, write a recursive rule for the explicit rule.

73. $a_n = \frac{1}{2}n + 1$

74. $a_n = -3(5)^{n-1}$

75. Does the graph represent a *linear* or *nonlinear* function? Explain.

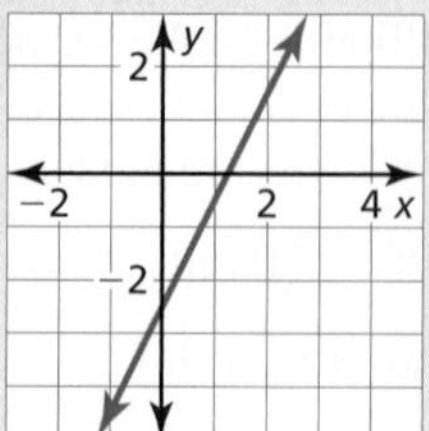

In Exercises 76 and 77, simplify the expression.

76. $5(2r + 1) - 3(-4r + 2)$

77. $\frac{1}{2}(4c + 10) + \frac{1}{3}(2c - 6)$

7.2 Multiplying and Dividing Polynomials

Learning Target Multiply and divide polynomials.

Success Criteria

- I can multiply and divide polynomials by monomials.
- I can multiply binomials using the Distributive Property.
- I can multiply binomials using the FOIL Method.
- I can multiply binomials and trinomials.

EXPLORE IT! Multiplying Polynomials Using Algebra Tiles

Work with a partner. You can use algebra tiles to find products of polynomials.

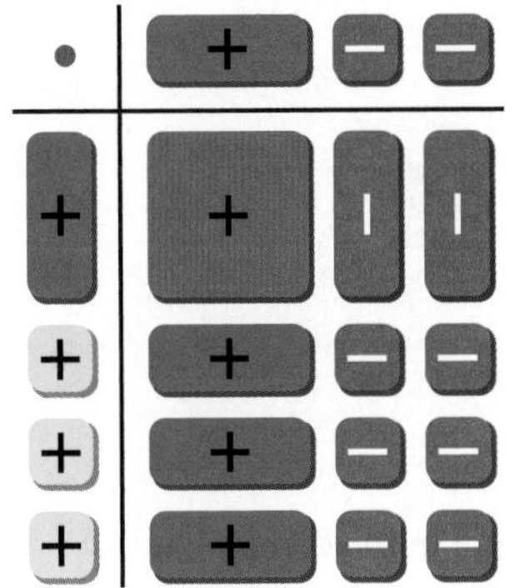

a. Write the equation modeled by the rectangular array of algebra tiles shown. What types of polynomials are being multiplied? What type of polynomial is the product?

b. Write the product modeled by each array of algebra tiles. Use additional algebra tiles to complete the model. Then write each product as a polynomial.

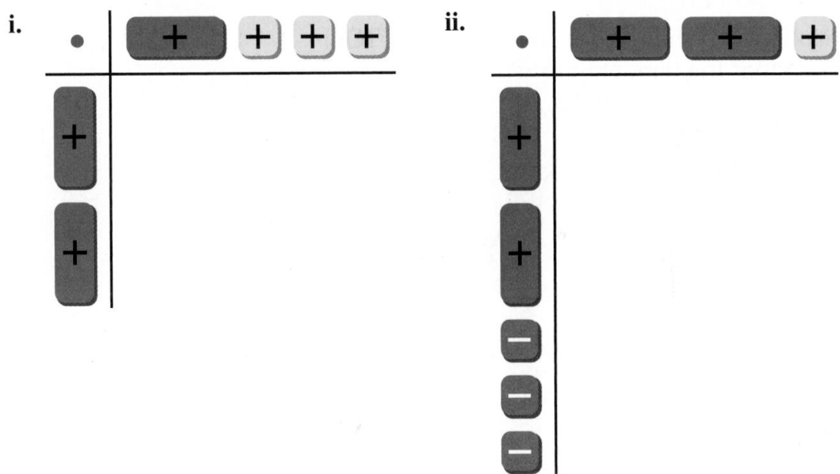

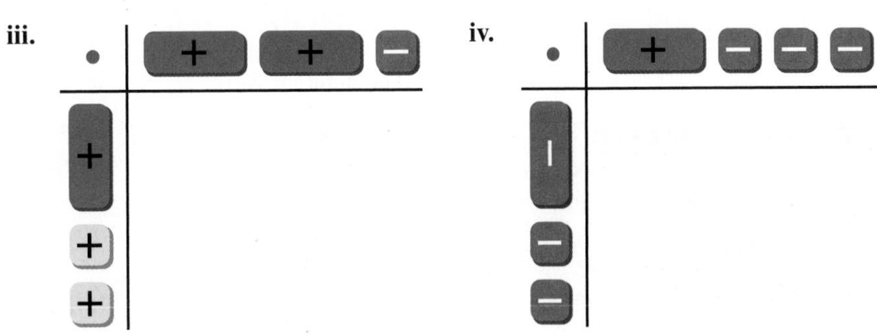

c. Explain how you can multiply two polynomials without using algebra tiles.

d. Does multiplying two polynomials result in an expression that is also a polynomial? Explain your reasoning.

Math Practice

Consider Similar Problems

Consider some of the strategies you have previously learned to multiply numbers. Which of these might be useful when multiplying polynomials?

Multiplying and Dividing by Monomials and Binomials

Vocabulary 

FOIL Method, *p. 374*

The product of two polynomials is always a polynomial. So, like the set of integers, the set of polynomials is *closed* under multiplication. You can use the Distributive Property to multiply polynomials.

EXAMPLE 1 Multiplying Polynomials and Monomials

Find (a) $-2x(3x + 7)$ and (b) $3x^2(5x^2 - 2x + 6)$.

SOLUTION

a. $-2x(3x + 7) = -2x(3x) + (-2x)(7)$ — Distribute $-2x$ to each term of $(3x + 7)$.

$= -6x^2 - 14x$ — Multiply.

b. $3x^2(5x^2 - 2x + 6) = 3x^2(5x^2) - 3x^2(2x) + 3x^2(6)$ — Distribute $3x^2$ to each term of $(5x^2 - 2x + 6)$.

$= 15x^4 - 6x^3 + 18x^2$ — Multiply.

EXAMPLE 2 Dividing Polynomials

Find (a) $\dfrac{x^4 + 4x^3 + 11x^2}{x^2}$ and (b) $\dfrac{6y - 30}{y - 5}$.

STUDY TIP

Notice in Examples 2(a) and 2(b) that the denominators cannot be equal to 0. So, $x \neq 0$ in part (a) and $y \neq 5$ in part (b).

SOLUTION

a. Divide each term in the numerator by the monomial in the denominator.

$$\frac{x^4 + 4x^3 + 11x^2}{x^2} = \frac{x^4}{x^2} + \frac{4x^3}{x^2} + \frac{11x^2}{x^2}$$ Divide each term in the numerator by x^2.

$$= x^2 + 4x + 11$$ Simplify. (Use the Quotient of Powers Property.)

▶ The quotient is $x^2 + 4x + 11$.

b. The GCF of $6y$ and 30 is 6. Use 6 to factor the expression in the numerator.

$$\frac{6y - 30}{y - 5} = \frac{6(y - 5)}{y - 5}$$ Factor the numerator.

$$= \frac{6\cancel{(y - 5)}}{\cancel{y - 5}}$$ Divide out common factor.

$$= 6$$ Simplify.

▶ The quotient is 6.

SELF-ASSESSMENT

1 I do not understand. 2 I can do it with help. 3 I can do it on my own. 4 I can teach someone else.

Find the product.

1. $(-8x^4)(11x^3)$

2. $4y^2(8y - 5)$

3. $-3b^3(6b^2 + b - 9)$

4. **MP STRUCTURE** In Example 1, why is the degree of the product different from the degree of the factors?

Find the quotient.

5. $\dfrac{-4h^4 + 6h^3 - 2h^2}{h}$

6. $\dfrac{2k^5 - 2k^4}{2k^3}$

7. $\dfrac{4z + 28}{z + 7}$

8. **MP REASONING** Is the set of polynomials closed under division? Explain your reasoning.

EXAMPLE 3 Multiplying Binomials Using the Distributive Property

Find each product.

a. $(x + 2)(x + 5)$ **b.** $(x + 3)(x - 4)$

SOLUTION

a. Use the horizontal method.

$(x + 2)(x + 5) = x(x + 5) + 2(x + 5)$	Distribute $(x + 5)$ to each term of $(x + 2)$.
$= x(x) + x(5) + 2(x) + 2(5)$	Distributive Property
$= x^2 + 5x + 2x + 10$	Multiply.
$= x^2 + 7x + 10$	Combine like terms.

▶ The product is $x^2 + 7x + 10$.

b. Use the vertical method.

$$\begin{array}{r} x + 3 \\ \times \quad x - 4 \\ \hline -4x - 12 \\ x^2 + 3x \quad\quad \\ \hline x^2 - x - 12 \end{array}$$

Align like terms vertically.

Multiply $-4(x + 3)$. → $-4x - 12$ — Distributive Property

Multiply $x(x + 3)$. → $x^2 + 3x$ — Distributive Property

$x^2 - x - 12$ — Combine like terms.

▶ The product is $x^2 - x - 12$.

EXAMPLE 4 Multiplying Binomials Using a Table

Find $(2x - 3)(x + 5)$.

SOLUTION

Write each binomial as a sum of terms and make a table of products.

$$(2x - 3)(x + 5) = [2x + (-3)](x + 5)$$

	2x	**−3**
x	$2x^2$	$-3x$
5	$10x$	-15

▶ The product is $2x^2 - 3x + 10x - 15$, or $2x^2 + 7x - 15$.

SELF-ASSESSMENT

1 I do not understand. 2 I can do it with help. 3 I can do it on my own. 4 I can teach someone else.

Use the Distributive Property to find the product.

9. $(y + 4)(y + 1)$ **10.** $(z - 2)(z + 6)$ **11.** $(4q - 1)(7q - 5)$

Use a table to find the product.

12. $(p + 3)(p - 8)$ **13.** $(r - 5)(2r - 1)$ **14.** $(6s - 1)(3s + 6)$

15. **MP REASONING** Explain why the set of polynomials is closed under multiplication.

16. **WRITING** Explain how to simplify the expression $4d(2d - 7) + (5d + 4)(4d - 1)$.

Using the FOIL Method

The **FOIL Method**, a method of applying the Distributive Property, is a shortcut for multiplying two binomials.

KEY IDEA

FOIL Method

To multiply two binomials using the FOIL Method, find the sum of the products of the

First terms,	$(x + 1)(x + 2)$	$x(x) = x^2$
Outer terms,	$(x + 1)(x + 2)$	$x(2) = 2x$
Inner terms, and	$(x + 1)(x + 2)$	$1(x) = x$
Last terms.	$(x + 1)(x + 2)$	$1(2) = 2$

$$(x + 1)(x + 2) = x^2 + 2x + x + 2 = x^2 + 3x + 2$$

EXAMPLE 5 Multiplying Binomials Using the FOIL Method

Find each product.

a. $(x - 3)(x - 6)$ **b.** $(2x + 1)(3x - 5)$

SOLUTION

Use the FOIL Method.

a. First Outer Inner Last

$$(x - 3)(x - 6) = x(x) + x(-6) + (-3)(x) + (-3)(-6)$$ FOIL Method

$$= x^2 + (-6x) + (-3x) + 18$$ Multiply.

$$= x^2 - 9x + 18$$ Combine like terms.

▶ The product is $x^2 - 9x + 18$.

b. First Outer Inner Last

$$(2x + 1)(3x - 5) = 2x(3x) + 2x(-5) + 1(3x) + 1(-5)$$ FOIL Method

$$= 6x^2 + (-10x) + 3x + (-5)$$ Multiply.

$$= 6x^2 - 7x - 5$$ Combine like terms.

▶ The product is $6x^2 - 7x - 5$.

SELF-ASSESSMENT 1 I do not understand. 2 I can do it with help. 3 I can do it on my own. 4 I can teach someone else.

Use the FOIL Method to find the product.

17. $(z + 5)(z + 10)$ **18.** $(m - 3)(m - 7)$ **19.** $(x - 4)(x + 2)$

20. $\left(2u + \frac{1}{2}\right)\left(u - \frac{3}{2}\right)$ **21.** $(4c - 7)(3c + 8)$ **22.** $(n + 2)(n^2 + 3)$

23. WRITING Explain why the FOIL Method is a valid method.

Multiplying Binomials and Trinomials

Multiplying a Binomial and a Trinomial

Find $(x + 5)(x^2 - 3x - 2)$.

SOLUTION

$$\begin{array}{rrrrl} & x^2 & -\ 3x & -\ 2 & \text{Align like terms vertically.} \\ \times & & x & +\ 5 & \\ \hline & 5x^2 & -\ 15x & -\ 10 & \text{Distributive Property} \\ x^3 & -\ 3x^2 & -\ 2x & & \text{Distributive Property} \\ \hline x^3 & +\ 2x^2 & -\ 17x & -\ 10 & \text{Combine like terms.} \end{array}$$

Multiply $5(x^2 - 3x - 2)$.

Multiply $x(x^2 - 3x - 2)$.

▶ The product is $x^3 + 2x^2 - 17x - 10$.

EXAMPLE 7

Modeling Real Life

In hockey, a goalie behind the goal line can only play a puck in the trapezoidal region.

a. Write a polynomial that represents the area of the trapezoidal region.

b. Find the area of the trapezoidal region when the shorter base is 22 feet.

x ft

$(x - 11)$ ft

$(x + 6)$ ft

SOLUTION

a.

$\frac{1}{2}h(b_1 + b_2) = \frac{1}{2}(x - 11)[x + (x + 6)]$	Substitute.
$= \frac{1}{2}(x - 11)(2x + 6)$	Combine like terms.
$= \frac{1}{2}[2x^2 + 6x + (-22x) + (-66)]$	FOIL Method
$= \frac{1}{2}(2x^2 - 16x - 66)$	Combine like terms.
$= x^2 - 8x - 33$	Distributive Property

▶ A polynomial that represents the area of the trapezoidal region is $x^2 - 8x - 33$.

b. Find the value of $x^2 - 8x - 33$ when $x = 22$.

$x^2 - 8x - 33 = 22^2 - 8(22) - 33$	Substitute 22 for x.
$= 484 - 176 - 33$	Simplify.
$= 275$	Subtract.

▶ The area of the trapezoidal region is 275 square feet.

SELF-ASSESSMENT 1 I do not understand. 2 I can do it with help. 3 I can do it on my own. 4 I can teach someone else.

Find the product.

24. $(x + 1)(x^2 + 5x + 8)$ **25.** $(n - 3)(n^2 - 2n + 4)$ **26.** $(2 - w)(3w^2 + w - 1)$

27. In Example 7, the longer base is extended by 1 foot and the shorter base remains 22 feet. Explain how the polynomial changes. Then find the percent of change in the area of the trapezoidal region.

7.2 Practice WITH CalcChat® AND CalcView®

In Exercises 1–8, find the product. *Example 1*

1. $2c(5c^2)$
2. $6d^4(-3c^3)$
3. $-4r^2(9r + 6)$
4. $12t^3(5t^5 - 2)$
5. $7w^3(w^2 - 4w - 1)$
6. $-z^2(2z^4 + 10z^2 - 16)$
7. $(15 - 3g^2)(8g^5)$
8. $(9h^2 - 18 + 9h^4)(-4h^3)$

In Exercises 9–16, find the quotient. *Example 2*

9. $\dfrac{2n^3 + 8n^2 - 20n}{2n}$
10. $\dfrac{-6k^4 + 15k^3 - 9k^2}{3k^2}$
11. $\dfrac{4x^5 - x^7 + 7x^4}{x^3}$
12. $\dfrac{10y^2 + 6y^4 + 8y^3}{2y^2}$
13. $\dfrac{7b + 14}{b + 2}$
14. $\dfrac{-9h + 27}{h - 3}$
15. $\dfrac{(5p - 20)(p - 3)}{p - 4}$
16. $\dfrac{(3q + 12)(2q - 1)}{(2q - 1)(q + 4)}$

In Exercises 17–24, use the Distributive Property to find the product. *Example 3*

17. $(x + 1)(x + 3)$
18. $(y + 6)(y + 4)$
19. $(z - 5)(z + 3)$
20. $(a + 8)(a - 3)$
21. $\left(g - \frac{1}{2}\right)\left(g - \frac{3}{2}\right)$
22. $(n - 0.4)(n - 0.5)$
23. $(3m + 1)(m + 9)$
24. $(5s + 6)(s - 2)$

In Exercises 25–30, use a table to find the product. *Example 4*

25. $(x + 3)(x + 2)$
26. $(h - 8)(h - 9)$
27. $(3k - 1)(4k + 9)$
28. $(5g + 3)(g + 8)$
29. $(-3 + 2j)(4j - 7)$
30. $(5d - 12)(-7 + 3d)$

In Exercises 31–40, use the FOIL Method to find the product. *Example 5*

31. $(b + 3)(b + 7)$
32. $(w + 9)(w + 6)$
33. $(k + 5)(k - 1)$
34. $(x - 4)(x + 8)$
35. $\left(q - \frac{3}{4}\right)\left(q + \frac{1}{4}\right)$
36. $\left(z - \frac{5}{3}\right)\left(z - \frac{2}{3}\right)$
37. $(9 - r)(2 - 3r)$
38. $(8 - 4x)(2x + 6)$
39. $(w + 5)(w^2 + 3w)$
40. $(v - 3)(v^2 + 8v)$

ERROR ANALYSIS In Exercises 41 and 42, describe and correct the error in finding the product of the binomials.

41.

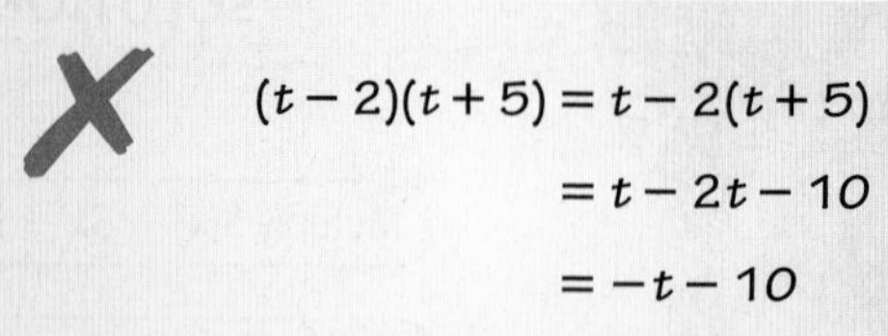

42.

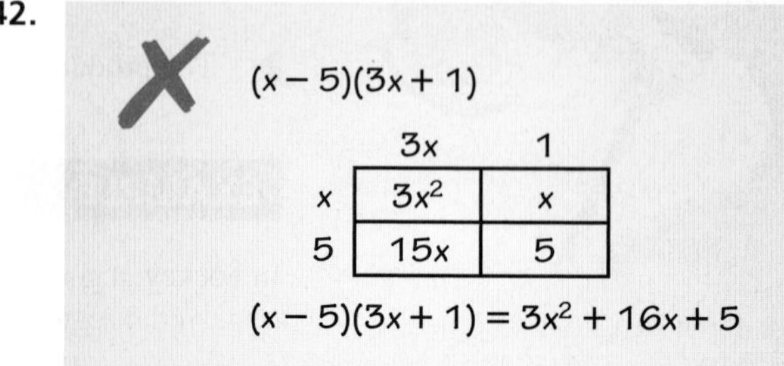

CONNECTING CONCEPTS In Exercises 43–46, write a polynomial that represents the area of the shaded region.

43.

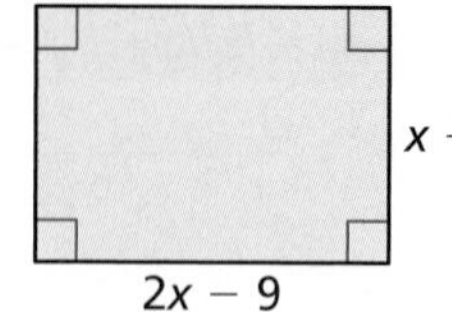

44.

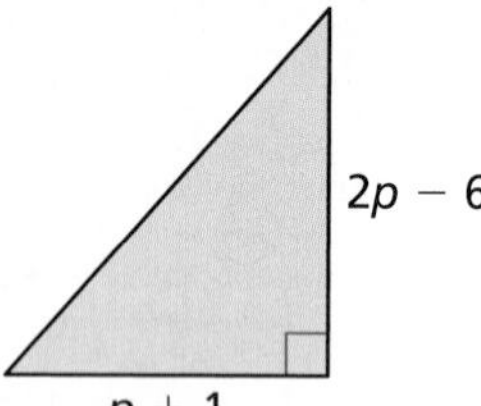

45.

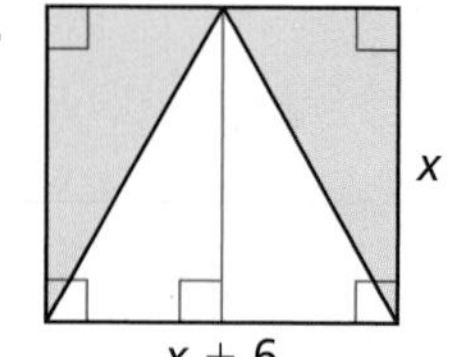

46.

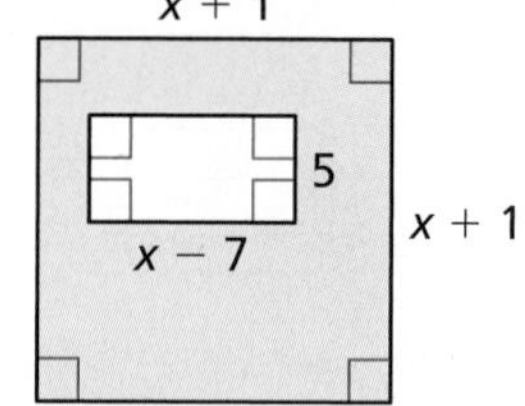

In Exercises 47–54, find the product. *Example 6*

47. $(x + 4)(x^2 + 3x + 2)$
48. $(f + 1)(f^2 + 4f + 8)$
49. $(y + 3)(y^2 + 8y - 2)$
50. $(t - 2)(t^2 - 5t + 1)$
51. $(4 - b)(5b^2 + 5b - 4)$
52. $(6 + d)(2d^2 - d + 7)$
53. $(3e^2 - 5e + 7)(6e + 1)$
54. $(6v^2 + 2v - 9)(4 - 5v)$

55. **MODELING REAL LIFE** You design a frame to surround a rectangular photo. The width of the frame is the same on each side, as shown. *Example 7*

a. Write a polynomial that represents the combined area of the photo and the frame.

b. Find the combined area of the photo and the frame when the width of the frame is 4 inches.

56. **MODELING REAL LIFE** The football field is rectangular.

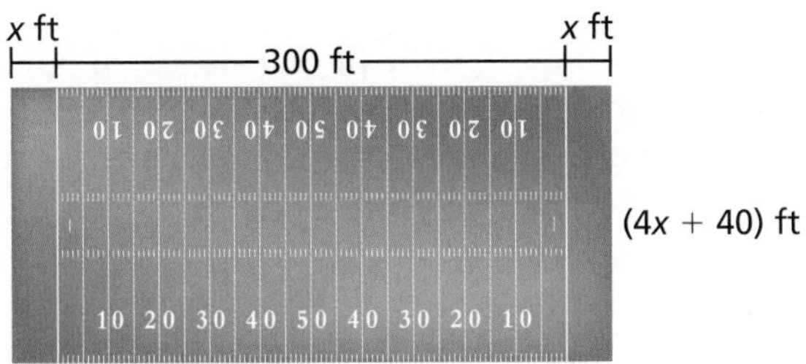

a. Write a polynomial that represents the area of the football field.

b. Find the area of the football field when the length of the field is 360 feet.

57. **COMPARING METHODS** Describe two ways to find the product of two binomials. Which method do you prefer? Explain.

58. **MP REASONING** Can you use the FOIL Method to multiply a binomial by a trinomial? two trinomials? Explain your reasoning.

59. **MAKING AN ARGUMENT** You use the Distributive Property to multiply $(x + 3)(x - 5)$. Your friend uses the FOIL Method to multiply $(x - 5)(x + 3)$. Should your answers be equivalent? Justify your answer.

60. **MP STRUCTURE** Find the values of a, b, and c that make the equation true.

$$(2x - 1)(3x + 4) = ax^2 + bx + c$$

61. **WRITING** When multiplying two binomials, explain how the degree of the product is related to the degree of each binomial.

62. **HOW DO YOU SEE IT?**
The table shows one method of finding the product of two binomials.

	$-4x$	3
$-8x$	a	b
-9	c	d

a. Write the two binomials being multiplied.

b. Determine whether a, b, c, and d will be positive or negative when $x > 0$.

GO DIGITAL

63. **COLLEGE PREP** The shipping container is a rectangular prism. Which polynomial represents the volume of the container?

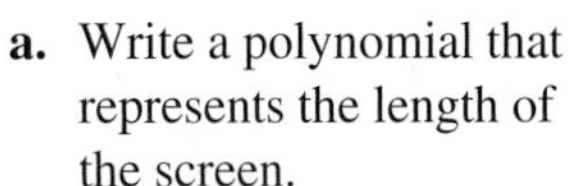
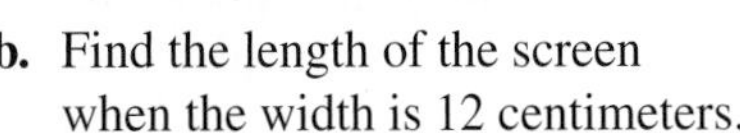

Ⓐ $4x^3 + 9x^2 - x - 6$ Ⓑ $4x^3 - 3x^2 + 12x - 9$

Ⓒ $4x^3 + 8x^2 - 3x - 6$ Ⓓ $4x^3 + 4x^2 - 6x - 6$

64. **MP REPEATED REASONING** When dividing two monomials, is it possible for the degree of the quotient to be greater than the degree of the dividend? the divisor? Explain.

65. **MODELING REAL LIFE** The area of the tablet screen (in square centimeters) is represented by $2x^2 - 4x$.

a. Write a polynomial that represents the length of the screen.

b. Find the length of the screen when the width is 12 centimeters.

66. **DIG DEEPER** The volume of the locker (in cubic inches) is represented by $(5x^2 + 15x)(x + 3)$.

a. Write a polynomial that represents the height of the locker.

b. Find the height of the locker (in feet) when the side length of the base is 15 inches.

67. OPEN-ENDED Write two polynomials that are not monomials whose product is a trinomial of degree 3.

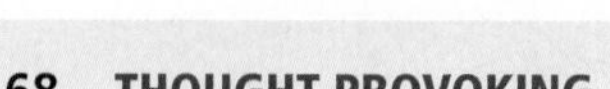

68. THOUGHT PROVOKING Find the value of k that makes the equation true. Justify your answer.

$$(12x^2 + 84x)(x - k)^{-2} = \frac{12x}{x + 7}$$

69. ABSTRACT REASONING The product of $(x + m)(x + n)$ is $x^2 + bx + c$.

a. What do you know about m and n when $c > 0$?

b. What do you know about m and n when $c < 0$?

REVIEW & REFRESH

WATCH

In Exercises 70 and 71, write the absolute value function as a piecewise function.

70. $y = |x| + 4$

71. $y = 6|x - 3|$

72. Write the first six terms of the sequence $a_1 = -1$, $a_n = 2a_{n-1}$. Then graph the sequence.

73. MP LOGIC The sum of two polynomials is $3x^2 - 7x + 5$. One of the polynomials is $x - 2$. What is the product of the polynomials?

74. Find the difference of $(s^4 - 2s^2 - 4)$ and $(-9s^2 + 5s - 7)$.

75. Use the graph to solve the system $6x + 4y = 12$ and $-x + 3y = 20$. Check your solution.

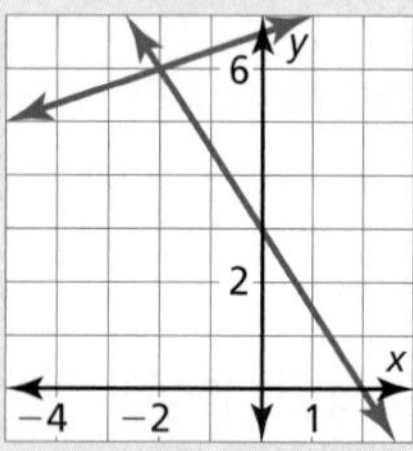

In Exercises 76–79, simplify the expression. Write your answer using only positive exponents.

76. $10^2 \cdot 10^9$

77. $\frac{x^5 \cdot x}{x^8}$

78. $(3z^6)^{-3}$

79. $\left(\frac{2y^4}{y^3}\right)^{-2}$

80. Write an equation for the nth term of the geometric sequence 256, 128, 64, 32, ... Then find a_{10}.

81. Write an inequality that represents the graph.

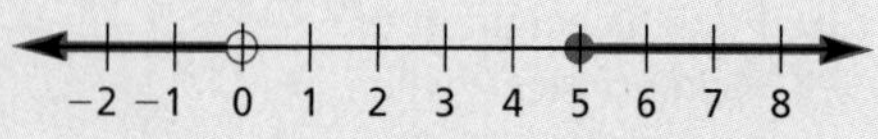

82. Determine whether the relation is a function. Explain.

Input, x	8	−2	−6	5	8
Output, y	−1	2	5	−7	2

83. Find the sum of $(8y^3 - y^2 + 12)$ and $(2y^2 + 3y - 4)$.

In Exercises 84–87, write the polynomial in standard form. Identify the degree and leading coefficient of the polynomial. Then classify the polynomial by the number of terms.

84. $9 + z^2$

85. $3d^4 - 6d^6$

86. $-2c - 4c^3 + c^2$

87. $\frac{1}{2}w^5 + 5w^3 + 7w^8$

88. WRITING Explain how you can determine whether a graph represents an arithmetic sequence or a geometric sequence.

In Exercises 89–92, find the product.

89. $-2a^2(4a + 9)$

90. $(b - 3)(b - 6)$

91. $(g^2 + 8)(2g + 5)$

92. $(v + 4)(-6v^2 - 6v + 10)$

93. MODELING REAL LIFE On a fishing trip, you catch two fish. The weight of the first fish is shown. The second fish weighs at least 0.5 pound more than the first fish. Write an inequality that represents the possible weights of the second fish.

7.3 Special Products of Polynomials

Learning Target Use patterns to find products of polynomials.

Success Criteria
- I can use the square of a binomial pattern.
- I can multiply binomials using the sum and difference pattern.
- I can solve problems using special product patterns.

EXPLORE IT! Identifying Patterns in Products of Binomials

Work with a partner. You can use algebra tiles to find special products of polynomials.

a. Write the product modeled by each array of algebra tiles. Use additional algebra tiles to complete the model. Then write the product as a polynomial.

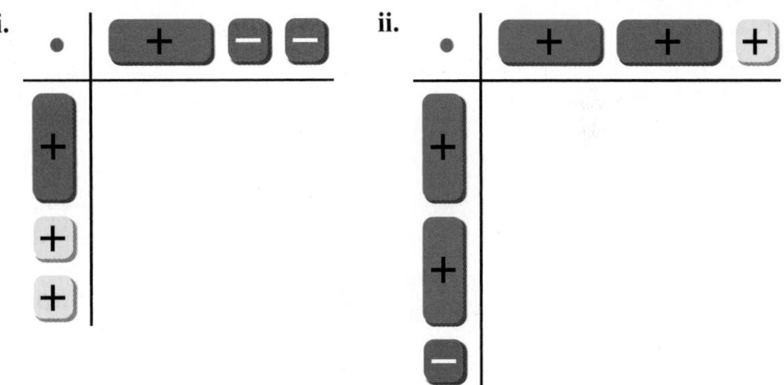

What pattern(s) do you notice? Explain your reasoning.

b. Use algebra tiles to model each product. Then write the product asa polynomial.

i. $(x + 2)^2$ **ii.** $(2x - 1)^2$

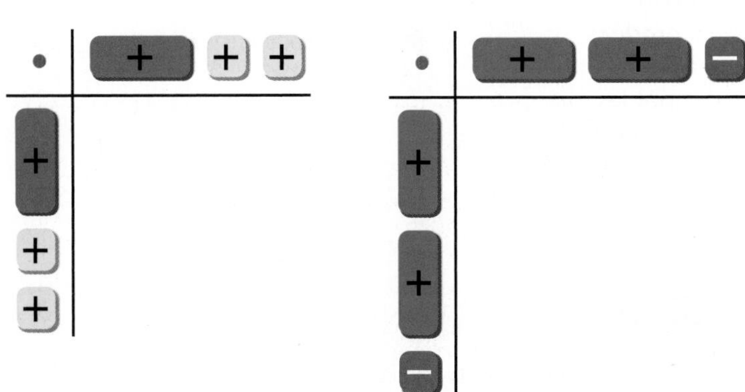

What pattern(s) do you notice? Explain your reasoning.

c. Use the patterns you found above to find each product. Check your answers using algebra tiles.

i. $(x + 3)(x - 3)$ **ii.** $(x - 4)(x + 4)$ **iii.** $(3x + 1)(3x - 1)$

iv. $(x + 3)^2$ **v.** $(x - 2)^2$ **vi.** $(3x + 1)^2$

Math Practice

Look for Structure

Why does each product in part (a) result in a binomial and not a trinomial like in part (b)?

Using the Square of a Binomial Pattern

The diagram shows a square with a side length of $(a + b)$ units. You can see that the area of the square is

$$(a + b)^2 = a^2 + 2ab + b^2.$$

a b
a a^2 ab
b ab b^2

This is one version of a pattern called the square of a binomial. To find another version of this pattern, use algebra: replace b with $-b$.

$(a + (-b))^2 = a^2 + 2a(-b) + (-b)^2$ — Replace b with $-b$ in the pattern above.

$(a - b)^2 = a^2 - 2ab + b^2$ — Simplify.

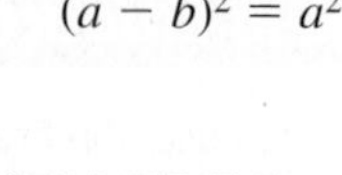

KEY IDEA

Square of a Binomial Pattern

Algebra	Example
$(a + b)^2 = a^2 + 2ab + b^2$	$(x + 5)^2 = (x)^2 + 2(x)(5) + (5)^2$ $= x^2 + 10x + 25$
$(a - b)^2 = a^2 - 2ab + b^2$	$(2x - 3)^2 = (2x)^2 - 2(2x)(3) + (3)^2$ $= 4x^2 - 12x + 9$

STUDY TIP

The square of a binomial, a polynomial such as $x^2 + 10x + 25$ or $4x^2 - 12x + 9$, is called a *perfect square trinomial.*

EXAMPLE 1 Using the Square of a Binomial Pattern

Find each product.

a. $(3x + 4)^2$ **b.** $(5x - 2y)^2$

SOLUTION

a. $(3x + 4)^2 = (3x)^2 + 2(3x)(4) + 4^2$ — Square of a binomial pattern

$= 9x^2 + 24x + 16$ — Simplify.

▶ The product is $9x^2 + 24x + 16$.

b. $(5x - 2y)^2 = (5x)^2 - 2(5x)(2y) + (2y)^2$ — Square of a binomial pattern

$= 25x^2 - 20xy + 4y^2$ — Simplify.

▶ The product is $25x^2 - 20xy + 4y^2$.

Math Practice

Look for Structure

In a special product pattern, a and b can be numbers, variables, or variable expressions.

SELF-ASSESSMENT

1 I do not understand. 2 I can do it with help. 3 I can do it on my own. 4 I can teach someone else.

1. **WRITING** Explain how to use the square of a binomial pattern.

Find the product.

2. $(x + 7)^2$
3. $(7x - 3)^2$
4. $(4x - y)^2$
5. $(3m + n)^2$
6. **MP STRUCTURE** Explain how to find $(-3h + 6)^2$ using each pattern shown above.
7. **MP REASONING** Find the products in Exercises 2–5 without using a special product pattern. Compare the methods.

Using the Sum and Difference Pattern

To find the product $(x + 2)(x - 2)$, you can multiply the two binomials using the FOIL Method.

$(x + 2)(x - 2) = x^2 - 2x + 2x - 4$	FOIL Method
$= x^2 - 4$	Combine like terms.

This suggests a pattern for the product of the sum and difference of two terms.

KEY IDEA

Sum and Difference Pattern

Algebra	**Example**
$(a + b)(a - b) = a^2 - b^2$	$(x + 3)(x - 3) = x^2 - 9$

EXAMPLE 2 Using the Sum and Difference Pattern

Find (a) $(t + 5)(t - 5)$ and (b) $(3x + y)(3x - y)$.

SOLUTION

a. $(t + 5)(t - 5) = t^2 - 5^2$ — Sum and difference pattern

$= t^2 - 25$ — Simplify.

▶ The product is $t^2 - 25$.

b. $(3x + y)(3x - y) = (3x)^2 - y^2$ — Sum and difference pattern

$= 9x^2 - y^2$ — Simplify.

▶ The product is $9x^2 - y^2$.

The special product patterns can help you use mental math to find certain products of numbers.

EXAMPLE 3 Using Special Product Patterns and Mental Math

Use special product patterns to find the product $26 \cdot 34$.

SOLUTION

Notice that 26 is 4 less than 30, while 34 is 4 greater than 30.

$26 \cdot 34 = (30 - 4)(30 + 4)$ — Write as product of difference and sum.

$= 30^2 - 4^2$ — Sum and difference pattern

$= 884$ — Evaluate powers and simplify.

▶ The product is 884.

SELF-ASSESSMENT 1 I do not understand. 2 I can do it with help. 3 I can do it on my own. 4 I can teach someone else.

Find the product.

8. $(x + 10)(x - 10)$

9. $(2x + 1.5)(2x - 1.5)$

10. $(x + 6y)(x - 6y)$

11. Describe how to use special product patterns to find $41 \cdot 39$.

Solving Real-Life Problems

EXAMPLE 4 Modeling Real Life

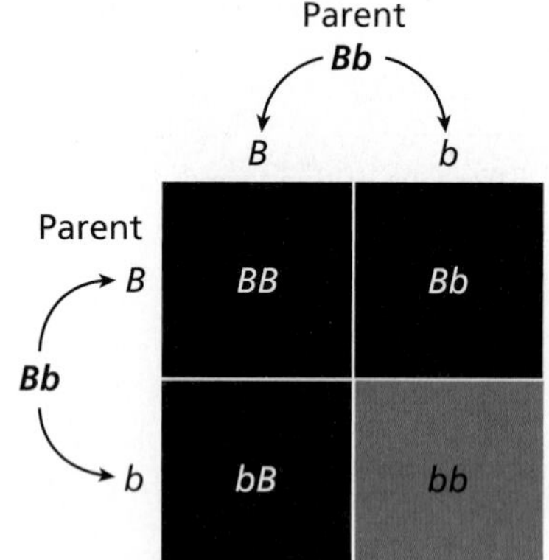

A combination of two genes determines the color of the dark patches on a border collie's coat. Each offspring inherits one patch-color gene from each parent. Each parent has two patch-color genes, and the offspring has an equal chance of inheriting either one.

Each parent has the same gene combination *Bb*. The Punnett square shows the possible outcomes for the gene combinations of the offspring: black patches (*BB*), black patches (*Bb*), black patches (*bB*), and red patches (*bb*).

a. What percent of the possible gene combinations result in black patches?

b. Show how you can use a polynomial to model the possible gene combinations.

SOLUTION

a. Notice that the Punnett square shows four possible outcomes for the gene combinations of the offspring. Of these combinations, three result in black patches.

▶ So, $\frac{3}{4} = 75\%$ of the possible gene combinations result in black patches.

b. Notice that you can think of the Punnett square as a square with side length $B + b$, where B and b are the probabilities that the offspring inherits a black or a red gene from each parent. The area of each section of the Punnett square is equal to the probability of an offspring inheriting that gene combination. So, find the area of the Punnett square using the square of a binomial pattern.

$$(B + b)^2 = B^2 + 2(B)(b) + b^2$$
$$= B^2 + 2Bb + b^2$$

Because the offspring has an equal chance of inheriting either gene, $B = 0.5$ and $b = 0.5$. Evaluate each term of the polynomial.

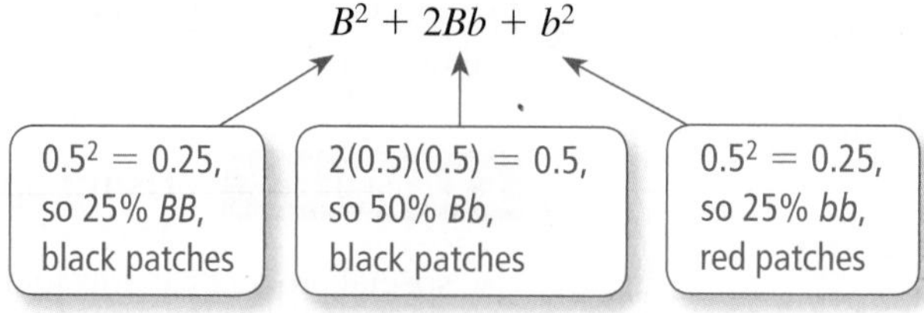

▶ So, $25\% + 50\% = 75\%$ of the possible gene combinations result in black patches and 25% result in red patches.

SELF-ASSESSMENT

1 I do not understand. 2 I can do it with help. 3 I can do it on my own. 4 I can teach someone else.

12. Each of two dogs has the same gene combination *BW*. The Punnett square shows the possible outcomes for the gene combinations of an offspring and the resulting coat colors.

a. What percent of the possible gene combinations result in a black coat?

b. Show how you can use a polynomial to model the possible gene combinations of the offspring.

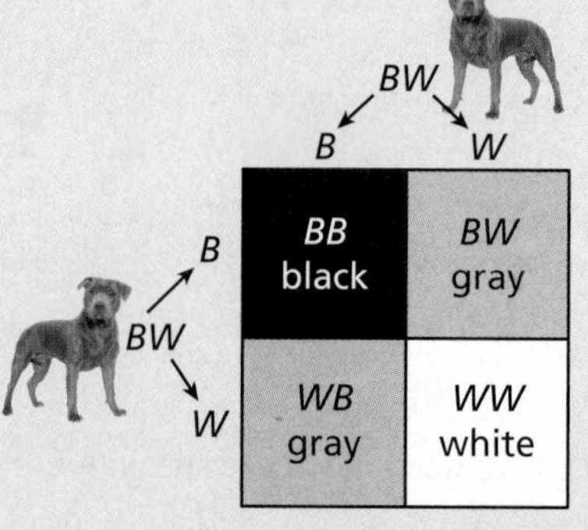

13. **MP PATTERNS** Find $(x + 1)^3$ and $(x + 2)^3$. Find a pattern in the terms and use it to write a pattern for the cube of a binomial $(a + b)^3$.

7.3 Practice WITH CalcChat® AND CalcView®

GO DIGITAL

In Exercises 1–8, find the product. ▶ *Example 1*

1. $(x + 8)^2$
2. $(a - 6)^2$
3. $(2f - 1)^2$
4. $(5p + 2)^2$
5. $(-7t + 4)^2$
6. $(-12 - n)^2$
7. $(2a + b)^2$
8. $(6x - 3y)^2$

CONNECTING CONCEPTS In Exercises 9–12, write a polynomial that represents the area of the square.

9. 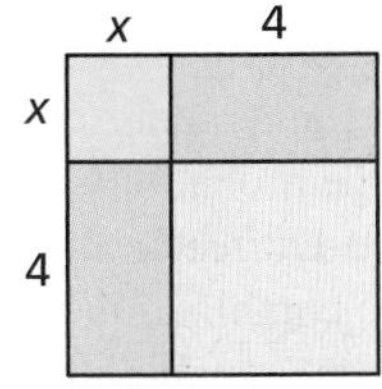

10. 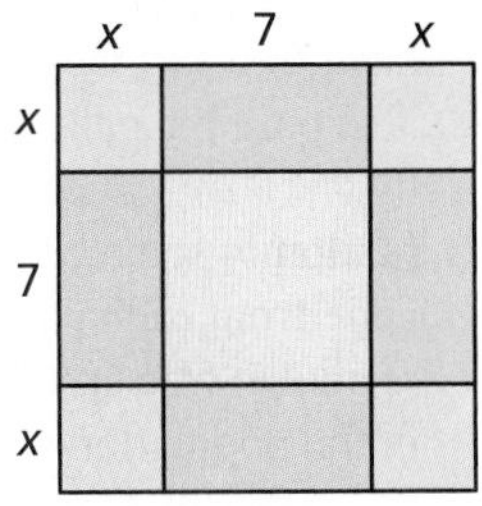

11. 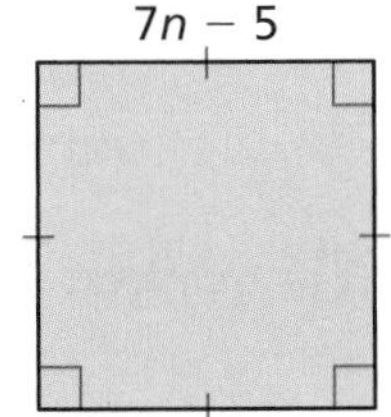

12. 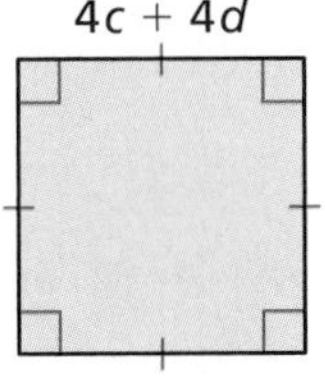

In Exercises 13–22, find the product. ▶ *Example 2*

13. $(t - 7)(t + 7)$
14. $(m + 6)(m - 6)$
15. $(4x + 1)(4x - 1)$
16. $(2k - 4)(2k + 4)$
17. $\left(\frac{1}{2} - c\right)\left(\frac{1}{2} + c\right)$
18. $(2.5 + 3a)(2.5 - 3a)$
19. $(p - 10q)(p + 10q)$
20. $(7m + 8n)(7m - 8n)$
21. $(-y + 4z)(-y - 4z)$
22. $(-5g - 2h)(-5g + 2h)$

In Exercises 23–28, use special product patterns to find the product. ▶ *Example 3*

23. $16 \cdot 24$
24. $33 \cdot 27$
25. 42^2
26. 29^2
27. 30.5^2
28. $10\frac{1}{3} \cdot 9\frac{2}{3}$

ERROR ANALYSIS In Exercises 29 and 30, describe and correct the error in finding the product.

29. 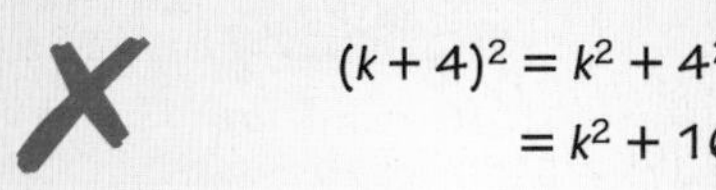

30. 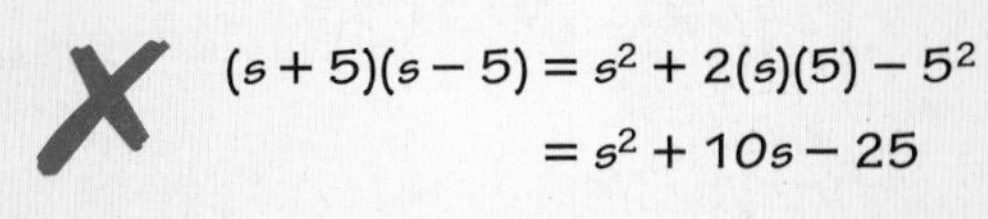

31. **MODELING REAL LIFE** A combination of two genes determines the coloring of a deer. Each offspring inherits one color gene from each parent. Each parent has the same gene combination *Nn*. The Punnett square shows the possible outcomes for the gene combinations of the offspring. ▶ *Example 4*

    a. What percent of the possible gene combinations result in albino coloring?

    b. Show how you can use a polynomial to model the possible gene combinations of the offspring.

Parent A: *Nn* → *N*, *n*; Parent B: *Nn* → *N*, *n*

	N	*n*
N	*NN* normal	*Nn* normal
n	*nN* normal	*nn* albino

32. **MODELING REAL LIFE** A square-shaped parking lot with 100-foot sides is reduced by *x* feet on one side and extended by *x* feet on an adjacent side.

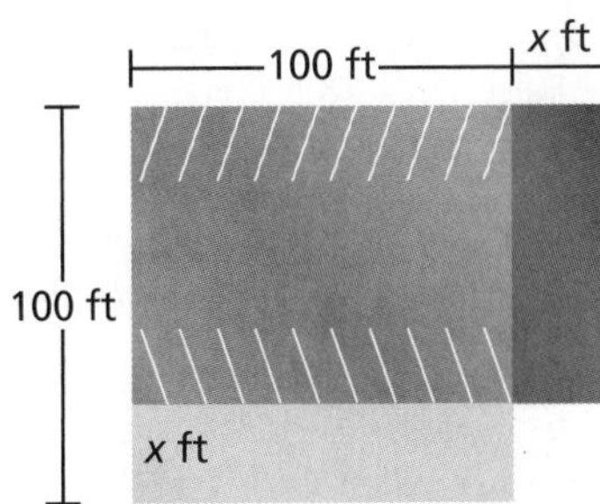

    a. Write a polynomial that represents the new area of the parking lot.

    b. Does the area of the parking lot increase, decrease, or stay the same? Explain.

33. **CRITICAL THINKING** Write two binomials that have the product $x^2 - 121$. Explain.

34. HOW DO YOU SEE IT?
Each offspring of two pea plants inherits one color gene from each parent. Each parent has the same gene combination Gg. The Punnett square shows the possible outcomes for the gene combinations of the offspring.

A polynomial that models the possible gene combinations of the offspring is

$$(G + g)^2 = G^2 + 2Gg + g^2.$$

Describe two ways to determine the percent of possible gene combinations that result in green pods.

In Exercises 35 and 36, find the product.

35. $(2m^2 - 5n^2)^2$

36. $(r^3 - 6t^4)(r^3 + 6t^4)$

37. MP **REASONING** Find k so that $9x^2 - 48x + k$ is the square of a binomial.

38. THOUGHT PROVOKING
Modify the dimensions of the parking lot in Exercise 32 so that the area can be represented by two other types of special product patterns discussed in this section. Is there a positive x-value for which the three area expressions are equivalent? Explain.

39. DIG DEEPER In a population of 8000 people, 95% have free earlobes and 5% have attached earlobes. The possible gene combinations can be represented by $(F + a)^2$, where F and a are the probability that a randomly selected person inherited a free or attached gene from each parent. Any gene combination with F results in free earlobes. Estimate the number of people in the population who carry *both* genes. (*Hint*: Find the values of F and a. Remember that $F + a = 1$.)

REVIEW & REFRESH

In Exercises 40 and 41, graph the function. Find the domain and range.

40. $y = \begin{cases} -2x, & \text{if } x \le 0 \\ x + 3, & \text{if } x > 0 \end{cases}$

41. $y = \begin{cases} \frac{1}{2}x + 1, & \text{if } x < 2 \\ 3x - 5, & \text{if } x > 2 \end{cases}$

42. Find the missing values in the ratio table. Then write the equivalent ratios.

Feet	18.5		92.5	
Seconds	1	2		7

In Exercises 43–45, find the sum or difference.

43. $(k + 5) - (3k - 2)$

44. $(6g^2 + 3g - 8) - (-g^2 + 12)$

45. $\left(\frac{1}{2}d - 4\right) + \left(\frac{1}{4}d^2 - 2d + 9\right)$

46. MODELING REAL LIFE The value of a building is \$180,000. The value is expected to increase by 3.5% each year. Write a function that represents the value y (in dollars) of the building after x years. Then predict the value after 10 years.

In Exercises 47–54, find the product or quotient.

47. $(x - 3)(x + 5)$

48. $(y^2 + 3y - 1)(y - 6)$

49. $(x - 6)^2$

50. $(2n + 9y)^2$

51. $(p + 4)(p - 4)$

52. $(w - 5z)(w + 5z)$

53. $\dfrac{4p^5 + 5p^3 - 3p - 2}{p}$

54. $\dfrac{(24h + 8)(3h - 4)}{3h + 1}$

55. MODELING REAL LIFE A movie theater sells 12 large bags of popcorn and 25 small bags of popcorn for \$227. A large bag of popcorn costs \$3.50 more than a small bag of popcorn. How much does each size cost?

56. Write an explicit and a recursive rule for the sequence.

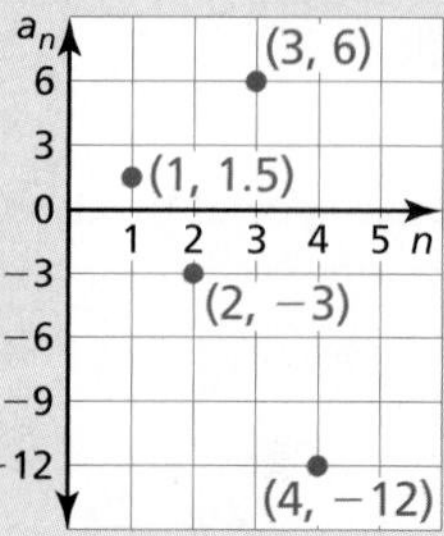

7.4 Solving Polynomial Equations in Factored Form

Learning Target Solve polynomial equations in factored form.

Success Criteria
- I can use the Zero-Product Property to solve polynomial equations in factored form.
- I can factor polynomials using the greatest common factor.
- I can solve polynomial equations by rewriting them in factored form.

EXPLORE IT! Understanding the Zero-Product Property

Math Practice

Find Entry Points
You can interpret $7x = 0$ as, "7 times something equals 0." What must "something" be? How can this help you solve the equations in part (b)?

Work with a partner.

a. Solve each equation. Explain your reasoning.

i. $x - 3 = 0$ **ii.** $x + 4 = 0$

iii. $3z + 2 = 0$ **iv.** $-2z + 4 = 0$

v. $7x = 0$ **vi.** $\frac{1}{2}z = 0$

b. Use your results in part (a) to solve each equation below. Explain how you found your answers.

i. $2(x - 3) = 0$ **ii.** $-12(x + 4) = 0$

iii. $7x(x + 4) = 0$ **iv.** $\frac{1}{2}z(3z + 2) = 0$

v. $(x - 3)(x + 4) = 0$ **vi.** $(3z + 2)(-2z + 4) = 0$

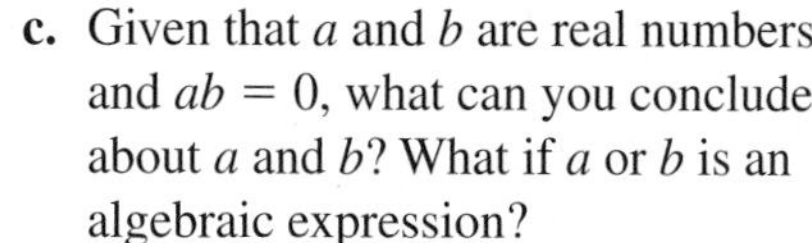

c. Given that a and b are real numbers and $ab = 0$, what can you conclude about a and b? What if a or b is an algebraic expression?

d. The property in part (c) is called the Zero-Product Property. Why do you think it is called the Zero-Product Property? Explain how it is used in algebra and why it is important.

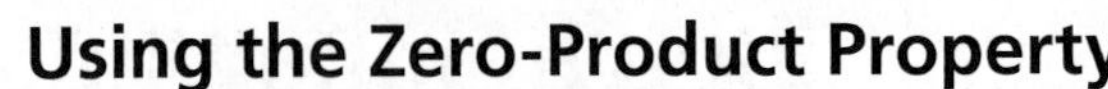

Using the Zero-Product Property

GO DIGITAL

Vocabulary

factored form, *p. 386*
Zero-Product Property, *p. 386*
roots, *p. 386*
repeated roots, *p. 387*

A polynomial is in **factored form** when it is written as a product of factors.

Standard form	Factored form
$x^2 + 2x$	$x(x + 2)$
$x^2 + 5x - 24$	$(x - 3)(x + 8)$

When one side of an equation is a polynomial in factored form and the other side is 0, use the **Zero-Product Property** to solve the polynomial equation. The solutions of an equation are also called **roots**.

KEY IDEA

Zero-Product Property

Words If the product of two real numbers is 0, then at least one of the numbers is 0.

Algebra If a and b are real numbers and $ab = 0$, then $a = 0$ or $b = 0$.

EXAMPLE 1 Solving Polynomial Equations

Solve each equation.

a. $2x(x - 4) = 0$ **b.** $(x - 3)(x - 9) = 0$ **c.** $(2x + 7)(2x - 7) = 0$

SOLUTION

a. $2x(x - 4) = 0$ Write equation.

$2x = 0$ *or* $x - 4 = 0$ Zero-Product Property

$x = 0$ *or* $x = 4$ Solve for x.

▶ The roots are $x = 0$ and $x = 4$.

Check
To check the solutions of Example 1(a), substitute each solution in the original equation.

$2(0)(0 - 4) \stackrel{?}{=} 0$
$0(-4) \stackrel{?}{=} 0$
$0 = 0$ ✓

$2(4)(4 - 4) \stackrel{?}{=} 0$
$8(0) \stackrel{?}{=} 0$
$0 = 0$ ✓

b. $(x - 3)(x - 9) = 0$ Write equation.

$x - 3 = 0$ *or* $x - 9 = 0$ Zero-Product Property

$x = 3$ *or* $x = 9$ Solve for x.

▶ The roots are $x = 3$ and $x = 9$.

c. $(2x + 7)(2x - 7) = 0$ Write equation.

$2x + 7 = 0$ *or* $2x - 7 = 0$ Zero-Product Property

$x = -\frac{7}{2}$ *or* $x = \frac{7}{2}$ Solve for x.

▶ The roots are $x = -\frac{7}{2}$ and $x = \frac{7}{2}$.

SELF-ASSESSMENT 1 I do not understand. 2 I can do it with help. 3 I can do it on my own. 4 I can teach someone else.

Solve the equation. Check your solutions.

1. $3t(t + 2) = 0$ **2.** $(z - 4)(z - 6) = 0$ **3.** $(3z - 4)(3z + 4) = 0$

4. OPEN-ENDED Write an equation that you can solve using the Zero-Product Property. Then explain why you can use the property to solve the equation.

When two or more roots of an equation are the same number, the equation has **repeated roots**.

EXAMPLE 2 **Solving Polynomial Equations** 

Solve (a) $(x - 1)^2 = 0$ and (b) $(x + 1)(x - 3)(x + 1) = 0$.

SOLUTION

a.

$(x - 1)^2 = 0$	Write equation.
$(x - 1)(x - 1) = 0$	Expand equation.
$x - 1 = 0$ *or* $x - 1 = 0$	Zero-Product Property
$x = 1$ *or* $x = 1$	Solve for x.

▶ The equation has repeated roots of $x = 1$.

STUDY TIP

You can extend the Zero-Product Property to products of more than two real numbers.

b.

$(x + 1)(x - 3)(x + 1) = 0$	Write equation.
$x + 1 = 0$ *or* $x - 3 = 0$ *or* $x + 1 = 0$	Zero-Product Property
$x = -1$ *or* $x = 3$ *or* $x = -1$	Solve for x.

▶ The equation has repeated roots of $x = -1$. The roots are $x = -1$ and $x = 3$.

Factoring Polynomials Using the GCF

To solve a polynomial equation using the Zero-Product Property, you may need to *factor* the polynomial. Look for the *greatest common factor* (GCF) of the terms of the polynomial. This is a monomial that divides evenly into each term.

EXAMPLE 3 **Factoring a Polynomial Using the GCF** 

Factor out the greatest common factor from $4x^4 + 24x^3$.

SOLUTION

The GCF of 4 and 24 is 4. The GCF of x^4 and x^3 is x^3. So, the greatest common factor of the terms is $4x^3$.

▶ So, $4x^4 + 24x^3 = 4x^3(x + 6)$.

SELF-ASSESSMENT 1 I do not understand. 2 I can do it with help. 3 I can do it on my own. 4 I can teach someone else.

Solve the equation. Check your solutions.

5. $(3s + 5)(3s + 5) = 0$ **6.** $(b + 7)^2 = 0$ **7.** $(d - 2)(d + 6)(d + 8) = 0$

8. DIFFERENT WORDS, SAME QUESTION Which is different? Find *both* answers.

Solve the equation $(2k + 4)(k - 3) = 0$.	Find the values of k for which $2k + 4 = 0$ *or* $k - 3 = 0$.	Find the value of k for which $(2k + 4) + (k - 3) = 0$.	Find the roots of the equation $(2k + 4)(k - 3) = 0$.

Factor the polynomial.

9. $8y^2 - 24y$ **10.** $15z^3 + 12z^2$

11. $2m^4 + 10m^2$ **12.** $13n^5 - 4n$

EXAMPLE 4 Solving Equations by Factoring

Solve each equation.

a. $2x^2 + 8x = 0$ **b.** $6n^2 = 15n$

SOLUTION

a.

$2x^2 + 8x = 0$	Write equation.
$2x(x + 4) = 0$	Factor left side.
$2x = 0 \quad or \quad x + 4 = 0$	Zero-Product Property
$x = 0 \quad or \quad x = -4$	Solve for x.

▶ The roots are $x = 0$ and $x = -4$.

b.

$6n^2 = 15n$	Write equation.
$6n^2 - 15n = 0$	Subtract $15n$ from each side.
$3n(2n - 5) = 0$	Factor left side.
$3n = 0 \quad or \quad 2n - 5 = 0$	Zero-Product Property
$n = 0 \quad or \quad n = \frac{5}{2}$	Solve for n.

▶ The roots are $n = 0$ and $n = \frac{5}{2}$.

Math Practice

Build Arguments

Is it valid to solve $6n^2 = 15n$ by first dividing each side by n? Explain your reasoning.

EXAMPLE 5 Modeling Real Life

You can model the arch of a fireplace using the equation $y = -\frac{1}{9}(x + 18)(x - 18)$, where x and y are measured in inches. The x-axis represents the floor. Find the width of the arch at floor level.

SOLUTION

Use the x-coordinates of the points where the arch meets the floor to find the width. At floor level, $y = 0$. So, substitute 0 for y and solve for x.

$y = -\frac{1}{9}(x + 18)(x - 18)$	Write equation.
$0 = -\frac{1}{9}(x + 18)(x - 18)$	Substitute 0 for y.
$0 = (x + 18)(x - 18)$	Multiply each side by -9.
$x + 18 = 0 \quad or \quad x - 18 = 0$	Zero-Product Property
$x = -18 \quad or \quad x = 18$	Solve for x.

The width is the distance between the x-coordinates, -18 and 18.

▶ So, the width of the arch at floor level is $|-18 - 18| = 36$ inches.

SELF-ASSESSMENT

1 I do not understand. 2 I can do it with help. 3 I can do it on my own. 4 I can teach someone else.

Solve the equation. Check your solutions.

13. $a^2 + 5a = 0$ **14.** $3s^2 - 9s = 0$ **15.** $4x^2 = 2x$

16. You can model the entrance to a mine shaft using the equation $y = -\frac{1}{2}(x + 4)(x - 4)$, where x and y are measured in feet. The x-axis represents the ground. Find the width of the entrance at ground level.

7.4 Practice WITH CalcChat® AND CalcView®

In Exercises 1–10, solve the equation. *Example 1*

1. $x(x + 7) = 0$
2. $r(r - 10) = 0$
3. $12t(t - 5) = 0$
4. $-2v(v + 1) = 0$
5. $(s - 9)(s - 1) = 0$
6. $(y + 2)(y - 6) = 0$
7. $(2a - 6)(3a + 15) = 0$
8. $(4q + 3)(q + 2) = 0$
9. $(3 - 2g)(7 - g) = 0$
10. $(2 - 4d)(2 + 4d) = 0$

In Exercises 11–18, solve the equation. *Example 2*

11. $(h - 8)(h - 8) = 0$
12. $(5m + 4)^2 = 0$
13. $(r - 4)^2(r + 8) = 0$
14. $w(w - 6)(w - 6) = 0$
15. $z(z + 2)(z - 1) = 0$
16. $5p(2p - 3)(p + 7) = 0$
17. $(15 - 5c)(5c + 5)(-c + 6) = 0$
18. $(2 - n)\left(6 + \frac{2}{3}n\right)(n - 2) = 0$

In Exercises 19 and 20, find the x-intercepts of the graph.

19.

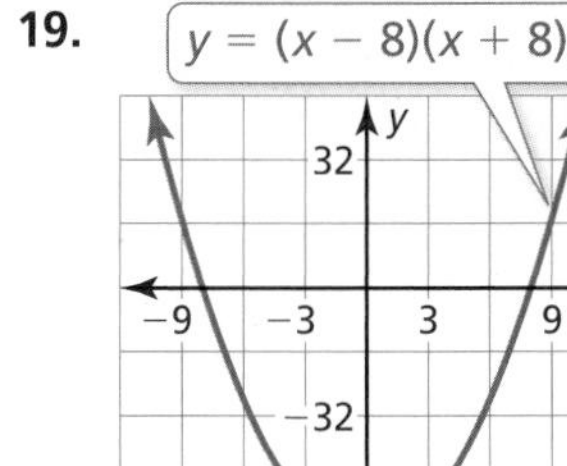

20.

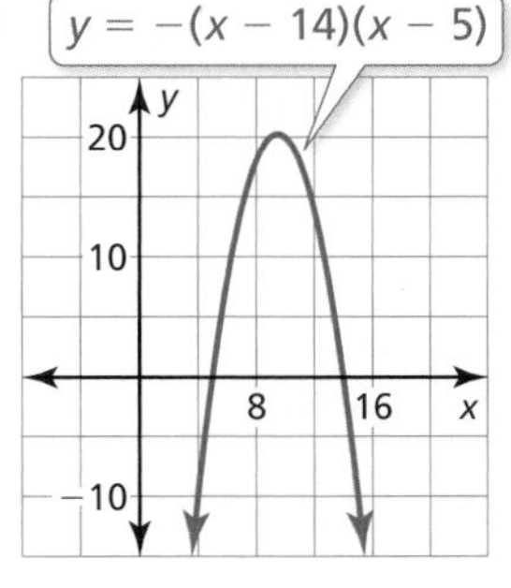

In Exercises 21–26, factor the polynomial. *Example 3*

21. $5z^2 + 45z$
22. $6d^2 - 21d$
23. $3y^3 - 9y^2$
24. $20x^3 + 30x^2$
25. $5n^6 + 2n^5$
26. $12a^4 + 8a$

In Exercises 27–32, solve the equation. *Example 4*

27. $4p^2 - p = 0$
28. $6m^2 + 12m = 0$
29. $25c + 10c^2 = 0$
30. $18q - 2q^2 = 0$
31. $7n^2 = 35n$
32. $-28r = 4r^2$

ERROR ANALYSIS In Exercises 33 and 34, describe and correct the error in solving the equation.

33.

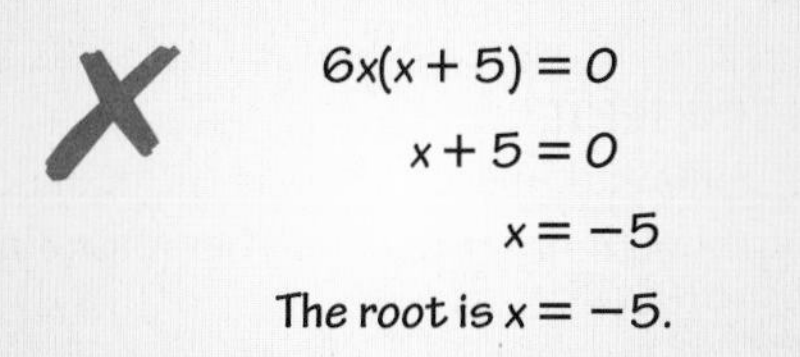

34.

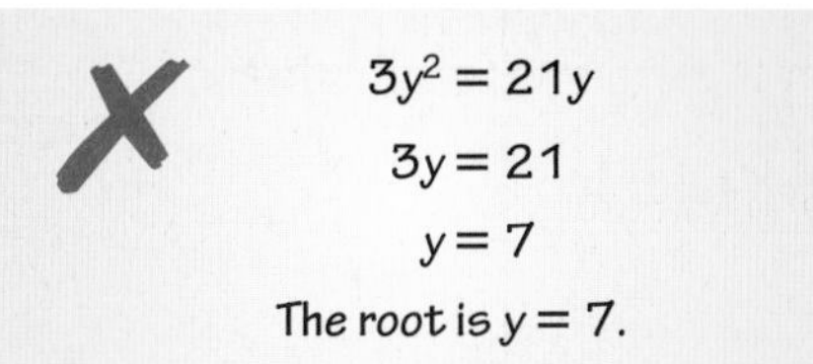

35. **MODELING REAL LIFE** The entrance of a tunnel can be modeled by $y = -\frac{11}{50}(x - 4)(x - 24)$, where x and y are measured in feet. The x-axis represents the ground. Find the width of the tunnel at ground level. *Example 5*

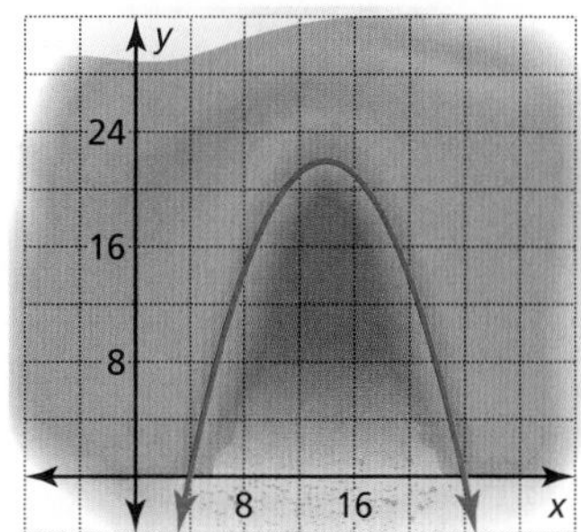

36. **MODELING REAL LIFE** The Gateway Arch in St. Louis can be modeled by $y = -\frac{2}{315}(x + 315)(x - 315)$, where x and y are measured in feet. The x-axis represents the ground.

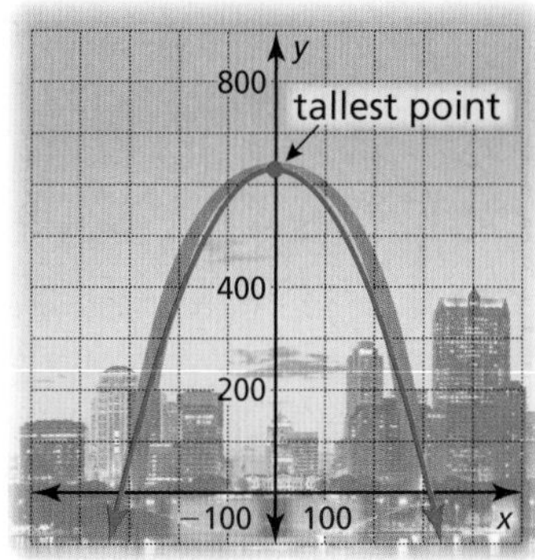

a. Find the width of the arch at ground level.

b. How tall is the arch? Explain how you found your answer.

37. MODELING REAL LIFE A penguin leaps out of the water while swimming. This action is called porpoising. The height y (in feet) of a porpoising penguin can be modeled by $y = -16x^2 + 4.8x$, where x is the time (in seconds) since the penguin leaped out of the water. Find the roots of the equation when $y = 0$. Explain what the roots mean in this situation.

38. HOW DO YOU SEE IT?
Use the graph to fill in each blank in the equation with the symbol + or −. Explain your reasoning.

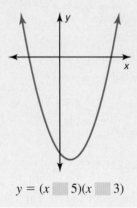

$y = (x \;\square\; 5)(x \;\square\; 3)$

39. MAKING AN ARGUMENT Your friend says that the graph of the equation $y = (x - a)(x - b)$ always has two x-intercepts for any values of a and b. Is your friend correct? Explain.

40. CRITICAL THINKING How many x-intercepts does the graph of $y = (2x + 5)(x - 9)^2$ have? Explain.

41. CRITICAL THINKING Does the equation $(x^2 + 3)(x^4 + 1) = 0$ have any real roots? Explain.

42. THOUGHT PROVOKING
Write a polynomial equation of degree 4 whose only roots are $x = 1$, $x = 2$, and $x = 3$.

43. MP REASONING Find the values of x in terms of y that are solutions of each equation.

a. $(x + y)(2x - y) = 0$

b. $(x^2 - y^2)(4x + 16y) = 0$

44. DIG DEEPER Solve $(4^{x-5} - 16)(3^x - 81) = 0$.

REVIEW & REFRESH

45. List the factor pairs of 48.

In Exercises 46–51, find the product or quotient.

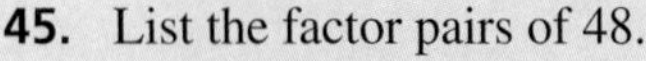

46. $(3 - 4d)(2d - 5)$

47. $(3z - 5)(3z + 5)$

48. $(y + 9)(y^2 + 2y - 3)$

49. $(t + 5)^2$

50. $\dfrac{6x^6 - 3x^5 + 12x^3}{3x^3}$

51. $\dfrac{5h - 35}{h - 7}$

52. MP NUMBER SENSE The sum of three consecutive integers is −45. What is the greatest integer?

In Exercises 53 and 54, determine whether the table or equation represents a *linear* or *nonlinear* function. Explain.

53.

x	−1	−0.5	0	0.5
y	12	7	2	−3

54. $y = \dfrac{3}{x} - 6$

55. Write $-1.3z + 3z^4 + 7.4z^2$ in standard form. Identify the degree and leading coefficient of the polynomial. Then classify the polynomial by the number of terms.

56. MODELING REAL LIFE You sell coupon books for \$25 and candles for \$15 as a fundraiser. Your total sales must be at least \$300. Write and graph an inequality that represents the numbers of coupon books and candles you must sell. Identify and interpret two solutions of the inequality.

57. Factor $18x^5 - 63x^2$.

In Exercises 58 and 59, solve the inequality. Graph the solution.

58. $-8 < \frac{1}{3}x - 7 \leq -5$

59. $12 > x + 8$ *or* $-4x + 5 \leq -27$

60. MP STRUCTURE Compare the graphs. Find the value of k.

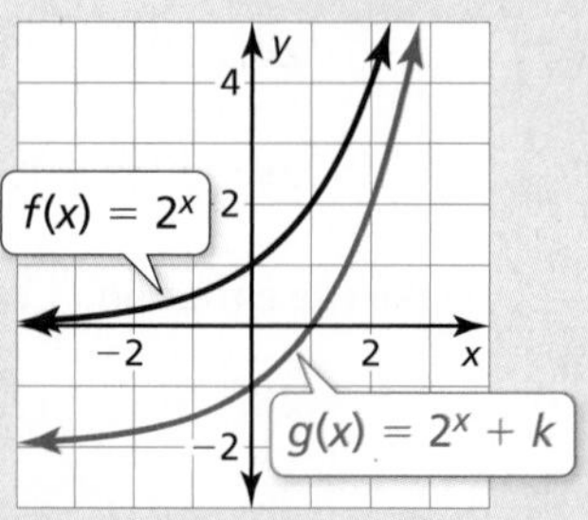

61. Solve $-10n(5n - 2) = 0$.

7.5 Factoring $x^2 + bx + c$

Learning Target Factor polynomials of the form $x^2 + bx + c$.

Success Criteria
- I can identify the three terms of a trinomial.
- I can factor polynomials of the form $x^2 + bx + c$.
- I can explain how to use b and c to find binomial factors of a polynomial $x^2 + bx + c$.

EXPLORE IT! Identifying Binomial Factors of a Polynomial

Work with a partner. In some cases, you can write a polynomial as a product of binomials. One way to do this is to first represent the polynomial using a rectangular array of algebra tiles.

a. Write the polynomial represented by the algebra tiles at the left. Then arrange the algebra tiles into a rectangular array.

b. Use algebra tiles to model the dimensions of the rectangular array in part (a). Then use the model to write the polynomial in factored form.

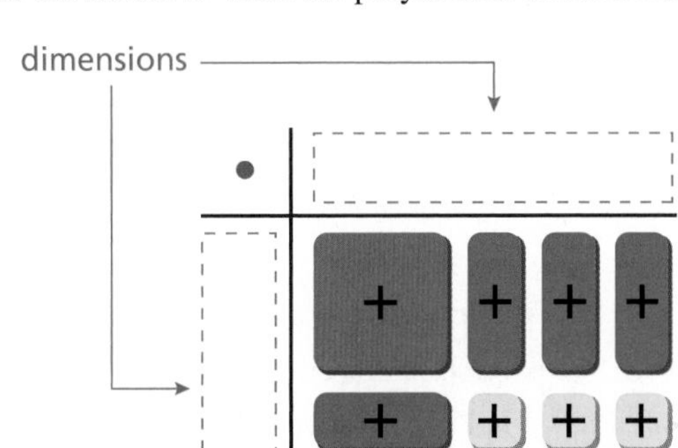

Math Practice

Look for Structure

When writing $x^2 + bx + c$ as $(x + p)(x + q)$, how do the values of b and c relate to the values of p and q?

c. Use algebra tiles to write each polynomial in factored form. Check your answers by multiplying.

i. $x^2 - 3x + 2 =$

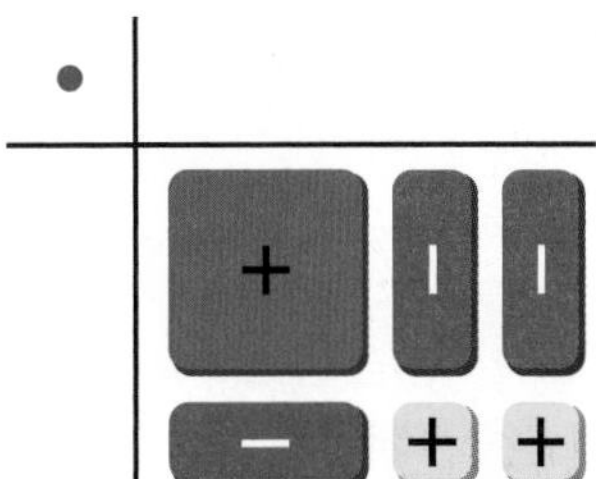

ii. $x^2 + 5x + 4 =$

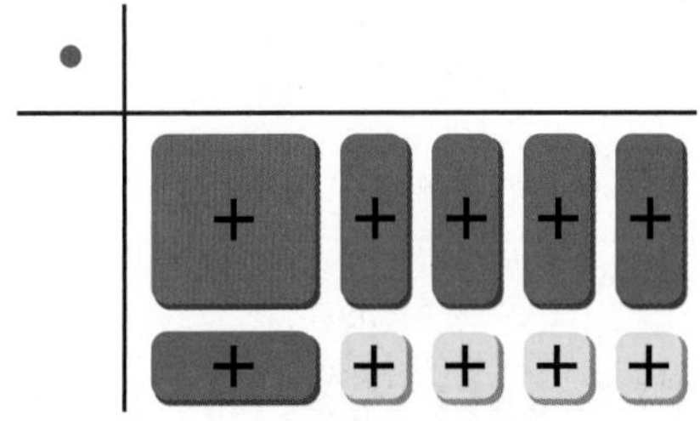

iii. $x^2 - 7x + 12 =$

iv. $x^2 + 7x + 12 =$

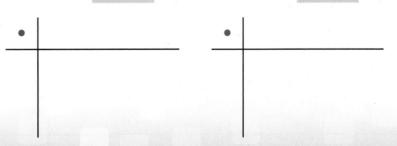

Factoring $x^2 + bx + c$

Writing a polynomial as a product of factors is called *factoring*. To factor $x^2 + bx + c$ as $(x + p)(x + q)$, you need to find p and q such that $p + q = b$ and $pq = c$.

$$(x + p)(x + q) = x^2 + px + qx + pq$$
$$= x^2 + (p + q)x + pq$$

KEY IDEA

Factoring $x^2 + bx + c$ When c Is Positive

Algebra $x^2 + bx + c = (x + p)(x + q)$ when $p + q = b$ and $pq = c$.
When c is positive, p and q have the same sign as b.

Examples $x^2 + 6x + 5 = (x + 1)(x + 5)$
$x^2 - 6x + 5 = (x - 1)(x - 5)$

EXAMPLE 1 Factoring $x^2 + bx + c$ When b and c Are Positive

Factor $x^2 + 10x + 16$.

SOLUTION

Notice that $b = 10$ and $c = 16$.

- Because c is positive, the factors p and q must have the same sign so that pq is positive.
- Because b is also positive, p and q must each be positive so that $p + q$ is positive.

Find two positive integer factors of 16 whose sum is 10.

Factors of	Sum of factors
1, 16	17
2, 8	10
4, 4	8

The values of p and q are 2 and 8.

▶ So, $x^2 + 10x + 16 = (x + 2)(x + 8)$.

Check Use the FOIL Method.
$(x + 2)(x + 8) = x^2 + 8x + 2x + 16$
$= x^2 + 10x + 16$ ✓

SELF-ASSESSMENT 1 I do not understand. 2 I can do it with help. 3 I can do it on my own. 4 I can teach someone else.

Factor the polynomial.

1. $x^2 + 7x + 6$ **2.** $x^2 + 9x + 8$ **3.** $x^2 + 12x + 27$

4. OPEN-ENDED Write a trinomial that can be factored as $(x + p)(x + q)$, where p and q are positive.

5. MP REASONING Can $x^2 + 9x + 1$ be written in the form $(x + p)(x + q)$, where p and q are integers? Explain your reasoning.

EXAMPLE 2 Factoring $x^2 + bx + c$ When b Is Negative and c Is Positive

Factor $x^2 - 8x + 12$.

SOLUTION

Notice that $b = -8$ and $c = 12$.

- Because c is positive, the factors p and q must have the same sign so that pq is positive.
- Because b is negative, p and q must each be negative so that $p + q$ is negative.

Find two negative integer factors of 12 whose sum is -8.

Factors of 12	$-1, -12$	$-2, -6$	$-3, -4$
Sum of factors	-13	-8	-7

The values of p and q are -2 and -6.

▶ So, $x^2 - 8x + 12 = (x - 2)(x - 6)$.

Check

Use the FOIL Method.

$(x - 2)(x - 6)$

$= x^2 - 6x - 2x + 12$

$= x^2 - 8x + 12$ ✓

KEY IDEA

Factoring $x^2 + bx + c$ When c Is Negative

Algebra $x^2 + bx + c = (x + p)(x + q)$ when $p + q = b$ and $pq = c$.

When c is negative, p and q have different signs.

Example $x^2 - 4x - 5 = (x + 1)(x - 5)$

EXAMPLE 3 Factoring $x^2 + bx + c$ When c Is Negative

Factor $x^2 + 4x - 21$.

SOLUTION

Notice that $b = 4$ and $c = -21$. Because c is negative, the factors p and q must have different signs so that pq is negative.

Find two integer factors of -21 whose sum is 4.

Factors of −21	$-21, 1$	$-1, 21$	$-7, 3$	$-3, 7$
Sum of factors	-20	20	-4	4

The values of p and q are -3 and 7.

▶ So, $x^2 + 4x - 21 = (x - 3)(x + 7)$.

Check

Use the FOIL Method.

$(x - 3)(x + 7)$

$= x^2 + 7x - 3x - 21$

$= x^2 + 4x - 21$ ✓

SELF-ASSESSMENT

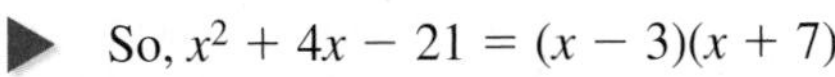

1 I do not understand. 2 I can do it with help. 3 I can do it on my own. 4 I can teach someone else.

Factor the polynomial.

6. $w^2 - 4w + 3$ **7.** $n^2 - 12n + 35$ **8.** $x^2 - 14x + 24$

9. $x^2 + 2x - 15$ **10.** $y^2 + 13y - 30$ **11.** $v^2 - v - 42$

12. WRITING You are factoring $x^2 + 11x - 26$. What do the signs of the terms tell you about the factors? Explain.

GO DIGITAL

CONCEPT SUMMARY

Factoring $x^2 + bx + c$ as $(x + p)(x + q)$

The diagram shows the relationships between the signs of b and c and the signs of p and q.

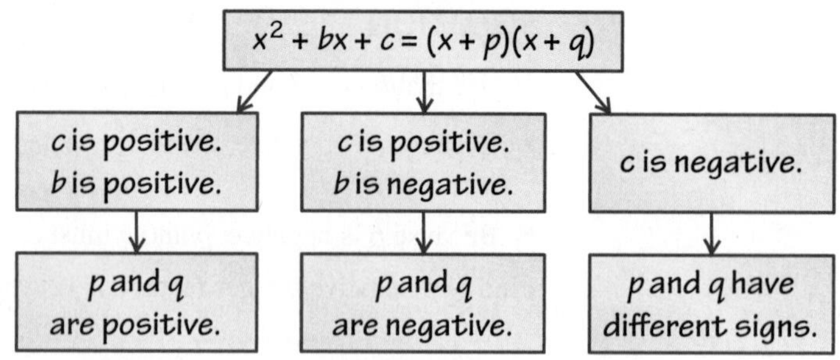

x² + bx + c = (x + p)(x + q)
c is positive. b is positive.
c is positive. b is negative.
c is negative.
p and q are positive.
p and q are negative.
p and q have different signs.

Solving Real-Life Problems

EXAMPLE 4 **Modeling Real Life** 
WATCH

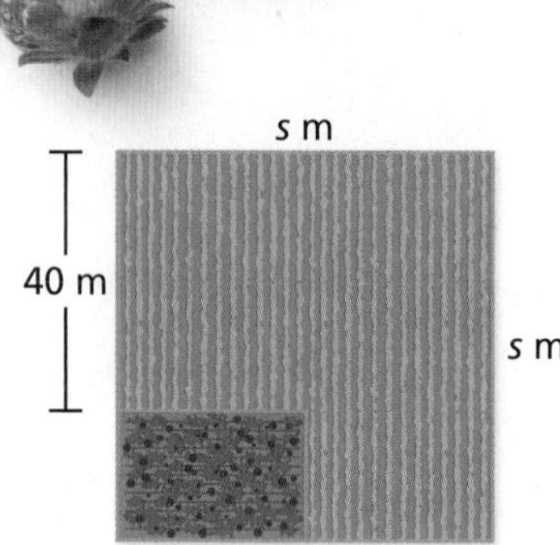

s m
40 m
s m

30 m

A farmer plants a rectangular strawberry patch in a corner of a square plot of land. The area of the strawberry patch is 600 square meters. What is the area of the square plot of land?

SOLUTION

1. **Understand the Problem** You are given the area of a strawberry patch and a diagram showing dimensions of a plot of land that contains the strawberry patch. You are asked to find the total area of the plot of land.
2. **Make a Plan** The length of the strawberry patch is $(s - 30)$ meters and the width is $(s - 40)$ meters. Write and solve an equation to find the side length s. Then use the solution to find the area of the square plot of land.
3. **Solve and Check** Use the formula for the area of a rectangle to write an equation. Then solve to find the side length s of the square plot of land.

$600 = (s - 30)(s - 40)$	Write an equation.
$600 = s^2 - 70s + 1200$	Multiply.
$0 = s^2 - 70s + 600$	Subtract 600 from each side.
$0 = (s - 10)(s - 60)$	Factor the polynomial.
$s - 10 = 0$ *or* $s - 60 = 0$	Zero-Product Property
$s = 10$ *or* $s = 60$	Solve for s.

STUDY TIP
The diagram shows that the side length is more than 40 meters, so a side length of 10 meters does not make sense in this situation. So, the side length must be 60 meters.

▶ So, the area of the square plot of land is 60(60) = 3600 square meters.

Check Use the diagram to check your answer. Using $s = 60$, the length of the strawberry patch is $60 - 30 = 30$ meters and the width is $60 - 40 = 20$ meters. So, the area of the strawberry patch is

$30(20) = 600$ square meters. ✓

SELF-ASSESSMENT 1 I do not understand. 2 I can do it with help. 3 I can do it on my own. 4 I can teach someone else.

13. **WHAT IF?** The area of the strawberry patch is 200 square meters. What is the area of the square plot of land?

7.5 Practice WITH CalcChat® AND CalcView®

In Exercises 1–6, factor the polynomial. *Example 1*

1. $x^2 + 8x + 7$
2. $z^2 + 10z + 21$
3. $n^2 + 9n + 20$
4. $s^2 + 11s + 30$
5. $h^2 + 11h + 18$
6. $y^2 + 13y + 40$

In Exercises 7–12, factor the polynomial. *Example 2*

7. $v^2 - 5v + 4$
8. $x^2 - 13x + 22$
9. $d^2 - 5d + 6$
10. $k^2 - 10k + 24$
11. $w^2 - 17w + 72$
12. $j^2 - 13j + 42$

In Exercises 13–22, factor the polynomial. *Example 3*

13. $x^2 + 3x - 4$
14. $z^2 + 7z - 18$
15. $n^2 + 4n - 12$
16. $s^2 + 3s - 40$
17. $y^2 + 2y - 48$
18. $h^2 + 6h - 27$
19. $x^2 - x - 20$
20. $m^2 - 6m - 7$
21. $-6t - 16 + t^2$
22. $-7y + y^2 - 30$

ERROR ANALYSIS In Exercises 23 and 24, describe and correct the error in factoring the polynomial.

23.

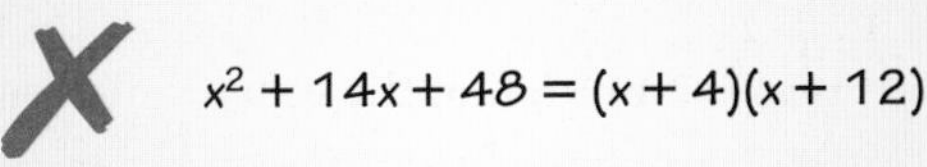

24.
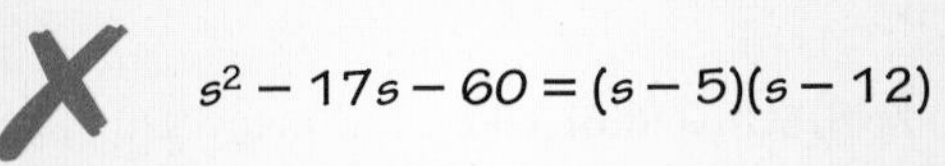

25. **MODELING REAL LIFE** A projector displays an image on a wall. The area (in square feet) of the projection is represented by $x^2 - 8x + 15$.

 a. Write a binomial that represents the height of the projection.

 b. Find the perimeter of the projection when the height of the wall is 8 feet.

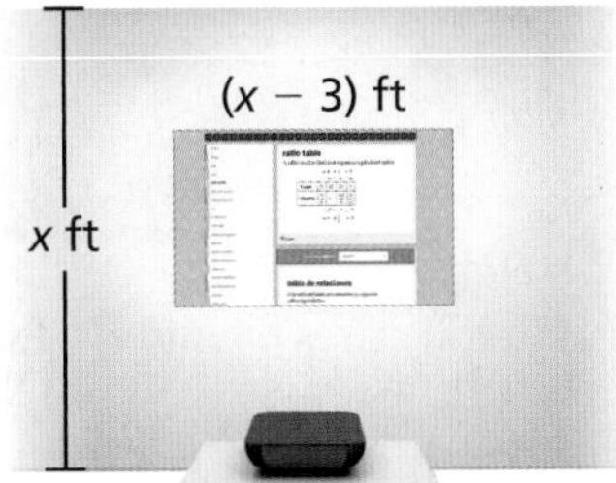

26. **MODELING REAL LIFE** A dentist's office and parking lot are on a rectangular piece of land. The area (in square meters) of the land is represented by $x^2 + x - 30$.

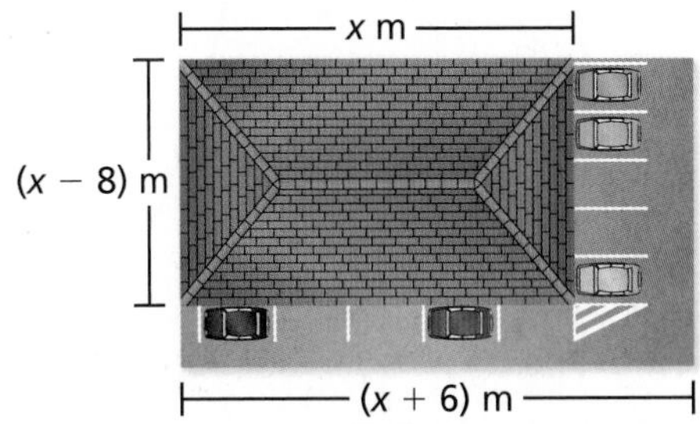

 a. Write a binomial that represents the width of the land.

 b. Find the perimeter of the land when the length of the dentist's office is 20 meters.

In Exercises 27–36, solve the equation.

27. $m^2 + 3m + 2 = 0$
28. $n^2 - 9n + 18 = 0$
29. $v^2 + 25v - 26 = 0$
30. $x^2 + 5x - 14 = 0$
31. $n^2 - 5n = 24$
32. $t^2 + 15t = -36$
33. $a^2 + 5a - 20 = 30$
34. $y^2 - 2y - 8 = 7$
35. $m^2 + 10 = 15m - 34$
36. $b^2 + 5 = 8b - 10$

37. **MODELING REAL LIFE** You trim a large square picture so that it fits into a frame. The area of the cut picture is 20 square inches. What is the area of the original picture? *Example 4*

38. **MODELING REAL LIFE** An architect creates a drawing of an apartment with an area (including the balcony) of 768 square feet. What is the area of the balcony?

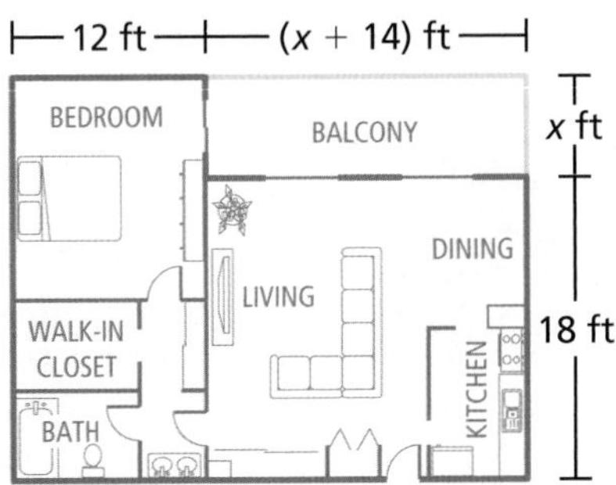

39. **CONNECTING CONCEPTS** The area of the triangle is 35 square meters. Find the dimensions of the triangle.

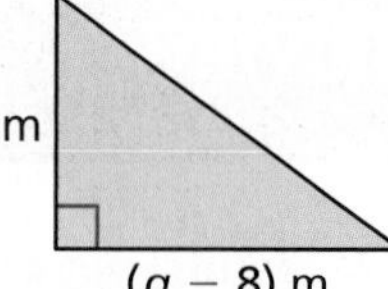

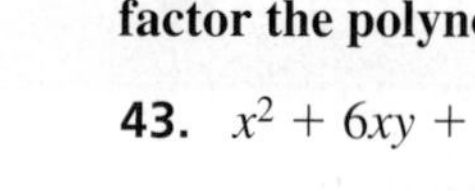

40. **HOW DO YOU SEE IT?** The graph of $y = x^2 + x - 6$ is shown.

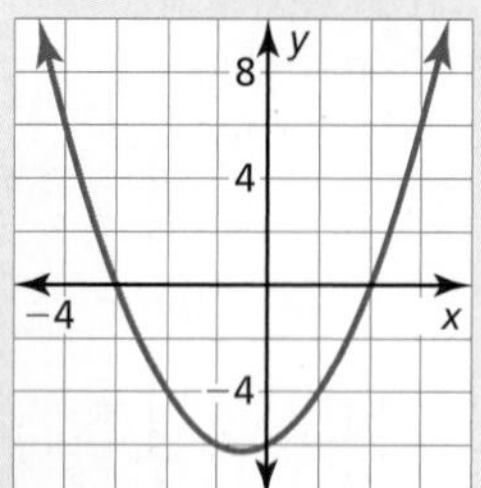

a. Explain how you can use the graph to factor the polynomial $x^2 + x - 6$.

b. Factor the polynomial.

41. **MAKING AN ARGUMENT** Your friend says there are six integer values of b for which the trinomial $x^2 + bx - 12$ has two binomial factors of the form $(x + p)$ and $(x + q)$, where p and q are integers. Is your friend correct? Explain.

42. **MP REASONING** Write an equation of the form $x^2 + bx + c = 0$ that has the solutions $x = -4$ and $x = 6$. Explain how you found your answer.

MP STRUCTURE In Exercises 43–46, factor the polynomial.

43. $x^2 + 6xy + 8y^2$

44. $r^2 + 14rs + 45s^2$

45. $a^2 + 11ab - 60b^2$

46. $x^2 - 2xy - 35y^2$

47. **MP PROBLEM SOLVING** Road construction workers are paving the area shown. The area being paved is 280 square meters. Find the width x of the road.

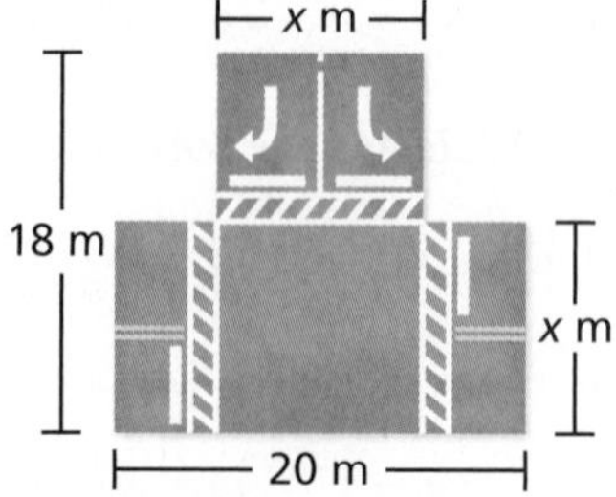

48. **THOUGHT PROVOKING** Write a polynomial of the form $x^2 + bx + c$ where $b = c$ that can be written as $(x + p)(x + q)$, where p and q are nonzero integers. Then write the polynomial in factored form.

49. **DIG DEEPER** Factor $(7n + 5)^2 - 21(7n + 5) - 100$.

REVIEW & REFRESH

In Exercises 50–53, solve the equation.

50. $p - 9 = 0$

51. $z + 12 = -5$

52. $6 = \frac{c}{-7}$

53. $4k = 0$

In Exercises 54 and 55, find the product.

54. $-6x^2(3x^3 + 7x - 1)$

55. $(5w + 4x)(5w - 4x)$

MP STRUCTURE In Exercises 56 and 57, find the value of k so that the graph of the equation has the given slope m or y-intercept b.

56. $5y = 10kx - 20;\ m = -\frac{2}{3}$

57. $y + \frac{1}{2}k = -4x;\ b = -7$

58. Write a recursive rule for the sequence.

n	1	2	3	4
a_n	85	60	35	10

In Exercises 59 and 60, solve the equation.

59. $(5p + 6)(2 - p) = 0$

60. $18x^2 - 12x = 0$

In Exercises 61 and 62, solve the inequality. Graph the solution.

61. $\frac{m}{3.5} > -2$

62. $t - 4 \geq 12t - 37$

In Exercises 63 and 64, find the sum or difference.

63. $(-p^2 + 4p) - (p^2 - 3p + 15)$

64. $(a^2 - 3ab + b^2) + (-a^2 + ab + b^2)$

65. **MODELING REAL LIFE** How many \$20 bills can you withdraw from the account without going below the minimum balance?

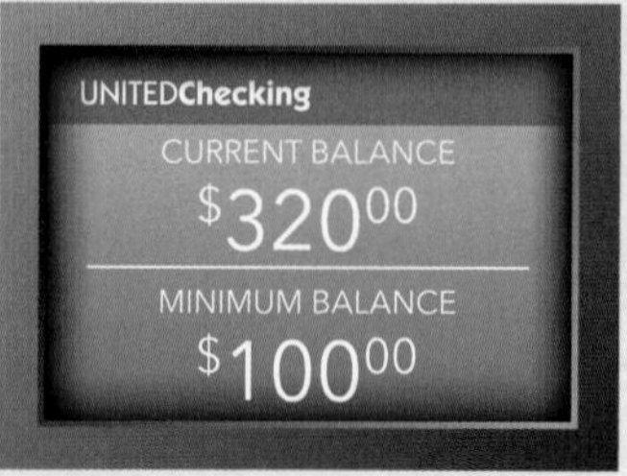

In Exercises 66 and 67, factor the polynomial.

66. $d^2 + 16d + 28$

67. $x^2 - 5x - 36$

7.6 Factoring $ax^2 + bx + c$

Learning Target Factor polynomials of the form $ax^2 + bx + c$.

Success Criteria

- I can factor a polynomial using the GCF of the terms of the polynomial.
- I can factor polynomials of the form $ax^2 + bx + c$.
- I can explain how to use a, b, and c to find binomial factors of a polynomial $ax^2 + bx + c$.

EXPLORE IT! Finding Binomial Factors

Work with a partner. You can use rectangular arrays of algebra tiles to factor polynomials that do not have a leading coefficient of 1.

a. Write the polynomial represented by the algebra tiles below. Then use the model to write the polynomial in factored form.

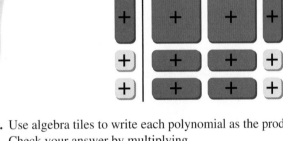

b. Use algebra tiles to write each polynomial as the product of two binomials. Check your answer by multiplying.

i. $3x^2 + 5x + 2 =$ ______

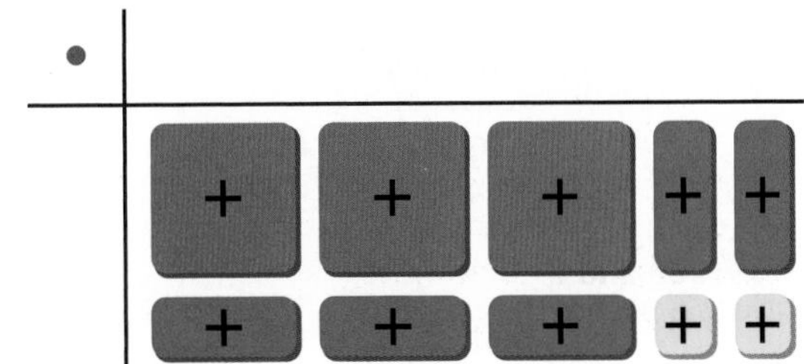

ii. $4x^2 + 4x - 3 =$ ______

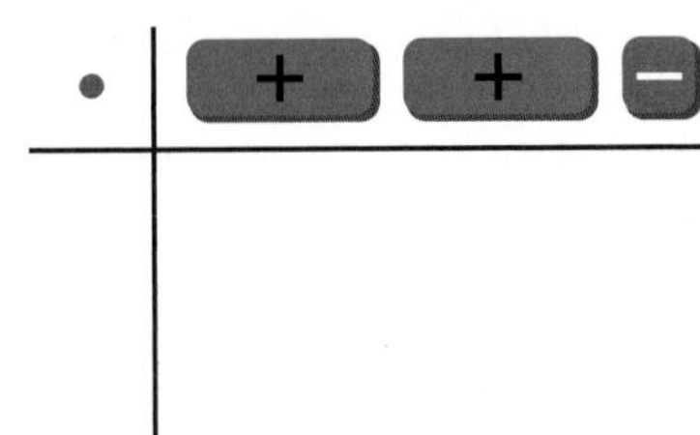

iii. $2x^2 - 11x + 5 =$ ______

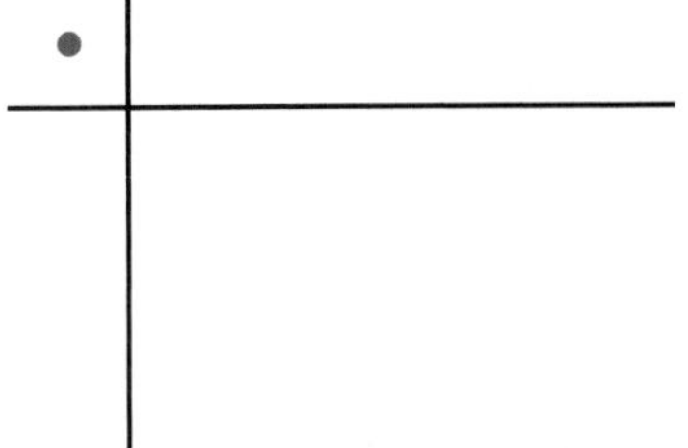

c. Describe a strategy for factoring the trinomial $ax^2 + bx + c$ that does not use algebra tiles.

Math Practice

Recognize Usefulness of Tools

Why might using algebra tiles be an inefficient way to factor polynomials involving greater numbers, such as $2x^2 + 47x + 23$?

Factoring $ax^2 + bx + c$

In the previous section, you factored polynomials of the form $ax^2 + bx + c$, where $a = 1$. To factor polynomials of the form $ax^2 + bx + c$, where $a \neq 1$, first look for the GCF of the terms of the polynomial and then factor further, if possible. When there is no GCF, consider the possible factors of a and c.

EXAMPLE 1 Factoring Out the GCF

Factor $5x^2 + 15x + 10$.

SOLUTION

Notice that the GCF of the terms $5x^2$, $15x$, and 10 is 5.

$5x^2 + 15x + 10 = 5(x^2 + 3x + 2)$ Factor out GCF.

$= 5(x + 1)(x + 2)$ Factor $x^2 + 3x + 2$.

▶ So, $5x^2 + 15x + 10 = 5(x + 1)(x + 2)$.

SELF-ASSESSMENT 1 I do not understand. 2 I can do it with help. 3 I can do it on my own. 4 I can teach someone else.

Factor the polynomial.

1. $2x^2 + 14x + 12$
2. $8x^2 - 56x + 48$
3. $3x^2 - 6x - 24$

EXAMPLE 2 Factoring $ax^2 + bx + c$ When a and c Are Positive

Factor each polynomial.

a. $4x^2 + 13x + 3$ **b.** $3x^2 - 7x + 2$

SOLUTION

a. There is no GCF, so you need to consider the possible factors of a and c. Because b and c are both positive, the factors of c must be positive. Use a table to organize information about the factors of a and c.

STUDY TIP

You must consider the order of the factors of 3, because the middle terms formed by the possible factorizations are different.

Factors of 4	Factors of 3	Possible factorization	Middle term	
1, 4	1, 3	$(x + 1)(4x + 3)$	$3x + 4x = 7x$	✗
1, 4	3, 1	$(x + 3)(4x + 1)$	$x + 12x = 13x$	✓
2, 2	1, 3	$(2x + 1)(2x + 3)$	$6x + 2x = 8x$	✗

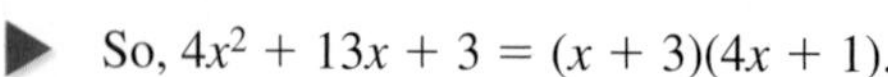

▶ So, $4x^2 + 13x + 3 = (x + 3)(4x + 1)$.

b. There is no GCF, so you need to consider the possible factors of a and c. Because b is negative and c is positive, both factors of c must be negative. Use a table to organize information about the factors of a and c.

Factors of 3	Factors of 2	Possible factorization	Middle term	
1, 3	$-1, -2$	$(x - 1)(3x - 2)$	$-2x - 3x = -5x$	✗
1, 3	$-2, -1$	$(x - 2)(3x - 1)$	$-x - 6x = -7x$	✓

▶ So, $3x^2 - 7x + 2 = (x - 2)(3x - 1)$.

EXAMPLE 3 Factoring $ax^2 + bx + c$ When a Is Positive and c Is Negative

Factor $2x^2 - 5x - 7$.

SOLUTION

There is no GCF, so you need to consider the possible factors of a and c. Because c is negative, the factors of c must have different signs. Use a table to organize information about the factors of a and c.

Factors of 2	Factors of −7	Possible factorization	Middle term	
1, 2	1, −7	$(x + 1)(2x - 7)$	$-7x + 2x = -5x$	✓
1, 2	7, −1	$(x + 7)(2x - 1)$	$-x + 14x = 13x$	✗
1, 2	−1, 7	$(x - 1)(2x + 7)$	$7x - 2x = 5x$	✗
1, 2	−7, 1	$(x - 7)(2x + 1)$	$x - 14x = -13x$	✗

▶ So, $2x^2 - 5x - 7 = (x + 1)(2x - 7)$.

EXAMPLE 4 Factoring $ax^2 + bx + c$ When a Is Negative

STUDY TIP

When a is negative, factor -1 from each term of $ax^2 + bx + c$. Then factor the resulting trinomial as in the previous examples.

Factor $-4x^2 - 8x + 5$.

SOLUTION

Step 1 Factor -1 from each term of the trinomial.

$$-4x^2 - 8x + 5 = -(4x^2 + 8x - 5)$$

Step 2 Factor the trinomial $4x^2 + 8x - 5$. Because c is negative, the factors of c must have different signs. Use a table to organize information about the factors of a and c.

Factors of 4	Factors of −5	Possible factorization	Middle term	
1, 4	1, −5	$(x + 1)(4x - 5)$	$-5x + 4x = -x$	✗
1, 4	5, −1	$(x + 5)(4x - 1)$	$-x + 20x = 19x$	✗
1, 4	−1, 5	$(x - 1)(4x + 5)$	$5x - 4x = x$	✗
1, 4	−5, 1	$(x - 5)(4x + 1)$	$x - 20x = -19x$	✗
2, 2	1, −5	$(2x + 1)(2x - 5)$	$-10x + 2x = -8x$	✗
2, 2	−1, 5	$(2x - 1)(2x + 5)$	$10x - 2x = 8x$	✓

▶ So, $-4x^2 - 8x + 5 = -(2x - 1)(2x + 5)$.

SELF-ASSESSMENT

1 I do not understand. 2 I can do it with help. 3 I can do it on my own. 4 I can teach someone else.

Factor the polynomial.

4. $2x^2 - 7x + 5$

5. $3x^2 - 14x + 8$

6. $4x^2 - 19x - 5$

7. $6x^2 + x - 12$

8. $-5m^2 + 6m - 1$

9. $-3x^2 - x + 2$

10. WRITING Compare factoring $6x^2 - x - 2$ with factoring $x^2 - x - 2$.

Solving Real-Life Problems

EXAMPLE 5 **Modeling Real Life**

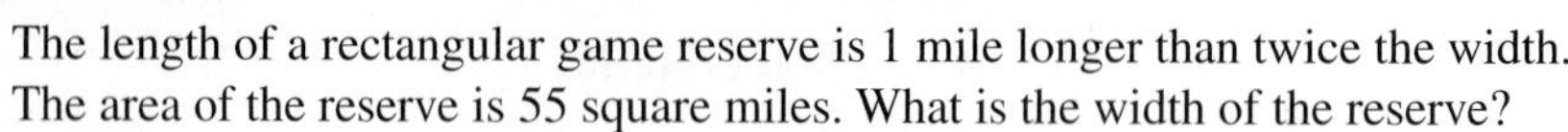

The length of a rectangular game reserve is 1 mile longer than twice the width. The area of the reserve is 55 square miles. What is the width of the reserve?

Pangolin are the only known mammal to be completely covered in scales. Eight species of pangolin are classified as threatened with extinction.

SOLUTION

Use the formula for the area of a rectangle to write an equation for the area of the reserve. Let w represent the width. Then $2w + 1$ represents the length. Solve for w.

$A = \ell w$	Area of a rectangle
$55 = (2w + 1)w$	Substitute 55 for A and $2w + 1$ for ℓ.
$55 = 2w^2 + w$	Distributive Property
$0 = 2w^2 + w - 55$	Subtract 55 from each side.

Factor the right side of the equation. There is no GCF, so you need to consider the possible factors of a and c. Because c is negative, the factors of c must have different signs. Use a table to organize information about the factors of a and c.

Factors of 2	Factors of −55	Possible factorization	Middle term	
1, 2	1, −55	$(w + 1)(2w - 55)$	$-55w + 2w = -53w$	✗
1, 2	55, −1	$(w + 55)(2w - 1)$	$-w + 110w = 109w$	✗
1, 2	−1, 55	$(w - 1)(2w + 55)$	$55w - 2w = 53w$	✗
1, 2	−55, 1	$(w - 55)(2w + 1)$	$w - 110w = -109w$	✗
1, 2	5, −11	$(w + 5)(2w - 11)$	$-11w + 10w = -w$	✗
1, 2	11, −5	$(w + 11)(2w - 5)$	$-5w + 22w = 17w$	✗
1, 2	−5, 11	$(w - 5)(2w + 11)$	$11w - 10w = w$	✓
1, 2	−11, 5	$(w - 11)(2w + 5)$	$5w - 22w = -17w$	✗

So, you can rewrite $2w^2 + w - 55$ as $(w - 5)(2w + 11)$. Continue solving for w.

$(w - 5)(2w + 11) = 0$	Rewrite equation.
$w - 5 = 0$ *or* $2w + 11 = 0$	Zero-Product Property
$w = 5$ *or* $w = -\frac{11}{2}$	Solve for w.

Because a negative width does not make sense, use the positive solution.

▶ So, the width of the reserve is 5 miles.

Check

Use mental math.

The width is 5 miles, so the length is $5(2) + 1 = 11$ miles and the area is $5(11) = 55$ square miles. ✓

SELF-ASSESSMENT

1 I do not understand. 2 I can do it with help. 3 I can do it on my own. 4 I can teach someone else.

11. WHAT IF? In Example 5, the area of the reserve is 136 square miles. How wide is the reserve?

12. A rectangular swimming pool is bordered by a concrete patio. The width of the patio is the same on each side. The area of the surface of the pool is equal to the area of the patio. What is the width of the patio?

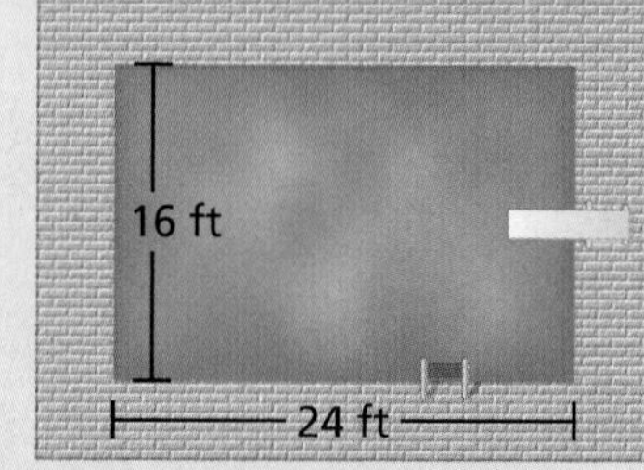

7.6 Practice WITH CalcChat® AND CalcView®

In Exercises 1–6, factor the polynomial. *Example 1*

1. $3x^2 + 3x - 6$
2. $8v^2 + 8v - 48$
3. $4k^2 + 28k + 48$
4. $6y^2 - 24y + 18$
5. $7b^2 - 63b + 140$
6. $9r^2 - 36r - 45$

In Exercises 7–14, factor the polynomial. *Examples 2 and 3*

7. $3h^2 + 11h + 6$
8. $8m^2 + 30m + 7$
9. $6x^2 - 5x + 1$
10. $10w^2 - 31w + 15$
11. $3n^2 + 5n - 2$
12. $4z^2 + 4z - 3$
13. $8g^2 - 10g - 12$
14. $18v^2 - 15v - 18$

In Exercises 15–20, factor the polynomial. *Example 4*

15. $-3t^2 + 11t - 6$
16. $-7v^2 - 25v - 12$
17. $-4c^2 + 19c + 5$
18. $-8h^2 - 13h + 6$
19. $-15w^2 - w + 28$
20. $-22d^2 + 29d - 9$

ERROR ANALYSIS In Exercises 21 and 22, describe and correct the error in factoring the polynomial.

21. 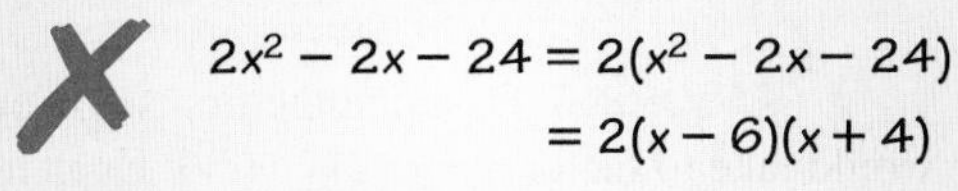

22. 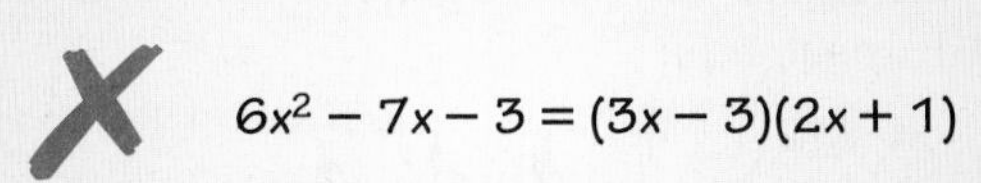

23. **MODELING REAL LIFE** The area (in square feet) of the school sign can be represented by $15x^2 - x - 2$.
    a. Write an expression that represents the length of the sign.
    b. Describe two ways to find the area of the sign when $x = 3$.

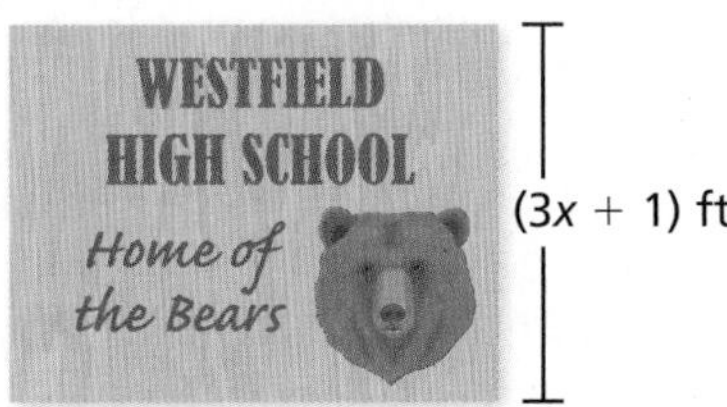

24. **MODELING REAL LIFE** The height h (in feet) above the water of a cliff diver is modeled by $h = -16t^2 + 8t + 80$, where t is the time (in seconds). What does the constant term represent? How long is the diver in the air?

In Exercises 25–28, solve the equation.

25. $5x^2 - 5x - 30 = 0$
26. $2k^2 - 5k - 18 = 0$
27. $-12n^2 - 11n = -15$
28. $14b^2 - 2 = -3b$

In Exercises 29 and 30, find the x-intercepts of the graph.

29. 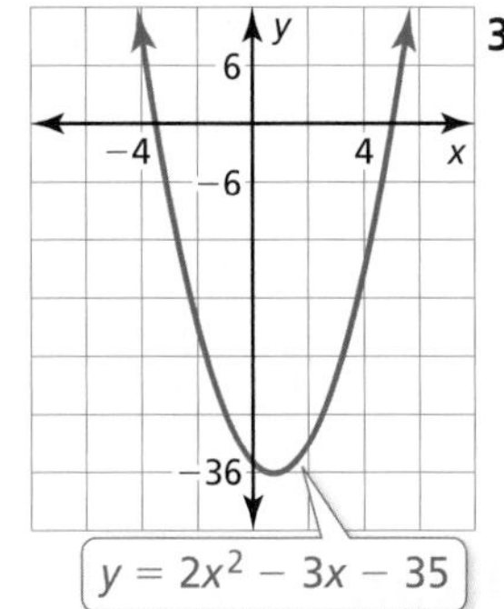

30. 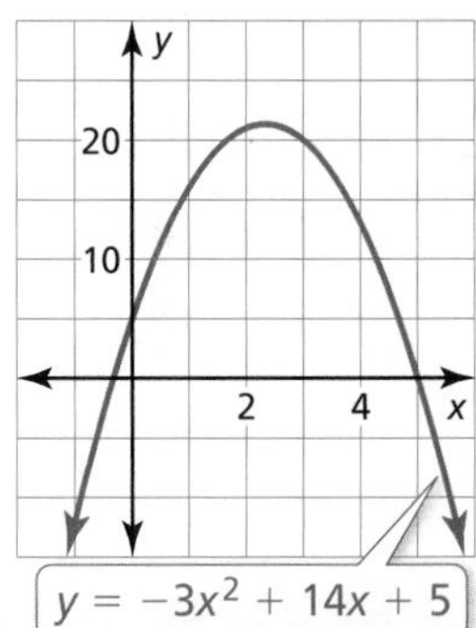

31. **MODELING REAL LIFE** The Parthenon in Athens, Greece, is an ancient structure that has a rectangular base. The length of the base of the Parthenon is 8 meters more than twice its width. The area of the base is about 2170 square meters. Find the length and width of the base. *Example 5*

32. **MODELING REAL LIFE** The length of a rectangular birthday party invitation is 1 inch less than twice its width. The area of the invitation is 15 square inches. Will the invitation fit in the envelope shown without being folded? Explain.

$3\frac{5}{8}$ in.

$5\frac{1}{8}$ in.

33. **MP REASONING** When is it not possible to factor $ax^2 + bx + c$, where $a \neq 1$? Give an example.

34. **MAKING AN ARGUMENT** Your friend begins to solve the equation $5x^2 + x - 4 = 2$ by factoring the left side as $(5x - 4)(x + 1)$. Is your friend correct? Explain.

35. **MP REASONING** For what values of t can $2x^2 + tx + 10$ be written as the product of two binomials with integer coefficients and constants?

36. **HOW DO YOU SEE IT?**
Without factoring, determine which of the graphs represents the function $g(x) = 21x^2 + 37x + 12$ and which represents the function $h(x) = 21x^2 - 37x + 12$. Explain.

37. **MP LOGIC** The length of a rectangle is 1 inch more than twice its width. The value of the area of the rectangle (in square inches) is 5 more than the value of the perimeter (in inches). Find the width.

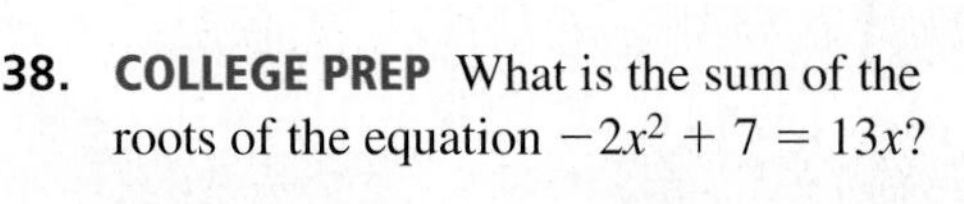

38. **COLLEGE PREP** What is the sum of the roots of the equation $-2x^2 + 7 = 13x$?

Ⓐ $-\frac{13}{2}$ Ⓑ $-\frac{5}{2}$

Ⓒ $\frac{5}{2}$ Ⓓ $\frac{13}{2}$

39. **DIG DEEPER** Find the quotient.

$$\frac{-4x^3 - 8x^2 + 60x}{2x^2 - 6x}$$

40. **THOUGHT PROVOKING**
Rewrite the expression below as the product of three factors. None of the factors should be monomials or have a leading coefficient greater than 2. What do you notice about the factors for any value of k? Explain.

$$(4k^3 + 6k^2 + 2k)(2k^2 + 2k + 1)$$

MP STRUCTURE In Exercises 41–44, factor the polynomial.

41. $4k^2 + 7jk - 2j^2$
42. $6x^2 + 5xy - 4y^2$
43. $-6a^2 + 19ab - 14b^2$
44. $18m^3 + 39m^2n - 15mn^2$

REVIEW & REFRESH

WATCH

In Exercises 45–48, find the square root(s).

45. $\pm\sqrt{64}$
46. $\sqrt{4}$
47. $-\sqrt{225}$
48. $\pm\sqrt{\frac{9}{49}}$

In Exercises 49 and 50, solve the system using any method. Explain your choice of method.

49. $y = 3 + 7x$
$y - x = -3$

50. $2x - y = 2$
$-x + 3y = 14$

51. Write an equation of the line that passes through $(-5, 6)$ and is parallel to $y = -3x + 8$.

52. **MODELING REAL LIFE** The table shows the total numbers of visitors to a website t days after it is online.

t	42	43	44	45
Visitors	11,000	12,100	13,310	14,641

a. Determine whether the table represents an *exponential growth function*, an *exponential decay function*, or *neither*.

b. How many people will have visited the website after it is online 47 days?

In Exercises 53–56, solve the equation.

53. $-3n(n - 2) = 0$
54. $(p + 7)(p - 3) = 0$
55. $(q + 6)^2 = 0$
56. $9r^2 = 108r$

57. **MP REASONING** Describe the first step you would take to factor $3y^2 - 21y + 36$. Explain.

58. Determine whether the graph represents a function. Explain.

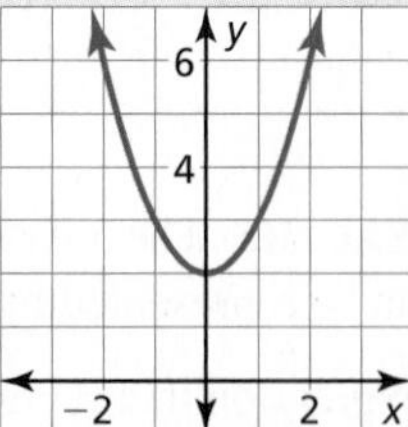

In Exercises 59–62, factor the polynomial.

59. $z^2 + 11z + 28$
60. $v^2 + 3v - 54$
61. $14x^2 + 31x + 15$
62. $-2y^2 - 5y - 3$

63. Solve $12 - t \geq -20$. Graph the solution.

64. Find the product $(2x + 3)(2x - 3)$.

7.7 Factoring Special Products

Learning Target Recognize and factor special products.

Success Criteria

- I can factor the difference of two squares.
- I can factor perfect square trinomials.
- I can solve real-life problems by factoring using special product patterns.

EXPLORE IT! Factoring Special Products

Work with a partner.

a. Use algebra tiles to write each polynomial as the product of two binomials. Check your answer by multiplying. Explain how each polynomial relates to a special product pattern.

i. $4x^2 - 4x + 1 =$ ______ **ii.** $4x^2 - 1 =$ ______

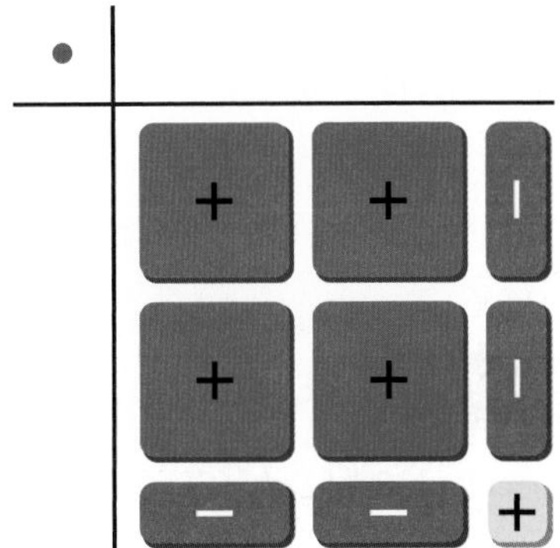

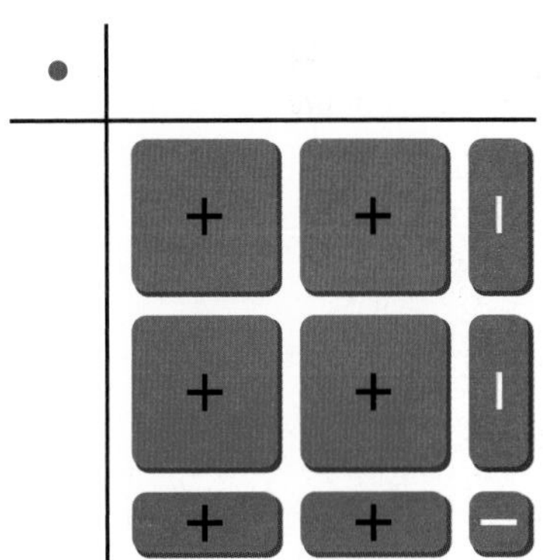

iii. $4x^2 + 4x + 1 =$ ______ **iv.** $4x^2 - 6x + 2 =$ ______

b. Use algebra tiles to complete the rectangular array below in three different ways. Each way should represent a different special product. Then write each special product in standard form and in factored form.

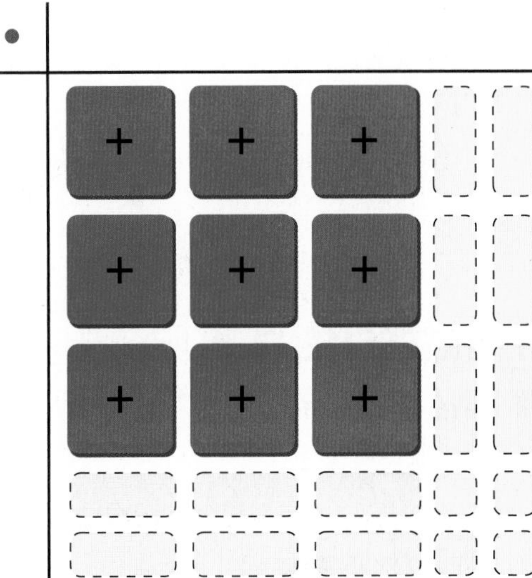

Math Practice

Repeat Calculations
Use algebra tiles to model other polynomials of the form $a^2 - b^2$. Do you notice a pattern in the factored form?

c. Describe a method for recognizing which polynomials can be factored using special products.

Factoring the Difference of Two Squares

You can use special product patterns to factor polynomials.

KEY IDEA

Difference of Two Squares Pattern

Algebra	**Example**
$a^2 - b^2 = (a + b)(a - b)$	$x^2 - 9 = x^2 - 3^2 = (x + 3)(x - 3)$

EXAMPLE 1 Factoring the Difference of Two Squares

Factor (a) $x^2 - 25$ and (b) $4z^2 - 1$.

SOLUTION

a. $x^2 - 25 = x^2 - 5^2$ — Write as $a^2 - b^2$.

$= (x + 5)(x - 5)$ — Difference of two squares pattern

▶ So, $x^2 - 25 = (x + 5)(x - 5)$.

b. $4z^2 - 1 = (2z)^2 - 1^2$ — Write as $a^2 - b^2$.

$= (2z + 1)(2z - 1)$ — Difference of two squares pattern

▶ So, $4z^2 - 1 = (2z + 1)(2z - 1)$.

EXAMPLE 2 Evaluating a Numerical Expression

Use a special product pattern to evaluate the expression $54^2 - 48^2$.

SOLUTION

Notice that $54^2 - 48^2$ is a difference of two squares. So, you can rewrite the expression in a form that it is easier to evaluate using the difference of two squares pattern.

$54^2 - 48^2 = (54 + 48)(54 - 48)$ — Difference of two squares pattern

$= 102(6)$ — Simplify.

$= 612$ — Multiply.

▶ So, $54^2 - 48^2 = 612$.

SELF-ASSESSMENT

1 I do not understand. 2 I can do it with help. 3 I can do it on my own. 4 I can teach someone else.

Factor the polynomial.

1. $x^2 - 36$ **2.** $100 - m^2$ **3.** $9n^2 - 16$

4. MP **REASONING** Can you use the difference of two squares pattern to factor $100x^2 - 49y^3$? Explain your reasoning.

Use a special product pattern to evaluate the expression.

5. $36^2 - 34^2$ **6.** $55^2 - 50^2$ **7.** $28^2 - 24^2$

Factoring Perfect Square Trinomials

KEY IDEA

Perfect Square Trinomial Pattern

Algebra	Example
$a^2 + 2ab + b^2 = (a + b)^2$	$x^2 + 6x + 9 = x^2 + 2(x)(3) + 3^2 = (x + 3)^2$
$a^2 - 2ab + b^2 = (a - b)^2$	$x^2 - 6x + 9 = x^2 - 2(x)(3) + 3^2 = (x - 3)^2$

EXAMPLE 3 Factoring Perfect Square Trinomials

Factor (a) $n^2 + 8n + 16$ and (b) $4x^2 - 12x + 9$.

SOLUTION

a. $n^2 + 8n + 16 = n^2 + 2(n)(4) + 4^2$ — Write as $a^2 + 2ab + b^2$.

$= (n + 4)^2$ — Perfect square trinomial pattern

▶ So, $n^2 + 8n + 16 = (n + 4)^2$.

REMEMBER
You can check your answers by multiplying the factors.

b. $4x^2 - 12x + 9 = (2x)^2 - 2(2x)(3) + 3^2$ — Write as $a^2 - 2ab + b^2$.

$= (2x - 3)^2$ — Perfect square trinomial pattern

▶ So, $4x^2 - 12x + 9 = (2x - 3)^2$.

EXAMPLE 4 Solving a Polynomial Equation

Solve $x^2 + \frac{2}{3}x + \frac{1}{9} = 0$.

SOLUTION

$x^2 + \frac{2}{3}x + \frac{1}{9} = 0$	Write equation.
$9x^2 + 6x + 1 = 0$	Multiply each side by 9.
$(3x)^2 + 2(3x)(1) + 1^2 = 0$	Write left side as $a^2 + 2ab + b^2$.
$(3x + 1)^2 = 0$	Perfect square trinomial pattern
$3x + 1 = 0$	Zero-Product Property
$x = -\frac{1}{3}$	Solve for x.

▶ The solution is $x = -\frac{1}{3}$.

Math Practice
Look for Structure
What is true about the roots of every equation of the form $(x + a)^2 = 0$?

SELF-ASSESSMENT

1 I do not understand. 2 I can do it with help. 3 I can do it on my own. 4 I can teach someone else.

Factor the polynomial.

8. $m^2 - 2m + 1$ **9.** $d^2 - 10d + 25$ **10.** $9z^2 + 36z + 36$

11. WHICH ONE DOESN'T BELONG? Which polynomial does *not* belong with the other three? Explain your reasoning.

$n^2 - 4$ $g^2 - 6g + 9$ $r^2 + 18r + 81$ $k^2 + 144$

Solve the equation.

12. $a^2 + 6a + 9 = 0$ **13.** $n^2 - 81 = 0$ **14.** $w^2 - \frac{7}{3}w + \frac{49}{36} = 0$

Solving Real-Life Problems

EXAMPLE 5 Modeling Real Life

A bird picks up a golf ball and drops it while flying. The function represents the height y (in feet) of the golf ball t seconds after it is dropped. The ball hits the top of a roof that is 32 feet high. After how many seconds does the ball hit the roof?

$y = 81 - 16t^2$

SOLUTION

1. **Understand the Problem** You are given the height of the golf ball as a function of the amount of time after it is dropped and the height of the roof that the golf ball hits. You are asked to determine how many seconds it takes for the ball to hit the roof.

2. **Make a Plan** Use the function for the height of the golf ball. Substitute the height of the roof for y and solve for the time t.

3. **Solve and Check** Substitute 32 for y and solve for t.

$y = 81 - 16t^2$		Write equation.
$32 = 81 - 16t^2$		Substitute 32 for y.
$0 = 49 - 16t^2$		Subtract 32 from each side.
$0 = 7^2 - (4t)^2$		Write as $a^2 - b^2$.
$0 = (7 + 4t)(7 - 4t)$		Difference of two squares pattern
$7 + 4t = 0$ *or*	$7 - 4t = 0$	Zero-Product Property
$t = -\frac{7}{4}$ *or*	$t = \frac{7}{4}$	Solve for t.

Because a negative time does not make sense, use the positive solution.

▶ So, the golf ball hits the roof after $\frac{7}{4}$, or 1.75 seconds.

Check You can check that your answer is correct by substituting $t = \frac{7}{4}$ into the equation $y = 81 - 16t^2$. Verify that a time of $\frac{7}{4}$ seconds gives a height of 32 feet.

$$32 = 81 - 16t^2$$
$$32 \stackrel{?}{=} 81 - 16\left(\frac{7}{4}\right)^2$$
$$32 \stackrel{?}{=} 81 - 16\left(\frac{49}{16}\right)$$
$$32 \stackrel{?}{=} 81 - 49$$
$$32 = 32 \checkmark$$

Math Practice

Understand Quantities

What are the meanings of the terms of $y = 81 - 16t^2$ in this situation?

SELF-ASSESSMENT

1 I do not understand. 2 I can do it with help. 3 I can do it on my own. 4 I can teach someone else.

15. **WHAT IF?** The golf ball does not hit the roof. After how many seconds does the ball hit the ground?

16. **MP REASONING** The area of a rectangular piece of land is represented by the polynomial $8x^2 + 40x + 50$. The length of the piece of land is equal to two times its width. What expressions represent the dimensions of the piece of land? Explain your reasoning.

7.7 Practice WITH CalcChat® AND CalcView®

In Exercises 1–6, factor the polynomial. *Example 1*

1. $m^2 - 49$
2. $z^2 - 81$
3. $64 - 81d^2$
4. $25 - 4x^2$
5. $225a^2 - 36b^2$
6. $16x^2 - 169y^2$

In Exercises 7–12, use a special product pattern to evaluate the expression. *Example 2*

7. $12^2 - 9^2$
8. $19^2 - 11^2$
9. $78^2 - 72^2$
10. $54^2 - 52^2$
11. $53^2 - 47^2$
12. $39^2 - 36^2$

In Exercises 13–20, factor the polynomial. *Example 3*

13. $h^2 + 12h + 36$
14. $p^2 + 30p + 225$
15. $y^2 - 22y + 121$
16. $x^2 - 4x + 4$
17. $a^2 - 28a + 196$
18. $m^2 + 24m + 144$
19. $25n^2 + 20n + 4$
20. $49a^2 - 14a + 1$

ERROR ANALYSIS In Exercises 21 and 22, describe and correct the error in factoring the polynomial.

21. ✗
$$n^2 - 64 = n^2 - 8^2 = (n - 8)^2$$

22. ✗
$$y^2 - 6y + 9 = y^2 - 2(y)(3) + 3^2 = (y - 3)(y + 3)$$

23. **MODELING REAL LIFE** The area (in square centimeters) of a square drink coaster can be represented by $d^2 + 8d + 16$. Write an expression that represents the perimeter of the coaster.

24. **MODELING REAL LIFE** The polynomial represents the area (in square feet) of the square playground. Write an expression that represents the perimeter of the playground.

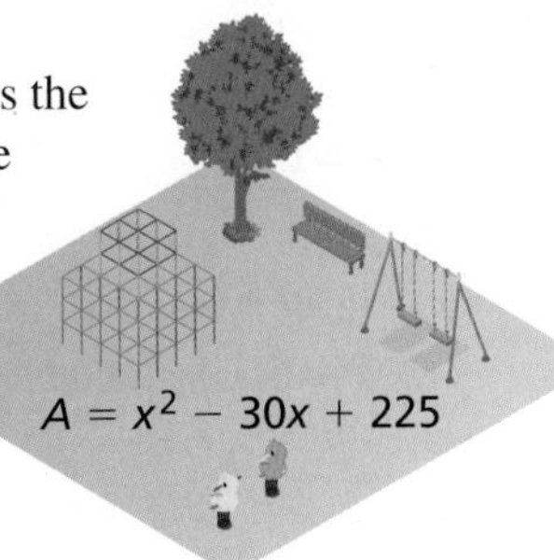

In Exercises 25–32, solve the equation. *Example 4*

25. $z^2 - 4 = 0$
26. $4x^2 = 49$
27. $k^2 - 16k + 64 = 0$
28. $s^2 + 20s + 100 = 0$
29. $n^2 + 9 = 6n$
30. $y^2 = 12y - 36$
31. $y^2 + \frac{1}{2}y = -\frac{1}{16}$
32. $-\frac{4}{3}x + \frac{4}{9} = -x^2$

33. **MODELING REAL LIFE** While standing on a ladder, you drop a roller. The function

$$y = 25 - 16t^2$$

represents the height y (in feet) of the roller t seconds after it is dropped. After how many seconds does the roller land on the ground? *Example 5*

34. **MODELING REAL LIFE** The function

$$y = -16t^2 + 8t$$

represents the height y (in feet) of a grasshopper jumping straight up from the ground t seconds after the start of the jump. After how many seconds is the grasshopper 1 foot off the ground?

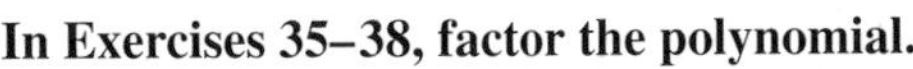

In Exercises 35–38, factor the polynomial.

35. $3z^2 - 27$
36. $2m^2 - 50$
37. $50y^2 + 120y + 72$
38. $27m^2 - 36m + 12$

39. **MP REASONING** Tell whether each polynomial can be factored. If not, change the constant term so that the polynomial is a perfect square trinomial.

a. $w^2 + 18w + 84$

b. $y^2 - 10y + 23$

40. HOW DO YOU SEE IT?
The figure shows a large square with an area of a^2 that contains a smaller square with an area of b^2.

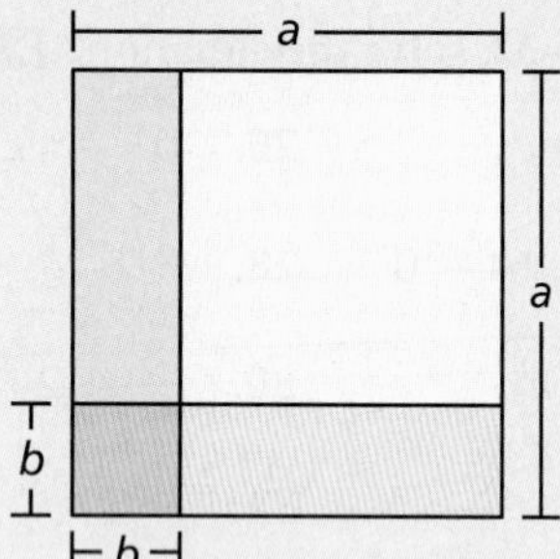

a. Describe the regions that represent $a^2 - b^2$. How can you rearrange these regions to show the difference of two squares pattern?

b. How can you use the figure to show the perfect square trinomial pattern?

41. MAKING AN ARGUMENT Describe two methods you can use to simplify $(2x - 5)^2 - (x - 4)^2$. Which one would you use? Explain.

42. THOUGHT PROVOKING
Consider the function $f(x) = x^2 + 6x + 9$. Complete the function below so that $g(x) = 0$ has solutions of $x = -2$ and $x = 2$. Justify your answer.

$$g(x) = f(x + \square) + \square$$

43. CONNECTING CONCEPTS
The composite solid is made up of a cube and a rectangular prism. The volume of the solid is $25x$ cubic inches. Find the value of x.

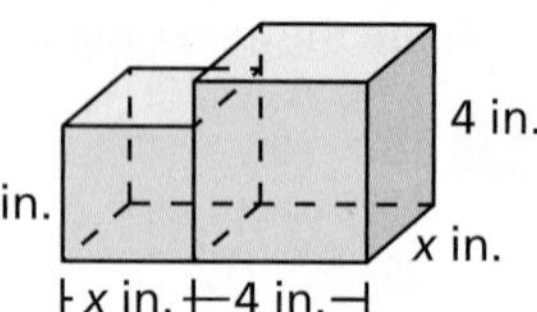

REVIEW & REFRESH

WATCH

In Exercises 44 and 45, find the x-intercepts of the graph.

44.

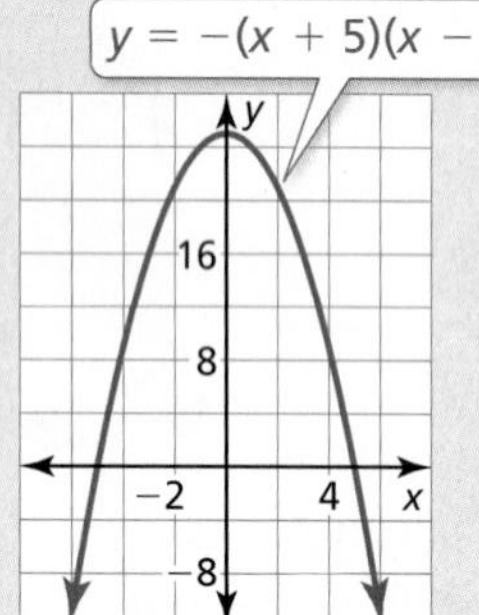

45.

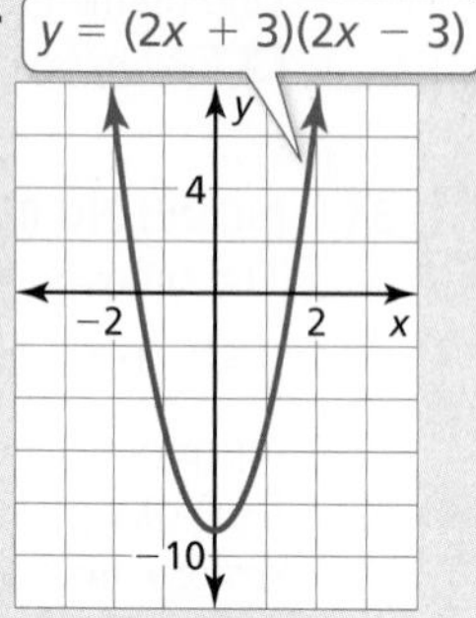

In Exercises 46–49, graph the inequality in a coordinate plane.

46. $y \le 4x - 1$

47. $y > -\frac{1}{2}x + 3$

48. $4y - 12 \ge 8x$

49. $3y + 3 < x$

50. Determine whether the sequence is *arithmetic* or *geometric*. Then write a recursive rule for the sequence.

$$4x + 9, x + 15, -2x + 21, -5x + 27, \ldots$$

In Exercises 51–54, factor the polynomial.

51. $x^2 + 2x - 3$

52. $w^2 - 4w - 21$

53. $3h^2 + 2h - 8$

54. $2p^2 - 6p - 80$

55. Determine whether the table represents a *linear* or an *exponential* function. Explain.

x	−3	−2	−1	0	1
y	0.1	0.3	0.9	2.7	8.1

56. Solve $\frac{3}{4}(x - 12) = 6$ for x by (a) using the Distributive Property and (b) interpreting the expression $x - 12$ as a single quantity. Justify your answers.

In Exercises 57–60, factor the polynomial.

57. $x^2 - 144$

58. $x^2 - 8x + 16$

59. $x^2 + \frac{4}{3}x + \frac{4}{9}$

60. $4x^2 + 36x + 81$

61. MODELING REAL LIFE The table shows the costs x (in dollars) of several meals ordered by customers at a restaurant and the amounts y (in dollars) of the tips left by the customers.

Cost, x	17.50	14	9.75	18.25	17	13.50
Tip, y	2.75	2.25	1.50	3	2.75	2

a. Use technology to find an equation of the line of best fit.

b. Approximate the amount of a tip for a meal that costs $15.

c. Predict the amount of a tip for a meal that costs $25.

7.8 Factoring Polynomials Completely

Learning Target Factor a polynomial by grouping and recognize when a polynomial is factored completely.

Success Criteria
- I can factor polynomials by grouping.
- I can factor polynomials completely.
- I can solve real-life problems by factoring.

EXPLORE IT! Factoring a Polynomial Completely

Work with a partner. Five students are asked to factor the polynomial below.

$$4x^3 + 16x^2 - 84x$$

The results are shown.

Student 1	Student 2
$4(x^3 + 4x^2 - 21x)$	$4x(x^2 + 4x - 21)$

Student 3	Student 4
$4x(x + 7)(x - 3)$	$\frac{1}{4}(16x^3 + 64x^2 - 336x)$

Student 5
$x(4x - 12)(x + 7)$

Math Practice

Explain the Meaning In your own words, explain what it means for a polynomial to be *unfactorable*.

a. Are the answers above equivalent? Explain.

b. Explain how you think the students obtained each result.

c. Which student's answer would you provide if you were asked to factor the polynomial? Why?

d. What does it mean for a polynomial to be *factored completely*?

e. Find a polynomial with the given description. Justify your answers.

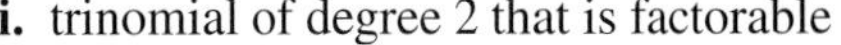

i. trinomial of degree 2 that is factorable

ii. trinomial of degree 2 that is unfactorable

iii. polynomial of degree 3 that is factorable

iv. polynomial of degree 3 that is unfactorable

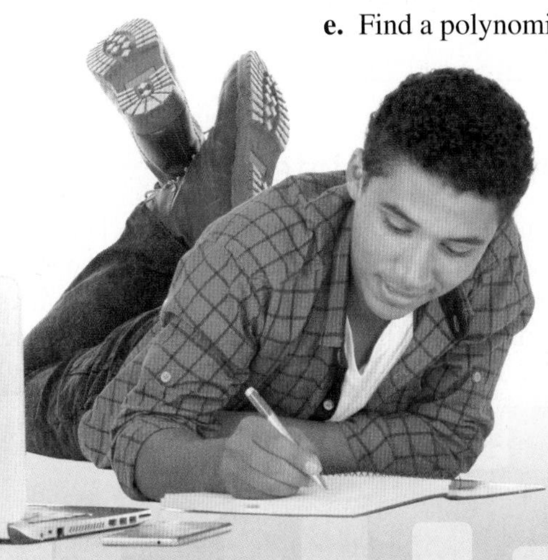

Factoring Polynomials by Grouping

GO DIGITAL

Vocabulary 

factoring by grouping, *p. 410*
factored completely, *p. 410*

You have used the Distributive Property to factor out a greatest common monomial from a polynomial. Sometimes, you can factor out a common binomial. You may be able to use the Distributive Property to factor polynomials with four terms, as described below.

KEY IDEA

Factoring by Grouping

To factor a polynomial with four terms, group the terms into pairs. Factor the GCF out of each pair of terms. Look for and factor out the common binomial factor. This process is called **factoring by grouping**.

EXAMPLE 1 Factoring Polynomials by Grouping

Factor each polynomial by grouping.

a. $x^3 + 3x^2 + 2x + 6$ **b.** $x^2 + y + x + xy$

SOLUTION

a. $x^3 + 3x^2 + 2x + 6 = (x^3 + 3x^2) + (2x + 6)$ Group terms with common factors.

Common binomial factor is $x + 3$. → $= x^2(x + 3) + 2(x + 3)$ Factor out GCF of each pair of terms.

$= (x + 3)(x^2 + 2)$ Factor out $(x + 3)$.

▶ So, $x^3 + 3x^2 + 2x + 6 = (x + 3)(x^2 + 2)$.

b. $x^2 + y + x + xy = x^2 + x + xy + y$ Rewrite polynomial.

$= (x^2 + x) + (xy + y)$ Group terms with common factors.

Common binomial factor is $x + 1$. → $= x(x + 1) + y(x + 1)$ Factor out GCF of each pair of terms.

$= (x + 1)(x + y)$ Factor out $(x + 1)$.

▶ So, $x^2 + y + x + xy = (x + 1)(x + y)$.

SELF-ASSESSMENT

1 I do not understand. 2 I can do it with help. 3 I can do it on my own. 4 I can teach someone else.

1. **WRITING** Explain how to choose which terms to group together when factoring by grouping.

Factor the polynomial by grouping.

2. $a^3 + 3a^2 + a + 3$
3. $3p^3 - 30 - 5p^2 + 18p$
4. $y^2 + 2x + yx + 2y$
5. **MP REASONING** In Example 1(b), can you group the first term x^2 with the fourth term xy, and then factor? Explain.

Factoring Polynomials Completely

You have seen that the polynomial $x^2 - 1$ can be factored as $(x + 1)(x - 1)$. This polynomial is *factorable*. Notice that the polynomial $x^2 + 1$ cannot be written as the product of polynomials with integer coefficients. This polynomial is *unfactorable*. A factorable polynomial with integer coefficients is **factored completely** when it is written as a product of unfactorable polynomials with integer coefficients.

GO DIGITAL

CONCEPT SUMMARY

Guidelines for Factoring Polynomials Completely

To factor a polynomial completely, you should try each of these steps.

1. Factor out the greatest common monomial factor. $3x^2 + 6x = 3x(x + 2)$
2. Look for a difference of two squares or a perfect square trinomial. $x^2 + 4x + 4 = (x + 2)^2$
3. Factor a trinomial of the form $ax^2 + bx + c$ into a product of binomial factors. $3x^2 - 5x - 2 = (3x + 1)(x - 2)$
4. Factor a polynomial with four terms by grouping. $x^3 + x - 4x^2 - 4 = (x^2 + 1)(x - 4)$

EXAMPLE 2 Factoring Polynomials Completely

Factor (a) $3x^3 + 6x^2 - 18x$ and (b) $7x^4 - 28x^2$ completely.

SOLUTION

a. $3x^3 + 6x^2 - 18x = 3x(x^2 + 2x - 6)$ — Factor out $3x$.

$x^2 + 2x - 6$ is unfactorable, so the polynomial is factored completely.

▶ So, $3x^3 + 6x^2 - 18x = 3x(x^2 + 2x - 6)$.

b. $7x^4 - 28x^2 = 7x^2(x^2 - 4)$ — Factor out $7x^2$.

$= 7x^2(x^2 - 2^2)$ — Write as $a^2 - b^2$.

$= 7x^2(x + 2)(x - 2)$ — Difference of two squares pattern

▶ So, $7x^4 - 28x^2 = 7x^2(x + 2)(x - 2)$.

EXAMPLE 3 Solving an Equation by Factoring Completely

Solve $2x^3 + 8x^2 = 10x$.

SOLUTION

$2x^3 + 8x^2 = 10x$	Original equation
$2x^3 + 8x^2 - 10x = 0$	Subtract $10x$ from each side.
$2x(x^2 + 4x - 5) = 0$	Factor out $2x$.
$2x(x + 5)(x - 1) = 0$	Factor $x^2 + 4x - 5$.
$2x = 0$ *or* $x + 5 = 0$ *or* $x - 1 = 0$	Zero-Product Property
$x = 0$ *or* $x = -5$ *or* $x = 1$	Solve for x.

▶ The roots are $x = -5$, $x = 0$, and $x = 1$.

SELF-ASSESSMENT

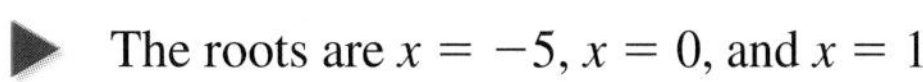

Factor the polynomial completely.

6. $3x^3 - 12x$
7. $2y^3 - 12y^2 + 18y$
8. $m^3 - 2m^2 - 8m$

Solve the equation.

9. $w^3 - 8w^2 + 16w = 0$
10. $2x^3 - 50x = 0$
11. $c^3 - 7c^2 + 12c = 0$

NASA's Neutral Buoyancy Laboratory (NBL) is an astronaut training facility in Houston, Texas. The main feature of the lab is a massive indoor pool that helps astronauts train for spacewalks.

Solving Real-Life Problems

GO DIGITAL

EXAMPLE 4 Modeling Real Life

A piece of equipment is submerged in the pool at the Neutral Buoyancy Laboratory for training. The piece of equipment is in the shape of a rectangular prism that has a volume of 72 cubic meters, a length of x meters, a width of $(x - 1)$ meters, and a height of $(x + 9)$ meters. Find the dimensions of the piece of equipment.

SOLUTION

1. **Understand the Problem** You are given the shape and volume of the piece of equipment. The dimensions are written in terms of its length. You are asked to find the length, width, and height.
2. **Make a Plan** Use the formula for the volume of a rectangular prism to write and solve an equation for the length of the piece of equipment. Then substitute that value in the expressions for the width and height.
3. **Solve and Check**

$\text{Volume} = \ell wh$	Volume of a rectangular prism
$72 = x(x - 1)(x + 9)$	Write equation.
$72 = x^3 + 8x^2 - 9x$	Multiply.
$0 = x^3 + 8x^2 - 9x - 72$	Subtract 72 from each side.
$0 = (x^3 + 8x^2) + (-9x - 72)$	Group terms with common factors.
$0 = x^2(x + 8) - 9(x + 8)$	Factor out GCF of each pair of terms.
$0 = (x + 8)(x^2 - 9)$	Factor out $(x + 8)$.
$0 = (x + 8)(x - 3)(x + 3)$	Difference of two squares pattern
$x + 8 = 0$ *or* $x - 3 = 0$ *or* $x + 3 = 0$	Zero-Product Property
$x = -8$ *or* $x = 3$ *or* $x = -3$	Solve for x.

Because a negative length does not make sense, use the positive solution. So, the length is 3 meters. Use $x = 3$ to find the width and height, as shown.

$$\text{width} = x - 1 = 3 - 1 = 2 \qquad \text{height} = x + 9 = 3 + 9 = 12$$

▶ The piece of equipment has a length of 3 meters, a width of 2 meters, and a height of 12 meters.

Check Substitute the values for the length, width, and height when the length is 3 meters into the formula for volume. The volume of the piece of equipment should be 72 cubic meters.

$$V = \ell wh$$
$$72 \stackrel{?}{=} 3(2)(12)$$
$$72 = 72 \checkmark$$

SELF-ASSESSMENT

1 I do not understand. 2 I can do it with help. 3 I can do it on my own. 4 I can teach someone else.

12. The terrarium has width w and is in the shape of a rectangular prism. The volume of the terrarium is 4608 cubic inches. Your friend says that there is more than one possible set of dimensions. Is your friend correct? If so, does each set of dimensions make sense in the context of the problem? Explain your reasoning.

In Exercises 1–8, factor the polynomial by grouping. *Example 1*

1. $x^3 + x^2 + 2x + 2$
2. $y^3 - 9y^2 + y - 9$
3. $3z^3 - 8 - 12z^2 + 2z$
4. $2s^3 + 27 + 18s + 3s^2$
5. $x^2 + xy + 8x + 8y$
6. $q^2 + q + 5pq + 5p$
7. $m^2 - 3n - 3m + mn$
8. $2a^2 - 12b + 8ab - 3a$

In Exercises 9–20, factor the polynomial completely. *Example 2*

9. $2x^3 - 2x$
10. $36a^4 - 4a^2$
11. $2c^2 - 7c + 19$
12. $m^2 - 5m - 35$
13. $6g^3 - 24g^2 + 24g$
14. $-15d^3 + 21d^2 - 6d$
15. $3r^5 + 3r^4 - 90r^3$
16. $5w^4 - 40w^3 + 80w^2$
17. $-4c^4 + 8c^3 - 28c^2$
18. $8t^2 + 8t - 72$
19. $b^3 - 5b^2 - 4b + 20$
20. $h^3 + 4h^2 - 25h - 100$

In Exercises 21–26, solve the equation. *Example 3*

21. $5n^3 - 30n^2 + 40n = 0$
22. $k^4 - 100k^2 = 0$
23. $x^3 + x^2 = 4x + 4$
24. $2t^5 + 2t^4 - 144t^3 = 0$
25. $147s - 3s^3 = 0$
26. $4y^3 - 7y^2 + 28 = 16y$

In Exercises 27–30, find the x-intercepts of the graph.

27.
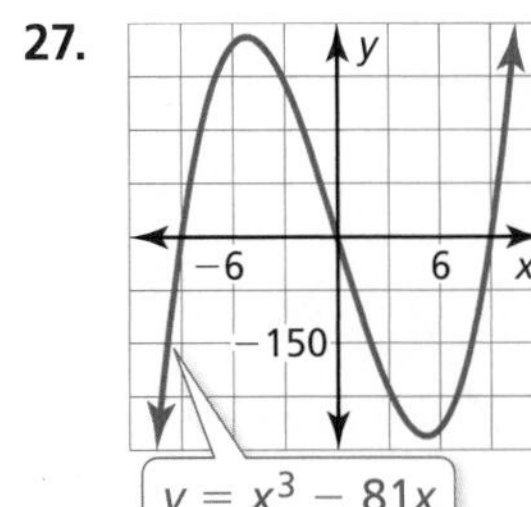

28.
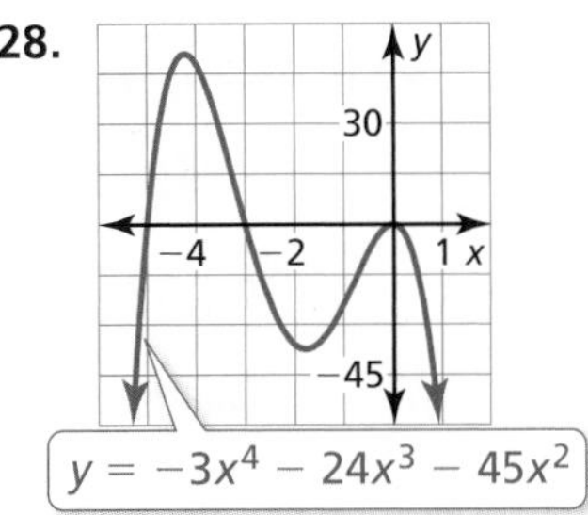

29.
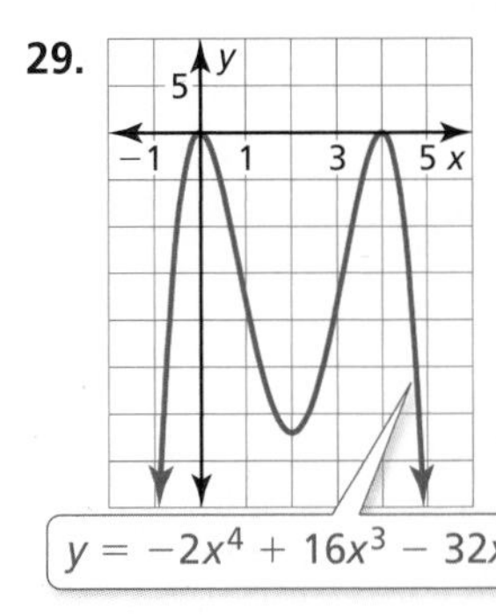

30.
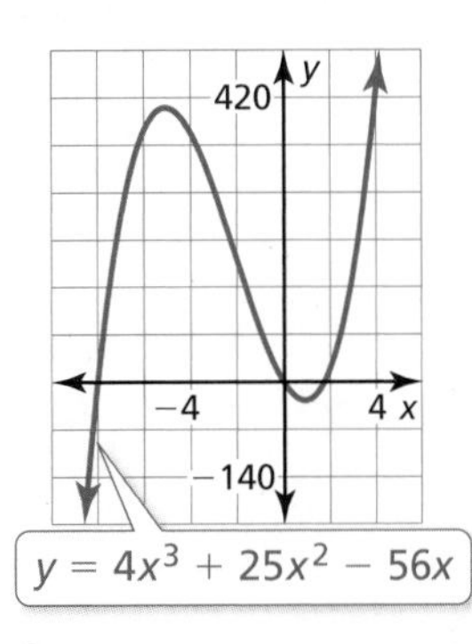

ERROR ANALYSIS In Exercises 31 and 32, describe and correct the error in factoring the polynomial completely.

31.
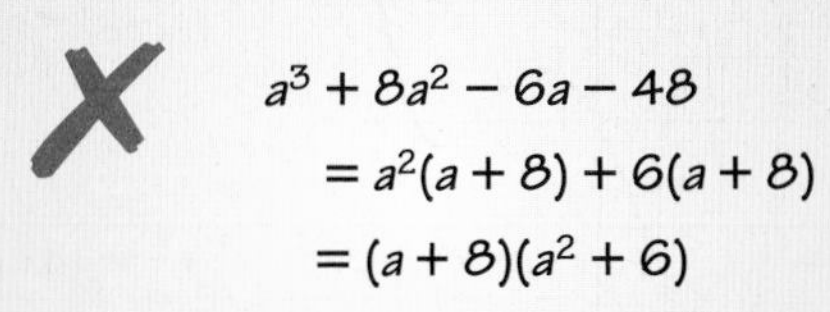

32.
$x^3 - 6x^2 - 9x + 54$
$= x^2(x - 6) - 9(x - 6)$
$= (x - 6)(x^2 - 9)$

33. **MODELING REAL LIFE** A birdhouse in the shape of a rectangular prism has a volume of 128 cubic inches. The width is w inches, the depth is 4 inches, and the height is 4 inches greater than the width. What are the dimensions of the birdhouse? *Example 4*

34. **MODELING REAL LIFE** A gift bag has width w and is in the shape of a rectangular prism. The volume of the gift bag is 1152 cubic inches. The height is greater than the width. What are the dimensions of the gift bag?

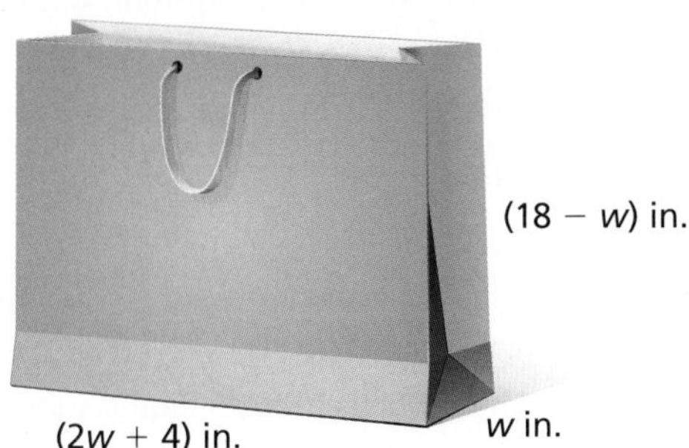

In Exercises 35–38, factor the polynomial completely.

35. $x^3 + 2x^2y - x - 2y$
36. $8b^3 - 4b^2a - 18b + 9a$
37. $4s^2 - s + 12st - 3t$
38. $6m^3 - 12mn + m^2n - 2n^2$

39. **COLLEGE PREP** When $9h^3 - 25h - 27h^2 + 75$ is factored completely, which of the following is one of the factors? Select all that apply.

(A) $9h^2 - 25$
(B) $h - 3$
(C) $3h - 5$
(D) $3h + 5$

40. HOW DO YOU SEE IT?
How can you use the factored form of the polynomial
$x^4 - 2x^3 - 9x^2 + 18x = x(x - 3)(x + 3)(x - 2)$
to find the x-intercepts of the graph of the function?

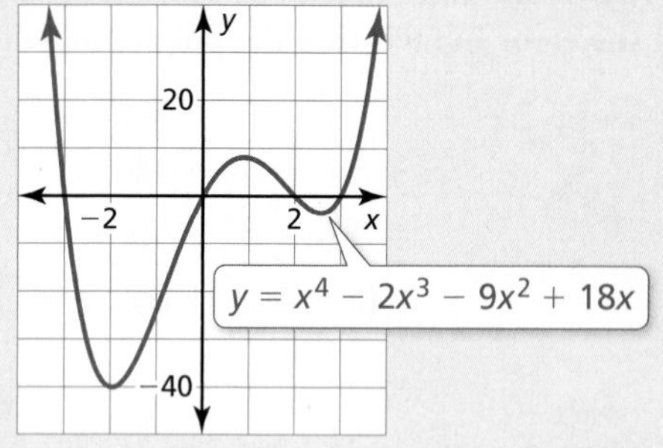

41. WRITING Is it possible to find three real solutions of the equation $x^3 + 2x^2 + 3x + 6 = 0$? Explain your reasoning.

42. MAKING AN ARGUMENT Your friend says that if a trinomial cannot be factored as the product of two binomials, then the trinomial is factored completely. Is your friend correct? Explain.

43. CONNECTING CONCEPTS
Find the dimensions of the cylinder.

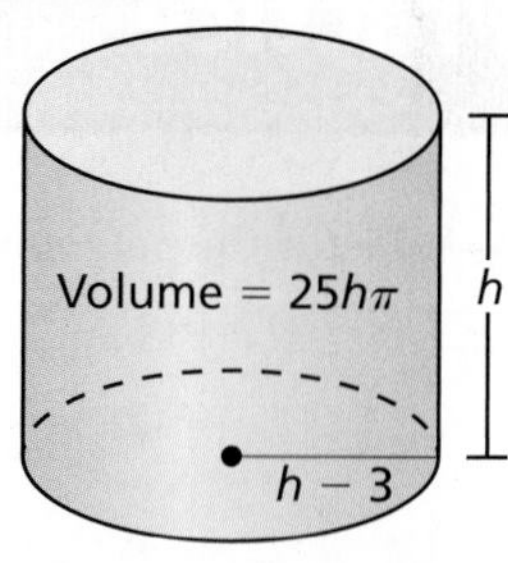

GO DIGITAL

44. THOUGHT PROVOKING
Factor the polynomial
$x^5 - x^4 - 5x^3 + 5x^2 + 4x - 4$ completely.

45. MP **REPEATED REASONING** Find a value for w so that the equation $5x^3 + wx^2 + 80x = 0$ has (a) two solutions and (b) three solutions. Explain your reasoning.

46. DIG DEEPER The width of a box in the shape of a rectangular prism is 4 inches more than the height h. The length is the difference of 9 inches and the height. The volume of the box is 180 cubic inches. Of the possible dimensions of the box, which result in a box with the least possible surface area? Explain your reasoning.

REVIEW & REFRESH

WATCH

In Exercises 47–50, solve the system. Explain your choice of method.

47. $y = \frac{1}{2}x + 2$
$y = 3x - 3$

48. $5x - y = 12$
$2x + y = 16$

49. $x = 3y$
$y - 10 = 2x$

50. $9x - 6y = 20$
$-3x + 2y = -7$

51. Determine whether the relation is a function. Explain.

Input, x	−5	−1	1	3	7
Output, y	−4	−2	1	−4	0

In Exercises 52 and 53, factor the polynomial completely.

52. $3y^2 - 12y - 63$

53. $z^3 + 2z^2 - 100z - 200$

54. MODELING REAL LIFE The total cost (in dollars) of printing x photographs is represented by the piecewise function

$$c(x) = \begin{cases} 0.33x, & \text{if } 0 \le x < 75 \\ 0.23x, & \text{if } x \ge 75 \end{cases}.$$

Determine the total cost of printing (a) 50 photographs and (b) 75 photographs.

In Exercises 55 and 56, graph the function. Find the domain and range.

55. $y = 9\left(\frac{1}{3}\right)^x$

56. $f(x) = -3(4)^x$

57. MP **NUMBER SENSE** Complete the inequality with < or > so that it has no solution.

$|7x - 8|$ ▢ 0

In Exercises 58–61, solve the equation.

58. $25n^2 - 81 = 0$

59. $6x^2 + 7x - 5 = 0$

60. $h^2 - 15h = -54$

61. $5x^3 + 125x = -50x^2$

62. Write an equation of the line in slope-intercept form.

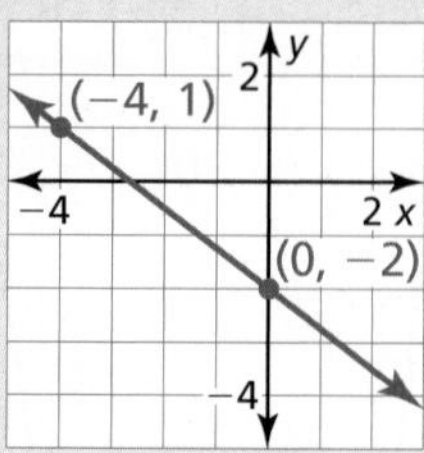

63. Solve $p = x - qx - r$ for x.

7 Chapter Review WITH CalcChat®

Chapter Learning Target Understand polynomial equations and factoring.

Chapter Success Criteria
- ◆ I can classify polynomials by degree and number of terms.
- ◆ I can add, subtract, multiply, and divide polynomials.
- ■ I can solve polynomial equations.
- ■ I can factor polynomials and use factoring to solve real-life problems.

◆ Surface
■ Deep

SELF-ASSESSMENT 1 I do not understand. 2 I can do it with help. 3 I can do it on my own. 4 I can teach someone else.

7.1 Adding and Subtracting Polynomials (pp. 363–370)

Learning Target: Add and subtract polynomials.

Vocabulary
monomial
degree of a monomial
polynomial
binomial
trinomial
degree of a polynomial
standard form
leading coefficient
closed

Write the polynomial in standard form. Identify the degree and leading coefficient of the polynomial. Then classify the polynomial by the number of terms.

1. $-3p^3 + 5p^6 - 4$
2. $9x^7 - 6x^2 + 13x^5$

Find the sum or difference.

3. $(3a + 7) + (a - 1)$
4. $(x^2 + 6x - 5) + (2x^2 + 15)$
5. $(-y^2 + y + 2) - (y^2 - 5y - 2)$
6. $(p + 7) - (6p^2 + 13p)$

7.2 Multiplying and Dividing Polynomials (pp. 371–378)

Learning Target: Multiply and divide polynomials.

Vocabulary
FOIL Method

Find the product or quotient.

7. $(x + 6)(x - 4)$
8. $(-3y + 1)(4y^2 - y - 7)$
9. $\dfrac{(3n - 18)(n + 8)}{n - 6}$
10. Find $\dfrac{(3x - 15)(x + 1)}{x - 5}$. Then find the x-value(s) for which the original expression has a value of 18. Explain your reasoning.

7.3 Special Products of Polynomials (pp. 379–384)

Learning Target: Use patterns to find products of polynomials.

Find the product.

11. $(x + 9)(x - 9)$
12. $(2y + 4)(2y - 4)$
13. $(p + 4)^2$
14. $(-1 + 2d)^2$
15. A square-shaped quilt with 72-inch sides is expanded by x inches on one pair of opposite sides and is reduced by x inches on the other pair of opposite sides. By how much does the area change? Explain.

7.4 Solving Polynomial Equations in Factored Form (pp. 385–390) WATCH

Learning Target: Solve polynomial equations in factored form.

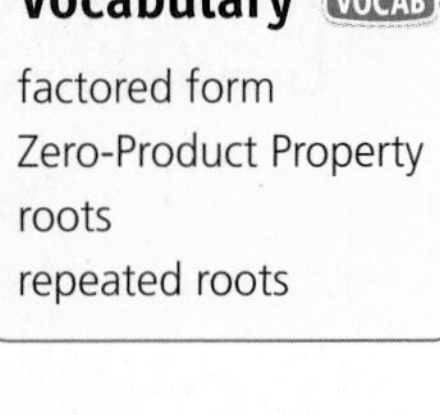

Solve the equation.

16. $(z + 3)(z - 7) = 0$

17. $(b + 13)^2 = 0$

18. $2y(y - 9)(y + 4) = 0$

19. $x^2 + 5x = 0$

20. The front of a storage bunker can be modeled by $y = -\frac{5}{216}(x - 72)(x + 72)$, where x and y are measured in inches. The x-axis represents the ground. Find the width of the bunker at ground level.

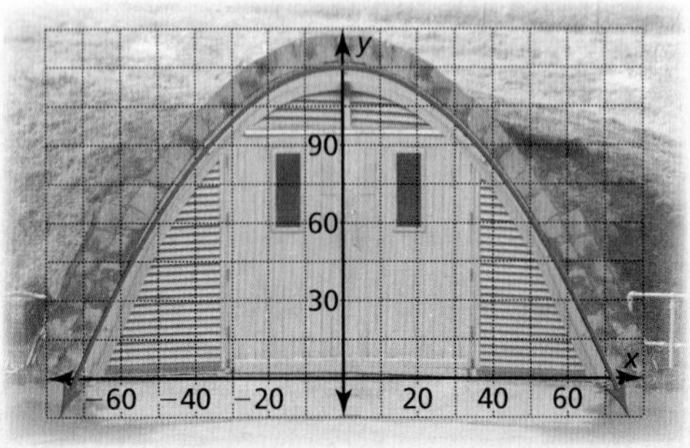

21. Solve $ax^3 = bx^2$, where a and b are nonzero constants. Check your solution.

7.5 Factoring $x^2 + bx + c$ (pp. 391–396)

Learning Target: Factor polynomials of the form $x^2 + bx + c$.

Factor the polynomial.

22. $p^2 + 2p - 35$

23. $b^2 + 18b + 80$

24. $z^2 - 4z - 21$

25. $x^2 - 11x + 28$

26. A contractor tiles a rectangular section of floor in a square room. The tile covers 18 square feet. What is the area of the room?

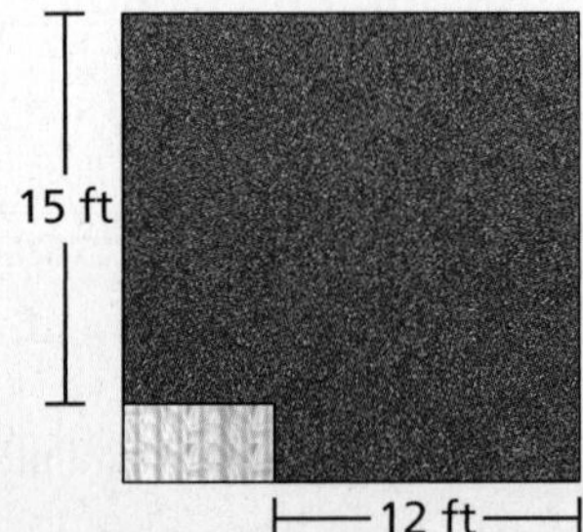

27. A polynomial is factored as $x^2 + bx + c = (x + p)(x - q)$, where p and q are whole numbers. Compare the values of p and q when b is negative. Explain your reasoning.

7.6 Factoring $ax^2 + bx + c$ (pp. 397–402) WATCH

Learning Target: Factor polynomials of the form $ax^2 + bx + c$.

Factor the polynomial.

28. $3t^2 + 16t - 12$

29. $-5y^2 - 22y - 8$

30. $6x^2 + 17x + 7$

31. $-2y^2 + 7y - 6$

32. $3z^2 + 26z - 9$

33. $10a^2 - 13a - 3$

34. Find each possible integer value of k so that $2x^2 + kx + 18 = 0$ has integer solutions. Explain your reasoning.

7.7 Factoring Special Products (pp. 403–408)

GO DIGITAL

Learning Target: Recognize and factor special products.

Factor the polynomial.

35. $x^2 - 9$

36. $y^2 - 100$

37. $z^2 - 6z + 9$

38. $m^2 + 16m + 64$

39. Find each possible value of b so that $4x^2 + bx + 25$ is a perfect square trinomial.

40. A rugby player kicks a rugby ball. The function

$$y = -\frac{1}{50}(x^2 - 225)$$

represents the path of the ball, where x and y are measured in meters and $x = 0$ represents the middle of the field. How far does the ball travel horizontally before hitting the ground?

7.8 Factoring Polynomials Completely (pp. 409–414)

WATCH

Learning Target: Factor a polynomial by grouping and recognize when a polynomial is factored completely.

Vocabulary AZ VOCAB

factoring by grouping
factored completely

Factor the polynomial completely.

41. $n^3 - 9n$

42. $x^2 - 3x + 4ax - 12a$

43. $2x^4 + 2x^3 - 20x^2$

Solve the equation.

44. $3x^3 - 9x^2 - 54x = 0$

45. $16x^2 - 36 = 0$

46. $z^3 + 3z^2 - 25z - 75 = 0$

47. A box in the shape of a rectangular prism has a volume of 96 cubic feet. The box has a length of $(x + 8)$ feet, a width of x feet, and a height of $(x - 2)$ feet. Find the dimensions of the box.

Mathematical Practices

Look for and Make Use of Structure

Mathematically proficient students are able to see complicated things as single objects or as being composed of several objects.

1. When factoring a polynomial by grouping, why is it necessary to see the polynomial as being composed of multiple polynomials?
2. How did you use the structure of a trinomial to answer Exercise 48 on page 369?
3. Assume that a and b are real numbers and $ab = 0$. You know that either $a = 0$ or $a \neq 0$. Use these two cases and the structure of the equation to prove that the Zero-Product Property is true.

7 Practice Test WITH CalcChat®

Find the sum or difference. Then identify the degree of the sum or difference and classify it by the number of terms.

1. $(4s^4 + 2st + t) + (2s^4 - 2st - 4t)$
2. $(-2p + 4) - (p^2 - 6p + 8)$

Find the product or quotient.

3. $(h - 5)(h + 5)$
4. $(2w - 3)(3w + 5)$
5. $\dfrac{3p^4 - 9p^3 - 18p}{3p}$
6. $\dfrac{7y + 42}{y + 6}$
7. Explain how you can determine whether a polynomial is a perfect square trinomial.
8. Is 18 a polynomial? Explain your reasoning.

Factor the polynomial completely.

9. $s^2 - 15s + 50$
10. $h^3 + 2h^2 - 9h - 18$
11. $-5k^2 - 22k + 15$

Solve the equation.

12. $(n - 1)(n + 6)(n + 5) = 0$
13. $d^2 + 14d + 49 = 0$
14. $6x^4 + 8x^2 = 26x^3$
15. $x^3 - 5x^2 - 16x = -80$
16. The expression $\pi(r - 3)^2$ represents the area covered by the hour hand on a clock in one rotation, where r is the radius of the entire clock. Write a polynomial in standard form that represents the area covered by the hour hand in one rotation.
17. A magician's stage has a trapdoor.
    a. The total area (in square feet) of the stage can be represented by $x^2 + 27x + 176$. Write an expression that represents the width of the stage.
    b. The magician wants the area of the stage to be at least 20 times the area of the trapdoor. Does the stage satisfy his requirement when the area of the trapdoor is 10 square feet?

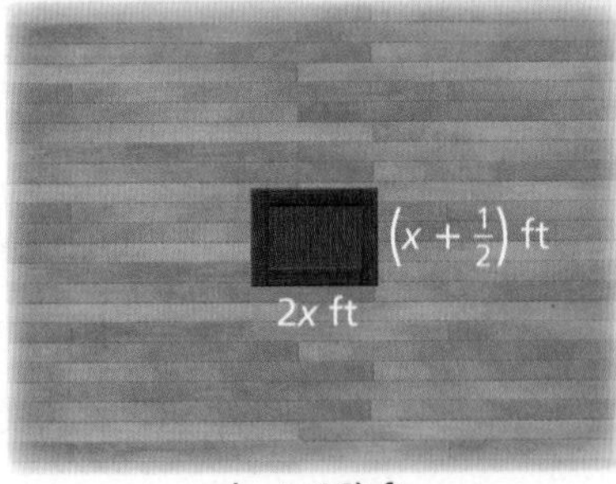

18. You are jumping on a trampoline. For one jump, your height y (in feet) above the trampoline after t seconds can be represented by $y = -16t^2 + 24t$. Find and interpret the domain of the function in this situation.
19. A cardboard box in the shape of a rectangular prism has the dimensions shown. The volume of the box is 60 cubic inches. Find the length, width, and height of the box.

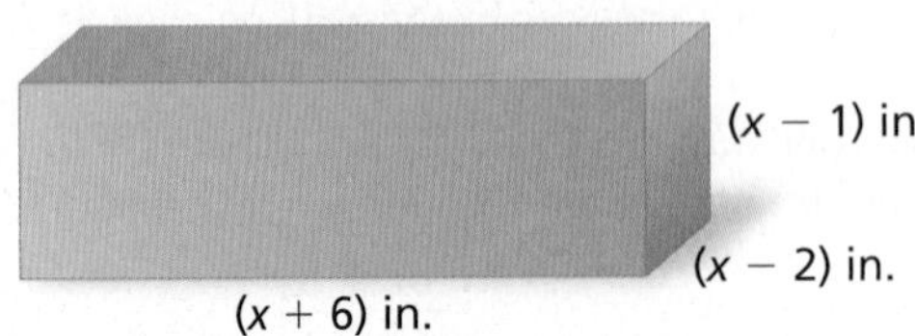

7 Performance Task
Gravity Check

GO DIGITAL

Mercury
Mass: 0.330×10^{24} kg
Diameter: 4879 km

Venus
Mass: 4.87×10^{24} kg
Diameter: 12,104 km

Earth
Mass: 5.97×10^{24} kg
Diameter: 12,756 km

Mars
Mass: 0.642×10^{24} kg
Diameter: 6792 km

Jupiter
Mass: 1898×10^{24} kg
Diameter: 142,984 km

Saturn
Mass: 568×10^{24} kg
Diameter: 120,536 km

Uranus
Mass: 86.8×10^{24} kg
Diameter: 51,118 km

Neptune
Mass: 102×10^{24} kg
Diameter: 49,528 km

The value of *a* is negative because gravity pulls objects *down*, toward the center of the planet.

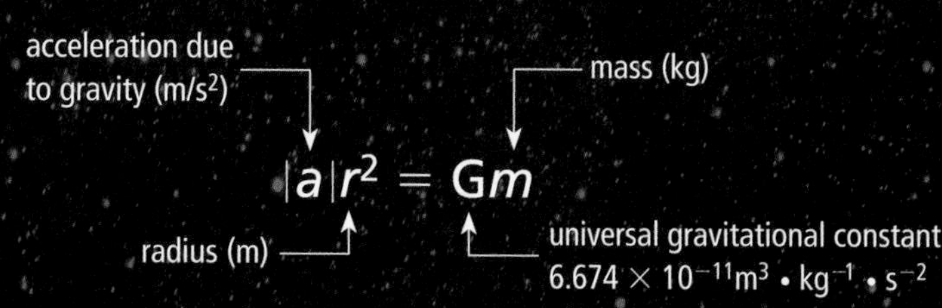

COMPARING GRAVITIES

INFO

A dropped object hits the ground after *n* seconds. The expression $\frac{1}{2}a(t+n)(t-n)$ represents the height (in meters) of the object *t* seconds after it is dropped.

- Write the expression as a polynomial in standard form and explain the meaning of each term.
- Predict the initial height of an object that takes 0.5 second to hit the ground on Earth. Perform an experiment to check your answer.
- Create a display that compares the initial height of an object that hits the ground after 1 second on each planet.

7 College and Career Readiness WITH CalcChat®

Tutorial videos are available for each exercise.

1. Which polynomial represents the product of $2x - 4$ and $x^2 + 6x - 2$?

Ⓐ $2x^3 + 16x^2 + 20x - 8$

Ⓑ $2x^3 + 8x^2 - 28x + 8$

Ⓒ $2x^3 + 8x^2 + 20x - 8$

Ⓓ $-2x^2 - 12x + 4$

2. Which exponential function has the greatest percent rate of change?

Ⓐ $f(x) = 4(2.5)^x$

Ⓑ
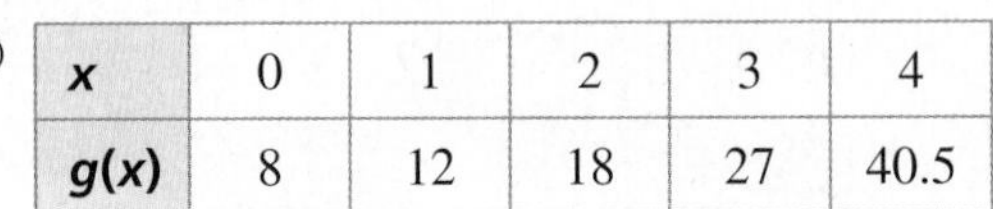

x	0	1	2	3	4
g(x)	8	12	18	27	40.5

Ⓒ
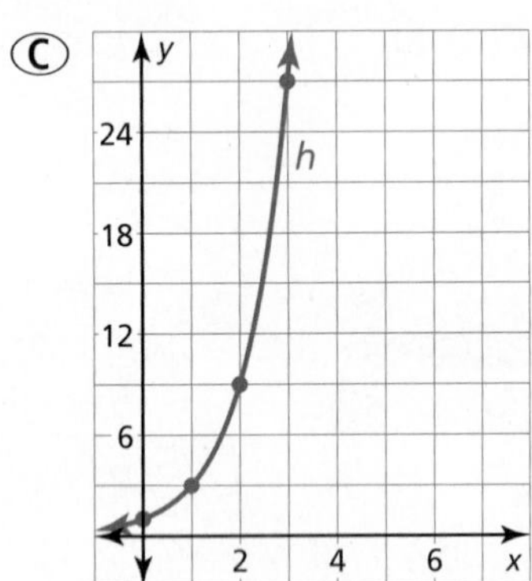

Ⓓ An exponential function j models a relationship in which as x increases by 2, $j(x)$ is multiplied by 4.

3. Find the roots of $x^3 + 8x^2 - 9x = 72$. Select all that apply.

Ⓐ -9

Ⓑ -8

Ⓒ -3

Ⓓ 0

Ⓔ 1

Ⓕ 3

Ⓖ 8

Ⓗ 9

4. The table shows the distances you travel over a 6-hour period. Write an equation that represents your distance traveled as a function of the number of hours.

Hours, x	1	2	3	4	5	6
Distance (miles), y	62	123	184	245	306	367

5. Convert $4\frac{1}{2}$ gallons per minute to cups per second.

GO DIGITAL

6. Which inequality is represented by the graph?

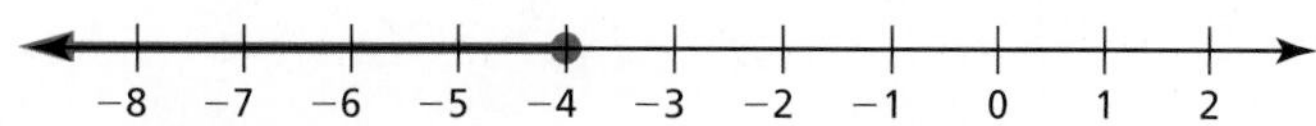

Ⓐ $x \leq -4$ Ⓑ $x < -4$

Ⓒ $x \geq -4$ Ⓓ $x > -4$

7. A carnival earns \$2125 by selling 600 tickets. Adult tickets cost \$5 and child tickets cost \$2.50. How many of each type of ticket are sold?

8. Which expression is equivalent to $-2x + 15x^2 - 8$?

Ⓐ $(5x + 4)(3x + 2)$ Ⓑ $(5x + 4)(3x - 2)$

Ⓒ $(3x - 2)(5x - 4)$ Ⓓ $(5x - 4)(3x + 2)$

9. Consider the graphs of functions f and g. Find the value of h.

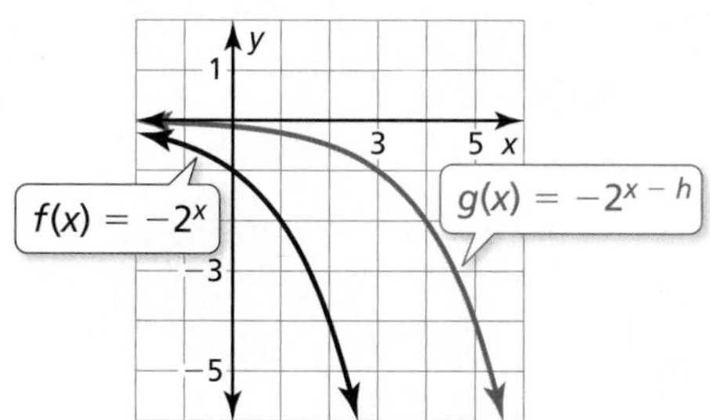

10. You design a hole for a miniature golf course as shown. Find the perimeter when the area is 216 square feet.

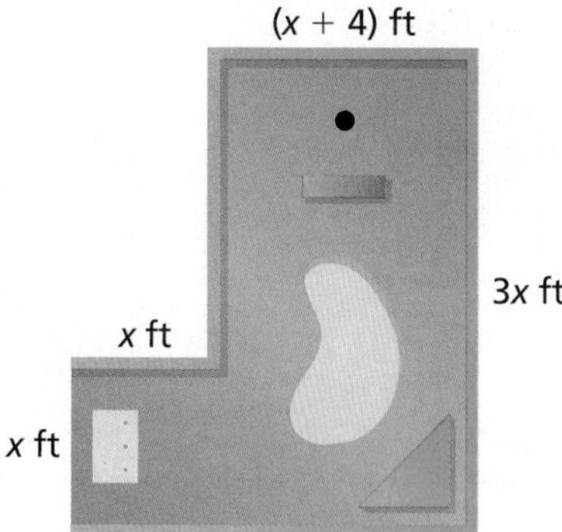

11. Which is a recursive rule for $a_n = -3n + 5$?

Ⓐ $a_1 = 5, a_n = a_{n-1} - 3$ Ⓑ $a_1 = 2, a_n = a_{n-1} + 5$

Ⓒ $a_1 = 2, a_n = a_{n-1} - 3$ Ⓓ $a_1 = 2, a_n = a_{n-1} + 3$

8 Graphing Quadratic Functions

NATIONAL GEOGRAPHIC EXPLORER

José Urteaga

Conservationist José Urteaga has been working in sea turtle and coastal habitat conservation in Central America since 2002. He uses interdisciplinary methods and common sense to find solutions that integrate human needs and conservation. He is an active member of several sea turtle conservation networks.

- What is an *endangered species*? What is an *extinct species*?
- How many endangered species are there on Earth? What are some reasons that a species becomes endangered?
- Of the seven species of sea turtles, which are considered endangered?

STEM

The United States Fish and Wildlife Service maintains a worldwide list of endangered species. In the Performance Task you will analyze sea turtle nesting trends in a region. You will write a report that includes methods to increase the population.

Wildlife Conservation

Preparing for Chapter 8

Chapter Learning Target Understand graphing quadratic functions.

Chapter Success Criteria
- ◆ I can identify characteristics of quadratic functions.
- ◆ I can describe how to graph quadratic functions in different forms.
- ■ I can find zeros of functions using intercept form.
- ■ I can choose an appropriate function to model data.

◆ Surface
■ Deep

Chapter Vocabulary

Work with a partner. Discuss each of the vocabulary terms.

vertex	zero of a function	minimum value
axis of symmetry	maximum value	average rate of change

Mathematical Practices

Construct Viable Arguments and Critique the Reasoning of Others

Mathematically proficient students understand and use previously established results in constructing arguments.

Work with a partner. The graphs of three different parent functions are shown.

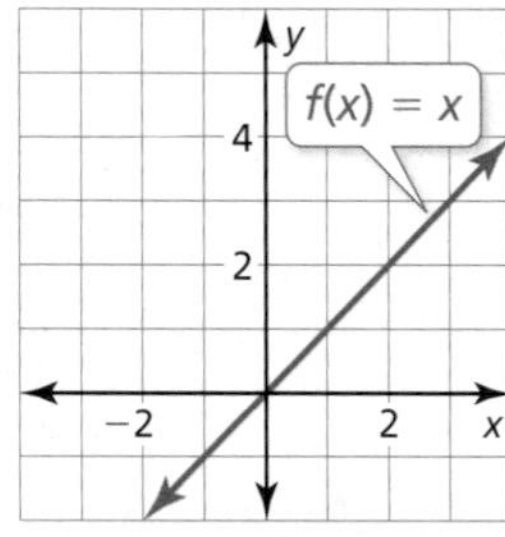

linear function

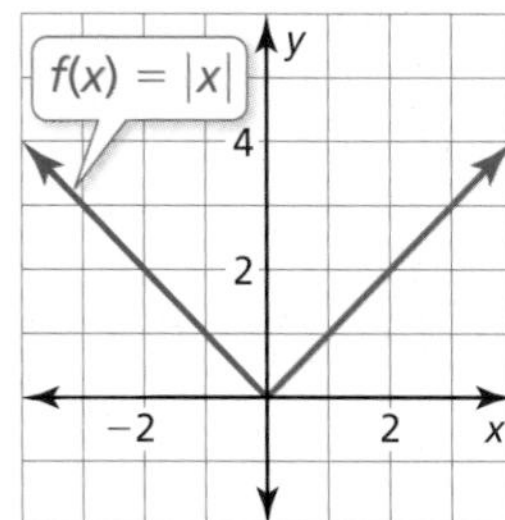

absolute value function

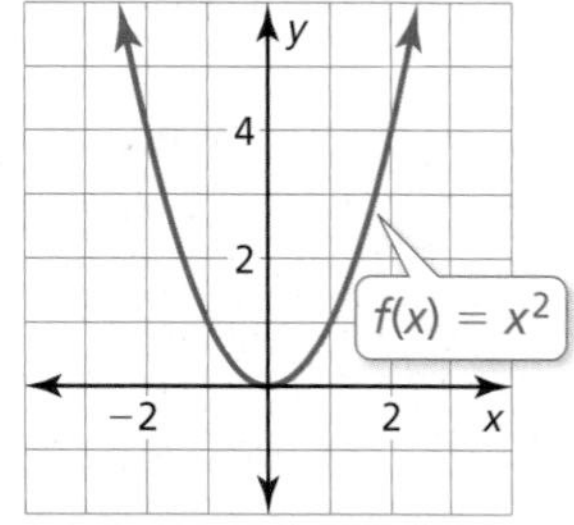

quadratic function

1. For each case below, describe the effect of n on the graph of the parent linear and absolute value functions. Then make an argument about the effects of n on the graph of the parent quadratic function. Explain your reasoning.

   $n \cdot f(x)$ $\quad f(nx)$ $\quad f(x - n)$ $\quad f(x) + n$

2. Use technology to graph each of the following quadratic functions. Do the results support your argument? Explain.

   $y = 3x^2$ $\quad y = \left(\frac{1}{4}x\right)^2$ $\quad y = (x - 5)^2$ $\quad y = x^2 + 1$

   $y = \frac{1}{2}x^2$ $\quad y = (2x)^2$ $\quad y = (x + 4)^2$ $\quad y = x^2 - 6$

8 Prepare WITH CalcChat®

Graphing Linear Equations

Example 1 **Graph $y = -x - 1$.**

Make a table of values.

x	$y = -x - 1$	y	(x, y)
-1	$y = -(-1) - 1$	0	$(-1, 0)$
0	$y = -(0) - 1$	-1	$(0, -1)$
1	$y = -(1) - 1$	-2	$(1, -2)$
2	$y = -(2) - 1$	-3	$(2, -3)$

Plot the ordered pairs. Then draw a line through the points.

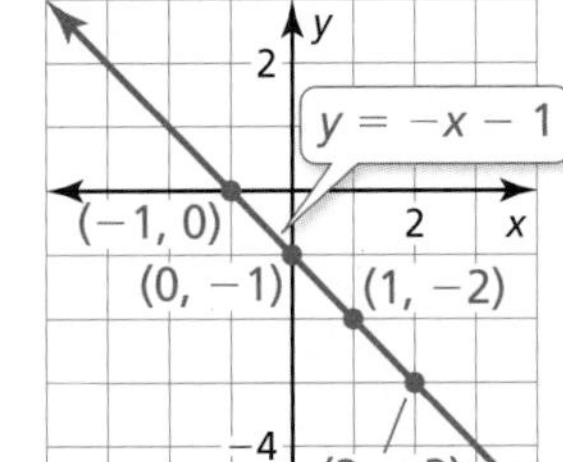

Graph the linear equation.

1. $y = 2x - 3$
2. $y = -3x + 4$
3. $y = -\frac{1}{2}x - 2$
4. $y = \frac{2}{3}x + 5$

Evaluating Expressions

Example 2 **Evaluate $2x^2 + 3x - 5$ when $x = -1$.**

$$2x^2 + 3x - 5 = 2(-1)^2 + 3(-1) - 5 \quad \text{Substitute } -1 \text{ for } x.$$
$$= 2(1) + 3(-1) - 5 \quad \text{Evaluate the power.}$$
$$= 2 - 3 - 5 \quad \text{Multiply.}$$
$$= -6 \quad \text{Subtract.}$$

Evaluate the expression when $x = -2$.

5. $5x^2 - 9$
6. $3x^2 + x - 2$
7. $-x^2 + 4x + 1$
8. $x^2 + 8x + 5$
9. $-\frac{1}{2}x^2 - 4x + 3$
10. $-4x^2 + \frac{3}{4}x - 6$
11. **MP PATTERNS** Complete the table. Find a pattern in the differences of consecutive values and use the pattern to identify the next three terms.

x	1	2	3	4	5
$y = ax^2$					

8.1 Graphing $f(x) = ax^2$

Learning Target Graph and describe functions of the form $f(x) = ax^2$.

Success Criteria
- I can identify characteristics of quadratic functions and their graphs.
- I can graph quadratic functions of the form $f(x) = ax^2$.
- I can compare the graph of $f(x) = ax^2$ to the graph of the parent quadratic function $f(x) = x^2$.

EXPLORE IT! Understanding Graphs of Quadratic Functions

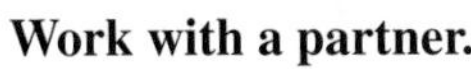

Work with a partner.

a. Graph $y = x^2$. Make several observations about the graph.

b. Let f be the parent quadratic function $f(x) = x^2$. Which of the following functions open up? open down? Which is the widest? narrowest? Explain your reasoning.

$m(x) = \frac{1}{2} \bullet f(x)$	$n(x) = -2 \bullet f(x)$
$p(x) = -f(x)$	$q(x) = 1.5 \bullet f(x)$

c. Match each function with its graph. Use technology to check your answers.

i. $g(x) = 3x^2$ **ii.** $g(x) = -5x^2$

iii. $g(x) = -0.6x^2$ **iv.** $g(x) = \frac{1}{10}x^2$

A.

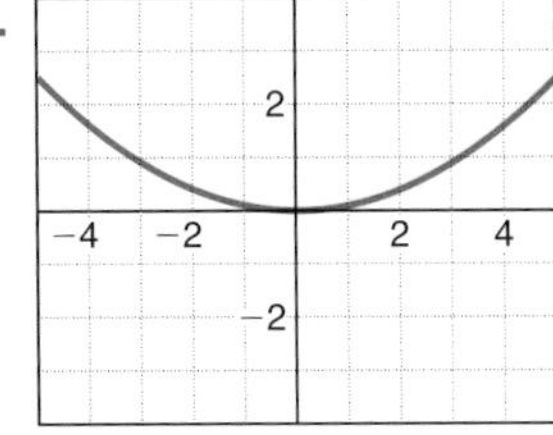

B.

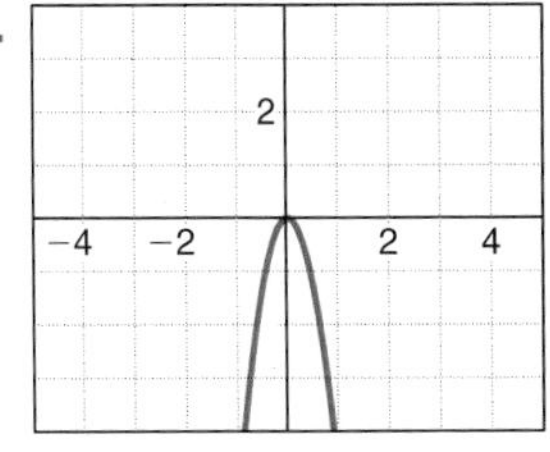

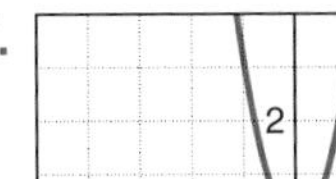

C.

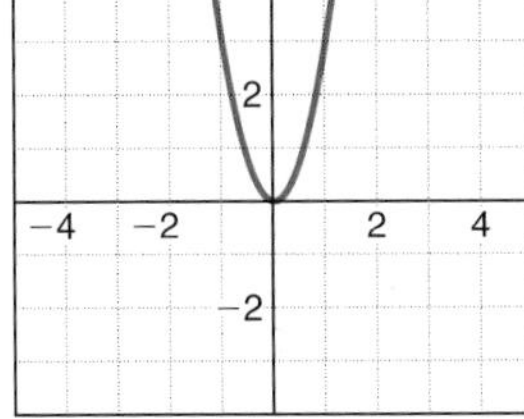

D.

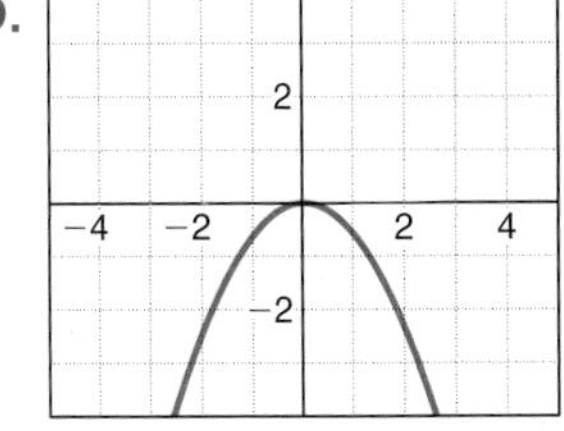

d. How does the value of a affect the graph of $g(x) = ax^2$? Use technology to verify your answer.

Math Practice

Find Entry Points
Given $f(x) = x^2$ and $g(x) = 3x^2$, explain how $f(c)$ compares to $g(c)$ for any value of c.

Identifying Characteristics of Quadratic Functions

GO DIGITAL

Vocabulary

quadratic function, *p. 426*
parabola, *p. 426*
vertex, *p. 426*
axis of symmetry, *p. 426*

A **quadratic function** is a nonlinear function that can be written in the standard form $y = ax^2 + bx + c$, where $a \neq 0$. The U-shaped graph of a quadratic function is called a **parabola**. In this lesson, you will graph quadratic functions where b and c equal 0.

KEY IDEA

Characteristics of Quadratic Functions

The *parent quadratic function* is $f(x) = x^2$. The graphs of all other quadratic functions are *transformations* of the graph of the parent quadratic function.

The lowest point on a parabola that opens up or the highest point on a parabola that opens down is the **vertex**. The vertex of the graph of $f(x) = x^2$ is (0, 0).

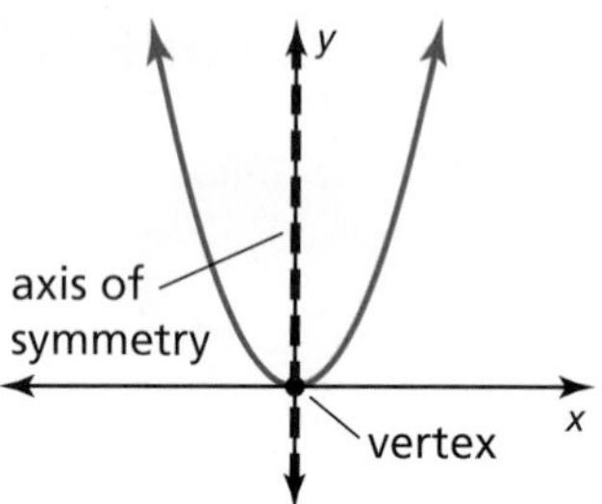

The vertical line that divides the parabola into two symmetric parts is the **axis of symmetry**. The axis of symmetry passes through the vertex. For the graph of $f(x) = x^2$, the axis of symmetry is the y-axis, or $x = 0$.

REMEMBER

The notation $f(x)$ is another name for y.

EXAMPLE 1 Identifying Characteristics of a Quadratic Function

Identify characteristics of the quadratic function and its graph.

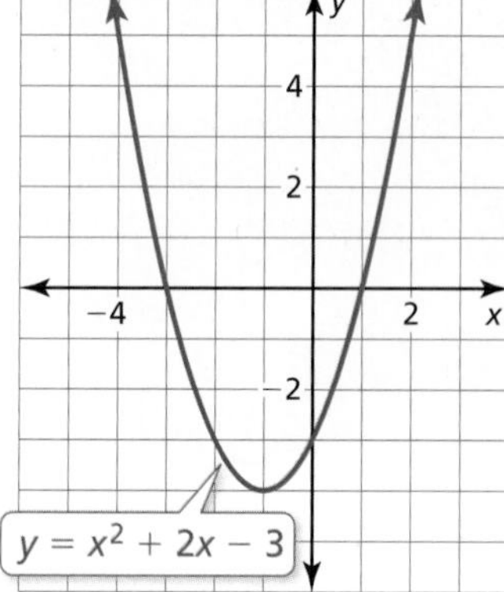

SOLUTION

Using the graph, you can identify characteristics such as the vertex and the axis of symmetry.

Vertex: $(-1, -4)$

Axis of symmetry: $x = -1$

You can also determine the following characteristics:

- The domain is all real numbers. The range is all real numbers greater than or equal to -4.
- The function is decreasing when $x < -1$ and increasing when $x > -1$.
- The y-intercept is -3. The x-intercepts are -3 and 1.
- The function is positive when $x < -3$, negative when $-3 < x < 1$, and positive when $x > 1$.
- end behavior: $y \to +\infty$ as $x \to -\infty$ and $y \to +\infty$ as $x \to +\infty$

STUDY TIP

The points $(-1, -4)$, $(0, -3)$, $(-3, 0)$, and $(1, 0)$ are solutions of the equation. This verifies that the vertex and intercepts are correct.

SELF-ASSESSMENT

1 I do not understand. 2 I can do it with help. 3 I can do it on my own. 4 I can teach someone else.

Identify characteristics of the quadratic function and its graph.

1.

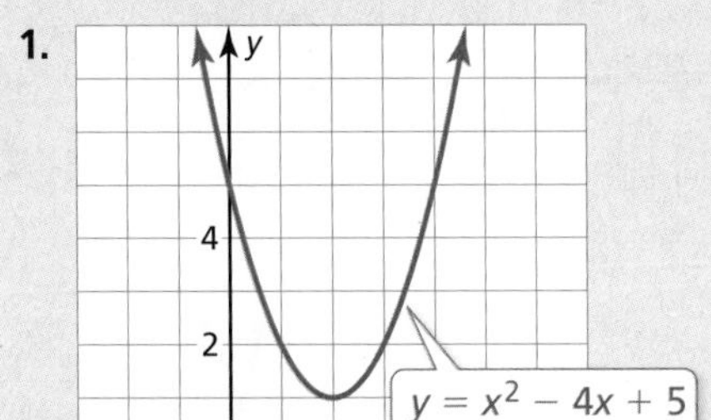

2.

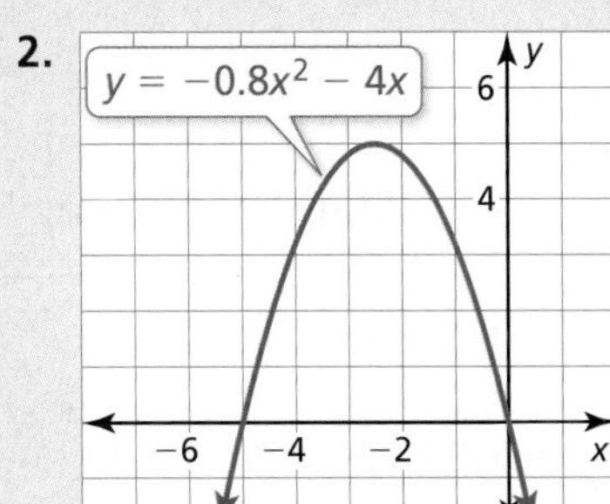

Graphing and Using $f(x) = ax^2$

REMEMBER

The graph of $y = a \cdot f(x)$ is a vertical stretch or shrink by a factor of a of the graph of $y = f(x)$, where $a > 0$ and $a \neq 1$.

The graph of $y = -f(x)$ is a reflection in the x-axis of the graph of $y = f(x)$.

KEY IDEA

Graphing $f(x) = ax^2$ When $a > 0$

- When $0 < a < 1$, the graph of $f(x) = ax^2$ is a vertical shrink of the graph of $f(x) = x^2$.
- When $a > 1$, the graph of $f(x) = ax^2$ is a vertical stretch of the graph of $f(x) = x^2$.

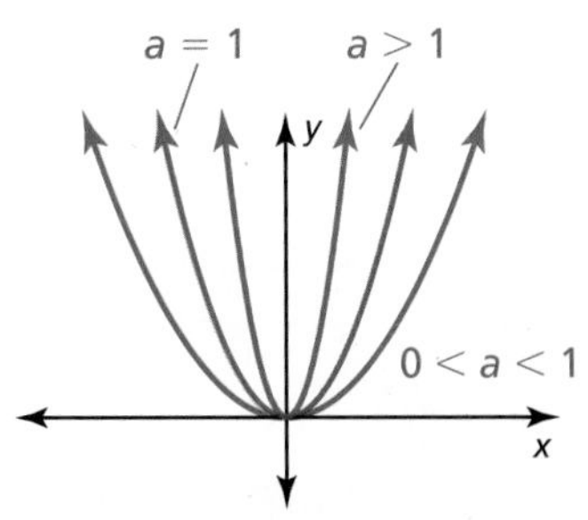

Graphing $f(x) = ax^2$ When $a < 0$

- When $-1 < a < 0$, the graph of $f(x) = ax^2$ is a vertical shrink with a reflection in the x-axis of the graph of $f(x) = x^2$.
- When $a < -1$, the graph of $f(x) = ax^2$ is a vertical stretch with a reflection in the x-axis of the graph of $f(x) = x^2$.

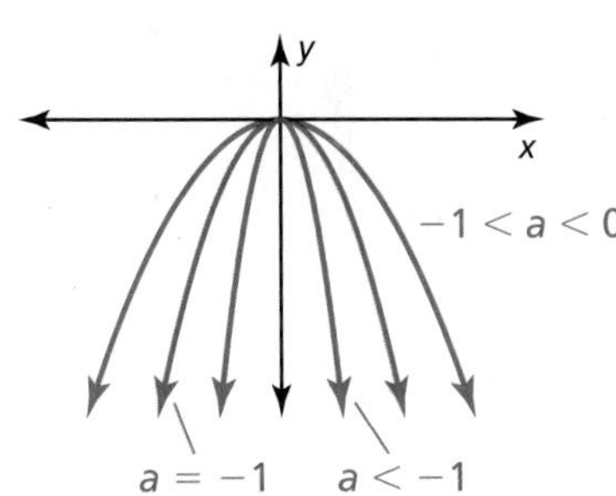

EXAMPLE 2 Graphing $y = ax^2$ When $a > 0$

Graph $g(x) = 2x^2$. Compare the graph to the graph of $f(x) = x^2$.

SOLUTION

Step 1 Make a table of values.

Step 2 Plot the ordered pairs.

x	−2	−1	0	1	2
$g(x)$	8	2	0	2	8

Step 3 Draw a smooth curve through the points.

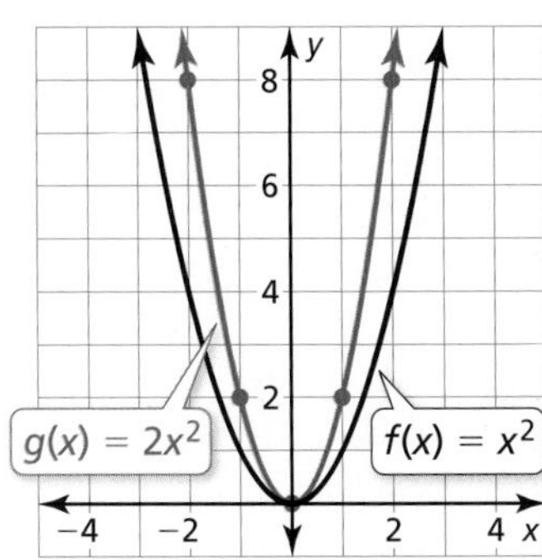

▶ Both graphs open up and have the same vertex, (0, 0), and the same axis of symmetry, $x = 0$. The graph of g is narrower than the graph of f because the graph of g is a vertical stretch by a factor of 2 of the graph of f.

EXAMPLE 3 Graphing $y = ax^2$ When $a < 0$

Graph $h(x) = -\frac{1}{3}x^2$. Compare the graph to the graph of $f(x) = x^2$.

SOLUTION

Step 1 Make a table of values.

> **STUDY TIP**
> To make the calculations easier, choose x-values that are multiples of 3.

x	−6	−3	0	3	6
$h(x)$	−12	−3	0	−3	−12

Step 2 Plot the ordered pairs.

Step 3 Draw a smooth curve through the points.

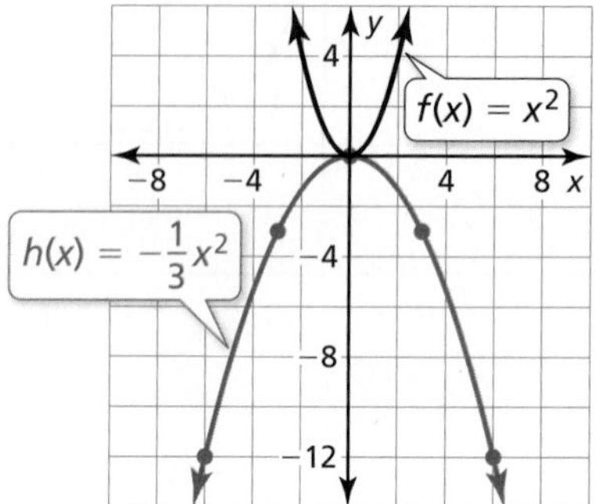

▶ The graphs have the same vertex, (0, 0), and the same axis of symmetry, $x = 0$, but the graph of h opens down and is wider than the graph of f. So, the graph of h is a vertical shrink by a factor of $\frac{1}{3}$ and a reflection in the x-axis of the graph of f.

EXAMPLE 4 Modeling Real Life

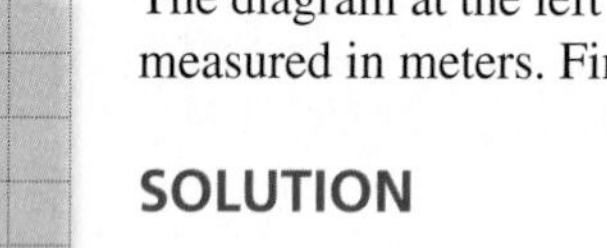

The diagram at the left shows the cross section of a satellite dish, where x and y are measured in meters. Find the width and depth of the dish.

SOLUTION

Use the domain of the function to find the width of the dish. Use the range to find the depth.

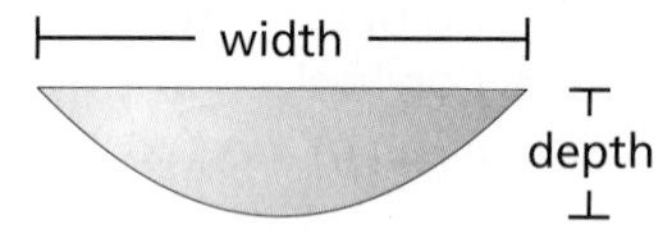

The leftmost point on the graph is $(-2, 1)$, and the rightmost point is $(2, 1)$. So, the domain is $-2 \le x \le 2$, which represents 4 meters.

The lowest point on the graph is $(0, 0)$, and the highest points on the graph are $(-2, 1)$ and $(2, 1)$. So, the range is $0 \le y \le 1$, which represents 1 meter.

▶ So, the satellite dish is 4 meters wide and 1 meter deep.

SELF-ASSESSMENT

1 I do not understand. 2 I can do it with help. 3 I can do it on my own. 4 I can teach someone else.

Graph the function. Compare the graph to the graph of $f(x) = x^2$.

3. $g(x) = 5x^2$

4. $h(x) = \frac{1}{3}x^2$

5. $n(x) = \frac{3}{2}x^2$

6. $p(x) = -3x^2$

7. $q(x) = -0.1x^2$

8. $g(x) = -\frac{1}{4}x^2$

9. WRITING When does the graph of a quadratic function open up? open down?

10. MP REASONING Explain why graphs of quadratic functions have a different shape than graphs of linear functions and exponential functions.

11. The cross section of another dish can be modeled by the graph of $f(x) = 0.75x^2$, where x and $f(x)$ are measured in feet and $-2 \le x \le 2$. Your friend says that the dish is deeper than the dish in Example 4 because the highest points on the graph of f are $(-2, 3)$ and $(2, 3)$. Is your friend correct? Explain.

8.1 Practice WITH CalcChat® AND CalcView®

GO DIGITAL

In Exercises 1–4, identify characteristics of the quadratic function and its graph. Example 1

1. 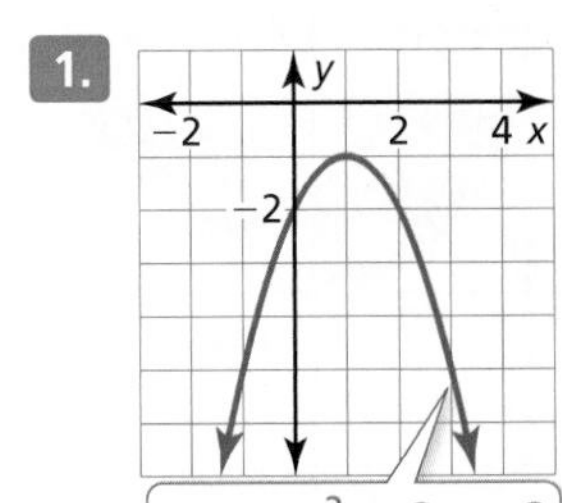

2. 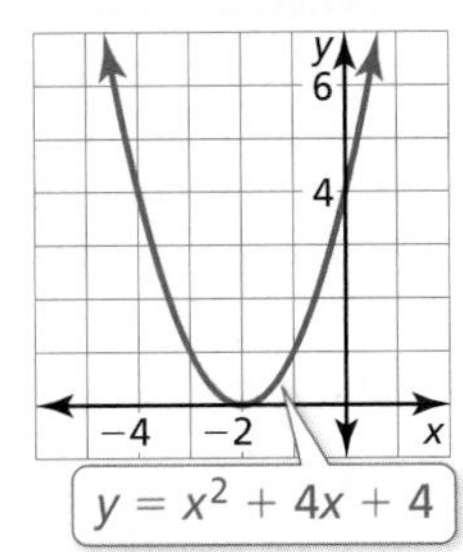

3. 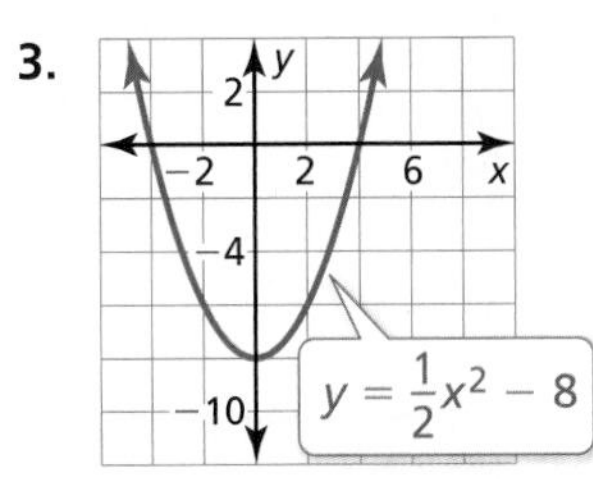

4. 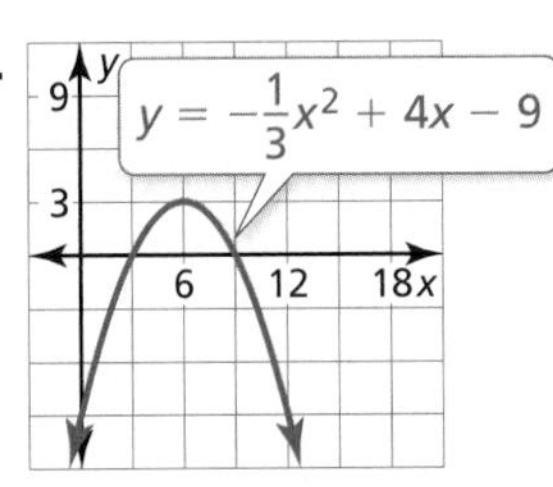

In Exercises 5–12, graph the function. Compare the graph to the graph of $f(x) = x^2$. Examples 2 and 3

5. $g(x) = 6x^2$
6. $b(x) = 2.5x^2$
7. $h(x) = \frac{1}{4}x^2$
8. $j(x) = 0.75x^2$
9. $m(x) = -2x^2$
10. $q(x) = -\frac{9}{2}x^2$
11. $k(x) = -0.2x^2$
12. $p(x) = -\frac{2}{3}x^2$

In Exercises 13 and 14, graph the function. Compare the graph to the graph of $y = -4x^2$.

13. $y = 4x^2$
14. $y = -0.4x^2$

15. **MODELING REAL LIFE** The arch support of a bridge can be modeled by $y = -0.0012x^2$, where x and y are measured in feet. Find the height and width of the arch. Example 4

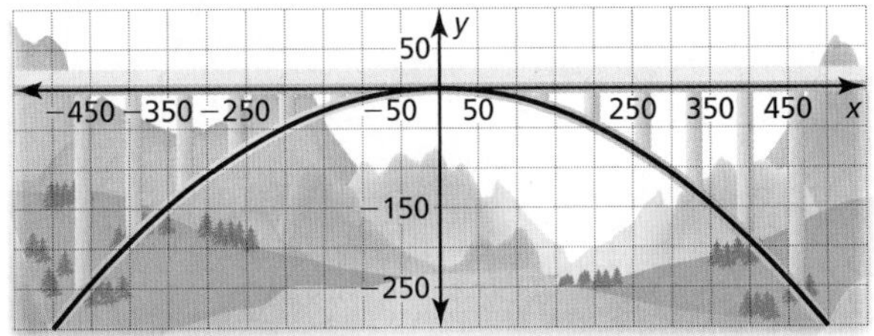

16. **MODELING REAL LIFE** The cross section of a parabolic solar cooker can be modeled by $f(x) = \frac{1}{45}x^2$, where x and $f(x)$ are measured in inches and $-30 \le x \le 30$. Graph the function. Then find the width and depth of the solar cooker.

17. **ERROR ANALYSIS** Describe and correct the error in graphing and comparing $f(x) = x^2$ and $g(x) = -0.5x^2$.

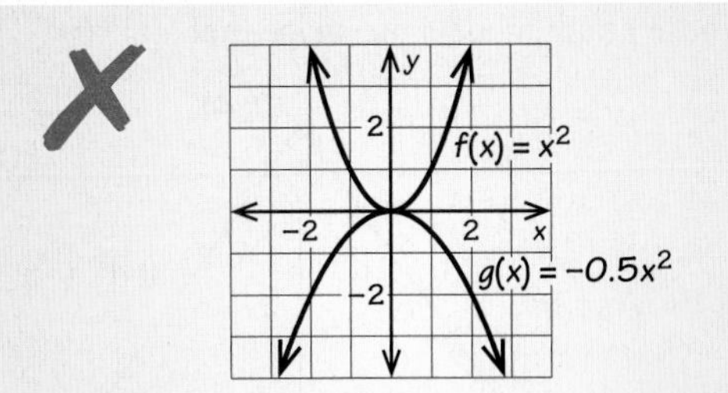

The graphs have the same vertex and the same axis of symmetry. The graph of g is a vertical stretch by a factor of 0.5 and a reflection in the x-axis of the graph of f.

18. **HOW DO YOU SEE IT?**
Describe the possible values of a.

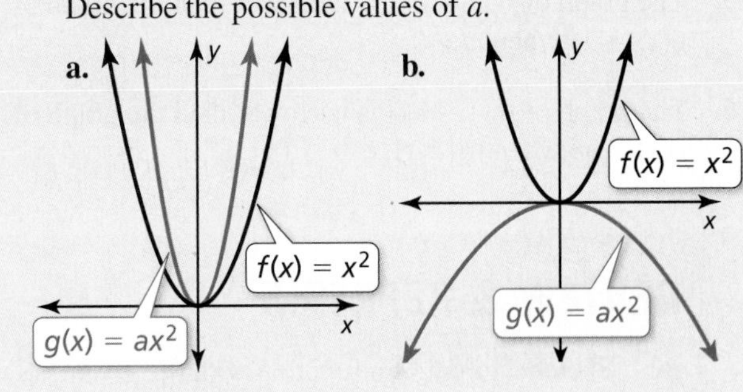

ANALYZING GRAPHS In Exercises 19–21, use the graph.

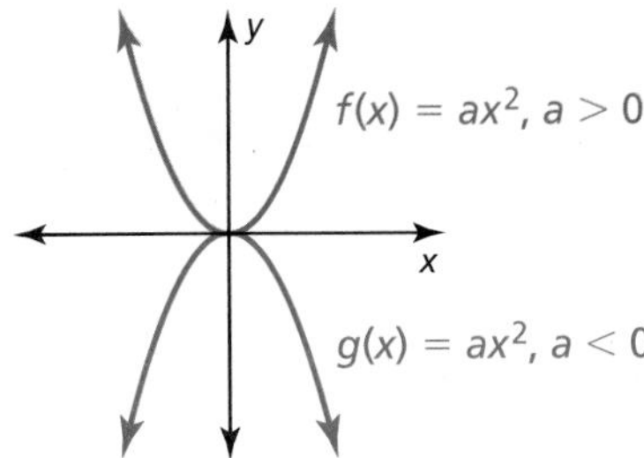

19. When is each function increasing? decreasing?
20. Describe the end behavior of each function.
21. Which function could include the point $(-2, 3)$? Find the value of a when the graph passes through $(-2, 3)$.
22. **MP REASONING** Is the x-intercept of the graph of $f(x) = ax^2$ always 0? Justify your answer.
23. **MP REASONING** A parabola opens up and passes through $(-4, 2)$ and $(6, -3)$. How do you know that $(-4, 2)$ is not the vertex?

24. **THOUGHT PROVOKING**
Draw the isosceles triangle shown. Divide each leg into eight congruent segments. Connect the highest point of one leg with the lowest point of the other leg. Then connect the second highest point of one leg to the second lowest point of the other leg. Continue this process. Write a quadratic function whose graph models the shape that appears.

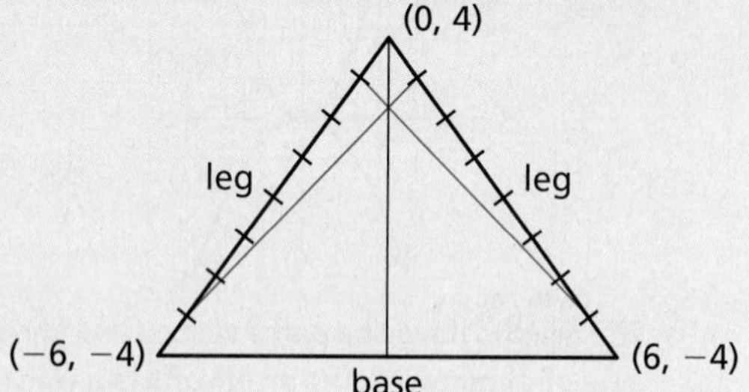

ABSTRACT REASONING In Exercises 25–28, determine whether the statement is *always*, *sometimes*, or *never* true. Explain your reasoning.

25. The graph of $f(x) = ax^2$ is narrower than the graph of $g(x) = x^2$ when $a > 0$.

26. The graph of $f(x) = ax^2$ is narrower than the graph of $g(x) = x^2$ when $|a| > 1$.

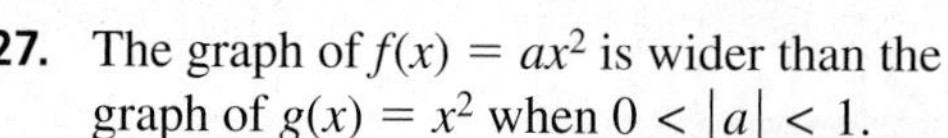

27. The graph of $f(x) = ax^2$ is wider than the graph of $g(x) = x^2$ when $0 < |a| < 1$.

28. The graph of $f(x) = ax^2$ is wider than the graph of $g(x) = dx^2$ when $|a| > |d|$.

29. **MAKING AN ARGUMENT**
The diagram shows the parabolic cross section of a swirling glass of water, where x and y are measured in centimeters.

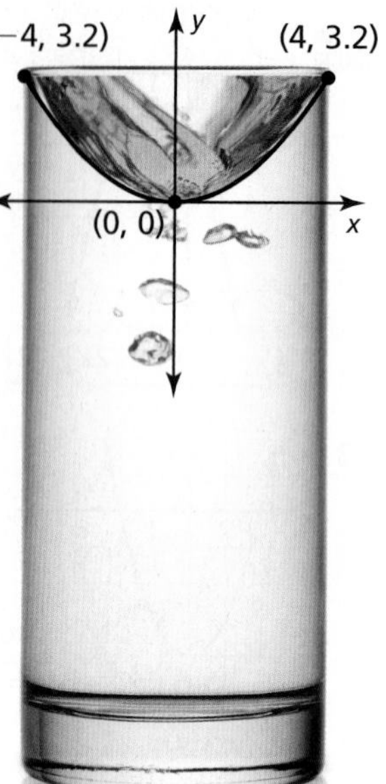

a. About how wide is the mouth of the glass?

b. Does the rotational speed of the water have to increase or decrease for the cross section to be modeled by $y = 0.1x^2$? Explain your reasoning.

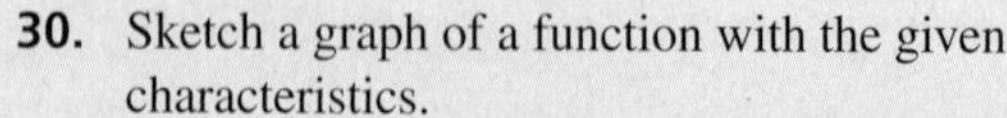

REVIEW & REFRESH

30. Sketch a graph of a function with the given characteristics.
- The x-intercepts are -4, -1, and 2.5.
- $y \to -\infty$ as $x \to -\infty$ and $y \to +\infty$ as $x \to +\infty$.

In Exercises 31 and 32, evaluate the expression when $n = 3$ and $x = -2$.

31. $-4n^2 + 11$

32. $n + 2x^2$

In Exercises 33–36, factor the polynomial completely.

33. $121 - 4h^2$

34. $-4t^2 - 3t + 7$

35. $x^2 - 6x - 55$

36. $5r^4 - 5r^3 + 30r^2$

37. **MP STRUCTURE** The function $y = 500\left(1 + \frac{0.03}{4}\right)^{4t}$ represents the balance y (in dollars) of a savings account after t years. Identify the principal, the annual interest rate, and the number of times the interest is compounded per year.

38. Write an equation for the nth term of the arithmetic sequence shown. Then find a_{13}.

25, 14, 3, −8, . . .

In Exercises 39 and 40, graph the function. Compare the graph to the graph of $f(x) = x^2$.

39. $h(x) = -x^2$

40. $b(x) = 8x^2$

41. **MODELING REAL LIFE** You buy ribbon and scrapbook paper for a project. Each spool of ribbon costs \$4, and each piece of scrapbook paper costs \$0.80. You spend \$28 on a total of 23 items. How many of each item do you buy?

42. Describe the slope of the line. Then find the slope.

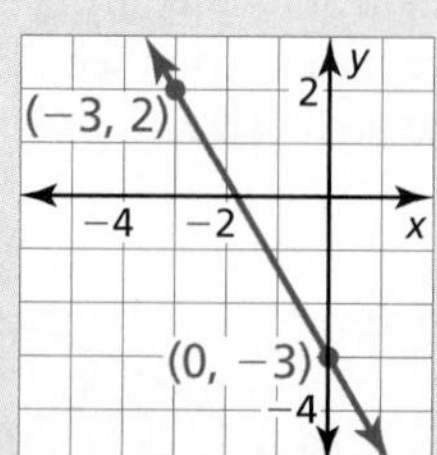

In Exercises 43 and 44, graph the system. Identify a solution.

43. $y \geq -3x + 4$
$y < 5$

44. $\frac{1}{2}x - y > 0$
$x \leq 4$
$y > -2$

8.2 Graphing $f(x) = ax^2 + c$

Learning Target Graph and describe functions of the form $f(x) = ax^2 + c$.

Success Criteria

- I can graph quadratic functions of the form $f(x) = ax^2 + c$.
- I can compare the graph of $f(x) = ax^2 + c$ to the graph of the parent quadratic function.
- I can describe translations of the graph of $f(x) = ax^2 + c$.
- I can find zeros of $f(x) = ax^2 + c$.

EXPLORE IT! Graphing $y = ax^2 + c$

Work with a partner.

a. Describe what you expect the graphs of f and g to look like. Then sketch the graphs of the functions in the same coordinate plane.

i. $f(x) = x^2$ and $g(x) = x^2 + 2$

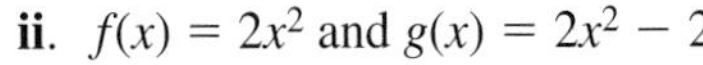

ii. $f(x) = 2x^2$ and $g(x) = 2x^2 - 2$

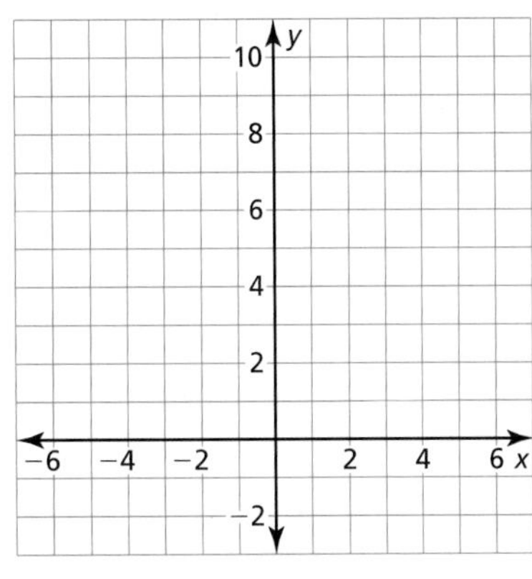

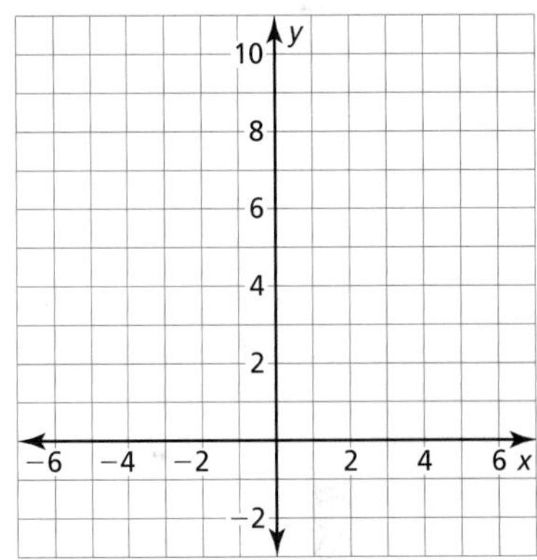

iii. $f(x) = x^2$ and $g(x) = f(x) - 6$

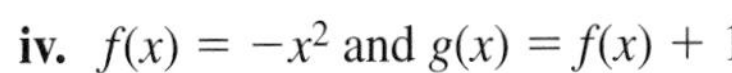

iv. $f(x) = -x^2$ and $g(x) = f(x) + 1$

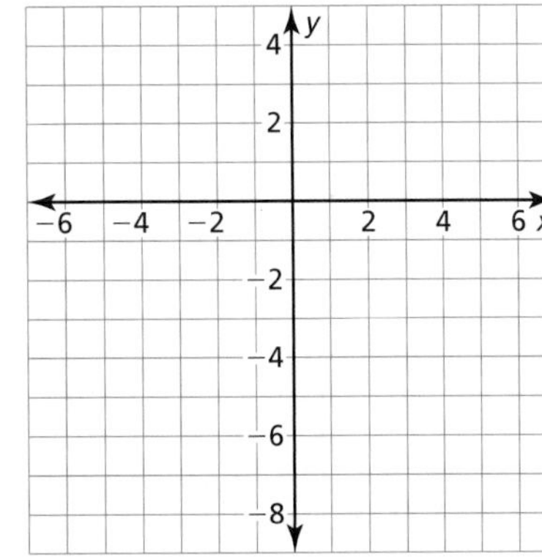

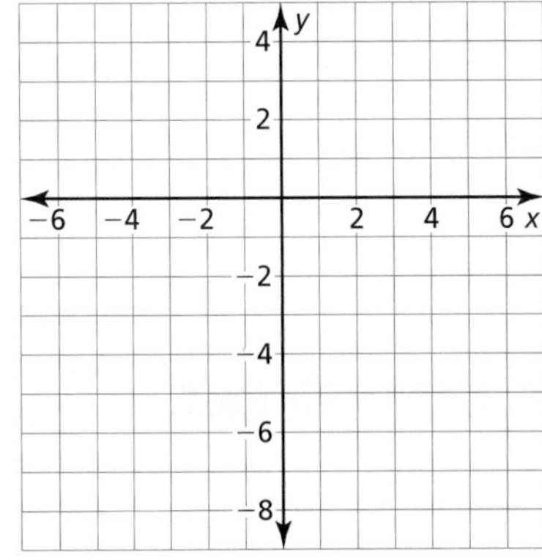

b. What is the y-intercept of the graph of $f(x) = ax^2 + c$? Justify your answer.

c. How does changing the value of c affect the graph of $f(x) = ax^2 + c$?

Math Practice

Construct Arguments
Explain how you can use the signs of a and c to determine the number of x-intercepts of the graph of $y = ax^2 + c$.

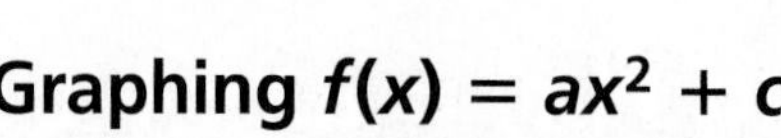

Graphing $f(x) = ax^2 + c$

Vocabulary 

zero of a function, *p. 434*

KEY IDEA

Graphing $f(x) = ax^2 + c$

- When $c > 0$, the graph of $f(x) = ax^2 + c$ is a vertical translation c units up of the graph of $f(x) = ax^2$.
- When $c < 0$, the graph of $f(x) = ax^2 + c$ is a vertical translation $|c|$ units down of the graph of $f(x) = ax^2$.

The vertex of the graph of $f(x) = ax^2 + c$ is $(0, c)$, and the axis of symmetry is $x = 0$.

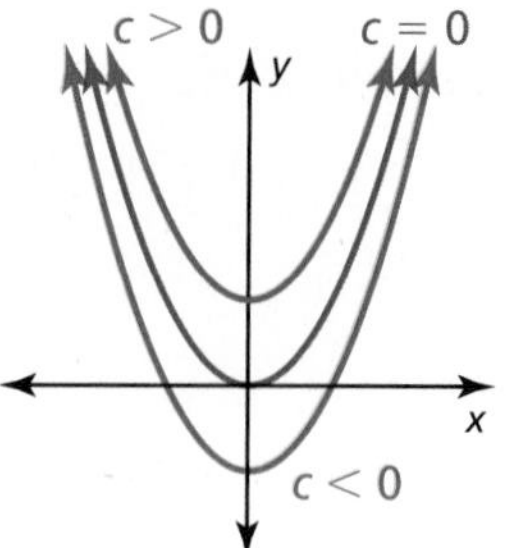

EXAMPLE 1 **Graphing $y = x^2 + c$** 

Graph $g(x) = x^2 - 2$. Compare the graph to the graph of $f(x) = x^2$.

SOLUTION

Step 1 Make a table of values.

x	-2	-1	0	1	2
$g(x)$	2	-1	-2	-1	2

Step 2 Plot the ordered pairs.

Step 3 Draw a smooth curve through the points.

REMEMBER
The graph of $y = f(x) + k$ is a vertical translation, and the graph of $y = f(x - h)$ is a horizontal translation of the graph of f.

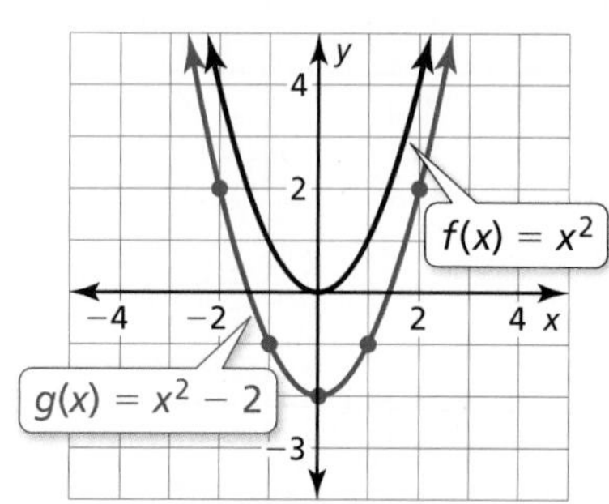

▶ Both graphs open up and have the same axis of symmetry, $x = 0$. The vertex of the graph of g, $(0, -2)$, is below the vertex of the graph of f, $(0, 0)$, because the graph of g is a vertical translation 2 units down of the graph of f.

SELF-ASSESSMENT 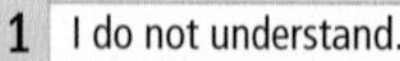 1 I do not understand. 2 I can do it with help. 3 I can do it on my own. 4 I can teach someone else.

Graph the function. Compare the graph to the graph of $f(x) = x^2$.

1. $g(x) = x^2 - 5$

2. $h(x) = x^2 + 3$

3. **MP REASONING** The figure shows the graph of a quadratic function of the form $y = x^2 + c$. Find the value of c. Explain your reasoning.

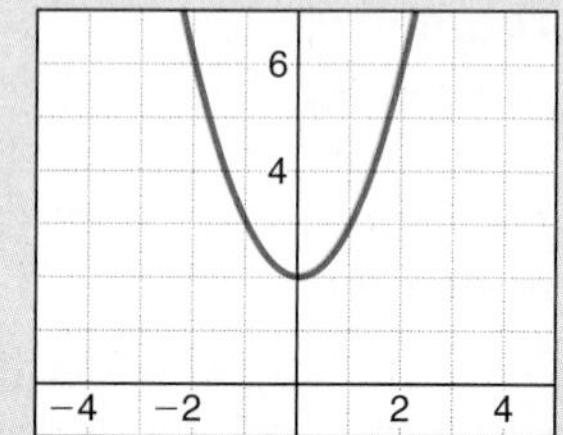

EXAMPLE 2 Graphing $y = ax^2 + c$

Graph $g(x) = 4x^2 + 1$. Compare the graph to the graph of $f(x) = x^2$.

SOLUTION

Step 1 Make a table of values.

x	−2	−1	0	1	2
$g(x)$	17	5	1	5	17

Step 2 Plot the ordered pairs.

Step 3 Draw a smooth curve through the points.

▶ Both graphs open up and have the same axis of symmetry, $x = 0$. The graph of g is narrower, and its vertex, (0, 1), is above the vertex of the graph of f, (0, 0). So, the graph of g is a vertical stretch by a factor of 4 and a vertical translation 1 unit up of the graph of f.

EXAMPLE 3 Translating the Graph of $y = ax^2 + c$

Let $f(x) = -0.5x^2 + 2$ and $g(x) = f(x) - 7$.

a. Describe the transformation from the graph of f to the graph of g. Then graph f and g in the same coordinate plane.

b. Write an equation that represents g in terms of x.

SOLUTION

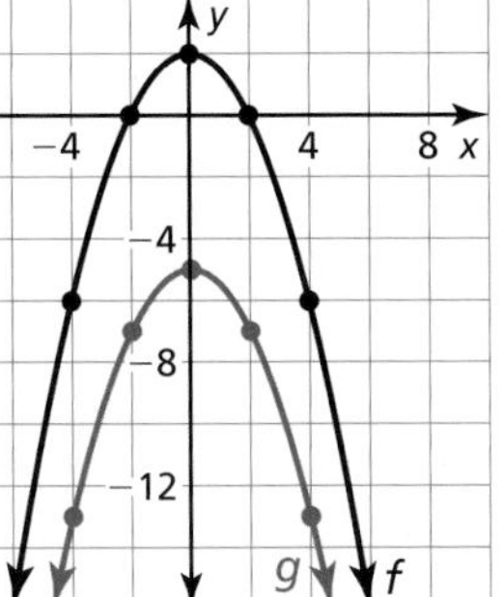

a. The function g is of the form $y = f(x) + k$, where $k = -7$. So, the graph of g is a vertical translation 7 units down of the graph of f.

x	−4	−2	0	2	4
$f(x)$	−6	0	2	0	−6
$g(x)$	−13	−7	−5	−7	−13

$-0.5x^2 + 2$

$f(x) - 7$

b. $g(x) = f(x) - 7$ Write the function g.

$= -0.5x^2 + 2 - 7$ Substitute for $f(x)$.

$= -0.5x^2 - 5$ Subtract.

▶ So, the equation $g(x) = -0.5x^2 - 5$ represents g in terms of x.

SELF-ASSESSMENT

1 I do not understand. 2 I can do it with help. 3 I can do it on my own. 4 I can teach someone else.

Graph the function. Compare the graph to the graph of $f(x) = x^2$.

4. $g(x) = 2x^2 - 5$

5. $m(x) = -x^2 - 3$

6. $h(x) = -\frac{1}{4}x^2 + 4$

7. Let $f(x) = 3x^2 - 1$ and $g(x) = f(x) + 3$.

a. Describe the transformation from the graph of f to the graph of g. Then graph f and g in the same coordinate plane.

b. Write an equation that represents g in terms of x.

8. WRITING How does the graph of $y = ax^2 + c$ compare to the graph of $y = x^2$?

Solving Real-Life Problems

A **zero of a function** f is an x-value for which $f(x) = 0$. A zero of a function is an x-intercept of the graph of the function.

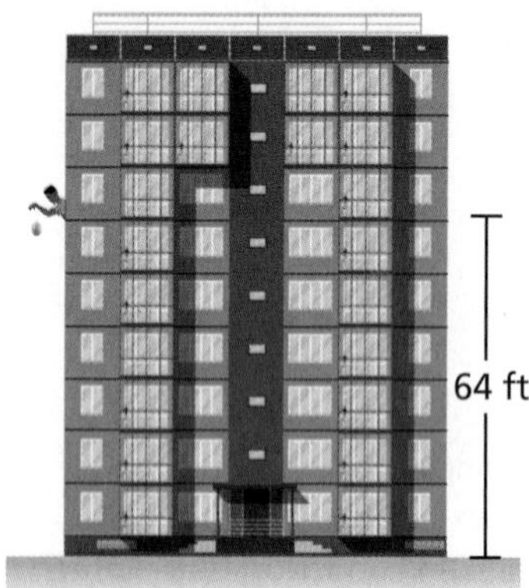

EXAMPLE 4 Modeling Real Life

The function $f(t) = 16t^2$ represents the distance (in feet) a dropped object falls in t seconds. The function $g(t) = s_0$ represents the initial height (in feet) of the object.

a. Find and interpret $h(t) = -f(t) + g(t)$.

b. You drop an egg from a height of 64 feet. After how many seconds does the egg hit the ground?

c. Suppose the initial height changes by k feet. How will this affect part (b)?

SOLUTION

a. $h(t) = -f(t) + g(t)$ — Write the function h.

$= -(16t^2) + s_0$ — Substitute for $f(t)$ and $g(t)$.

$= -16t^2 + s_0$ — Simplify.

▶ The function $h(t) = -16t^2 + s_0$ represents the height (in feet) of a falling object t seconds after it is dropped from an initial height s_0 (in feet).

b. The initial height is 64 feet. So, the function $h(t) = -16t^2 + 64$ represents the height of the egg t seconds after you drop it. The egg hits the ground when $h(t) = 0$.

COMMON ERROR

The graph in Step 1 shows the height of the object over time, not the path the object follows.

Step 1 Make a table of values and sketch the graph.

t	0	1	2
$h(t)$	64	48	0

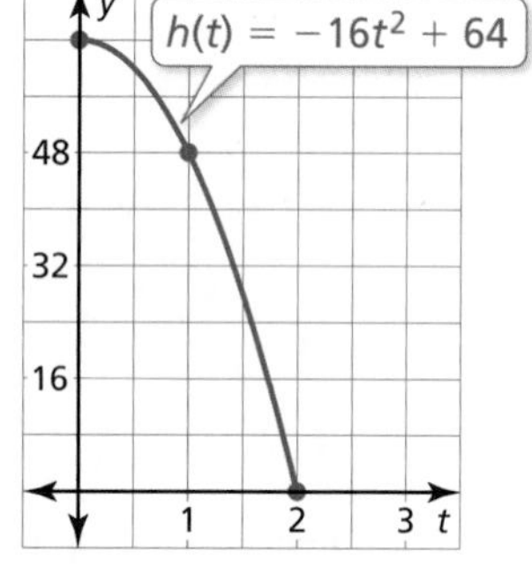

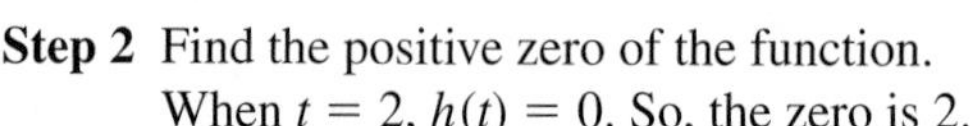

Step 2 Find the positive zero of the function. When $t = 2$, $h(t) = 0$. So, the zero is 2.

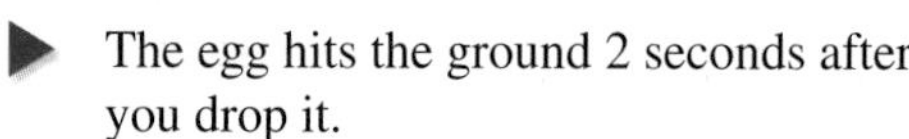

▶ The egg hits the ground 2 seconds after you drop it.

c. When the initial height changes by k feet, the graph of h is translated up k units when $k > 0$ or down $|k|$ units when $k < 0$. So, the x-intercept of the graph of h will move right when $k > 0$ or left when $k < 0$.

▶ When $k > 0$, the egg will take more than 2 seconds to hit the ground. When $k < 0$, the egg will take less than 2 seconds to hit the ground.

SELF-ASSESSMENT 1 I do not understand. 2 I can do it with help. 3 I can do it on my own. 4 I can teach someone else.

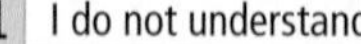
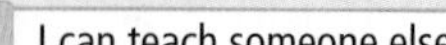

9. VOCABULARY A ______ of a function is an input for which the output is zero.

10. WHAT IF? In Example 4, you drop the egg from a height of 100 feet. After how many seconds does the egg hit the ground? Explain why only nonnegative values of t and $h(t)$ make sense in this situation.

8.2 Practice WITH CalcChat® AND CalcView®

GO DIGITAL

In Exercises 1–4, graph the function. Compare the graph to the graph of $f(x) = x^2$. *Example 1*

1. $g(x) = x^2 + 6$
2. $h(x) = x^2 + 8$
3. $p(x) = x^2 - 3$
4. $q(x) = x^2 - 1$

In Exercises 5–10, graph the function. Compare the graph to the graph of $f(x) = x^2$. *Example 2*

5. $g(x) = -x^2 + 3$
6. $h(x) = -x^2 - 7$
7. $s(x) = 2x^2 - 4$
8. $t(x) = -3x^2 + 1$
9. $p(x) = -\frac{1}{3}x^2 - 2$
10. $q(x) = \frac{1}{2}x^2 + 6$

In Exercises 11–14, describe the transformation from the graph of f to the graph of g. Then graph f and g in the same coordinate plane. Write an equation that represents g in terms of x. *Example 3*

11. $f(x) = 3x^2 + 4$
    $g(x) = f(x) + 2$
12. $f(x) = \frac{1}{2}x^2 + 1$
    $g(x) = f(x) - 4$
13. $f(x) = -\frac{1}{4}x^2 - 6$
    $g(x) = f(x) - 3$
14. $f(x) = 4x^2 - 5$
    $g(x) = f(x) + 7$

In Exercises 15–22, find the zeros of the function.

15. $y = x^2 - 1$
16. $y = x^2 - 36$
17. $f(x) = -x^2 + 25$
18. $f(x) = -x^2 + 49$
19. $f(x) = 4x^2 - 16$
20. $f(x) = 3x^2 - 27$
21. $f(x) = -12x^2 + 3$
22. $f(x) = -8x^2 + 98$

23. **MODELING REAL LIFE** You drop a water balloon from a height of 144 feet. *Example 4*
    a. What does the function $h(t) = -16t^2 + 144$ represent in this situation?
    b. After how many seconds does the water balloon hit the ground?

24. **MODELING REAL LIFE** An apple falls off a tree from a height of 36 feet.
    a. What does the function $h(t) = -16t^2 + 36$ represent in this situation?
    b. After how many seconds does the apple hit the ground?

25. **ERROR ANALYSIS** Describe and correct the error in finding the zero(s) of $f(x) = -\frac{1}{4}x^2 + 16$.

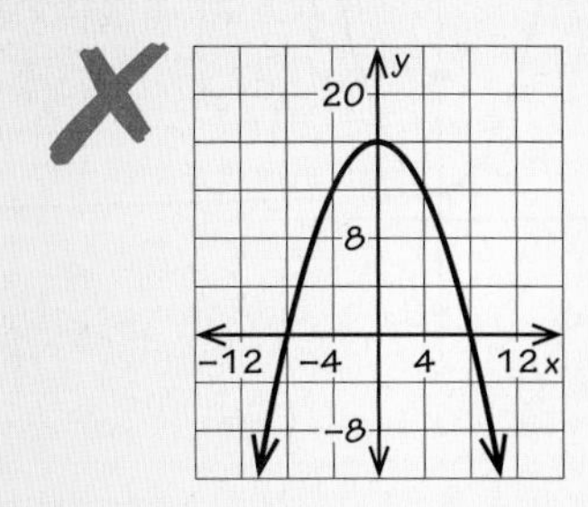

26. **DRAWING CONCLUSIONS** You and your friend both drop a ball at the same time. The functions represent the heights (in feet) of the balls after x seconds.

    Your ball: $h(x) = -16x^2 + 256$

    Friend's ball: $g(x) = -16x^2 + 300$

    a. Who drops the ball from a higher point?
    b. Write the function $T(x) = h(x) - g(x)$. What does $T(x)$ represent?
    c. When the first ball hits the ground, what is the height of the other ball? Use a graph to justify your answer.

In Exercises 27–30, sketch a parabola with the given characteristics.

27. The parabola opens up, and the vertex is (0, 3).
28. The vertex is (0, 4), and one of the x-intercepts is 2.
29. The related function is increasing when $x < 0$, and the zeros are −1 and 1.
30. The highest point on the parabola is (0, −5).

31. **MAKING AN ARGUMENT** Does the vertex of the graph of $y = ax^2 + c$ change when the value of a changes? Explain your reasoning.

32. **CONNECTING CONCEPTS** The area A (in square feet) of a square patio is represented by $A = x^2$, where x is the length of one side of the patio. You add 48 square feet to the patio, resulting in a total area of 192 square feet. What are the dimensions of the original patio? Use a graph to justify your answer.

33. MP **REASONING** Describe two methods you can use to find the zeros of the function $f(t) = -16t^2 + 400$.

34. HOW DO YOU SEE IT? The graph of $f(x) = ax^2 + c$ is shown. Points A and B are the same distance from the vertex of the graph of f. Which point is closer to the vertex of the graph of f as c increases?

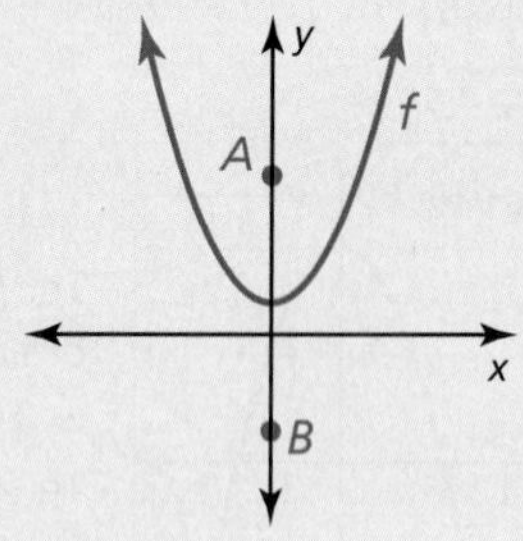

35. MP PROBLEM SOLVING The paths of water from three different garden waterfalls are given below. Each function gives the height h (in feet) and the horizontal distance d (in feet) of the water.

Waterfall 1 $h = -3.1d^2 + 4.8$

Waterfall 2 $h = -3.5d^2 + 1.9$

Waterfall 3 $h = -1.1d^2 + 1.6$

a. Which waterfall drops water from the highest point?

b. Which waterfall follows the narrowest path?

c. Which waterfall sends water the farthest?

36. WRITING EQUATIONS Two acorns fall to the ground from an oak tree. One falls 45 feet, while the other falls 32 feet. For each acorn, write an equation that represents the height h (in feet) as a function of the time t (in seconds). Then describe how the graphs of the two equations are related.

GO DIGITAL

37. CRITICAL THINKING A cross section of the parabolic surface of the antenna shown can be modeled by $y = 0.012x^2$, where x and y are measured in feet. The antenna is moved up so that the outer edges of the dish are 25 feet above the x-axis. Where is the vertex of the cross section located? Explain.

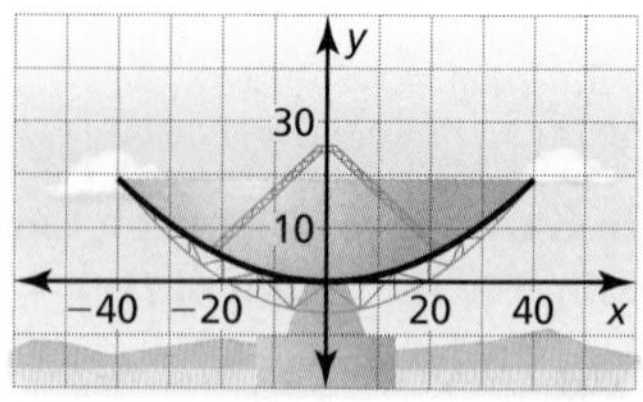

38. THOUGHT PROVOKING One of two classic problems in calculus is to find the area under a curve. Approximate the area of the region bounded by the parabola and the x-axis. Show your work.

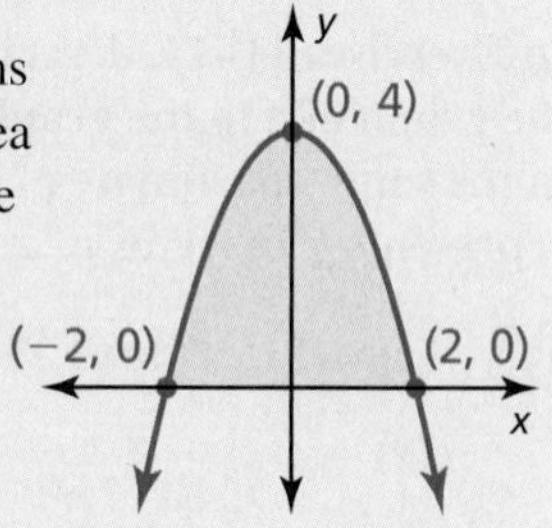

REVIEW & REFRESH

WATCH

In Exercises 39 and 40, evaluate the expression when $a = 4$ and $b = -3$.

39. $-\dfrac{b}{2a}$ **40.** $\dfrac{a - b}{3a + b}$

In Exercises 41 and 42, solve the equation.

41. $100 - 9x^2 = 0$ **42.** $6h^3 + 54h = -36h^2$

43. Write an equation of the line that passes through $(-3, -1)$ and is (a) parallel and (b) perpendicular to the line $3y = 9x - 15$.

44. MP STRUCTURE Complete the system so that it has infinitely many solutions.

$$4x - 6y = -15$$
$$\square x + 6y = \square$$

In Exercises 45 and 46, simplify the expression. Write your answer using only positive exponents.

45. $\dfrac{b^6}{b^{10}}$ **46.** $(12m)^{-2}$

In Exercises 47 and 48, graph the linear equation.

47. $9x - 6y = -18$ **48.** $y = -4x - 12$

49. Identify the characteristics of the quadratic function and its graph.

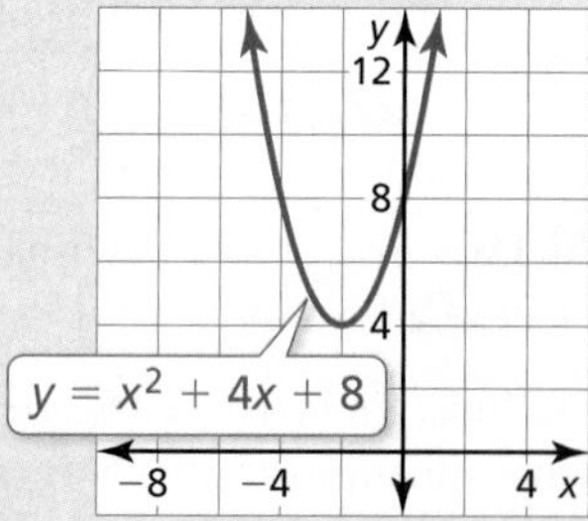

50. MODELING REAL LIFE A classroom can seat at most 30 students. There are 17 students currently in the class. What are the possible numbers of students who can be added to the class?

In Exercises 51 and 52, graph the function. Compare the graph to the graph of $f(x) = x^2$.

51. $p(x) = 2x^2 + 2$ **52.** $m(x) = -\frac{1}{2}x^2 - 4$

8.3 Graphing $f(x) = ax^2 + bx + c$

Learning Target Graph and describe functions of the form $f(x) = ax^2 + bx + c$.

Success Criteria

- I can find the axis of symmetry and vertex of a quadratic function.
- I can graph quadratic functions of the form $f(x) = ax^2 + bx + c$.
- I can determine a maximum or minimum value of a quadratic function.

EXPLORE IT! Identifying Characteristics of Quadratic Functions

Work with a partner.

a. Sketch the graph of $y = 2x^2 - 8x$.

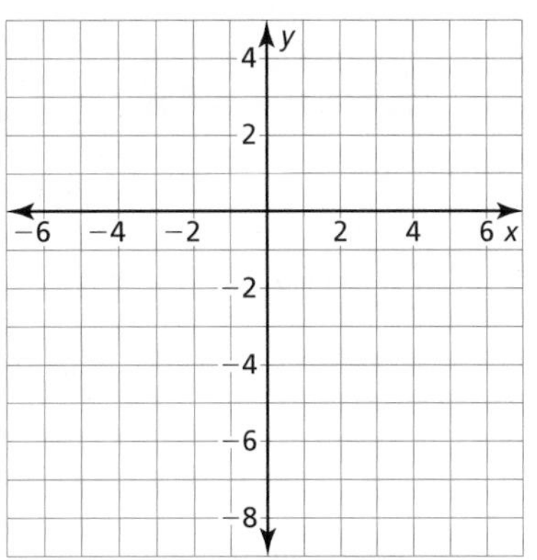

b. Compare the value of the x-coordinate of the vertex with the values of the x-intercepts. Explain why this occurs.

c. Sketch the graphs of $y = 2x^2 - 8x - 10$ and $y = 2x^2 - 8x + 6$. Is the relationship you found in part (b) true for these functions? Explain your reasoning.

d. What are the x-intercepts of the graph of $y = ax^2 + bx$? Explain how you found your answer.

e. Write an expression that represents the value of the x-coordinate of the vertex of the graph of $y = ax^2 + bx$. Is the expression different for the graph of $y = ax^2 + bx + c$? Explain your reasoning.

f. Without graphing, explain how you can find each of the following for $f(x) = ax^2 + bx + c$.

- x-coordinate of the vertex of the graph of f
- axis of symmetry of the graph of f
- y-intercept of the graph of f
- the *maximum value* or *minimum value* of f

g. Write a quadratic function of the form $y = ax^2 + bx + c$. Without graphing, find the characteristics listed in part (f). Then check your results by graphing.

Math Practice

Build Arguments

Why does it help to start with $y = ax^2 + bx$ rather than $y = ax^2 + bx + c$ to find an expression for the axis of symmetry of a quadratic function?

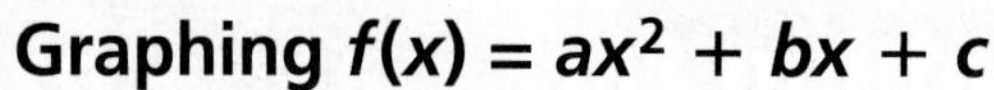

Graphing $f(x) = ax^2 + bx + c$

Vocabulary AZ VOCAB

maximum value, *p. 439*
minimum value, *p. 439*

KEY IDEA

Graphing $f(x) = ax^2 + bx + c$

- The graph opens up when $a > 0$, and the graph opens down when $a < 0$.
- The y-intercept is c.
- The x-coordinate of the vertex is $-\frac{b}{2a}$.
- The axis of symmetry is $x = -\frac{b}{2a}$.

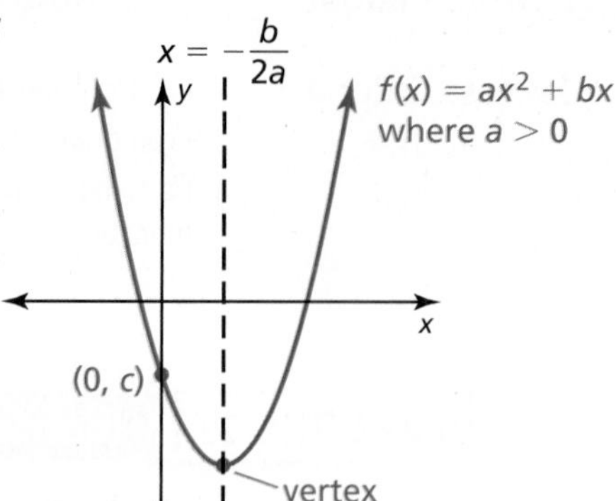

EXAMPLE 1 **Finding the Axis of Symmetry and the Vertex**

Find (a) the axis of symmetry and (b) the vertex of the graph of $f(x) = 2x^2 + 8x - 1$.

SOLUTION

a. Find the axis of symmetry when $a = 2$ and $b = 8$.

$x = -\frac{b}{2a}$ Write the equation for the axis of symmetry.

$x = -\frac{8}{2(2)}$ Substitute 2 for *a* and 8 for *b*.

$x = -2$ Simplify.

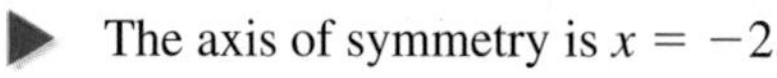

▶ The axis of symmetry is $x = -2$.

Check

$f(x) = 2x^2 + 8x - 1$

$(-2, -9)$

b. The axis of symmetry is $x = -2$, so the x-coordinate of the vertex is -2. Use the function to find the y-coordinate of the vertex.

$f(x) = 2x^2 + 8x - 1$ Write the function.

$f(-2) = 2(-2)^2 + 8(-2) - 1$ Substitute -2 for *x*.

$= 8 + (-16) - 1$ Multiply.

$= -9$ Simplify.

▶ The vertex is $(-2, -9)$.

SELF-ASSESSMENT 1 I do not understand. 2 I can do it with help. 3 I can do it on my own. 4 I can teach someone else.

Find (a) the axis of symmetry and (b) the vertex of the graph of the function.

1. $f(x) = 3x^2 - 2x$

2. $g(x) = x^2 + 6x + 5$

3. $h(x) = -\frac{1}{2}x^2 + 7x - 4$

4. OPEN-ENDED Write a quadratic function that has an axis of symmetry of $x = 4$.

GO DIGITAL

EXAMPLE 2 **Graphing $f(x) = ax^2 + bx + c$** WATCH

COMMON ERROR

Be sure to include the negative sign before the fraction when finding the axis of symmetry.

Graph $f(x) = 3x^2 - 6x + 5$. Find the domain and range.

SOLUTION

Step 1 Find and graph the axis of symmetry.

$$x = -\frac{b}{2a} = -\frac{(-6)}{2(3)} = 1$$ Substitute and simplify.

Step 2 Find and plot the vertex.

The axis of symmetry is $x = 1$, so the x-coordinate of the vertex is 1. Use the function to find the y-coordinate of the vertex.

$f(x) = 3x^2 - 6x + 5$ Write the function.

$f(1) = 3(1)^2 - 6(1) + 5$ Substitute 1 for x.

$= 2$ Simplify.

So, the vertex is (1, 2).

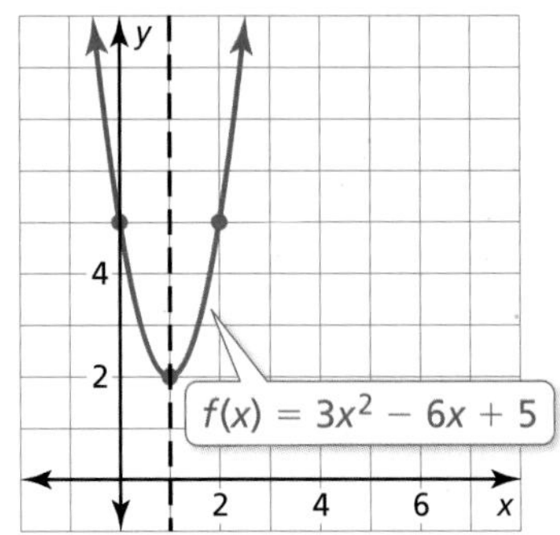

Step 3 Use the y-intercept to find two more points on the graph.

Because $c = 5$, the y-intercept is 5. So, (0, 5) lies on the graph. Because the axis of symmetry is $x = 1$, the point (2, 5) also lies on the graph.

Step 4 Draw a smooth curve through the points.

▶ The domain is all real numbers. The range is $y \geq 2$.

SELF-ASSESSMENT 1 I do not understand. 2 I can do it with help. 3 I can do it on my own. 4 I can teach someone else.

Graph the function. Find the domain and range.

5. $h(x) = 2x^2 + 4x + 1$ **6.** $k(x) = x^2 - 8x + 7$ **7.** $p(x) = -5x^2 - 10x - 2$

8. MP **REASONING** Can the graph of a quadratic function have a vertex of $(2, -1)$ and pass through the points (0, 3) and (5, 3)? Explain.

Finding Maximum and Minimum Values

KEY IDEA

Maximum and Minimum Values

The y-coordinate of the vertex of the graph of $f(x) = ax^2 + bx + c$ is the **maximum value** of the function when $a < 0$ or the **minimum value** of the function when $a > 0$.

$f(x) = ax^2 + bx + c, a < 0$

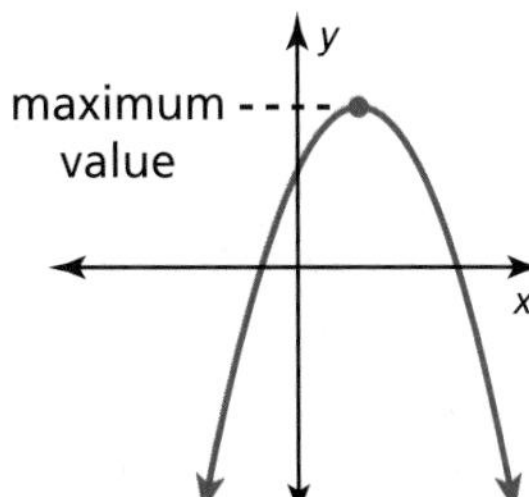

$f(x) = ax^2 + bx + c, a > 0$

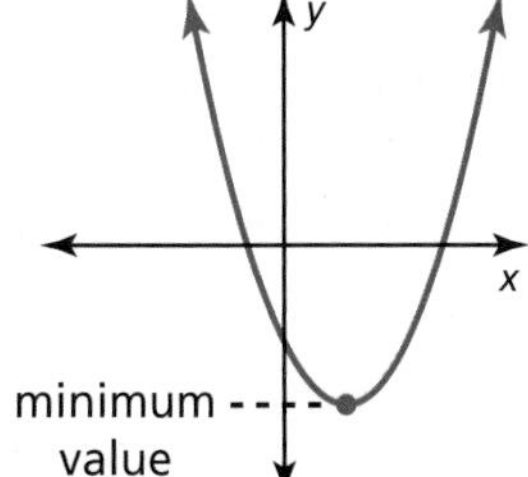

EXAMPLE 3 Finding a Maximum or Minimum Value

Tell whether the function $f(x) = -4x^2 - 24x - 19$ has a *maximum value* or a *minimum value*. Then find the value.

SOLUTION

For $f(x) = -4x^2 - 24x - 19$, $a = -4$ and $-4 < 0$. So, the parabola opens down and the function has a maximum value. To find the maximum value, find the y-coordinate of the vertex.

First, find the x-coordinate of the vertex. Use $a = -4$ and $b = -24$.

$$x = -\frac{b}{2a} = -\frac{(-24)}{2(-4)} = -3 \qquad \text{Substitute and simplify.}$$

Then evaluate the function when $x = -3$ to find the y-coordinate of the vertex.

$$f(-3) = -4(-3)^2 - 24(-3) - 19 \qquad \text{Substitute } -3 \text{ for } x.$$

$$= 17 \qquad \text{Simplify.}$$

▶ The maximum value is 17.

EXAMPLE 4 Modeling Real Life

The suspension cables between the two towers of the Mackinac Bridge in Michigan form a parabola that can be modeled by $y = 0.000098x^2 - 0.37x + 552$, where x and y are measured in feet. Estimate and interpret the minimum value of the function.

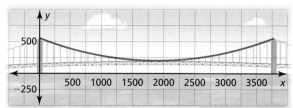

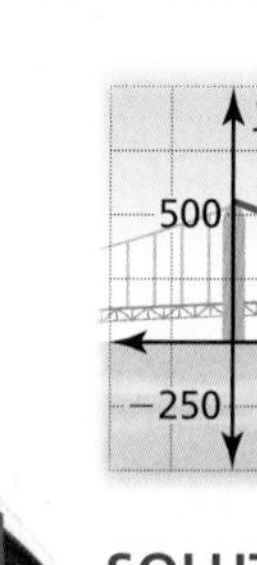

SOLUTION

To find the minimum value, find the y-coordinate of the vertex.

First, find the x-coordinate of the vertex. Use $a = 0.000098$ and $b = -0.37$.

$$x = -\frac{b}{2a} = -\frac{(-0.37)}{2(0.000098)} = \frac{0.37}{0.000196}$$

Use technology to find the y-coordinate of the vertex.

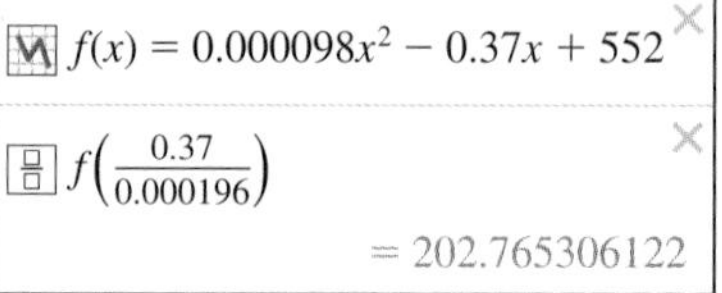

▶ The minimum value is about 203. So, at its lowest point, the cable is about 203 feet above the water.

Math Practice

Recognize Usefulness of Tools
Why is it helpful to use technology to find the y-coordinate of the vertex?

SELF-ASSESSMENT

1 I do not understand. 2 I can do it with help. 3 I can do it on my own. 4 I can teach someone else.

Tell whether the function has a *maximum value* or a *minimum value*. Then find the value.

9. $g(x) = x^2 + 4x$

10. $g(x) = 8x^2 - 8x + 6$

11. $h(x) = -\frac{1}{4}x^2 + 3x + 1$

12. The cables between the two towers of the Tacoma Narrows Bridge in Washington form a parabola that can be modeled by $y = 0.00016x^2 - 0.46x + 507$, where x and y are measured in feet. Estimate and interpret the minimum value of the function.

EXAMPLE 5 Modeling Real Life

GO DIGITAL

A group of friends is launching water balloons. The function $f(t) = -16t^2 + 80t + 5$ represents the height (in feet) of the first water balloon t seconds after it is launched. The height of the second water balloon t seconds after it is launched is shown in the graph. Which water balloon reaches a greater height?

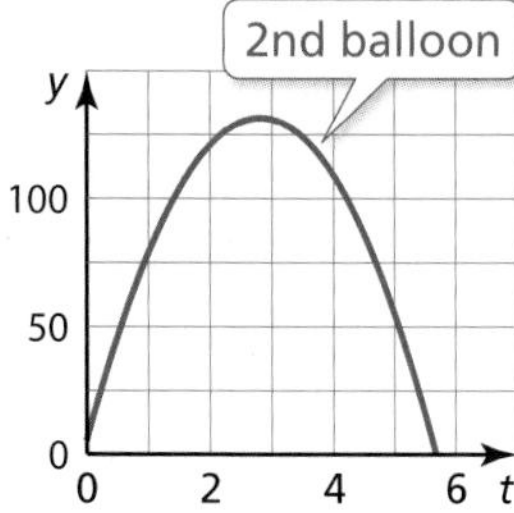

SOLUTION

1. **Understand the Problem** You are given a function and a graph that represent heights of water balloons. You are asked to compare the maximum heights.

2. **Make a Plan** Use technology to graph $f(t) = -16t^2 + 80t + 5$ in an appropriate viewing window. Then compare the maximum heights using the graphs.

3. **Solve and Check** Graph $f(t) = -16t^2 + 80t + 5$.

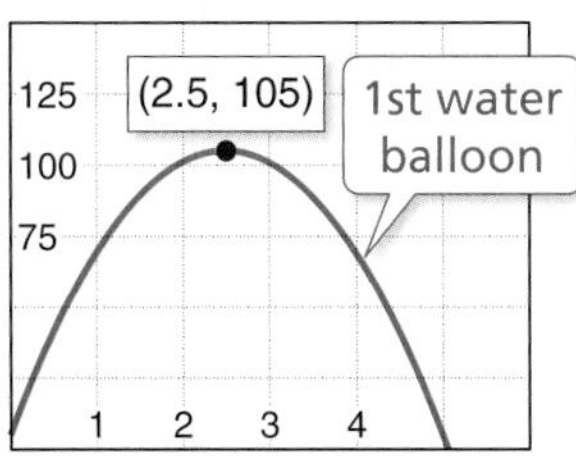

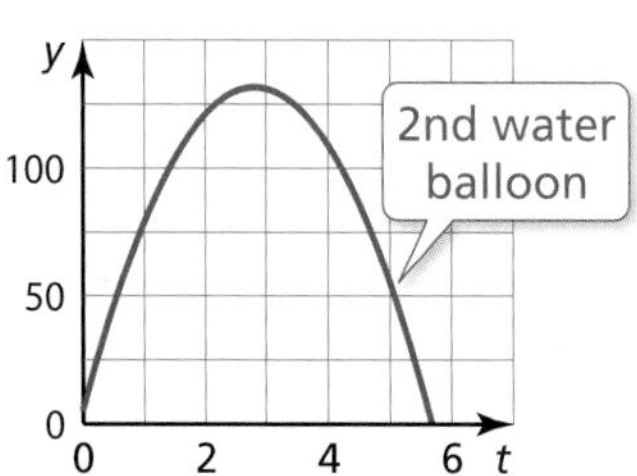

You can see that the second water balloon reaches a height of about 125 feet, while the first water balloon reaches a height of 105 feet.

▶ So, the second water balloon reaches a greater height.

Check Find the maximum value of $f(t) = -16t^2 + 80t + 5$ algebraically. First, find the x-coordinate of the vertex.

$$x = -\frac{b}{2a} = -\frac{80}{2(-16)} = 2.5$$

Evaluate the function when $x = 2.5$.

$$f(2.5) = -16(2.5)^2 + 80(2.5) + 5$$
$$= -100 + 200 + 5$$
$$= 105$$

So, the first water balloon reached a height of 105 feet. Use a straightedge to represent a height of 105 feet on the graph that represents the second water balloon. ✓

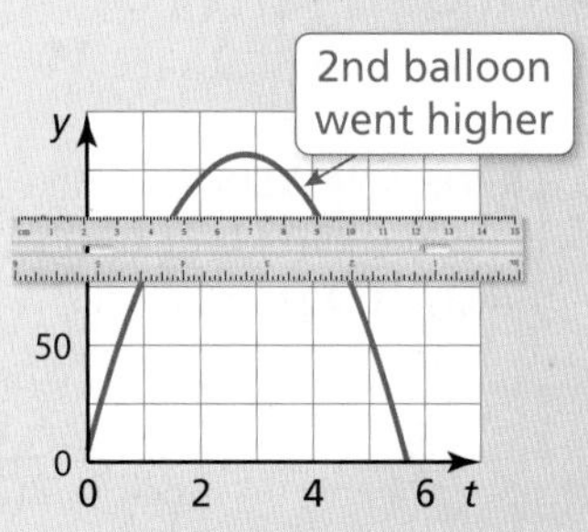

Math Practice

Understand Quantities

Why is the graph of f restricted to the first quadrant?

SELF-ASSESSMENT

1 I do not understand. 2 I can do it with help. 3 I can do it on my own. 4 I can teach someone else.

13. The function $g(t) = -16t^2 + 72t + 4$ represents the height (in feet) of a third water balloon t seconds after it is launched.

a. Did the third balloon travel higher than the first two? Explain your reasoning.

b. Which balloon was in the air longest? Explain your reasoning.

c. Which balloon reached its maximum height in the least amount of time? Explain your reasoning.

8.3 Practice WITH CalcChat® AND CalcView®

GO DIGITAL

In Exercises 1 and 2, find the vertex, the axis of symmetry, and the y-intercept of the graph.

1. 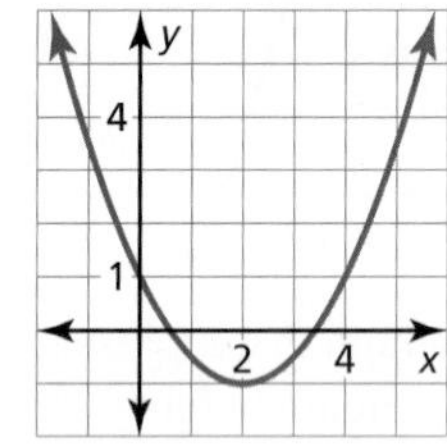

2. 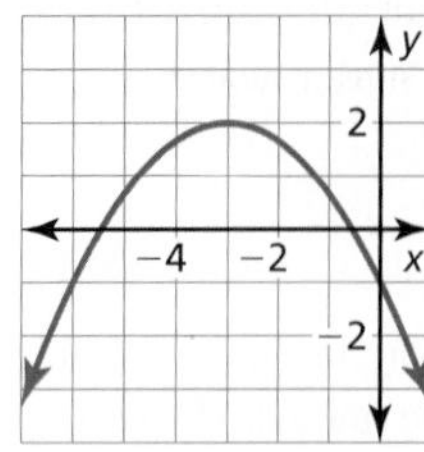

In Exercises 3–8, find (a) the axis of symmetry and (b) the vertex of the graph of the function. *Example 1*

3. $f(x) = 2x^2 - 4x$
4. $y = 3x^2 + 2x$
5. $y = -9x^2 - 18x - 1$
6. $f(x) = -6x^2 + 24x - 20$
7. $f(x) = \frac{2}{5}x^2 - 4x + 14$
8. $y = -\frac{3}{4}x^2 + 9x - 18$

In Exercises 9–14, graph the function. Find the domain and range. *Example 2*

9. $f(x) = 2x^2 + 12x + 4$
10. $y = 4x^2 + 24x + 13$
11. $y = -8x^2 - 16x - 9$
12. $f(x) = -5x^2 + 20x - 7$
13. $y = \frac{2}{3}x^2 - 6x + 5$
14. $f(x) = -\frac{1}{2}x^2 - 3x - 4$

15. **ERROR ANALYSIS** Describe and correct the error in finding the axis of symmetry of the graph of $y = 3x^2 - 12x + 11$.

$$x = -\frac{b}{2a} = \frac{-12}{2(3)} = -2$$

The axis of symmetry is $x = -2$.

16. **ERROR ANALYSIS** Describe and correct the error in finding the vertex of the graph of $f(x) = x^2 + 2x + 3$.

$$x = -\frac{b}{2a} = -\frac{2}{2(1)} = -1$$

$c = 3$

The vertex is $(-1, 3)$.

In Exercises 17–22, tell whether the function has a *maximum value* or a *minimum value*. Then find the value. *Example 3*

17. $y = 3x^2 - 18x + 15$
18. $f(x) = -5x^2 + 10x + 7$
19. $f(x) = -4x^2 + 4x - 2$
20. $y = 2x^2 - 10x + 13$
21. $y = -\frac{1}{2}x^2 - 11x + 6$
22. $f(x) = \frac{1}{5}x^2 - 5x + 27$

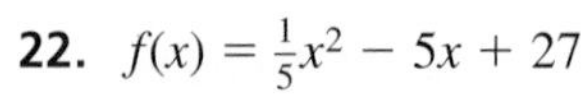

23. **MODELING REAL LIFE** The height (in feet) of a javelin t seconds after it is thrown can be represented by the function $h(t) = -16t^2 + 82t + 5$. Estimate and interpret the maximum value of the function. *Example 4*

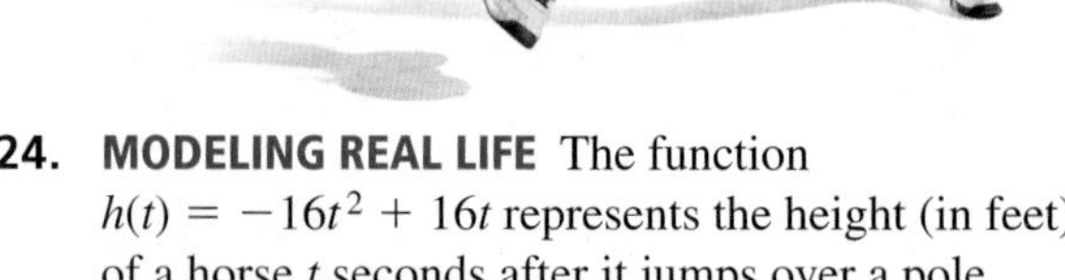

24. **MODELING REAL LIFE** The function $h(t) = -16t^2 + 16t$ represents the height (in feet) of a horse t seconds after it jumps over a pole.
    a. When does the horse reach its maximum height?
    b. Can the horse clear a pole that is 3.5 feet high? If so, by how much?
    c. How long is the horse in the air?

25. **MP REASONING** The vertex of a parabola is $(3, -1)$. One point on the parabola is $(6, 8)$. Find another point on the parabola. Explain your reasoning.

26. **MP REASONING** The graph of a quadratic function passes through $(3, 2)$, $(4, 7)$, and $(9, 2)$. Does the graph open up or down? Explain your reasoning.

MP USING TOOLS In Exercises 27–30, use technology to approximate the vertex of the graph of the function.

27. $y = 0.5x^2 + \sqrt{2}x - 3$
28. $y = -6.2x^2 + 4.8x - 1$
29. $y = -\pi x^2 + 3x$
30. $y = 0.25x^2 - 5^{2/3}x + 2$

31. **MODELING REAL LIFE** The front of an aircraft hangar is a parabolic arch that can be modeled by the equation $y = -0.006x^2 + 1.5x$, where x and y are measured in feet. The front of a second aircraft hangar is shown in the graph. *Example 5*

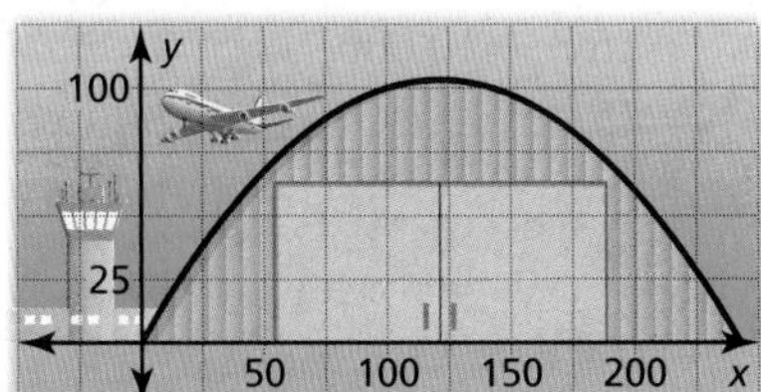

a. Which aircraft hangar is taller?

b. Which aircraft hangar is wider?

32. **MODELING REAL LIFE** An electronics store sells about 80 drones per month for \$120 each. For each \$6 decrease in price, the store expects to sell eight more drones. The revenue from drone sales is given by the function $R(n) = $ (unit price)(units sold), or $R(n) = (120 - 6n)(80 + 8n)$, where n is the number of \$6 price decreases.

a. How much should the store charge to maximize monthly revenue?

b. Using a different revenue model, the store expects to sell five more drones for each \$4 decrease in price. Which revenue model results in a greater maximum monthly revenue? Explain.

33. **MP REASONING** Find the axis of symmetry of the graph of the equation $y = ax^2 + bx + c$ when $b = 0$. Can you find the axis of symmetry when $a = 0$? Explain.

34. **MAKING AN ARGUMENT** Is it possible to draw a parabola through any two points with different x-coordinates? Explain.

CONNECTING CONCEPTS In Exercises 35 and 36, (a) find the value of x that maximizes the area of the figure and (b) find the maximum area.

35.

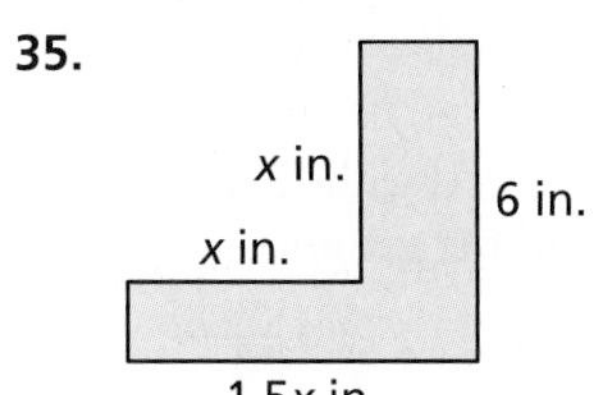

36.

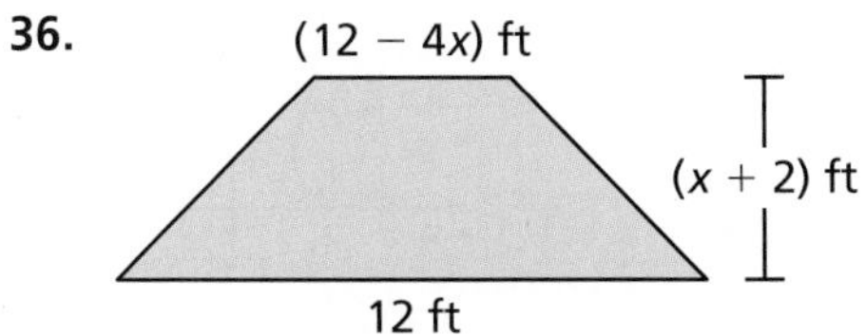

37. **WRITING** Compare the graph of $g(x) = x^2 + 4x + 1$ with the graph of $h(x) = x^2 - 4x + 1$.

38. **HOW DO YOU SEE IT?**
During an archery competition, an archer shoots an arrow. The arrow follows the parabolic path shown, where x and y are measured in meters.

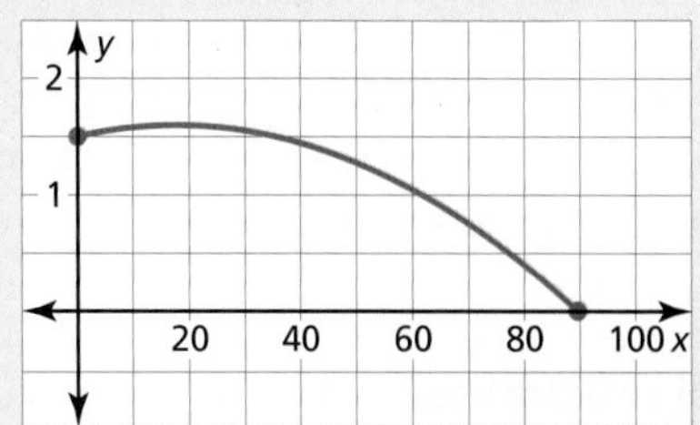

a. What is the initial height of the arrow?

b. Estimate the maximum height of the arrow.

c. How far does the arrow travel?

In Exercises 39 and 40, write and graph a quadratic function that has the given characteristics.

39. y-intercept: 2; decreasing when $x < 1.5$, increasing when $x > 1.5$; range: $y \geq -2.5$

40. vertex: $(0, -3)$; end behavior: $y \to -\infty$ as $x \to -\infty$ and $y \to -\infty$ as $x \to +\infty$; passes through $(1, -7)$

41. **CRITICAL THINKING** A parabola contains the points shown. Identify characteristics of each parabola, if possible. Explain your reasoning.

a. $(2, 3), (6, 4)$

b. $(1, 4), (3, -4), (5, 4)$

42. **THOUGHT PROVOKING**
One of two classic problems in calculus is finding the slope of a *tangent line* to a curve. A tangent line touches a curve at exactly one point.

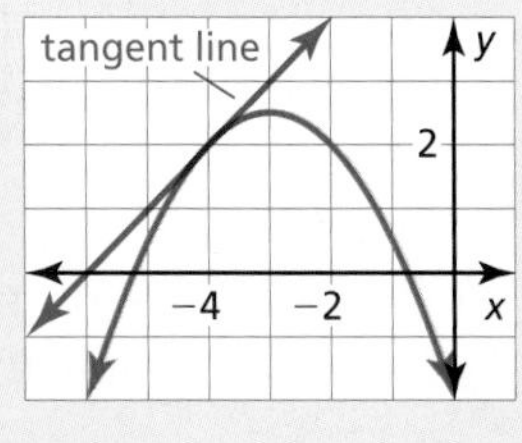

Approximate the slope of the tangent line to the graph of $y = x^2$ at the point $(1, 1)$. Explain your reasoning.

43. **MODELING REAL LIFE** The function $y = -\frac{1}{8}x^2 + 4x$ represents the path of a T-shirt from an air cannon at a basketball game. The function $3y = 2x - 14$ represents the height of the bleachers. In both functions, y represents vertical height (in feet) and x represents horizontal distance (in feet). At what height does the T-shirt land in the bleachers?

44. **MP PRECISION** For a quadratic function f, explain the meaning of $f\left(-\frac{b}{2a}\right)$.

45. **PERFORMANCE TASK** Research the projectile motion function, which can be used to represent the height of a firework after it is launched from the ground. A firework will explode at its highest point. The table shows the approximate velocities of fireworks with different shell sizes. Use this information to plan a fireworks display. Your plan should include the shell sizes used, the approximate times and heights at which each firework will explode, and the total length of the display.

Shell size (inches)	4	6	10	12	24
Velocity, v_0 (feet per second)	165	200	260	285	400

46. **MP PROBLEM SOLVING** The function shown represents the height y (in feet) of a skydiver x seconds after jumping from an airplane. When and at what height does the skydiver open the parachute?

$$y = \begin{cases} -16x^2 + 10{,}000, & \text{if } 0 < x \leq 20 \\ -15x + 3900, & \text{if } 20 < x \leq 260 \end{cases}$$

47. **DIG DEEPER** The landscape architects at a zoo plan to build a rectangular outdoor orangutan exhibit. They have k feet of fencing. What is the maximum area of the outdoor exhibit in terms of k?

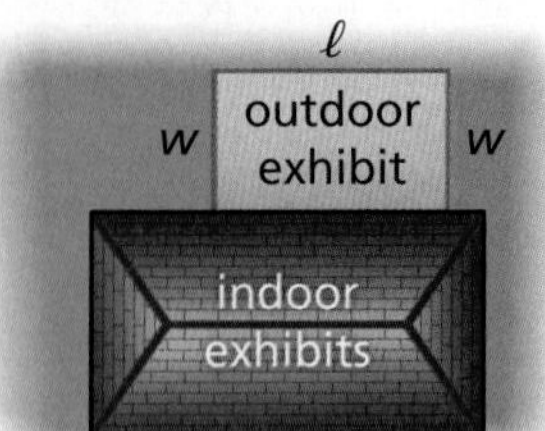

REVIEW & REFRESH

In Exercises 48–51, describe the transformation(s) from the graph of $f(x) = |x|$ to the graph of the given function.

48. $q(x) = |x + 6|$

49. $h(x) = -0.5|x|$

50. $g(x) = |x - 2| + 5$

51. $p(x) = 3|x + 1|$

52. Determine whether the graph represents an *arithmetic sequence*, a *geometric sequence*, or *neither*. Explain your reasoning.

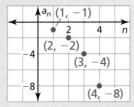

In Exercises 53–56, graph the function. Compare the graph to the graph of $f(x) = x^2$.

53. $g(x) = 3x^2$

54. $h(x) = -\frac{1}{2}x^2$

55. $d(x) = -x^2 + 6$

56. $p(x) = 4x^2 - 10$

57. **WRITING** When does the function $y = ab^x$ represent exponential decay?

In Exercises 58 and 59, find the sum or difference.

58. $(2y^2 - 9) + (-y^2 + 3y - 12)$

59. $(-k^2 + 4k^3 - 8k) - (2k - 6k^2 + 10)$

60. Graph $f(x) = -4x^2 + 16x - 6$. Find the domain and range.

61. **MODELING REAL LIFE** The linear function $m = 3.75 - 0.25q$ represents the amount of money m (in dollars) you have left after putting q quarters into a parking meter.

a. Find the domain of the function. Is the domain discrete or continuous?

b. Graph the function using its domain.

In Exercises 62–69, factor the polynomial completely.

62. $z^2 - 49$

63. $w^2 + 2w + 1$

64. $n^2 + 11n + 24$

65. $q^2 + 4q - 5$

66. $2s^2 - 21s + 27$

67. $-9r^2 - 12r + 12$

68. $b^3 + b^2 - 4b - 4$

69. $2c^3 + 2c^2 - 24c$

70. Solve the literal equation $4y - ky = x$ for y.

In Exercises 71 and 72, find the vertex, the axis of symmetry, and the y-intercept of the graph.

71.

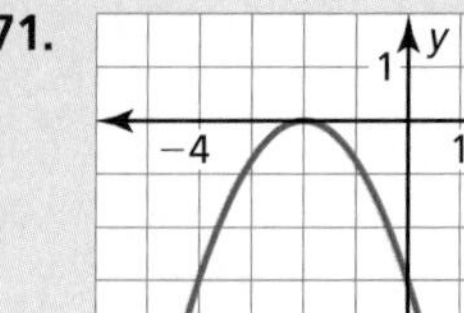

72.

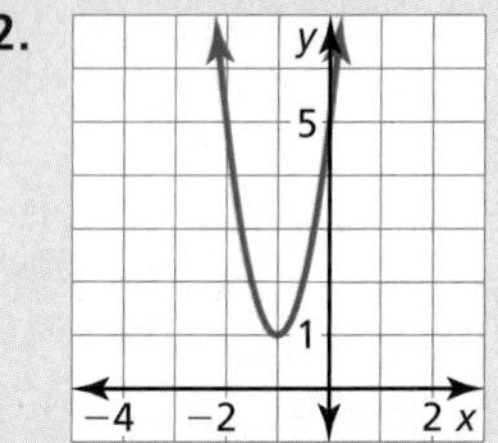

8.4 Graphing $f(x) = a(x - h)^2 + k$

Learning Target Graph and describe functions of the form $f(x) = a(x - h)^2 + k$.

Success Criteria

- I can identify even and odd functions.
- I can graph quadratic functions of the form $f(x) = a(x - h)^2 + k$.
- I can compare the graph of $f(x) = a(x - h)^2$ to the graph of the parent quadratic function.
- I can compare the graph of $f(x) = a(x - h)^2 + k$ to the graph of the parent quadratic function.

EXPLORE IT! Graphing $y = a(x - h)^2$ and $y = a(x - h)^2 + k$

Work with a partner.

a. Describe what you expect the graphs of f and g to look like. Then sketch the graphs of the functions in the same coordinate plane.

i. $f(x) = x^2$ and $g(x) = (x - 2)^2$

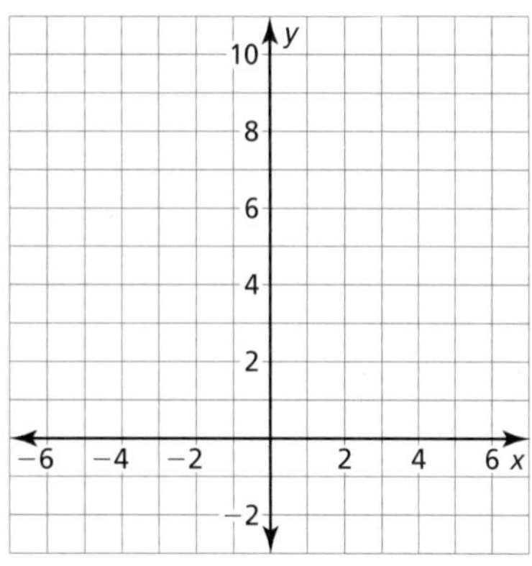

ii. $f(x) = 2x^2$ and $g(x) = 2(x + 3)^2$

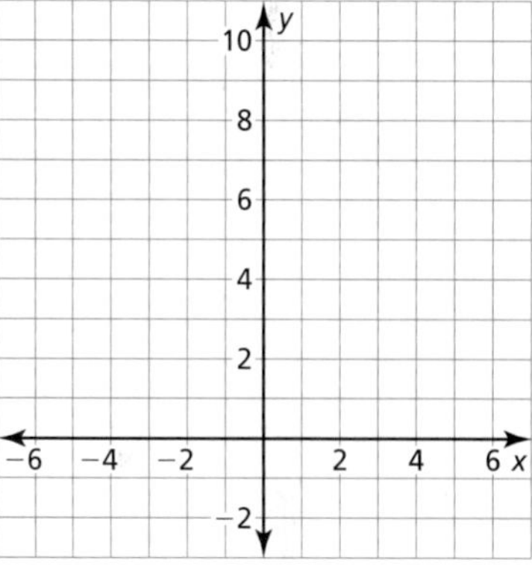

iii. $f(x) = -x^2$ and $g(x) = f(x + 2)$

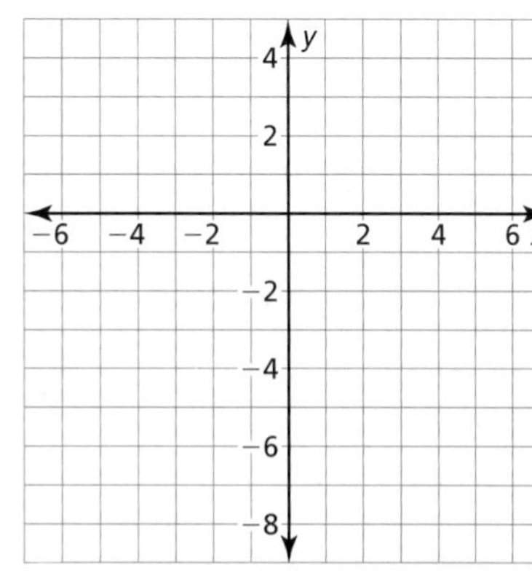

iv. $f(x) = -2x^2$ and $g(x) = f(x - 3)$

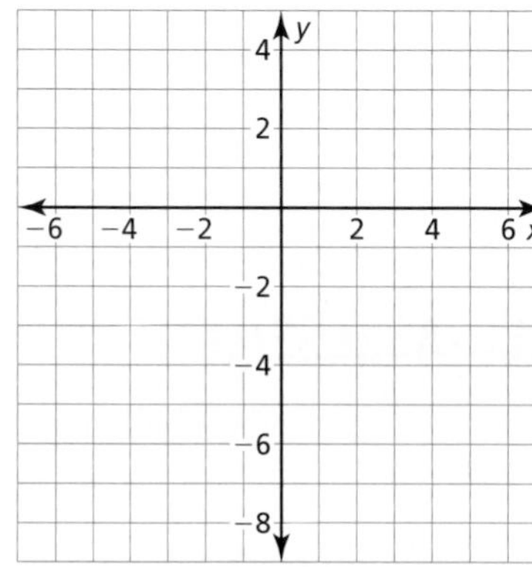

v. $f(x) = x^2$ and $g(x) = (x + 2)^2 + 1$

vi. $f(x) = -x^2$ and $g(x) = f(x - 1) - 2$

b. In each graph from part (a), find the vertex of the graph of g. What do you notice?

c. How does the value of h affect the graph of $y = a(x - h)^2$? How does the value of k affect the graph of $y = a(x - h)^2 + k$?

Math Practice

Use Technology to Explore

Use technology to explore how the values of a, h, and k affect the graph of $f(x) = a(x - h)^2 + k$.

GO DIGITAL

Identifying Even and Odd Functions

Vocabulary 

even function, *p. 446*
odd function, *p. 446*
vertex form (of a quadratic function), *p. 448*

KEY IDEA

Even and Odd Functions

A function $y = f(x)$ is **even** when $f(-x) = f(x)$ for each x in the domain of f. The graph of an even function is symmetric about the y-axis.

A function $y = f(x)$ is **odd** when $f(-x) = -f(x)$ for each x in the domain of f. The graph of an odd function is symmetric about the origin. A graph is *symmetric about the origin* when it looks the same after reflections in the x-axis and then in the y-axis.

STUDY TIP

The graph of an odd function looks the same after a 180° rotation about the origin.

EXAMPLE 1 Identifying Even and Odd Functions

Determine whether each function is *even*, *odd*, or *neither*.

a. $f(x) = 2x$ **b.** $g(x) = x^2 - 2$ **c.** $h(x) = 2x^2 + x - 2$

SOLUTION

a.

$f(x) = 2x$	Write the original function.
$f(-x) = 2(-x)$	Substitute $-x$ for x.
$= -2x$	Simplify.
$= -f(x)$	Substitute $f(x)$ for $2x$.

▶ Because $f(-x) = -f(x)$, the function is odd.

b.

$g(x) = x^2 - 2$	Write the original function.
$g(-x) = (-x)^2 - 2$	Substitute $-x$ for x.
$= x^2 - 2$	Simplify.
$= g(x)$	Substitute $g(x)$ for $x^2 - 2$.

▶ Because $g(-x) = g(x)$, the function is even.

c.

$h(x) = 2x^2 + x - 2$	Write the original function.
$h(-x) = 2(-x)^2 + (-x) - 2$	Substitute $-x$ for x.
$= 2x^2 - x - 2$	Simplify.

STUDY TIP

Most functions are neither even nor odd.

▶ Because $h(x) = 2x^2 + x - 2$ and $-h(x) = -2x^2 - x + 2$, you can conclude that $h(-x) \neq h(x)$ and $h(-x) \neq -h(x)$. So, the function is neither even nor odd.

SELF-ASSESSMENT

1 I do not understand. 2 I can do it with help. 3 I can do it on my own. 4 I can teach someone else.

Determine whether the function is *even*, *odd*, or *neither*.

1. $f(x) = 5x$
2. $g(x) = 2^x$
3. $h(x) = 2x^2 + 3$
4. **VOCABULARY** Compare the graph of an even function with the graph of an odd function.
5. Determine whether the function represented by the graph is *even*, *odd*, or *neither*. Explain your reasoning.

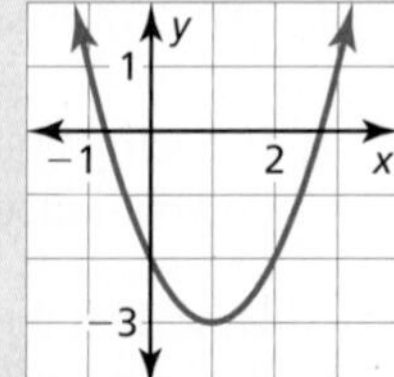

Graphing $f(x) = a(x - h)^2$

KEY IDEA

Graphing $f(x) = a(x - h)^2$

- When $h > 0$, the graph of $f(x) = a(x - h)^2$ is a horizontal translation h units right of the graph of $f(x) = ax^2$.
- When $h < 0$, the graph of $f(x) = a(x - h)^2$ is a horizontal translation $|h|$ units left of the graph of $f(x) = ax^2$.

The vertex of the graph of $f(x) = a(x - h)^2$ is $(h, 0)$, and the axis of symmetry is $x = h$.

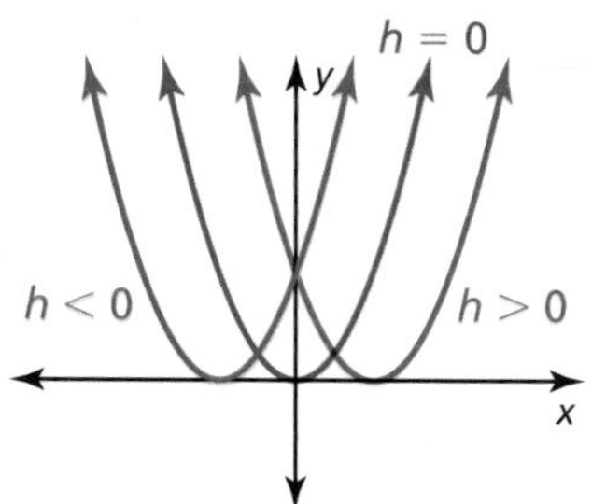

EXAMPLE 2 Graphing $y = a(x - h)^2$ 

Graph $g(x) = \frac{1}{2}(x - 4)^2$. Compare the graph to the graph of $f(x) = x^2$.

SOLUTION

Step 1 Graph the axis of symmetry. Because $h = 4$, graph $x = 4$.

Step 2 Plot the vertex. Because $h = 4$, plot $(4, 0)$.

Step 3 Find and plot two more points on the graph. Choose two x-values less than the x-coordinate of the vertex. Then find $g(x)$ for each x-value.

ANOTHER WAY

In Steps 3 and 4, you can also choose two x-values greater than the x-coordinate of the vertex, and reflect the resulting points in the axis of symmetry.

When $x = 0$:

$$g(0) = \frac{1}{2}(0 - 4)^2$$
$$= 8$$

When $x = 2$:

$$g(2) = \frac{1}{2}(2 - 4)^2$$
$$= 2$$

So, plot $(0, 8)$ and $(2, 2)$.

Step 4 Reflect the points plotted in Step 3 in the axis of symmetry. So, plot $(8, 8)$ and $(6, 2)$.

Step 5 Draw a smooth curve through the points.

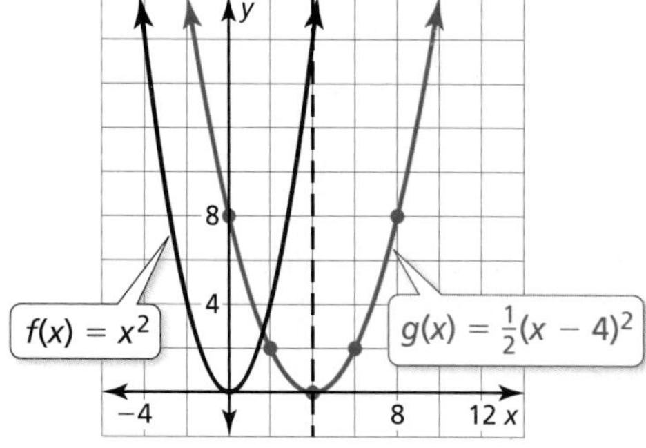

Both graphs open up. The graph of g is wider than the graph of f. The axis of symmetry $x = 4$ and the vertex $(4, 0)$ of the graph of g are 4 units right of the axis of symmetry $x = 0$ and the vertex $(0, 0)$ of the graph of f. So, the graph of g is a translation 4 units right and a vertical shrink by a factor of $\frac{1}{2}$ of the graph of f.

SELF-ASSESSMENT 1 I do not understand. 2 I can do it with help. 3 I can do it on my own. 4 I can teach someone else.

Graph the function. Compare the graph to the graph of $f(x) = x^2$.

6. $g(x) = (x - 6)^2$

7. $g(x) = 2(x + 5)^2$

8. $h(x) = -(x - 2)^2$

9. MP **REASONING** When graphing a quadratic function, why is it helpful to identify the axis of symmetry?

Graphing $f(x) = a(x - h)^2 + k$

KEY IDEA

Graphing $f(x) = a(x - h)^2 + k$

The **vertex form** of a quadratic function is $f(x) = a(x - h)^2 + k$, where $a \neq 0$. The graph of $f(x) = a(x - h)^2 + k$ is a translation h units horizontally and k units vertically of the graph of $f(x) = ax^2$.

The vertex of the graph of $f(x) = a(x - h)^2 + k$ is (h, k), and the axis of symmetry is $x = h$.

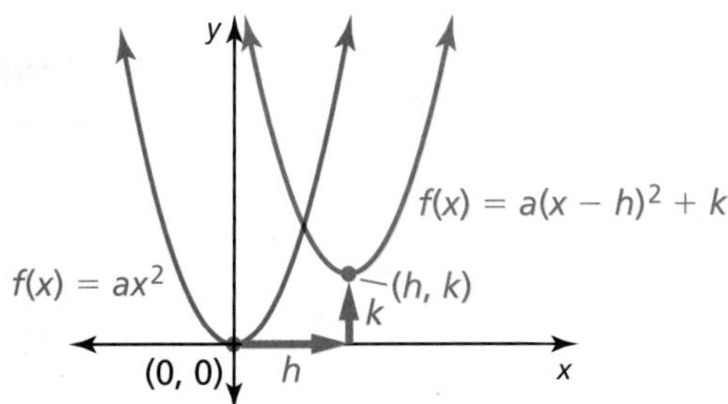

EXAMPLE 3 Graphing $y = a(x - h)^2 + k$

a. Graph $g(x) = -2(x + 2)^2 + 3$. Compare the graph to the graph of $f(x) = x^2$.

b. Consider function g in part (a). Graph $p(x) = g(x + 3)$.

SOLUTION

a. Step 1 Graph the axis of symmetry. Because $h = -2$, graph $x = -2$.

Step 2 Plot the vertex. Because $h = -2$ and $k = 3$, plot $(-2, 3)$.

Step 3 Find and plot two more points on the graph. Choose two x-values less than the x-coordinate of the vertex. Because $g(-4) = -5$ and $g(-3) = 1$, you can plot $(-4, -5)$ and $(-3, 1)$.

Step 4 Reflect the points plotted in Step 3 in the axis of symmetry. So, plot $(0, -5)$ and $(-1, 1)$.

Step 5 Draw a smooth curve through the points.

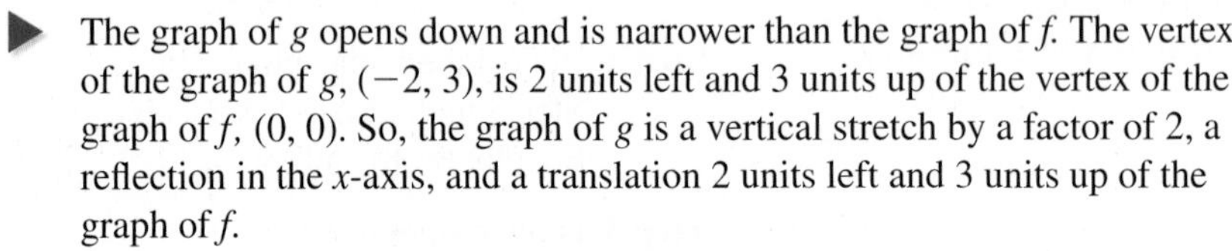

▶ The graph of g opens down and is narrower than the graph of f. The vertex of the graph of g, $(-2, 3)$, is 2 units left and 3 units up of the vertex of the graph of f, $(0, 0)$. So, the graph of g is a vertical stretch by a factor of 2, a reflection in the x-axis, and a translation 2 units left and 3 units up of the graph of f.

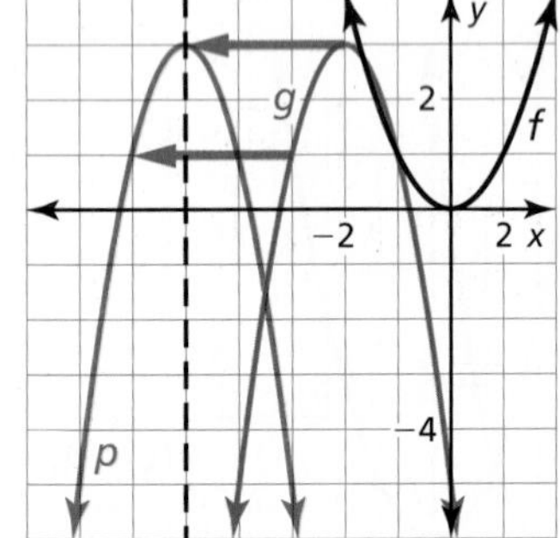

b. The function p is of the form $y = g(x - h)$, where $h = -3$. So, the graph of p is a horizontal translation 3 units left of the graph of g. To graph p, subtract 3 from the x-coordinates of the points on the graph of g.

SELF-ASSESSMENT

1 I do not understand. 2 I can do it with help. 3 I can do it on my own. 4 I can teach someone else.

Graph the function. Compare the graph to the graph of $f(x) = x^2$.

10. $g(x) = 3(x - 1)^2 + 6$

11. $h(x) = \frac{1}{2}(x + 4)^2 - 2$

12. $p(x) = -(x - 5)^2 - 5$

13. Consider function g in Example 3. Graph $f(x) = g(x) - 3$.

14. WHICH ONE DOESN'T BELONG? Which function does *not* belong with the other three? Explain your reasoning.

$f(x) = 8(x + 4)^2$	$f(x) = 4(x - 2)^2 + 4$	$f(x) = 2(x + 0)^2$	$f(x) = 3(x + 1)^2 + 1$

Modeling Real-Life Problems

Modeling Real Life

The water fountain shown consists of streams of water that are shaped like parabolas. Write and graph a quadratic function that models the path of a stream of water with a maximum height of 5 feet, represented by a vertex of (3, 5), landing on a spotlight 6 feet from the water jet, represented by (6, 0).

SOLUTION

1. **Understand the Problem** You know the vertex and another point on the graph that represents the parabolic path. You are asked to write and graph a quadratic function that models the path.
2. **Make a Plan** Use the given points and the vertex form to write a quadratic function. Then graph the function.
3. **Solve and Check** Use the vertex form, vertex (3, 5), and point (6, 0) to find the value of a.

$f(x) = a(x - h)^2 + k$	Write the vertex form of a quadratic function.
$f(x) = a(x - 3)^2 + 5$	Substitute 3 for h and 5 for k.
$0 = a(6 - 3)^2 + 5$	Substitute 6 for x and 0 for $f(x)$.
$0 = 9a + 5$	Simplify.
$-\frac{5}{9} = a$	Solve for a.

So, $f(x) = -\frac{5}{9}(x - 3)^2 + 5$ models the path. Now graph the function.

Step 1 Graph the axis of symmetry. Because $h = 3$, graph $x = 3$.

Step 2 Plot the vertex, (3, 5).

Step 3 Find and plot two more points on the graph. Because the x-axis represents the base of the fountain, the graph should only contain points with nonnegative values of $f(x)$. You know that (6, 0) is on the graph. To find another point, choose an x-value between $x = 3$ and $x = 6$. Then find the corresponding value of $f(x)$.

$$f(4.5) = -\frac{5}{9}(4.5 - 3)^2 + 5 = 3.75$$

So, plot (6, 0) and (4.5, 3.75).

Step 4 Reflect the points plotted in Step 3 in the axis of symmetry. So, plot (0, 0) and (1.5, 3.75).

Step 5 Draw a smooth curve through the points.

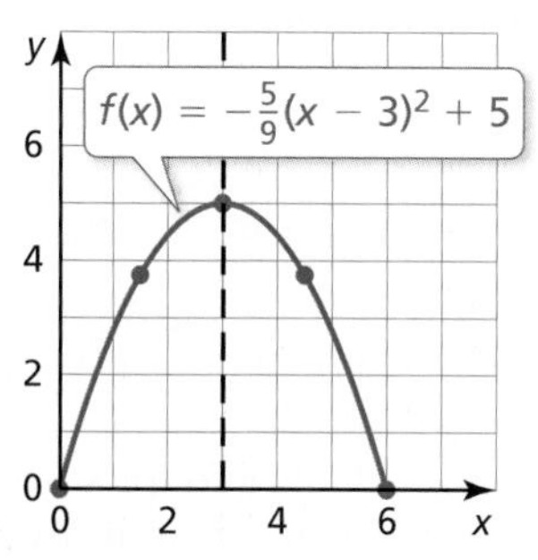

Check Use technology to graph $f(x) = -\frac{5}{9}(x - 3)^2 + 5$. Verify that the maximum value is 5 and $x = 6$ is a zero of the function.

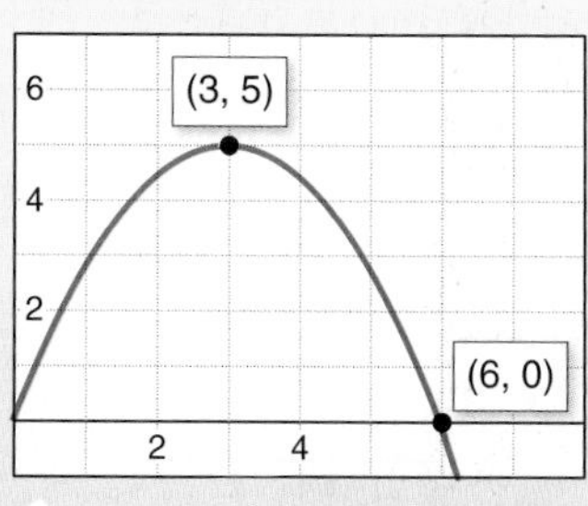

SELF-ASSESSMENT

1 I do not understand. 2 I can do it with help. 3 I can do it on my own. 4 I can teach someone else.

15. **WHAT IF?** The maximum height of the stream of water increases by 60%, but the water still lands on the spotlight. Write and graph a quadratic function that models the path.

8.4 Practice WITH CalcChat® AND CalcView®

In Exercises 1–8, determine whether the function is *even, odd,* or *neither.* ▶ *Example 1*

1. $f(x) = 4x + 3$
2. $g(x) = 3x^2$
3. $h(x) = 5^x + 2$
4. $m(x) = 2x^2 - 7x$
5. $p(x) = -x^2 + 8$
6. $f(x) = -\frac{1}{2}x$
7. $n(x) = 2x^2 - 7x + 3$
8. $r(x) = -6x^2 + 5$

In Exercises 9–12, determine whether the function represented by the graph is *even, odd,* or *neither.*

9\.

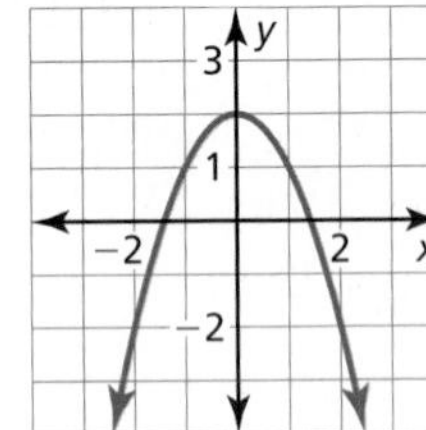

10\.

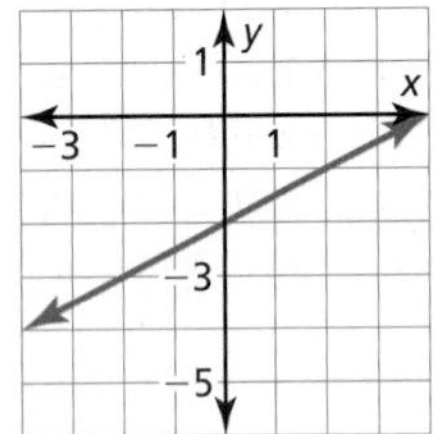

11\.

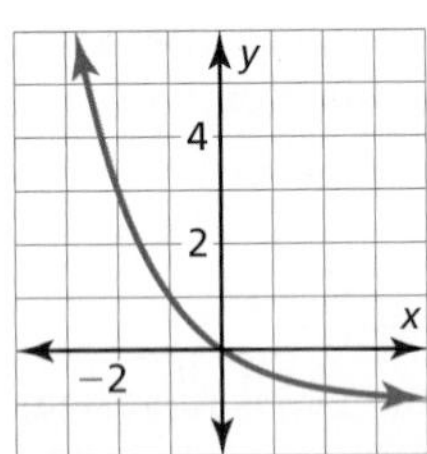

12\.

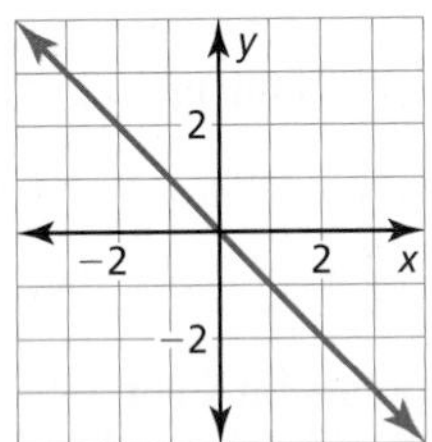

In Exercises 13–16, find the vertex and the axis of symmetry of the graph of the function.

13. $f(x) = 3(x + 1)^2$
14. $f(x) = \frac{1}{4}(x - 6)^2$
15. $y = -\frac{1}{8}(x - 4)^2$
16. $y = -5(x + 9)^2$

In Exercises 17–22, graph the function. Compare the graph to the graph of $f(x) = x^2$. ▶ *Example 2*

17. $g(x) = 2(x + 3)^2$
18. $p(x) = 3(x - 1)^2$
19. $r(x) = \frac{1}{4}(x + 10)^2$
20. $n(x) = \frac{1}{3}(x - 6)^2$
21. $d(x) = \frac{1}{5}(x - 5)^2$
22. $q(x) = 6(x + 2)^2$

In Exercises 23–26, find the vertex and the axis of symmetry of the graph of the function.

23. $y = -6(x + 4)^2 - 3$
24. $f(x) = 3(x - 3)^2 + 6$
25. $f(x) = -4(x + 3)^2 + 1$
26. $y = -(x - 6)^2 - 5$

In Exercises 27–32, graph the function. Compare the graph to the graph of $f(x) = x^2$. ▶ *Example 3*

27. $h(x) = (x - 2)^2 + 4$
28. $g(x) = (x + 1)^2 - 7$
29. $r(x) = 4(x - 1)^2 - 5$
30. $n(x) = -(x + 4)^2 + 2$
31. $g(x) = -\frac{1}{3}(x + 3)^2 - 2$
32. $r(x) = \frac{1}{2}(x - 2)^2 - 4$

33\. **ERROR ANALYSIS** Describe and correct the error in determining whether the function $f(x) = x^2 + 3$ is even, odd, or neither.

$f(x) = x^2 + 3$
$f(-x) = (-x)^2 + 3$
$= x^2 + 3$
$= f(x)$

So, f is an odd function.

34\. **ERROR ANALYSIS** Describe and correct the error in finding the vertex of the graph of the function.

$y = -(x + 8)^2$

Because $h = -8$, the vertex is $(0, -8)$.

MP STRUCTURE In Exercises 35–38, let $f(x) = (x - 2)^2 + 1$. Match the function with its graph.

35. $g(x) = f(x - 1)$
36. $r(x) = f(x + 2)$
37. $h(x) = f(x) + 2$
38. $p(x) = f(x) - 3$

A.

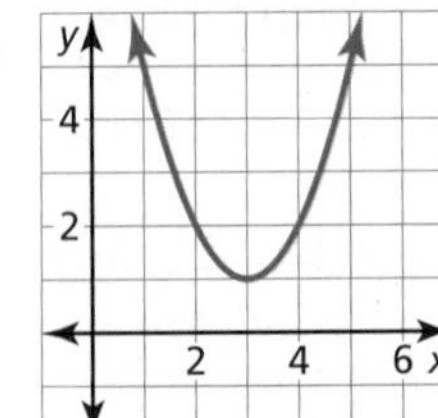

B.

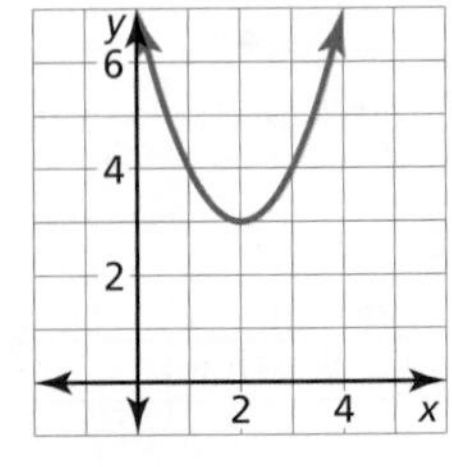

C.

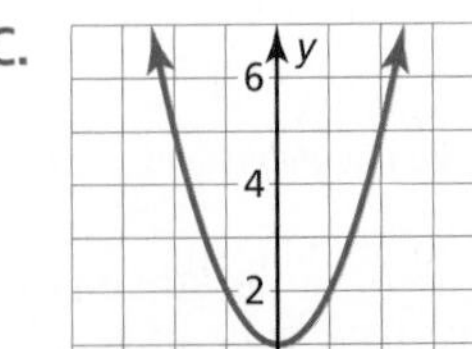

D.

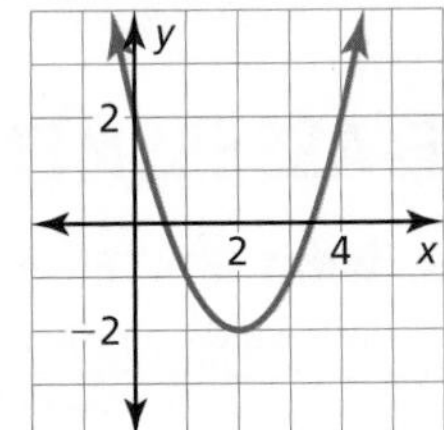

In Exercises 39–46, graph g. Example 3

39. $f(x) = 2(x - 1)^2 + 1$; $g(x) = f(x + 3)$

40. $f(x) = (x + 3)^2 + 5$; $g(x) = f(x - 4)$

41. $f(x) = -3(x + 5)^2 - 6$; $g(x) = 2f(x)$

42. $f(x) = -(x + 1)^2 + 2$; $g(x) = \frac{1}{2}f(x)$

43. $f(x) = 5(x - 3)^2 - 1$; $g(x) = f(x) - 6$

44. $f(x) = -2(x - 4)^2 - 8$; $g(x) = -f(x)$

45. $f(x) = (x + 1)^2 - 3$; $g(x) = f(2x)$

46. $f(x) = 2(x - 4)^2 + 5$; $g(x) = f\left(\frac{1}{2}x\right)$

47. **MODELING REAL LIFE** The height (in meters) of a bird diving to catch a fish is represented by $h(t) = 5(t - 2.5)^2$, where t is the number of seconds after beginning the dive.

a. Graph h.

b. Another bird's dive is represented by $r(t) = 2h(t)$. Graph r.

c. Compare the graphs. Which bird starts its dive from a greater height? Explain.

48. **MODELING REAL LIFE** A kicker punts a football. The height (in yards) of the football is represented by $f(x) = -\frac{1}{9}(x - 30)^2 + 25$, where x is the horizontal distance (in yards) from the kicker's goal line.

a. Graph f. Find the domain and range.

b. On the next possession, the kicker punts the football again. The height of the football is represented by $g(x) = f(x + 5)$. Graph g. Find the domain and range.

c. Compare the graphs. On which possession does the kicker punt closer to his goal line? Explain.

In Exercises 49–52, write a quadratic function in vertex form whose graph has the given vertex and passes through the given point.

49. vertex: (1, 2); passes through (3, 10)

50. vertex: (−3, 5); passes through (0, −14)

51. vertex: (−2, −4); passes through (−1, −6)

52. vertex: (−5, −1); passes through (−2, 2)

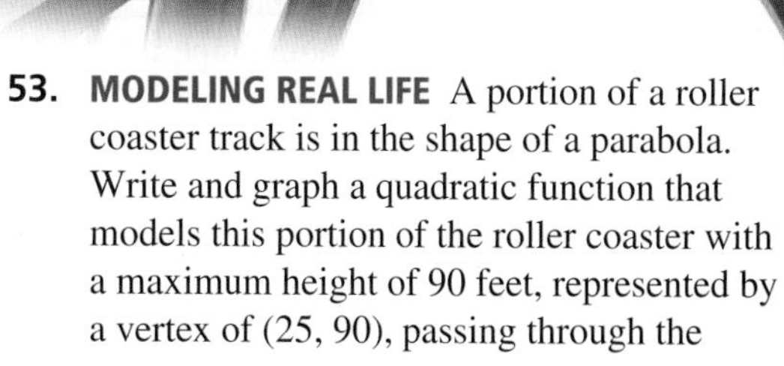

53. **MODELING REAL LIFE** A portion of a roller coaster track is in the shape of a parabola. Write and graph a quadratic function that models this portion of the roller coaster with a maximum height of 90 feet, represented by a vertex of (25, 90), passing through the point (50, 0). Example 4

54. **MODELING REAL LIFE** A flare is launched from a boat and travels in a parabolic path until reaching the water. Write and graph a quadratic function that models the path of the flare with a maximum height of 300 meters, represented by a vertex of (59, 300), landing in the water at the point (119, 0).

55. **COLLEGE PREP** The graph of $g(x) = -\frac{1}{2}(x + 3)^2 - 4$ is translated 4 units right and 1 unit up. What is the value of h when the equation of the transformed graph is written in vertex form?

Ⓐ −7 Ⓑ −3 Ⓒ −1
Ⓓ 1 Ⓔ 4 Ⓕ 7

56. **HOW DO YOU SEE IT?**
Use the symbols + or − to complete the vertex form of the quadratic function shown. Explain.

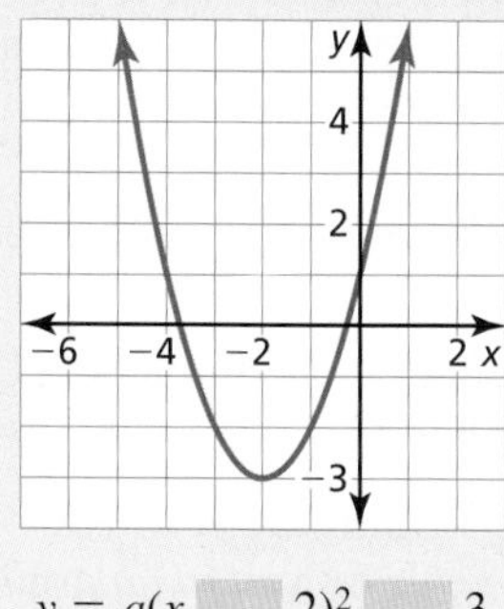

$y = a(x \;\square\; 2)^2 \;\square\; 3$

In Exercises 57–60, describe the transformation from the graph of f to the graph of h. Write an equation that represents h in terms of x.

57. $f(x) = -(x + 1)^2 - 2$
$h(x) = f(x) + 4$

58. $f(x) = 2(x - 1)^2 + 1$
$h(x) = f(x - 5)$

59. $f(x) = 4(x - 2)^2 + 3$
$h(x) = 2f(x)$

60. $f(x) = -(x + 5)^2 - 6$
$h(x) = \frac{1}{3}f(x)$

61. MP **REASONING** The graph of $y = x^2$ is translated 2 units right and 5 units down. Write an equation that represents the function in vertex form and in standard form. Describe advantages of writing the function in each form.

62. MP **REASONING** Compare the graphs of $y = 2x^2 + 8x + 8$ and $y = x^2$ without graphing the functions. How can factoring help you compare the parabolas? Explain.

In Exercises 63–66, rewrite the quadratic function in vertex form.

63. $y = 2x^2 - 8x + 4$
64. $y = 3x^2 + 6x - 1$
65. $f(x) = -x^2 - 4x + 2$
66. $f(x) = -5x^2 + 10x + 3$

67. **MAKING AN ARGUMENT** Are all quadratic functions of the form $y = ax^2 + c$ even? Explain.

68. **THOUGHT PROVOKING**
Which of the following are true? Justify your answers.

a. Any constant multiple of an even function is even.

b. Any constant multiple of an odd function is odd.

c. The sum or difference of two even functions is even.

d. The sum or difference of two odd functions is odd.

e. The sum or difference of an even function and an odd function is odd.

REVIEW & REFRESH

69. Identify characteristics of the quadratic function and its graph.

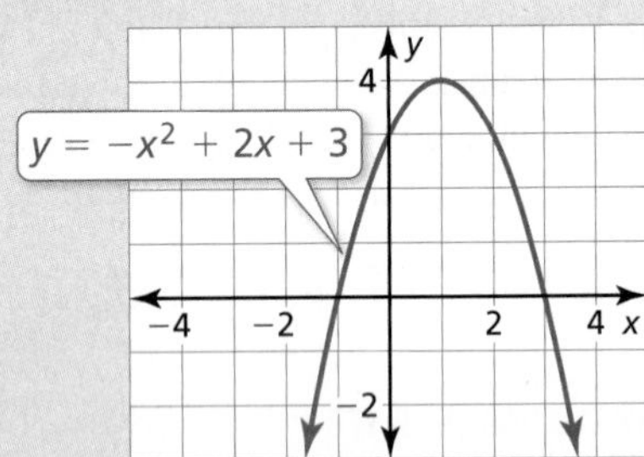

70. **WRITING** Describe the transformation from the graph of $f(x) = ax^2$ to the graph of $g(x) = a(x - h)^2 + k$.

In Exercises 71 and 72, solve the inequality. Graph the solution.

71. $4t - 12 \geq 6 - 2t$
72. $1 < \frac{1}{2}v + 5 \leq 9$

In Exercises 73 and 74, tell whether the function has a *maximum value* or a *minimum value*. Then find the value.

73. $f(x) = 5x^2 + 10x - 3$
74. $y = -x^2 + 4x + 12$

75. Solve $-2(8x + 6) = 12 - 16x$.

76. Determine whether the table represents a *linear* or an *exponential* function. Explain.

x	−3	−2	−1	0	1
y	192	48	12	3	$\frac{3}{4}$

77. Describe the transformation from the graph of $f(x) = \frac{1}{2}x^2 - 2$ to the graph of $g(x) = f(x) - 6$. Then graph f and g in the same coordinate plane. Write an equation that represents g in terms of x.

78. Graph $y = \begin{cases} \frac{1}{2}x - 3, & \text{if } x \leq -2 \\ -3x + 2, & \text{if } x > -2 \end{cases}$. Find the domain and range.

In Exercises 79–82, graph the function. Compare the graph to the graph of $f(x) = x^2$.

79. $g(x) = 2(x - 5)^2$
80. $h(x) = -(x + 3)^2 + 1$
81. $m(x) = -(x + 8)^2$
82. $n(x) = \frac{1}{3}(x - 6)^2 - 2$

83. Write a rule for the nth term of the geometric sequence. Then find a_{10}.

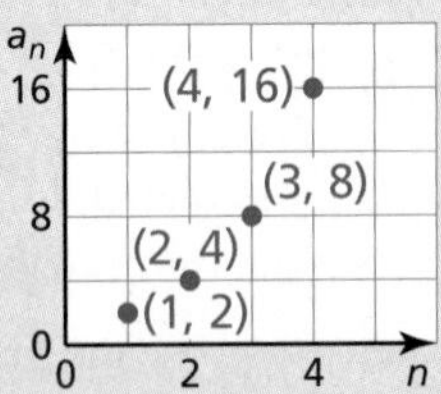

84. **MODELING REAL LIFE** A bicycle rental company charges $12 per hour to rent a standard bicycle and $20 per hour to rent a tandem bicycle. In 1 hour, the company earns $240 from a total of 18 bicycle rentals. How many of each type of bicycle are rented?

In Exercises 85–88, solve the equation.

85. $x(x - 1) = 0$
86. $(x + 3)(x - 8) = 0$
87. $(2x - 3)^2 = 0$
88. $(3x - 9)(4x + 1) = 0$

8.5 Using Intercept Form

Learning Target Graph and use functions in intercept form.

Success Criteria
- I can graph quadratic functions of the form $f(x) = a(x - p)(x - q)$.
- I can find zeros of functions using intercept form.
- I can use characteristics to graph and write quadratic functions and cubic functions.

EXPLORE IT! Using Different Forms of Quadratic Functions

Work with a partner. Consider the equations shown.

$y_1 = x^2 + 2x - 8$ $y_2 = (x + 1)^2 - 9$ $y_3 = (x + 4)(x - 2)$

a. What do you notice about their graphs?

b. Which equation from part (a) would you use to find each of the following? Explain your reasoning.

i. vertex **ii.** x-intercepts **iii.** y-intercept

Math Practice

Look for Structure
Why is it important to be familiar with different ways of representing the same quadratic function?

c. Each graph represents a function of the form $f(x) = (x - p)(x - q)$ or $f(x) = -(x - p)(x - q)$. Write the function represented by each graph. Explain your reasoning.

i.
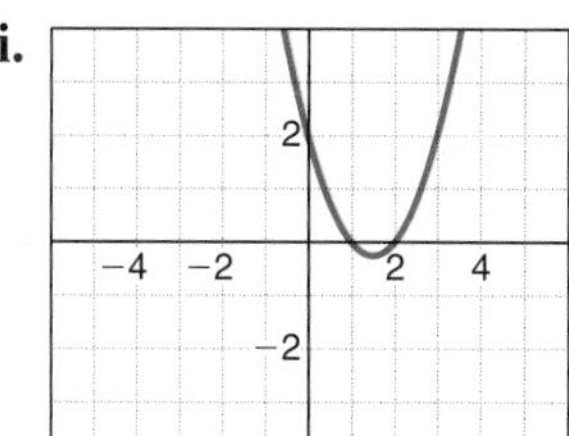

ii.
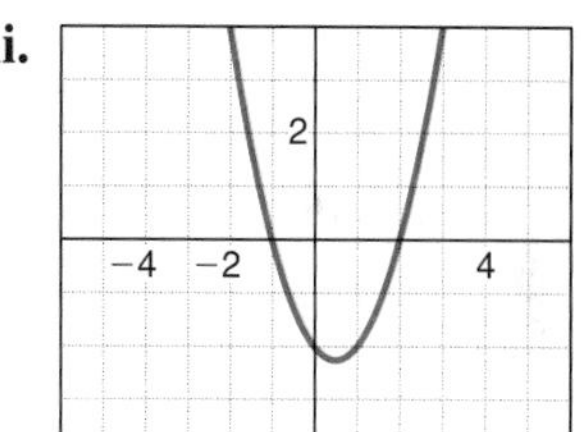

iii.
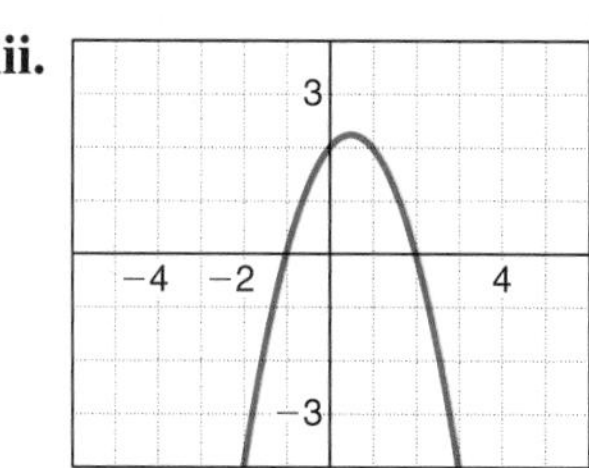

iv.
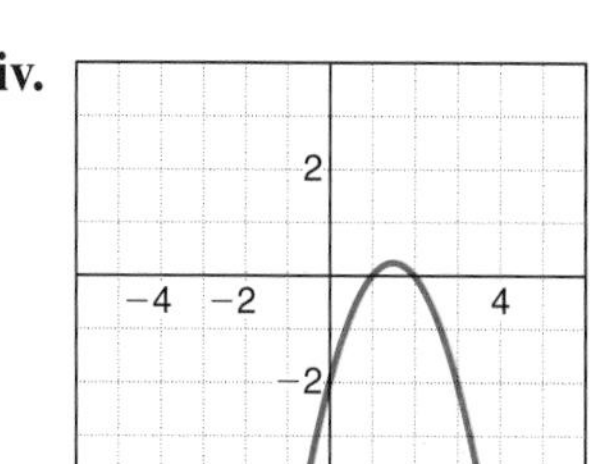

d. Without graphing, explain how you can find each of the following for $f(x) = a(x - p)(x - q)$.

- x-intercept(s) of the graph of f
- axis of symmetry of the graph of f
- x-coordinate of the vertex of the graph of f
- y-intercept of the graph of f

e. Consider the graph of $f(x) = a(x - p)(x - q)$.

i. Does changing the sign of a change the x-intercepts? Does changing the sign of a change the y-intercept? Explain your reasoning.

ii. Does changing the value of p or q change the x-intercepts? Does changing the value of p or q change the y-intercept? Explain your reasoning.

Graphing $f(x) = a(x - p)(x - q)$

Vocabulary 

intercept form, *p. 454*

You have already graphed quadratic functions written in several different forms, such as $f(x) = ax^2 + bx + c$ (standard form) and $f(x) = a(x - h)^2 + k$ (vertex form). Quadratic functions can also be written in **intercept form**.

$$f(x) = a(x - p)(x - q),\ a \neq 0 \qquad \text{Intercept form of a quadratic function}$$

In this form, the polynomial that defines a function is in factored form and the x-intercepts of the graph can be easily determined.

KEY IDEA

Graphing $f(x) = a(x - p)(x - q)$

- The x-intercepts are p and q.
- The axis of symmetry is halfway between $(p, 0)$ and $(q, 0)$. So, the axis of symmetry is $x = \frac{p + q}{2}$.
- The graph opens up when $a > 0$, and the graph opens down when $a < 0$.
- The x-coordinate of the vertex is $\frac{p + q}{2}$.

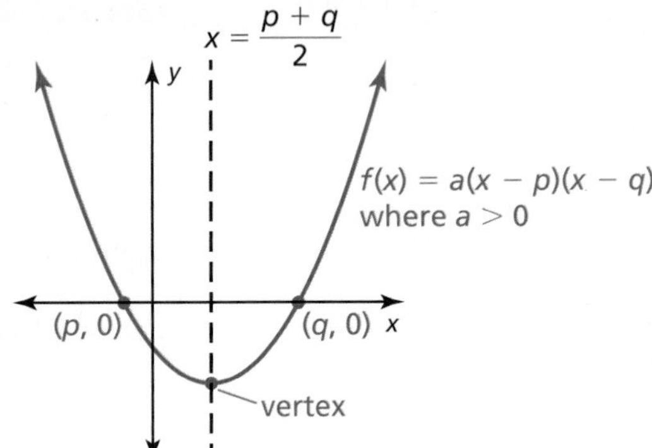

EXAMPLE 1 Graphing $f(x) = a(x - p)(x - q)$ 

Graph $f(x) = -(x + 1)(x - 5)$. Find the domain and range.

SOLUTION

Step 1 Identify the x-intercepts. Because the x-intercepts are $p = -1$ and $q = 5$, plot $(-1, 0)$ and $(5, 0)$.

Step 2 Find and graph the axis of symmetry.

$$x = \frac{p + q}{2} = \frac{-1 + 5}{2} = 2$$

Step 3 Find and plot the vertex. The x-coordinate of the vertex is 2. To find the y-coordinate of the vertex, substitute 2 for x and evaluate.

$$f(2) = -(2 + 1)(2 - 5) = 9$$

So, the vertex is $(2, 9)$.

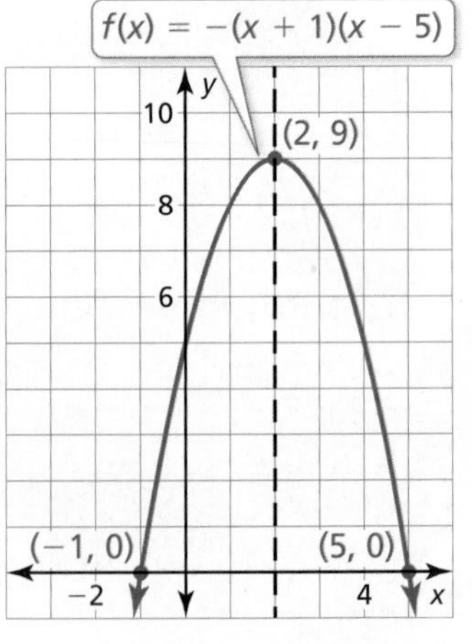

Step 4 Draw a parabola through the vertex and the points where the x-intercepts occur.

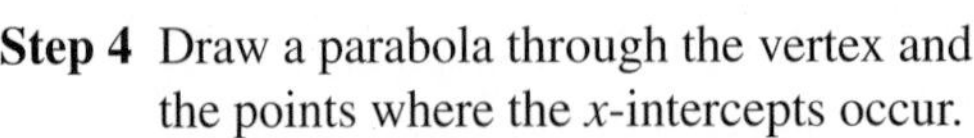

▶ The domain is all real numbers. The range is $y \leq 9$.

EXAMPLE 2 Graphing a Quadratic Function

GO DIGITAL

Graph $f(x) = 2x^2 - 8$. Find the domain and range.

SOLUTION

Notice that $2x^2 - 8$ is factorable. One way to graph is to use intercept form.

Step 1 Rewrite the quadratic function in intercept form.

$f(x) = 2x^2 - 8$	Write the function.
$= 2(x^2 - 4)$	Factor out common factor.
$= 2(x + 2)(x - 2)$	Difference of two squares pattern

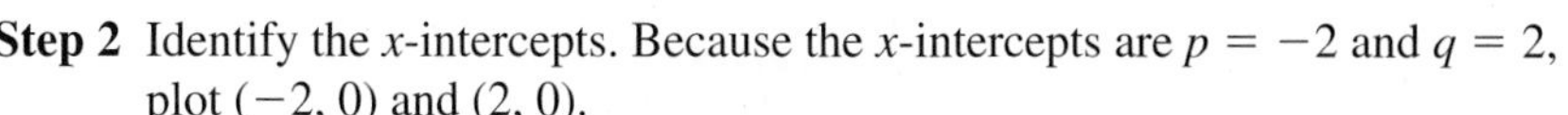

Step 2 Identify the x-intercepts. Because the x-intercepts are $p = -2$ and $q = 2$, plot $(-2, 0)$ and $(2, 0)$.

Step 3 Find and graph the axis of symmetry.

$$x = \frac{p + q}{2} = \frac{-2 + 2}{2} = 0$$

Step 4 Find and plot the vertex.

The x-coordinate of the vertex is 0. The y-coordinate of the vertex is

$$f(0) = 2(0)^2 - 8 = -8.$$

So, the vertex is $(0, -8)$.

Step 5 Draw a parabola through the vertex and the points where the x-intercepts occur.

▶ The domain is all real numbers. The range is $y \geq -8$.

SELF-ASSESSMENT

1 I do not understand. 2 I can do it with help. 3 I can do it on my own. 4 I can teach someone else.

Graph the quadratic function. Label the vertex, axis of symmetry, and x-intercepts. Find the domain and range of the function.

1. $f(x) = (x + 2)(x - 3)$

2. $g(x) = -(x + 5)(x - 5)$

3. $g(x) = -2(x - 4)(x + 1)$

4. $f(x) = x^2 - 25$

5. $g(x) = x^2 + 10x + 16$

6. $h(x) = 4x^2 - 36$

Using Intercept Form to Find Zeros of Functions

In Section 8.2, you learned that a zero of a function is an x-value for which $f(x) = 0$. You can use the intercept form of a function to find the zeros of the function.

REMEMBER

Functions have zeros, and *graphs* have x-intercepts.

EXAMPLE 3 Finding Zeros of a Function

WATCH

Find the zeros of $f(x) = (x - 1)(x + 2)$.

SOLUTION

To find the zeros, determine the x-values for which $f(x)$ is 0.

$f(x) = (x - 1)(x + 2)$	Write the function.
$0 = (x - 1)(x + 2)$	Substitute 0 for $f(x)$.
$x - 1 = 0$ *or* $x + 2 = 0$	Zero-Product Property
$x = 1$ *or* $x = -2$	Solve for x.

▶ So, the zeros of the function are -2 and 1.

Check

KEY IDEA

Factors and Zeros

For any factor $x - n$ of a polynomial, n is a zero of the function defined by the polynomial.

EXAMPLE 4 Finding Zeros of Functions

Find the zeros of each function.

a. $f(x) = -2x^2 - 10x - 12$

b. $h(x) = (x - 1)(x^2 - 16)$

SOLUTION

Write each function in intercept form to identify the zeros.

a. $f(x) = -2x^2 - 10x - 12$ — Write the function.

$= -2(x^2 + 5x + 6)$ — Factor out common factor.

$= -2(x + 3)(x + 2)$ — Factor the trinomial.

▶ So, the zeros of the function are -3 and -2.

b. $h(x) = (x - 1)(x^2 - 16)$ — Write the function.

$= (x - 1)(x + 4)(x - 4)$ — Difference of two squares pattern

▶ So, the zeros of the function are -4, 1, and 4.

Math Practice

Look for Structure

The function in Example 4(b) is called a *cubic function*. You can extend the concept of intercept form to cubic functions. You will graph a cubic function in Example 7.

SELF-ASSESSMENT 1 I do not understand. 2 I can do it with help. 3 I can do it on my own. 4 I can teach someone else.

Find the zero(s) of the function.

7. $f(x) = (x - 6)(x - 7)$

8. $g(x) = 3x^2 - 12x + 12$

9. $h(x) = x(x^2 - 1)$

Using Characteristics to Graph and Write Quadratic Functions

EXAMPLE 5 Graphing a Quadratic Function Using Zeros

Use zeros to graph $h(x) = x^2 - 2x - 3$.

SOLUTION

The function is in standard form. You know that the parabola opens up ($a > 0$) and the y-intercept is -3. So, begin by plotting $(0, -3)$.

Notice that the polynomial that defines the function is factorable. So, write the function in intercept form and identify the zeros.

$h(x) = x^2 - 2x - 3$ — Write the function.

$= (x + 1)(x - 3)$ — Factor the trinomial.

The zeros of the function are -1 and 3. So, plot $(-1, 0)$ and $(3, 0)$. Draw a parabola through the points.

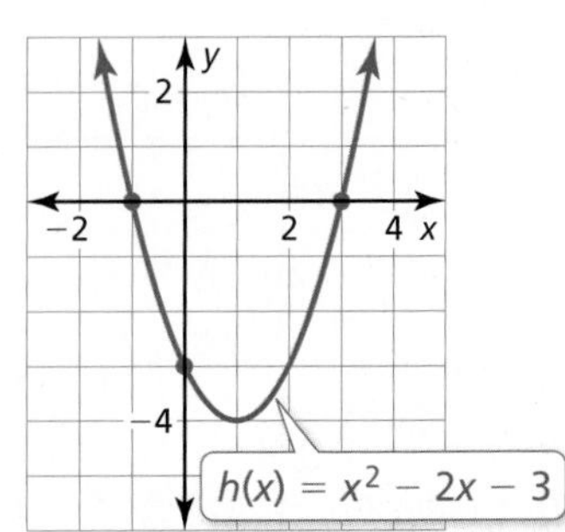

EXAMPLE 6 Writing Quadratic Functions

Write a quadratic function in standard form that has the given characteristic(s).

a. vertex: $(-3, 4)$

b. zeros: -5 and 4

c. passes through $(-9, 0)$, $(-2, 0)$, and $(-4, 20)$

SOLUTION

a. Because you know the vertex, use vertex form to write a function.

$f(x) = a(x - h)^2 + k$	Vertex form
$= 1(x + 3)^2 + 4$	Substitute for a, h, and k.
$= x^2 + 6x + 9 + 4$	Find the product $(x + 3)^2$.
$= x^2 + 6x + 13$	Combine like terms.

STUDY TIP

In parts (a) and (b), many possible functions satisfy the given condition. The value a can be *any* nonzero number. To allow easier calculations in part (a), let $a = 1$. By letting $a = 2$, the resulting function would be $f(x) = 2x^2 + 12x + 22$.

b. Remember that a zero of a function is an x-intercept of the graph of the function. So, the x-intercepts are -5 and 4. Use intercept form to write a function.

$f(x) = a(x - p)(x - q)$	Intercept form
$= 1(x + 5)(x - 4)$	Substitute for a, p, and q.
$= x^2 + x - 20$	Multiply.

c. The given points indicate that the x-intercepts are -9 and -2. So, use intercept form to write a function.

$f(x) = a(x - p)(x - q)$	Intercept form
$= a(x + 9)(x + 2)$	Substitute for p and q.

Use the other given point, $(-4, 20)$, to find the value of a.

$20 = a(-4 + 9)(-4 + 2)$	Substitute -4 for x and 20 for $f(x)$.
$20 = a(5)(-2)$	Simplify.
$-2 = a$	Solve for a.

Use the value of a to write the function.

$f(x) = -2(x + 9)(x + 2)$	Substitute -2 for a.
$= -2x^2 - 22x - 36$	Simplify.

SELF-ASSESSMENT

1 I do not understand. **2** I can do it with help. **3** I can do it on my own. **4** I can teach someone else.

Use zeros to graph the function.

10. $f(x) = (x - 1)(x - 4)$

11. $g(x) = x^2 + x - 12$

12. $h(x) = 2x^2 + 3x - 2$

Write a quadratic function in standard form that has the given characteristic(s).

13. x-intercepts: -1 and 1

14. vertex: $(8, 8)$

15. zeros: -7 and -2

16. passes through $(0, 0)$, $(10, 0)$, and $(4, 12)$

17. passes through $(-5, 0)$, $(4, 0)$, and $(3, -16)$

18. MP **REASONING** Write a quadratic function whose graph passes through the points $(-1, 5)$ and $(4, 5)$. Explain how you found your answer.

Using Characteristics to Graph and Write Cubic Functions

In Example 4, you extended the concept of intercept form to cubic functions.

$f(x) = a(x - p)(x - q)(x - r),\ a \neq 0$ — Intercept form of a cubic function

The x-intercepts of the graph of f are p, q, and r.

EXAMPLE 7 Graphing a Cubic Function Using Zeros

Use zeros to graph $f(x) = x^3 - 4x$.

SOLUTION

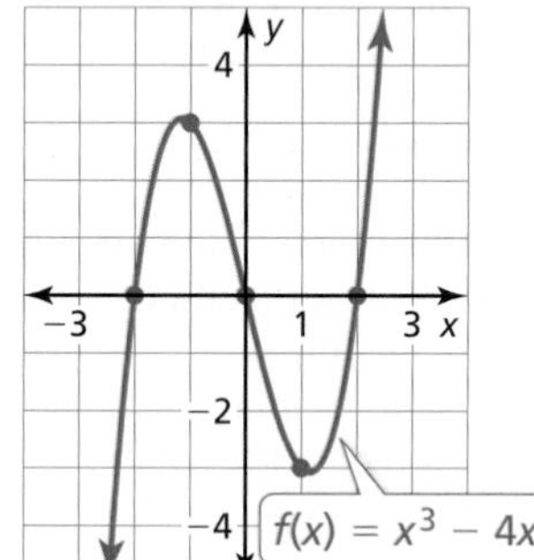

Notice that the polynomial that defines the function is factorable. So, write the function in intercept form and identify the zeros.

$f(x) = x^3 - 4x$	Write the function.
$= x(x^2 - 4)$	Factor out x.
$= x(x + 2)(x - 2)$	Difference of two squares pattern

The zeros of the function are -2, 0, and 2. So, plot $(-2, 0)$, $(0, 0)$, and $(2, 0)$.

To help determine the shape of the graph, find and plot points between the zeros, such as $(-1, 3)$ and $(1, -3)$. Draw a smooth curve through the points.

EXAMPLE 8 Writing a Cubic Function

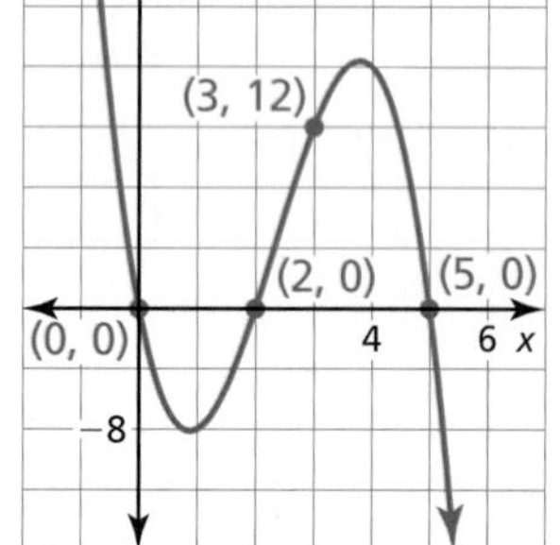

The graph represents a cubic function. Write the function in standard form.

SOLUTION

From the graph, you can see that the x-intercepts are 0, 2, and 5. Use intercept form to write a function.

$f(x) = a(x - p)(x - q)(x - r)$	Intercept form
$= a(x - 0)(x - 2)(x - 5)$	Substitute for p, q, and r.
$= a(x)(x - 2)(x - 5)$	Simplify.

Use the other given point, $(3, 12)$, to find the value of a.

$12 = a(3)(3 - 2)(3 - 5)$	Substitute 3 for x and 12 for $f(x)$.
$-2 = a$	Solve for a.

Use the value of a to write the function.

$f(x) = -2(x)(x - 2)(x - 5)$	Substitute -2 for a.
$= -2x^3 + 14x^2 - 20x$	Simplify.

▶ The function represented by the graph is $f(x) = -2x^3 + 14x^2 - 20x$.

SELF-ASSESSMENT 1 I do not understand. 2 I can do it with help. 3 I can do it on my own. 4 I can teach someone else.

Use zeros to graph the function.

19. $g(x) = (x - 1)(x - 3)(x + 3)$ **20.** $f(x) = x^3 + 2x^2 - 8x$ **21.** $h(x) = x^3 - 6x^2 + 5x$

8.5 Practice WITH CalcChat® AND CalcView®

In Exercises 1–4, find the x-intercepts and axis of symmetry of the graph of the function.

1. 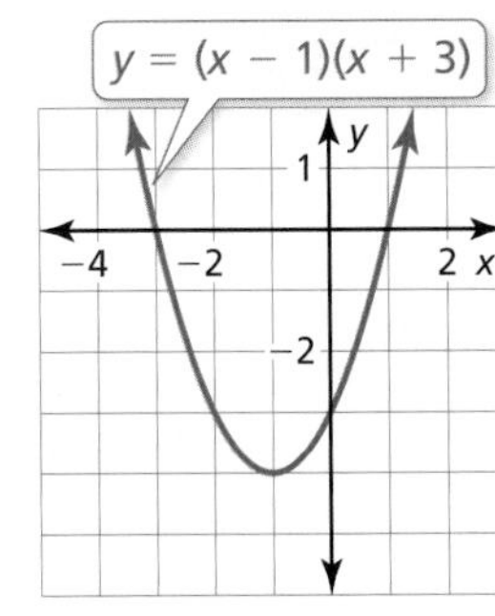

2. 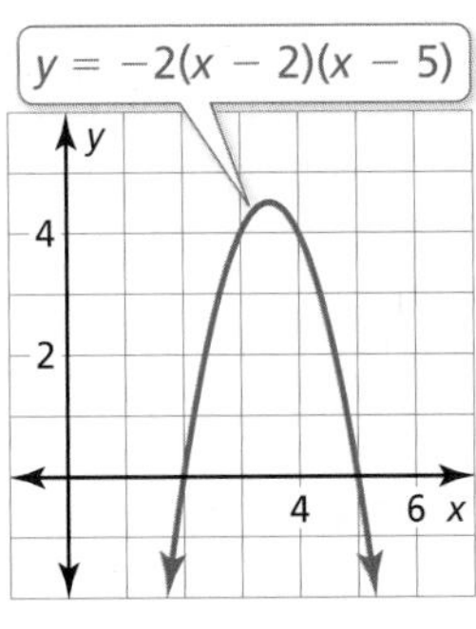

3. $f(x) = -5(x + 7)(x - 5)$
4. $g(x) = \frac{2}{3}x(x + 8)$

In Exercises 5–10, graph the quadratic function. Label the vertex, axis of symmetry, and x-intercepts. Find the domain and range of the function. *Example 1*

5. $f(x) = (x + 4)(x + 1)$
6. $y = (x - 2)(x + 2)$
7. $y = -(x + 6)(x - 4)$
8. $h(x) = -4(x - 7)(x - 3)$
9. $g(x) = 5(x + 1)(x + 2)$
10. $y = -2(x - 3)(x + 4)$

In Exercises 11–18, graph the quadratic function. Label the vertex, axis of symmetry, and x-intercepts. Find the domain and range of the function. *Example 2*

11. $y = x^2 - 9$
12. $f(x) = x^2 - 8x$
13. $h(x) = -5x^2 + 5x$
14. $y = 3x^2 - 48$
15. $q(x) = x^2 + 9x + 14$
16. $p(x) = x^2 + 6x - 27$
17. $y = 4x^2 - 36x + 32$
18. $y = -2x^2 - 4x + 30$

In Exercises 19–28, find the zero(s) of the function. *Examples 3 and 4*

19. $y = -2(x - 2)(x - 10)$
20. $f(x) = \frac{1}{3}(x + 5)(x - 1)$
21. $g(x) = x^2 + 5x - 24$
22. $y = x^2 - 17x + 52$
23. $y = 3x^2 - 15x - 42$
24. $g(x) = -4x^2 - 8x - 4$
25. $f(x) = (x + 5)(x^2 - 4)$
26. $h(x) = (x^2 - 36)(x - 11)$
27. $y = x^3 - 49x$
28. $y = x^3 - x^2 - 9x + 9$

ERROR ANALYSIS In Exercises 29 and 30, describe and correct the error in finding the zeros of the function.

29. 

$y = 5(x + 3)(x - 2)$

The zeros of the function are 3 and −2.

30. 

$y = (x + 4)(x^2 - 9)$

The zeros of the function are −4 and 9.

In Exercises 31–34, match the function with its graph.

31. $y = (x + 5)(x + 3)$
32. $y = (x + 5)(x - 3)$
33. $y = (x - 5)(x + 3)$
34. $y = (x - 5)(x - 3)$

A. 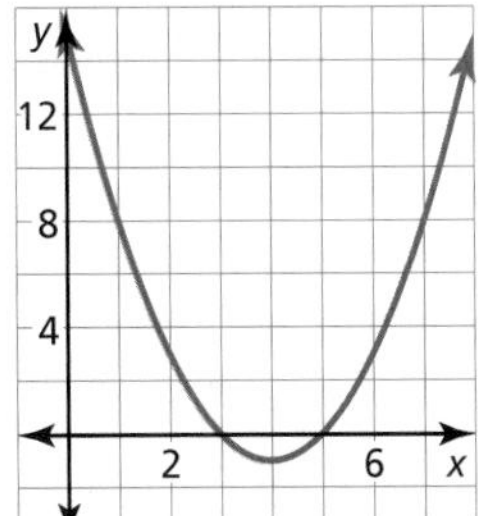

B. 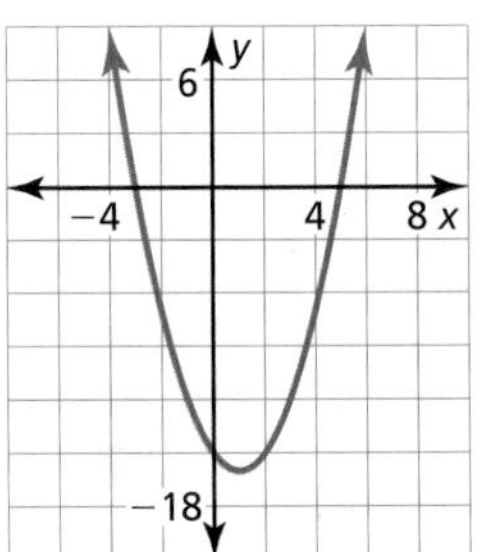

C. 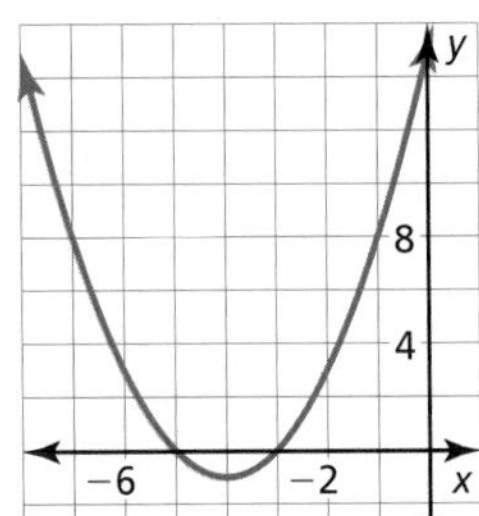

D. 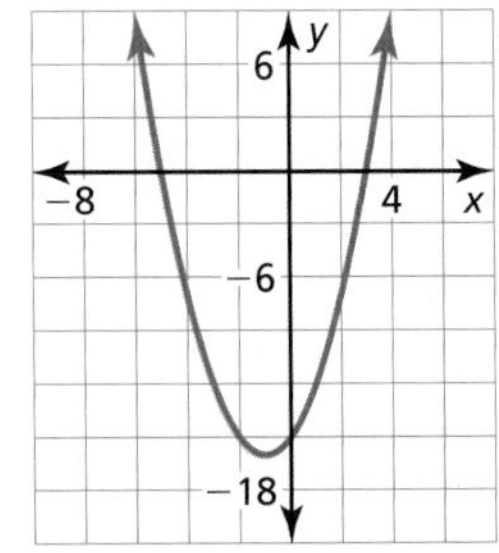

In Exercises 35–40, use zeros to graph the function. *Example 5*

35. $f(x) = (x + 2)(x - 6)$
36. $g(x) = -3(x + 1)(x + 7)$
37. $y = x^2 - 11x + 18$
38. $y = x^2 - x - 30$
39. $y = -5x^2 - 10x + 40$
40. $h(x) = 8x^2 - 8$

In Exercises 41–52, write a quadratic function in standard form that has the given characteristic(s). ▶ *Example 6*

41. vertex: $(7, -3)$

42. vertex: $(4, 8)$

43. x-intercepts: 1 and 9

44. zeros: -2 and -5

45. passes through $(-4, 0)$, $(3, 0)$, and $(2, -18)$

46. passes through $(-5, 0)$, $(-1, 0)$, and $(-4, 3)$

47. increasing when $x < 4$; decreasing when $x > 4$

48. decreasing when $x < -1$; increasing when $x > -1$

49. range: $y \geq -3$

50. range: $y \leq 10$

51. axis of symmetry: $x = -5$

52. end behavior: $y \to -\infty$ as $x \to -\infty$ and $y \to -\infty$ as $x \to +\infty$

In Exercises 53–60, use zeros to graph the function. ▶ *Example 7*

53. $y = 5x(x + 2)(x - 6)$

54. $f(x) = -x(x + 9)(x + 3)$

55. $h(x) = (x - 2)(x + 2)(x + 7)$

56. $y = (x + 1)(x - 5)(x - 4)$

57. $f(x) = 3x^3 - 48x$

58. $y = -2x^3 + 20x^2 - 50x$

59. $y = -x^3 - 16x^2 - 28x$

60. $g(x) = 6x^3 + 30x^2 - 36x$

In Exercises 61–64, write the standard form of the cubic function represented by the graph . ▶ *Example 8*

61.

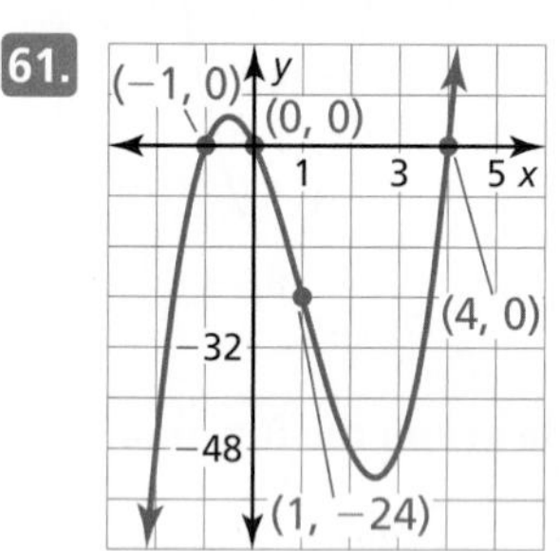

62.

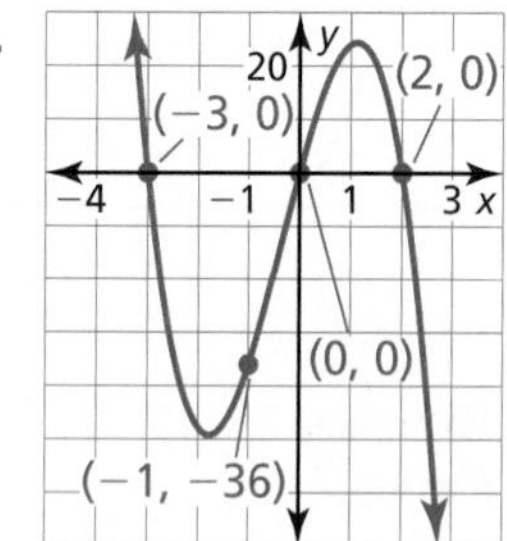

63.

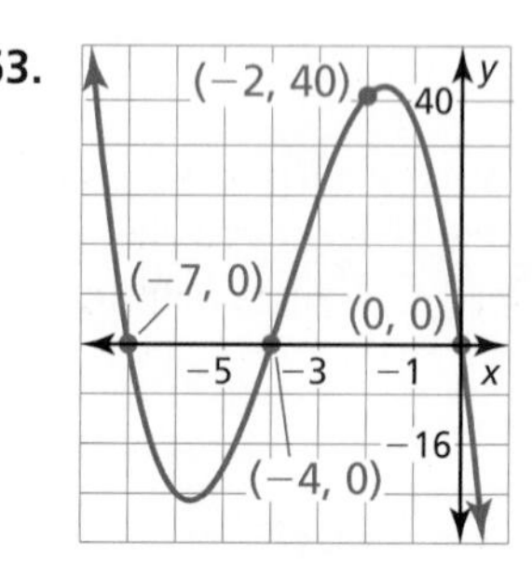

64.

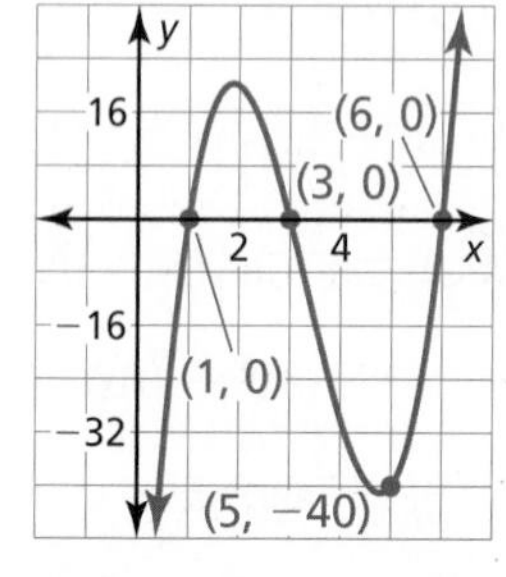

In Exercises 65–68, write a cubic function in standard form that has the given characteristic(s).

65. x-intercepts: -2, 3, and 8

66. zeros: -7, -5, and 0

67. passes through $(0, 0)$, $(1, 0)$, and $(7, 0)$

68. passes through $(-4, 0)$, $(-2, 0)$, $(0, -32)$, and $(2, 0)$

In Exercises 69 and 70, all the zeros of a function are given. Use the zeros and the other point given to write a quadratic or cubic function represented by the table in standard form.

69.

x	y
0	0
2	30
7	0

70.

x	y
-8	0
-6	-36
-3	0
0	0

In Exercises 71–74, sketch a parabola that has the given characteristic(s).

71. zeros: -4 and 2; range: $y \geq -3$

72. axis of symmetry: $x = 6$; passes through $(4, 15)$

73. range: $y \leq 5$; passes through $(0, 2)$

74. x-intercept: 6; y-intercept: 1; range: $y \geq -4$

75. MODELING REAL LIFE Satellite dishes are shaped like parabolas to optimally receive signals. The cross section of a satellite dish is modeled by the function shown, where x and y are measured in feet. The x-axis represents the top of the opening of the dish.

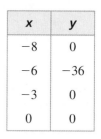

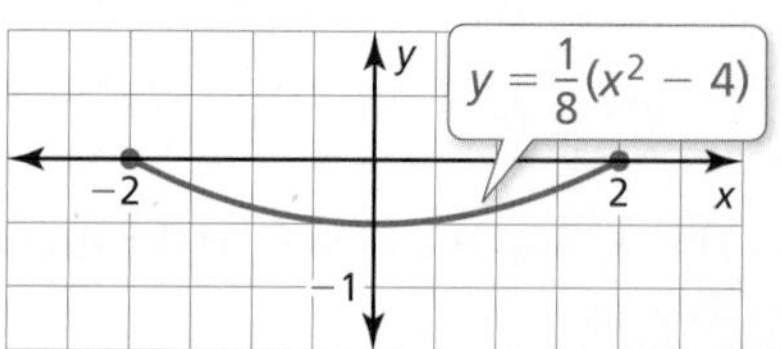

a. How wide is the satellite dish?

b. How deep is the satellite dish?

c. Write a quadratic function in standard form that models the cross section of a satellite dish that is 6 feet wide and 1.5 feet deep.

76. MODELING REAL LIFE A professional basketball player's shot is modeled by the function shown, where x and y are measured in feet.

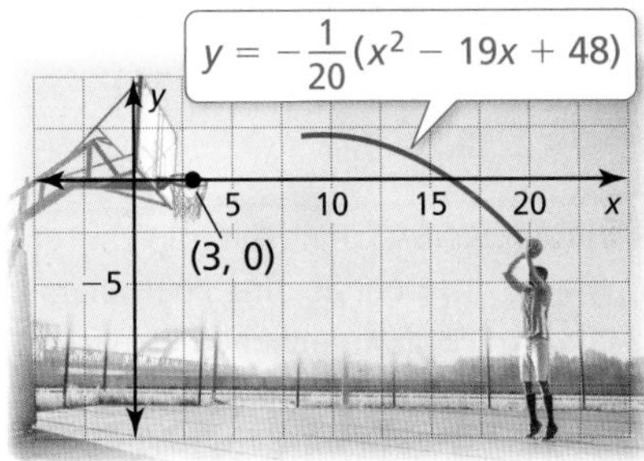

a. Does the player make the shot? Explain.

b. The basketball player releases another shot from the point (13, 0) and makes the shot. The shot also passes through the point (10, 1.4). Write a quadratic function in standard form that models the path of the shot.

77. COLLEGE PREP Which of the following functions could be represented by the graph? Select all that apply.

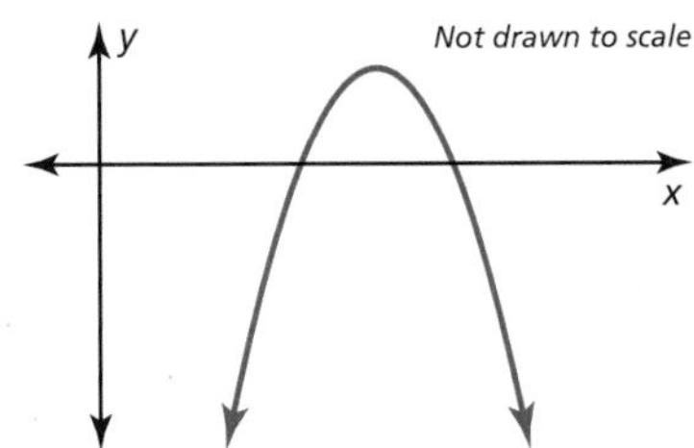

Ⓐ $y = (x - 4)(x - 6)$ Ⓑ $y = -2(x - 12)^2 + 5$

Ⓒ $y = -(x + 8)^2 + 3$ Ⓓ $y = -\frac{1}{2}(x + 3)(x + 5)$

Ⓔ $y = (x - 30)^2 + 10$ Ⓕ $y = -(x - 8)(x - 14)$

78. HOW DO YOU SEE IT?
The graph shows the parabolic arch that supports the roof of a convention center, where x and y are measured in feet.

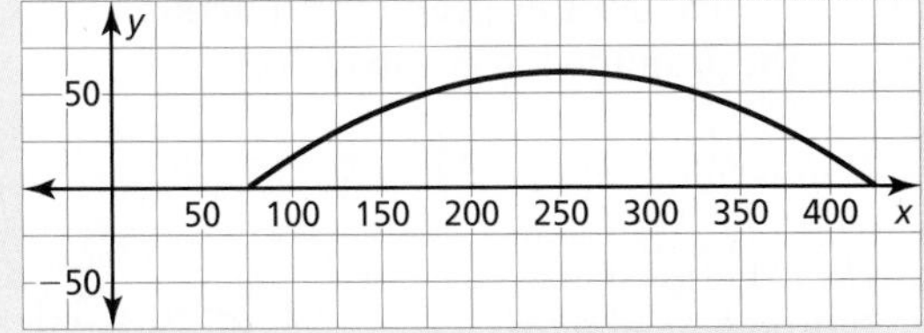

a. The arch can be represented by a function of the form $f(x) = a(x - p)(x - q)$. Estimate the values of p and q.

b. Estimate the width and height of the arch. Explain how you can use your height estimate to calculate a.

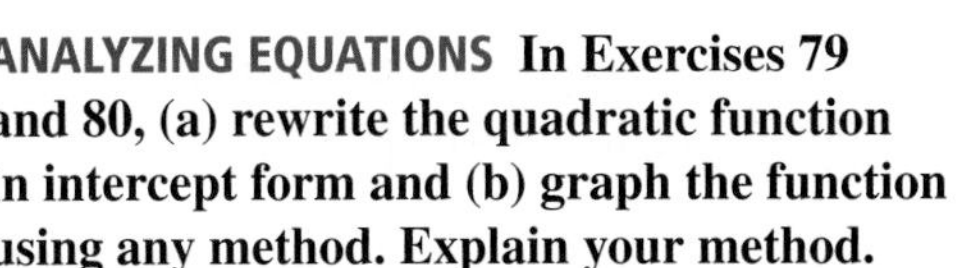

ANALYZING EQUATIONS In Exercises 79 and 80, (a) rewrite the quadratic function in intercept form and (b) graph the function using any method. Explain your method.

79. $f(x) = -3(x + 1)^2 + 27$

80. $g(x) = 2(x - 1)^2 - 2$

81. WRITING Can a quadratic function with exactly one real zero be written in intercept form? Explain.

82. MULTIPLE REPRESENTATIONS The profit (in hundreds of dollars) that a company makes selling an item for x dollars is represented by each of the following equivalent functions:

$$p(x) = -2x^2 + 28x - 80$$
$$p(x) = -2(x - 4)(x - 10)$$
$$p(x) = -2(x - 7)^2 + 18.$$

Answer each question and explain which function you used to find your answer.

a. What selling price(s) yield no profit?

b. What is the profit when the product is free?

c. What selling price maximizes the profit?

83. MAKING AN ARGUMENT Is it possible to write a quadratic function represented by the table? Explain.

x	−5	−3	−1	1
y	0	12	4	0

84. DRAWING CONCLUSIONS Consider the points (−2, 8), (−1, 6), and (2, 0).

a. The graphs of which of the following functions contain all three points?

$f(x) = -2x + 4$ $g(x) = x^2 - 2x$

$h(x) = x^3 + x^2 - 6x$

b. Is it possible for three points that lie on the same line to also lie on the graph of a quadratic function? a cubic function? Explain your reasoning.

MP PROBLEM SOLVING In Exercises 85 and 86, write a system of two quadratic functions whose graphs intersect at the given points. Explain your reasoning.

85. (−4, 0) and (2, 0)

86. (3, 6) and (7, 6)

87. **MP PROBLEM SOLVING** Write the function represented by the graph in intercept form.

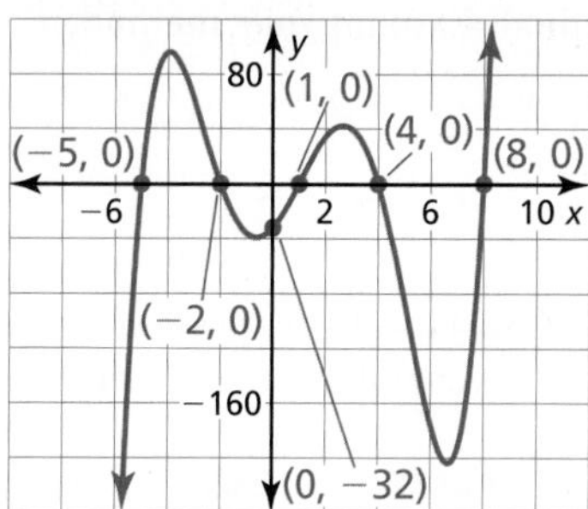

88. **THOUGHT PROVOKING** Sketch the graph of each function. Explain your procedure.

a. $f(x) = (x^2 - 1)(x^2 - 4)$

b. $g(x) = x(x^2 - 1)(x^2 - 4)$

GO DIGITAL

89. **MP REPEATED REASONING** Graph several cubic functions with different leading coefficients. Then make a conjecture about the end behavior of cubic functions.

90. **DIG DEEPER** Let k be a constant. Find the zeros of the function $f(x) = kx^2 - k^2x - 2k^3$ in terms of k.

REVIEW & REFRESH

In Exercises 91–93, determine whether the sequence is *arithmetic*, *geometric*, or *neither*. Explain your reasoning.

91. 3, 11, 21, 33, 47, . . .

92. −2, −6, −18, −54, . . .

93. 26, 18, 10, 2, −6, . . .

94. Write a system of linear inequalities represented by the graph.

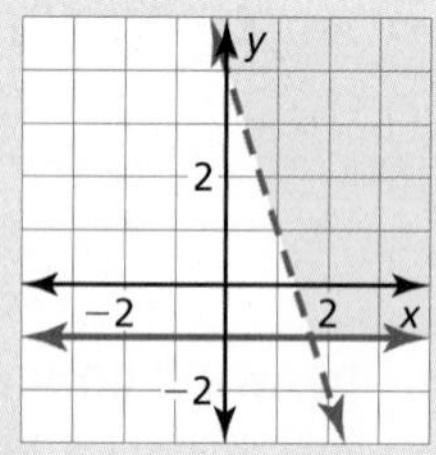

95. Find the zeros of $f(x) = -\frac{1}{3}(x + 6)(x - 9)$.

In Exercises 96 and 97, write an inequality that represents the graph.

96.

97.

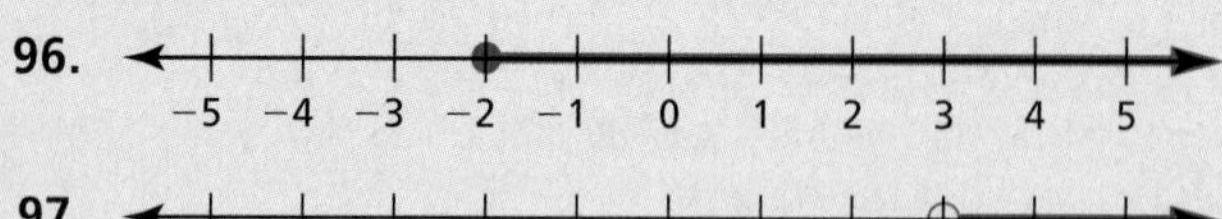

98. Graph $f(x) = -\frac{1}{2}x + 3$ and $g(x) = f(x - 2)$. Describe the transformation from the graph of f to the graph of g.

In Exercises 99 and 100, write an equation in slope-intercept form of the line that passes through the given points.

99. (0, −2), (9, 1)

100. (1, 3), (3, −5)

In Exercises 101–104, find the vertex and the axis of symmetry of the graph of the function.

101. $y = 4(x - 1)^2 + 7$

102. $f(x) = -(x + 3)^2 - 5$

103. $f(x) = x^2 + 6x - 4$

104. $f(x) = \frac{1}{2}x^2 - 2x + 12$

105. Write a recursive rule for the sequence.

n	1	2	3	4
a_n	$\frac{1}{3}$	1	3	9

106. **MP STRUCTURE** Tell whether you would use a quadratic function in *standard form*, *vertex form*, or *intercept form* to find the given feature(s) of its graph without graphing. Explain your reasoning.

a. x-intercepts

b. y-intercept

c. axis of symmetry

d. vertex

e. maximum or minimum value

107. Factor $6x^2 + 7x - 20$.

In Exercises 108 and 109, graph the function. Compare the graph to the graph of $f(x) = x^2$.

108. $r(x) = 4x^2 - 16$

109. $g(x) = \frac{2}{5}x^2$

110. Write the quadratic function represented by the graph.

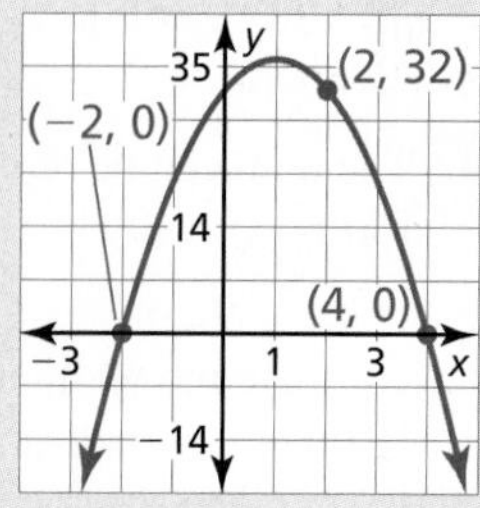

8.6 Comparing Linear, Exponential, and Quadratic Functions

Learning Target Compare the characteristics of linear, exponential, and quadratic functions.

Success Criteria
- I can determine whether data can be represented by a linear, exponential, or quadratic function.
- I can write functions to model data.
- I can compare functions using average rates of change.

EXPLORE IT! Comparing Speeds

MP CHOOSE TOOLS Work with a partner. Three cars start traveling at the same time. Let y represent the distance (in miles) traveled by each car in t minutes, where $0 \le t \le 5$.

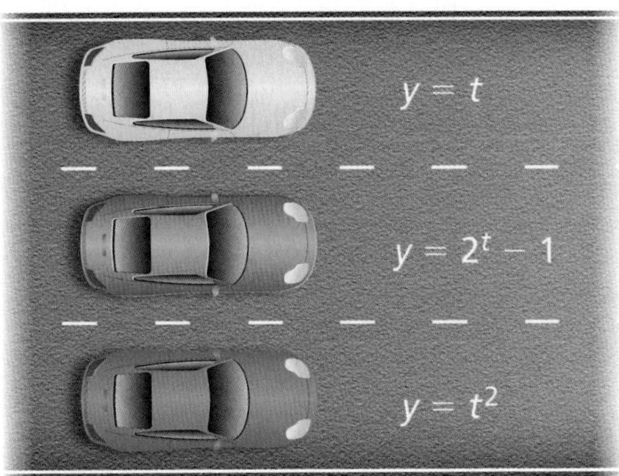

a. Graph the functions in the same coordinate plane for $0 \le t \le 1$. Compare the speeds of the cars. Which car has a constant speed? Which car has the greatest acceleration? Explain your reasoning.

b. Extend the graphs of the functions in the same coordinate plane for $1 \le t \le 5$. Compare the speeds of the cars. How do the values of the three functions compare for greater values of t? Which car has the greatest acceleration? Explain your reasoning.

c. Which of the functions has a growth rate that is eventually much greater than the growth rates of the other functions? Do you think this is true in general? Explain your reasoning.

Math Practice

Look for Structure
How does the structure of a function help explain its growth rate?

Choosing Functions to Model Data

Vocabulary

average rate of change, *p. 467*

So far, you have studied linear functions, exponential functions, and quadratic functions. You can use these functions to model data.

KEY IDEA

Linear, Exponential, and Quadratic Functions

Linear Function	Exponential Function	Quadratic Function
$y = mx + b$	$y = ab^x$	$y = ax^2 + bx + c$

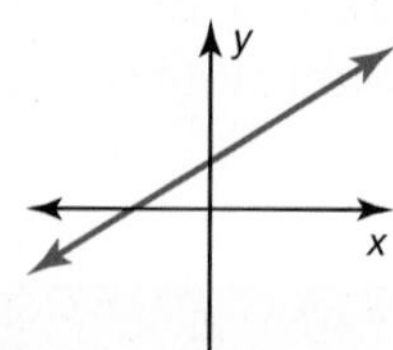

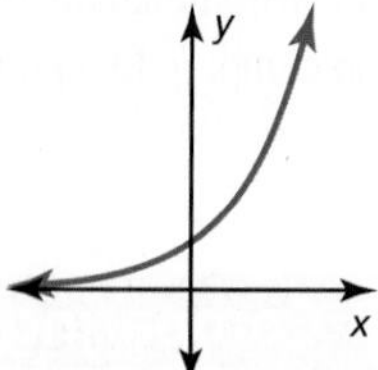

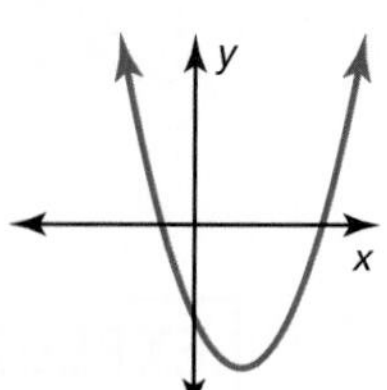

EXAMPLE 1 Using Graphs to Identify Functions

Plot the points. Tell whether the points appear to represent a *linear*, an *exponential*, or a *quadratic* function.

a. $(4, 4), (2, 0), (0, 0), \left(1, -\frac{1}{2}\right), (-2, 4)$

b. $(0, 1), (2, 4), (4, 7), (-2, -2), (-4, -5)$

c. $(0, 2), (2, 8), (1, 4), (-1, 1), \left(-2, \frac{1}{2}\right)$

SOLUTION

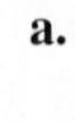

a.

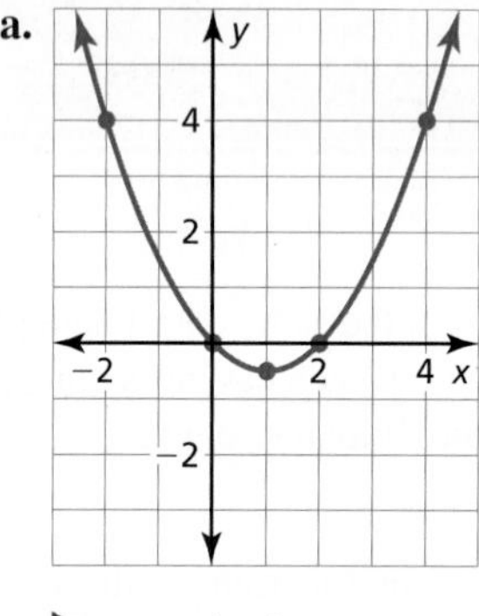

▶ quadratic

b.

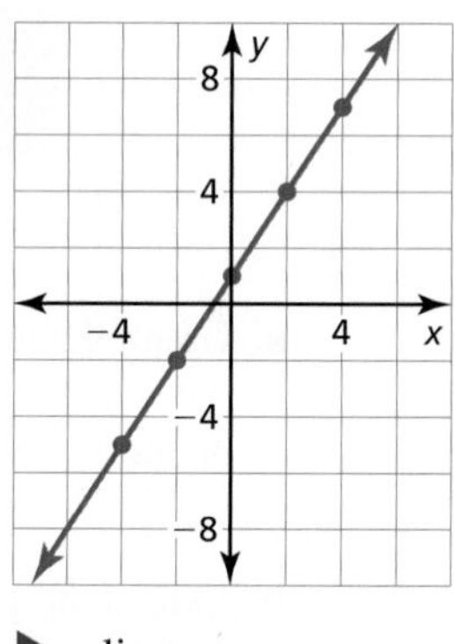

▶ linear

c.

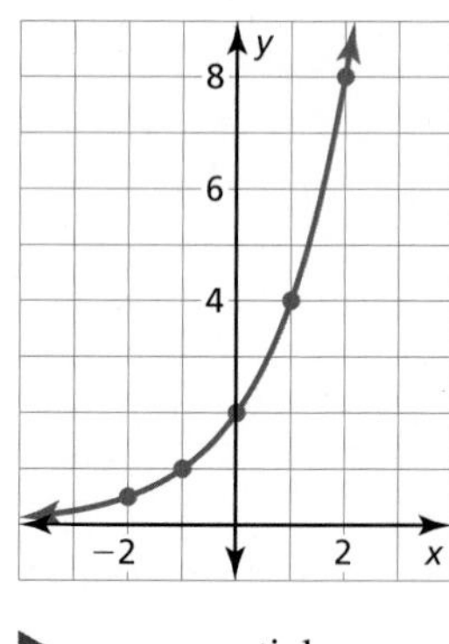

▶ exponential

SELF-ASSESSMENT 1 I do not understand. 2 I can do it with help. 3 I can do it on my own. 4 I can teach someone else.

Plot the points. Tell whether the points appear to represent a *linear*, an *exponential*, or a *quadratic* function.

1. $(-1, 5), (2, -1), (0, -1), (3, 5), (1, -3)$
2. $(-1, 2), (-2, 8), (-3, 32), \left(0, \frac{1}{2}\right), \left(1, \frac{1}{8}\right)$
3. $(-3, 5), (0, -1), (2, -5), (-4, 7), (1, -3)$
4. $\left(-1, \frac{1}{6}\right), \left(0, \frac{1}{2}\right), \left(1, \frac{3}{2}\right), \left(2, \frac{9}{2}\right), \left(-2, \frac{1}{18}\right)$

STUDY TIP
Linear functions have a *constant rate of change*. So, for equally-spaced *x*-values, the differences of consecutive *y*-values are constant. Exponential and quadratic functions do *not* have a constant rate of change.

KEY IDEA
Differences and Ratios of Functions

You can use patterns between consecutive data pairs to determine which type of function models the data. The differences of consecutive *y*-values are called *first differences*. The differences of consecutive first differences are called *second differences*.

- **Linear Function** The first differences are constant.
- **Exponential Function** Consecutive *y*-values have a common *ratio*.
- **Quadratic Function** The second differences are constant.

In all cases, the differences of consecutive *x*-values need to be constant.

EXAMPLE 2 Using Differences or Ratios to Identify Functions

Tell whether each table of values represents a *linear*, an *exponential*, or a *quadratic* function.

a.

x	−3	−2	−1	0	1
y	11	8	5	2	−1

b.

x	−2	−1	0	1	2
y	1	2	4	8	16

c.

x	−2	−1	0	1	2
y	−1	−2	−1	2	7

SOLUTION

STUDY TIP
First determine that the differences of consecutive *x*-values are constant. Then check whether the first differences are constant or consecutive *y*-values have a common ratio. If neither of these is true, then check whether the second differences are constant.

a.

+1 +1 +1 +1

x	−3	−2	−1	0	1
y	11	8	5	2	−1

−3 −3 −3 −3

▶ The first differences are constant. So, the table represents a linear function.

b.

+1 +1 +1 +1

x	−2	−1	0	1	2
y	1	2	4	8	16

×2 ×2 ×2 ×2

▶ Consecutive *y*-values have a common ratio. So, the table represents an exponential function.

c.

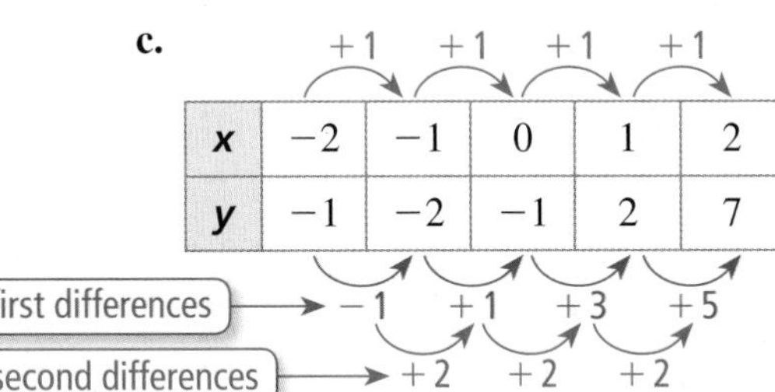

+1 +1 +1 +1
x −2 −1 0 1 2
y −1 −2 −1 2 7
first differences → −1 +1 +3 +5
second differences → +2 +2 +2

▶ The second differences are constant. So, the table represents a quadratic function.

SELF-ASSESSMENT
1 I do not understand. **2** I can do it with help. **3** I can do it on my own. **4** I can teach someone else.

Tell whether the table of values represents a *linear*, an *exponential*, or a *quadratic* function.

5.

x	−1	0	1	2	3
y	1	3	9	27	81

6.

x	−3	−2	−1	0	1
y	16	7	2	1	4

Writing Functions to Model Data

EXAMPLE 3 Writing a Function to Model Data

x	0	1	2	3	4
$f(x)$	12	0	−4	0	12

Write a function that models the data.

SOLUTION

Step 1 Determine which type of function the table of values represents.

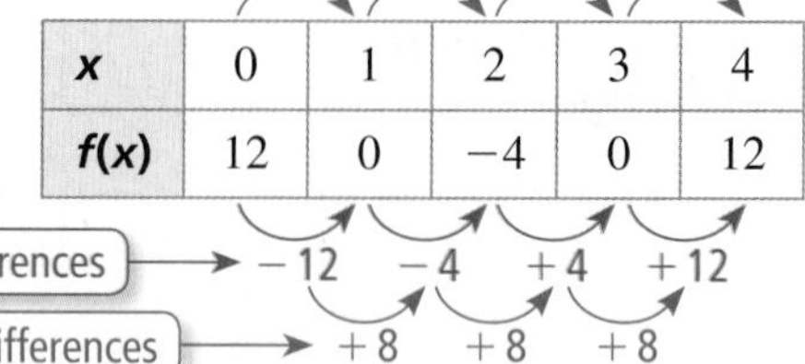

x	0	1	2	3	4
$f(x)$	12	0	−4	0	12

The second differences are constant. So, the table represents a quadratic function.

Step 2 Write an equation of the quadratic function. Using the table, notice that the x-intercepts are 1 and 3. So, use intercept form to write a function.

$f(x) = a(x - 1)(x - 3)$ — Substitute for p and q in intercept form.

Use another point from the table, such as (0, 12), to find a.

$12 = a(0 - 1)(0 - 3)$ — Substitute 0 for x and 12 for $f(x)$.

$4 = a$ — Solve for a.

Use the value of a to write the function.

$f(x) = 4(x - 1)(x - 3)$ — Substitute 4 for a.

$= 4x^2 - 16x + 12$ — Use the FOIL Method and combine like terms.

STUDY TIP

To check your function in Example 3, substitute the other points from the table to verify that they satisfy the function.

▶ So, the quadratic function $f(x) = 4x^2 - 16x + 12$ models the data.

Previously, you wrote recursive rules for linear and exponential functions. You can use the pattern in the first differences to write recursive rules for quadratic functions.

EXAMPLE 4 Writing a Recursive Rule

Write a recursive rule for the quadratic function f in Example 3.

SOLUTION

An expression for the nth term of the sequence of first differences is $-12 + 8(n - 1)$, or $8n - 20$. Notice that $f(n) - f(n - 1) = 8n - 20$.

▶ So, a recursive rule for the quadratic function is $f(0) = 12$, $f(n) = f(n - 1) + 8n - 20$.

SELF-ASSESSMENT

1 I do not understand. 2 I can do it with help. 3 I can do it on my own. 4 I can teach someone else.

Write a function that models the data.

7.

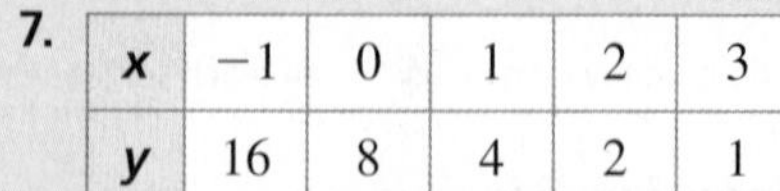

x	−1	0	1	2	3
y	16	8	4	2	1

8.

x	−2	2	6	10	14
y	0	16	0	−48	−128

9. Write a recursive rule for the function represented by the table of values.

x	0	1	2	3	4
$f(x)$	−8	−1	10	25	44

Comparing Functions Using Average Rates of Change

For nonlinear functions, the rate of change is not constant. You can compare two nonlinear functions over the same interval using their *average rates of change*. The **average rate of change** of a function $y = f(x)$ between $x = a$ and $x = b$ is the slope of the line through $(a, f(a))$ and $(b, f(b))$.

$$\text{average rate of change} = \frac{\text{change in } y}{\text{change in } x} = \frac{f(b) - f(a)}{b - a}$$

Exponential Function

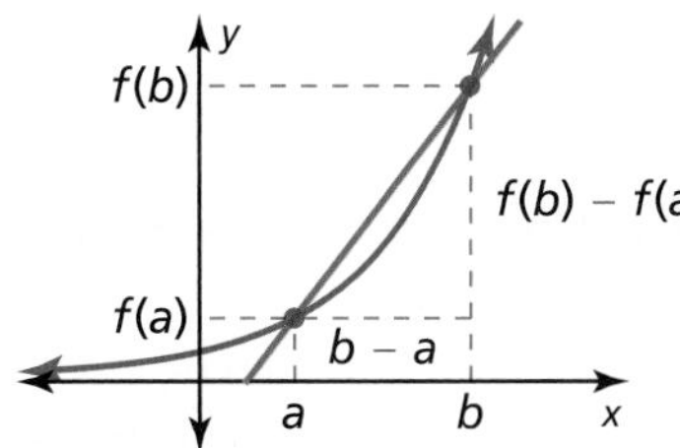

Quadratic Function

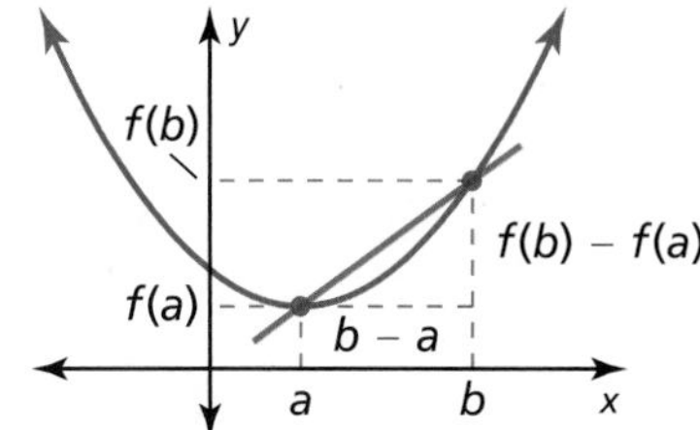

EXAMPLE 5 Using and Interpreting Average Rates of Change

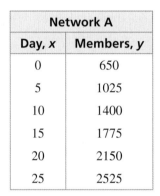

Network A	
Day, x	**Members, y**
0	650
5	1025
10	1400
15	1775
20	2150
25	2525

Two social media networks open their memberships to the public. Compare the network memberships by calculating and interpreting the average rates of change from Day 10 to Day 20.

Network B

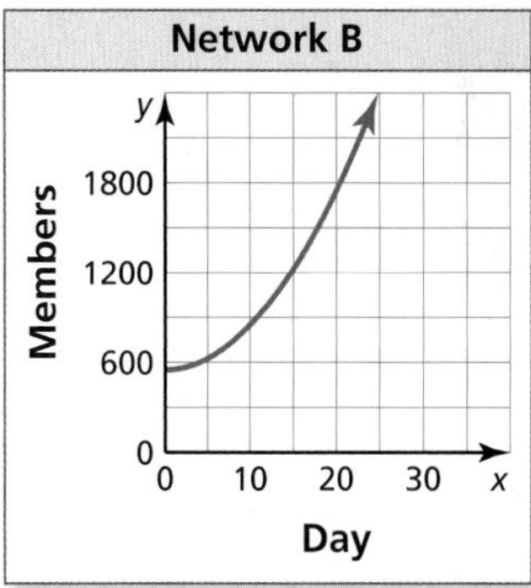

SOLUTION

Calculate the average rates of change by using the points whose x-coordinates are 10 and 20.

Network A: Use (10, 1400) and (20, 2150).

$$\text{average rate of change} = \frac{f(b) - f(a)}{b - a} = \frac{2150 - 1400}{20 - 10} = \frac{750}{10} = 75$$

Network B: Use the graph to estimate the points when $x = 10$ and $x = 20$. Use (10, 850) and (20, 1800).

$$\text{average rate of change} = \frac{f(b) - f(a)}{b - a} \approx \frac{1800 - 850}{20 - 10} = \frac{950}{10} = 95$$

▶ From Day 10 to Day 20, Network A membership increases at an average rate of 75 people per day, and Network B membership increases at an average rate of about 95 people per day. So, Network B membership is growing faster from Day 10 to Day 20.

SELF-ASSESSMENT

1 I do not understand. 2 I can do it with help. 3 I can do it on my own. 4 I can teach someone else.

10. VOCABULARY Describe how to find the average rate of change of a function $y = f(x)$ between $x = a$ and $x = b$.

11. Compare the networks in Example 5 by calculating and interpreting the average rates of change from Day 0 to Day 10.

KEY IDEA

Comparing Functions Using Average Rates of Change

- As a and b increase, the average rate of change between $x = a$ and $x = b$ of an increasing exponential function $y = f(x)$ will eventually exceed the average rate of change between $x = a$ and $x = b$ of an increasing quadratic function $y = g(x)$ or an increasing linear function $y = h(x)$. So, as x increases, $f(x)$ will eventually exceed $g(x)$ or $h(x)$.
- As a and b increase, the average rate of change between $x = a$ and $x = b$ of an increasing quadratic function $y = g(x)$ will eventually exceed the average rate of change between $x = a$ and $x = b$ of an increasing linear function $y = h(x)$. So, as x increases, $g(x)$ will eventually exceed $h(x)$.

Math Practice

Use Technology to Explore

Why can technology be helpful for exploring these concepts for greater values of x?

EXAMPLE 6 Modeling Real Life

Each year a team of researchers counts the numbers of sea turtle nests on an island and in a coastal wildlife refuge. The function $L(x) = 4x^2 + 72x + 1750$ represents the numbers of sea turtle nests counted on the island x years after 1990. In the wildlife refuge, the team counted 1275 nests in 1990 and observed that the number of nests increased by about 6% each year.

a. From 1990 to 2010, which location had a greater average rate of change?

b. Which location will eventually have a greater number of nests? Explain.

SOLUTION

a. Write a function $y = R(x)$ to model the number of nests at the wildlife refuge where x represents the number of years since 1990.

Island: $L(x) = 4x^2 + 72x + 1750$ — Quadratic function

Refuge: $R(x) = 1275(1.06)^x$ — Exponential function

Find the average rate of change from 1990 to 2010 for the number of nests at each location.

$$\text{Island: } \frac{L(20) - L(0)}{20 - 0} = \frac{4790 - 1750}{20} = \frac{3040}{20} = 152$$

$$\text{Refuge: } \frac{R(20) - R(0)}{20 - 0} \approx \frac{4089 - 1275}{20} = \frac{2814}{20} \approx 141$$

▶ From 1990 to 2010, the average rate of change on the island was greater.

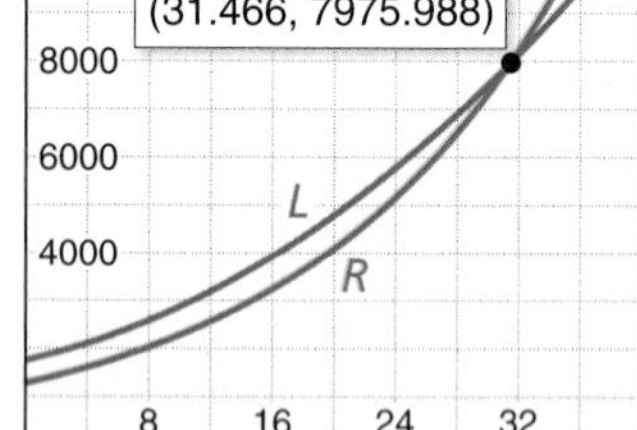

b. The number of nests on the island is represented by a quadratic function and the number of nests at the refuge is represented by an exponential function. So, the refuge will eventually have a greater number of nests.

Using technology, you can determine that the number of nests at each location are about equal when $x \approx 31.5$. So, the number of nests at the refuge exceeds the number of nests on the island between $x = 31$ and $x = 32$, which corresponds to 2021.

SELF-ASSESSMENT

1 I do not understand. 2 I can do it with help. 3 I can do it on my own. 4 I can teach someone else.

12. In Example 5, predict which network will have more members after 50 days. Explain your reasoning.

13. **WHAT IF?** In Example 6, suppose the initial number of nests on the island in 1990 was doubled and maintained the same average rate of change. Does the number of nests at the wildlife refuge still eventually exceed the number of nests on the island? Explain.

8.6 Practice WITH CalcChat® AND CalcView®

GO DIGITAL

In Exercises 1–4, tell whether the points appear to represent a *linear*, an *exponential*, or a *quadratic* function.

1. 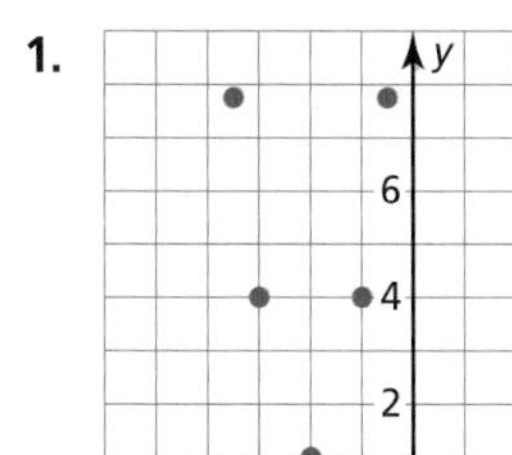

2. 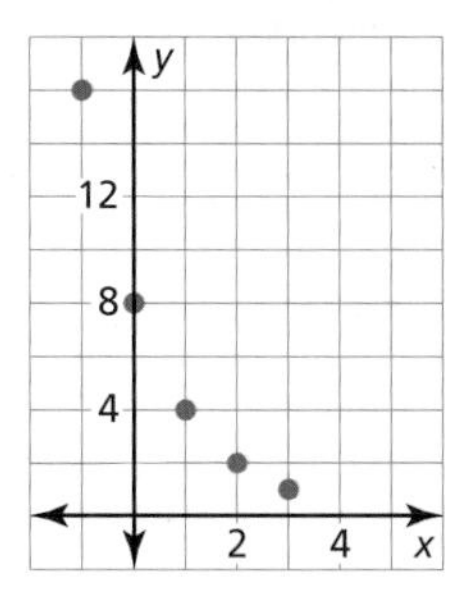

3. 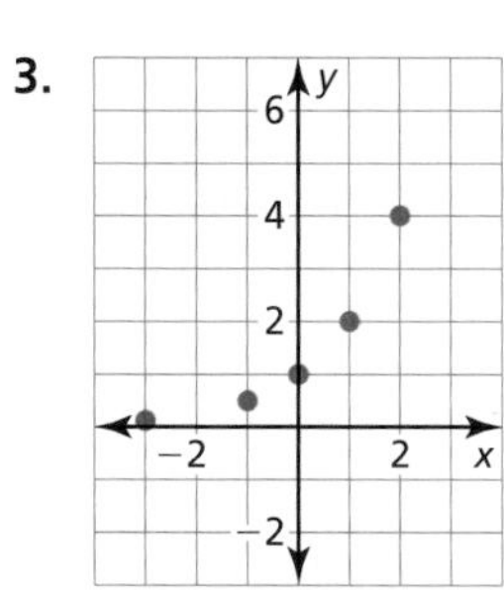

4. 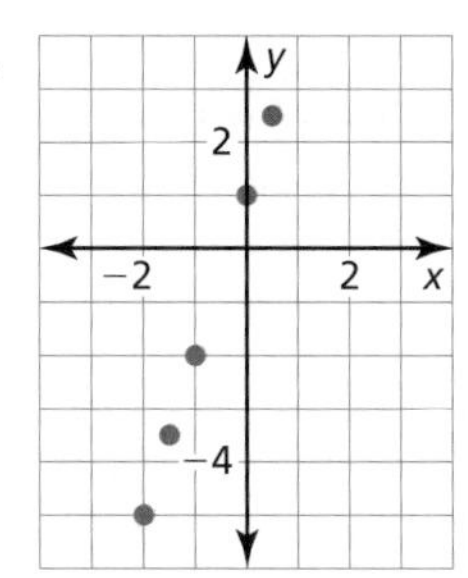

In Exercises 5–8, plot the points. Tell whether the points appear to represent a *linear*, an *exponential*, or a *quadratic* function. Example 1

5. $(-2, -1), (-1, 0), (1, 2), (2, 3), (0, 1)$

6. $(0, -3), (1, 0), (2, 9), (-2, 9), (-1, 0)$

7. $\left(0, \frac{1}{4}\right), (1, 1), (2, 4), (3, 16), \left(-1, \frac{1}{16}\right)$

8. $(-4, -4), (-2, -3.4), (0, -3), (2, -2.6), (4, -2)$

In Exercises 9–12, tell whether the table of values represents a *linear*, an *exponential*, or a *quadratic* function. Example 2

9.

x	−2	−1	0	1	2
y	0	0.5	1	1.5	2

10.

x	−1	0	1	2	3
y	0.2	1	5	25	125

11.

x	2	3	4	5	6
y	2	6	18	54	162

12.

x	−3	−2	−1	0	1
y	2	4.5	8	12.5	18

13. **MODELING REAL LIFE** A student takes a subway to a public library. The table shows the distances (in miles) the student travels over time (in minutes). Tell whether the data can be modeled by a *linear*, an *exponential*, or a *quadratic* function. Explain.

Time	1	3	5	7
Distance	0.67	2.01	3.35	4.69

14. **MODELING REAL LIFE** A store sells custom circular rugs. The table shows the costs (in dollars) of rugs with different diameters (in feet). Tell whether the data can be modeled by a *linear*, an *exponential*, or a *quadratic* function. Explain.

Diameter	3	4	5	6
Cost	63.90	113.60	177.50	255.60

In Exercises 15–20, write a function that models the data. Example 3

15. $(-2, 8), (-1, 0), (0, -4), (1, -4), (2, 0), (3, 8)$

16. $(-3, 8), (-2, 4), (-1, 2), (0, 1), (1, 0.5)$

17.

x	−2	−1	0	1	2
y	4	1	−2	−5	−8

18.

x	−1	0	1	2	3
y	2.5	5	10	20	40

19. 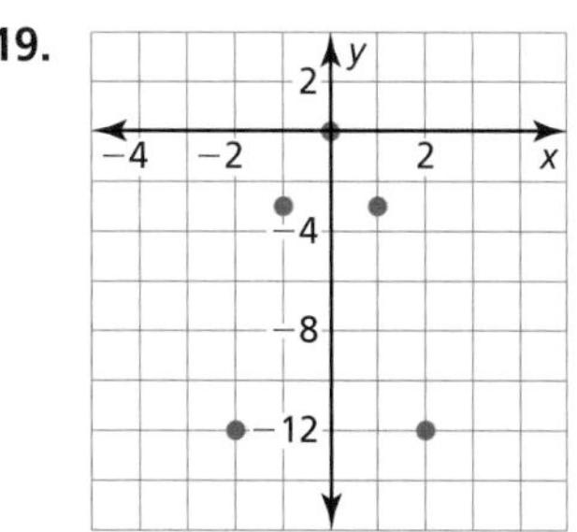

20. 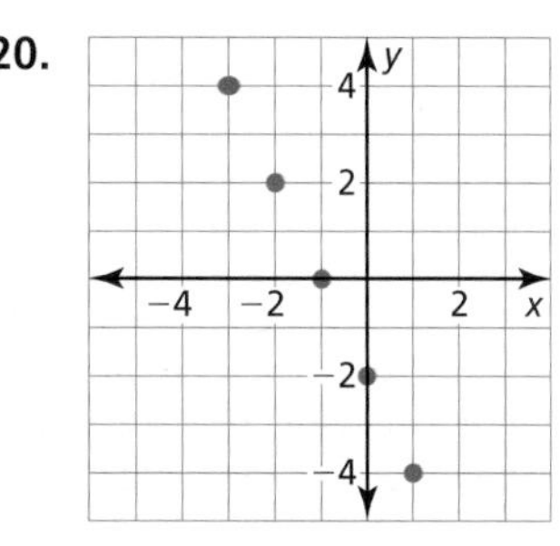

21. **MODELING REAL LIFE** The table shows the central air pressures (in millibars) of a hurricane at different sustained wind speeds (in kilometers per hour).

Sustained wind speed	136	165	194	223	252
Central air pressure	980	965	950	935	920

a. Write a function f that models the data.

b. Find and interpret $f(150)$.

22. **MODELING REAL LIFE** The table shows the breathing rates (in liters of air per minute) of a cyclist traveling at different speeds (in miles per hour).

Speed	Breathing rate
20	51.4
21	57.1
22	63.3
23	70.3
24	78.0

a. Write a function f that models the data.

b. Find and interpret $f(18)$.

In Exercises 23–28, write a recursive rule for the function represented by the table of values.
Example 4

23.

x	0	1	2	3	4
$f(x)$	3	6	12	24	48

24.

x	0	1	2	3	4
$f(x)$	64	16	4	1	0.25

25.

x	0	1	2	3	4
$f(x)$	2	1	2	5	10

26.

x	0	1	2	3	4
$f(x)$	1	−2	−7	−14	−23

27.

x	0	1	2	3	4
$f(x)$	$-\frac{7}{3}$	−3	$-\frac{11}{3}$	$-\frac{13}{3}$	−5

28.

x	0	1	2	3	4
$f(x)$	−45	−25	−11	−3	−1

29. **ERROR ANALYSIS** Describe and correct the error in determining whether the table represents a *linear*, an *exponential*, or a *quadratic* function.

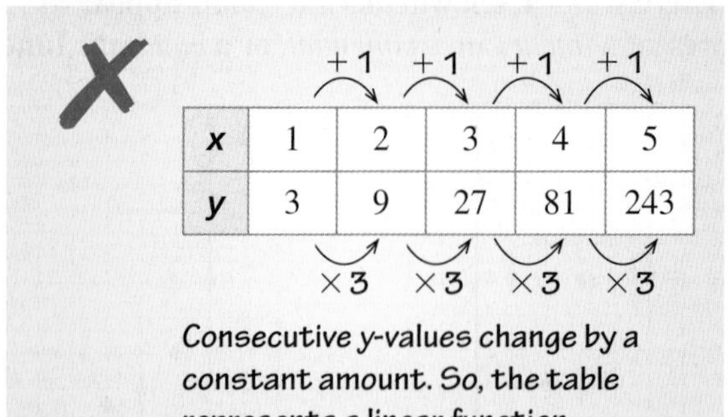

30. **ERROR ANALYSIS** Describe and correct the error in writing the function represented by the table.

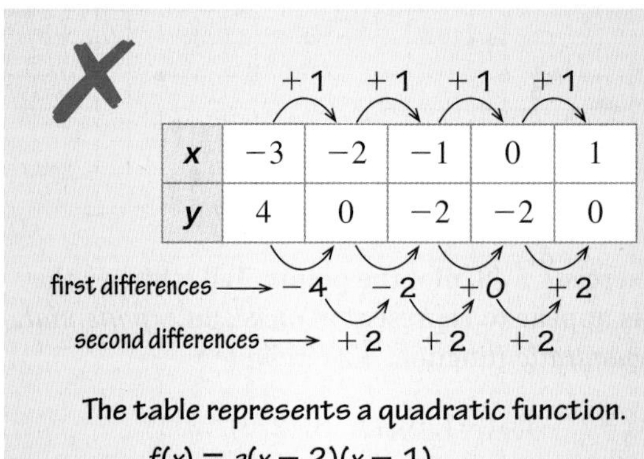

+1 +1 +1 +1
x −3 −2 −1 0 1
y 4 0 −2 −2 0
first differences → −4 −2 +0 +2
second differences → +2 +2 +2
The table represents a quadratic function.
$f(x) = a(x - 2)(x - 1)$
$4 = a(-3 - 2)(-3 - 1)$
$\frac{1}{5} = a$
$f(x) = \frac{1}{5}(x - 2)(x - 1)$
$= \frac{1}{5}x^2 - \frac{3}{5}x + \frac{2}{5}$
So, the function is $f(x) = \frac{1}{5}x^2 - \frac{3}{5}x + \frac{2}{5}$.

31. **ANALYZING RELATIONSHIPS** The population of Town A in 1980 was 3000. The population of Town A increased by 20% every decade. Let x represent the number of decades since 1980. The graph shows the population of Town B. Compare the populations of the towns by calculating and interpreting the average rates of change from 2000 to 2020.
Example 5

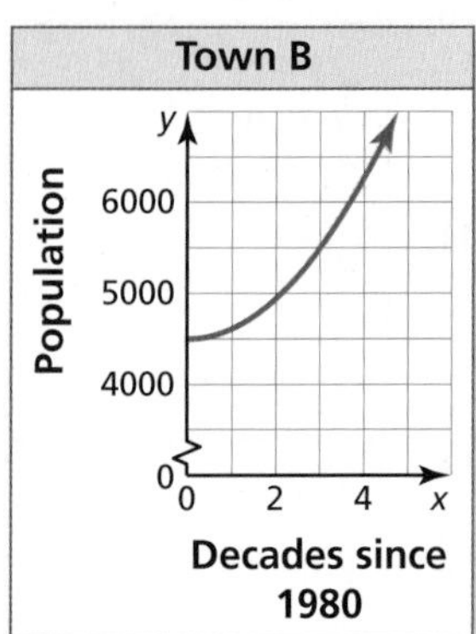

32. ANALYZING RELATIONSHIPS Three organizations are collecting donations for a cause. Organization A begins with one donation, and the number of donations quadruples each hour. The numbers of donations collected by Organizations B and C are shown.

Organization B

Time (hours), t	Number of donations, y
0	0
1	4
2	8
3	12
4	16
5	20
6	24

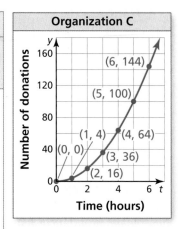

Organization C

Number of donations; Time (hours); (0, 0); (1, 4); (2, 16); (3, 36); (4, 64); (5, 100); (6, 144)

a. What type of function represents the numbers of donations collected by each organization?

b. Find the average rates of change of each function for each 1-hour interval from $t = 0$ to $t = 6$.

c. For which function does the average rate of change increase most quickly? What does this tell you about the numbers of donations collected by the three organizations?

33. MODELING REAL LIFE Let x represent the number of years since 1970. The function $H(x) = 10x^2 + 10x + 500$ represents the population of Oak Hill. In 1970, Poplar Grove had a population of 200 people. Poplar Grove's population increased by 8% each year. *Example 6*

a. From 1970 to 2020, which town's population had a greater average rate of change?

b. Which town will eventually have a greater population? Explain.

34. MODELING REAL LIFE Let x represent the number of years since 2005. The function

$$R(x) = 0.01x^2 + 0.22x + 1.08$$

represents the revenue (in millions of dollars) of Company A. In 2005, Company B had a revenue of \$2.12 million. Company B's revenue increased by \$0.32 million each year.

a. From 2005 to 2020, which company's revenue had a greater average rate of change?

b. Which company will eventually have a greater revenue? Explain.

35. MP REASONING Explain why the average rate of change of a linear function is constant and the average rate of change of a quadratic or exponential function is not constant.

36. HOW DO YOU SEE IT?
Match each graph with its function. Explain your reasoning.

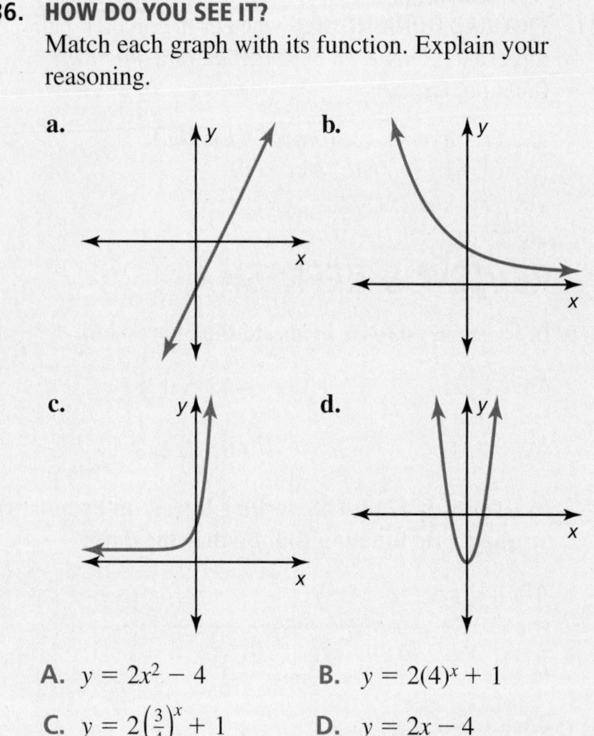

A. $y = 2x^2 - 4$

B. $y = 2(4)^x + 1$

C. $y = 2\left(\frac{3}{4}\right)^x + 1$

D. $y = 2x - 4$

37. MP REASONING The table shows the numbers of people attending the first five football games at a high school. Can a linear, an exponential, or a quadratic function represent this situation? Explain.

Game	1	2	3	4	5
Number of people	252	325	270	249	310

38. MAKING AN ARGUMENT Function p is an exponential function and function q is a quadratic function. Your friend says that after about $x = 3$, function q will always have a greater y-value than function p. Is your friend correct? Explain.

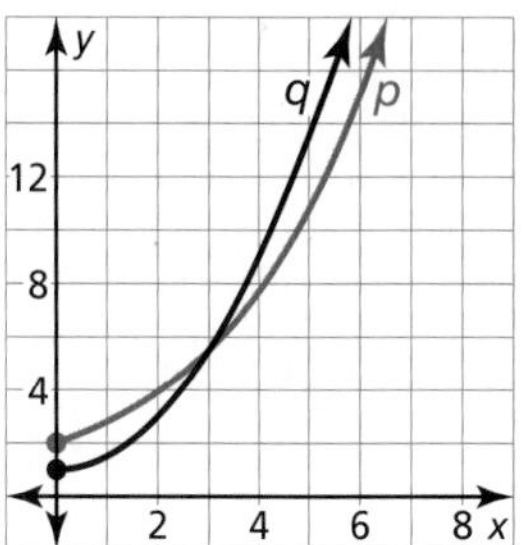

DIG DEEPER **In Exercises 39 and 40, write a function that satisfies the given condition.**

39. The function has constant second differences of 3.

40. The function has constant second differences of 4.5.

41. **CRITICAL THINKING** Tell whether the ordered pairs represent a *linear*, an *exponential*, or a *quadratic* function. Explain.

$(1, 3n - 1), (2, 10n + 2), (3, 26n),$
$(4, 51n - 7), (5, 85n - 19)$

42. **THOUGHT PROVOKING** Find four different patterns in the figure. Determine whether each pattern represents a *linear*, an *exponential*, or a *quadratic* function. Write a model for each pattern.

GO DIGITAL

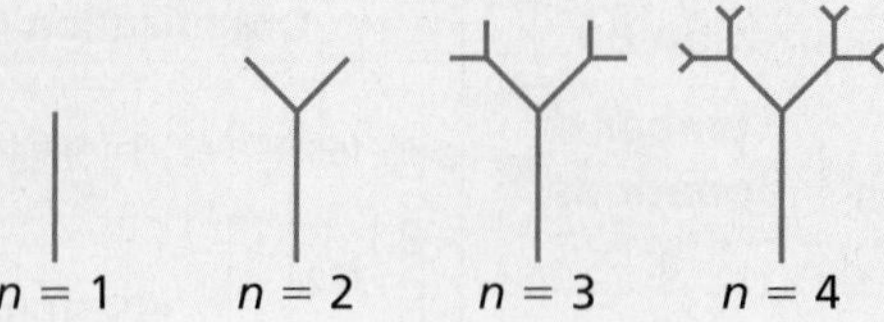

REVIEW & REFRESH

WATCH

In Exercises 43–46, evaluate the expression.

43. $\sqrt{121}$ **44.** $\sqrt[3]{125}$

45. $\sqrt[3]{512}$ **46.** $\sqrt[5]{243}$

In Exercises 47 and 48, write a linear, an exponential, or quadratic function that models the data.

47.

x	−3	−2	−1	0	1
y	81	27	9	3	1

48.

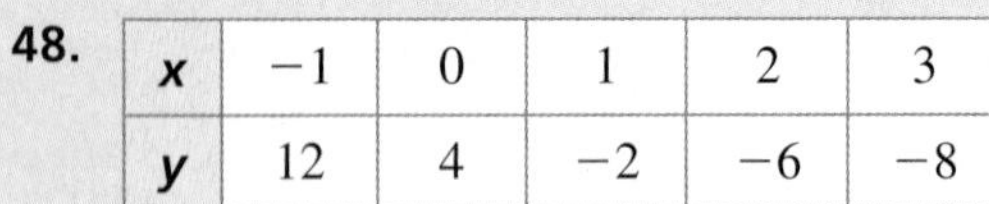

x	−1	0	1	2	3
y	12	4	−2	−6	−8

In Exercises 49–52, find the product.

49. $(x + 8)(x - 8)$ **50.** $(4y + 2)(4y - 2)$

51. $(3a - 5b)(3a + 5b)$

52. $(-2r + 6s)(-2r - 6s)$

In Exercises 53 and 54, write the cubic function in standard form represented by the graph.

53.

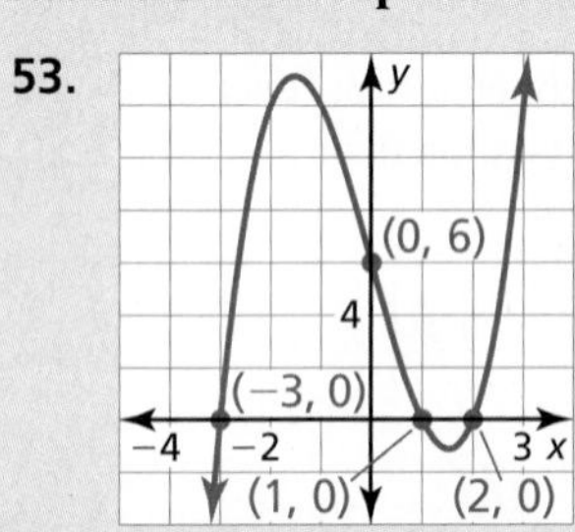

54.

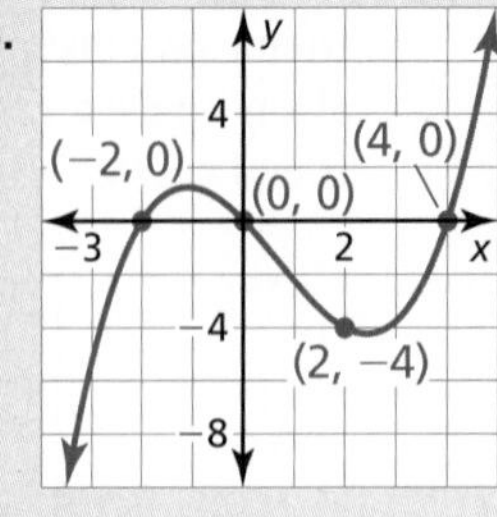

In Exercises 55 and 56, graph *g*.

55. $f(x) = (x - 4)^2 + 1;\ g(x) = 2f(x)$

56. $f(x) = -(x + 2)^2 - 5;\ g(x) = f(x - 6) + 3$

In Exercises 57–60, solve the equation by graphing. Determine whether the equation has *one solution*, *no solution*, or *infinitely many solutions*.

57. $x - 3 = 5x + 1$ **58.** $3x + 2 = 5x - 2$

59. $2(x - 6) = 2x - 4$ **60.** $4(x + 4) = 2(2x + 8)$

61. The scatter plot shows the sizes (in carats) and the prices (in dollars) of several diamonds.

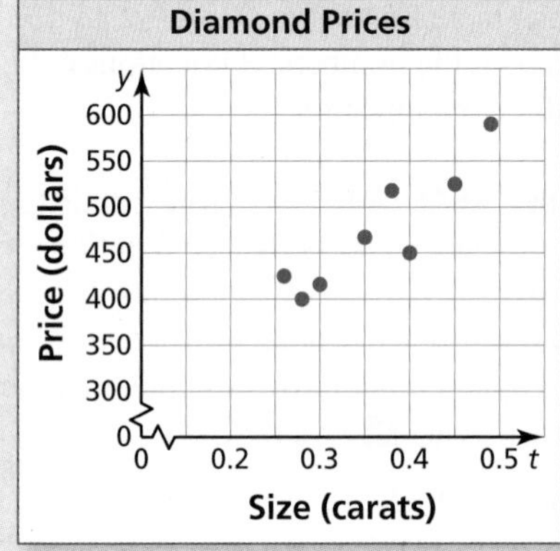

a. What is the price of the 0.4-carat diamond?

b. What is the size of the diamond that costs $416?

In Exercises 62–65, tell whether the function has a *maximum value* or a *minimum value*. Then find the value.

62. $y = 2x^2 + 8x + 8$ **63.** $f(x) = 3x^2 - 6x + 1$

64. $f(x) = 4x^2 - 6x + 2$ **65.** $y = -\frac{1}{2}x^2 + 3x - 1$

66. **MP STRUCTURE** Without solving completely, determine whether each equation has *no solution*, *one solution*, or *two solutions*. Explain your reasoning.

a. $|x - 2| - 5 = -3$ **b.** $|x + 7| + 6 = 4$

8 Chapter Review WITH CalcChat®

Chapter Learning Target Understand graphing quadratic functions.

Chapter Success Criteria
- ◆ I can identify characteristics of quadratic functions.
- ◆ I can describe how to graph quadratic functions in different forms.
- ■ I can find zeros of functions using intercept form.
- ■ I can choose an appropriate function to model data.

◆ Surface
■ Deep

SELF-ASSESSMENT 1 I do not understand. 2 I can do it with help. 3 I can do it on my own. 4 I can teach someone else.

8.1 Graphing $f(x) = ax^2$ (pp. 425–430)

Learning Target: Graph and describe functions of the form $f(x) = ax^2$.

Vocabulary
quadratic function
parabola
vertex
axis of symmetry

Identify characteristics of the quadratic function and its graph.

1. 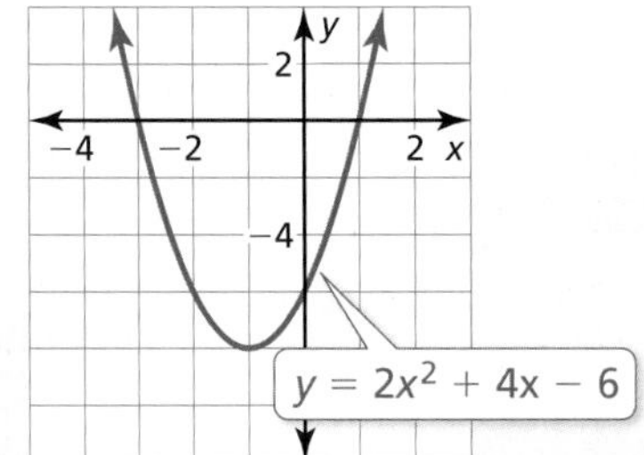

2. 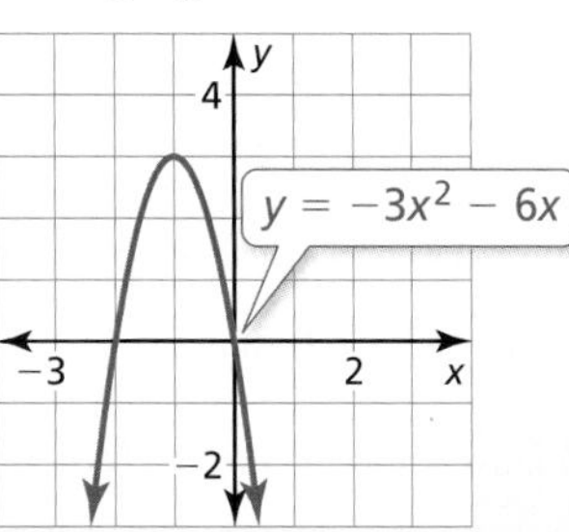

Graph the function. Compare the graph to the graph of $f(x) = x^2$.

3. $p(x) = 7x^2$

4. $q(x) = 0.25x^2$

5. $g(x) = -\frac{3}{4}x^2$

6. $h(x) = -6x^2$

8.2 Graphing $f(x) = ax^2 + c$ (pp. 431–436)

Learning Target: Graph and describe functions of the form $f(x) = ax^2 + c$.

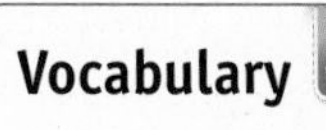

zero of a function

Graph the function. Compare the graph to the graph of $f(x) = x^2$.

7. $g(x) = x^2 + 5$

8. $h(x) = -x^2 - 4$

9. $m(x) = -2x^2 + 6$

10. $n(x) = \frac{1}{3}x^2 - 5$

11. Compare the graph of $f(x) = ax^2 + c$ to the graph of $g(x) = a(x^2 + c)$.

12. The function $y = -16x^2 + 256$ represents the height y (in feet) of a sandal x seconds after falling off your foot while riding a roller coaster. Find and interpret the x- and y-intercepts.

8.3 Graphing $f(x) = ax^2 + bx + c$ (pp. 437–444)

Learning Target: Graph and describe functions of the form $f(x) = ax^2 + bx + c$.

Vocabulary
maximum value
minimum value

Find (a) the axis of symmetry and (b) the vertex of the graph of the function.

13. $f(x) = 4x^2 + 8x - 1$

14. $g(x) = -\frac{1}{4}x^2 + 6x + 3$

Graph the function. Find the domain and range.

15. $y = x^2 - 2x + 7$

16. $f(x) = -3x^2 + 3x - 4$

17. $y = \frac{1}{2}x^2 - 6x + 10$

18. $g(x) = -\frac{1}{3}x^2 - 4x + 1$

19. The graph of $f(x) = ax^2 + bx + c$ is shown. Describe the possible values of a, b, and c. Explain your reasoning.

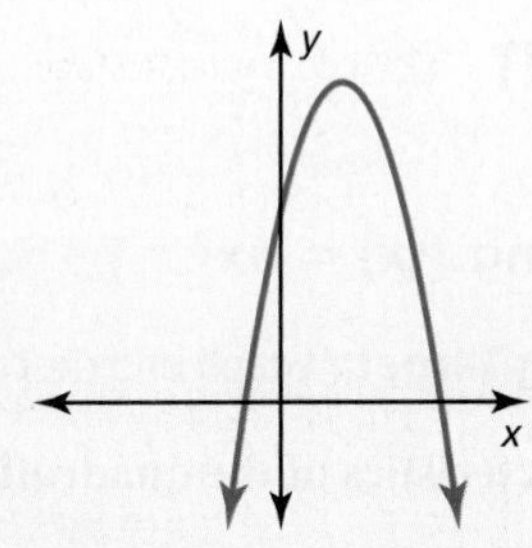

20. The function $f(t) = -16t^2 + 88t + 12$ represents the height (in feet) of a pumpkin t seconds after it is launched from a catapult. When does the pumpkin reach its maximum height? What is the maximum height of the pumpkin?

8.4 Graphing $f(x) = a(x - h)^2 + k$ (pp. 445–452)

Learning Target: Graph and describe functions of the form $f(x) = a(x - h)^2 + k$.

Vocabulary
even function
odd function
vertex form (of a quadratic function)

Determine whether the function is *even*, *odd*, or *neither*.

21. $r(x) = -8x$

22. $h(x) = 3x^2 - 2$

23.

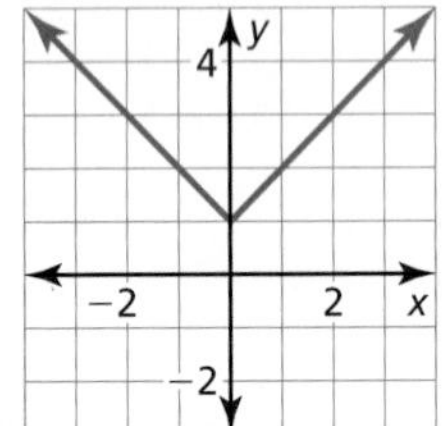

24.

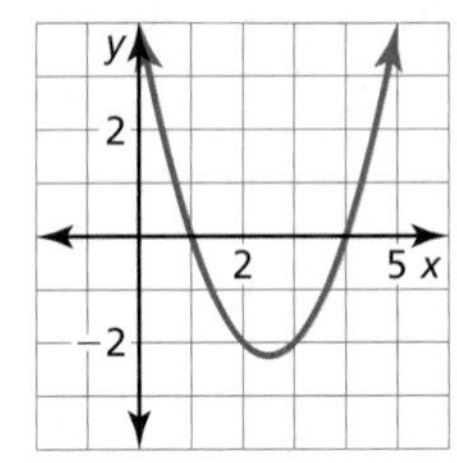

Graph the function. Compare the graph to the graph of $f(x) = x^2$.

25. $h(x) = 2(x - 4)^2$

26. $g(x) = \frac{1}{2}(x - 1)^2 + 1$

27. $q(x) = -(x + 4)^2 + 7$

28. Consider the function $g(x) = -3(x + 2)^2 - 4$. Graph $h(x) = g(x - 1)$.

29. Write and graph a quadratic function whose graph has a vertex of $(3, 2)$ and passes through the point $(4, 7)$.

30. Write and graph a quadratic function that models the path of a skateboarder who jumps off a ramp at the point $(0, 4)$ and reaches a maximum height of 8 feet, represented by a vertex of $(12, 8)$.

31. Write the function $f(x) = x^2 - 6x + 7$ in vertex form. Then graph the function.

8.5 Using Intercept Form (pp. 453–462) 

Learning Target: Graph and use functions in intercept form.

Vocabulary
intercept form

Graph the quadratic function. Label the vertex, axis of symmetry, and *x*-intercepts. Find the domain and range of the function.

32. $y = (x - 4)(x + 2)$

33. $f(x) = -3(x + 3)(x + 1)$

34. $y = x^2 - 8x + 15$

Use zeros to graph the function.

35. $y = -2x^2 + 6x + 8$

36. $f(x) = x^2 + x - 2$

37. $f(x) = 2x^3 - 18x$

38. Write a quadratic function in standard form whose graph passes through (4, 0) and (6, 0).

39. Write and graph a function that has zeros of −4.5, −1.5, and 2.

8.6 Comparing Linear, Exponential, and Quadratic Functions (pp. 463–472) 

Learning Target: Compare the characteristics of linear, exponential, and quadratic functions.

Vocabulary
average rate of change

Tell whether the data represent a *linear*, an *exponential*, or a *quadratic* function. Then write the function.

40. (−1, 0), (0, 12), (1, 16), (2, 12), (3, 0)

41. (−2, −9), (−1, −4), (0, 1), (1, 6), (2, 11)

42. 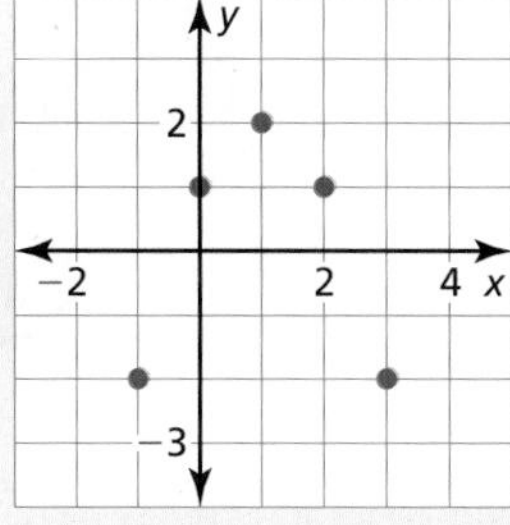

43.

x	−1	0	1	2	3
y	512	128	32	8	2

44. You and your friend each open a savings account at the same time. The balance *y* (in dollars) of your account after *t* years is represented by $y = 100(1.1)^t$. The beginning balance of your friend's account is \$150, and the balance increases by \$50 each year. (a) From Year 0 to Year 10, which account had a greater average rate of change? (b) Which account will eventually have a greater balance? Explain.

Mathematical Practices

Construct Viable Arguments and Critique the Reasoning of Others

Mathematically proficient students understand and use previously established results in constructing arguments.

1. In Exercises 63–66 on page 452, how did you use a previously established result to rewrite each function?
2. Explain how you can use the zeros of a quadratic function to find the maximum or minimum value.

8 Practice Test WITH CalcChat®

Graph the function. Compare the graph to the graph of $f(x) = x^2$.

1. $h(x) = 2x^2 - 3$

2. $g(x) = -\frac{1}{5}x^2$

3. $p(x) = \frac{1}{2}(x + 1)^2 - 1$

4. Consider the graph of the function f.

a. Find the domain, range, and zeros of the function.

b. Write the function f in standard form.

c. Compare the graph of f to the graph of $g(x) = x^2$.

d. Graph $h(x) = f(x - 6)$.

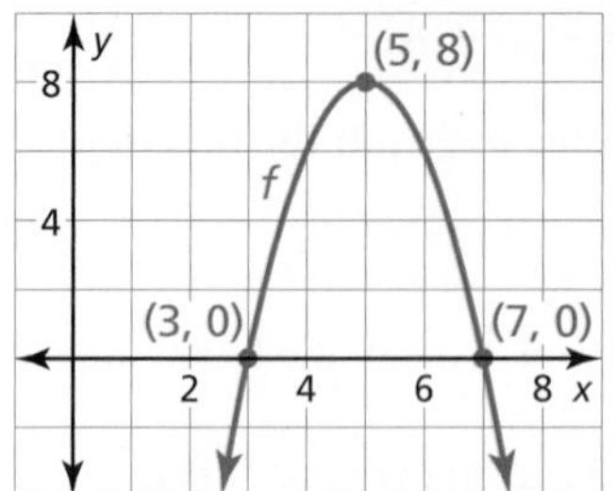

Use zeros to graph the function. Find the domain and range of the function.

5. $f(x) = 2x^2 - 8x + 8$

6. $y = -(x + 5)(x - 1)$

7. $h(x) = 16x^2 - 4$

Tell whether the table of values represents a *linear*, an *exponential*, or a *quadratic* function. Explain your reasoning. Then write the function.

8.

x	−1	0	1	2	3
y	4	8	16	32	64

9.

x	−2	−1	0	1	2
y	−8	−2	0	−2	−8

10. You are playing table tennis with a friend. The path of the ball after you return a serve can be modeled by the function $y = -0.001x^2 + 0.2x + 10$, where x is the horizontal distance (in centimeters) from where you hit the ball and y is the height (in centimeters) of the ball above the table. What is the maximum height of the ball?

Write a quadratic function in standard form whose graph has the given characteristics.

11. is even and has a range of $y \geq 3$

12. passes through (4, 0) and (1, 9)

13. The creator of two apps records the numbers of downloads over time.

App A						
Week, x	0	2	4	6	8	10
Downloads, y	150	400	650	900	1150	1400

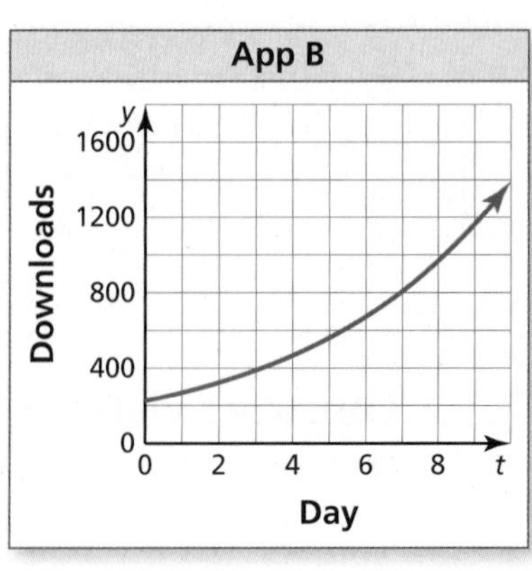

a. From Week 6 to Week 8, which app had a greater average rate of change?

b. Which app will eventually have a greater number of downloads? Explain.

14. Find values of a, b, and c so that the function $f(x) = ax^2 + bx + c$ is (a) even, (b) odd, and (c) neither even nor odd.

15. Write a function of the form $y = ax^2 + bx$ whose graph contains the points (1, 6) and (3, 6).

8 Performance Task
Endangered!

6 of the 7 species of sea turtles are endangered.

90% of hatchlings do not survive longer than 1 year.

50–100 year lifespan

Loggerheads *are the most common sea turtles in the United States' coastal waters.*

Only the ***flatback*** *sea turtle is not considered endangered.*

1 in 1000 survive to maturity

LEATHERBACK

LOGGERHEAD

GREEN

FLATBACK

HAWKSBILL

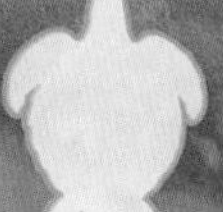

OLIVE RIDLEY

KEMP'S RIDLEY

CONSERVATION PLAN

For the past 18 years, a wildlife commission has estimated the number of loggerhead sea turtle nests in a region and summarized the data in the table shown. Write a report for the commission that analyzes the data. Include the following features in your report:

- a function and its graph that models the number of nests
- future nesting predictions based on the current trend
- threats to loggerhead turtles in the United States
- conservation methods to increase the loggerhead turtle population
- nesting goals for specific years, including the average rate of change needed to accomplish those goals.

Year	1	2	3	4	5	6	7	8	9
Nests (thousands)	41	43	55	49	54	59	64	65	60

Year	10	11	12	13	14	15	16	17	18
Nests (thousands)	51	57	51	46	51	42	31	35	30

8 College and Career Readiness WITH CalcChat®

Tutorial videos are available for each exercise.

1. Which function is represented by the graph?

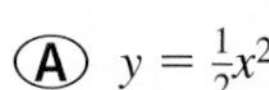

Ⓐ $y = \frac{1}{2}x^2$

Ⓑ $y = 2x^2$

Ⓒ $y = -\frac{1}{2}x^2$

Ⓓ $y = -2x^2$

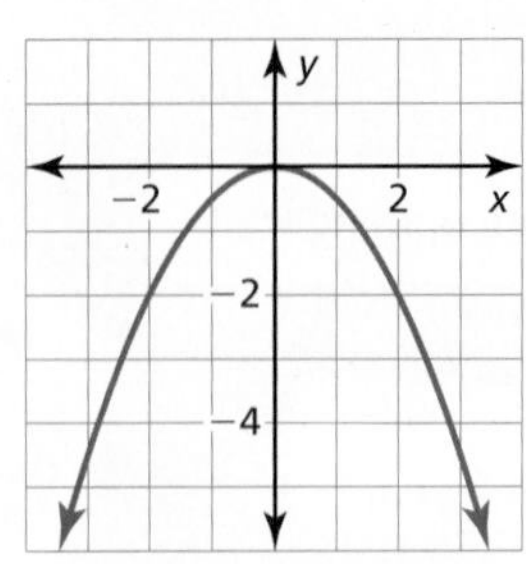

2. Which is an explicit rule for $a_1 = -2, a_n = a_{n-1} - 4$?

Ⓐ $a_n = -4n + 2$

Ⓑ $a_n = -4n - 2$

Ⓒ $a_n = 4n - 6$

Ⓓ $a_n = -2n - 2$

3. Without solving, classify each system of equations by the number of solutions. Explain your reasoning.

$y = 6x + 9$	$3x + y = 5$	$y - 5 = -3x$
$y = -\frac{1}{6}x + 9$	$9x + 3y = 15$	$y - 9 = -3x$

4. The function $f(t) = -16t^2 + v_0t + s_0$ represents the height (in feet) of a ball t seconds after it is thrown from an initial height s_0 (in feet) with an initial vertical velocity v_0 (in feet per second). The ball reaches its maximum height after $\frac{7}{8}$ second. What is the initial vertical velocity?

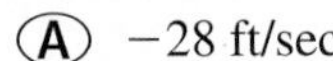

Ⓐ −28 ft/sec

Ⓑ −14 ft/sec

Ⓒ 14 ft/sec

Ⓓ 28 ft/sec

5. Which polynomial represents the area (in square feet) of the shaded region of the figure?

Ⓐ $x^2 + 2ax$

Ⓑ $x^2 - a^2$

Ⓒ $x^2 - 2ax + a^2$

Ⓓ $x^2 + 2ax + a^2$

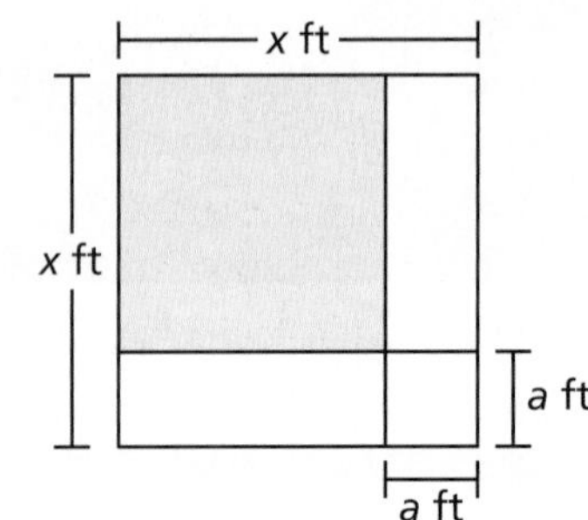

GO DIGITAL

6. The table represents a quadratic function. Identify the axis of symmetry of the graph of f.

x	-2	-1.5	-1	-0.5	0	0.5	1
$f(x)$	-2.5	0	-1.5	-2	-1.5	0	2.5

Ⓐ $x = -1.5$

Ⓑ $x = -0.5$

Ⓒ $x = 0.5$

Ⓓ $x = 1$

7. Complete each function using the symbols $+$ or $-$ so that the graph of the quadratic function satisfies the given conditions.

a. $f(x) = 5(x \,\square\, 3)^2 \,\square\, 4$; vertex: $(-3, 4)$

b. $g(x) = -(x \,\square\, 2)(x \,\square\, 8)$; x-intercepts: -8 and 2

c. $h(x) = \square\, 3x^2 \,\square\, 6$; range: $y \geq -6$

d. $j(x) = \square\, 4(x \,\square\, 1)(x \,\square\, 1)$; range: $y \leq 4$

8. Which expressions are equivalent to $(b^{-5})^{-4}$? Select all that apply.

Ⓐ $b^{12}b^8$

Ⓑ $(b^{-4})^{-5}$

Ⓒ $b^{-5}b^{-4}$

Ⓓ $b^{-6}b^{-14}$

Ⓔ $(b^{10})^2$

Ⓕ b^{-9}

Ⓖ b^{-20}

Ⓗ $(b^{-2})^{-7}$

9. The graph shows the amounts y (in dollars) that a referee earns for officiating x high school volleyball games.

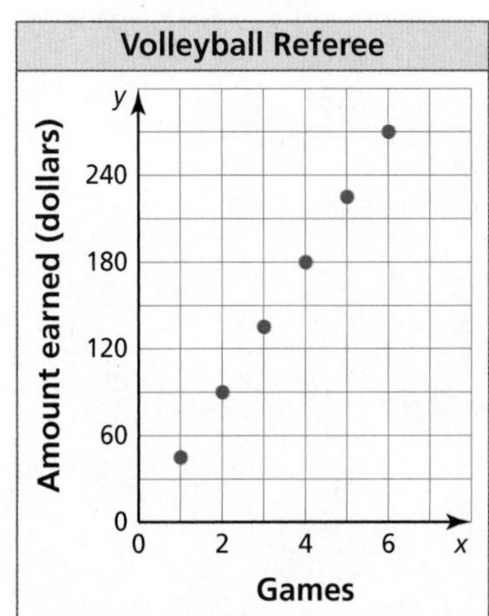

a. Does the graph represent a linear or nonlinear function? Explain.

b. Find the domain of the function. Is the domain discrete or continuous?

c. Write a function that models the data.

d. Can the referee earn exactly \$500? Explain.

10. Find the slope and y-intercept of the line that passes through the points $(-3, 7)$ and $(3, -9)$.

9 Solving Quadratic Equations

NATIONAL GEOGRAPHIC EXPLORER

Munazza Alam

Munazza Alam studies astrophysics. She investigates nearby low-mass stars and unusual brown dwarfs (astronomical objects that form like stars, but cool and fade over time to resemble gas giant planets like Jupiter). To conduct her research, she uses powerful telescopes at some of the best observatories in the world, such as the Kitt Peak National Observatory in Arizona and the Las Campanas Observatory in Chile.

- What is astrophysics? What is the Big Bang Theory?
- Why do scientists believe that the universe is expanding? At what rate is the universe thought to be expanding?
- Suppose the radius of the universe is expanding at a linear rate. At what rate is a cross-sectional area of the universe expanding?

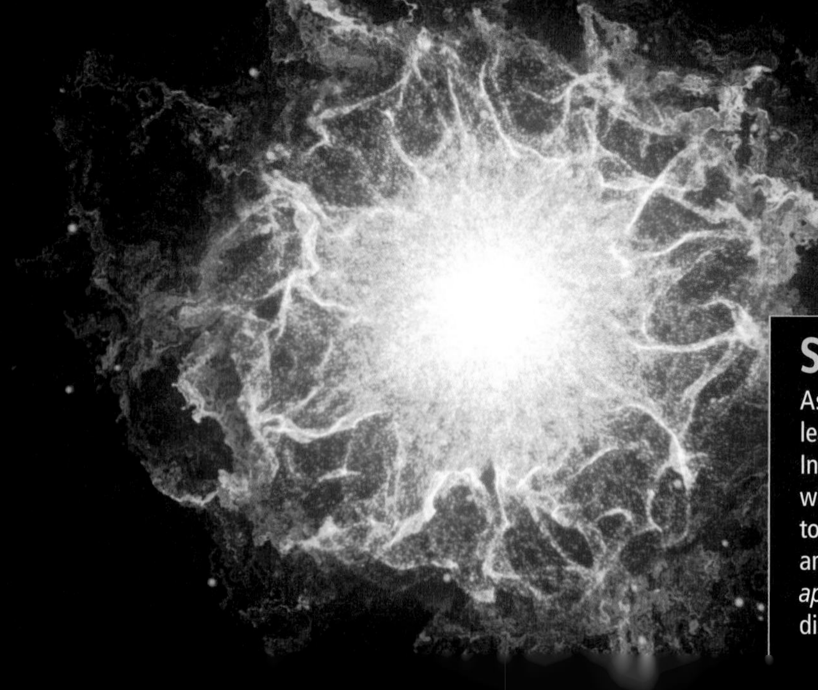

STEM

Astrophysicists study stars to learn more about the universe. In the Performance Task, you will use a quadratic equation to show the relationship among a star's *luminosity*, *apparent brightness*, and distance from Earth.

Preparing for Chapter 9

Chapter Learning Target Understand solving quadratic equations.

Chapter Success Criteria
- ◆ I can simplify expressions using properties of radicals.
- ◆ I can describe different methods for solving quadratic equations.
- ■ I can solve quadratic equations.
- ■ I can solve nonlinear systems of equations graphically and algebraically.

◆ Surface
■ Deep

Chapter Vocabulary

Work with a partner. Discuss each of the vocabulary terms.

radical expression
rationalizing the denominator
like radicals
quadratic equation
system of nonlinear equations

Mathematical Practices

Make Sense of Problems and Persevere in Solving Them

Mathematically proficient students analyze givens, constraints, relationships, and goals.

Work with a partner. The equation $f(t) = -0.8t^2 + s_0$ represents the height (in meters) of a falling object t seconds after it is dropped from an initial height s_0 on the moon.

In 2009, a rocket carried by the Lunar Crater Observation and Sensing Satellite (LCROSS) intentionally crashed into the moon. Scientists collected data about the debris plume created by the impact. How long did it take for the debris to fall back to the surface of the moon after reaching its maximum height?

The debris plume created by the LCROSS impact reached a maximum height of about 10 kilometers.

1. Analyze the given information. Then describe what you are asked to do.
2. Explain the meaning of each of the following statements in this situation. Then write an equation that you can use to solve the problem.

   $f(0) = 10{,}000$ $\quad f(60) = 7120$ $\quad f(t) = 0$

3. Before solving, analyze your equation: What must be true about the value of t? What must be true about the value of $-0.8t^2$? Then solve the equation.

9 Prepare WITH CalcChat®

Factoring Perfect Square Trinomials

WATCH

Example 1 **Factor $x^2 + 14x + 49$.**

$$x^2 + 14x + 49 = x^2 + 2(x)(7) + 7^2 \qquad \text{Write as } a^2 + 2ab + b^2.$$

$$= (x + 7)^2 \qquad \text{Perfect square trinomial pattern}$$

Factor the trinomial.

1. $x^2 + 10x + 25$

2. $x^2 - 20x + 100$

3. $x^2 + 12x + 36$

4. $x^2 - 18x + 81$

5. $x^2 + 16x + 64$

6. $x^2 - 30x + 225$

Solving Systems of Linear Equations by Graphing

Example 2 **Solve the system of linear equations by graphing.**

$y = 2x + 1$ Equation 1

$y = -\frac{1}{3}x + 8$ Equation 2

Step 1 Graph each equation.

Step 2 Estimate the point of intersection.
The graphs appear to intersect at (3, 7).

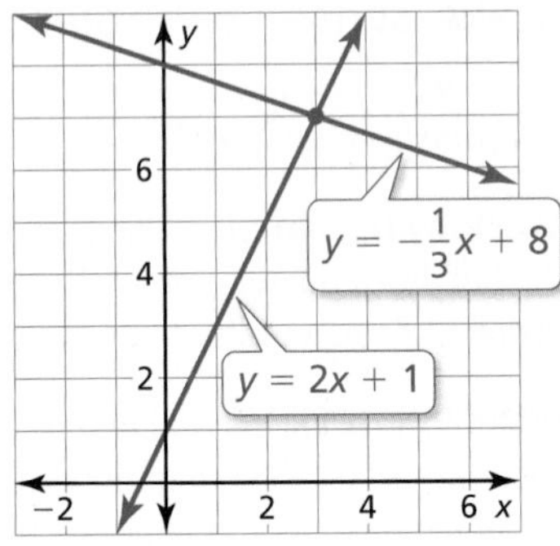

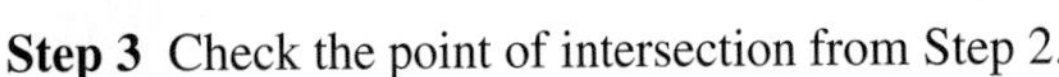

Step 3 Check the point of intersection from Step 2.

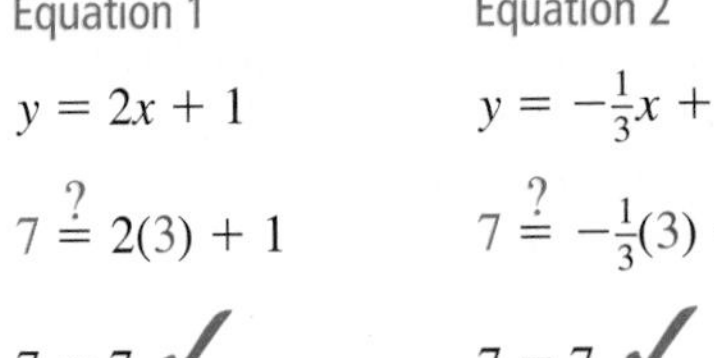

Equation 1	Equation 2
$y = 2x + 1$	$y = -\frac{1}{3}x + 8$
$7 \stackrel{?}{=} 2(3) + 1$	$7 \stackrel{?}{=} -\frac{1}{3}(3) + 8$
$7 = 7$ ✓	$7 = 7$ ✓

▶ The solution is (3, 7).

Solve the system of linear equations by graphing.

7. $y = -5x + 3$
$y = 2x - 4$

8. $y = \frac{3}{2}x - 2$
$y = -\frac{1}{4}x + 5$

9. $y = \frac{1}{2}x + 4$
$y = -3x - 3$

10. MP **STRUCTURE** What value of c makes $x^2 + bx + c$ a perfect square trinomial?

9.1 Properties of Radicals

Learning Target Use properties of radicals to write equivalent expressions.

Success Criteria
- I can use properties of square roots to write equivalent expressions.
- I can use properties of cube roots to write equivalent expressions.
- I can rationalize the denominator of a fraction.
- I can perform operations with radicals.

EXPLORE IT! Performing Operations with Square Roots

Work with a partner.

a. Determine which of the following are general rules by choosing various values for a and b. Use what you know about radicals and rational exponents to justify your answer.

Math Practice

Find Entry Points
What types of values of a and b make the expressions easier to evaluate?

i. $\sqrt{a} + \sqrt{b} \stackrel{?}{=} \sqrt{a + b}$

ii. $\sqrt{a} \bullet \sqrt{b} \stackrel{?}{=} \sqrt{a \bullet b}$

iii. $\sqrt{a} - \sqrt{b} \stackrel{?}{=} \sqrt{a - b}$

iv. $\dfrac{\sqrt{a}}{\sqrt{b}} \stackrel{?}{=} \sqrt{\dfrac{a}{b}}$

b. Explain how to add, subtract, multiply, and divide square roots in your own words.

c. Consider the following list of rational and irrational numbers. Add two more rational numbers and two more irrational numbers to the list.

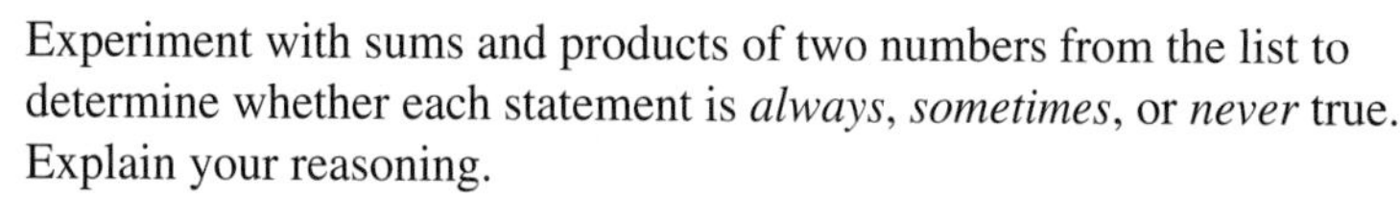

Experiment with sums and products of two numbers from the list to determine whether each statement is *always*, *sometimes*, or *never* true. Explain your reasoning.

i. The sum of two rational numbers is rational.

ii. The sum of a rational number and an irrational number is irrational.

iii. The sum of two irrational numbers is irrational.

iv. The product of two rational numbers is rational.

v. The product of a nonzero rational number and an irrational number is irrational.

vi. The product of two irrational numbers is irrational.

Using Properties of Radicals

Vocabulary AZ VOCAB

radical expression, *p. 484*
simplest form of a radical, *p. 484*
rationalizing the denominator, *p. 486*
conjugates, *p. 486*
like radicals, *p. 488*

A **radical expression** is an expression that contains a radical. An expression involving a radical with index n is in **simplest form** when these three conditions are met.

- No radicands have perfect nth powers as factors other than 1.
- No radicands contain fractions.
- No radicals appear in the denominator of a fraction.

You can use the properties below to simplify radical expressions involving square roots.

STUDY TIP

In this course, whenever a variable appears in the radicand, assume that it has only *nonnegative* values.

KEY IDEAS

Product Property of Square Roots

Words The square root of a product equals the product of the square roots of the factors.

Numbers $\sqrt{9 \cdot 5} = \sqrt{9} \cdot \sqrt{5} = 3\sqrt{5}$

Algebra $\sqrt{ab} = \sqrt{a} \cdot \sqrt{b}$, where $a \geq 0$ and $b \geq 0$

Quotient Property of Square Roots

Words The square root of a quotient equals the quotient of the square roots of the numerator and denominator.

Numbers $\sqrt{\frac{3}{4}} = \frac{\sqrt{3}}{\sqrt{4}} = \frac{\sqrt{3}}{2}$

Algebra $\sqrt{\frac{a}{b}} = \frac{\sqrt{a}}{\sqrt{b}}$, where $a \geq 0$ and $b > 0$

There can be more than one way to factor a radicand. An efficient method is to find the greatest perfect square factor.

EXAMPLE 1 Using the Product Property of Square Roots

a. $\sqrt{108} = \sqrt{36 \cdot 3}$ Factor using the greatest perfect square factor.

$= \sqrt{36} \cdot \sqrt{3}$ Product Property of Square Roots

$= 6\sqrt{3}$ Simplify.

b. $\sqrt{9x^3} = \sqrt{9 \cdot x^2 \cdot x}$ Factor using the greatest perfect square factors.

$= \sqrt{9} \cdot \sqrt{x^2} \cdot \sqrt{x}$ Product Property of Square Roots

$= 3x\sqrt{x}$ Simplify.

EXAMPLE 2 Using the Quotient Property of Square Roots

a. $\sqrt{\frac{15}{64}} = \frac{\sqrt{15}}{\sqrt{64}}$ Quotient Property of Square Roots

$= \frac{\sqrt{15}}{8}$ Simplify.

b. $\sqrt{\frac{81}{x^2}} = \frac{\sqrt{81}}{\sqrt{x^2}}$

$= \frac{9}{x}$

You can extend the Product and Quotient Properties of Square Roots to other radicals, such as cube roots. When using these *properties of cube roots*, the radicands can contain negative numbers.

EXAMPLE 3 **Using Properties of Cube Roots** 

STUDY TIP

To write a cube root in simplest form, find factors of the radicand that are perfect cubes.

a. $\sqrt[3]{-128} = \sqrt[3]{-64 \cdot 2}$ — Factor using the greatest perfect cube factor.

$= \sqrt[3]{-64} \cdot \sqrt[3]{2}$ — Product Property of Cube Roots

$= -4\sqrt[3]{2}$ — Simplify.

b. $\sqrt[3]{125x^7} = \sqrt[3]{125 \cdot x^6 \cdot x}$ — Factor using the greatest perfect cube factors.

$= \sqrt[3]{125} \cdot \sqrt[3]{x^6} \cdot \sqrt[3]{x}$ — Product Property of Cube Roots

$= 5x^2\sqrt[3]{x}$ — Simplify.

c. $\sqrt[3]{\frac{y}{216}} = \frac{\sqrt[3]{y}}{\sqrt[3]{216}}$ — Quotient Property of Cube Roots

$= \frac{\sqrt[3]{y}}{6}$ — Simplify.

d. $\sqrt[3]{\frac{8x^4}{27y^3}} = \frac{\sqrt[3]{8x^4}}{\sqrt[3]{27y^3}}$ — Quotient Property of Cube Roots

$= \frac{\sqrt[3]{8 \cdot x^3 \cdot x}}{\sqrt[3]{27 \cdot y^3}}$ — Factor using the greatest perfect cube factors.

$= \frac{\sqrt[3]{8} \cdot \sqrt[3]{x^3} \cdot \sqrt[3]{x}}{\sqrt[3]{27} \cdot \sqrt[3]{y^3}}$ — Product Property of Cube Roots

$= \frac{2x\sqrt[3]{x}}{3y}$ — Simplify.

SELF-ASSESSMENT

1 I do not understand. 2 I can do it with help. 3 I can do it on my own. 4 I can teach someone else.

Simplify the expression.

1. $\sqrt{24}$

2. $\sqrt{75n^5}$

3. $-\sqrt{\frac{17}{100}}$

4. $\sqrt{\frac{36}{z^2}}$

5. $\sqrt{\frac{4x^2}{64}}$

6. $\sqrt[3]{54}$

7. $\sqrt[3]{\frac{a}{-27}}$

8. $\sqrt[3]{\frac{25c^7d^3}{64}}$

9. VOCABULARY Is $\sqrt{63}$ in simplest form? Explain your reasoning.

10. MP REASONING Simplify $\sqrt{8x^2}$. Find the value of the original expression and the value of the expression in simplest form when $x = -1$. What do you notice? Why does this occur?

11. MP REASONING Are the expressions $\frac{1}{3}\sqrt{2x}$ and $\sqrt{\frac{2x}{9}}$ equivalent? Explain your reasoning.

Rationalizing the Denominator

When a radical is in the denominator of a fraction, you can multiply the fraction by an appropriate form of 1 to eliminate the radical from the denominator. This process is called **rationalizing the denominator**.

GO DIGITAL

EXAMPLE 4 Rationalizing the Denominator

STUDY TIP

Rationalizing the denominator works because you multiply the numerator and denominator by the same nonzero number a, which is the same as multiplying by $\frac{a}{a}$, or 1.

a. $\dfrac{\sqrt{5}}{\sqrt{3n}} = \dfrac{\sqrt{5}}{\sqrt{3n}} \cdot \dfrac{\sqrt{3n}}{\sqrt{3n}}$ Multiply by $\dfrac{\sqrt{3n}}{\sqrt{3n}}$.

$= \dfrac{\sqrt{15n}}{\sqrt{9n^2}}$ Product Property of Square Roots

$= \dfrac{\sqrt{15n}}{3n}$ Simplify.

b. $\dfrac{2}{\sqrt[3]{9}} = \dfrac{2}{\sqrt[3]{9}} \cdot \dfrac{\sqrt[3]{3}}{\sqrt[3]{3}}$ Multiply by $\dfrac{\sqrt[3]{3}}{\sqrt[3]{3}}$.

$= \dfrac{2\sqrt[3]{3}}{\sqrt[3]{27}}$ Product Property of Cube Roots

$= \dfrac{2\sqrt[3]{3}}{3}$ Simplify.

The binomials $a\sqrt{b} + c\sqrt{d}$ and $a\sqrt{b} - c\sqrt{d}$, where a, b, c, and d are rational numbers, are called **conjugates**. You can use conjugates to simplify radical expressions that contain a sum or difference involving square roots in the denominator.

EXAMPLE 5 Rationalizing the Denominator Using Conjugates

Simplify $\dfrac{7}{2 - \sqrt{3}}$.

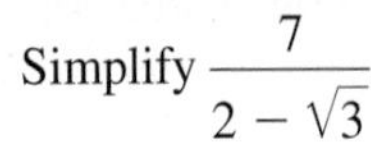

SOLUTION

$\dfrac{7}{2 - \sqrt{3}} = \dfrac{7}{2 - \sqrt{3}} \cdot \dfrac{2 + \sqrt{3}}{2 + \sqrt{3}}$ The conjugate of $2 - \sqrt{3}$ is $2 + \sqrt{3}$.

$= \dfrac{7(2 + \sqrt{3})}{2^2 - (\sqrt{3})^2}$ Sum and difference pattern

$= \dfrac{14 + 7\sqrt{3}}{1}$ Simplify.

$= 14 + 7\sqrt{3}$ Simplify.

SELF-ASSESSMENT 1 I do not understand. 2 I can do it with help. 3 I can do it on my own. 4 I can teach someone else.

Simplify the expression.

12. $\dfrac{\sqrt{10}}{\sqrt{3}}$ **13.** $\dfrac{5}{\sqrt[3]{32}}$ **14.** $\dfrac{8}{1 + \sqrt{3}}$ **15.** $\dfrac{12}{\sqrt{2} + \sqrt{7}}$

16. MP **LOGIC** Find the product of the conjugates $a\sqrt{b} + c\sqrt{d}$ and $a\sqrt{b} - c\sqrt{d}$. What does the result tell you about using conjugates to rationalize the denominator?

GO DIGITAL

EXAMPLE 6 Modeling Real Life

The distance d (in miles) that you can see to the horizon with your eye level h feet above the water is given by $d = \sqrt{\frac{3h}{2}}$. Estimate how far you can see when your eye level is 5 feet above the water.

SOLUTION

Use the equation to find the value of d when $h = 5$.

$$d = \sqrt{\frac{3(5)}{2}} \qquad \text{Substitute 5 for } h.$$

$$= \frac{\sqrt{15}}{\sqrt{2}} \qquad \text{Quotient Property of Square Roots}$$

$$= \frac{\sqrt{15}}{\sqrt{2}} \cdot \frac{\sqrt{2}}{\sqrt{2}} \qquad \text{Multiply by } \frac{\sqrt{2}}{\sqrt{2}}.$$

$$= \frac{\sqrt{30}}{2} \qquad \text{Simplify.}$$

▶ You can see $\frac{\sqrt{30}}{2} \approx 2.7$ miles.

EXAMPLE 7 Modeling Real Life

The ratio of the length to the width of a *golden rectangle* is $(1 + \sqrt{5}) : 2$. The dimensions of the face of the Parthenon in Greece form a golden rectangle. Estimate the height h of the Parthenon.

SOLUTION

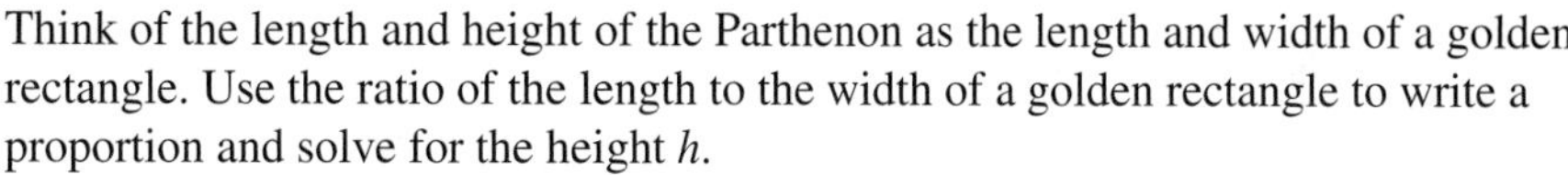

Think of the length and height of the Parthenon as the length and width of a golden rectangle. Use the ratio of the length to the width of a golden rectangle to write a proportion and solve for the height h.

$$\frac{1 + \sqrt{5}}{2} = \frac{31}{h} \qquad \text{Write a proportion.}$$

$$h(1 + \sqrt{5}) = 62 \qquad \text{Cross Products Property}$$

$$h = \frac{62}{1 + \sqrt{5}} \qquad \text{Divide each side by } 1 + \sqrt{5}.$$

$$h = \frac{62}{1 + \sqrt{5}} \cdot \frac{1 - \sqrt{5}}{1 - \sqrt{5}} \qquad \text{Multiply the numerator and denominator by the conjugate.}$$

$$h = \frac{62 - 62\sqrt{5}}{-4} \qquad \text{Simplify.}$$

$$h = \frac{31\sqrt{5} - 31}{2} \qquad \text{Simplify.}$$

▶ The height is $\frac{31\sqrt{5} - 31}{2} \approx 19$ meters.

SELF-ASSESSMENT

1 I do not understand. 2 I can do it with help. 3 I can do it on my own. 4 I can teach someone else.

17. WHAT IF? In Example 6, how far can you see when your eye level is 35 feet above the water?

18. The dimensions of a dance floor form a golden rectangle. The width of the dance floor is 50 feet. Estimate the perimeter and area of the dance floor.

Performing Operations with Radicals

Radicals with the same index and radicand are called **like radicals**. You can add and subtract like radicals the same way you combine like terms by using the Distributive Property.

EXAMPLE 8 Adding and Subtracting Radicals

a. $5\sqrt{7} + \sqrt{11} - 8\sqrt{7} = 5\sqrt{7} - 8\sqrt{7} + \sqrt{11}$ — Commutative Property of Addition

$= (5 - 8)\sqrt{7} + \sqrt{11}$ — Distributive Property

$= -3\sqrt{7} + \sqrt{11}$ — Subtract.

b. $10\sqrt{5} + \sqrt{20} = 10\sqrt{5} + 2\sqrt{5}$ — Simplify.

$= (10 + 2)\sqrt{5}$ — Distributive Property

$= 12\sqrt{5}$ — Add.

c. $6\sqrt[3]{x} + 2\sqrt[3]{x} = (6 + 2)\sqrt[3]{x}$ — Distributive Property

$= 8\sqrt[3]{x}$ — Add.

STUDY TIP

Do not assume that radicals with different radicands cannot be added or subtracted. Always check to see whether you can simplify the radicals. In some cases, the radicals can be written as like radicals.

EXAMPLE 9 Multiplying Radicals

Simplify $\sqrt{5}(\sqrt{3} - \sqrt{75})$.

SOLUTION

Method 1 $\sqrt{5}(\sqrt{3} - \sqrt{75}) = \sqrt{5} \cdot \sqrt{3} - \sqrt{5} \cdot \sqrt{75}$ — Distributive Property

$= \sqrt{15} - \sqrt{375}$ — Product Property of Square Roots

$= \sqrt{15} - 5\sqrt{15}$ — Simplify.

$= (1 - 5)\sqrt{15}$ — Distributive Property

$= -4\sqrt{15}$ — Subtract.

Method 2 $\sqrt{5}(\sqrt{3} - \sqrt{75}) = \sqrt{5}(\sqrt{3} - 5\sqrt{3})$ — Simplify $\sqrt{75}$.

$= \sqrt{5}[(1 - 5)\sqrt{3}]$ — Distributive Property

$= \sqrt{5}(-4\sqrt{3})$ — Subtract.

$= -4\sqrt{15}$ — Product Property of Square Roots

SELF-ASSESSMENT

1 I do not understand. 2 I can do it with help. 3 I can do it on my own. 4 I can teach someone else.

Simplify the expression.

19. $3\sqrt{2} - \sqrt{6} + 10\sqrt{2}$

20. $4\sqrt{7} - 6\sqrt{63}$

21. $4\sqrt[3]{5x} - 11\sqrt[3]{5x}$

22. $\sqrt{3}(8\sqrt{2} + 7\sqrt{32})$

23. $(2\sqrt{5} - 4)^2$

24. $\sqrt[3]{-4}(\sqrt[3]{2} - \sqrt[3]{16})$

25. WHICH ONE DOESN'T BELONG? Which expression does *not* belong with the other three? Explain your reasoning.

$-\frac{1}{3}\sqrt{6}$ | $6\sqrt{3}$ | $\frac{1}{6}\sqrt{3}$ | $-3\sqrt{3}$

9.1 Practice WITH CalcChat® AND CalcView®

In Exercises 1–6, determine whether the expression is in simplest form. If it is not, explain why not.

1. $\sqrt{19}$ **2.** $\sqrt{\frac{1}{7}}$

3. $\sqrt{34}$ **4.** $\frac{5}{\sqrt{2}}$

5. $\frac{3\sqrt{10}}{4}$ **6.** $\frac{1}{2+\sqrt[3]{2}}$

In Exercises 7–14, simplify the expression. *Example 1*

7. $\sqrt{20}$ **8.** $\sqrt{32}$

9. $\sqrt{128}$ **10.** $-\sqrt{72}$

11. $\sqrt{125b}$ **12.** $\sqrt{4x^2}$

13. $-\sqrt{81m^3}$ **14.** $\sqrt{48n^5}$

In Exercises 15–22, simplify the expression. *Example 2*

15. $\sqrt{\frac{4}{49}}$ **16.** $-\sqrt{\frac{7}{81}}$

17. $-\sqrt{\frac{23}{64}}$ **18.** $\sqrt{\frac{65}{121}}$

19. $\sqrt{\frac{a^3}{49}}$ **20.** $\sqrt{\frac{144}{k^2}}$

21. $\sqrt{\frac{100}{4x^2}}$ **22.** $\sqrt{\frac{25v^2}{36}}$

In Exercises 23–30, simplify the expression. *Example 3*

23. $\sqrt[3]{16}$ **24.** $\sqrt[3]{-108}$

25. $\sqrt[3]{-64x^5}$ **26.** $-\sqrt[3]{343n^2}$

27. $\sqrt[3]{\frac{6c}{-125}}$ **28.** $\sqrt[3]{\frac{8h^4}{27}}$

29. $-\sqrt[3]{\frac{81y^2}{1000x^3}}$ **30.** $\sqrt[3]{\frac{21}{-64a^3b^6}}$

31. ERROR ANALYSIS Describe and correct the error in writing $\sqrt{72}$ in simplest form.

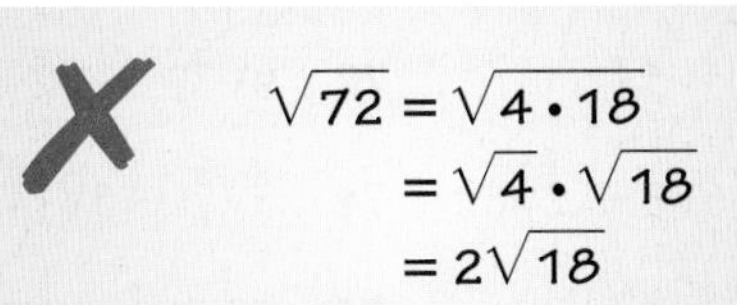

32. ERROR ANALYSIS Describe and correct the error in writing $\sqrt[3]{\frac{128y^3}{125}}$ in simplest form.

$$\sqrt[3]{\frac{128y^3}{125}} = \frac{\sqrt[3]{128y^3}}{125}$$
$$= \frac{\sqrt[3]{64 \cdot 2 \cdot y^3}}{125}$$
$$= \frac{\sqrt[3]{64} \cdot \sqrt[3]{2} \cdot \sqrt[3]{y^3}}{125}$$
$$= \frac{4y\sqrt[3]{2}}{125}$$

In Exercises 33–38, write a form of 1 that you can use to rationalize the denominator of the expression.

33. $\frac{4}{\sqrt{6}}$ **34.** $\frac{1}{\sqrt{13z}}$

35. $\frac{2}{\sqrt[3]{x^2}}$ **36.** $\frac{3m}{\sqrt[3]{4}}$

37. $\frac{\sqrt{2}}{\sqrt{5}-8}$ **38.** $\frac{5}{\sqrt{3}+\sqrt{7}}$

In Exercises 39–48, simplify the expression. *Example 4*

39. $\frac{2}{\sqrt{2}}$ **40.** $\frac{4}{\sqrt{3}}$

41. $\frac{\sqrt{5}}{\sqrt{48}}$ **42.** $\sqrt{\frac{4}{52}}$

43. $\frac{3}{\sqrt{a}}$ **44.** $\frac{1}{\sqrt{2x}}$

45. $\sqrt{\frac{3d^2}{5}}$ **46.** $\frac{\sqrt{8}}{\sqrt{3n^3}}$

47. $\frac{4}{\sqrt[3]{25}}$ **48.** $\frac{\sqrt[3]{2}}{\sqrt[3]{49t}}$

In Exercises 49–54, simplify the expression. *Example 5*

49. $\frac{1}{\sqrt{7}+1}$ **50.** $\frac{2}{5-\sqrt{3}}$

51. $\frac{10}{7-\sqrt{2}}$ **52.** $\frac{5}{6+\sqrt{5}}$

53. $\frac{3}{\sqrt{5}-\sqrt{2}}$ **54.** $\frac{9}{\sqrt{3}+\sqrt{11}}$

55. **MODELING REAL LIFE** The time t (in seconds) it takes a dropped object to fall h feet is given by $t = \sqrt{\frac{h}{16}}$.

a. Estimate how long it takes an earring to hit the ground when it falls from the roof of the building.

b. Estimate how much sooner the earring hits the ground when it is dropped from two stories (22 feet) below the roof.

56. **MODELING REAL LIFE** The orbital period of a planet is the time it takes the planet to travel around the Sun. You can find the orbital period P (in Earth years) using the formula $P = \sqrt{d^3}$, where d is the average distance (in astronomical units, abbreviated AU) of the planet from the Sun.

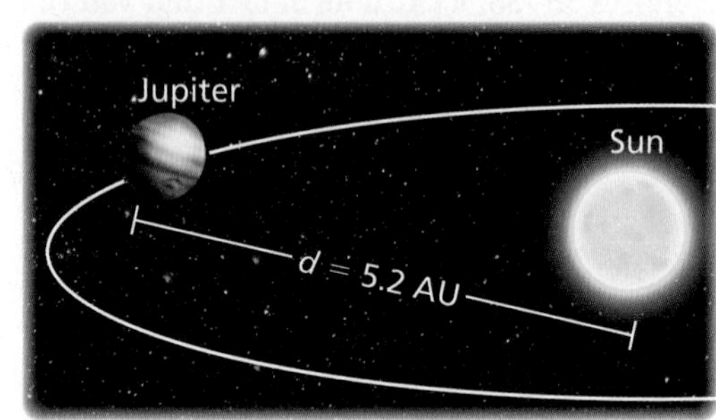

a. Simplify the right side of the formula.

b. Estimate Jupiter's orbital period.

57. **MODELING REAL LIFE** The electric current I (in amperes) an appliance uses is given by $I = \sqrt{\frac{P}{R}}$, where P is the power (in watts) and R is the resistance (in ohms). Estimate the current an appliance uses when the power is 147 watts and the resistance is 5 ohms. *Example 6*

58. **MP PROBLEM SOLVING** The radius r of a cylinder is given by

$$r = \sqrt{\frac{V}{\pi h}}$$

where V is the volume and h is the height of the cylinder.

a. Estimate the radius of a cylinder with a volume of 44π cubic centimeters and a height of 7 centimeters.

b. The radius of Cylinder A is 30 inches. Cylinder B has the same volume as Cylinder A but is 9 times taller. What is the radius of Cylinder B?

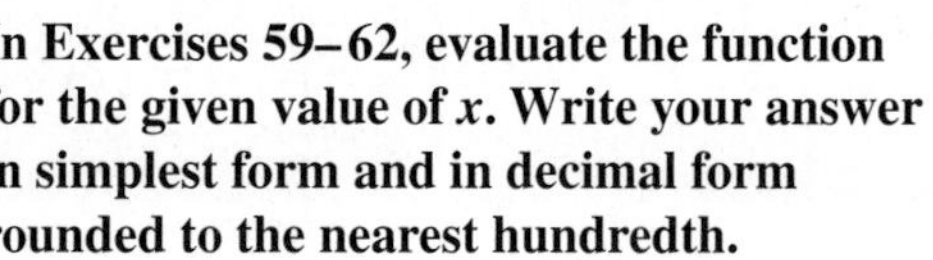

In Exercises 59–62, evaluate the function for the given value of x. Write your answer in simplest form and in decimal form rounded to the nearest hundredth.

59. $h(x) = \sqrt{5x}; x = 10$

60. $g(x) = \sqrt{3x}; x = 60$

61. $r(x) = \sqrt{\frac{3x}{3x^2 + 6}}; x = 4$

62. $p(x) = \sqrt{\frac{x - 1}{5x}}; x = 8$

In Exercises 63–66, evaluate the expression when $a = -2$, $b = 8$, and $c = \frac{1}{2}$. Write your answer in simplest form and in decimal form rounded to the nearest hundredth.

63. $\sqrt{a^2 + bc}$

64. $-\sqrt{4c - 6ab}$

65. $-\sqrt{2a^2 + b^2}$

66. $\sqrt{b^2 - 4ac}$

67. **MODELING REAL LIFE** The text in the book shown forms a golden rectangle. Estimate the width w of the text. *Example 7*

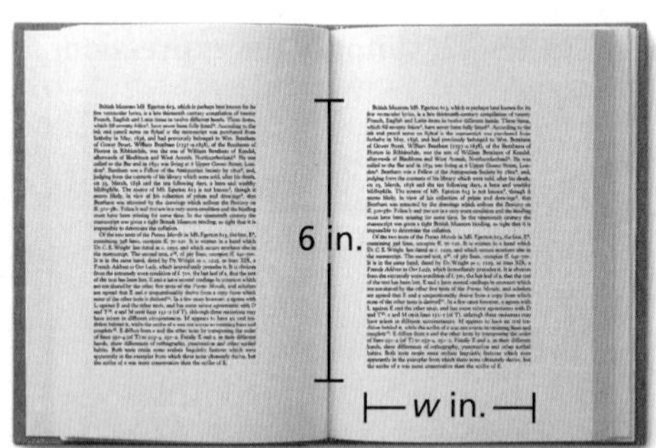

68. **MODELING REAL LIFE** The flag of Togo is approximately the shape of a golden rectangle. Estimate the width w of the flag.

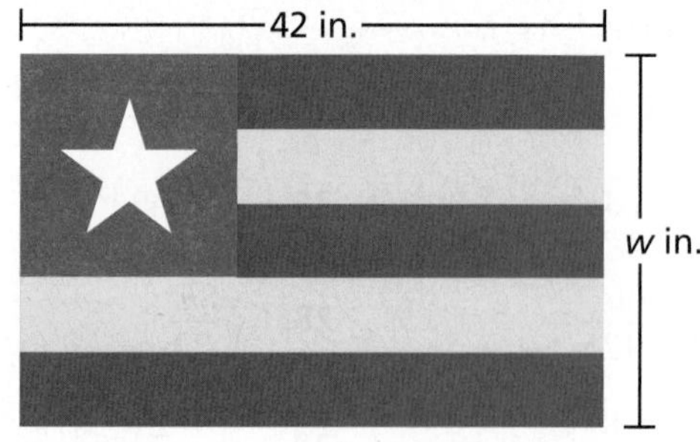

In Exercises 69–76, simplify the expression. *Example 8*

69. $\sqrt{3} - 2\sqrt{2} + 6\sqrt{2}$

70. $\sqrt{5} - 5\sqrt{13} - 8\sqrt{5}$

71. $2\sqrt{6} - 5\sqrt{54}$

72. $9\sqrt{32} + \sqrt{2}$

73. $\sqrt{12} + 6\sqrt{3} + 2\sqrt{6}$

74. $3\sqrt{7} - 5\sqrt{14} + 2\sqrt{28}$

75. $\sqrt[3]{-81} + 4\sqrt[3]{3}$

76. $6\sqrt[3]{128t} - 2\sqrt[3]{2t}$

In Exercises 77–84, simplify the expression.
Example 9

77. $\sqrt{2}(\sqrt{45} + \sqrt{5})$

78. $\sqrt{3}(\sqrt{72} - 3\sqrt{2})$

79. $\sqrt{5}(2\sqrt{6x} - \sqrt{96x})$

80. $\sqrt{7y}(\sqrt{27y} + 5\sqrt{12y})$

81. $(4\sqrt{2} - \sqrt{98})^2$

82. $(\sqrt{3} + \sqrt{48})(\sqrt{20} - \sqrt{5})$

83. $\sqrt[3]{3}(\sqrt[3]{4} + \sqrt[3]{32})$

84. $\sqrt[3]{2}(\sqrt[3]{135} - 4\sqrt[3]{5})$

In Exercises 85 and 86, simplify the expression.

85. $\dfrac{\sqrt{3}}{\sqrt{7} + \sqrt{3}}$

86. $\dfrac{\sqrt{6}}{\sqrt{15} - \sqrt{10}}$

87. **MODELING REAL LIFE** The circumference C of the art room in a mansion is approximated by the formula $C \approx 2\pi\sqrt{\dfrac{a^2 + b^2}{2}}$. Approximate the circumference of the room.

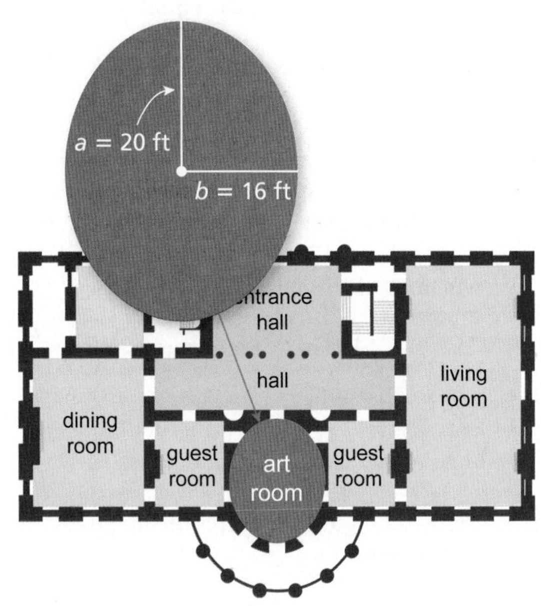

88. **COLLEGE PREP** What is the value of y when $x = 2\sqrt{11}$ and $3x = \sqrt{11y}$?

Ⓐ 6 Ⓑ 12

Ⓒ 36 Ⓓ 108

In Exercises 89–94, simplify the expression.

89. $\sqrt[4]{\dfrac{10}{81}}$

90. $\sqrt[5]{\dfrac{13}{5x^5}}$

91. $\sqrt[5]{160x^6}$

92. $\sqrt[4]{256y}$

93. $6\sqrt[4]{9} - \sqrt[5]{9} + 3\sqrt[4]{9}$

94. $\sqrt[5]{2}(\sqrt[4]{7} + \sqrt[5]{16})$

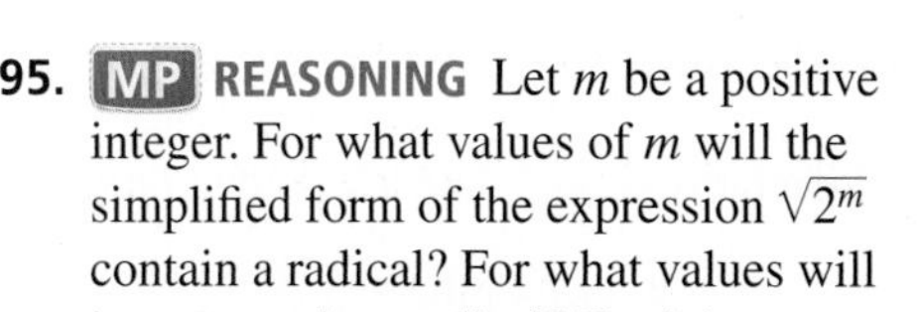

95. MP **REASONING** Let m be a positive integer. For what values of m will the simplified form of the expression $\sqrt{2^m}$ contain a radical? For what values will it *not* contain a radical? Explain.

96. **HOW DO YOU SEE IT?**
The edge length s of a cube is an irrational number, the surface area is an irrational number, and the volume is a rational number. Give a possible value of s.

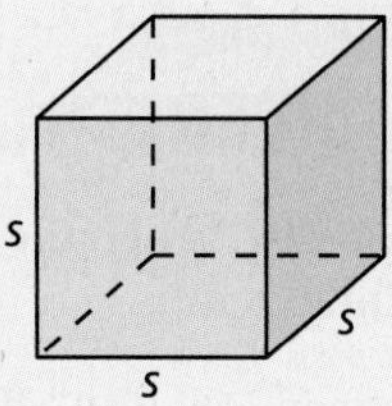

97. MP **REASONING** Let a and b be positive numbers. Explain why $\sqrt{ab}$ lies between a and b on a number line. (*Hint:* Let $a < b$ and multiply each side of $a < b$ by a. Then let $a < b$ and multiply each side by b.)

98. **MAKING AN ARGUMENT** Can you rationalize the denominator of the expression $\dfrac{2}{4 + \sqrt[3]{5}}$ by multiplying the numerator and denominator by $4 - \sqrt[3]{5}$? Explain.

99. **CONNECTING CONCEPTS** Write a quadratic function in standard form that has $5 + \sqrt{7}$ and its conjugate as zeros.

100. MP **PROBLEM SOLVING** The ratio of consecutive terms $\dfrac{a_n}{a_{n-1}}$ in the Fibonacci sequence gets closer and closer to the golden ratio $\dfrac{1 + \sqrt{5}}{2}$ as n increases. Find the term that precedes 610 in the sequence.

101. **CRITICAL THINKING** Determine whether each expression represents a *rational* or an *irrational* number. Explain your reasoning.

a. $4 + \sqrt{6}$

b. $\dfrac{\sqrt{48}}{\sqrt{3}}$

c. $\dfrac{8}{\sqrt{12}}$

d. $\sqrt{3} + \sqrt{7}$

e. $\dfrac{a}{\sqrt{10} - \sqrt{2}}$, where a is a positive integer

f. $\dfrac{2 + \sqrt{5}}{2b + \sqrt{5b^2}}$, where b is a positive integer

102. THOUGHT PROVOKING

Use the golden ratio $\frac{1+\sqrt{5}}{2}$ and the golden ratio conjugate $\frac{1-\sqrt{5}}{2}$ for each of the following.

a. Show that the golden ratio and golden ratio conjugate are both solutions of $x^2 - x - 1 = 0$.

b. Construct a geometric diagram that has the golden ratio as the length of a part of the diagram.

103. **DIG DEEPER** Use the special product pattern

$$(a + b)(a^2 - ab + b^2) = a^3 + b^3$$

to simplify the expression $\frac{2}{\sqrt[3]{x} + 1}$. Explain your reasoning.

REVIEW & REFRESH

In Exercises 104–107, graph the linear equation. Identify the *x*-intercept.

104. $y = x - 4$ **105.** $y = -2x + 6$

106. $y + 1 = -\frac{1}{3}x$ **107.** $2y = 3x + 12$

In Exercises 108–111, solve the equation.

108. $8^5 = 8^{2x+1}$ **109.** $27^x = 3^{x-6}$

110. $625^x = \left(\frac{1}{25}\right)^{x+2}$ **111.** $\left(\frac{1}{36}\right)^x = 216^{1-x}$

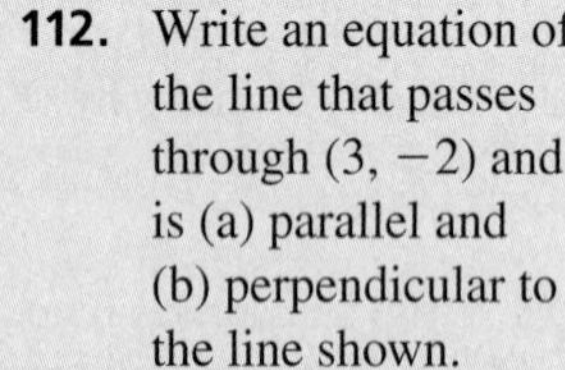

112. Write an equation of the line that passes through $(3, -2)$ and is (a) parallel and (b) perpendicular to the line shown.

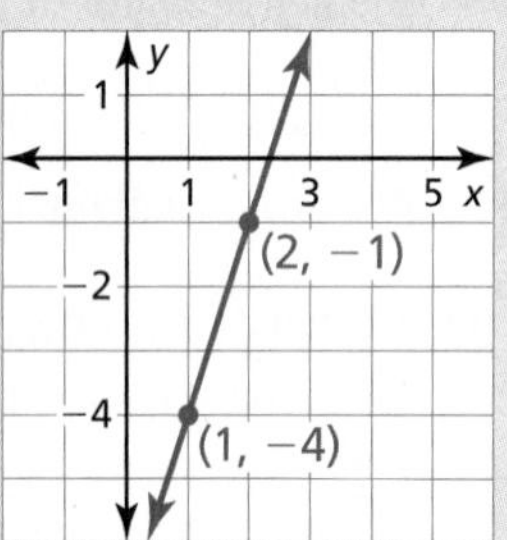

113. Simplify the expression.

$$(x - 3)[(x^2 - 5x + 4) - (x^2 - 7x - 1)]$$

In Exercises 114–116, graph the function.

114. $f(x) = (x - 6)^2 + 4$ **115.** $g(x) = 3x^2 + 6x - 2$

116. $p(x) = -2(x + 1)(x + 5)$

117. **MODELING REAL LIFE** The costs for Internet service from two companies are shown. After how many months are the total costs the same at both companies?

	Installation fee	Price per month
Company A	\$60.00	\$42.95
Company B	\$25.00	\$49.95

In Exercises 118–121, simplify the expression.

118. $\sqrt{200}$ **119.** $\sqrt[3]{\frac{54x^4}{343y^6}}$

120. $\frac{12}{\sqrt{32}}$ **121.** $\sqrt{6}\left(7\sqrt{12} - 4\sqrt{3}\right)$

In Exercises 122–125, solve the equation.

122. $(n + 10)(n - 5) = 0$ **123.** $b^2 - 12b - 45 = 0$

124. $x^2 + 22x = -121$ **125.** $4t^2 - 15 = -4t$

126. A bag contains 75 tickets. You randomly draw a ticket from the bag and replace it. The table shows the results after 30 draws. Predict the number of winning tickets in the bag.

Ticket	Frequency
Win	6
Lose	24

In Exercises 127 and 128, graph the inequality in a coordinate plane.

127. $x \leq -5$ **128.** $x - 2y < 8$

In Exercises 129 and 130, tell whether the points appear to represent a *linear*, an *exponential*, or a *quadratic* function.

129.

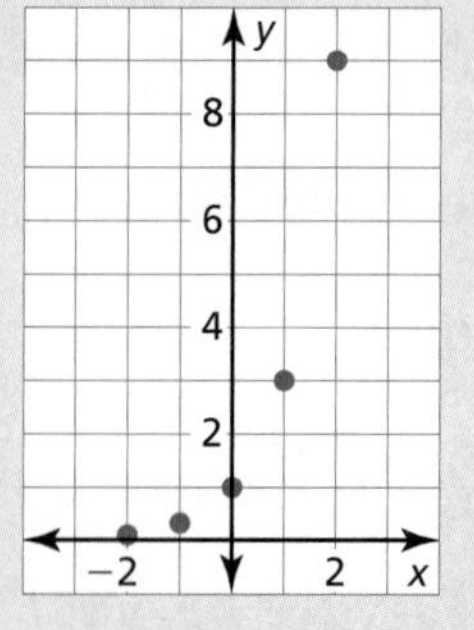

130.

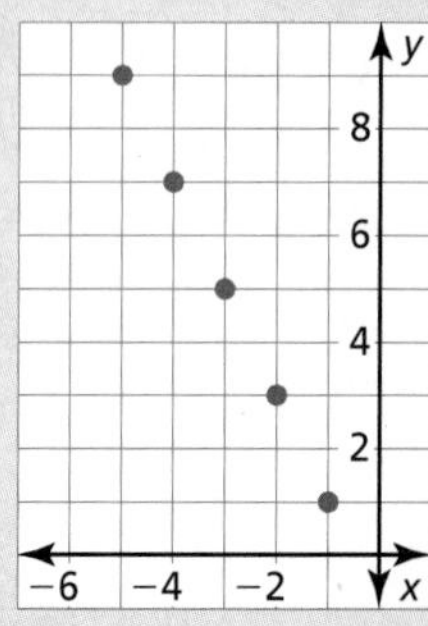

9.2 Solving Quadratic Equations by Graphing

Learning Target Use graphs to solve quadratic equations and find zeros of functions.

Success Criteria

- I can solve quadratic equations by graphing.
- I can use graphs to find and approximate zeros of functions.
- I can use technology to find a quadratic model for a set of data.

EXPLORE IT! Solving a Quadratic Equation by Graphing

Work with a partner.

a. Sketch the graph of $y = x^2 - 2x$.

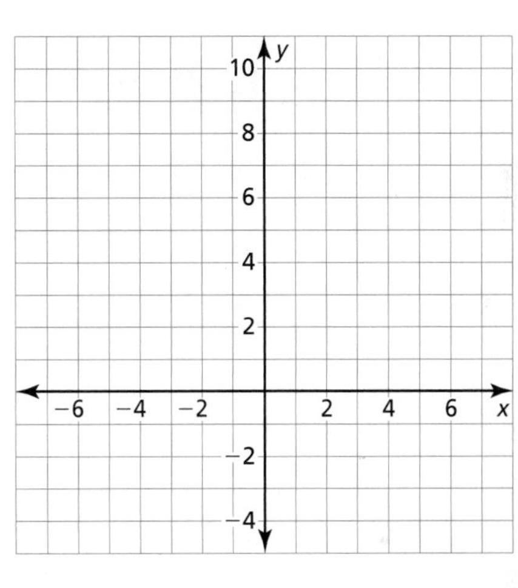

b. Explain how you can use the graph to find the solutions of $x^2 - 2x = 0$.

c. Explain how you can use the graph to find the solutions of $x^2 - 2x = 3$.

A **quadratic equation** is a nonlinear equation that can be written in the standard form $ax^2 + bx + c = 0$, where $a \neq 0$.

d. How many real solutions can a quadratic equation have? Explain your reasoning.

e. Describe two ways that you can use a graph to solve $x^2 + 4x = -5$.

f. **MP CHOOSE TOOLS** Solve each equation by graphing.

i. $x^2 - 4 = 0$ **ii.** $x^2 + 3x = 0$

iii. $-x^2 + 2x = 0$ **iv.** $x^2 - 2x = -1$

v. $x^2 - 3x = -5$ **vi.** $-x^2 + 3x = 6$

g. After you find a solution graphically, how can you check your result algebraically? Check your solutions for parts i–iv in part (f) algebraically.

Math Practice

View as Components
When solving quadratic equations, how can it help to view each side of the equation as a function?

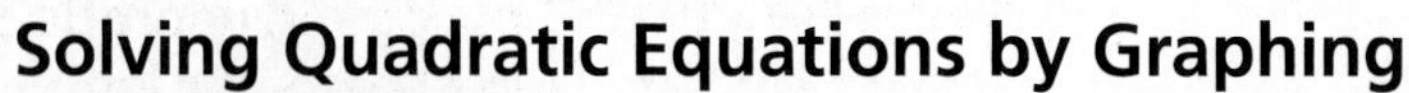

GO DIGITAL

Solving Quadratic Equations by Graphing

Vocabulary

quadratic equation, *p. 494*

A **quadratic equation** is a nonlinear equation that can be written in the standard form $ax^2 + bx + c = 0$, where $a \neq 0$.

Previously, you solved quadratic equations by factoring. You can also solve quadratic equations by graphing.

KEY IDEA

Solving Quadratic Equations by Graphing

Step 1 Write the equation in standard form, $ax^2 + bx + c = 0$.

Step 2 Graph the related function $y = ax^2 + bx + c$.

Step 3 Find the x-intercepts, if any.

The real solutions, or *roots*, of $ax^2 + bx + c = 0$ are the x-intercepts of the graph.

EXAMPLE 1 Solving a Quadratic Equation: Two Real Solutions

Solve $x^2 + 2x = 3$ by graphing.

SOLUTION

Step 1 Write the equation in standard form.

$x^2 + 2x = 3$ Write original equation.

$x^2 + 2x - 3 = 0$ Subtract 3 from each side.

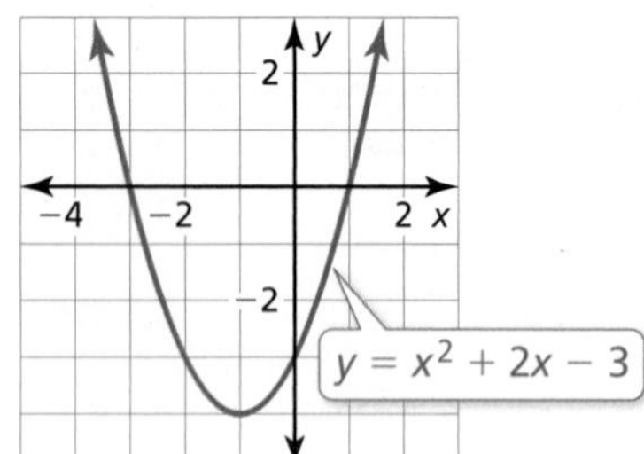

Step 2 Graph the related function $y = x^2 + 2x - 3$.

Step 3 Find the x-intercepts. The x-intercepts appear to be -3 and 1.

▶ So, the solutions are $x = -3$ and $x = 1$.

Check

$x^2 + 2x = 3$	Original equation	$x^2 + 2x = 3$
$(-3)^2 + 2(-3) \stackrel{?}{=} 3$	Substitute.	$1^2 + 2(1) \stackrel{?}{=} 3$
$3 = 3$ ✓	Simplify.	$3 = 3$ ✓

SELF-ASSESSMENT

1 I do not understand. 2 I can do it with help. 3 I can do it on my own. 4 I can teach someone else.

Solve the equation by graphing. Check your solutions.

1. $x^2 - x - 2 = 0$ **2.** $x^2 + 7x = -10$ **3.** $x^2 + x = 12$

4. WHICH ONE DOESN'T BELONG? Which equation does *not* belong with the other three? Explain your reasoning.

$x^2 + 5x = 20$ $x^2 + x - 4 = 0$ $x^2 - 6 = 4x$ $7x + 12 = x^2$

5. WRITING How can you use a graph to find the number of solutions of a quadratic equation?

EXAMPLE 2 Solving a Quadratic Equation: One Real Solution

Solve $x^2 - 8x = -16$ by graphing.

SOLUTION

Step 1 Write the equation in standard form.

$$x^2 - 8x = -16 \quad \text{Write original equation.}$$

$$x^2 - 8x + 16 = 0 \quad \text{Add 16 to each side.}$$

Step 2 Graph the related function $y = x^2 - 8x + 16$.

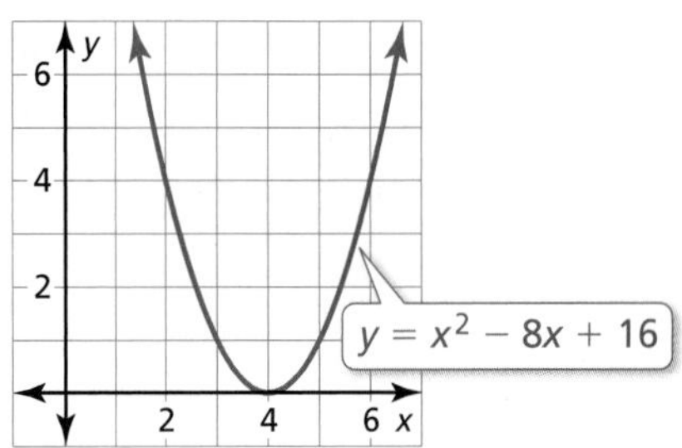

Step 3 Find the x-intercept. The only x-intercept appears to be at the vertex, (4, 0).

▶ So, the solution is $x = 4$.

Check

$x^2 - 8x = -16$ Original equation

$4^2 - 8(4) \stackrel{?}{=} -16$ Substitute.

$-16 = -16$ ✓ Simplify.

EXAMPLE 3 Solving a Quadratic Equation: No Real Solutions

Solve $-x^2 = 2x + 4$ by graphing.

SOLUTION

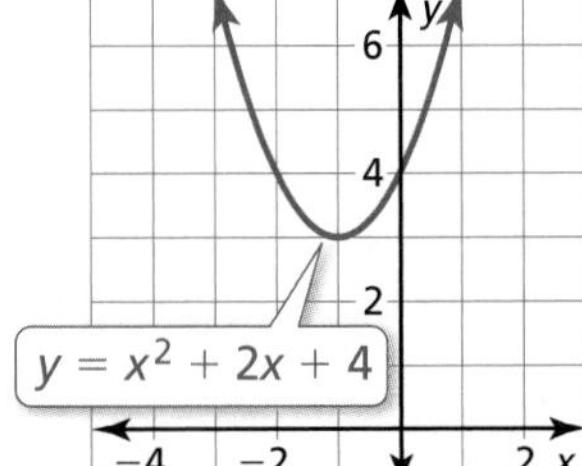

Method 1 Write the equation in standard form, $x^2 + 2x + 4 = 0$. Then graph the related function $y = x^2 + 2x + 4$, as shown at the left.

▶ There are no x-intercepts. So, $-x^2 = 2x + 4$ has no real solutions.

Method 2 Graph each side of the equation.

$y = -x^2$ Left side

$y = 2x + 4$ Right side

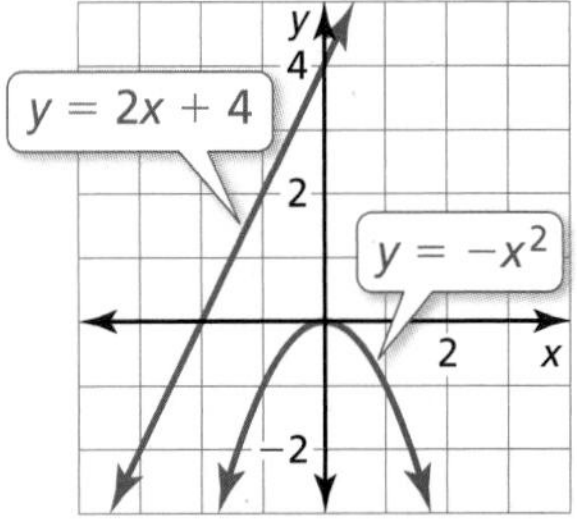

▶ The graphs do not intersect. So, $-x^2 = 2x + 4$ has no real solutions.

SELF-ASSESSMENT

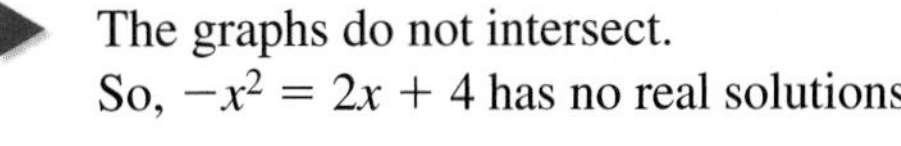

Solve the equation by graphing.

6. $x^2 + 36 = 12x$

7. $x^2 + 4x = 0$

8. $x^2 + 10x = -25$

9. $x^2 = 3x - 3$

10. $x^2 + 7x = -6$

11. $2x + 5 = -x^2$

12. WRITING Explain why the x-coordinates of the points where the graphs of the equations $y = x^2 - x$ and $y = 20$ intersect are the solutions of the equation $x^2 - x = 20$.

13. WRITING Describe the number of solutions a quadratic equation has when its related function has two x-intercepts, one x-intercept, or no x-intercepts.

Finding Zeros of Functions

Recall that a zero of a function is an x-intercept of the graph of the function. The zeros of a function are not necessarily integers. To approximate zeros, analyze the signs of function values. When two function values have different signs, a zero lies between the x-values that correspond to the function values.

EXAMPLE 4 **Finding Zeros of Functions** WATCH

Find the zero(s) of f. Round to the nearest tenth, if necessary.

a.

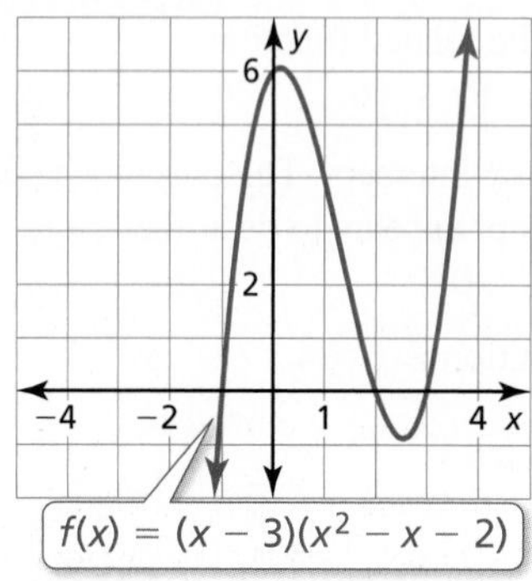

b.

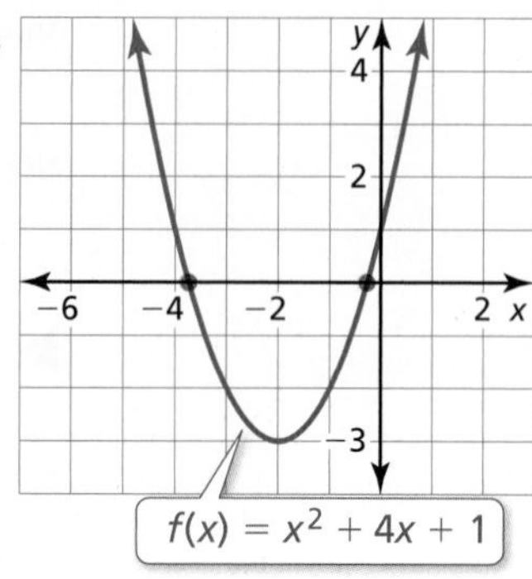

SOLUTION

a. The x-intercepts appear to be -1, 2, and 3. Substitute the estimates into the equation to check whether they are exact.

$$f(-1) = (-1 - 3)[(-1)^2 - (-1) - 2] = 0 \checkmark$$

$$f(2) = (2 - 3)(2^2 - 2 - 2) = 0 \checkmark$$

$$f(3) = (3 - 3)(3^2 - 3 - 2) = 0 \checkmark$$

▶ So, the zeros of f are -1, 2, and 3.

b. There are two x-intercepts: one between -4 and -3, and another between -1 and 0. Make tables using x-values between -4 and -3, and between -1 and 0. Use an increment of 0.1. Look for a change in the signs of the function values.

x	−3.9	−3.8	(−3.7)	−3.6	−3.5	−3.4	−3.3	−3.2	−3.1
$f(x)$	0.61	0.24	−0.11	−0.44	−0.75	−1.04	−1.31	−1.56	−1.79

change in signs

x	−0.9	−0.8	−0.7	−0.6	−0.5	−0.4	(−0.3)	−0.2	−0.1
$f(x)$	−1.79	−1.56	−1.31	−1.04	−0.75	−0.44	−0.11	0.24	0.61

change in signs

ANOTHER WAY

You could approximate one zero using a table and then use the axis of symmetry $x = -2$ to find the other zero.

The function values that are closest to 0 correspond to x-values that approximate the zeros of the function to the nearest tenth. In each table, the function value closest to 0 is -0.11.

▶ So, the zeros of f are about -3.7 and -0.3.

EXAMPLE 5 Modeling Real Life

WATCH

GO DIGITAL

A football player kicks a football 2 feet above the ground with an initial vertical velocity of 75 feet per second. The function $h = -16t^2 + 75t + 2$ represents the height h (in feet) of the football after t seconds. (a) Find the height of the football each second after it is kicked. (b) Estimate when the height of the football is 50 feet. (c) Using a graph, after how many seconds is the football 50 feet above the ground?

SOLUTION

Seconds, t	Height, h
0	2
1	61
2	88
3	83
4	46
5	−23

a. Make a table of values starting with $t = 0$ seconds using an increment of 1. Continue the table until a function value is negative.

▶ The height of the football is 61 feet after 1 second, 88 feet after 2 seconds, 83 feet after 3 seconds, and 46 feet after 4 seconds.

b. From part (a), you can estimate that the height of the football is 50 feet between 0 and 1 second and between 3 and 4 seconds.

▶ Based on the function values, it is reasonable to estimate that the height of the football is 50 feet slightly less than 1 second and slightly less than 4 seconds after it is kicked.

c. To determine when the football is 50 feet above the ground, find the t-values for which $h = 50$. So, solve the equation $-16t^2 + 75t + 2 = 50$ by graphing.

Step 1 Write the equation in standard form.

$$-16t^2 + 75t + 2 = 50 \quad \text{Write the equation.}$$

$$-16t^2 + 75t - 48 = 0 \quad \text{Subtract 50 from each side.}$$

Step 2 Use technology to graph the related function $h = -16t^2 + 75t - 48$.

Step 3 Use technology to find the zeros of the function.

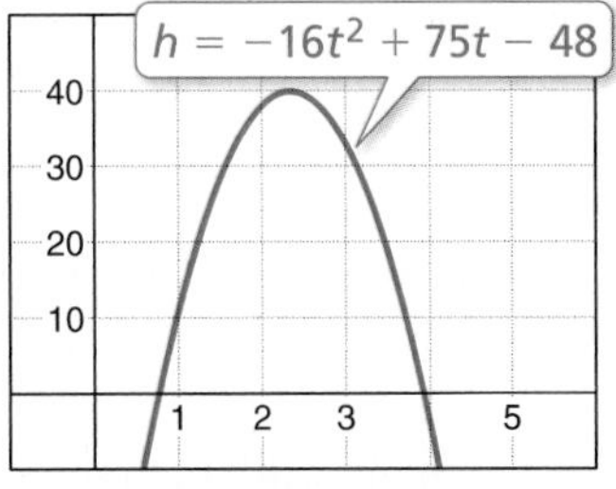

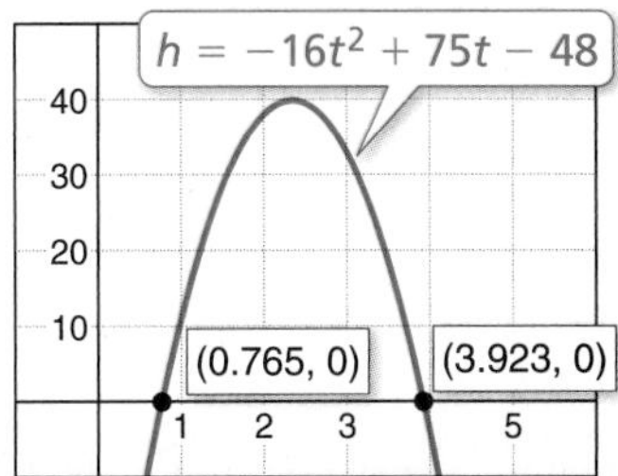

▶ The football is 50 feet above the ground after about 0.8 second and about 3.9 seconds, which supports the estimates in part (b).

SELF-ASSESSMENT 1 I do not understand. 2 I can do it with help. 3 I can do it on my own. 4 I can teach someone else.

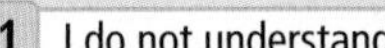

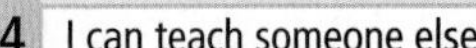

Find the zero(s) of *f*. Round to the nearest tenth, if necessary.

14. $f(x) = x^2 + x - 6$ **15.** $f(x) = (x - 4)(x^2 + 5x + 6)$ **16.** $f(x) = -x^2 + 2x + 2$

17. WHAT IF? After how many seconds is the football 65 feet above the ground?

18. WRITING How are solutions, roots, x-intercepts, and zeros related?

In previous sections, you used technology to perform linear and exponential regression to find models for sets of data. You can also perform *quadratic regression*.

EXAMPLE 6 Modeling Real Life

Time	Temperature (°F)
6 A.M.	58
8 A.M.	68
10 A.M.	76
12 P.M.	82
2 P.M.	84
4 P.M.	81
6 P.M.	75

The table shows the recorded temperatures (in degrees Fahrenheit) for a portion of a day. (a) Use technology to find a quadratic model for the data. Then determine whether the model is a good fit. (b) At what time(s) during the day is the temperature 77°F?

SOLUTION

a. Step 1 Enter the data from the table into two lists. Let x represent the number of hours after midnight.

x	y
6	58
8	68
10	76
12	82
14	84
16	81
18	75

Step 2 Use *quadratic regression.* The values in the equation can be rounded to obtain $y = -0.43x^2 + 11.7x + 2$.

$y = ax^2 + bx + c$

PARAMETERS

$a = -0.425595$ $b = 11.7321$

$c = 2.16667$

STATISTICS

$R^2 = 0.9933$

STUDY TIP

Some technology does not calculate the correlation coefficient r but does calculate R^2, which is called the *coefficient of determination.*

Step 3 Graph the equation $y = -0.43x^2 + 11.7x + 2$ with the data.

▶ The graph of the equation passes through or is close to all of the data points. So, the model is a good fit.

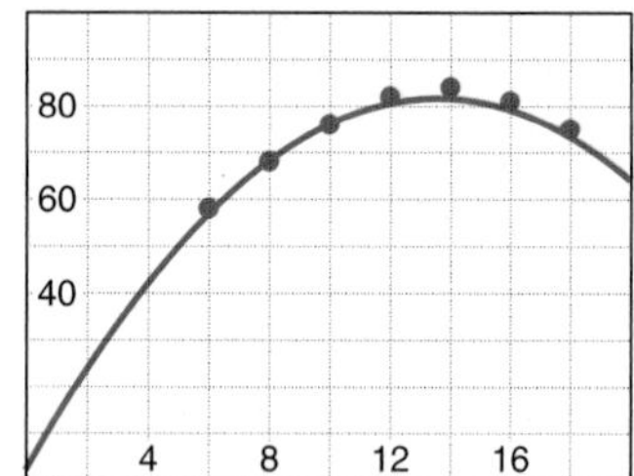

b. Find the x-values for which $y = 77$ by writing $-0.43x^2 + 11.7x + 2 = 77$ in standard form, graphing the related function $y = -0.43x^2 + 11.7x - 75$, and finding its zeros.

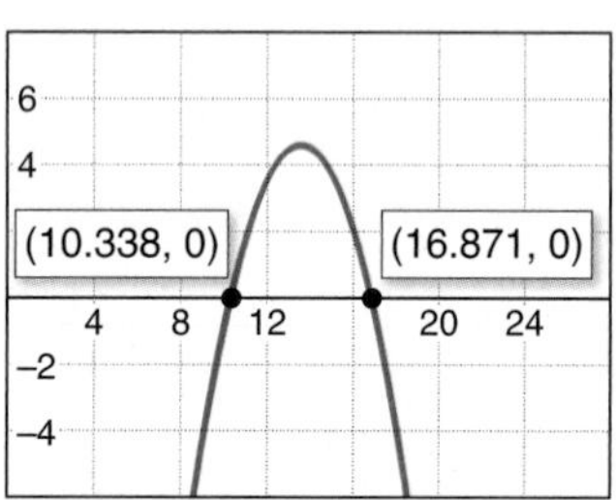

▶ The temperature is 77°F at about 10.3, or 10:18 A.M., and at about 16.9, or 4:54 P.M.

SELF-ASSESSMENT

1 I do not understand. 2 I can do it with help. 3 I can do it on my own. 4 I can teach someone else.

19. After a break, two students come to school with the flu. The table shows the total numbers of students infected with the flu x days after the break. (a) Use technology to find a quadratic model for the data. Then determine whether the model is a good fit. (b) How many days after the break are 26 students infected?

Days after break	0	7	14	21	28	35	42	49
Students with flu	2	3	5	8	18	30	42	55

20. MP **REASONING** In Example 6, the local news station reports a high temperature of 87°F for the day at 3:00 P.M. Is this possible? Explain your reasoning.

9.2 Practice WITH CalcChat® AND CalcView®

GO DIGITAL

In Exercises 1 and 2, use the graph to solve the equation.

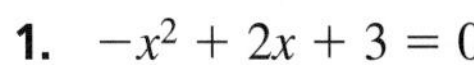

1. $-x^2 + 2x + 3 = 0$
2. $x^2 - 6x + 8 = 0$

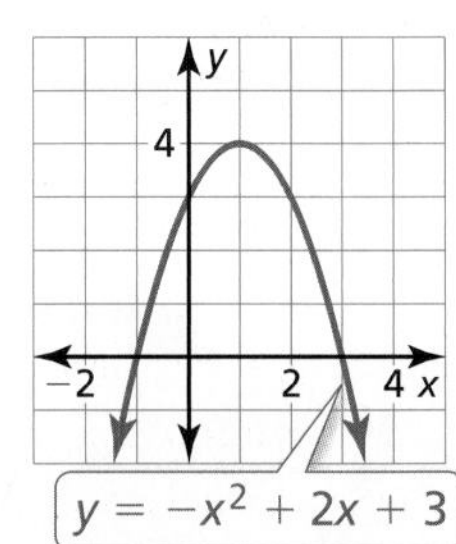

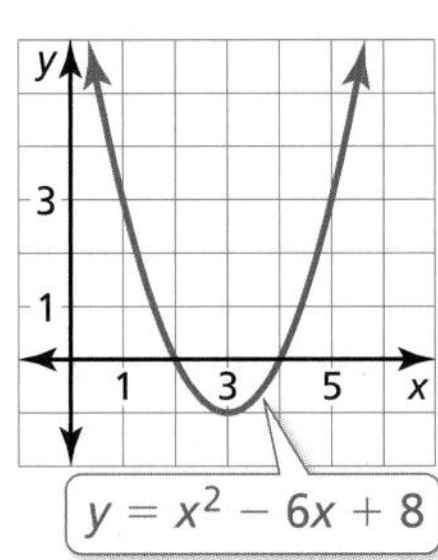

In Exercises 3–8, write the equation in standard form.

3. $4x^2 = 12$
4. $-x^2 = 15$
5. $-5x = 2x^2$
6. $x^2 = 14x$
7. $2x - x^2 = 1$
8. $5 + x = 3x^2$

In Exercises 9–20, solve the equation by graphing.
▶ *Examples 1, 2, and 3*

9. $x^2 - 5x = 0$
10. $x^2 - 4x + 4 = 0$
11. $x^2 - 2x + 5 = 0$
12. $x^2 - 6x - 7 = 0$
13. $x^2 = 6x - 9$
14. $-x^2 = 8x + 20$
15. $x^2 = -1 - 2x$
16. $x^2 = -x - 3$
17. $4x - 12 = -x^2$
18. $5x - 6 = x^2$
19. $x^2 - 2 = -x$
20. $16 + x^2 = -8x$

21. **ERROR ANALYSIS** Describe and correct the error in solving $x^2 + 3x = 18$ by graphing.

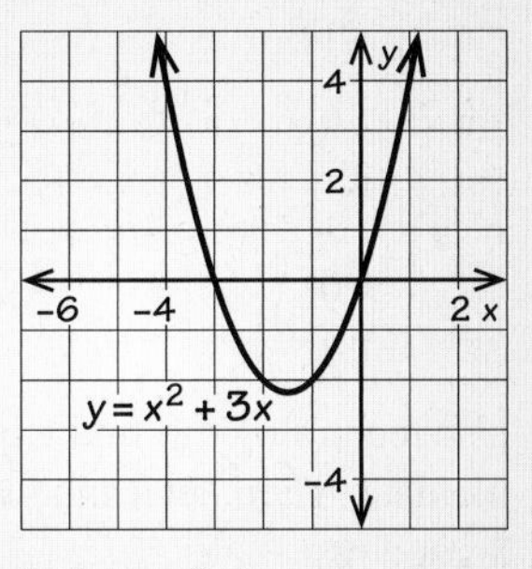

The solutions of the equation $x^2 + 3x = 18$ are $x = -3$ and $x = 0$.

22. **ERROR ANALYSIS** Describe and correct the error in solving $x^2 + 6x + 9 = 0$ by graphing.

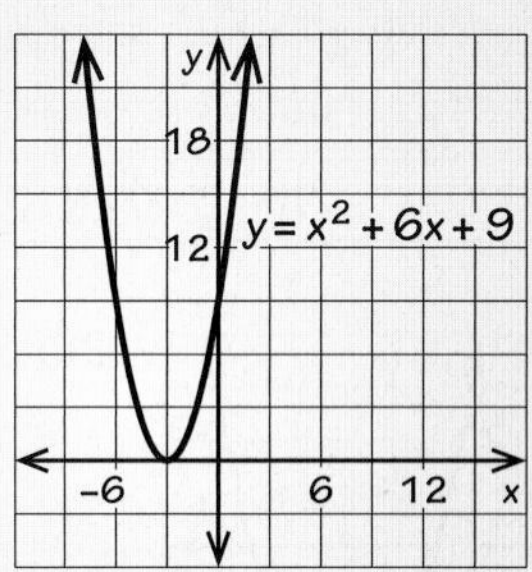

The solution of the equation $x^2 + 6x + 9 = 0$ is $x = 9$.

23. **MODELING REAL LIFE** The height y (in yards) of a flop shot in golf can be modeled by $y = -x^2 + 5x$, where x is the horizontal distance (in yards).
    a. Interpret the x-intercepts of the graph of the equation.
    b. How far away does the golf ball land?

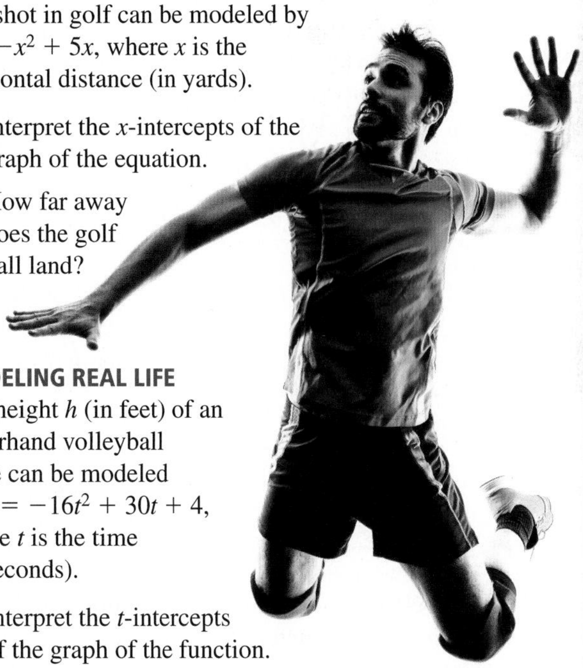

24. **MODELING REAL LIFE** The height h (in feet) of an underhand volleyball serve can be modeled by $h = -16t^2 + 30t + 4$, where t is the time (in seconds).
    a. Interpret the t-intercepts of the graph of the function.
    b. No one receives the serve. After how many seconds does the volleyball hit the ground?

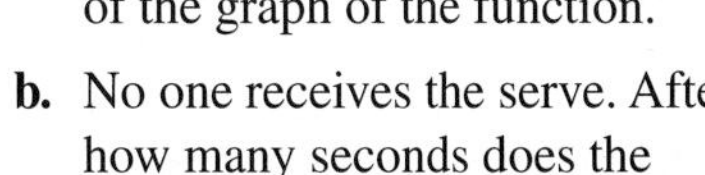

In Exercises 25–32, solve the equation by graphing each side of the equation.

25. $x^2 = 10 - 3x$
26. $2x - 3 = x^2$
27. $5x - 7 = x^2$
28. $x^2 = 6x - 5$
29. $x^2 + 12x = -20$
30. $x^2 + 8x = 9$
31. $-x^2 - 5 = -2x$
32. $-x^2 - 4 = -4x$

In Exercises 33–40, find the zero(s) of f. Round to the nearest tenth, if necessary. ▶ *Example 4*

33.

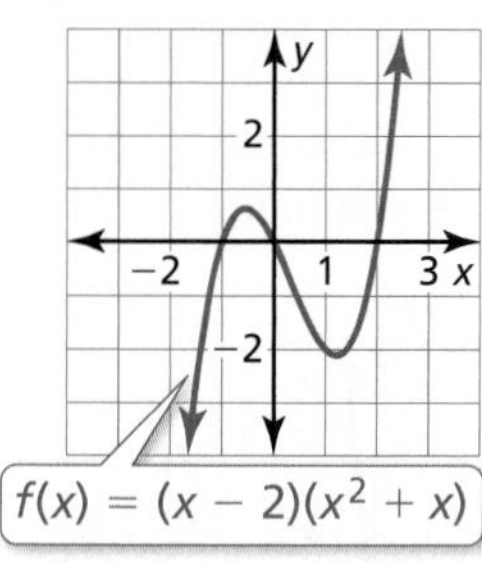

34.

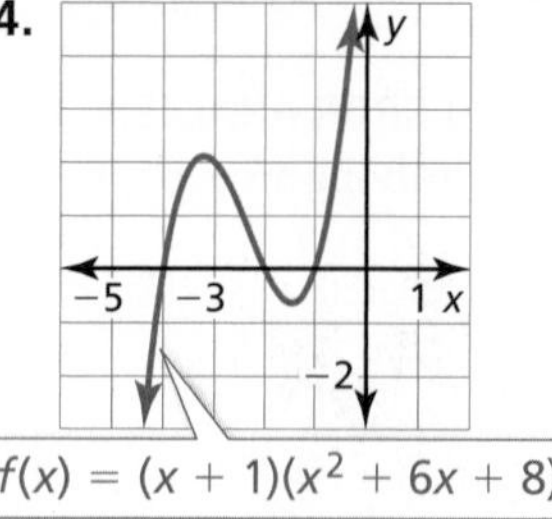

35.

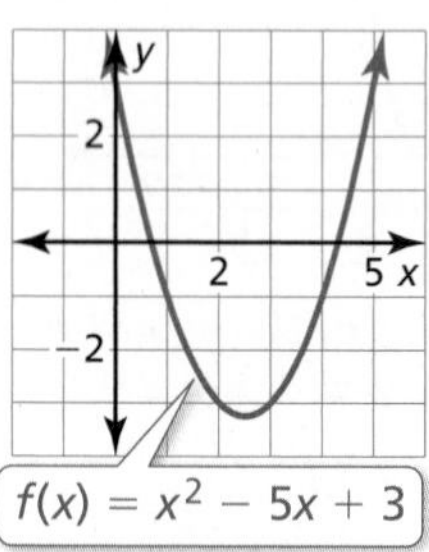

36.

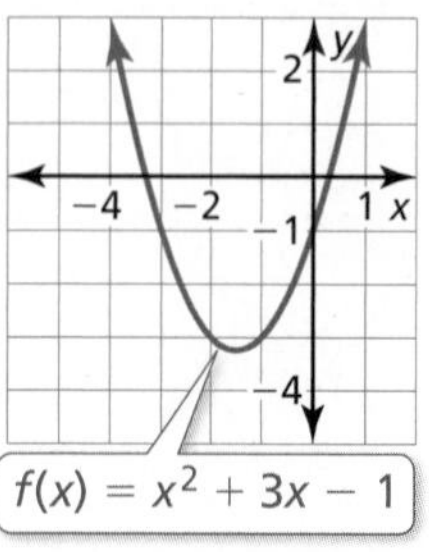

37.

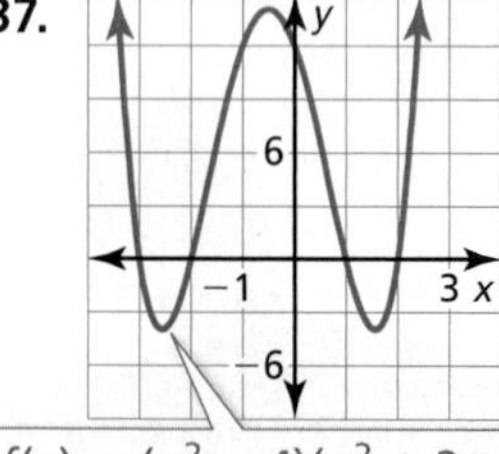

38.

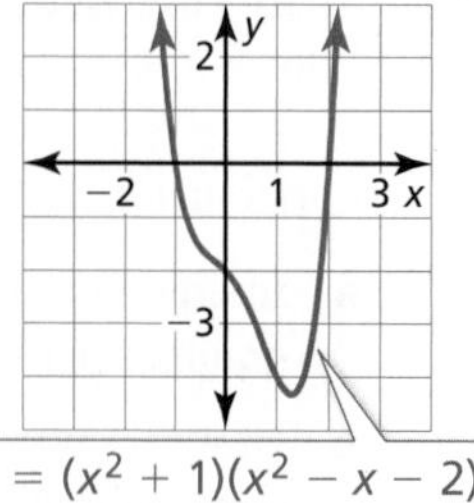

39.

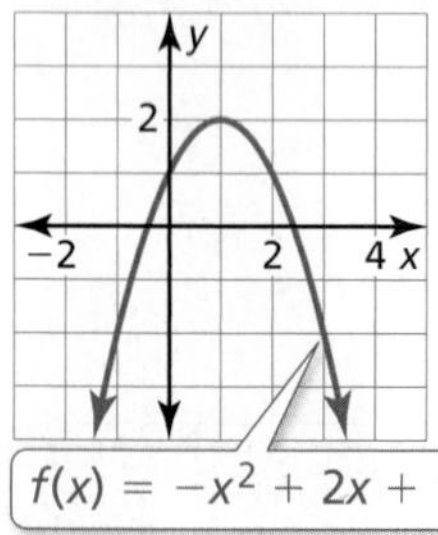

40.

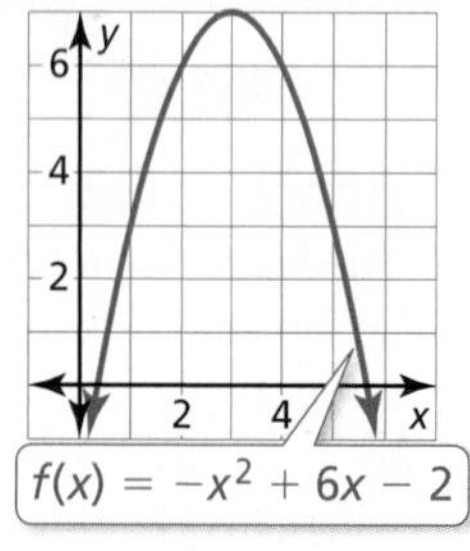

In Exercises 41–46, graph the function. Approximate the zeros of the function to the nearest tenth, if necessary.

41. $f(x) = x^2 + 6x + 1$

42. $f(x) = x^2 - 3x + 2$

43. $y = -x^2 + 4x - 2$

44. $y = -x^2 + 9x - 6$

45. $f(x) = \frac{1}{2}x^2 + 2x - 5$

46. $f(x) = -3x^2 + 4x + 3$

47. WRITING Explain how to approximate zeros of a function when the zeros are not integers.

48. COMPARING METHODS Describe two methods for solving a quadratic equation by graphing. Which method do you prefer? Explain your reasoning.

49. MODELING REAL LIFE At a Civil War demonstration, a cannonball is fired into the air with an initial vertical velocity of 128 feet per second. The release point is 6 feet above the ground. The function $h = -16t^2 + 128t + 6$ represents the height h (in feet) of the cannonball after t seconds. ▶ *Example 5*

a. Find the height of the cannonball each second after it is fired.

b. Estimate when the height of the cannonball is 150 feet.

c. Using a graph, after how many seconds is the cannonball 150 feet above the ground?

50. MODELING REAL LIFE You throw a softball straight up into the air with an initial vertical velocity of 40 feet per second. The release point is 5 feet above the ground. The function $h = -16t^2 + 40t + 5$ represents the height h (in feet) of the softball after t seconds.

a. Find the height of the softball each second after it is released.

b. Estimate when the height of the softball is 15 feet.

c. Using a graph, after how many seconds is the softball 15 feet above the ground?

51. MODELING REAL LIFE The table shows the projected revenues of a company when its product is sold for different prices. ▶ *Example 6*

Selling price (dollars)	Revenue (thousands of dollars)
2.5	5.8
4	21
5.5	32.75
6	36
7.5	43.4
9	47.25

a. Use technology to find a quadratic model for the data. Then determine whether the model is a good fit.

b. What selling price yields a revenue of $45,000?

c. Should the company sell the product for more than $10? Explain.

52. **MODELING REAL LIFE** The table shows the values of a car over time.

Age (years)	0	3	6	9	12
Value (dollars)	18,900	12,275	7972	5178	3363

a. Use technology to find a quadratic model for the data. Then determine whether the model is a good fit.

b. After how many years is the value of the car \$10,000? Round your answer to the nearest tenth.

c. Should you use the quadratic model you found in part (a) to predict the value of the car when it is more than 12 years old? Explain your reasoning.

53. **CONNECTING CONCEPTS** The table shows the numbers of line segments that you can draw whose endpoints are chosen from x points, no three of which are collinear.

Number of points, x	2	3	4	5	6
Number of line segments, y	1	3			

a. Complete the table. Use diagrams to support your answers.

b. Use technology to find a quadratic model for the data. Then determine whether the model is a good fit.

c. Predict the number of line segments that you can draw whose endpoints are chosen from 9 points.

d. Find the number of points when you can draw 66 line segments. Explain how you found your answer.

54. **PERFORMANCE TASK** Record the outside temperature each hour for 8 hours. Organize your results in a table.

a. Find a model for your data. Explain your reasoning.

b. Predict the temperature 2 hours after your last recording. Then compare the actual temperature at that time to your prediction.

c. Research the local hourly temperatures from the previous day and plot the results in a graph. Do the data show a pattern? If so, describe the pattern.

d. Use the results from part (c) to determine whether your model in part (a) is appropriate for a 24-hour period. Explain your reasoning.

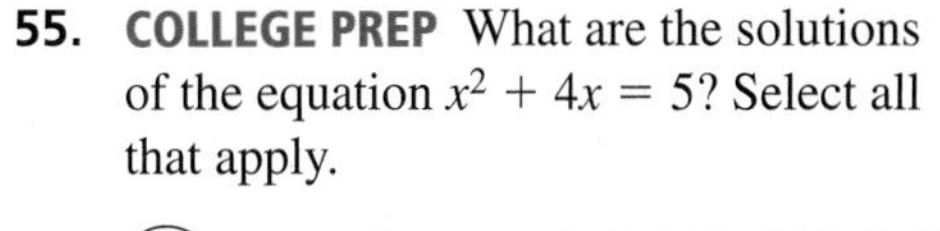

55. **COLLEGE PREP** What are the solutions of the equation $x^2 + 4x = 5$? Select all that apply.

Ⓐ $x = -5$

Ⓑ $x = 0$

Ⓒ $x = 1$

Ⓓ $x = 5$

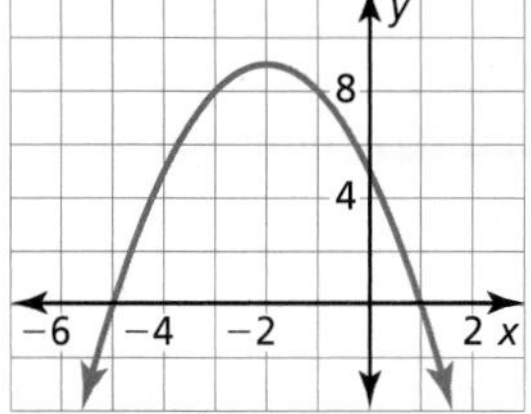

56. **HOW DO YOU SEE IT?**
Consider the graph shown.

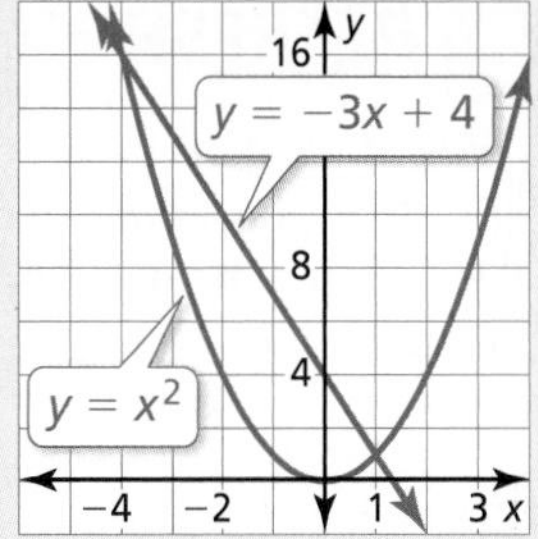

a. How many solutions does the quadratic equation $x^2 = -3x + 4$ have? Explain.

b. Without graphing, describe what you know about the x-intercepts of the graph of $y = x^2 + 3x - 4$.

CONNECTING CONCEPTS In Exercises 57 and 58, use the given surface area S of the cylinder to find the radius r to the nearest tenth.

57. $S = 225\ \text{ft}^2$

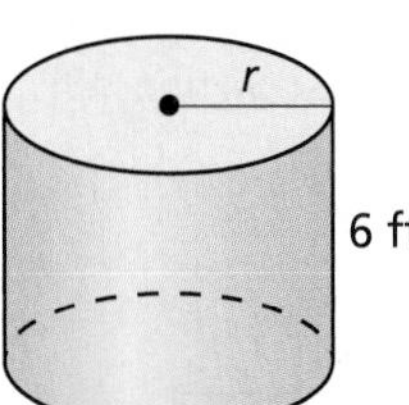

58. $S = 750\ \text{m}^2$

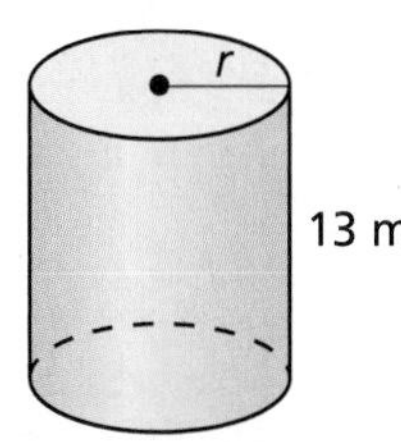

59. **MODELING REAL LIFE** To keep water off a road, the surface of the road is shaped like a parabola. A cross section of the road is shown in the diagram. The surface of the road can be modeled by $y = -0.0017x^2 + 0.041x$, where x and y are measured in feet. Find the width of the road to the nearest tenth of a foot.

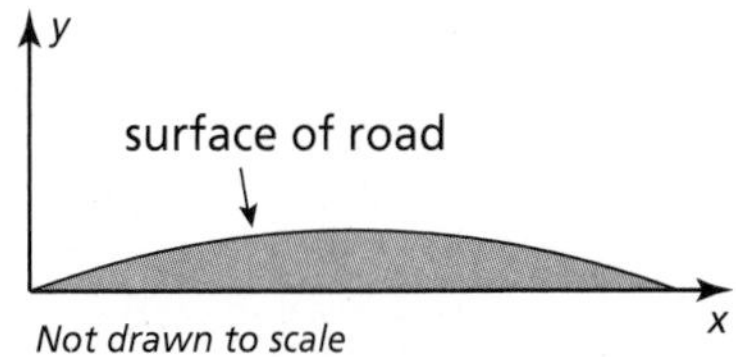

60. THOUGHT PROVOKING
How many different parabolas have -2 and 2 as x-intercepts? Sketch examples of parabolas that have these two x-intercepts.

61. MAKING AN ARGUMENT A stream of water from a fire hose can be modeled by $y = -0.003x^2 + 0.58x + 3$, where x and y are measured in feet. A firefighter standing 57 feet from a building is holding the hose 3 feet above the ground. The bottom of a window of the building is 26 feet above the ground. Will the stream of water pass through the window? Explain.

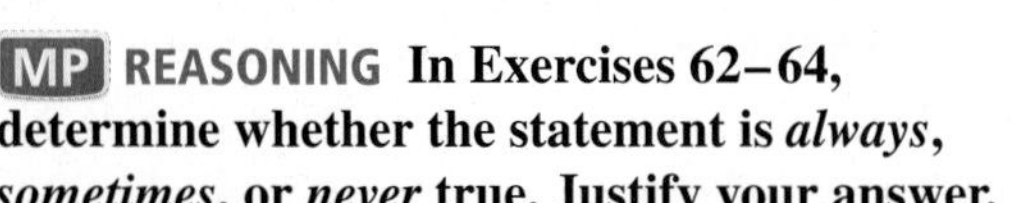

MP REASONING In Exercises 62–64, determine whether the statement is *always*, *sometimes*, or *never* true. Justify your answer.

62. The graph of $y = ax^2 + c$ has two x-intercepts when a is negative.

63. The graph of $y = ax^2 + c$ has no x-intercepts when a and c have the same sign.

64. The graph of $y = ax^2 + bx + c$ has more than two x-intercepts when $a \neq 0$.

REVIEW & REFRESH

In Exercises 65 and 66, determine whether the table represents an *exponential growth function*, an *exponential decay function*, or *neither*. Explain.

65.

x	-1	0	1	2
y	18	3	$\frac{1}{2}$	$\frac{1}{12}$

66.

x	0	1	2	3
y	2	8	32	128

In Exercises 67–69, solve the equation by graphing.

67. $-x^2 - 3x = 3$

68. $x^2 = -12x - 36$

69. $6x = x^2 + 27$

70. The graph represents a cubic function. Write the function in standard form.

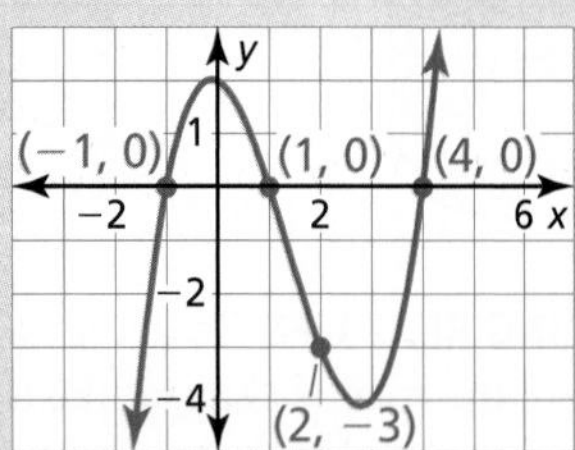

In Exercises 71–74, simplify the expression.

71. $\sqrt{36x^3}$

72. $\sqrt[3]{8x^8}$

73. $-\sqrt{\frac{21}{81}}$

74. $\frac{\sqrt{6}}{\sqrt{5}}$

75. Plot the points $(-1, 8)$, $(0, 4)$, $(1, 2)$, $(2, 1)$, and $\left(3, \frac{1}{2}\right)$ and tell whether they appear to represent a *linear*, an *exponential*, or a *quadratic* function.

76. WRITING Explain how the sum and difference pattern is related to the difference of two squares pattern.

77. Tell whether the ratios 2 : 5 and 4 : 15 form a proportion.

78. Solve the system $2x + 2y = 17$ and $-3x + 4y = -8$ using any method. Explain your choice of method.

79. MODELING REAL LIFE The scatter plot shows the storage capacities x (in gigabytes) and the prices y (in dollars) of 10 tablets.

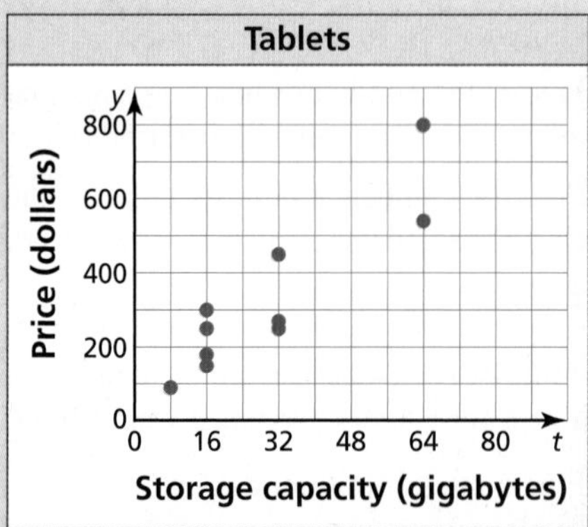

a. What is the price of the tablet with a storage capacity of 8 gigabytes?

b. What is the storage capacity of the \$450 tablet?

c. What tends to happen to the price as the storage capacity increases?

In Exercises 80–83, factor the polynomial completely.

80. $a^2 + 3a - 28$

81. $3b^2 - 14b - 5$

82. $c^2 - 144$

83. $-2x^3 - 3x^2 + 14x$

9.3 Solving Quadratic Equations Using Square Roots

Learning Target Solve quadratic equations using square roots.

Success Criteria
- I can find the square roots of a number.
- I can solve quadratic equations using square roots.
- I can approximate solutions of quadratic equations.

EXPLORE IT! Estimating Solutions of Quadratic Equations

Work with a partner.

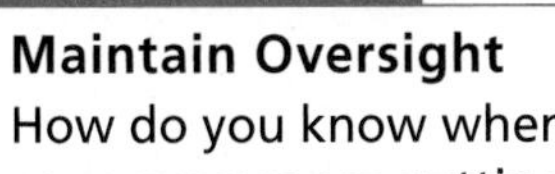

Math Practice

Maintain Oversight
How do you know when your guesses are getting closer to the solution?

a. Use *Guess, Check, and Revise* to estimate the solutions of the equation $x^2 - 5 = 0$ to the nearest hundredth. Organize your results in a spreadsheet.

	A	B
1	x	$x^2 - 5$
2		
3		
4		
5		
6		
7		
8		

b. Are the equations $x^2 - 5 = 0$ and $x^2 = 5$ equivalent? Explain your reasoning.

c. Use the square root key on a calculator to estimate the solutions of $x^2 - 5 = 0$. Compare these estimates to your estimates in part (a).

d. Write the exact solutions of $x^2 - 5 = 0$.

e. Write the exact solutions of each equation. Then use a calculator to estimate the solutions.

i. $x^2 - 2 = 0$

ii. $3x^2 - 18 = 0$

iii. $x^2 = 8$

f. Describe the values of d for which the equation $x^2 = d$ has the given number of solutions. Explain your reasoning.

i. no real solutions

ii. one real solution

iii. two real solutions

Solving Quadratic Equations Using Square Roots

Earlier in this chapter, you studied properties of square roots. Now, you will use square roots to solve quadratic equations of the form $ax^2 + c = 0$. First isolate x^2 on one side of the equation to obtain $x^2 = d$. Then solve by taking the square root of each side.

KEY IDEA

Solutions of $x^2 = d$

- When $d > 0$, $x^2 = d$ has two real solutions, $x = \pm\sqrt{d}$.
- When $d = 0$, $x^2 = d$ has one real solution, $x = 0$.
- When $d < 0$, $x^2 = d$ has no real solutions.

EXAMPLE 1 Solving Quadratic Equations Using Square Roots

a. Solve $3x^2 - 27 = 0$ using square roots.

$3x^2 - 27 = 0$	Write the equation.
$3x^2 = 27$	Add 27 to each side.
$x^2 = 9$	Divide each side by 3.
$x = \pm\sqrt{9}$	Take the square root of each side.
$x = \pm 3$	Simplify.

▶ The solutions are $x = 3$ and $x = -3$.

ANOTHER WAY

You can also solve $3x^2 - 27 = 0$ by factoring.

$$3(x^2 - 9) = 0$$
$$3(x - 3)(x + 3) = 0$$
$$x = 3 \text{ or } x = -3$$

b. Solve $x^2 - 10 = -10$ using square roots.

$x^2 - 10 = -10$	Write the equation.
$x^2 = 0$	Add 10 to each side.
$x = 0$	Take the square root of each side.

▶ The only solution is $x = 0$.

c. Solve $-5x^2 + 11 = 16$ using square roots.

$-5x^2 + 11 = 16$	Write the equation.
$-5x^2 = 5$	Subtract 11 from each side.
$x^2 = -1$	Divide each side by -5.

▶ The square of a real number cannot be negative. So, the equation has no real solutions.

SELF-ASSESSMENT

1 I do not understand. 2 I can do it with help. 3 I can do it on my own. 4 I can teach someone else.

Solve the equation using square roots.

1. $-3x^2 = -75$

2. $x^2 + 12 = 10$

3. $4x^2 - 15 = -15$

4. DIFFERENT WORDS, SAME QUESTION Which is different? Find "both" answers.

Solve $x^2 = 144$ using square roots.	Solve $x^2 - 144 = 0$ using square roots.	Solve $x^2 + 146 = 2$ using square roots.	Solve $x^2 + 2 = 146$ using square roots.

EXAMPLE 2 Solving a Quadratic Equation Using Square Roots

STUDY TIP

Each side of the equation $(x - 1)^2 = 25$ is a square. So, you can still solve by taking the square root of each side.

Solve $(x - 1)^2 = 25$ using square roots.

SOLUTION

$(x - 1)^2 = 25$	Write the equation.
$x - 1 = \pm 5$	Take the square root of each side.
$x = 1 \pm 5$	Add 1 to each side.

▶ The solutions are $x = 1 + 5 = 6$ and $x = 1 - 5 = -4$.

Check

Use technology to check your answer. Rewrite the equation as $(x - 1)^2 - 25 = 0$. Graph the related function $f(x) = (x - 1)^2 - 25$ and find the zeros of the function. The zeros are -4 and 6.

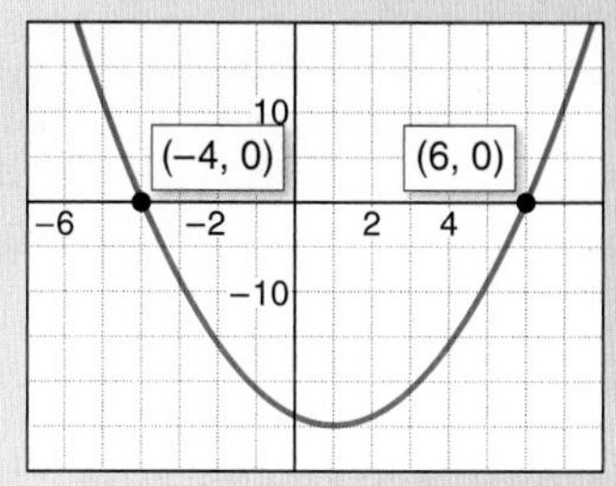

Approximating Solutions of Quadratic Equations

EXAMPLE 3 Approximating Solutions of a Quadratic Equation

Solve $4x^2 - 13 = 15$ using square roots. Round the solutions to the nearest hundredth.

SOLUTION

$4x^2 - 13 = 15$	Write the equation.
$4x^2 = 28$	Add 13 to each side.
$x^2 = 7$	Divide each side by 4.
$x = \pm\sqrt{7}$	Take the square root of each side.
$x \approx \pm 2.65$	Use technology.

▶ The solutions are $x \approx -2.65$ and $x \approx 2.65$.

Check

Graph each side of the equation and find the points of intersection. The x-values of the points of intersection are about -2.65 and 2.65.

SELF-ASSESSMENT

1 I do not understand. 2 I can do it with help. 3 I can do it on my own. 4 I can teach someone else.

Solve the equation using square roots.

5. $(x + 7)^2 = 0$ **6.** $4(x - 3)^2 = 9$ **7.** $(2x + 1)^2 = 36$

Solve the equation using square roots. Round your solutions to the nearest hundredth.

8. $x^2 + 8 = 19$ **9.** $5x^2 - 2 = 0$ **10.** $3x^2 - 30 = 4$

11. WRITING Given the equation $ax^2 + c = 0$, describe the values of a and c so the equation has the following number of solutions.

a. two real solutions **b.** one real solution **c.** no real solutions

EXAMPLE 4 Modeling Real Life

A touch tank in the shape of a rectangular prism has a height of 3 feet. Its length is three times its width. The volume of the tank is 270 cubic feet. Find the length and width of the tank.

SOLUTION

The length ℓ is three times the width w, so $\ell = 3w$. Write an equation using the formula for the volume of a rectangular prism.

$V = \ell wh$ — Write the formula.

$270 = 3w(w)(3)$ — Substitute 270 for V, $3w$ for ℓ, and 3 for h.

$270 = 9w^2$ — Multiply.

$30 = w^2$ — Divide each side by 9.

$\pm\sqrt{30} = w$ — Take the square root of each side.

The solutions are $\sqrt{30}$ and $-\sqrt{30}$. Use the positive solution.

▶ So, the width is $\sqrt{30} \approx 5.5$ feet and the length is $3\sqrt{30} \approx 16.4$ feet.

Math Practice

Interpret Results
Why should you only use the positive square root in this situation?

EXAMPLE 5 Rewriting and Evaluating a Formula

The area A of an equilateral triangle with side length s is given by the formula $A = \frac{\sqrt{3}}{4}s^2$. Solve the formula for s. Then approximate the side length of the traffic sign that has an area of 390 square inches.

s
YIELD
s
s

ANOTHER WAY

Notice that you can rewrite the formula as $s = \frac{2}{3^{1/4}}\sqrt{A}$, or $s \approx 1.52\sqrt{A}$. This can help you efficiently find the value of s for several values of A.

SOLUTION

Step 1 Solve the formula for s.

$A = \frac{\sqrt{3}}{4}s^2$ — Write the formula.

$\frac{4A}{\sqrt{3}} = s^2$ — Multiply each side by $\frac{4}{\sqrt{3}}$.

$\sqrt{\frac{4A}{\sqrt{3}}} = s$ — Take the positive square root of each side.

Step 2 Substitute 390 for A in the new formula and evaluate.

$s = \sqrt{\frac{4A}{\sqrt{3}}} = \sqrt{\frac{4(390)}{\sqrt{3}}} = \sqrt{\frac{1560}{\sqrt{3}}} \approx 30$ — Use technology.

▶ The side length of the traffic sign is about 30 inches.

SELF-ASSESSMENT

1 I do not understand. 2 I can do it with help. 3 I can do it on my own. 4 I can teach someone else.

12. WHAT IF? In Example 4, the volume of the tank is 315 cubic feet. Find the length and width of the tank.

13. The surface area S of a sphere with radius r is given by the formula $S = 4\pi r^2$. Solve the formula for r. Then find the radius of a globe with a surface area of 804 square inches.

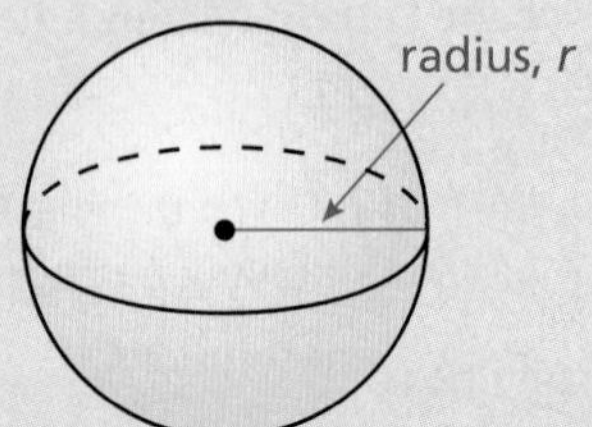

9.3 Practice WITH CalcChat® AND CalcView®

GO DIGITAL

In Exercises 1–4, determine the number of real solutions of the equation. Then solve the equation using square roots.

1. $x^2 = 25$
2. $x^2 = -36$
3. $x^2 = 0$
4. $x^2 = 169$

In Exercises 5–14, solve the equation using square roots. *Example 1*

5. $x^2 - 16 = 0$
6. $x^2 + 6 = 0$
7. $3x^2 + 12 = 0$
8. $x^2 - 55 = 26$
9. $2x^2 - 98 = 0$
10. $-x^2 + 9 = 9$
11. $-3x^2 - 5 = -5$
12. $4x^2 - 371 = 29$
13. $4x^2 + 10 = 11$
14. $9x^2 - 35 = 14$

In Exercises 15–20, solve the equation using square roots. *Example 2*

15. $(x + 3)^2 = 0$
16. $(x - 1)^2 = 4$
17. $(2x - 1)^2 = 81$
18. $(4x + 5)^2 = 9$
19. $9(x + 1)^2 = 16$
20. $4(x - 2)^2 = 25$

In Exercises 21–26, solve the equation using square roots. Round your solutions to the nearest hundredth. *Example 3*

21. $x^2 + 6 = 13$
22. $x^2 + 11 = 24$
23. $2x^2 - 9 = 11$
24. $5x^2 + 2 = 6$
25. $-21 = 15 - 2x^2$
26. $2 = 4x^2 - 5$

27. **ERROR ANALYSIS** Describe and correct the error in solving the equation $2x^2 - 33 = 39$ using square roots.

$$2x^2 - 33 = 39$$
$$2x^2 = 72$$
$$x^2 = 36$$
$$x = 6$$

The solution is $x = 6$.

28. **MAKING AN ARGUMENT** Your friend says that the solutions of the equation $x^2 + 4 = 0$ are $x = 2$ and $x = -2$. Is your friend correct? Explain.

29. **MODELING REAL LIFE** A person sitting in the top row of the bleachers at a sporting event drops a pair of sunglasses from a height of 24 feet. The function $h = -16x^2 + 24$ represents the height h (in feet) of the sunglasses after x seconds. How long does it take the sunglasses to hit the ground?

30. **WRITING** How can you approximate the roots of a quadratic equation when the roots are not integers?

31. **MODELING REAL LIFE** An in-ground pond has the shape of a rectangular prism. The pond has a depth of 24 inches and a volume of 72,000 cubic inches. The length of the pond is two times its width. Find the length and width of the pond. *Example 4*

32. **MODELING REAL LIFE** A square rug is shown. The area of the inner square is 25% of the total area of the rug. Find the side length x of the inner square.

6 ft

33. **CONNECTING CONCEPTS** The area A of a circle with radius r is given by the formula $A = \pi r^2$. *Example 5*

a. Solve the formula for r.

b. Use the formula from part (a) to find the radius of each circle.

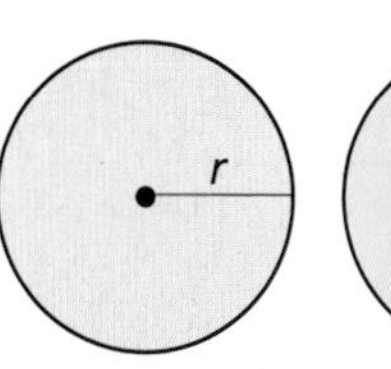

$A = 113\text{ ft}^2$

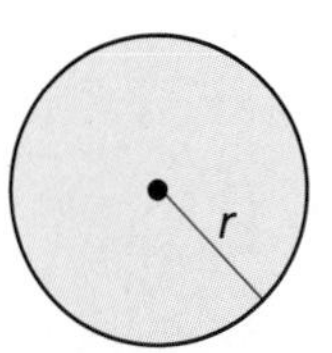

$A = 1810\text{ in.}^2$

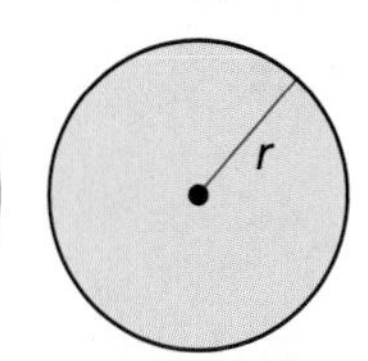

$A = 531\text{ m}^2$

c. Explain why it is beneficial to solve the formula for r before finding the radius.

34. **MODELING REAL LIFE** The kinetic energy (in joules) of an object in motion is given by the formula $KE = \frac{1}{2}mv^2$, where m is the mass (in kilograms) of the object and v is the velocity (in meters per second). Solve the formula for v. Then approximate the velocity of a 1200-kilogram car that has 360,000 joules of kinetic energy.

35. **MP REASONING** Without graphing, where do the graphs of $y = x^2$ and $y = 9$ intersect? Explain.

36. **HOW DO YOU SEE IT?** The graph represents the function $f(x) = (x - 1)^2$. How many solutions does the equation $(x - 1)^2 = 0$ have? Explain.

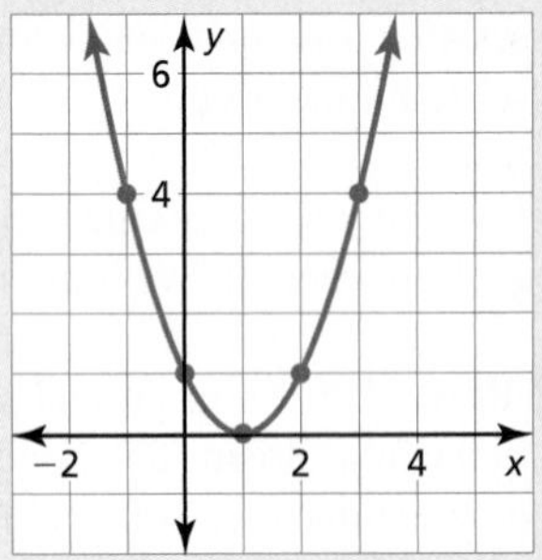

37. **MP REASONING** Solve $x^2 = 1.44$ without using technology. Explain your reasoning.

38. **THOUGHT PROVOKING** The quadratic equation

$$ax^2 + bx + c = 0$$

can be rewritten in the following form.

$$\left(x + \frac{b}{2a}\right)^2 = \frac{b^2 - 4ac}{4a^2}$$

Use this form to write the solutions of the equation.

39. **MP REASONING** An equation of the graph shown is $y = \frac{1}{2}(x - 2)^2 + 1$. Two points on the parabola have y-coordinates of 9. Find the x-coordinates of these points.

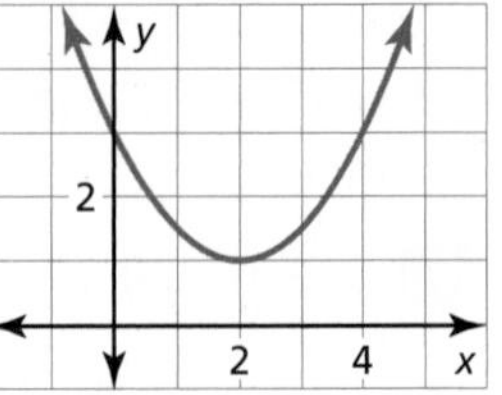

40. **CRITICAL THINKING** Solve each equation without graphing.

a. $x^2 - 12x + 36 = 64$ **b.** $x^2 + 14x + 49 = 16$

REVIEW & REFRESH

WATCH

In Exercises 41–44, factor the polynomial.

41. $x^2 + 18x + 81$

42. $x^2 - 22x + 121$

43. $x^2 + 2x - 8$

44. $2x^2 - 9x - 35$

45. Write the sentence as an inequality. Graph the inequality.

A number q is less than 10.5 and greater than 2.

In Exercises 46–49, solve the equation using square roots.

46. $x^2 = -21$

47. $x^2 = 400$

48. $3x^2 + 8 = 8$

49. $(2x - 3)^2 = 225$

50. Determine whether $y = \sqrt{5} + 2x$ represents a *linear* or *nonlinear* function. Explain.

51. Use the graph to solve $-x^2 - 4x - 6 = 0$.

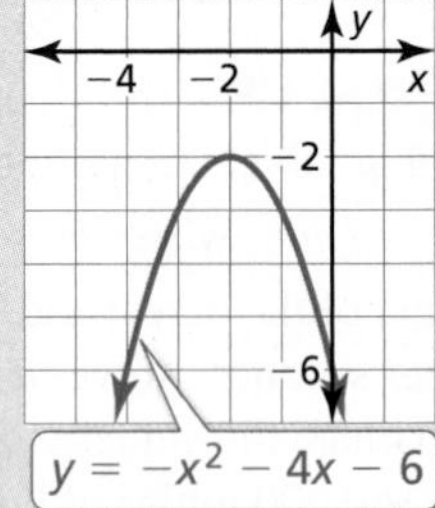

In Exercises 52–55, simplify the expression.

52. $5\sqrt[3]{4x} - 12\sqrt[3]{4x}$

53. $(3\sqrt{6} - 8)^2$

54. $\dfrac{8}{\sqrt{10x}}$

55. $\dfrac{7}{\sqrt{5} - 2}$

56. Tell whether the data represent a *linear*, an *exponential*, or a *quadratic* function. Then write the function.

x	−2	0	2	4	6
y	0	−16	−16	0	32

57. **MODELING REAL LIFE** You deposit \$500 in a savings account that earns 4% annual interest compounded quarterly. Write a function that represents the balance y (in dollars) after t years.

58. Graph the system. Identify a solution.

$$y - 3 > 2x$$
$$x \geq -1$$

In Exercises 59–62, solve the equation.

59. $-84 = 7t$

60. $3c + 15 = 120$

61. $9g - 2 = 12g + 7$

62. $|4b - 9| + 11 = 5$

63. What number is 30% of 50?

9.4 Solving Quadratic Equations by Completing the Square

Learning Target Solve quadratic equations and find maximum and minimum values of quadratic functions by completing the square.

Success Criteria

- I can complete the square for an expression of the form $x^2 + bx$.
- I can solve quadratic equations by solving the square.
- I can find maximum and minimum values of quadratic functions by completing the square.

EXPLORE IT! Solving by Completing the Square

Work with a partner.

a. Write the equation modeled by the algebra tiles.

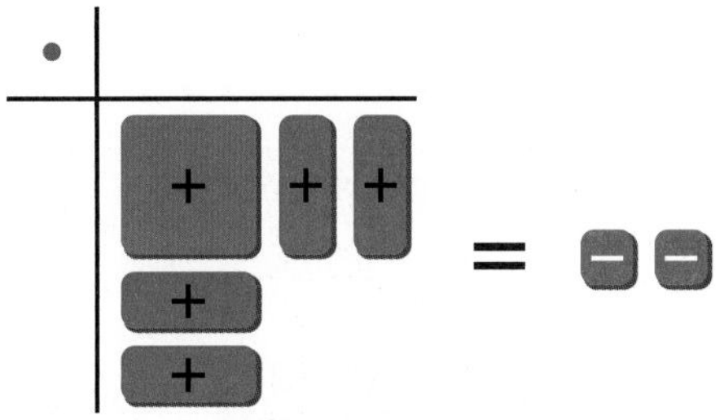

b. Notice that if the algebra tiles for the left side of the equation formed a square, you could solve the equation by taking the square root of each side. How can you make the left side a square? Explain your reasoning.

c. Use algebra tiles and your reasoning in part (b) to solve the equation. Explain your method.

d. Write the equation modeled by the algebra tiles. Use algebra tiles to "complete the square." Solve the equation.

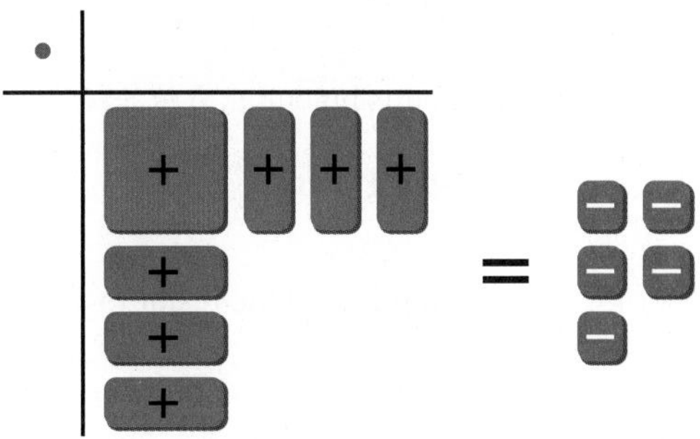

Math Practice

Find General Methods
How does the constant you add to complete the square relate to the coefficient of the x-term of the equation?

e. How can you use "completing the square" to solve a quadratic equation?

f. Solve each quadratic equation by completing the square.

i. $x^2 - 2x = 1$ **ii.** $x^2 - 4x = -1$ **iii.** $x^2 + 4x = -3$

GO DIGITAL

Vocabulary

completing the square, p. 510

Completing the Square

For an expression of the form $x^2 + bx$, you can add a constant c to the expression so that $x^2 + bx + c$ is a perfect square trinomial. This process is called **completing the square**.

KEY IDEA

Completing the Square

Words To complete the square for the expression $x^2 + bx$, add $\left(\frac{b}{2}\right)^2$.

Diagrams In each diagram, the combined area of the shaded regions is $x^2 + bx$. Adding $\left(\frac{b}{2}\right)^2$ completes the square in the second diagram.

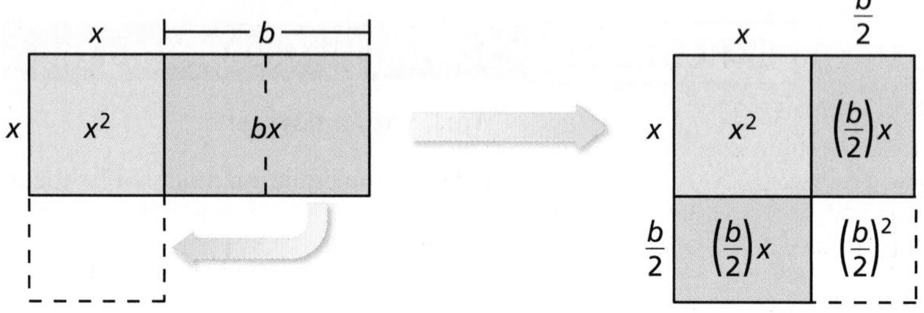

Algebra $x^2 + bx + \left(\frac{b}{2}\right)^2 = \left(x + \frac{b}{2}\right)\left(x + \frac{b}{2}\right) = \left(x + \frac{b}{2}\right)^2$

EXAMPLE 1 Completing the Square

Complete the square for (a) $x^2 + 6x$ and (b) $x^2 - 9x$. Then factor the trinomial.

SOLUTION

a. In this binomial, $b = 6$.

Step 1 Find $\left(\frac{b}{2}\right)^2$. $\quad \left(\frac{b}{2}\right)^2 = \left(\frac{6}{2}\right)^2 = 3^2 = 9$

Step 2 Add the result to $x^2 + bx$. $\quad x^2 + 6x + 9$

▶ $x^2 + 6x + 9 = (x + 3)(x + 3) = (x + 3)^2$

b. In this binomial, $b = -9$.

Step 1 Find $\left(\frac{b}{2}\right)^2$. $\quad \left(\frac{b}{2}\right)^2 = \left(\frac{-9}{2}\right)^2 = \frac{81}{4}$

Step 2 Add the result to $x^2 + bx$. $\quad x^2 - 9x + \frac{81}{4}$

▶ $x^2 - 9x + \frac{81}{4} = \left(x - \frac{9}{2}\right)\left(x - \frac{9}{2}\right) = \left(x - \frac{9}{2}\right)^2$

SELF-ASSESSMENT

1 I do not understand. 2 I can do it with help. 3 I can do it on my own. 4 I can teach someone else.

1. **VOCABULARY** Explain how to complete the square for an expression of the form $x^2 + bx$.

Complete the square for the expression. Then factor the trinomial.

2. $x^2 + 10x$
3. $x^2 - 4x$
4. $x^2 + 7x$

GO DIGITAL

Solving Quadratic Equations by Completing the Square

Completing the square can be used to solve any quadratic equation. To solve a quadratic equation by completing the square, you must write the equation in the form $x^2 + bx = d$.

EXAMPLE 2 Solving a Quadratic Equation: $x^2 + bx = d$

Solve $x^2 - 16x = -15$ by completing the square.

SOLUTION

$x^2 - 16x = -15$	Write the equation.
$x^2 - 16x + (-8)^2 = -15 + (-8)^2$	Complete the square by adding $\left(\frac{-16}{2}\right)^2$, or $(-8)^2$, to each side.
$(x - 8)^2 = 49$	Write the left side as the square of a binomial.
$x - 8 = \pm 7$	Take the square root of each side.
$x = 8 \pm 7$	Add 8 to each side.

▶ The solutions are $x = 8 + 7 = 15$ and $x = 8 - 7 = 1$.

COMMON ERROR

When completing the square to solve an equation, be sure to add $\left(\frac{b}{2}\right)^2$ to each side of the equation.

Check

$x^2 - 16x = -15$	Original equation	$x^2 - 16x = -15$
$15^2 - 16(15) \stackrel{?}{=} -15$	Substitute.	$1^2 - 16(1) \stackrel{?}{=} -15$
$-15 = -15$ ✓	Simplify.	$-15 = -15$ ✓

EXAMPLE 3 Solving a Quadratic Equation: $ax^2 + bx + c = 0$

Solve $2x^2 + 20x - 8 = 0$ by completing the square.

SOLUTION

$2x^2 + 20x - 8 = 0$	Write the equation.
$2x^2 + 20x = 8$	Add 8 to each side.
$x^2 + 10x = 4$	Divide each side by 2.
$x^2 + 10x + 5^2 = 4 + 5^2$	Complete the square by adding $\left(\frac{10}{2}\right)^2$, or 5^2, to each side.
$(x + 5)^2 = 29$	Write the left side as the square of a binomial.
$x + 5 = \pm\sqrt{29}$	Take the square root of each side.
$x = -5 \pm \sqrt{29}$	Subtract 5 from each side.

▶ The solutions are $x = -5 + \sqrt{29}$ and $x = -5 - \sqrt{29}$.

COMMON ERROR

Before you complete the square, be sure that the coefficient of the x^2-term is 1.

SELF-ASSESSMENT 1 I do not understand. 2 I can do it with help. 3 I can do it on my own. 4 I can teach someone else.

Solve the equation by completing the square.

5. $x^2 - 2x = 3$

6. $m^2 + 12m = -8$

7. $3g^2 - 24g + 27 = 0$

Finding and Using Maximum and Minimum Values

One way to find the maximum or minimum value of a quadratic function is to write the function in vertex form by completing the square. Recall that the vertex form of a quadratic function is $y = a(x - h)^2 + k$, where $a \neq 0$. The vertex of the graph is (h, k).

EXAMPLE 4 Finding Maximum and Minimum Values

Determine whether each quadratic function has a *maximum* or *minimum* value. Then find the value.

a. $y = x^2 + 4x - 1$

b. $y = -x^2 + 2x + 7$

SOLUTION

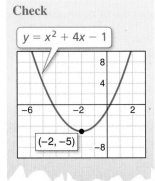

a. Because a is positive ($a = 1$), the parabola opens up and the y-coordinate of the vertex is the minimum value. Write the function in vertex form.

$y = x^2 + 4x - 1$	Write the function.
$y + 1 = x^2 + 4x$	Add 1 to each side.
$y + 1 + 4 = x^2 + 4x + 4$	Complete the square for $x^2 + 4x$.
$y + 5 = x^2 + 4x + 4$	Simplify the left side.
$y + 5 = (x + 2)^2$	Write the right side as the square of a binomial.
$y = (x + 2)^2 - 5$	Write in vertex form.

The vertex is $(-2, -5)$.

▶ So, the function has a minimum value of -5.

Check

$y = x^2 + 4x - 1$

(graph: vertex $(-2, -5)$; axes labeled -6, -2, 2, 8, 4, -8)

b. Because a is negative ($a = -1$), the parabola opens down and the y-coordinate of the vertex is the maximum value. Write the function in vertex form.

$y = -x^2 + 2x + 7$	Write the function.
$y - 7 = -x^2 + 2x$	Subtract 7 from each side.
$y - 7 = -(x^2 - 2x)$	Factor out -1.
$y - 7 - 1 = -(x^2 - 2x + 1)$	Complete the square for $x^2 - 2x$.
$y - 8 = -(x^2 - 2x + 1)$	Simplify the left side.
$y - 8 = -(x - 1)^2$	Write $x^2 - 2x + 1$ as the square of a binomial.
$y = -(x - 1)^2 + 8$	Write in vertex form.

The vertex is $(1, 8)$.

▶ So, the function has a maximum value of 8.

STUDY TIP

Adding 1 inside the parentheses results in subtracting 1 from the right side of the equation.

SELF-ASSESSMENT 1 I do not understand. 2 I can do it with help. 3 I can do it on my own. 4 I can teach someone else.

8. WRITING Describe how you can use completing the square to find the maximum or minimum value of a quadratic function.

Determine whether the quadratic function has a *maximum* or *minimum* value. Then find the value.

9. $y = -x^2 - 4x + 4$

10. $y = x^2 + 12x + 40$

11. $y = x^2 - 2x - 2$

GO DIGITAL

EXAMPLE 5 Interpreting Forms of Quadratic Functions

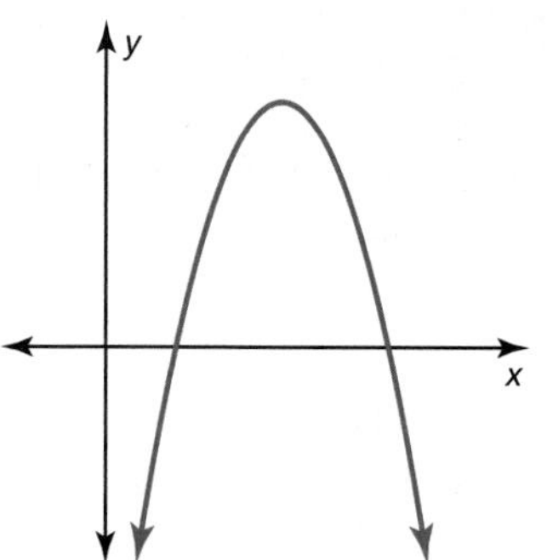

$f(x) = -\frac{1}{2}(x+4)^2 + 8$

$g(x) = -(x-5)^2 + 9$

$m(x) = (x-3)(x-12)$

$p(x) = -(x-2)(x-8)$

Which of the functions could be represented by the graph? Explain.

SOLUTION

To eliminate functions, consider the characteristics of the graph and the information provided by the form of each function. The graph appears to be a parabola that opens down, which means the function has a maximum value. The vertex of the graph is in the first quadrant. Both x-intercepts are positive.

- The graph of f opens down because $a < 0$, which means f has a maximum value. However, the vertex $(-4, 8)$ of the graph of f is in the second quadrant. So, the graph does not represent f.
- The graph of g opens down because $a < 0$, which means g has a maximum value. The vertex $(5, 9)$ of the graph of g is in the first quadrant. By solving $0 = -(x-5)^2 + 9$, you see that the x-intercepts of the graph of g are 2 and 8. So, the graph could represent g.
- The graph of m has two positive x-intercepts. However, its graph opens up because $a > 0$, which means m has a minimum value. So, the graph does not represent m.
- The graph of p has two positive x-intercepts, and its graph opens down because $a < 0$. This means that p has a maximum value and the vertex must be in the first quadrant. So, the graph could represent p.

▶ The graph could represent function g or function p.

EXAMPLE 6 Modeling Real Life

The function $y = -16x^2 + 96x$ represents the height y (in feet) of a model rocket x seconds after it is launched. (a) Find the maximum height of the rocket. (b) Find and interpret the axis of symmetry.

SOLUTION

a. To find the maximum height, identify the maximum value of the function.

$$y = -16x^2 + 96x \quad \text{Write the function.}$$
$$y = -16(x^2 - 6x) \quad \text{Factor out } -16.$$
$$y - 144 = -16(x^2 - 6x + 9) \quad \text{Complete the square for } x^2 - 6x.$$
$$y = -16(x-3)^2 + 144 \quad \text{Write in vertex form.}$$

Because the vertex is $(3, 144)$, the maximum value is 144.

▶ So, the model rocket reaches a maximum height of 144 feet.

b. The vertex is $(3, 144)$. So, the axis of symmetry is $x = 3$. On the left side of $x = 3$, the height increases as time increases. On the right side of $x = 3$, the height decreases as time increases.

STUDY TIP

Adding 9 inside the parentheses results in subtracting 144 from the right side of the equation.

SELF-ASSESSMENT

1 I do not understand. 2 I can do it with help. 3 I can do it on my own. 4 I can teach someone else.

Determine whether the function could be represented by the graph in Example 5. Explain.

12. $h(x) = (x-8)^2 + 10$

13. $n(x) = -2(x-5)(x-20)$

14. WHAT IF? Repeat Example 6 when the function is $y = -16x^2 + 128x$.

Solving Real-Life Problems

EXAMPLE 7 Modeling Real Life

3 ft
width of border, x ft
7 ft
chalkboard

You use chalkboard paint to create a chalkboard on a door. The area of the chalkboard is 6 square feet and has a uniform border, as shown. Find the width of the border to the nearest inch.

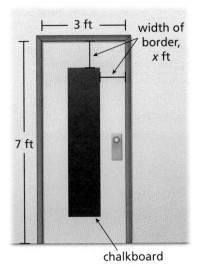

SOLUTION

1. **Understand the Problem** You know the dimensions of the door. You also know the area of the chalkboard and that it has a uniform border. You are asked to find the width of the border.
2. **Make a Plan** Use a verbal model to write an equation that represents the area of the chalkboard in terms of x. Then solve the equation and state the width in inches.
3. **Solve and Check** Let x be the width (in feet) of the border, as shown in the diagram.

Area of chalkboard (square feet)	=	Length of chalkboard (feet)	•	Width of chalkboard (feet)
6	=	$(7 - 2x)$	•	$(3 - 2x)$

$6 = (7 - 2x)(3 - 2x)$ Write the equation.

$6 = 21 - 20x + 4x^2$ Multiply the binomials.

$-15 = 4x^2 - 20x$ Subtract 21 from each side.

$-\frac{15}{4} = x^2 - 5x$ Divide each side by 4.

$-\frac{15}{4} + \frac{25}{4} = x^2 - 5x + \frac{25}{4}$ Complete the square for $x^2 - 5x$.

$\frac{5}{2} = x^2 - 5x + \frac{25}{4}$ Simplify the left side.

$\frac{5}{2} = \left(x - \frac{5}{2}\right)^2$ Write the right side as the square of a binomial.

$\pm\sqrt{\frac{5}{2}} = x - \frac{5}{2}$ Take the square root of each side.

$\frac{5}{2} \pm \sqrt{\frac{5}{2}} = x$ Add $\frac{5}{2}$ to each side.

The solutions of the equation are $x = \frac{5}{2} + \sqrt{\frac{5}{2}} \approx 4.08$ and $x = \frac{5}{2} - \sqrt{\frac{5}{2}} \approx 0.92$.

It is not possible for the width of the border to be 4.08 feet because the width of the door is 3 feet. So, the width of the border is about 0.92 foot.

$0.92 \text{ ft} \cdot \frac{12 \text{ in.}}{1 \text{ ft}} = 11.04 \text{ in.}$ Convert 0.92 foot to inches.

▶ The width of the border should be about 11 inches.

Check Reasonableness

When the width of the border is slightly less than 1 foot, the length of the chalkboard is slightly more than 5 feet and the width of the chalkboard is slightly more than 1 foot. Multiplying these dimensions gives an area close to 6 square feet. So, an 11-inch border is reasonable.

SELF-ASSESSMENT

1 I do not understand. 2 I can do it with help. 3 I can do it on my own. 4 I can teach someone else.

15. **WHAT IF?** The area of the chalkboard is 4 square feet. Find the width of the border to the nearest inch.

16. You have 80 feet of fencing to make a rectangular horse pasture that covers 750 square feet. A barn will be used as one side of the pasture, as shown. Write equations for the amount of fencing to be used and the area enclosed by the fencing. What are the possible dimensions of the pasture? Explain.

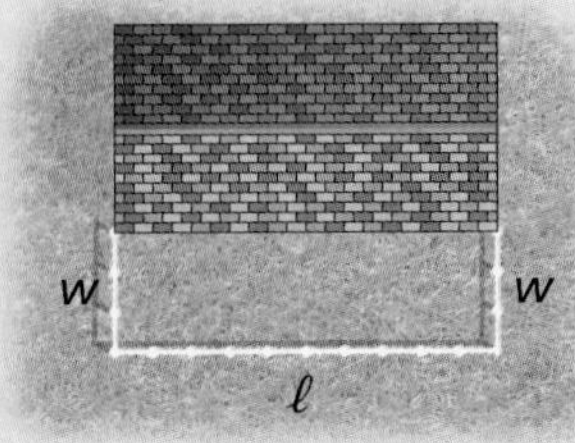

9.4 Practice WITH CalcChat® AND CalcView®

In Exercises 1–4, find the value of c that completes the square.

1. $x^2 - 8x + c$
2. $x^2 - 2x + c$
3. $x^2 + 12x + c$
4. $x^2 + 9x + c$

In Exercises 5–10, complete the square for the expression. Then factor the trinomial. *Example 1*

5. $x^2 - 10x$
6. $x^2 - 40x$
7. $x^2 + 16x$
8. $x^2 + 22x$
9. $x^2 + 5x$
10. $x^2 - 3x$

In Exercises 11–16, solve the equation by completing the square. *Example 2*

11. $x^2 + 14x = 15$
12. $x^2 - 6x = 16$
13. $x^2 - 4x = -2$
14. $x^2 + 2x = 5$
15. $x^2 - 5x = 8$
16. $x^2 + 11x = -10$

17. **MODELING REAL LIFE** The area of the patio is 216 square feet.

   a. Write an equation that represents the area of the patio.

   b. Find the dimensions of the patio by completing the square.

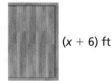

$(x + 6)$ ft

x ft

18. **MODELING REAL LIFE** Some sand art contains sand and water sealed in a glass case, similar to the one shown. When the art is turned upside down, the sand and water fall to create a new picture. The glass case has a depth of 1 centimeter and a volume of 768 cubic centimeters.

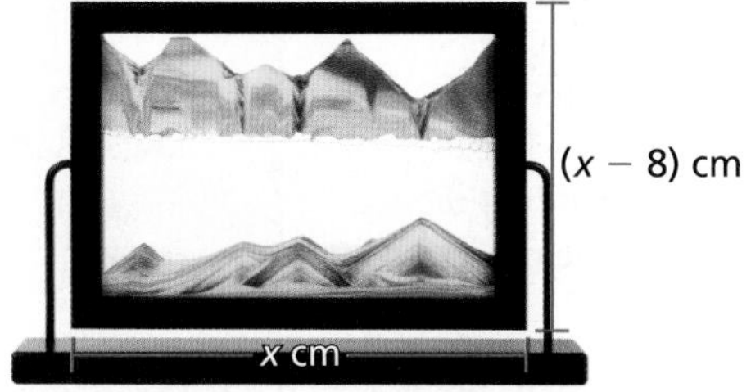

   a. Write an equation that represents the volume of the glass case.

   b. Find the dimensions of the glass case by completing the square.

In Exercises 19–24, solve the equation by completing the square. *Example 3*

19. $x^2 - 8x + 15 = 0$
20. $x^2 + 4x - 21 = 0$
21. $2x^2 + 20x + 44 = 0$
22. $3x^2 - 18x + 12 = 0$
23. $2x^2 - 14x + 10 = 26$
24. $4x^2 + 12x - 15 = 5$

25. **ERROR ANALYSIS** Describe and correct the error in solving $x^2 + 8x = 10$ by completing the square.

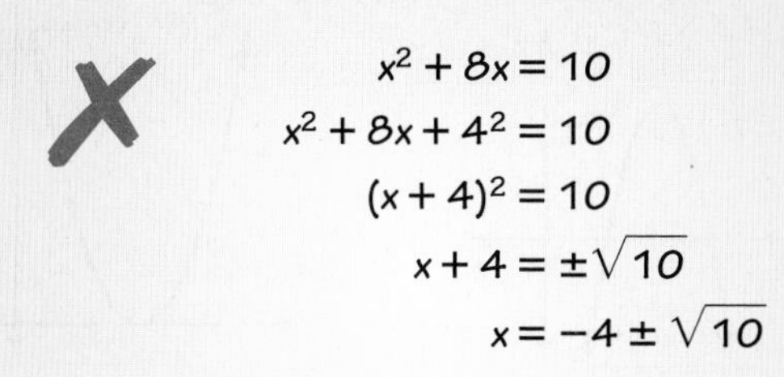

26. **ERROR ANALYSIS** Describe and correct the error in the first two steps of solving $2x^2 - 2x - 4 = 0$ by completing the square.

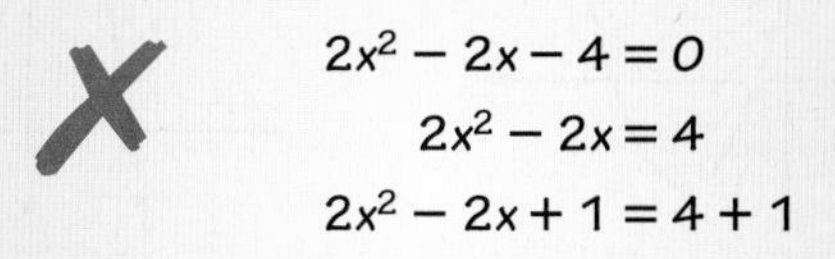

In Exercises 27–30, write the function in vertex form by completing the square. Then match the function with its graph.

27. $y = x^2 + 6x + 3$
28. $y = -x^2 + 8x - 12$
29. $y = -x^2 - 4x - 2$
30. $y = x^2 - 2x + 4$

A.
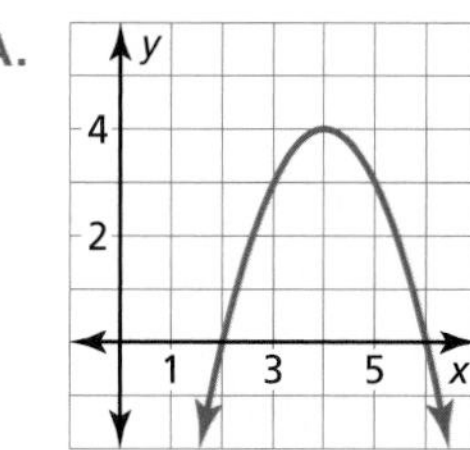

B.
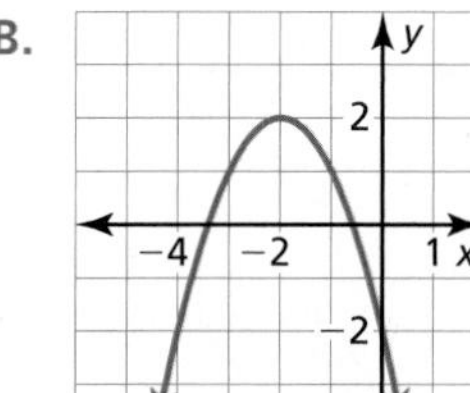

C.
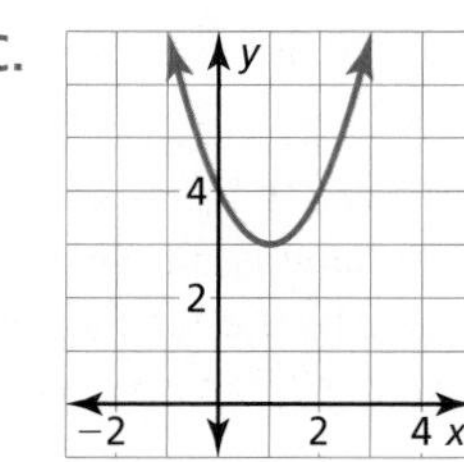

D.
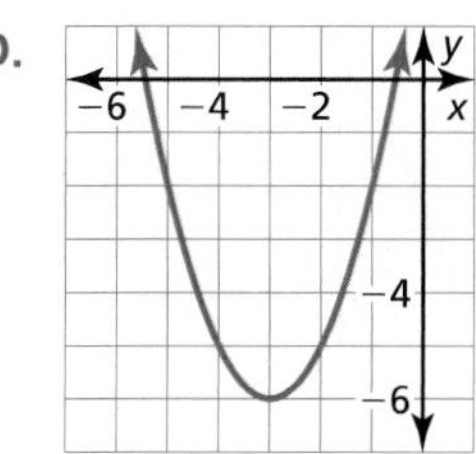

In Exercises 31–36, determine whether the quadratic function has a *maximum* or *minimum* value. Then find the value. *Example 4*

31. $y = x^2 - 4x - 2$

32. $y = x^2 + 6x + 10$

33. $y = -x^2 - 10x - 30$

34. $y = -x^2 + 14x - 34$

35. $f(x) = -3x^2 - 6x - 9$

36. $f(x) = 4x^2 - 28x + 32$

In Exercises 37–40, determine whether the graph could represent the function. Explain.

37. $y = -(x + 8)(x + 3)$

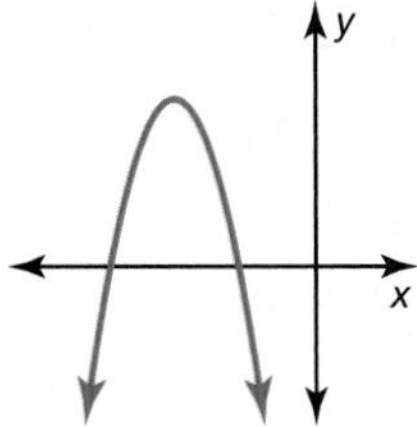

38. $y = (x - 5)^2$ 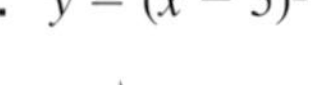

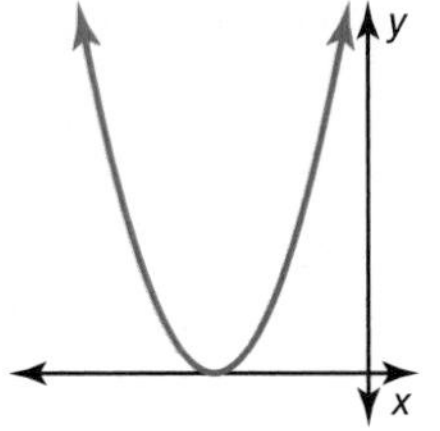

39. $y = \frac{1}{4}(x + 2)^2 - 4$

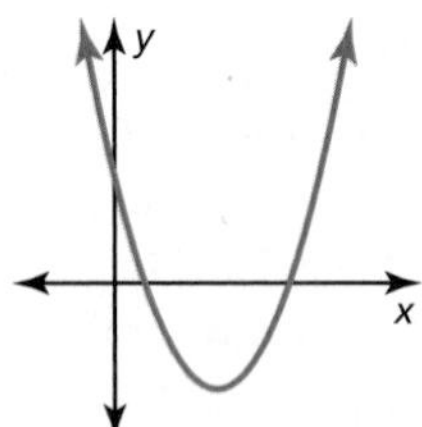

40. $y = -2(x - 1)(x + 2)$

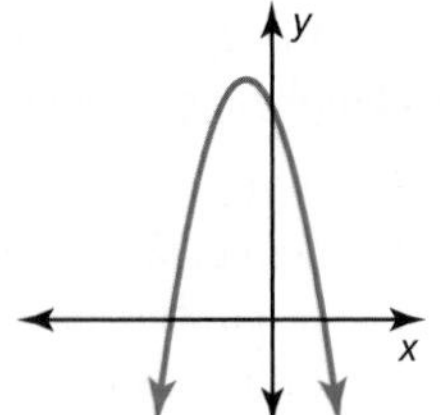

In Exercises 41 and 42, determine which of the functions could be represented by the graph. Explain. *Example 5*

41.

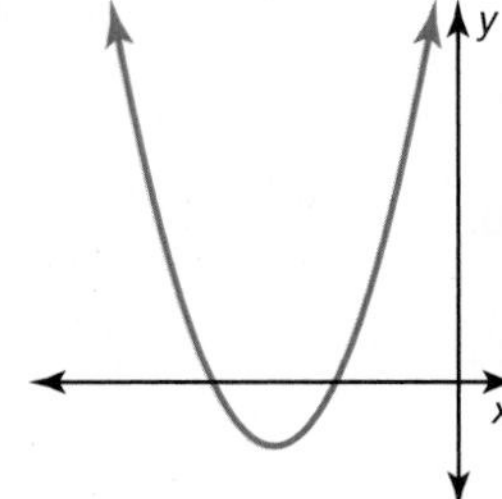

$h(x) = (x + 2)^2 + 3$

$g(x) = -\frac{1}{2}(x - 8)(x - 4)$

$f(x) = 2(x + 3)^2 - 2$

$m(x) = (x + 2)(x + 4)$

42.

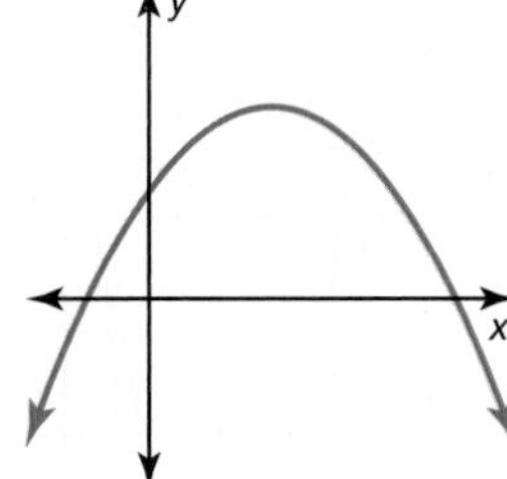

$r(x) = -\frac{1}{3}(x - 5)(x + 1)$

$p(x) = -2(x - 2)(x - 6)$

$q(x) = (x + 1)^2 + 4$

$n(x) = -(x - 2)^2 + 9$

GO DIGITAL

43. MODELING REAL LIFE The function $h = -16t^2 + 48t$ represents the height h (in feet) of a kickball t seconds after it is kicked from the ground. *Example 6*

a. Find the maximum height of the kickball.

b. Find and interpret the axis of symmetry.

44. MODELING REAL LIFE You throw a stone from a height of 16 feet with an initial vertical velocity of 32 feet per second. The function $h = -16t^2 + 32t + 16$ represents the height h (in feet) of the stone after t seconds.

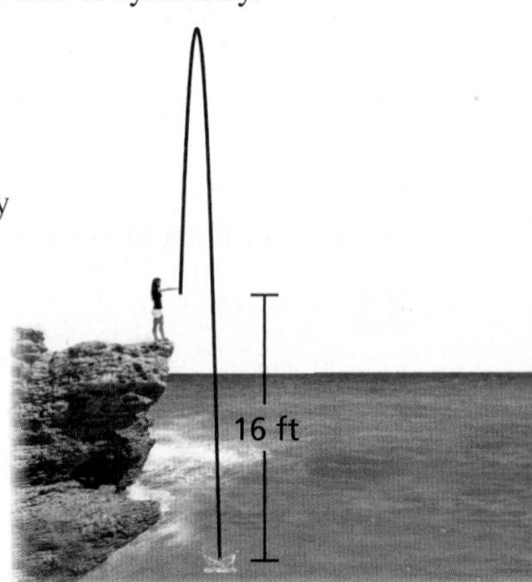

a. Find the maximum height of the stone.

b. Find and interpret the axis of symmetry.

45. MODELING REAL LIFE You are building a rectangular brick patio surrounded by a crushed stone border with a uniform width, as shown. You purchase patio bricks to cover 140 square feet. Find the width of the border. *Example 7*

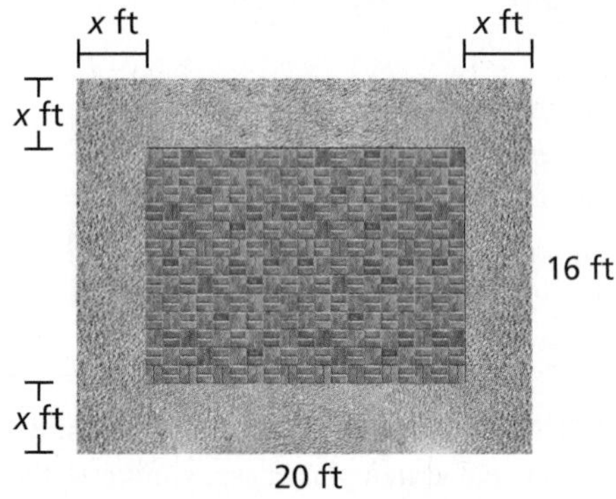

46. MODELING REAL LIFE You are making a poster that will have a uniform border, as shown. The area of the poster (including the border) is 722 square inches. Find the width of the border to the nearest inch.

47. COLLEGE PREP When $y = 2x^2 + 12x + 3$ is written in vertex form, $y = a(x - h)^2 + k$, what is the value of k?

Ⓐ -15

Ⓑ -6

Ⓒ 3

Ⓓ 21

48. **CONNECTING CONCEPTS** Let x_1 and x_2 be the solutions of $3x^2 - 30x - 9 = 0$, where $x_1 > x_2$. Find (a) $x_1 - x_2$ and (b) $x_1 \cdot x_2$. Write each answer in simplest form.

CONNECTING CONCEPTS In Exercises 49 and 50, find the value of x. Round your answer to the nearest hundredth, if necessary.

49. $A = 108 \text{ m}^2$

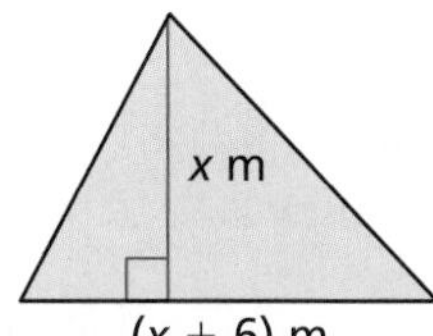

50. $A = 288 \text{ in.}^2$

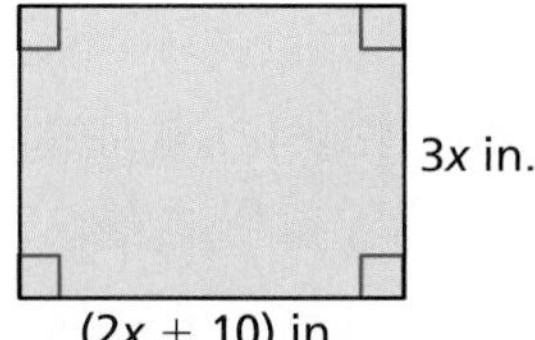

In Exercises 51–54, solve the equation by completing the square.

51. $0.5x^2 + x - 2 = 0$

52. $0.75x^2 + 1.5x = 4$

53. $\frac{8}{3}x - \frac{2}{3}x^2 = -\frac{5}{6}$

54. $\frac{1}{4}x^2 + \frac{1}{2}x - \frac{5}{4} = 0$

55. **MP PROBLEM SOLVING** The distance d (in feet) that it takes a car to come to a complete stop can be modeled by $d = 0.05s^2 + 2.2s$, where s is the speed of the car (in miles per hour). A car has 168 feet to come to a complete stop. Find the maximum speed at which the car can travel.

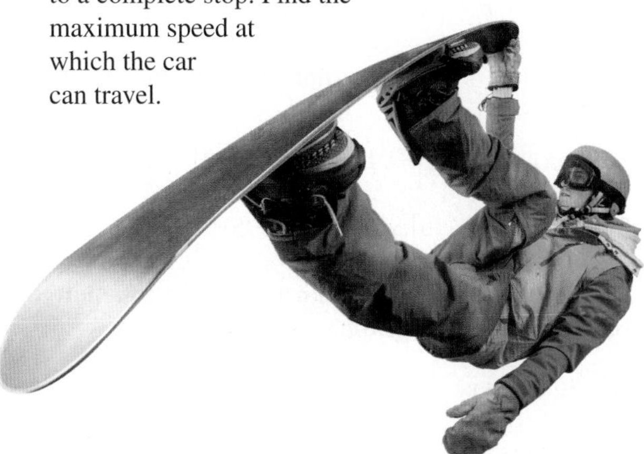

56. **MP PROBLEM SOLVING** During a "big air" competition, snowboarders launch themselves from a half-pipe, perform tricks in the air, and land back in the half-pipe. The height h (in feet) of a snowboarder above the bottom of the half-pipe can be modeled by $h = -16t^2 + 24t + 16.4$, where t is the time (in seconds) after the snowboarder launches into the air. The snowboarder lands 3.2 feet lower than the height of the launch. About how long is the snowboarder in the air?

57. **MP NUMBER SENSE** Find all values of b for which $x^2 + bx + 25$ is a perfect square trinomial. Explain how you found your answer.

58. **HOW DO YOU SEE IT?**
The graph represents the quadratic function $y = x^2 - 4x + 6$.

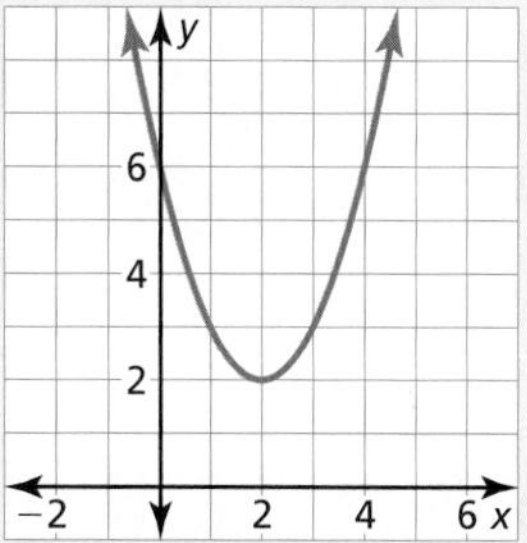

a. Use the graph to estimate the x-values for which $y = 3$.

b. Explain how you can use completing the square to check your estimates in part (a).

59. **COMPARING METHODS** Consider the quadratic equation $x^2 + 12x + 2 = 12$.

a. Solve the equation by completing the square and by using another method.

b. Compare the two methods. Which do you prefer? Explain.

60. **MAKING AN ARGUMENT** You purchase a stock for \$16 per share. You sell the stock 30 days later for \$23.50 per share. The price y (in dollars) of a share during the 30-day period can be modeled by $y = -0.025x^2 + x + 16$, where x is the number of days after the stock is purchased. Your friend says you could have sold the stock earlier for \$23.50 per share. Is your friend correct? Explain.

61. **MP PROBLEM SOLVING** You are knitting a rectangular scarf. The pattern results in a scarf that is 60 inches long and 4 inches wide. However, you have enough yarn to knit 396 square inches. You decide to increase the dimensions of the scarf so that you will use all your yarn. The increase in the length is three times the increase in the width. What are the dimensions of your scarf?

62. **MP REASONING** The product of two consecutive even integers that are positive is 48. Write and solve an equation to find the integers.

63. **MP REASONING** The product of two consecutive odd integers that are negative is 195. Write and solve an equation to find the integers.

64. **THOUGHT PROVOKING** Sketch the graph of the equation $x^2 - 2xy + y^2 - x - y = 0$. Identify the graph.

65. **DIG DEEPER** How many real solutions does $x^2 + bx = c$ have when $c < -\left(\frac{b}{2}\right)^2$? Explain.

REVIEW & REFRESH

In Exercises 66 and 67, solve the equation using square roots.

66. $x^2 - 150 = -29$

67. $(x - 8)^2 = 1$

In Exercises 68 and 69, write a recursive rule for the sequence.

68.

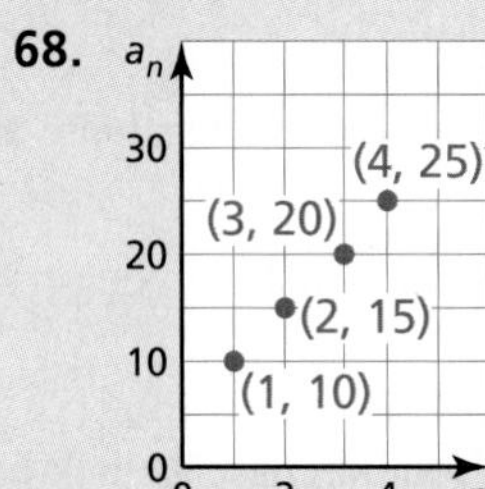

69.

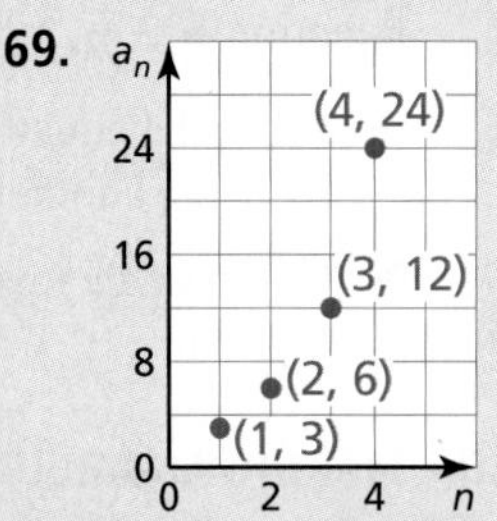

70. Solve $x^2 + 3x = 1$ by completing the square.

In Exercises 71–74, solve the inequality. Graph the solution, if possible.

71. $9x + 3 > 8 + 11x$

72. $\frac{2}{3}x - 6 \geq -\frac{1}{3}(9 - 2x)$

73. $|4x + 3| - 6 < -5$

74. $\frac{1}{4}x \leq -2$ *or* $-3x - 2 < 13$

75. **MODELING REAL LIFE** A rectangular garden has an area of 23 square meters. Its width is one-half of its length. Find the length and width of the garden.

76. Find the mean, median, and mode of the data.

Heights (inches)			
65	66	64	68
66	72	67	71
68	64	68	65

In Exercises 77 and 78, solve the equation by graphing.

77. $x^2 + 9x + 14 = 0$

78. $x + 4 = -x^2$

79. Sketch a parabola that has x-intercepts of -2 and 6 and a range of $y \leq 5$.

80. You are completing the square to solve $3x^2 + 6x = 12$. What is the first step?

In Exercises 81 and 82, the points represented by the table lie on a line. Find the slope of the line.

81.

x	-7	-2	3	8
y	-3	-2	-1	0

82.

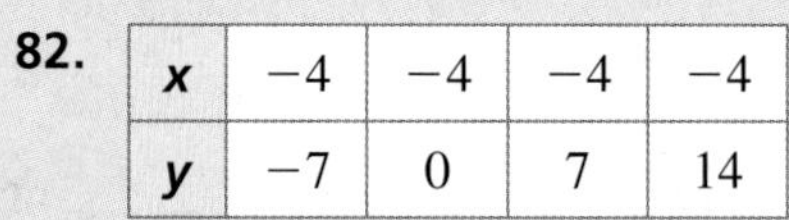

x	-4	-4	-4	-4
y	-7	0	7	14

In Exercises 83 and 84, simplify the expression $\sqrt{b^2 - 4ac}$ for the given values.

83. $a = 3, b = -6, c = 2$

84. $a = -2, b = 4, c = 7$

In Exercises 85 and 86, graph and compare the two functions.

85. $f(x) = |x - 2| - 4$; $g(x) = |x - 2| + 2$

86. $p(x) = |x + 5|$; $q(x) = |3x + 5|$

In Exercises 87 and 88, write a piecewise function represented by the graph.

87.

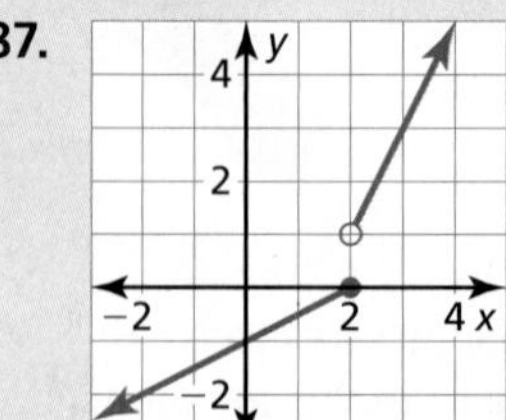

88.

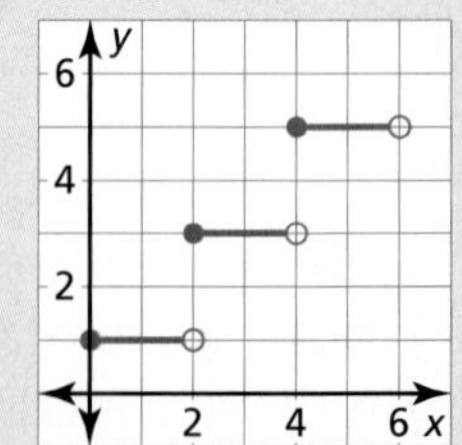

89. Determine whether $y = -x^2 + 8x - 28$ has a *maximum* or *minimum* value. Then find the value.

90. Tell whether $(3, -5)$ is a solution of the system of linear equations.

$$x - y = 8$$
$$4x + 6y = 18$$

9.5 Solving Quadratic Equations Using the Quadratic Formula

Learning Target Use the Quadratic Formula and its discriminant to solve and analyze quadratic equations.

Success Criteria
- I can solve quadratic equations using the Quadratic Formula.
- I can find and interpret the discriminant of an equation.
- I can choose an efficient method for solving a quadratic equation and explain my choice of method.

EXPLORE IT! Deriving the Quadratic Formula

Work with a partner.

a. Explain what is being done in each step when solving a quadratic equation of the form $ax^2 + bx + c = 0$.

$$ax^2 + bx + c = 0$$
$$4a^2x^2 + 4abx + 4ac = 0$$
$$4a^2x^2 + 4abx + 4ac + b^2 = b^2$$
$$4a^2x^2 + 4abx + b^2 = b^2 - 4ac$$
$$(2ax + b)^2 = b^2 - 4ac$$
$$2ax + b = \pm\sqrt{b^2 - 4ac}$$
$$2ax = -b \pm \sqrt{b^2 - 4ac}$$
$$x = \frac{-b \pm \sqrt{b^2 - 4ac}}{2a}$$

Math Practice

View as Components Can you write the right side of this equation as two separate fractions? If so, what do you notice about one of the fractions?

Explain the overall procedure. What does this show?

b. The last equation in part (a) is called the **Quadratic Formula**, which can be used to find the solutions of any quadratic equation. Show how to derive this formula by completing the square on the standard form of a quadratic equation, $ax^2 + bx + c = 0$.

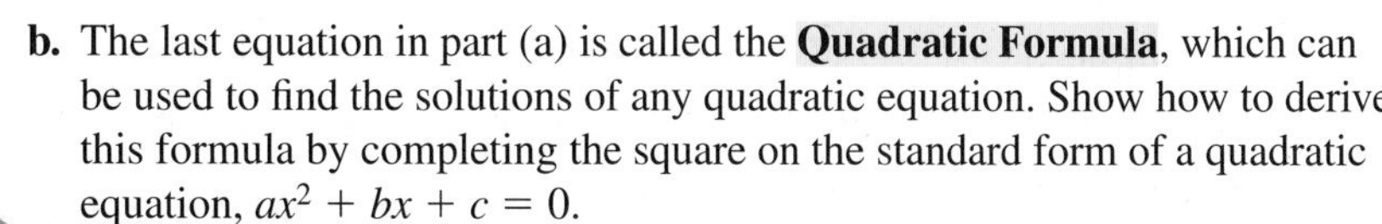

c. Compare this method with the method in part (a). Explain why you think $4a$ and b^2 were chosen in steps 2 and 3 of part (a).

d. Use the Quadratic Formula to solve each quadratic equation.

i. $x^2 + 2x - 3 = 0$

ii. $x^2 - 4x + 4 = 0$

e. Use the Quadratic Formula to solve $x^2 + 4x + 5 = 0$. What do you notice? Use the Internet to research *imaginary numbers.* How are they related to quadratic equations?

Using the Quadratic Formula

Vocabulary

Quadratic Formula, *p. 520*
discriminant, *p. 522*

By completing the square for the quadratic equation $ax^2 + bx + c = 0$, you can develop a formula that gives the solutions of any quadratic equation in standard form. This formula is called the **Quadratic Formula**.

KEY IDEA

Quadratic Formula

The real solutions of the quadratic equation $ax^2 + bx + c = 0$ are

$$x = \frac{-b \pm \sqrt{b^2 - 4ac}}{2a} \qquad \text{Quadratic Formula}$$

where $a \neq 0$ and $b^2 - 4ac \geq 0$.

EXAMPLE 1 Using the Quadratic Formula

Solve $2x^2 - 5x + 3 = 0$ using the Quadratic Formula.

SOLUTION

$$x = \frac{-b \pm \sqrt{b^2 - 4ac}}{2a} \qquad \text{Quadratic Formula}$$

$$= \frac{-(-5) \pm \sqrt{(-5)^2 - 4(2)(3)}}{2(2)} \qquad \text{Substitute 2 for } a, -5 \text{ for } b, \text{ and 3 for } c.$$

$$= \frac{5 \pm \sqrt{1}}{4} \qquad \text{Simplify.}$$

$$= \frac{5 \pm 1}{4} \qquad \text{Evaluate the square root.}$$

▶ So, the solutions are $x = \frac{5+1}{4} = \frac{3}{2}$ and $x = \frac{5-1}{4} = 1$.

STUDY TIP

You can use the roots of a quadratic equation to factor the related expression. In Example 1, you can use 1 and $\frac{3}{2}$ to factor $2x^2 - 5x + 3$ as $(x - 1)(2x - 3)$.

Check

$2x^2 - 5x + 3 = 0$	Original equation	$2x^2 - 5x + 3 = 0$
$2\left(\frac{3}{2}\right)^2 - 5\left(\frac{3}{2}\right) + 3 \stackrel{?}{=} 0$	Substitute.	$2(1)^2 - 5(1) + 3 \stackrel{?}{=} 0$
$\frac{9}{2} - \frac{15}{2} + 3 \stackrel{?}{=} 0$	Simplify.	$2 - 5 + 3 \stackrel{?}{=} 0$
$0 = 0$ ✓	Simplify.	$0 = 0$ ✓

SELF-ASSESSMENT

1 I do not understand. 2 I can do it with help. 3 I can do it on my own. 4 I can teach someone else.

Solve the equation using the Quadratic Formula.

1. $x^2 - 6x + 5 = 0$
2. $3x^2 + 11x + 10 = 0$
3. $\frac{1}{2}x^2 + x - 10 = 0$
4. $4x^2 - 4x = -1$
5. MP **STRUCTURE** Explain how the Quadratic Formula can be used to solve $12x^2 - 7 = 0$?
6. MP **REASONING** What is the value of b^2 when a quadratic equation of the form $ax^2 + bx + c = 0$ has exactly one real solution? Explain your reasoning.

EXAMPLE 2 Modeling Real Life

WATCH INFO

In British Columbia, Canada, the number y of purple martin nesting pairs x years since 2000 can be modeled by the function $y = 0.63x^2 + 51.8x + 144$. When were there about 1000 nesting pairs?

SOLUTION

1. **Understand the Problem** You are given a quadratic function that represents the numbers of purple martin nesting pairs for years after 2000. You need to use the model to determine when there were 1000 nesting pairs.
2. **Make a Plan** To determine when there were 1000 nesting pairs, find the x-value(s) for which $y = 1000$. So, solve the equation $1000 = 0.63x^2 + 51.8x + 144$.
3. **Solve and Check**

$$1000 = 0.63x^2 + 51.8x + 144$$ Write the equation.

$$0 = 0.63x^2 + 51.8x - 856$$ Write in standard form.

$$x = \frac{-b \pm \sqrt{b^2 - 4ac}}{2a}$$ Quadratic Formula

$$= \frac{-51.8 \pm \sqrt{51.8^2 - 4(0.63)(-856)}}{2(0.63)}$$ Substitute 0.63 for a, 51.8 for b, and -856 for c.

$$= \frac{-51.8 \pm \sqrt{4840.36}}{1.26}$$ Simplify.

The solutions are

$$x \approx \frac{-51.8 + \sqrt{4840.36}}{1.26} \approx 14.1 \text{ and } x \approx \frac{-51.8 - \sqrt{4840.36}}{1.26} \approx -96.3.$$

Because a negative solution represents a year that is not in the given time period, use the positive solution.

▶ So, there were about 1000 nesting pairs about 14 years after 2000, in 2014.

Check Use technology to graph the equations $y = 0.63x^2 + 51.8x + 144$ and $y = 1000$. Then find the point of intersection. The graphs intersect at about (14.1, 1000).

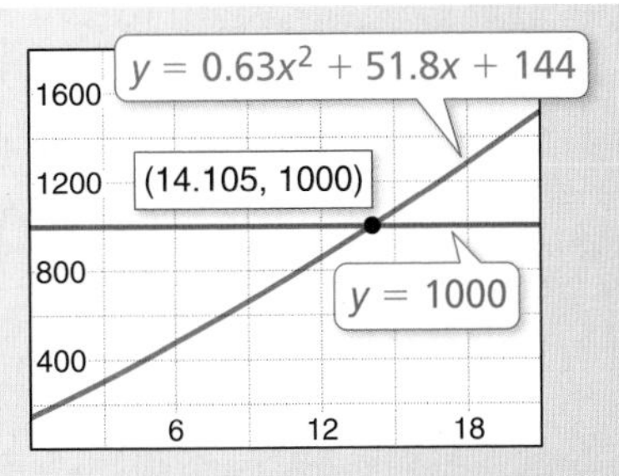

SELF-ASSESSMENT

1 I do not understand. 2 I can do it with help. 3 I can do it on my own. 4 I can teach someone else.

7. **WHAT IF?** When were there about 500 purple martin nesting pairs?
8. The number y of bald eagle nesting pairs in a state x years since 2000 can be modeled by the function $y = 0.34x^2 + 13.1x + 51$.
   a. When were there about 160 bald eagle nesting pairs?
   b. How many bald eagle nesting pairs were there in 2000?

Interpreting the Discriminant

The expression $b^2 - 4ac$ in the Quadratic Formula is called the **discriminant**.

$$x = \frac{-b \pm \sqrt{b^2 - 4ac}}{2a}$$ ← discriminant

Because the discriminant is under the radical symbol, you can use the value of the discriminant to determine the number of real solutions of a quadratic equation and the number of x-intercepts of the graph of the related function.

STUDY TIP

The solutions of a quadratic equation may be real numbers or *imaginary numbers*. You will study imaginary numbers in a future course.

KEY IDEA

Interpreting the Discriminant

$b^2 - 4ac > 0$

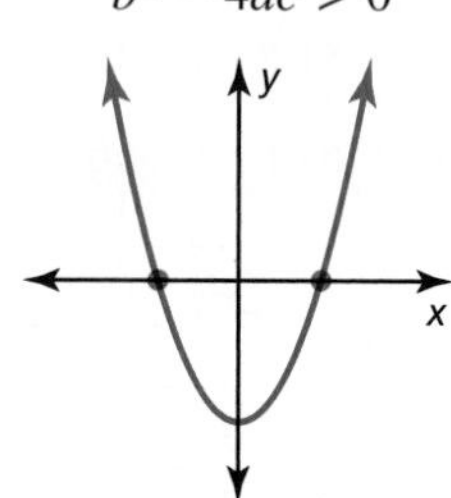

- two real solutions
- two x-intercepts

$b^2 - 4ac = 0$

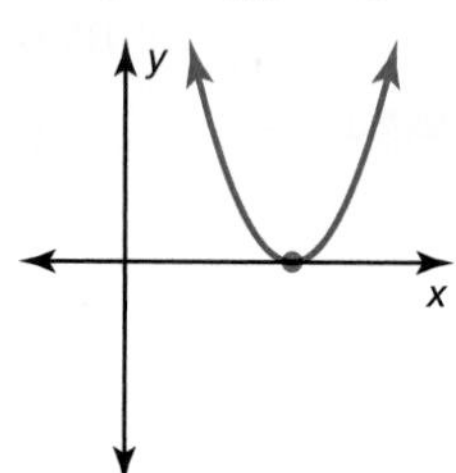

- one real solution
- one x-intercept

$b^2 - 4ac < 0$

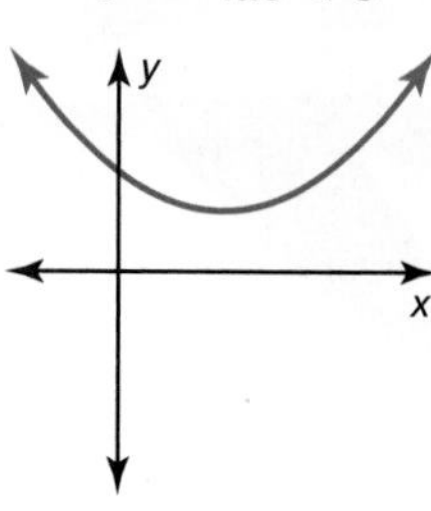

- no real solutions
- no x-intercepts

EXAMPLE 3 Determining the Number of Real Solutions

a. Determine the number of real solutions of $x^2 + 8x - 3 = 0$.

$b^2 - 4ac = 8^2 - 4(1)(-3)$ — Substitute 1 for a, 8 for b, and -3 for c.

$= 64 + 12$ — Simplify.

$= 76$ — Add.

▶ The discriminant is greater than 0. So, the equation has two real solutions.

b. Determine the number of real solutions of $9x^2 + 1 = 6x$.

Write the equation in standard form: $9x^2 - 6x + 1 = 0$.

$b^2 - 4ac = (-6)^2 - 4(9)(1)$ — Substitute 9 for a, -6 for b, and 1 for c.

$= 36 - 36$ — Simplify.

$= 0$ — Subtract.

▶ The discriminant is 0. So, the equation has one real solution.

SELF-ASSESSMENT

1 I do not understand. 2 I can do it with help. 3 I can do it on my own. 4 I can teach someone else.

Determine the number of real solutions of the equation.

9. $-x^2 + 4x - 4 = 0$ **10.** $6x^2 + 2x = -1$ **11.** $\frac{1}{2}x^2 = 7x - 1$

12. OPEN-ENDED Write a quadratic equation that has no real solutions.

13. MP REASONING The quadratic equation $3x^2 - 6x + 2n = 0$ has two real solutions. What are the possible values of n?

Finding the Number of x-Intercepts of a Parabola

Find the number of x-intercepts of the graph of $y = 2x^2 + 3x + 9$.

SOLUTION

To find the number of x-intercepts, determine the number of real solutions of $0 = 2x^2 + 3x + 9$.

$$b^2 - 4ac = 3^2 - 4(2)(9) \quad \text{Substitute 2 for } a, \text{ 3 for } b, \text{ and 9 for } c.$$
$$= 9 - 72 \quad \text{Simplify.}$$
$$= -63 \quad \text{Subtract.}$$

Because the discriminant is less than 0, the equation has no real solutions.

▶ So, the graph of $y = 2x^2 + 3x + 9$ has no x-intercepts.

Check

Use technology to check your answer. Notice that the graph of $y = 2x^2 + 3x + 9$ has no x-intercepts.

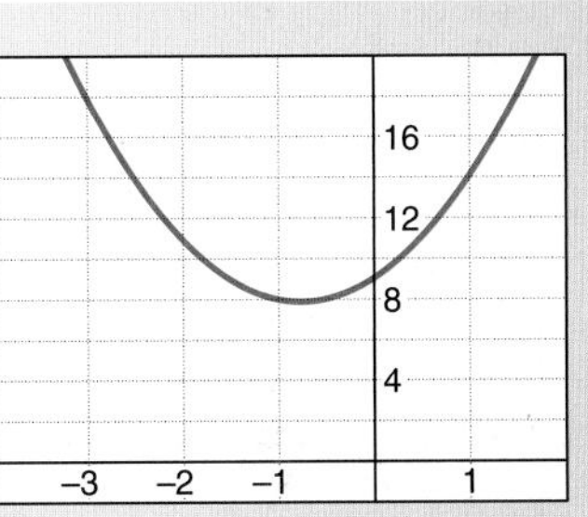

SELF-ASSESSMENT

1 I do not understand. 2 I can do it with help. 3 I can do it on my own. 4 I can teach someone else.

Find the number of x-intercepts of the graph of the function.

14. $y = -x^2 + x - 6$

15. $y = x^2 - x$

16. $f(x) = x^2 + 12x + 36$

Choosing an Efficient Method

Here are five methods for solving quadratic equations. For a given equation, you may find one method is more efficient than the others.

KEY IDEA

Methods for Solving Quadratic Equations

Method	Advantages	Disadvantages
Factoring *(Lessons 7.5–7.8)*	• Straightforward when the expression can be factored	• Some expressions are not factorable.
Graphing *(Lesson 9.2)*	• Can see the number of real solutions • Use when approximate solutions are sufficient. • Can use technology	• May not give exact solutions
Using Square Roots *(Lesson 9.3)*	• Use to solve equations of the form $x^2 = d$.	• Can only be used for certain equations
Completing the Square *(Lesson 9.4)*	• Best used when $a = 1$ and b is even	• May involve difficult calculations
Quadratic Formula *(Lesson 9.5)*	• Can be used for any quadratic equation • Gives exact solutions	• Takes time to do calculations

EXAMPLE 5 Choosing a Method

WATCH

Solve the equation using any method. Explain your choice of method.

a. $x^2 - 10x = 1$ **b.** $2x^2 - 13x - 24 = 0$ **c.** $x^2 + 8x + 12 = 0$

SOLUTION

a. The coefficient of the x^2-term is 1, and the coefficient of the x-term is an even number. So, solve by completing the square.

$x^2 - 10x = 1$ Write the equation.

$x^2 - 10x + 25 = 1 + 25$ Complete the square for $x^2 - 10x$.

$(x - 5)^2 = 26$ Write the left side as the square of a binomial.

$x - 5 = \pm\sqrt{26}$ Take the square root of each side.

$x = 5 \pm \sqrt{26}$ Add 5 to each side.

▶ The solutions are $x = 5 + \sqrt{26}$ and $x = 5 - \sqrt{26}$.

b. The expression $2x^2 - 13x - 24$ is not easily factorable, and the numbers are somewhat large. So, solve using the Quadratic Formula.

$x = \frac{-b \pm \sqrt{b^2 - 4ac}}{2a}$ Quadratic Formula

$= \frac{-(-13) \pm \sqrt{(-13)^2 - 4(2)(-24)}}{2(2)}$ Substitute 2 for a, −13 for b, and −24 for c.

$= \frac{13 \pm \sqrt{361}}{4}$ Simplify.

$= \frac{13 \pm 19}{4}$ Evaluate the square root.

▶ The solutions are $x = \frac{13 + 19}{4} = 8$ and $x = \frac{13 - 19}{4} = -\frac{3}{2}$.

Check

Graph the related function $f(x) = x^2 + 8x + 12$ and find the zeros. The zeros are −6 and −2.

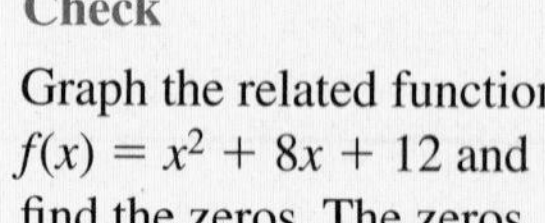

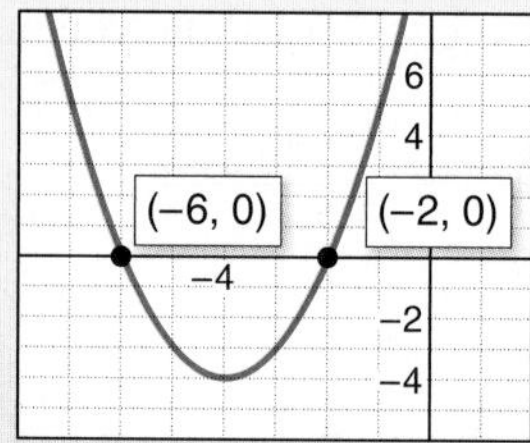

c. The expression $x^2 + 8x + 12$ is factorable. So, solve by factoring.

$x^2 + 8x + 12 = 0$ Write the equation.

$(x + 2)(x + 6) = 0$ Factor the polynomial.

$x + 2 = 0$ *or* $x + 6 = 0$ Zero-Product Property

$x = -2$ *or* $x = -6$ Solve for x.

▶ The solutions are $x = -2$ and $x = -6$.

SELF-ASSESSMENT

1 I do not understand. 2 I can do it with help. 3 I can do it on my own. 4 I can teach someone else.

Solve the equation using any method. Explain your choice of method.

17. $x^2 + 11x - 12 = 0$

18. $9x^2 - 5 = 4$

19. $5x^2 - x - 1 = 0$

20. $x^2 = 2x - 5$

21. MP **REASONING** Write a quadratic equation that you would solve using the given method. Explain your reasoning.

a. factoring **b.** graphing **c.** using square roots

d. completing the square **e.** Quadratic Formula

9.5 Practice WITH CalcChat® AND CalcView®

In Exercises 1–14, solve the equation using the Quadratic Formula. ▶ *Example 1*

1. $x^2 - 12x + 36 = 0$
2. $x^2 + 6x + 9 = 0$
3. $2x^2 - x - 1 = 0$
4. $x^2 - 10x - 11 = 0$
5. $0 = 9x^2 - 6x + 1$
6. $0 = -16x^2 + 8x - 1$
7. $6x^2 - 13x = -6$
8. $2x^2 + 9x + 7 = 3$
9. $2x^2 = 6x - 5$
10. $-3x^2 = 4 - 6x$
11. $x^2 + 2x - 9 = 0$
12. $x^2 - 5x + 3 = 0$
13. $5x^2 + 2 = 4x + 4$
14. $8x^2 + 8 = 6 - 9x$

15. **MODELING REAL LIFE** The function $h = -16t^2 + 26t$ models the height h (in feet) of a dolphin t seconds after jumping out of the water. After how many seconds is the dolphin 5 feet above the water?
▶ *Example 2*

16. **MODELING REAL LIFE** The amounts y (in tons) of trout caught in a lake from 2000 to 2019 can be modeled by the equation $y = -0.08x^2 + 1.6x + 10$, where x is the number of years since 2000.

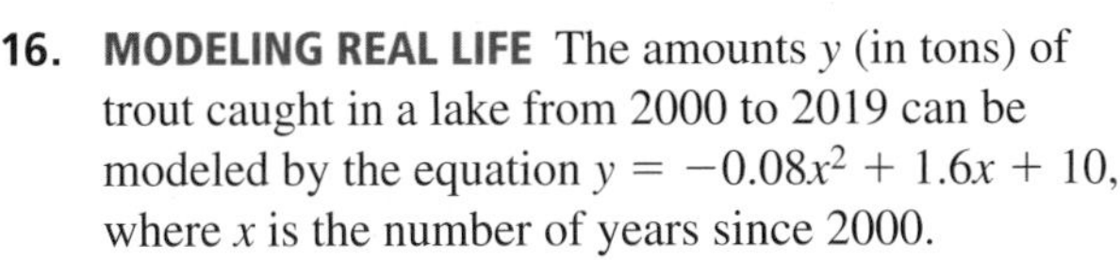

   a. When were about 15 tons of trout caught in the lake?

   b. Do you think this model can be used to accurately predict the amounts of trout caught in future years? Explain your reasoning.

In Exercises 17–22, determine the number of real solutions of the equation. ▶ *Example 3*

17. $x^2 - 6x + 10 = 0$
18. $x^2 - 5x - 3 = 0$
19. $2x^2 - 12x = -18$
20. $4x^2 = 4x - 1$
21. $-\frac{1}{4}x^2 + 4x = -2$
22. $-5x^2 + 8x = 9$

In Exercises 23–28, find the number of x-intercepts of the graph of the function. ▶ *Example 4*

23. $y = x^2 + 5x - 1$
24. $y = 4x^2 + 4x + 1$
25. $y = -6x^2 + 3x - 4$
26. $y = -x^2 + 5x + 13$
27. $f(x) = 4x^2 + 3x - 6$
28. $f(x) = 2x^2 + 8x + 8$

In Exercises 29–36, solve the equation using any method. Explain your choice of method. ▶ *Example 5*

29. $-10x^2 + 13x = 4$
30. $x^2 - 3x - 40 = 0$
31. $x^2 + 6x = 5$
32. $-5x^2 = -25$
33. $x^2 + x - 12 = 0$
34. $x^2 - 4x + 1 = 0$
35. $x^2 + 6x + 9 = 16$
36. $4x^2 - x = 17$

37. **ERROR ANALYSIS** Describe and correct the error in solving $3x^2 - 7x - 6 = 0$ using the Quadratic Formula.

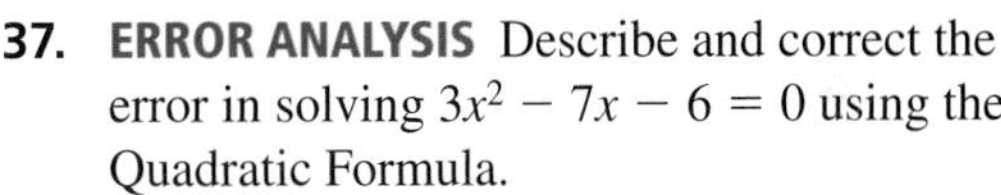

$$x = \frac{-7 \pm \sqrt{(-7)^2 - 4(3)(-6)}}{2(3)}$$
$$= \frac{-7 \pm \sqrt{121}}{6}$$
$$x = \frac{2}{3} \text{ and } x = -3$$

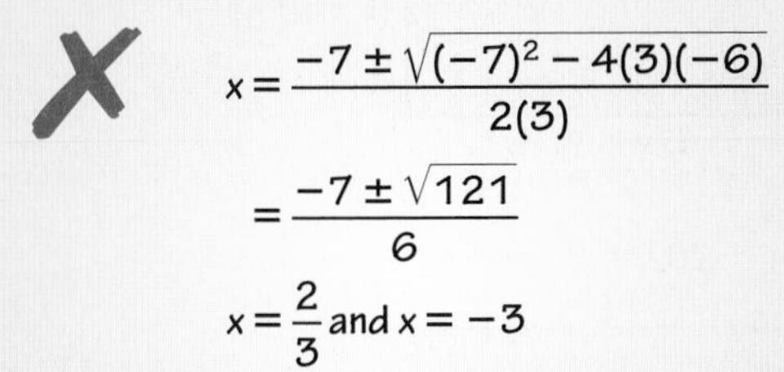

38. **ERROR ANALYSIS** Describe and correct the error in solving $-2x^2 + 9x = 4$ using the Quadratic Formula.

$$x = \frac{-9 \pm \sqrt{9^2 - 4(-2)(4)}}{2(-2)}$$
$$= \frac{-9 \pm \sqrt{113}}{-4}$$
$$x = \frac{9 - \sqrt{113}}{4} \text{ and } x = \frac{9 + \sqrt{113}}{4}$$

39. **MODELING REAL LIFE** The path of a fountain over a river can be modeled by $y = -0.006x^2 + 1.2x + 10$, where x is the horizontal distance (in feet) from the river's north shore and y is the height (in feet) above the river. Does the water reach a height of 50 feet? If so, about how far from the north shore is the water 50 feet above the river?

40. **MODELING REAL LIFE** From April 1 through September 30, the number y of hours of daylight per day in Seattle, Washington, can be modeled by $y = -0.0005x^2 + 0.074x + 12.78$, where x is the number of days since April 1.

    a. Do any of the days from the beginning of April through the end of September have 17 hours of daylight? If so, how many?

    b. Do any of the days from the beginning of April through the end of September have 14 hours of daylight? If so, how many?

CONNECTING CONCEPTS In Exercises 41 and 42, find the dimensions of the rectangle.

41. $A = 91\text{ m}^2$

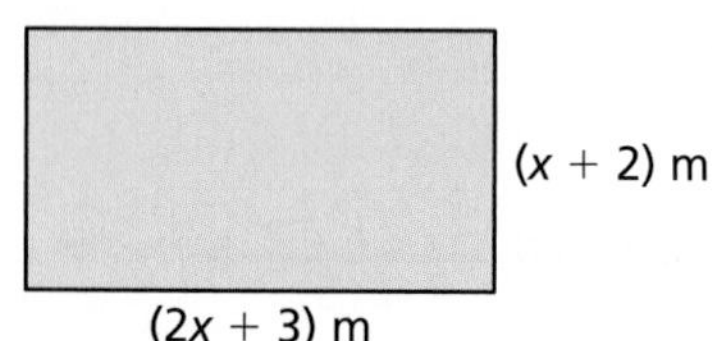

42. $A = 209\text{ ft}^2$

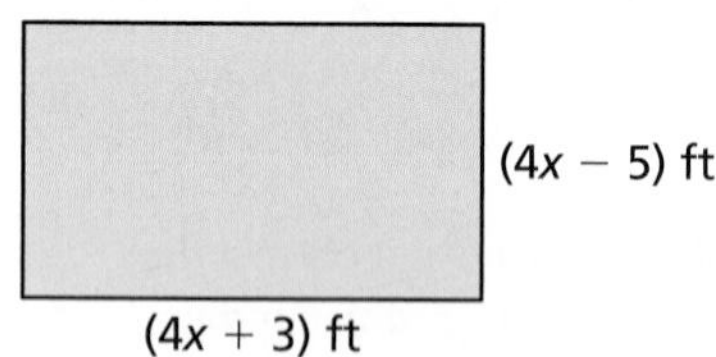

COMPARING METHODS In Exercises 43 and 44, solve the equation by (a) graphing, (b) factoring, and (c) using the Quadratic Formula. Which method do you prefer? Explain your reasoning.

43. $x^2 + 4x + 4 = 0$

44. $3x^2 + 11x + 6 = 0$

45. **MP REASONING** How many solutions does the equation $ax^2 + bx + c = 0$ have when a and c have different signs? Explain your reasoning.

46. **MAKING AN ARGUMENT** Your friend calculates the discriminant of the equation $2x^2 - 5x - 2 = -11$ as shown, and determines that the equation has two real solutions. Is your friend correct? Explain your reasoning.

$$b^2 - 4ac = (-5)^2 - 4(2)(-2)$$
$$= 41$$

47. **MODELING REAL LIFE** The fuel economy y (in miles per gallon) of a car can be modeled by the equation $y = -0.013x^2 + 1.25x + 5.6$, where $5 \le x \le 75$ and x is the speed (in miles per hour) of the car. Find the speed(s) at which you can travel and have a fuel economy of 32 miles per gallon.

48. **MODELING REAL LIFE** The depth d (in feet) of a river can be modeled by the equation $d = -0.25t^2 + 1.7t + 3.5$, where $0 \le t \le 7$ and t is the time (in hours) after a heavy rain begins. When is the river 6 feet deep?

In Exercises 49–54, tell whether the vertex of the graph of the function lies *above*, *below*, or *on* the x-axis. Explain your reasoning without using a graph.

49. $y = x^2 - 3x + 2$

50. $y = 3x^2 - 6x + 3$

51. $y = 6x^2 - 2x + 4$

52. $y = -15x^2 + 10x - 25$

53. $f(x) = -3x^2 - 4x + 8$

54. $f(x) = 9x^2 - 24x + 16$

55. **MODELING REAL LIFE** NASA creates a weightless environment by flying a plane in a series of parabolic paths. The height h (in feet) of a plane after t seconds in a parabolic flight path can be modeled by $h = -11t^2 + 700t + 21{,}000$. The passengers experience a weightless environment when the height of the plane is greater than or equal to 30,800 feet. How long do passengers experience weightlessness? Explain.

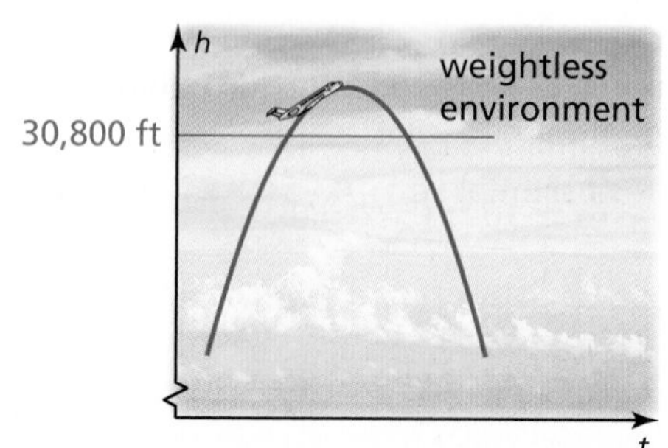

56. **MP STRUCTURE** Use the Quadratic Formula and the numbers below to create a quadratic equation with the solutions $x = \frac{3 \pm \sqrt{89}}{10}$.

$\_\_\_x^2 + \_\_\_x + \_\_\_ = 0$

−5	−4	−3	−2	−1
1	2	3	4	5

57. **MP PROBLEM SOLVING** A rancher constructs two rectangular horse pastures that share a side, as shown. The pastures are enclosed by 1050 feet of fencing. Each pasture has an area of 15,000 square feet. Find the possible lengths and widths of each pasture.

58. **MODELING REAL LIFE** A kicker punts a football from a height of 2.5 feet above the ground with an initial vertical velocity of 45 feet per second.

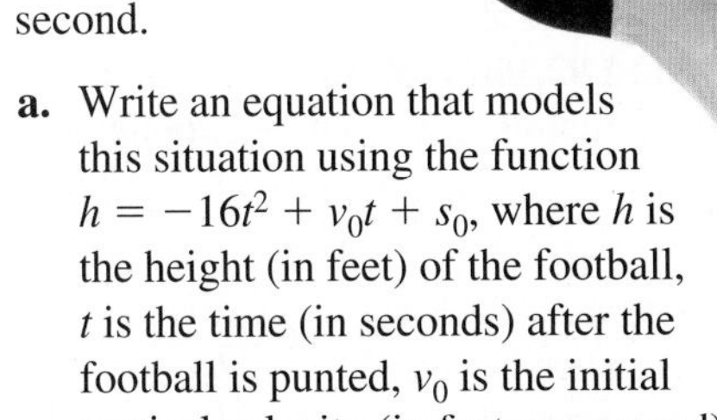

a. Write an equation that models this situation using the function $h = -16t^2 + v_0t + s_0$, where h is the height (in feet) of the football, t is the time (in seconds) after the football is punted, v_0 is the initial vertical velocity (in feet per second), and s_0 is the initial height (in feet).

b. The football is caught 5.5 feet above the ground. Find the amount of time that the football is in the air.

In Exercises 59 and 60, give a value of c for which the equation has (a) two real solutions, (b) one real solution, and (c) no real solutions.

59. $x^2 - 2x + c = 0$

60. $4x^2 + 12x + c = 0$

61. **CRITICAL THINKING** The solutions of the quadratic equation $ax^2 + bx + c = 0$ are

$$x = \frac{-b + \sqrt{b^2 - 4ac}}{2a} \text{ and}$$

$$x = \frac{-b - \sqrt{b^2 - 4ac}}{2a}.$$

Find the mean of the solutions. How is the mean of the solutions related to the graph of $y = ax^2 + bx + c$? Explain.

62. **HOW DO YOU SEE IT?**
Match each graph with its related discriminant. Explain your reasoning.

A.

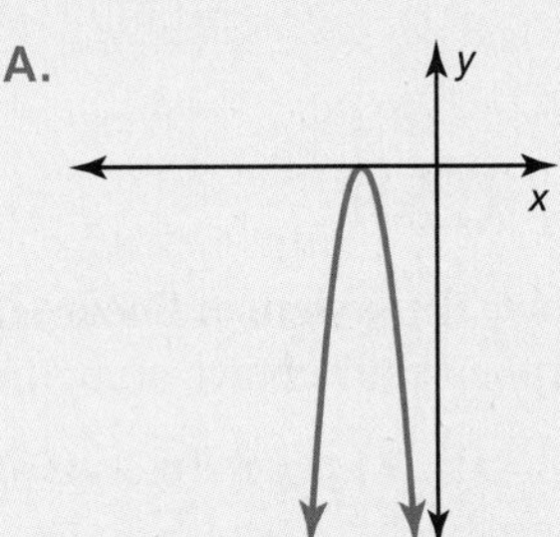

B.

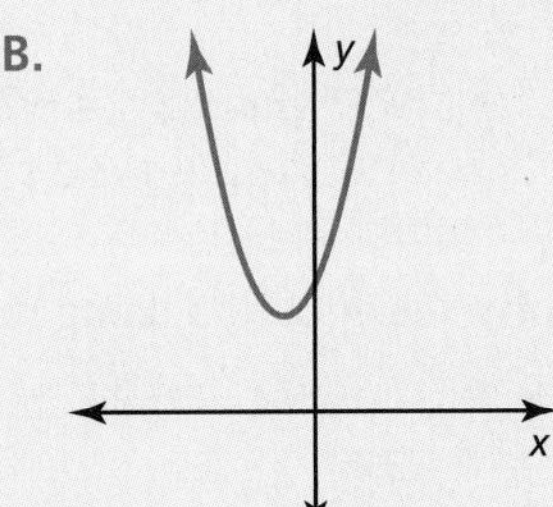

C.

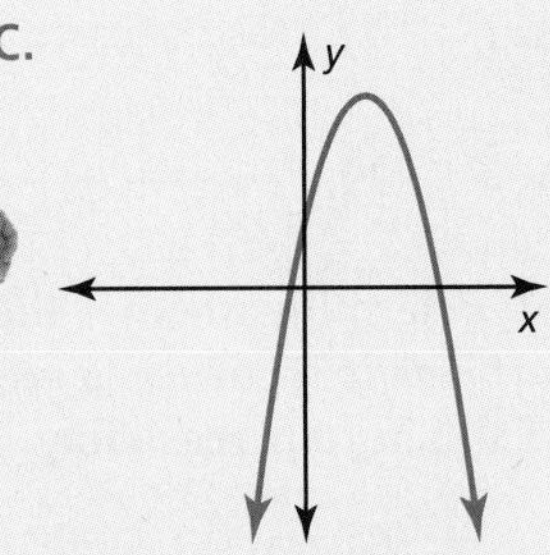

a. $b^2 - 4ac > 0$

b. $b^2 - 4ac = 0$

c. $b^2 - 4ac < 0$

63. **MP PROBLEM SOLVING** You are trying to hang a tire swing. To get the rope over a tree branch that is 15 feet high, you tie the rope to a weight and throw it over the branch. You release the weight at a height s_0 of 5.5 feet. What is the minimum initial vertical velocity v_0 needed to reach the branch? (*Hint*: Use the equation $h = -16t^2 + v_0t + s_0$.)

64. THOUGHT PROVOKING
Consider the graph of the standard form of a quadratic function $y = ax^2 + bx + c$. Then consider the Quadratic Formula as given by

$$x = -\frac{b}{2a} \pm \frac{\sqrt{b^2 - 4ac}}{2a}.$$

Write a graphical interpretation of the two parts of this formula.

65. WRITING A FORMULA Derive a formula that can be used to find the solutions of equations that have the form $ax^2 + x + c = 0$. Use your formula to solve $-2x^2 + x + 8 = 0$.

66. ANALYZING RELATIONSHIPS Find the sum and product of $\frac{-b + \sqrt{b^2 - 4ac}}{2a}$ and $\frac{-b - \sqrt{b^2 - 4ac}}{2a}$. Then write a quadratic equation whose solutions have a sum of 2 and a product of $\frac{1}{2}$.

GO DIGITAL

DIG DEEPER **In Exercises 67–69, find all values of k for which the equation has (a) two real solutions, (b) one real solution, and (c) no real solutions.**

67. $2x^2 + x + 3k = 0$

68. $x^2 - 4kx + 36 = 0$

69. $kx^2 + 5x - 16 = 0$

REVIEW & REFRESH

In Exercises 70–73, solve the system of linear equations using any method. Explain your choice of method.

70. $y = -x + 4$
$y = 2x - 8$

71. $x = 16 - 4y$
$3x + 4y = 8$

72. $2x - y = 7$
$2x + 7y = 31$

73. $3x - 2y = -20$
$x + 1.2y = 6.4$

In Exercises 74–79, solve the equation using the Quadratic Formula.

74. $x^2 - 8x - 3 = 0$

75. $4x^2 - 12x + 9 = 0$

76. $-9x^2 - 6x - 1 = 0$

77. $-x^2 + 7x - 11 = 0$

78. $7x^2 + x + 5 = 0$

79. $-6x^2 + 3x - 2 = 0$

In Exercises 80 and 81, determine whether the graph represents an *arithmetic sequence*, a *geometric sequence*, or *neither*. Explain your reasoning.

80.

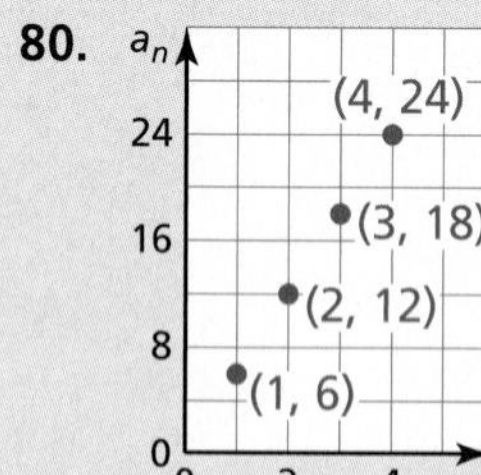

81.

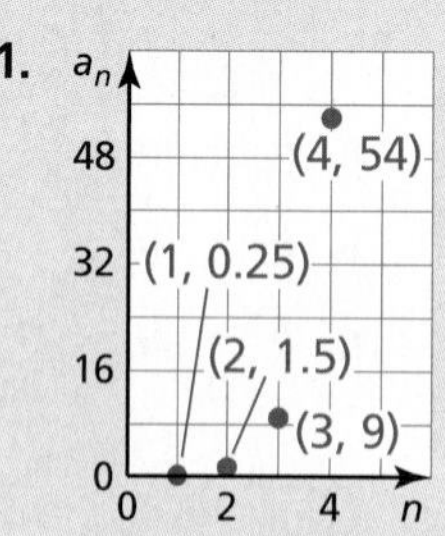

In Exercises 82–85, solve the proportion.

82. $\frac{x}{6} = \frac{5}{3}$

83. $\frac{7}{4} = \frac{d}{12}$

84. $\frac{4}{5} = \frac{10}{z}$

85. $\frac{8}{y} = \frac{9}{12}$

In Exercises 86–89, solve the equation using square roots.

86. $x^2 = 225$

87. $x^2 - 121 = 0$

88. $(x + 5)^2 = 0$

89. $6x^2 - 54 = 0$

90. MODELING REAL LIFE The table shows the numbers of people who view a video x days after it is posted online. (a) Use technology to find a quadratic model for the data. Then determine whether the model is a good fit. (b) After how many days is the video viewed by 1000 people?

Days	5	10	15	20	25	30
Views	258	540	835	1146	1462	1787

In Exercises 91 and 92, simplify the expression. Write your answer using only positive exponents.

91. $(-3.5m)^2$

92. $\left(\frac{2p}{4}\right)^{-3}$

93. Approximate when the function is positive, negative, increasing, or decreasing. Then describe the end behavior of the function.

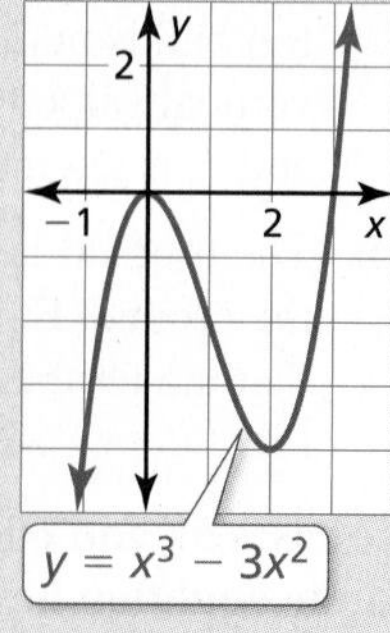

In Exercises 94 and 95, complete the square for the expression. Then factor the trinomial.

94. $x^2 - 20x$

95. $x^2 + 18x$

9.6 Solving Nonlinear Systems of Equations

Learning Target Solve nonlinear systems graphically and algebraically.

Success Criteria
- I can solve nonlinear systems graphically.
- I can solve nonlinear systems algebraically.
- I can approximate the solutions of nonlinear systems.

EXPLORE IT! Solving Systems of Equations

Work with a partner. Consider the graphs of the functions shown.

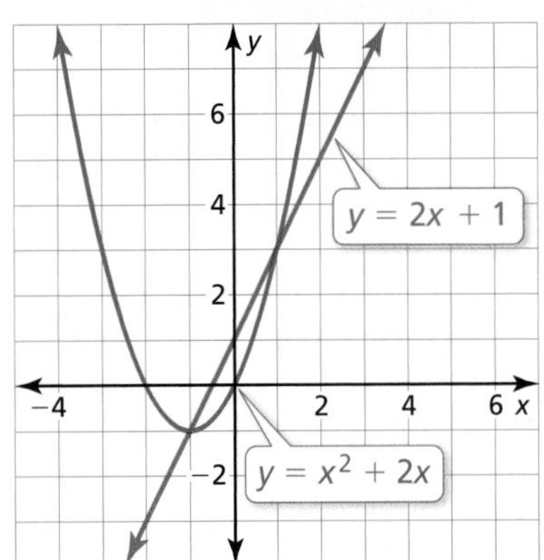

Math Practice

Communicate Precisely
How are the questions in parts (a) and (b) similar? How are they different?

a. Use the graph to solve the equation below. Explain your reasoning.

$$2x + 1 = x^2 + 2x$$

b. Use the graph to solve the system below. Explain your reasoning.

$$y = 2x + 1$$
$$y = x^2 + 2x$$

c. Find the solutions in parts (a) and (b) algebraically. Explain your method.

d. Does each system below have a solution? Justify your answer.

System 1	**System 2**
$y = 2x$	$y = 2x - 3$
$y = x^2 + 2x$	$y = x^2 + 2x$

e. A system consists of one linear equation and one quadratic equation. Describe the possible numbers of solutions of the system.

f. How can you solve a system consisting of one linear equation and one quadratic equation?

Solving Nonlinear Systems by Graphing

Vocabulary

system of nonlinear equations, *p. 530*

The methods for solving systems of linear equations can also be used to solve *systems of nonlinear equations*. A **system of nonlinear equations** is a system in which at least one of the equations is nonlinear.

When a nonlinear system consists of a linear equation and a quadratic equation, the graphs can intersect in zero, one, or two points. So, the system can have zero, one, or two solutions, as shown.

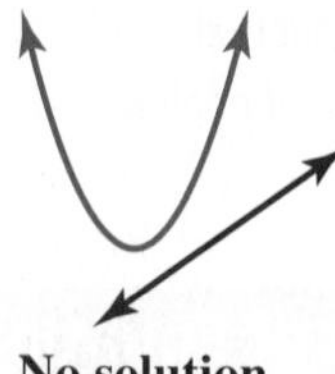

No solution

One solution

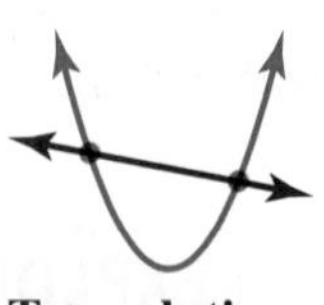

Two solutions

EXAMPLE 1 Solving a Nonlinear System by Graphing

Solve the system by graphing.

$y = 2x^2 + 5x - 1$ Equation 1

$y = x - 3$ Equation 2

SOLUTION

Step 1 Graph each equation.

Step 2 Estimate the point of intersection. The graphs appear to intersect at $(-1, -4)$.

Step 3 Check that $(-1, -4)$ is a solution of each equation.

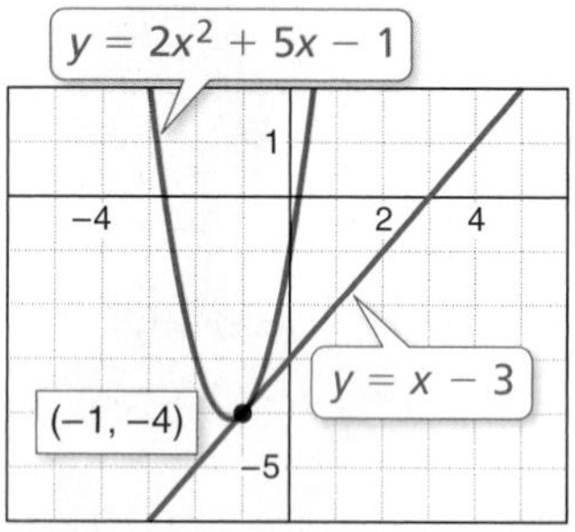

Equation 1

$y = 2x^2 + 5x - 1$

$-4 \stackrel{?}{=} 2(-1)^2 + 5(-1) - 1$

$-4 = -4$ ✓

Equation 2

$y = x - 3$

$-4 \stackrel{?}{=} -1 - 3$

$-4 = -4$ ✓

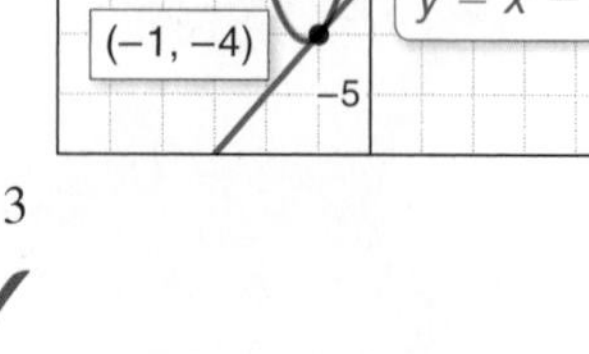

▶ The solution is $(-1, -4)$.

SELF-ASSESSMENT 1 I do not understand. 2 I can do it with help. 3 I can do it on my own. 4 I can teach someone else.

Solve the system by graphing.

1. $y = x^2 + 4x - 4$
$y = 2x - 5$

2. $y = -x + 6$
$y = -2x^2 - x + 3$

3. $y = 3x - 15$
$y = \frac{1}{2}x^2 - 2x - 7$

4. Find the solutions of the system whose graph is shown. Show that each solution satisfies each equation in the system.

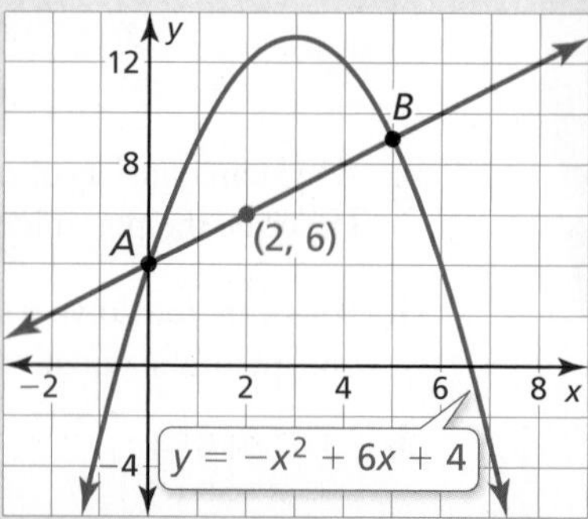

Solving Nonlinear Systems Algebraically

REMEMBER

The algebraic procedures that you use to solve nonlinear systems are similar to the procedures that you used to solve linear systems in Sections 5.2 and 5.3.

EXAMPLE 2 Solving a Nonlinear System by Substitution

WATCH

Solve the system by substitution.

$y = x^2 + x - 1$ Equation 1

$y = -2x + 3$ Equation 2

SOLUTION

Step 1 The equations are already solved for y.

Step 2 Substitute $-2x + 3$ for y in Equation 1 to obtain an equation in one variable, x. Then solve the equation to find the value(s) of x.

$y = x^2 + x - 1$	Equation 1
$-2x + 3 = x^2 + x - 1$	Substitute $-2x + 3$ for y.
$3 = x^2 + 3x - 1$	Add $2x$ to each side.
$0 = x^2 + 3x - 4$	Subtract 3 from each side.
$0 = (x + 4)(x - 1)$	Factor the polynomial.
$x + 4 = 0$ *or* $x - 1 = 0$	Zero-Product Property
$x = -4$ *or* $x = 1$	Solve for x.

Step 3 Substitute -4 and 1 for x in Equation 2 and solve for y.

$y = -2x + 3$	Equation 2	$y = -2x + 3$
$y = -2(-4) + 3$	Substitute for x.	$y = -2(1) + 3$
$= 11$	Simplify.	$= 1$

▶ So, the solutions are $(-4, 11)$ and $(1, 1)$.

Check

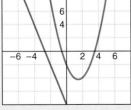

(−4, 11)
(1, 1)

EXAMPLE 3 Solving a Nonlinear System by Elimination

Solve the system by elimination.

$y = x^2 - 3x - 2$ Equation 1

$y = -3x - 8$ Equation 2

SOLUTION

Step 1 Because the coefficients of the y-terms are the same, you do not need to multiply either equation by a constant.

Step 2 Subtract the equations to eliminate the y-terms.

$y = x^2 - 3x - 2$	Equation 1
$y = \quad -3x - 8$	Equation 2
$0 = x^2 \quad + 6$	Subtract the equations.

Step 3 Solve for x.

$0 = x^2 + 6$	Resulting equation from Step 2
$-6 = x^2$	Subtract 6 from each side.

▶ The square of a real number cannot be negative. So, the system has no real solutions.

Check

SELF-ASSESSMENT

1 I do not understand. **2** I can do it with help. **3** I can do it on my own. **4** I can teach someone else.

Solve the system by substitution.

5. $y = x^2 + 9$
$y = 9$

6. $y = -5x$
$y = x^2 - 3x - 3$

7. $y = -3x^2 + 2x + 1$
$y = 5 - 3x$

Solve the system by elimination.

8. $y = x^2 + x$
$y = x + 5$

9. $y = 9x^2 + 8x - 6$
$y = 5x - 4$

10. $y = 2x + 5$
$y = -3x^2 + x - 4$

Approximating Solutions

When you cannot find the exact solution(s) of a system of equations, you can analyze output values to approximate the solution(s).

EXAMPLE 4 Approximating Solutions of a Nonlinear System

Approximate the solution(s) of the system to the nearest thousandth.

$y = \frac{1}{2}x^2 + 3$ Equation 1

$y = 3^x$ Equation 2

SOLUTION

$y = \frac{1}{2}x^2 + 3$

$y = 3^x$

Sketch a graph of the system. You can see that the system has one solution between $x = 1$ and $x = 2$.

Substitute 3^x for y in Equation 1 and rewrite the equation.

$3^x = \frac{1}{2}x^2 + 3$ Substitute 3^x for y in Equation 1.

$3^x - \frac{1}{2}x^2 - 3 = 0$ Rewrite the equation.

Because you do not know how to solve this equation algebraically, let $f(x) = 3^x - \frac{1}{2}x^2 - 3$. The solution of the system is the x-value for which $f(x) = 0$. Evaluate the function for x-values between 1 and 2.

$f(1.1) \approx -0.26$
$f(1.2) \approx 0.02$
Because $f(1.1) < 0$ and $f(1.2) > 0$, the zero is between 1.1 and 1.2.

$f(1.2)$ is closer to 0 than $f(1.1)$, so decrease your guess and evaluate $f(1.19)$.

REMEMBER
Function values closer to 0 correspond to x-values that better approximate the zeros.

$f(1.19) \approx -0.012$ Because $f(1.19) < 0$ and $f(1.2) > 0$, the zero is between 1.19 and 1.2. So, increase guess.

$f(1.191) \approx -0.009$ Result is negative. Increase guess.

$f(1.192) \approx -0.006$ Result is negative. Increase guess.

$f(1.193) \approx -0.003$ Result is negative. Increase guess.

$f(1.194) \approx -0.0002$ Result is negative. Increase guess.

$f(1.195) \approx 0.003$ Result is positive.

Because $f(1.194)$ is closer to 0 than $f(1.195)$, $x \approx 1.194$.

Substitute $x = 1.194$ into one of the original equations and solve for y.

$$y = \frac{1}{2}x^2 + 3 = \frac{1}{2}(1.194)^2 + 3 \approx 3.713$$

► So, the solution of the system is about (1.194, 3.713).

STUDY TIP

You can think of this as solving the system of equations

$y = f(x)$
$y = g(x)$

by graphing.

Recall that one way to solve $f(x) = g(x)$ is to first graph $y = f(x)$ and $y = g(x)$. The x-value of an intersection point of the graphs of the functions is a solution of the equation $f(x) = g(x)$.

EXAMPLE 5 Approximating Solutions of an Equation

Solve $-2(4)^x + 3 = 0.5x^2 - 2x$. Round the solution(s) to the nearest hundredth.

SOLUTION

You do not know how to solve this equation algebraically. One way to find the solutions is to use technology to find the x-coordinates of the intersection points of $y = -2(4)^x + 3$ and $y = 0.5x^2 - 2x$.

Method 1 Graph the functions and find the intersection points.

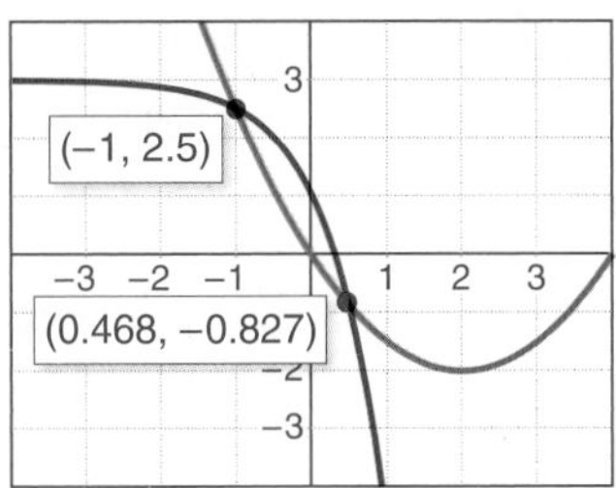

One point of intersection is $(-1, 2.5)$. The other point of intersection is about $(0.47, -0.83)$.

▶ So, the solutions of the equation are $x = -1$ and $x \approx 0.47$.

Method 2 Create a table of values for the functions. Find the x-values for which the corresponding y-values are approximately equal.

STUDY TIP

You can use the differences between the corresponding y-values of the two functions to determine the best approximation of a solution.

x	$-2(4)^x + 3$	$0.5x^2 - 2x$
−1.03	2.5204	2.5905
−1.02	2.5137	2.5602
−1.01	2.5069	2.5301
−1	2.5	2.5
−0.99	2.493	2.4701
−0.98	2.4859	2.4402
−0.97	2.4788	2.4105

When $x = -1$, the corresponding y-values are 2.5.

x	$-2(4)^x + 3$	$0.5x^2 - 2x$
0.44	−0.6808	−0.7832
0.45	−0.7321	−0.7988
0.46	−0.7842	−0.8142
0.47	−0.8371	−0.8296
0.48	−0.8906	−0.8448
0.49	−0.9449	−0.86
0.5	−1	−0.875

When $x = 0.47$, the corresponding y-values are approximately -0.83.

▶ So, the solutions of the equation are $x = -1$ and $x \approx 0.47$.

SELF-ASSESSMENT

1 I do not understand. 2 I can do it with help. 3 I can do it on my own. 4 I can teach someone else.

Use the method in Example 4 to approximate the solution(s) of the system to the nearest thousandth.

11. $y = 4^x$
$y = x^2 + x + 3$

12. $y = 4x^2 - 1$
$y = -2(3)^x + 4$

13. $y = x^2 + 3x$
$y = -x^2 + x + 10$

Solve the equation. Round your solution(s) to the nearest hundredth.

14. $3^x - 1 = x^2 - 2x + 5$

15. $4x^2 + x = -2\left(\frac{1}{2}\right)^x + 5$

16. WRITING Explain how the solutions of the equation and the system below are related.

Equation: $x^2 = 2^x$

System: $y = x^2$
$y = 2^x$

9.6 Practice WITH CalcChat® AND CalcView®

In Exercises 1–4, match the system of equations with its graph. Then solve the system.

1. $y = x^2 - 2x + 1$
   $y = x + 1$

2. $y = x^2 + 3x + 2$
   $y = -x - 3$

3. $y = x - 1$
   $y = -x^2 + x - 1$

4. $y = -x + 3$
   $y = -x^2 - 2x + 5$

A.
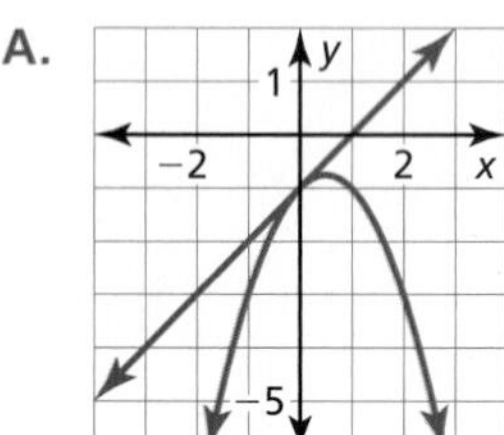

B.
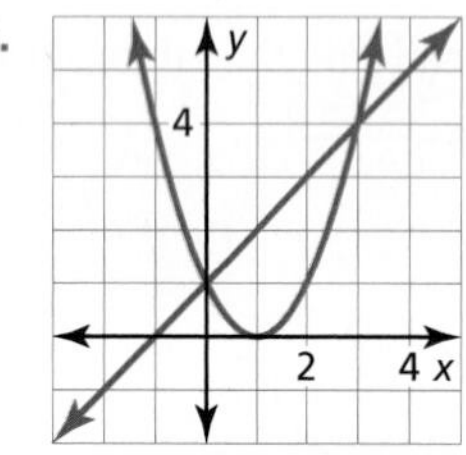

C.
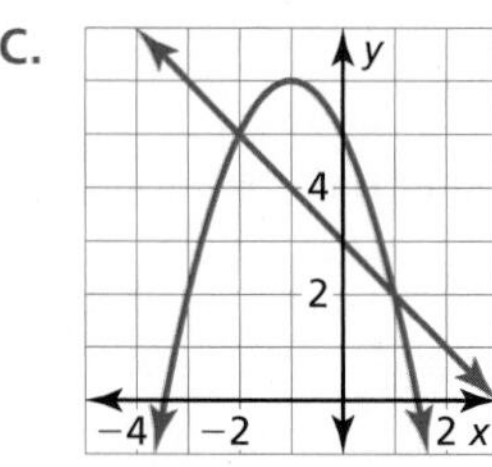

D.
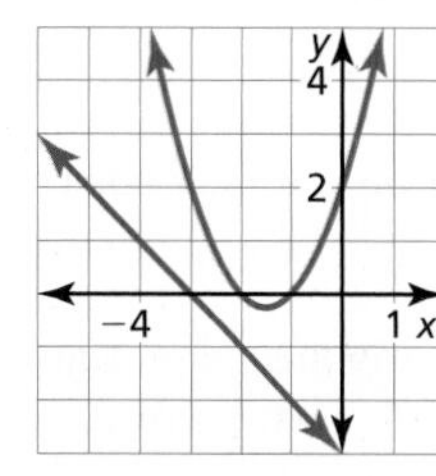

In Exercises 5–10, solve the system by graphing. *Example 1*

5. $y = 3x^2 - 2x + 1$
   $y = x + 7$

6. $y = x^2 + 2x + 5$
   $y = -2x - 5$

7. $y = -2x^2 - 4x$
   $y = 2$

8. $y = \frac{1}{2}x^2 - 3x + 4$
   $y = x - 2$

9. $y = \frac{1}{3}x^2 + 2x - 3$
   $y = 2x$

10. $y = 4x^2 + 5x - 7$
    $y = -3x + 5$

In Exercises 11–16, solve the system by substitution. *Example 2*

11. $y = x - 5$
    $y = x^2 + 4x - 5$

12. $y = -3x^2$
    $y = 6x + 3$

13. $y = -x + 7$
    $y = -x^2 - 2x - 1$

14. $y = -x^2 + 7$
    $y = 2x + 4$

15. $y - 5 = -x^2$
    $y = 5$

16. $y = 2x^2 + 3x - 4$
    $y - 4x = 2$

In Exercises 17–24, solve the system by elimination. *Example 3*

17. $y = x^2 - 5x - 7$
    $y = -5x + 9$

18. $y = -3x^2 + x + 2$
    $y = x + 4$

19. $y = -x^2 - 2x + 2$
    $y = 4x + 2$

20. $y = -2x^2 + x - 3$
    $y = 2x - 2$

21. $y = 2x - 1$
    $y = x^2$

22. $y = x^2 + x + 1$
    $y = -x - 2$

23. $y + 2x = 0$
    $y = x^2 + 4x - 6$

24. $y = 2x - 7$
    $y + 5x = x^2 - 2$

25. **ERROR ANALYSIS** Describe and correct the error in solving the system of equations by graphing.

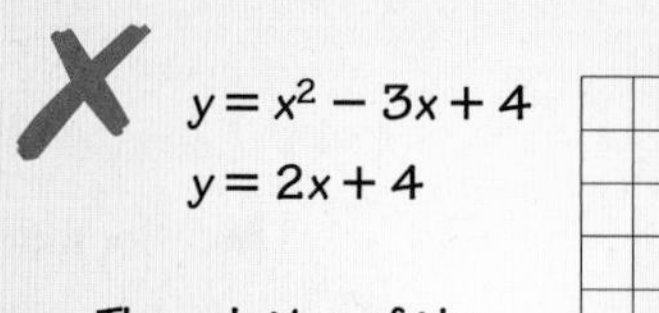

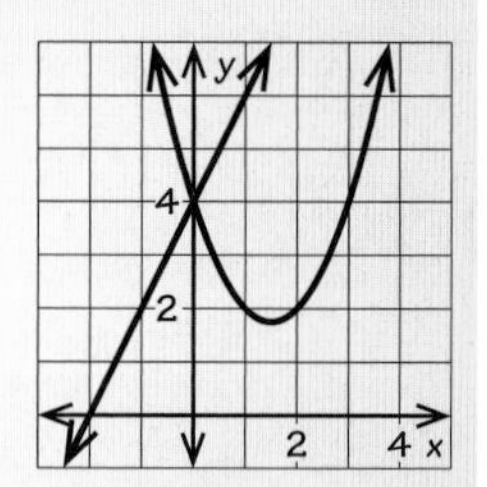

26. **ERROR ANALYSIS** Describe and correct the error in solving for one of the variables in the system.

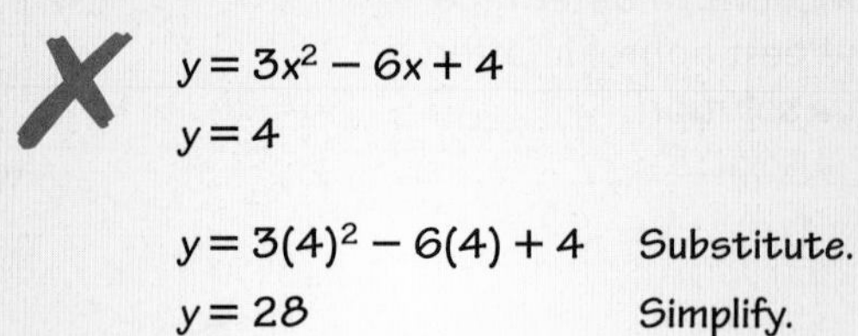

In Exercises 27 and 28, use the table to describe the locations of the zeros of the quadratic function *f*.

27.

x	−4	−3	−2	−1	0	1
$f(x)$	−2	2	4	4	2	−2

28.

x	−1	0	1	2	3	4
$f(x)$	11	5	1	−1	−1	1

In Exercises 29–34, use the method in Example 4 to approximate the solution(s) of the system to the nearest thousandth. *Example 4*

29. $y = x^2 + 2x + 3$
$y = 3^x$

30. $y = 2^x + 5$
$y = x^2 - 3x + 1$

31. $y = 2(4)^x - 1$
$y = 3x^2 + 8x$

32. $y = -x^2 - 4x - 4$
$y = -5^x - 2$

33. $y = -x^2 - x + 5$
$y = 2x^2 + 6x - 3$

34. $y = 2x^2 + x - 8$
$y = x^2 - 5$

In Exercises 35–42, solve the equation. Round your solution(s) to the nearest hundredth. *Example 5*

35. $3x + 1 = x^2 + 7x - 1$

36. $-x^2 + 2x = -2x + 5$

37. $x^2 - 6x + 4 = -x^2 - 2x$

38. $2x^2 + 8x + 10 = -x^2 - 2x + 5$

39. $-4\left(\frac{1}{2}\right)^x = -x^2 - 5$

40. $1.5(2)^x - 3 = -x^2 + 4x$

41. $8^{x-2} + 3 = 2\left(\frac{3}{2}\right)^x$

42. $-0.5(4)^x = 5^x - 6$

43. MODELING REAL LIFE The attendances y for two movies can be modeled by the following equations, where x is the number of days since the movies opened.

$y = -x^2 + 35x + 100$ Movie A
$y = -5x + 275$ Movie B

After how many days is the attendance for each movie the same?

44. MODELING REAL LIFE The arch of a bridge can be modeled by $y = -0.002x^2 + 1.06x$, where x is the distance (in meters) from the left pylons and y is the height (in meters) of the arch above the water. The road can be modeled by the equation $y = 52$. To the nearest meter, how far from the left pylons are the two points where the road intersects the arch of the bridge?

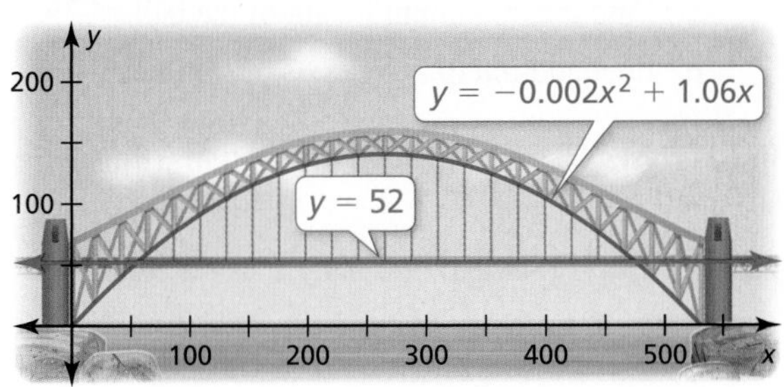

45. COMPARING METHODS Solve the system in Exercise 33 using substitution. Compare the exact solutions to the approximated solutions.

46. COMPARING METHODS Solve the system in Exercise 34 using elimination. Compare the exact solutions to the approximated solutions.

47. MP REASONING Is it possible for a system of equations that consists of a linear equation and a quadratic equation to have infinitely many solutions? Explain.

48. HOW DO YOU SEE IT?
The diagram shows the graphs of two equations in a system that has one solution.

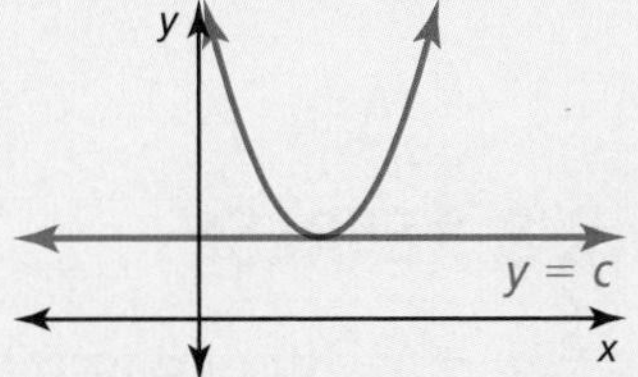

a. How many solutions will the system have when you change the linear equation to $y = c + 2$?

b. How many solutions will the system have when you change the linear equation to $y = c - 2$?

COMPARING METHODS In Exercises 49 and 50, solve the system of equations by (a) graphing, (b) substitution, and (c) elimination. Which method do you prefer? Explain your reasoning.

49. $y = 4x + 3$
$y = x^2 + 4x - 1$

50. $y = x^2 - 5$
$y = -x + 7$

51. MODELING REAL LIFE The function $y = -x^2 + 65x + 256$ models the number y of subscribers to a website, where x is the number of days since the website launched. The number of subscribers to a competitor's website can be modeled by a linear function. The websites have the same numbers of subscribers on Days 1 and 34. Write a linear function that models the number of subscribers to the competitor's website. Verify your answer.

52. COLLEGE PREP A system of equations consists of a quadratic equation whose graph opens up and a quadratic equation whose graph opens down. What are the possible numbers of solutions of the system? Select all that apply.

Ⓐ 0 Ⓑ 1
Ⓒ 2 Ⓓ infinitely many

53. **MP PROBLEM SOLVING** A country's population of 2 million people increases by 3% each year. The country's food supply, sufficient to feed 3 million people, increases at a constant rate that feeds 0.25 million additional people each year.

   a. After how many years will the country first experience a food shortage?

   b. The country doubles the rate at which its food supply increases. Will food shortages still occur? If so, after how many years?

54. **THOUGHT PROVOKING**
Is it possible for a system of two quadratic equations to have exactly three solutions? exactly four solutions? Explain your reasoning. (*Hint:* Rotations of the graphs of quadratic equations still represent quadratic equations.)

GO DIGITAL

55. **MAKING AN ARGUMENT** A system of equations consists of a linear equation and a quadratic equation. The system has one solution. Must the solution be the vertex of the graph of the quadratic equation? Explain.

56. **MP LOGIC** The product of two positive numbers is 25. The reciprocal of one of the numbers is equal to 16 times the reciprocal of the other number. What are the numbers?

57. **MP PROBLEM SOLVING** Solve the system of three equations shown.

$$y = 2x - 8$$
$$y = x^2 - 4x - 3$$
$$y = -3(2)^x$$

REVIEW & REFRESH

58. Solve $-3x^2 + 6 = 10$ using square roots.

In Exercises 59–62, graph the system. Identify a solution.

59. $y > 2x$, $y > -x + 4$

60. $y \geq 4x + 1$, $y \leq 7$

61. $y - 3 \leq -2x$, $y + 5 < 3x$

62. $x + y > -6$, $2y \leq 3x + 4$

In Exercises 63–66, graph the function. Find the domain and range.

63. $y = 3x^2 + 2$

64. $y = -x^2 - 6x$

65. $y = -2x^2 + 12x - 7$

66. $y = 5x^2 + 10x - 3$

67. Use the graph to solve $x^2 + 10x + 25 = 0$.

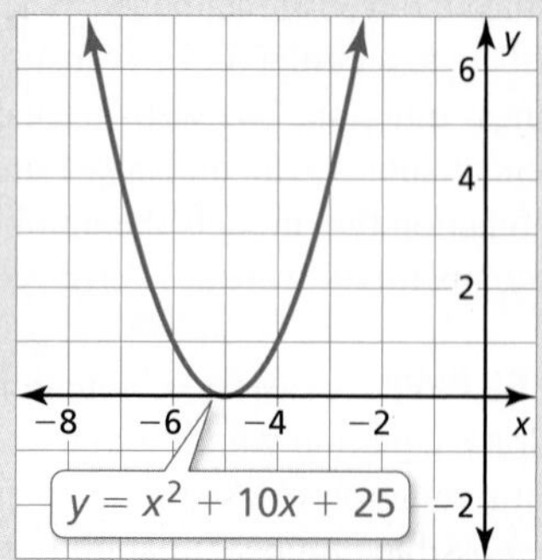

In Exercises 68 and 69, evaluate the expression.

68. $\sqrt[3]{-512}$

69. $32^{2/5}$

70. For $f(x) = \frac{3}{2}x - 10$, find the value of x for which $f(x) = -1$.

In Exercises 71 and 72, solve the equation using the Quadratic Formula.

71. $3x^2 + 2x - 8 = 0$

72. $2x^2 - 3x = 6$

In Exercises 73 and 74, write an inequality that represents the graph.

73. −15 −14 −13 −12 −11 −10 −9 −8 −7 −6 −5

74. −5 −4 −3 −2 −1 0 1 2 3 4 5

In Exercises 75 and 76, write an equation in slope-intercept form of the line that passes through the given points.

75. (2, −5), (4, 3)

76. (−8, 15), (0, 9)

77. **MODELING REAL LIFE** The function $h = -16t^2 + 64t + 4$ represents the height h (in feet) of a ball t seconds after it is thrown up into the air.

   a. Find the maximum height of the ball.

   b. Find and interpret the axis of symmetry.

In Exercises 78 and 79, solve the system using any method.

78. $y = -x^2 + 4x + 5$, $y = x + 1$

79. $y = 2x^2 + 6x + 7$, $y = -2x - 1$

9 Chapter Review WITH CalcChat®

Chapter Learning Target Understand solving quadratic equations.

Chapter Success Criteria

- ◆ I can simplify expressions using properties of radicals.
- ◆ I can describe different methods for solving quadratic equations.
- ■ I can solve quadratic equations.
- ■ I can solve nonlinear systems of equations graphically and algebraically.

◆ Surface ■ Deep

SELF-ASSESSMENT 1 I do not understand. 2 I can do it with help. 3 I can do it on my own. 4 I can teach someone else.

9.1 Properties of Radicals (pp. 483–492)

Learning Target: Use properties of radicals to write equivalent expressions.

Vocabulary
radical expression
simplest form of a radical
rationalizing the denominator
conjugates
like radicals

Simplify the expression.

1. $\sqrt{72p^7}$ **2.** $\sqrt{\dfrac{45}{7y}}$ **3.** $\sqrt[3]{\dfrac{125x^{11}}{4}}$

4. $\dfrac{8}{\sqrt{6}+2}$ **5.** $4\sqrt{3}+5\sqrt{12}$ **6.** $\sqrt{6}\left(\sqrt{18}+\sqrt{8}\right)$

7. The dimensions of a company logo form a golden rectangle. The logo has a length of 15 feet when displayed on a screen in Times Square. Estimate the height of the logo.

8. Determine whether the expression represents a *rational* or an *irrational* number. Justify your answer.

$$\frac{3-\sqrt{8}}{12d-\sqrt{128d^2}}, \text{ where } d \text{ is a positive integer}$$

9.2 Solving Quadratic Equations by Graphing (pp. 493–502)

Learning Target: Use graphs to solve quadratic equations and find zeros of functions.

Vocabulary
quadratic equation

Solve the equation by graphing.

9. $-x^2-5x-4=0$ **10.** $x^2-9x+18=0$

11. $x^2-2x=-4$ **12.** $-10x-25=x^2$

13. The graph of $f(x)=(x+1)(x^2+2x-3)$ is shown. Find the zeros of f.

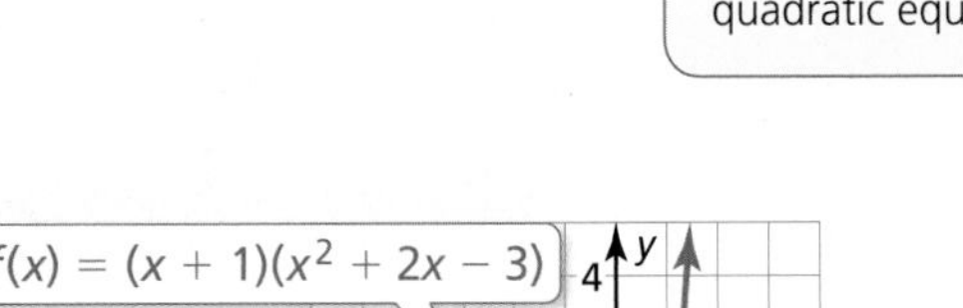

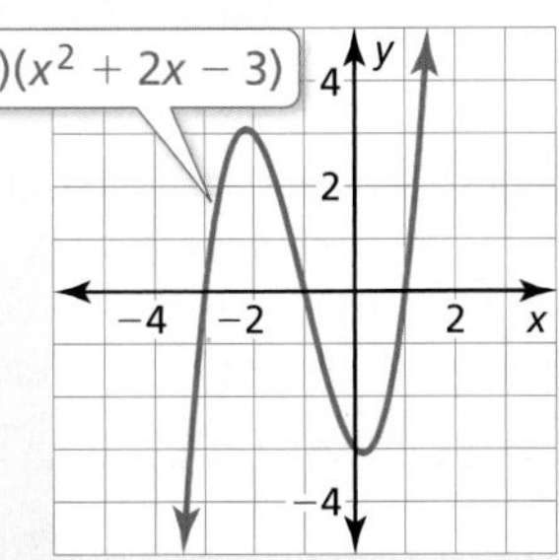

14. Graph $f(x)=x^2+2x-5$. Approximate the zeros of f to the nearest tenth.

9.3 Solving Quadratic Equations Using Square Roots (pp. 503–508)

WATCH

Learning Target: Solve quadratic equations using square roots.

Solve the equation using square roots.

15. $x^2 + 5 = 17$ **16.** $x^2 - 14 = -14$ **17.** $(x + 2)^2 = 64$

18. $(x - 1)^2 = 0$ **19.** $4x^2 + 25 = -75$ **20.** $19 = 30 - 5x^2$

21. A sprinkler sprays water to cover a circular region of 90π square feet. Find the diameter of the circle.

22. The length of the rectangular prism is four times its width. The volume of the prism is 380 cubic meters. Find the length and width of the prism.

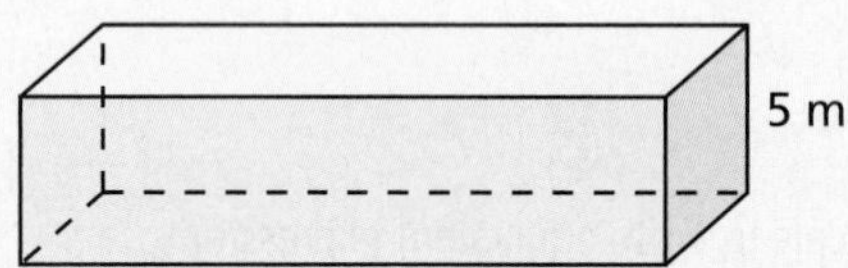

9.4 Solving Quadratic Equations by Completing the Square (pp. 509–518)

Learning Target: Solve quadratic equations and find maximum and minimum values of quadratic functions by completing the square.

Vocabulary AZ VOCAB
completing the square

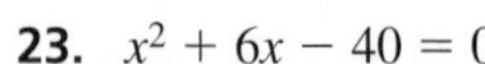

Solve the equation by completing the square.

23. $x^2 + 6x - 40 = 0$ **24.** $x^2 + 2x + 5 = 4$ **25.** $2x^2 - 4x = 10$

Determine whether the quadratic function has a *maximum* or *minimum* value. Then find the value.

26. $y = -x^2 + 6x - 1$ **27.** $f(x) = x^2 + 4x + 11$ **28.** $y = 3x^2 - 24x + 15$

29. The picture frame has three identical openings and a total area (including the openings) of 148 square inches. The distances between the openings are equal to the width x of the uniform border. Find the width of the border.

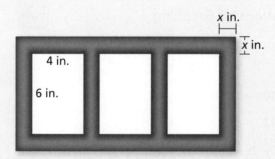

30. A store sells about 230 baseballs per month for \$15 each. For every \$1 decrease in price, the store expects to sell 35 more baseballs. The monthly revenue y (in dollars) from baseball sales is given by $y = (15 - x)(230 + 35x)$, where x is the number of \$1 price decreases. The store wants to sell the most baseballs possible while earning at least \$3800 in monthly revenue. How much should the store charge for each baseball?

9.5 Solving Quadratic Equations Using the Quadratic Formula (pp. 519–528)

Learning Target: Use the Quadratic Formula and its discriminant to solve and analyze quadratic equations.

Vocabulary

Quadratic Formula
discriminant

Solve the equation using the Quadratic Formula.

31. $x^2 + 2x - 15 = 0$

32. $2x^2 - x + 8 = 16$

33. $-5x^2 + 10x = 5$

Find the number of x-intercepts of the graph of the function.

34. $y = -x^2 + 6x - 9$

35. $y = 2x^2 + 4x + 8$

36. $y = -\frac{1}{2}x^2 + 2x$

37. Find a value of k so that the function $y = 4x^2 + kx + 49$ has exactly one zero.

38. The average difference y (in percent form) between declared fuel efficiency and actual fuel efficiency for cars in Europe x years after 2000 can be represented by $y = 0.13x^2 + 0.1x + 9$. In what year was there a 40% difference?

9.6 Solving Nonlinear Systems of Equations (pp. 529–536)

Learning Target: Solve nonlinear systems graphically and algebraically.

Vocabulary

system of nonlinear equations

Solve the system using any method.

39. $y = x^2 - 2x - 4$
$y = -5$

40. $y = 2x^2 - 4x - 1$
$y = x + 2$

41. $y = x^2 - 5x + 4$
$y = 2x^2 - 8x$

42. $y = x^2 - 9$
$y = 2x + 5$

43. $y = -4^x + 6$
$y = 3x - 7$

44. $y = 2\left(\frac{1}{2}\right)^x - 5$
$y = -x^2 - x + 4$

45. The graphs of a linear equation and quadratic equation intersect at $(-5, 4)$ and $(3, 4)$. Find (a) the slope and y-intercept of the line and (b) the axis of symmetry of the parabola. Explain your reasoning.

46. Write a system that consists of a linear equation and a quadratic equation whose only solution is $(4, 1)$.

Mathematical Practices

Make Sense of Problems and Persevere in Solving Them

Mathematically proficient students analyze givens, constraints, relationships, and goals.

1. In Exercise 56 on page 527, how did analyzing the given information help you make sense of the problem?

2. Analyze relationships among the terms to find the number of solutions of the equation $-4 = -3x^2 + 12x - 18$. Explain your reasoning.

9 Practice Test WITH CalcChat®

Simplify the expression.

1. $\sqrt{\frac{11}{25}}$

2. $\frac{3}{\sqrt{24}}$

3. $\frac{8}{\sqrt{6} - \sqrt{10}}$

Solve the equation using any method. Explain your choice of method.

4. $x^2 - 121 = 0$

5. $x^2 - 6x = 10$

6. $x^2 - 7x + 12 = 0$

7. $(4x + 3)^2 = 16$

8. $5x^2 + x - 4 = 0$

9. $-2x^2 + 3x + 7 = 0$

10. Can the function $f(x) = 2x^2 + 4x - 6$ be represented by the graph shown? Justify your answer.

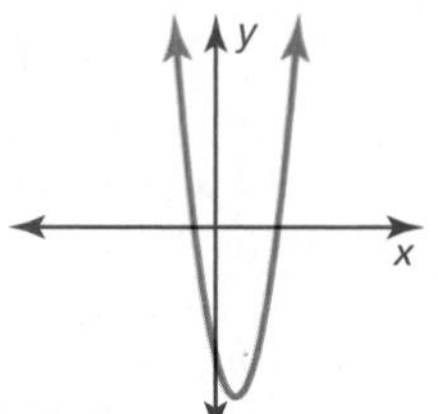

11. Write an expression involving radicals in which a conjugate can be used to simplify the expression. Then simplify the expression.

Solve the system using any method.

12. $y = x^2 - 4x - 2$
$y = -4x + 2$

13. $y = -5x^2 + x - 1$
$y = -7$

14. $y = \frac{1}{2}(4)^x + 1$
$y = x^2 - 2x + 4$

15. The function $h = -16t^2 + 28t + 8$ represents the height h (in feet) of a skier t seconds after jumping off a ramp in a competition. The skier has a perfect landing. How many points does the skier earn?

Criteria	Scoring
Maximum height	1 point per foot
Time in air	5 points per second
Perfect landing	25 points

16. An amusement park ride lifts seated riders 265 feet above the ground. The riders are then dropped and experience free fall until the brakes are activated 105 feet above the ground. The function $h = -16t^2 + 265$ represents the height h (in feet) of the riders t seconds after they are dropped. How long do the riders experience free fall?

17. Write an expression in simplest form that represents the area of the painting shown.

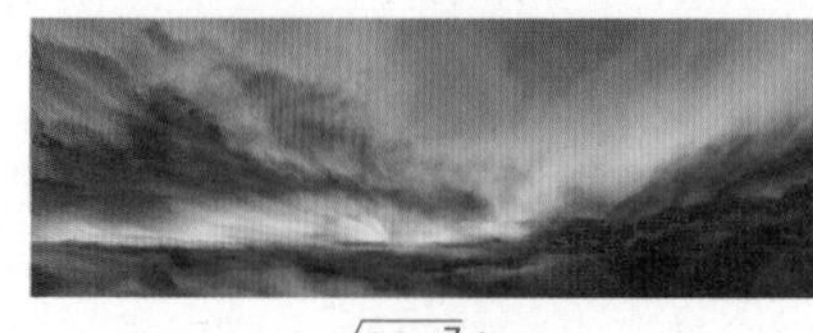

18. The graph of f is a line that passes through $(-6, 2)$ and $(2, 22)$. The graph of g is a parabola that has a vertex of $(4, 3)$ and a y-intercept of 7. Solve $f(x) = g(x)$.

19. The numbers y of two types of bacteria after x hours are represented by the models below. When are there more Type A bacteria than Type B? When are there more Type B bacteria than Type A? Use a graph to support your answers.

$y = 3x^2 + 8x + 20$ Type A

$y = 27x + 60$ Type B

9 Performance Task

A Stellar View

LUMINOSITY (L):
The rate (in watts) at which a star radiates energy.

Luminosity is often thought of as a measure of a star's intrinsic brightness.

BETELGEUSE
$L \approx 4.6 \times 10^{31}$ w
$b \approx 9.8 \times 10^{-8}$ w/m^2

ANTARES
$L \approx 3.7 \times 10^{31}$ w
$b \approx 1.1 \times 10^{-7}$ w/m^2

SUN
$L \approx 3.8 \times 10^{26}$ w
$b \approx 1300$ w/m^2

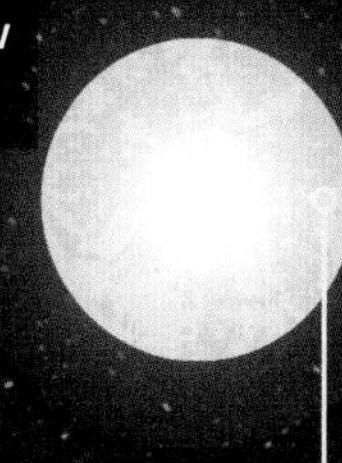

SIRIUS
$L \approx 9.7 \times 10^{27}$ w
$b \approx 1.2 \times 10^{-7}$ w/m^2

ALDEBARAN
$L \approx 2.0 \times 10^{29}$ w
$b \approx 4.1 \times 10^{-8}$ w/m^2

APPARENT BRIGHTNESS (b):
The rate (in watts per square meter) at which a star's radiated energy reaches an observer on Earth.

Apparent brightness is often thought of as a measure of the brightness of a star as observed from Earth.

Luminosity is often expressed in *solar luminosities* ($L_{\odot}$), where 1 $L_{\odot}$ is equal to the luminosity of the Sun.

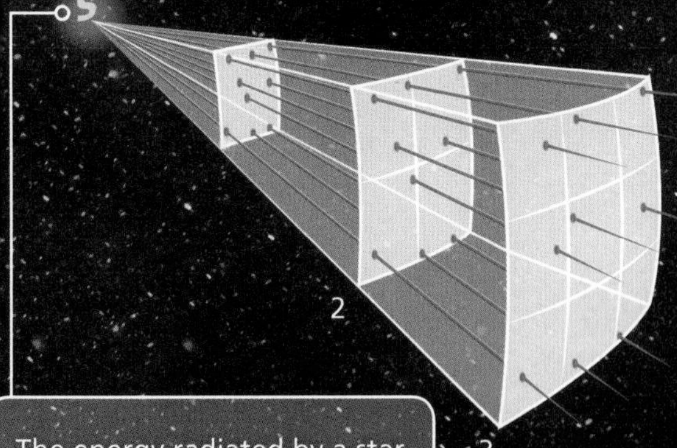

The energy radiated by a star (luminosity) spreads out more and more the farther it travels. The greater the distance between Earth and the star, the less energy is recorded on Earth (apparent brightness).

A JOURNEY THROUGH SPACE

Use the Internet or another resource to find an equation for luminosity in terms of apparent brightness and the distance of a star from Earth. Then use the formula for the surface area of a sphere to explain why the luminosity equation makes sense. Show how you can find the distance to each star above given the star's luminosity and apparent brightness.

Use the Internet to find the luminosity and the distance of a star other than those shown above. What is the apparent brightness of the star?

9 College and Career Readiness WITH CalcChat®

Tutorial videos are available for each exercise.

1. Identify the x- and y-intercepts, and the maximum or minimum value, of the graph of $f(x) = 6x^2 - x - 12$.

2. Which graph could represent the function $y = (x - 5)^2 + 2$?

Ⓐ 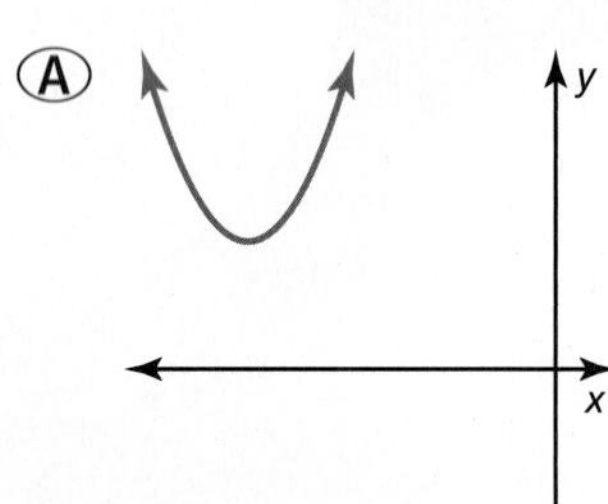

Ⓑ 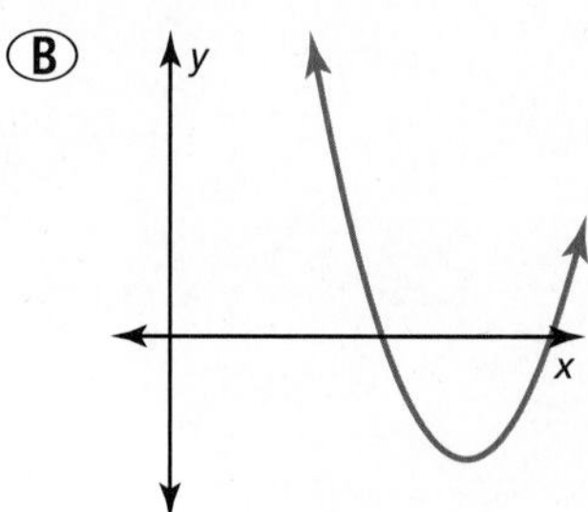

Ⓒ 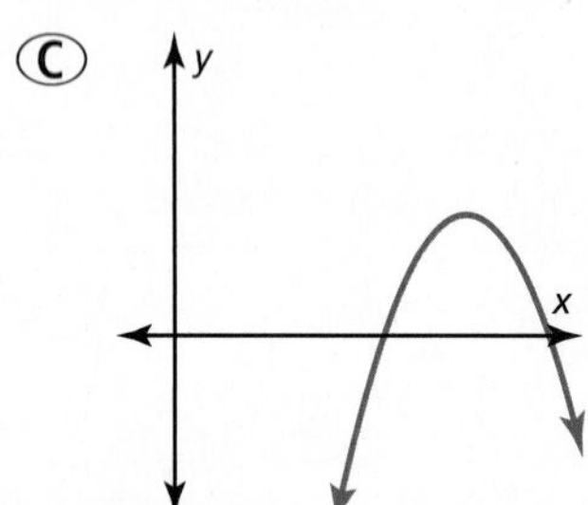

Ⓓ 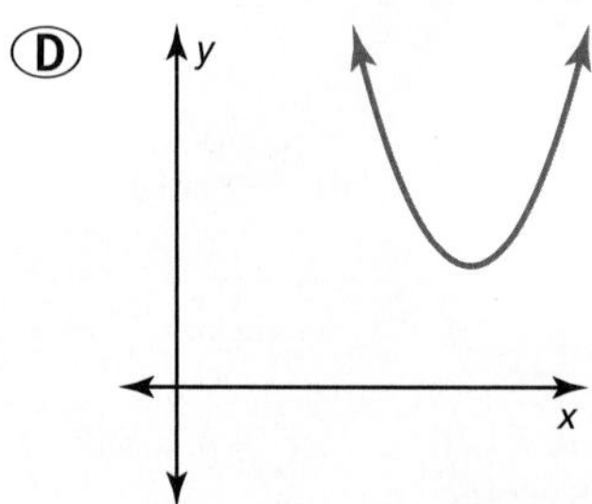

3. The domain of the function shown is restricted to all integers in the interval $-3 < x \leq 3$. Find all the ordered pairs that are solutions of the equation $y = f(x)$.

$$f(x) = 4x - 5$$

4. The table represents the numbers of cups of hot chocolate sold at a concession stand on days with different average temperatures. Interpret the slope and y-intercept of the line of best fit.

Temperature (°F), *x*	Cups of hot chocolate, *y*
73	1
48	11
32	22
62	5
27	28
41	15
14	35

5. Which graph shows exponential growth?

Ⓐ
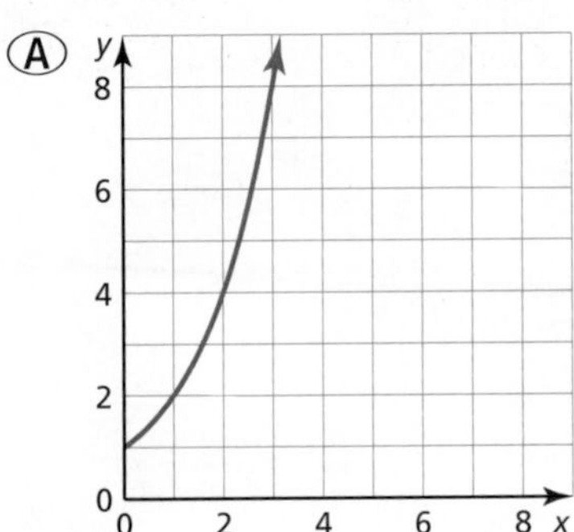

Ⓑ
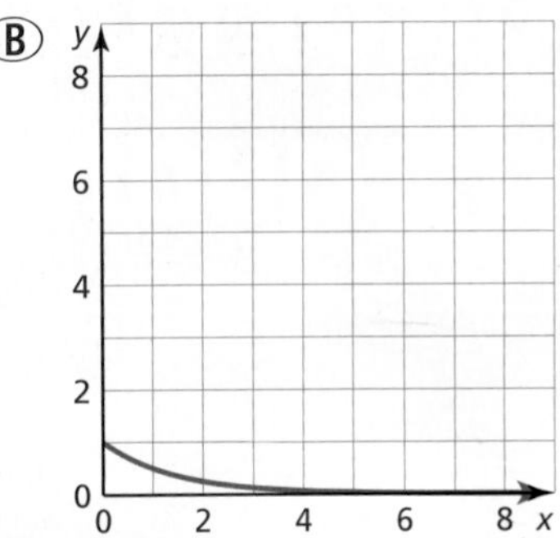

Ⓒ
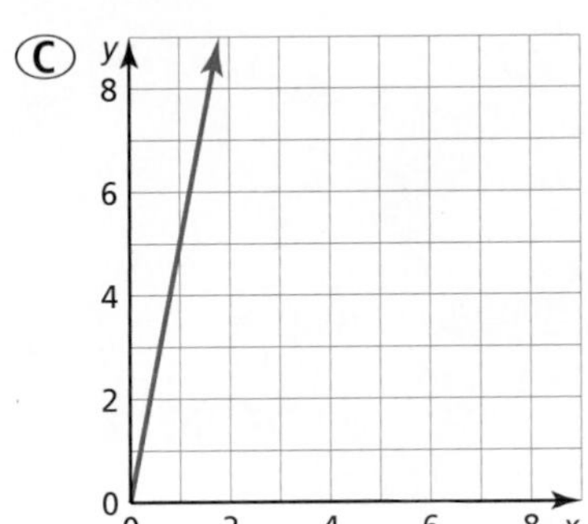

Ⓓ
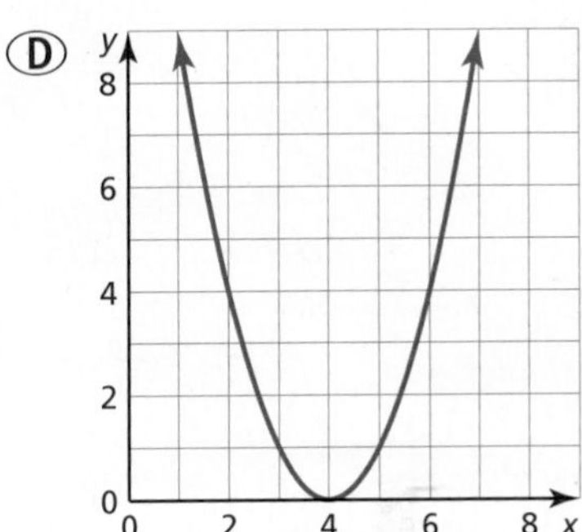

6. Which statement best describes the solution(s) of the system of equations?

$y = x^2 + 2x - 8$
$y = 5x + 2$

Ⓐ The graphs intersect at one point, $(-2, -8)$. So, there is one solution.

Ⓑ The graphs intersect at two points, $(-2, -8)$ and $(5, 27)$. So, there are two solutions.

Ⓒ The graphs do not intersect. So, there is no solution.

Ⓓ The graph of $y = x^2 + 2x - 8$ has two x-intercepts. So, there are two solutions.

7. Which expressions are equivalent to $\sqrt[3]{\dfrac{64x^6}{80}}$? Select all that apply.

Ⓐ $\dfrac{4x^2}{2\sqrt[3]{10}}$

Ⓑ $2x\sqrt[3]{\dfrac{x^2}{10}}$

Ⓒ $\dfrac{4x^2\sqrt[3]{10}}{20}$

Ⓓ $\dfrac{x^2\sqrt[3]{100}}{5}$

8. The function $f(x) = a(1.08)^x$ represents the balance (in dollars) of Account A after x years. The function $g(x) = 600(b)^x$ represents the balance (in dollars) of Account B after x years. Find values for a and b so that each statement is true.

a. Account B has a greater initial amount and increases at a faster rate than Account A.

b. Account B has a lesser initial amount than Account A but increases at a faster rate than Account A.

c. Account B and Account A have the same initial amount, and Account B increases at a slower rate than Account A.

10 Radical Functions and Equations

NATIONAL GEOGRAPHIC EXPLORER

Elora Hayter López

Elora Hayter López is a biologist who uses genomics to study a wide range of topics, including the health of coral reefs in American Samoa and DNA mutations in wildlife living at Bikini Atoll, a former nuclear testing site in the Marshall Islands. López's expedition to Bikini Atoll was featured on the PBS documentary series *Big Pacific*.

- What is DNA? What are DNA mutations?
- How do coral reefs help humans?
- What is coral bleaching? What are other threats to the health of coral reefs?
- How can humans protect the health of coral reefs?

STEM

Coral reefs play a critical role in sustaining aquatic life. In the Performance Task you will write a report that describes the *recovery* and *reassembly* of a damaged coral reef.

Marine Conservation

Preparing for Chapter 10

Chapter Learning Target Understand radical functions and equations.

Chapter Success Criteria
- ◆ I can identify domains and ranges of radical functions.
- ◆ I can graph square root and cube root functions.
- ■ I can solve radical equations.
- ■ I can find inverses of relations and functions.

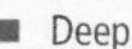

◆ Surface
■ Deep

Chapter Vocabulary

Work with a partner. Discuss each of the vocabulary terms.

square root function
radical function
cube root function
radical equation
inverse relation
inverse function

Mathematical Practices

Reason Abstractly and Quantitatively

Mathematically proficient students bring two complementary abilities to bear on problems involving quantitative relationships: the ability to decontextualize and the ability to contextualize.

Work with a partner. Two functions that undo each other are called *inverses*. For example, the functions shown below are inverses.

$h(x) = 2x + 3$ $\qquad k(x) = \dfrac{x - 3}{2}$

Notice that $h(5) = 13$ and $k(13) = 5$. For any value a, when $h(a) = b$, $k(b) = a$.

1. The function $f(x) = \pi x^2$, $x \geq 0$ gives the area (in square kilometers) enclosed by a circular *atoll* with a radius of x kilometers. Functions f and g are inverses.

a. Complete the table for g. Explain your reasoning.

x	6	7	8	9
$f(x)$	36π	49π	64π	81π

x				
$g(x)$				

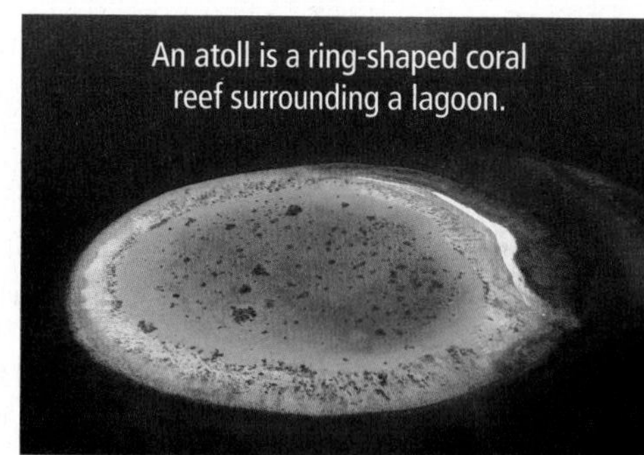
An atoll is a ring-shaped coral reef surrounding a lagoon.

b. What does g represent in this context?

c. Compare the meanings of f and g. How can you use the rule for f to write a rule for g? Can you use this method to find inverses of other functions?

2. Was it necessary to consider the context of the problem in order to complete the table in Exercise 1(a)? Explain.

3. How does considering the context help you write a rule for g in Exercise 1(c)?

10 Prepare WITH CalcChat®

Evaluating Expressions Involving Square Roots

Example 1 **Evaluate $-4(\sqrt{121} - 16)$.**

$$-4(\sqrt{121} - 16) = -4(11 - 16) \quad \text{Evaluate the square root.}$$
$$= -4(-5) \quad \text{Subtract.}$$
$$= 20 \quad \text{Multiply.}$$

Evaluate the expression.

1. $7\sqrt{25} + 10$ **2.** $-8 - \sqrt{\frac{64}{16}}$ **3.** $5\left(\frac{\sqrt{81}}{3} - 7\right)$ **4.** $-2(3\sqrt{9} + 13)$

Transforming Linear Functions

Example 2 **Graph $f(x) = x$ and $g(x) = -3x - 4$. Describe the transformations from the graph of f to the graph of g.**

Note that you can rewrite g as $g(x) = -3f(x) - 4$.

Step 1 There is no horizontal translation from the graph of f to the graph of g.

Step 2 Stretch the graph of f vertically by a factor of 3 to get the graph of $h(x) = 3x$.

Step 3 Reflect the graph of h in the x-axis to get the graph of $r(x) = -3x$.

Step 4 Translate the graph of r vertically 4 units down to get the graph of $g(x) = -3x - 4$.

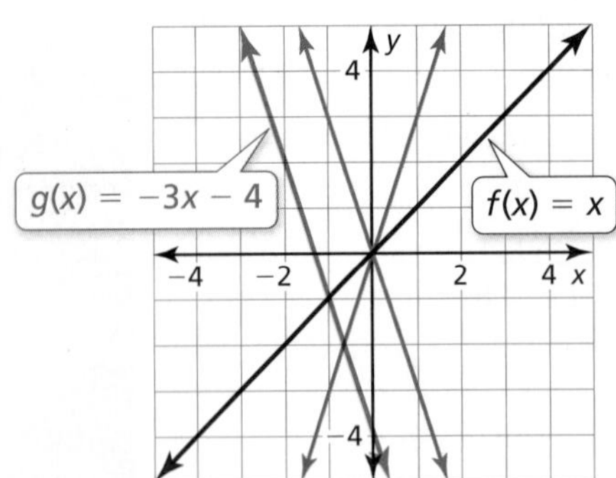

Graph f and g. Describe the transformations from the graph of f to the graph of g.

5. $f(x) = x;\ g(x) = 2x - 2$ **6.** $f(x) = x;\ g(x) = \frac{1}{3}x + 5$ **7.** $f(x) = x;\ g(x) = -x + 3$

8. MP **REASONING** Let a and b represent constants, where $b \geq 0$. Describe the transformations from the graph of $m(x) = ax + b$ to the graph of $n(x) = -2ax - 4b$.

10.1 Graphing Square Root Functions

Learning Target Graph and describe square root functions.

Success Criteria
- I can find the domain and range of a square root function.
- I can graph square root functions.
- I can graph and describe transformations of square root functions.
- I can use square root functions to solve real-life problems.

EXPLORE IT! Graphing Square Root Functions

Math Practice

Critique Reasoning
The expression $\sqrt{x}$ must be positive. Does this imply that the functions in part (b) do not have negative values? Explain.

Work with a partner.

a. Graph $f(x) = \sqrt{x}$. Find the domain and range of the function. Then make several observations about the graph.

b. Describe what you expect the graph of g to look like. Then sketch the graph of g and find the domain and range of the function.

i. $g(x) = 2\sqrt{x}$

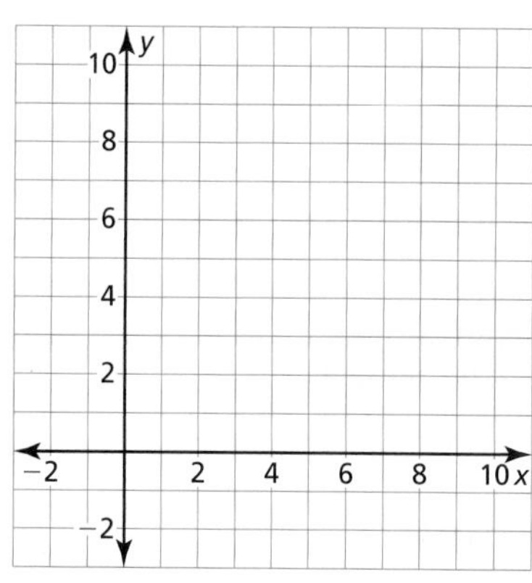

ii. $g(x) = \sqrt{x} - 2$

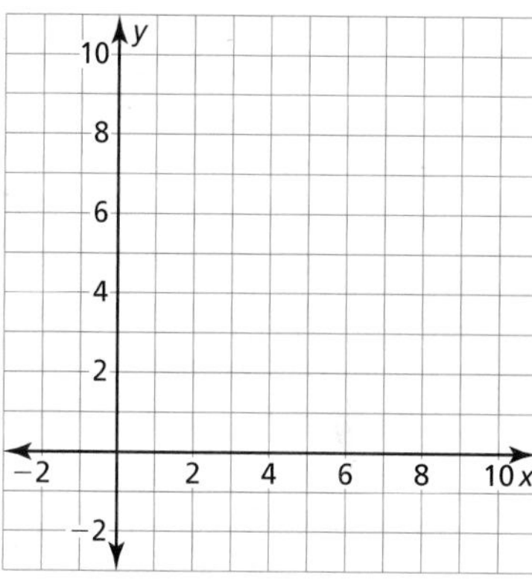

iii. $g(x) = -\sqrt{x}$

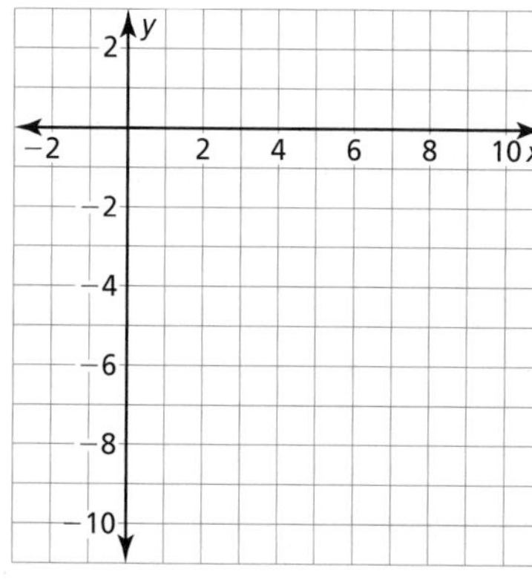

iv. $g(x) = \sqrt{x + 2}$

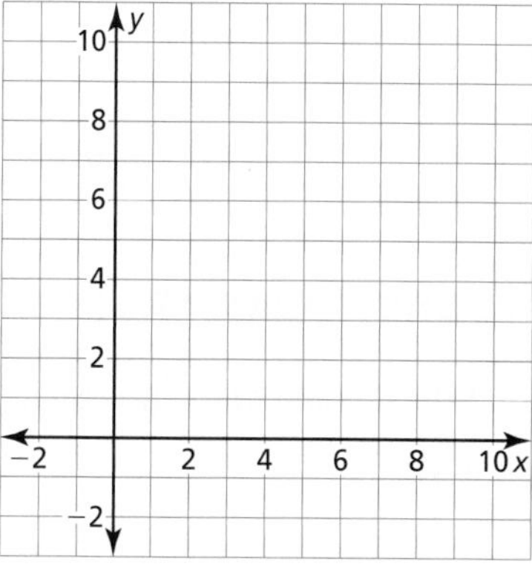

c. Without graphing, compare the graph of $g(x) = -\sqrt{x} - 3$ to the graph of $f(x) = \sqrt{x}$. Explain your reasoning.

d. How are graphs of square root functions similar to graphs of other types of functions you have studied in this course? How are they different?

Graphing Square Root Functions

Vocabulary 

square root function, *p. 548*
radical function, *p. 549*

KEY IDEA

Square Root Functions

A **square root function** is a function that contains a square root with the independent variable in the radicand. The parent function for the family of square root functions is $f(x) = \sqrt{x}$. The domain of f is $x \geq 0$, the range of f is $y \geq 0$, and the function increases over its entire domain.

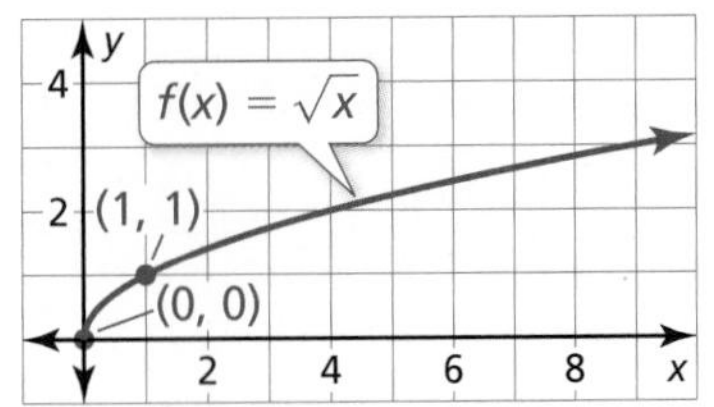

The value of the radicand in a square root function cannot be negative. So, the domain of a square root function includes x-values for which the radicand is greater than or equal to 0.

EXAMPLE 1 Finding the Domain of a Square Root Function

Find the domain of $f(x) = 3\sqrt{x - 5}$.

SOLUTION

The radicand cannot be negative. So, $x - 5$ is greater than or equal to 0.

$x - 5 \geq 0$ Write an inequality for the domain.

$x \geq 5$ Add 5 to each side.

▶ The domain is the set of real numbers greater than or equal to 5.

EXAMPLE 2 Graphing a Square Root Function

Graph $f(x) = \sqrt{x} + 3$. Find the range of the function.

SOLUTION

Step 1 Use the domain of f, $x \geq 0$, to make a table of values.

x	0	1	4	9	16
$f(x)$	3	4	5	6	7

Step 2 Plot the ordered pairs.

Step 3 Draw a smooth curve through the points, starting at (0, 3).

▶ From the graph, you can see that the range of f is $y \geq 3$.

SELF-ASSESSMENT

1 I do not understand. 2 I can do it with help. 3 I can do it on my own. 4 I can teach someone else.

Find the domain of the function.

1. $f(x) = 10\sqrt{x}$
2. $y = \sqrt{2x} + 7$
3. $h(x) = \sqrt{-x + 1}$

Graph the function. Find the range.

4. $g(x) = \sqrt{x} - 4$
5. $y = \sqrt{x + 5}$
6. $n(x) = 5\sqrt{x}$

7. **VOCABULARY** Is $y = 2x\sqrt{5}$ a square root function? Explain.

8. **MP REASONING** Can the domain of a square root function include negative numbers? Can the range include negative numbers? Explain your reasoning.

A **radical function** is a function that contains a radical expression with the independent variable in the radicand. A square root function is a radical function.

You can transform graphs of radical functions in the same way you transformed graphs of functions previously. In Example 2, notice that the graph of f is a vertical translation of the graph of the parent square root function.

KEY IDEA

Transformation	$f(x)$ Notation	Examples	
Horizontal Translation Graph shifts left or right.	$f(x - h)$	$g(x) = \sqrt{x - 2}$ $g(x) = \sqrt{x + 3}$	2 units right 3 units left
Vertical Translation Graph shifts up or down.	$f(x) + k$	$g(x) = \sqrt{x} + 7$ $g(x) = \sqrt{x} - 1$	7 units up 1 unit down
Reflection Graph flips over a line.	$f(-x)$ $-f(x)$	$g(x) = \sqrt{-x}$ $g(x) = -\sqrt{x}$	in the y-axis in the x-axis
Horizontal Stretch or Shrink Graph stretches away from or shrinks toward y-axis by a factor of $\frac{1}{a}$.	$f(ax)$	$g(x) = \sqrt{3x}$ $g(x) = \sqrt{\frac{1}{2}x}$	shrink by a factor of $\frac{1}{3}$ stretch by a factor of 2
Vertical Stretch or Shrink Graph stretches away from or shrinks toward x-axis by a factor of a.	$a \cdot f(x)$	$g(x) = 4\sqrt{x}$ $g(x) = \frac{1}{5}\sqrt{x}$	stretch by a factor of 4 shrink by a factor of $\frac{1}{5}$

EXAMPLE 3 Comparing Graphs of Square Root Functions

Graph $g(x) = -\sqrt{x - 2}$. Compare the graph to the graph of $f(x) = \sqrt{x}$.

SOLUTION

Step 1 Use the domain of g, $x \geq 2$, to make a table of values.

x	2	3	6	11
g(x)	0	−1	−2	−3

Step 2 Plot the ordered pairs.

Step 3 Draw a smooth curve through the points, starting at (2, 0).

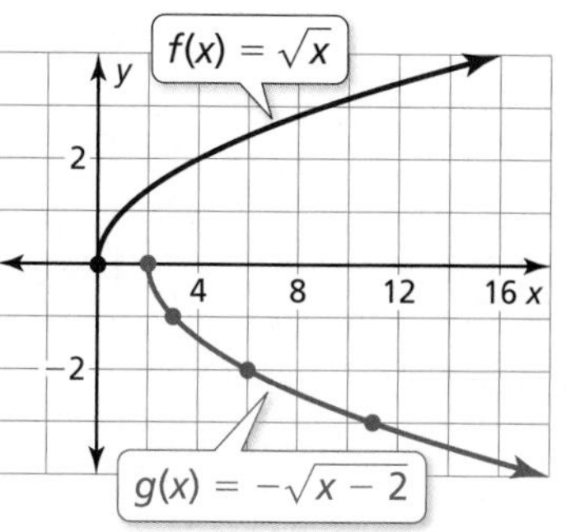

▶ The graph of g is a translation 2 units right and a reflection in the x-axis of the graph of f.

SELF-ASSESSMENT

1 I do not understand. 2 I can do it with help. 3 I can do it on my own. 4 I can teach someone else.

Graph the function. Compare the graph to the graph of $f(x) = \sqrt{x}$.

9. $h(x) = \sqrt{\frac{1}{4}x}$

10. $g(x) = \sqrt{x} - 6$

11. $m(x) = -3\sqrt{x}$

EXAMPLE 4 Graphing $y = a\sqrt{x - h} + k$

Graph $g(x) = -2\sqrt{x - 3} - 2$. Describe the transformations from the graph of $f(x) = \sqrt{x}$ to the graph of g.

SOLUTION

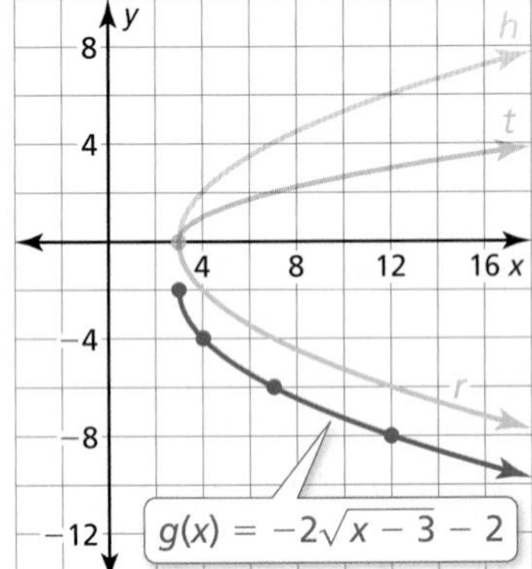

Refer to the steps in Section 3.7, which show you how to obtain the graph of $y = a \cdot f(x - h) + k$ from the graph of $y = f(x)$.

Step 1 Translate the graph of f horizontally 3 units right: $t(x) = \sqrt{x - 3}$

Step 2 Stretch the graph of t vertically by a factor of 2: $h(x) = 2\sqrt{x - 3}$

Step 3 Reflect the graph of h in the x-axis: $r(x) = -2\sqrt{x - 3}$

Step 4 Translate the graph of r vertically 2 units down: $g(x) = -2\sqrt{x - 3} - 2$

▶ The graph of g is a horizontal translation 3 units right, a vertical stretch by a factor of 2, a reflection in the x-axis, and a translation 2 units down of the graph of f.

SELF-ASSESSMENT

1 I do not understand. 2 I can do it with help. 3 I can do it on my own. 4 I can teach someone else.

12. Graph $g(x) = \frac{1}{2}\sqrt{x + 4} + 1$. Describe the transformations from the graph of $f(x) = \sqrt{x}$ to the graph of g.

13. **MP REASONING** What is the domain of a function of the form $f(x) = a\sqrt{x - h} + k$? At what point does the graph of a function of this form start?

Comparing Average Rates of Change

EXAMPLE 5 Comparing Square Root Functions

Free-Falling Object on Earth

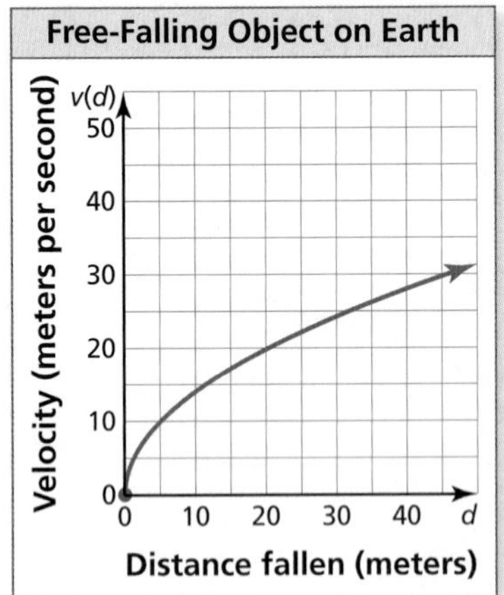

The velocity (in meters per second) of an object after free-falling d meters on Earth is different than its velocity after free-falling d meters on the moon. Compare the velocities using their average rates of change over the interval $d = 0$ to $d = 10$.

Free-Falling Object on the Moon
$v(d) = \sqrt{3.2d}$

SOLUTION

To calculate the average rates of change, use points whose d-coordinates are 0 and 10.

Earth: Use the graph to estimate. Use (0, 0) and (10, 14).

$$\frac{v(10) - v(0)}{10 - 0} \approx \frac{14 - 0}{10} = \frac{1.4 \text{ m/sec}}{\text{m}}$$ Average rate of change on Earth

Moon: Find $v(d)$ when $d = 0$ and $d = 10$.

$$v(0) = \sqrt{3.2(0)} = 0 \quad \text{and} \quad v(10) = \sqrt{3.2(10)} = \sqrt{32}$$

Use (0, 0) and $(10, \sqrt{32})$.

$$\frac{v(10) - v(0)}{10 - 0} = \frac{\sqrt{32} - 0}{10} \approx \frac{0.57 \text{ m/sec}}{\text{m}}$$ Average rate of change on the moon

▶ Because 1.4 > 0.57, the velocity of an object free-falling from 0 to 10 meters increases at a greater average rate on Earth than on the moon.

EXAMPLE 6 Modeling Real Life

The velocity (in meters per second) of a tsunami can be modeled by the function $v(x) = \sqrt{9.8x}$, where x is the water depth (in meters).

a. At what depth is the velocity of the tsunami about 200 meters per second?

b. What happens to the average rate of change of the velocity as the water depth increases?

SOLUTION

1. **Understand the Problem** You are given a model that represents the velocity of a tsunami as a function of water depth. You are asked to find the depth for a given velocity and to describe the average rate of change of the velocity as the water depth increases.
2. **Make a Plan** Use technology to graph the function and find where $v(x) \approx 200$. Then calculate and compare average rates of change of the velocity over different intervals.
3. **Solve and Check**

a. Use technology to graph the function. Find the value of x for which $v(x) \approx 200$.

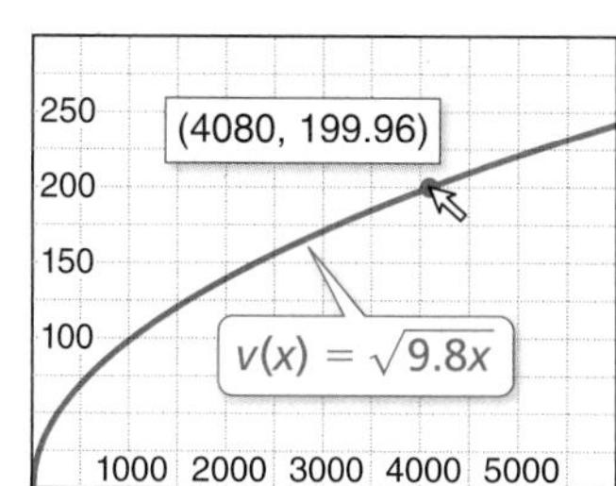

▶ The velocity is about 200 meters per second at a depth of about 4080 meters.

b. Calculate the average rates of change over the intervals $x = 0$ to $x = 1000$, $x = 1000$ to $x = 2000$, and $x = 2000$ to $x = 3000$.

$$\frac{v(1000) - v(0)}{1000 - 0} = \frac{\sqrt{9800} - 0}{1000} \approx 0.099 \qquad \text{0 to 1000 meters}$$

$$\frac{v(2000) - v(1000)}{2000 - 1000} = \frac{\sqrt{19{,}600} - \sqrt{9800}}{1000} \approx 0.041 \qquad \text{1000 to 2000 meters}$$

$$\frac{v(3000) - v(2000)}{3000 - 2000} = \frac{\sqrt{29{,}400} - \sqrt{19{,}600}}{1000} \approx 0.031 \qquad \text{2000 to 3000 meters}$$

▶ The average rate of change of the velocity decreases as the water depth increases.

Check To check the answer in part (a), find $v(x)$ when $x = 4080$.

$$v(4080) = \sqrt{9.8(4080)} \approx 200 \checkmark$$

In part (b), the slopes of the line segments that represent the average rates of change over the intervals are decreasing. So, the answer to part (b) is reasonable.

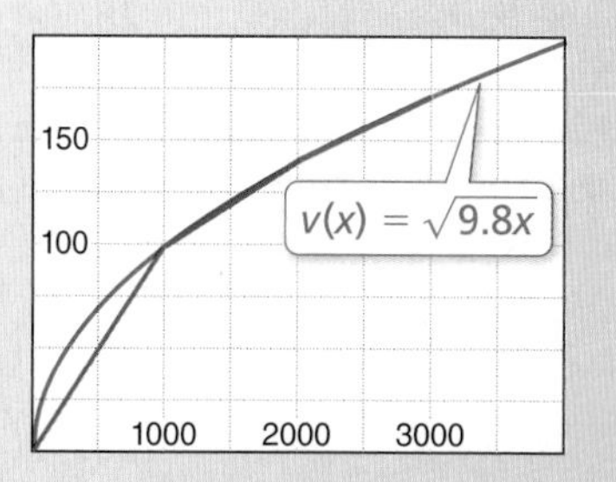

SELF-ASSESSMENT

1 I do not understand. 2 I can do it with help. 3 I can do it on my own. 4 I can teach someone else.

14. In Example 5, compare the velocities using their average rates of change over the interval $d = 30$ to $d = 40$.

15. WHAT IF? In Example 6(a), at what depth is the velocity of the tsunami about 100 meters per second? Does your answer in part (b) change when you compare the velocities using their average rates of change over the intervals $x = 0$ to $x = 2000$, $x = 2000$ to $x = 4000$, and $x = 4000$ to $x = 6000$?

10.1 Practice WITH CalcChat® AND CalcView®

In Exercises 1–10, find the domain of the function. *Example 1*

1. $y = 8\sqrt{x}$
2. $y = \sqrt{4x}$
3. $y = 4 + \sqrt{-x}$
4. $y = \sqrt{-\frac{1}{2}x} + 1$
5. $h(x) = \sqrt{x - 4}$
6. $p(x) = \sqrt{x + 7}$
7. $f(x) = \sqrt{-x + 8}$
8. $g(x) = \sqrt{-x - 1}$
9. $m(x) = 2\sqrt{x + 4}$
10. $n(x) = \frac{1}{2}\sqrt{-x} - 2$

In Exercises 11–18, graph the function. Find the range. *Example 2*

11. $y = \sqrt{3x}$
12. $y = 4\sqrt{-x}$
13. $y = \sqrt{x} + 5$
14. $y = -2 + \sqrt{x}$
15. $f(x) = -\sqrt{x - 3}$
16. $g(x) = \sqrt{x + 4}$
17. $h(x) = \sqrt{x + 2} - 2$
18. $f(x) = -\sqrt{x - 1} + 3$

In Exercises 19–26, graph the function. Compare the graph to the graph of $f(x) = \sqrt{x}$. *Example 3*

19. $g(x) = \frac{1}{4}\sqrt{x}$
20. $r(x) = \sqrt{2x}$
21. $h(x) = \sqrt{x + 3}$
22. $q(x) = \sqrt{x} + 8$
23. $p(x) = \sqrt{-\frac{1}{3}x}$
24. $g(x) = -5\sqrt{x}$
25. $m(x) = -\sqrt{x} - 6$
26. $n(x) = -\sqrt{x - 4}$

In Exercises 27–34, graph h. Describe the transformations from the graph of $f(x) = \sqrt{x}$ to the graph of h. *Example 4*

27. $h(x) = 4\sqrt{x + 2} - 1$
28. $h(x) = \frac{1}{2}\sqrt{x - 6} + 3$
29. $h(x) = 2\sqrt{-x} - 6$
30. $h(x) = -\sqrt{x - 3} - 2$
31. $h(x) = \frac{1}{3}\sqrt{x + 3} - 3$
32. $h(x) = 2\sqrt{x - 1} + 4$
33. $h(x) = -2\sqrt{x - 1} + 5$
34. $h(x) = -5\sqrt{x + 2} - 1$

35. **MP REASONING** Is the graph of $g(x) = 1.25\sqrt{x}$ a vertical stretch or a vertical shrink of the graph of $f(x) = \sqrt{x}$? Explain.

36. **MP REASONING** Without graphing, determine which function's graph increases at a greater rate, $f(x) = 5\sqrt{x}$ or $g(x) = \sqrt{5x}$. Explain your reasoning.

37. **ERROR ANALYSIS** Describe and correct the error in graphing the function $y = \sqrt{x + 1}$.

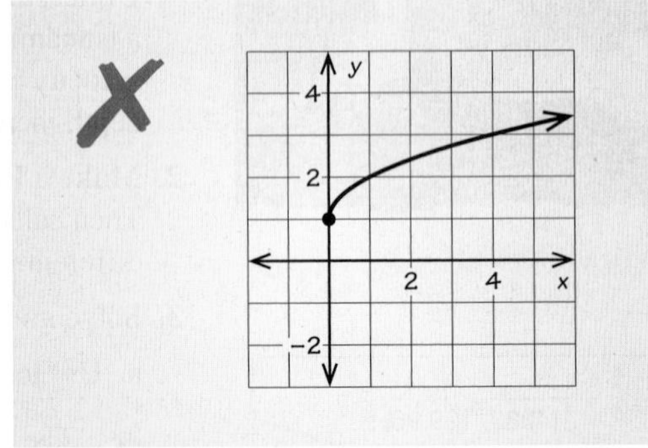

38. **ERROR ANALYSIS** Describe and correct the error in comparing the graph of $g(x) = -\frac{1}{4}\sqrt{x}$ to the graph of $f(x) = \sqrt{x}$.

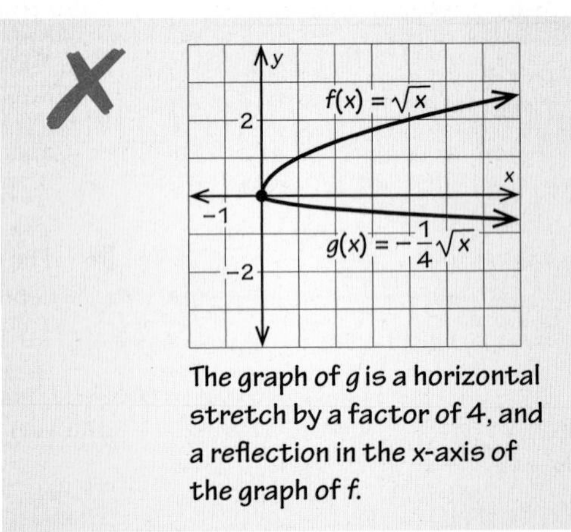

39. **COLLEGE PREP** The graph of which function is shown?

Ⓐ $y = \sqrt{x - 12}$

Ⓑ $y = \sqrt{x} - 12$

Ⓒ $y = \sqrt{x + 12}$

Ⓓ $y = \sqrt{-x + 12}$

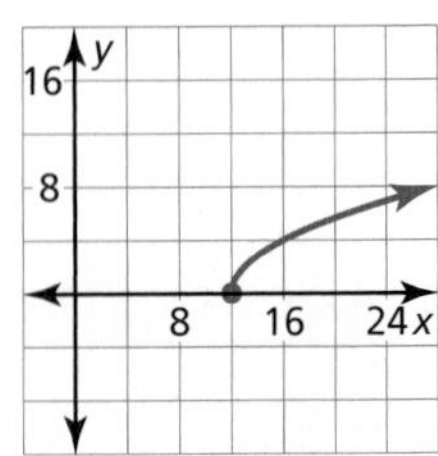

40. **MP REASONING** Consider a function of the form $f(x) = a\sqrt{x - h} + k$. Describe when the function is increasing or decreasing when (a) $a > 0$ and (b) $a < 0$.

41. **COMPARING FUNCTIONS** The model $S(d) = \sqrt{30df}$ represents the speed (in miles per hour) of a van before it skids to a stop, where f is the drag factor of the road surface and d is the length (in feet) of the skid marks. The drag factor of Road Surface A is 0.75. The graph shows the speed of the van on Road Surface B. Compare the speeds using their average rates of change over the interval $d = 0$ to $d = 15$. *Example 5*

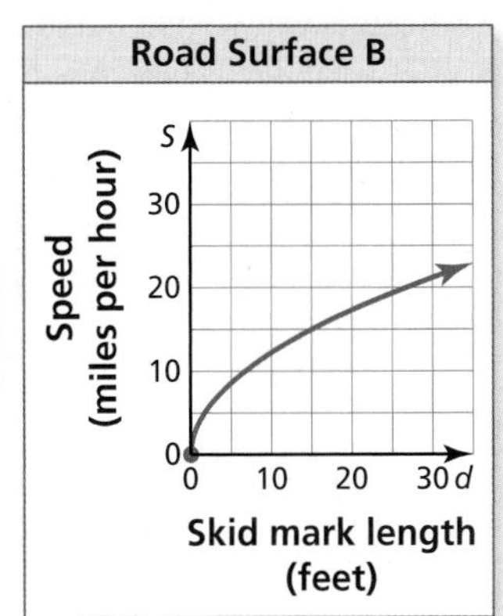

42. **COMPARING FUNCTIONS** The velocity (in meters per second) of an object in motion is given by $v(E) = \sqrt{\frac{2E}{m}}$, where E is the kinetic energy of the object (in joules) and m is the mass of the object (in kilograms). The mass of Object A is 4 kilograms. The graph shows the velocity of Object B. Compare the velocities of the objects using their average rates of change over the interval $E = 0$ to $E = 6$.

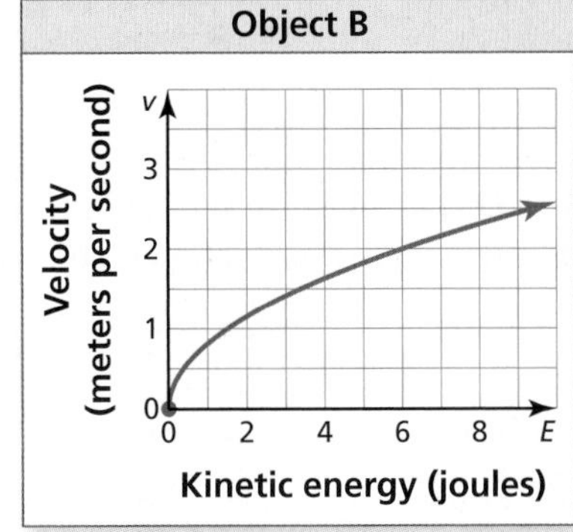

43. **MODELING REAL LIFE** The nozzle pressure of a fire hose allows firefighters to control the amount of water they spray on a fire. The flow rate f (in gallons per minute) can be modeled by the function $f = 120\sqrt{p}$, where p is the nozzle pressure (in pounds per square inch). *Example 6*

a. Use technology to graph the function. At what pressure is the flow rate about 300 gallons per minute?

b. What happens to the average rate of change of the flow rate as the pressure increases?

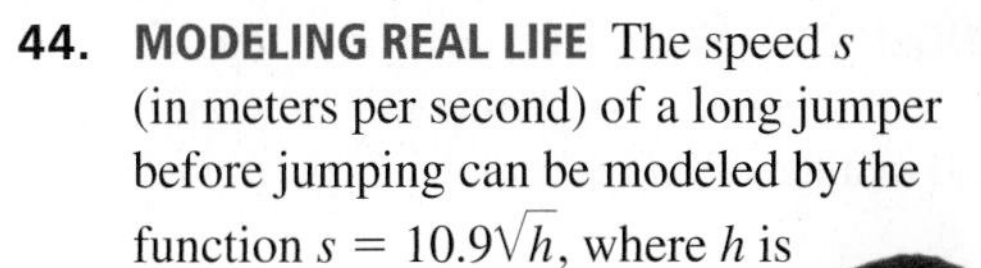

44. **MODELING REAL LIFE** The speed s (in meters per second) of a long jumper before jumping can be modeled by the function $s = 10.9\sqrt{h}$, where h is the maximum height (in meters from the ground) reached by the jumper.

a. Use technology to graph the function. Estimate the maximum height reached by a jumper running 9.2 meters per second.

b. Suppose the runway and pit are raised on a platform slightly higher than the ground. How would the graph of the function be transformed?

45. **CONNECTING CONCEPTS** The radius r of a circle is given by $r = \sqrt{\frac{A}{\pi}}$, where A is the area of the circle.

a. Find the domain of the function. Use technology to graph the function.

b. Approximate the area of a circle with a radius of 5.4 inches.

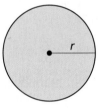

46. MP **REASONING** Consider the function $f(x) = 8a\sqrt{x}$.

a. For what value of a will the graph of f be identical to the graph of the parent square root function?

b. For what values of a will the graph of f be a vertical stretch of the graph of the parent square root function?

c. For what values of a will the graph of f be a vertical shrink and a reflection of the graph of the parent square root function?

47. **MAKING AN ARGUMENT** Can a square root function have a minimum value? a maximum value? both? Explain your reasoning.

48. **THOUGHT PROVOKING**
Use a graphical approach to find the solutions of $x - 1 = \sqrt{5x - 9}$. Show your work. Verify your solutions algebraically.

49. **OPEN-ENDED** Write a radical function that has a domain of all real numbers greater than or equal to -5 and a range of all real numbers less than or equal to 3.

50. **HOW DO YOU SEE IT?**
Match each function with its graph. Explain your reasoning.

i. $f(x) = \sqrt{x} + 2$ **ii.** $m(x) = f(x) - 4$

iii. $n(x) = f(-x)$ **iv.** $p(x) = f(3x)$

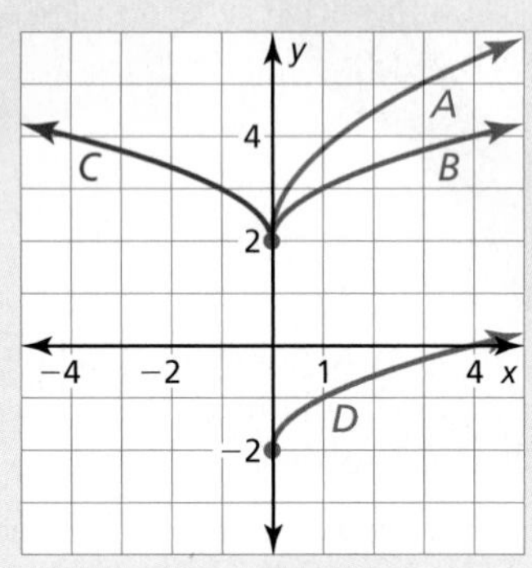

51. **PERFORMANCE TASK** When administering medication, it is critical for doctors to prescribe the correct dosage, especially for children. Body surface area (BSA) can be used to calculate appropriate dosages. Mosteller's Formula, shown below, estimates a person's body surface area (in square meters), where H is the height (in centimeters), and W is the weight (in kilograms) of the person. Use the heights and weights of at least two different children between the ages of 6 and 12 to calculate the correct dosage of each medication in the table. Research these medications and write a prescription for each child that includes how the medication should be administered, how often, and for how many days.

GO DIGITAL

Mosteller's Formula: $BSA = \sqrt{\dfrac{H \bullet W}{3600}}$

Medication	Recommended Daily Dose
Mitoxantrone	18 mg/m^2
Cytarabine	100 mg/m^2
Cyclophosphamide	600 mg/m^2

REVIEW & REFRESH

WATCH

In Exercises 52–55, evaluate the expression.

52. $\sqrt[3]{343}$

53. $\sqrt[3]{-64}$

54. $-\sqrt[3]{-\frac{1}{27}}$

55. $\sqrt[3]{\frac{8}{125}}$

56. **MODELING REAL LIFE** The table shows your daily usage time x (in minutes) and your cell phone's remaining battery percentage y.

x	24	40	55	67	79	92	107
y	88	83	80	76	68	63	54

a. Write a linear equation that models the battery percentage as a function of the usage time.

b. Interpret the slope and y-intercept of the line of fit.

In Exercises 57–59, factor the polynomial.

57. $x^2 + 7x + 6$

58. $d^2 - 11d + 28$

59. $y^2 - 3y - 40$

In Exercises 60–63, simplify the expression.

60. $\sqrt{108n^5}$

61. $6\sqrt{3} - \sqrt{7} + 8\sqrt{3}$

62. $\sqrt[3]{\dfrac{c}{-1000}}$

63. $\dfrac{20}{\sqrt{2} + \sqrt{6}}$

64. Does the graph represent a *linear* or *nonlinear* function? Explain.

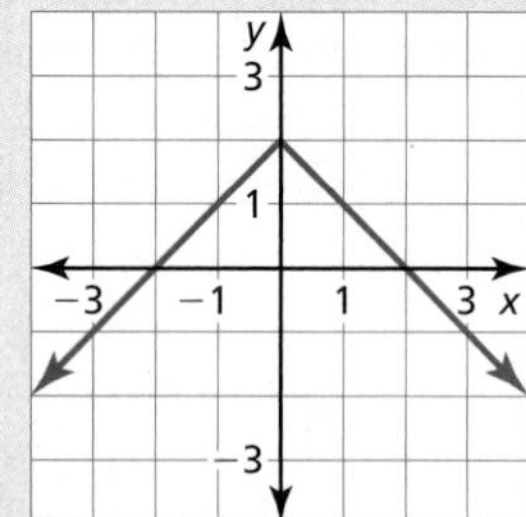

In Exercises 65 and 66, solve the equation using any method. Explain your choice of method.

65. $x^2 + 6x = 27$

66. $2x^2 - 11x + 13 = 0$

67. Graph $g(x) = \sqrt{x - 8} + 4$. Compare the graph to the graph of $f(x) = \sqrt{x}$.

68. **OPEN-ENDED** Write a quadratic function whose graph has a vertex of (1, 2).

In Exercises 69 and 70, approximate the solution(s) of the system to the nearest thousandth.

69. $y = \left(\frac{1}{2}\right)^x$
$y = -x^2 + 4x + 3$

70. $y = 3x^2 - x$
$y = -2(4)^x + 3$

71. Write the sentence as an inequality. Graph the inequality.

A number z is no less than 4 and fewer than 10.

10.2 Graphing Cube Root Functions

Learning Target Graph and describe cube root functions.

Success Criteria
- I can graph cube root functions.
- I can graph and describe transformations of cube root functions.
- I can use cube root functions to solve real-life problems.

EXPLORE IT! Graphing Cube Root Functions

Work with a partner.

a. Graph $f(x) = \sqrt[3]{x}$. Find the domain and range of the function. Then make several observations about the graph.

b. Describe what you expect the graph of g to look like. Then sketch the graph of g and find the domain and range of the function.

i. $g(x) = 2\sqrt[3]{x}$

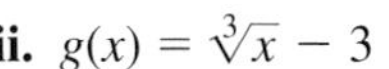
ii. $g(x) = \sqrt[3]{x} - 3$

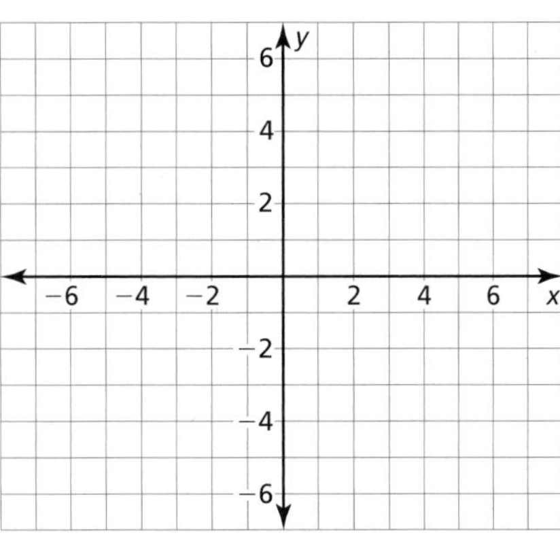

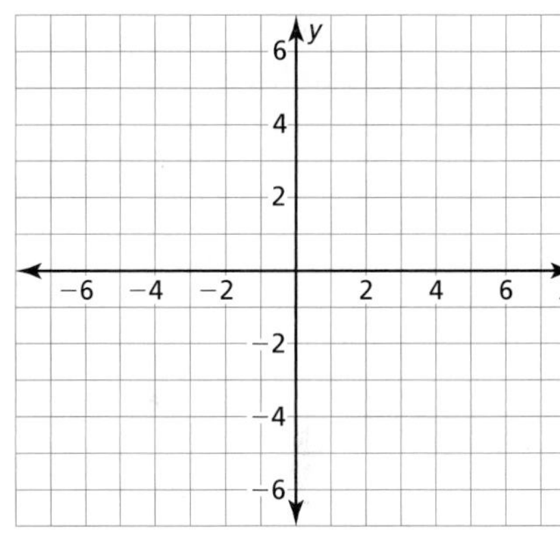

iii. $g(x) = -\sqrt[3]{x}$

iv. $g(x) = \sqrt[3]{x + 3}$

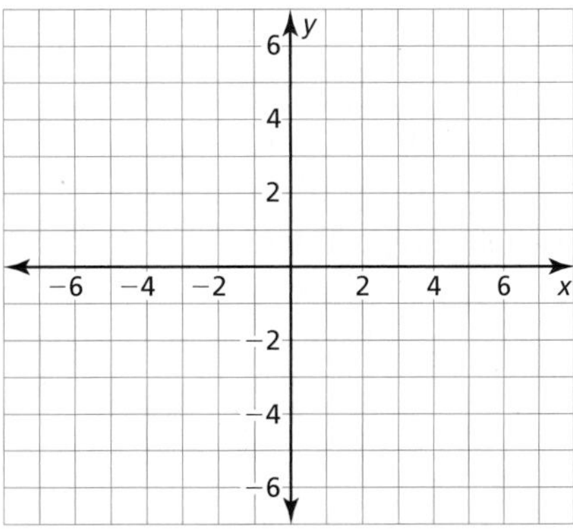

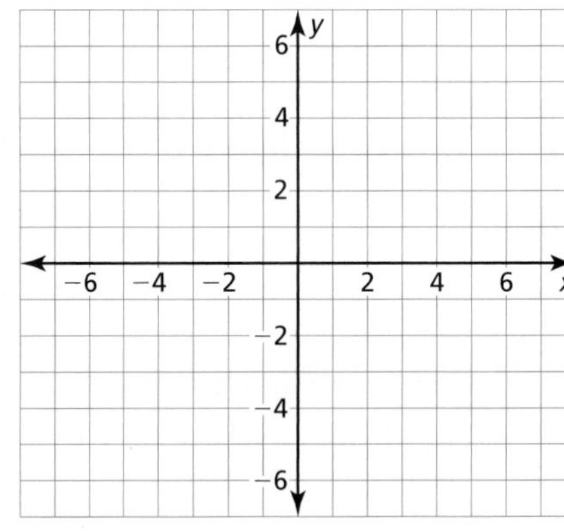

c. Without graphing, compare the graph of $g(x) = -\sqrt[3]{x + 3} + 1$ to the graph of $f(x) = \sqrt[3]{x}$. Explain your reasoning.

d. How are graphs of cube root functions similar to graphs of other types of functions? How are they different?

Math Practice

Critique Reasoning
All real numbers have a cube root. Does this imply that the domain of each function in part (b) is all real numbers? Explain.

Graphing Cube Root Functions

Vocabulary 

cube root function, *p. 556*

KEY IDEA

Cube Root Functions

A **cube root function** is a radical function with an index of 3. The parent function for the family of cube root functions is $f(x) = \sqrt[3]{x}$. The domain and range of f are all real numbers.

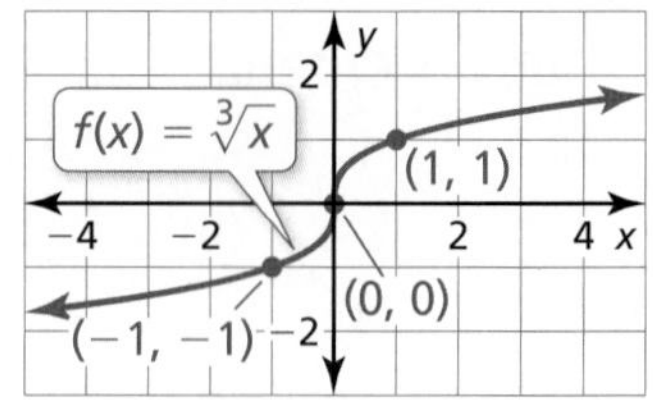

You can transform graphs of cube root functions in the same way you transformed graphs of square root functions.

EXAMPLE 1 Comparing Graphs of Cube Root Functions

Graph $h(x) = \sqrt[3]{x} - 4$. Compare the graph to the graph of $f(x) = \sqrt[3]{x}$.

SOLUTION

Step 1 Make a table of values.

x	−8	−1	0	1	8
$h(x)$	−6	−5	−4	−3	−2

Math Practice

Look for Structure
Explain how to choose convenient x-values when making the table.

Step 2 Plot the ordered pairs.

Step 3 Draw a smooth curve through the points.

▶ The graph of h is a translation 4 units down of the graph of f.

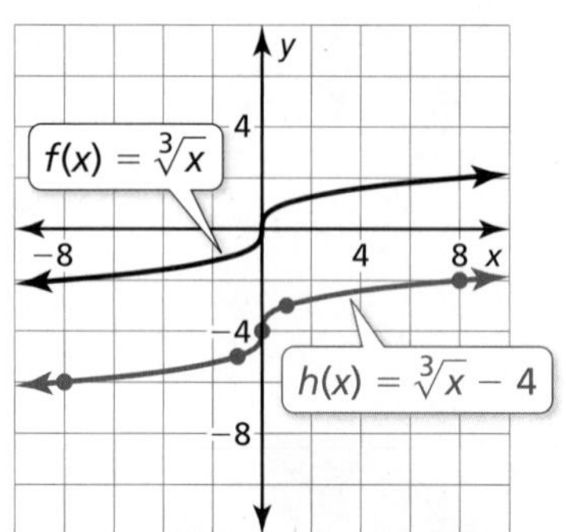

SELF-ASSESSMENT 1 I do not understand. 2 I can do it with help. 3 I can do it on my own. 4 I can teach someone else.

Graph the function. Compare the graph to the graph of $f(x) = \sqrt[3]{x}$.

1. $h(x) = \sqrt[3]{x} + 3$
2. $m(x) = \sqrt[3]{x - 5}$
3. $g(x) = 4\sqrt[3]{x}$

Match the function with its graph.

4. $h(x) = \sqrt[3]{x + 2}$
5. $m(x) = \sqrt[3]{x - 2}$
6. $g(x) = \sqrt[3]{x} + 2$
7. $g(x) = \sqrt[3]{x} - 2$

A. 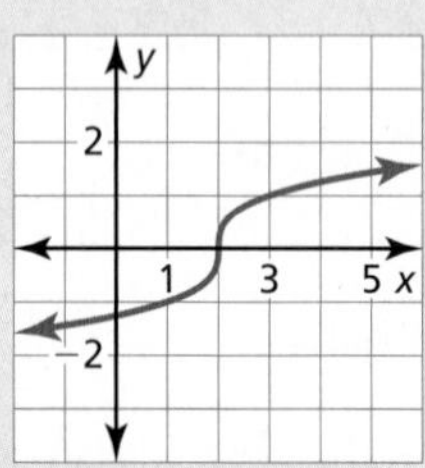

B. 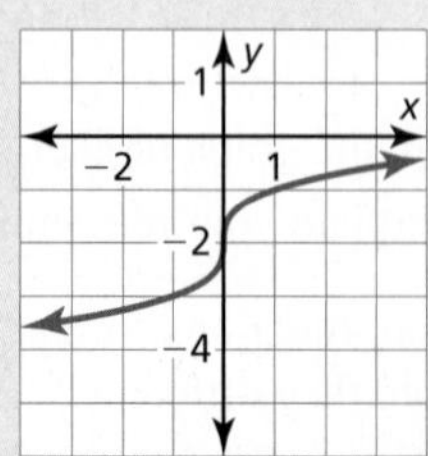

C. 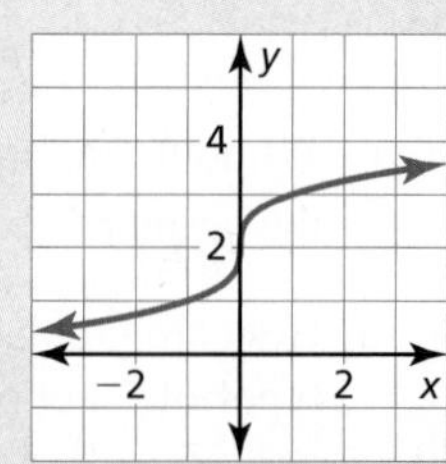

D. 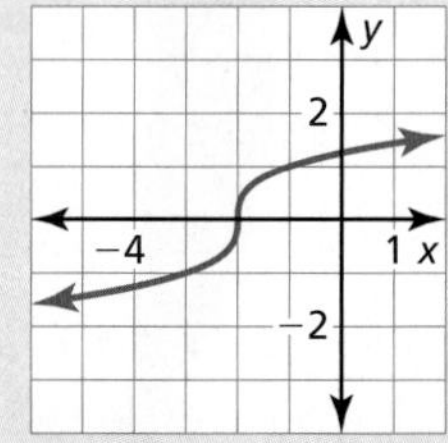

EXAMPLE 2 Comparing Graphs of Cube Root Functions

WATCH

Graph $g(x) = -\sqrt[3]{x+2}$. Compare the graph to the graph of $f(x) = \sqrt[3]{x}$.

SOLUTION

Step 1 Make a table of values.

x	−10	−3	−2	−1	6
$g(x)$	2	1	0	−1	−2

Step 2 Plot the ordered pairs.

Step 3 Draw a smooth curve through the points.

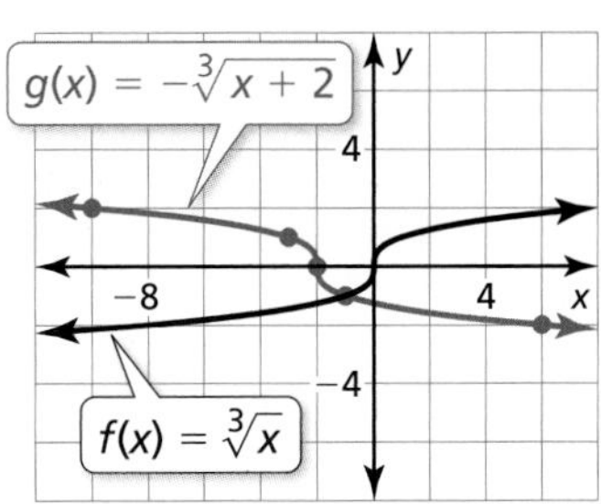

▶ The graph of g is a translation 2 units left and a reflection in the x-axis of the graph of f.

EXAMPLE 3 Graphing $y = a\sqrt[3]{x-h} + k$

Graph $g(x) = 2\sqrt[3]{x-3} + 4$. Describe the transformations from the graph of $f(x) = \sqrt[3]{x}$ to the graph of g.

SOLUTION

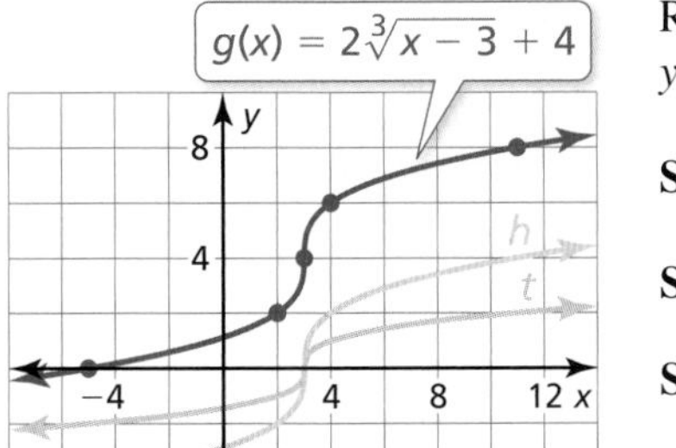

Refer to the steps in Section 3.7, which show you how to obtain the graph of $y = a \cdot f(x-h) + k$ from the graph of $y = f(x)$.

Step 1 Translate the graph of f horizontally 3 units right: $t(x) = \sqrt[3]{x-3}$

Step 2 Stretch the graph of t vertically by a factor of 2: $h(x) = 2\sqrt[3]{x-3}$

Step 3 Because $a > 0$, there is no reflection.

Step 4 Translate the graph of h vertically 4 units up: $g(x) = 2\sqrt[3]{x-3} + 4$

▶ The graph of g is a translation 3 units right, a vertical stretch by a factor of 2, and a translation 4 units up of the graph of f.

SELF-ASSESSMENT

1 I do not understand. 2 I can do it with help. 3 I can do it on my own. 4 I can teach someone else.

Graph the function. Compare the graph to the graph of $f(x) = \sqrt[3]{x}$.

8. $g(x) = \sqrt[3]{0.5x} + 5$ **9.** $h(x) = 4\sqrt[3]{x-1}$ **10.** $n(x) = \sqrt[3]{4-x}$

11. Graph $g(x) = -\frac{1}{2}\sqrt[3]{x+2} - 4$. Describe the transformations from the graph of $f(x) = \sqrt[3]{x}$ to the graph of g.

12. WRITING Explain why the domain and range of $y = a\sqrt[3]{x-h} + k$ are all real numbers.

13. MP REASONING Compare the graphs of $y = \sqrt[3]{-x}$ and $y = -\sqrt[3]{x}$. What does this mean in terms of transformations?

Comparing Average Rates of Change

EXAMPLE 4 Comparing Cube Root Functions

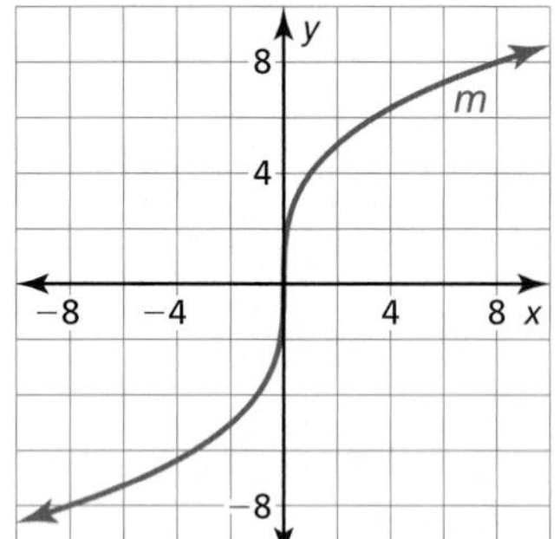

The graph of cube root function m is shown. Compare the average rate of change of m to the average rate of change of $h(x) = \sqrt[3]{\frac{1}{4}x}$ over the interval $x = 0$ to $x = 8$.

SOLUTION

To calculate the average rates of change, use points whose x-coordinates are 0 and 8.

Function m: Use the graph to estimate. Use (0, 0) and (8, 8).

$$\frac{m(8) - m(0)}{8 - 0} \approx \frac{8 - 0}{8} = 1 \qquad \text{Average rate of change of } m$$

Function h: Evaluate h when $x = 0$ and $x = 8$.

$$h(0) = \sqrt[3]{\tfrac{1}{4}(0)} = 0 \qquad \text{and} \qquad h(8) = \sqrt[3]{\tfrac{1}{4}(8)} = \sqrt[3]{2}$$

Use (0, 0) and $\left(8, \sqrt[3]{2}\right)$.

$$\frac{h(8) - h(0)}{8 - 0} = \frac{\sqrt[3]{2} - 0}{8} \approx 0.16 \qquad \text{Average rate of change of } h$$

▶ Because $1 > 0.16$, the average rate of change of m is greater than the average rate of change of h over the interval $x = 0$ to $x = 8$.

Solving Real-Life Problems

EXAMPLE 5 Modeling Real Life

The shoulder height h (in centimeters) of a male Asian elephant can be modeled by the function $h = 62.5\sqrt[3]{t} + 75.8$, where t is the age (in years) of the elephant. Estimate the age of an elephant whose shoulder height is 200 centimeters.

SOLUTION

The solution is the t-value for which $h = 200$. So, solve $200 = 62.5\sqrt[3]{t} + 75.8$.

One way to find the solution is to graph each side of the equation, as shown. Use technology to find the coordinates of the point of intersection.

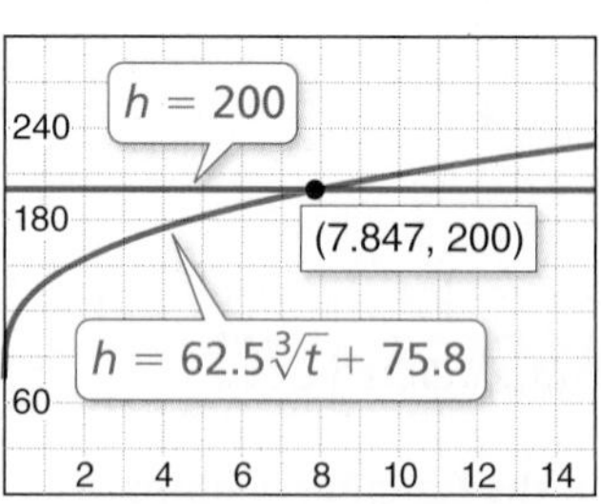

The two graphs intersect at about (8, 200).

▶ So, the elephant is about 8 years old.

SELF-ASSESSMENT 1 I do not understand. 2 I can do it with help. 3 I can do it on my own. 4 I can teach someone else.

14. In Example 4, compare the average rate of change of m to the average rate of change of $g(x) = 8\sqrt[3]{x}$ over the interval $x = 2$ to $x = 8$.

15. WHAT IF? Estimate the age of an elephant whose shoulder height is 175 centimeters.

10.2 Practice WITH CalcChat® AND CalcView®

In Exercises 1–6, graph the function. Compare the graph to the graph of $f(x) = \sqrt[3]{x}$. *Example 1*

1. $h(x) = \sqrt[3]{x - 4}$
2. $g(x) = \sqrt[3]{x + 1}$
3. $m(x) = \sqrt[3]{x} + 5$
4. $q(x) = \sqrt[3]{x} - 3$
5. $p(x) = 6\sqrt[3]{x}$
6. $j(x) = \sqrt[3]{\frac{1}{2}x}$

In Exercises 7–10, compare the graphs. Find the value of *h*, *k*, or *a*.

7.

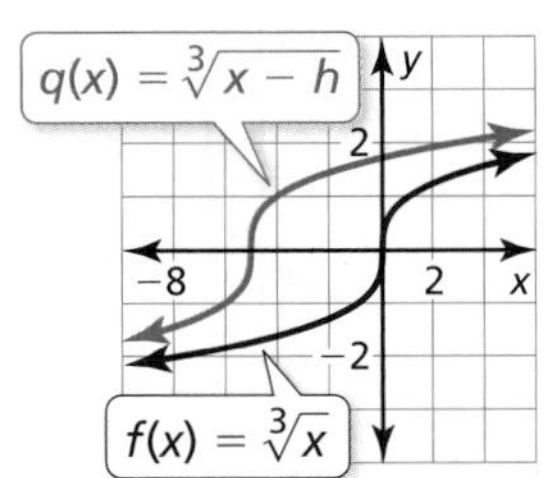

8.

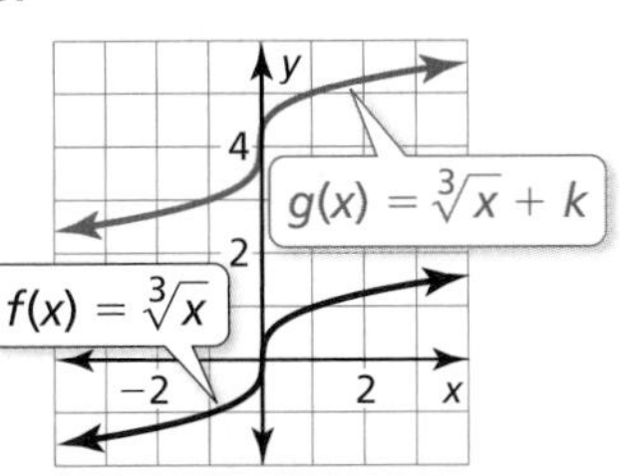

9.

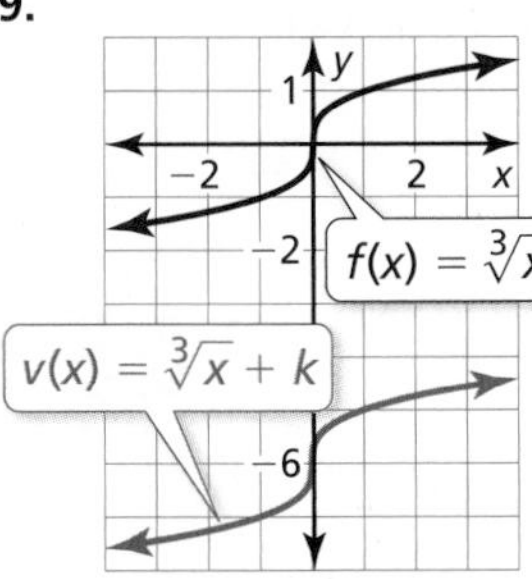

10.

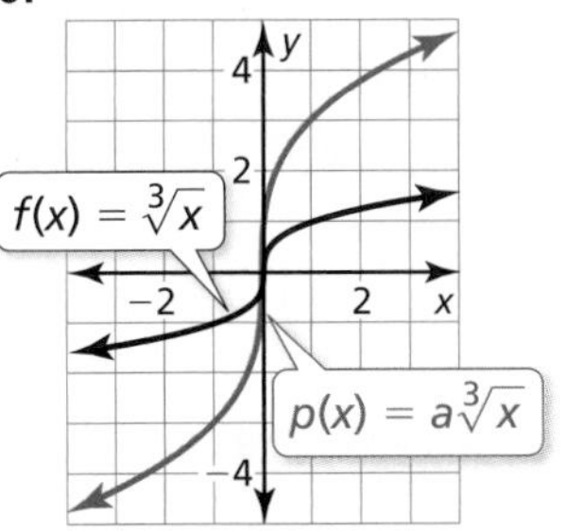

In Exercises 11–20, graph the function. Compare the graph to the graph of $f(x) = \sqrt[3]{x}$. *Example 2*

11. $r(x) = -\sqrt[3]{x - 2}$
12. $h(x) = -\sqrt[3]{x} + 3$
13. $k(x) = 5\sqrt[3]{x + 1}$
14. $j(x) = 0.5\sqrt[3]{x - 4}$
15. $g(x) = 4\sqrt[3]{x} - 3$
16. $m(x) = 3\sqrt[3]{x} + 7$
17. $n(x) = \sqrt[3]{-8x} - 1$
18. $v(x) = \sqrt[3]{5x} + 2$
19. $q(x) = \sqrt[3]{2(x + 3)}$
20. $p(x) = \sqrt[3]{3(1 - x)}$

In Exercises 21–26, graph the function. Describe the transformations from the graph of $f(x) = \sqrt[3]{x}$ to the graph of the given function. *Example 3*

21. $g(x) = \sqrt[3]{x - 4} + 2$
22. $n(x) = \sqrt[3]{x + 1} - 3$
23. $j(x) = -5\sqrt[3]{x + 3} + 2$
24. $k(x) = 6\sqrt[3]{x - 9} - 5$
25. $v(x) = \frac{1}{3}\sqrt[3]{x - 1} + 7$
26. $h(x) = -\frac{3}{2}\sqrt[3]{x + 4} - 3$

ERROR ANALYSIS In Exercises 27 and 28, describe and correct the error in graphing the function.

27. $f(x) = \sqrt[3]{x - 3}$

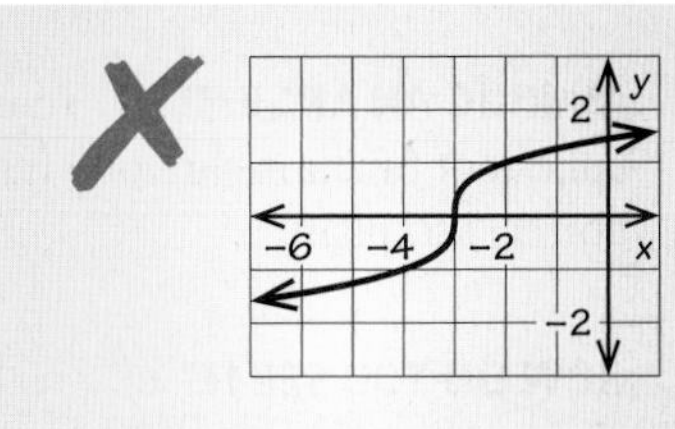

28. $h(x) = \sqrt[3]{x} + 1$

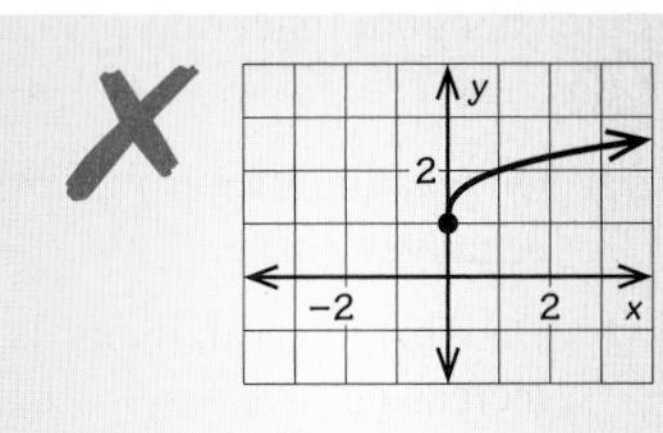

In Exercises 29 and 30, compare the average rate of change of *f* to the average rate of change of *q* over the given interval. *Example 4*

29. $f(x) = 3\sqrt[3]{x}$; $x = 0$ to $x = 6$
30. $f(x) = \sqrt[3]{0.5x}$; $x = -2$ to $x = 2$

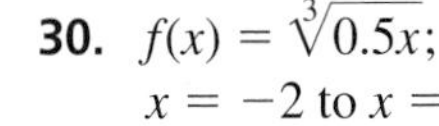

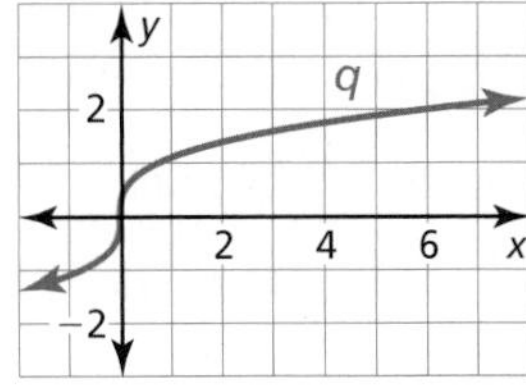

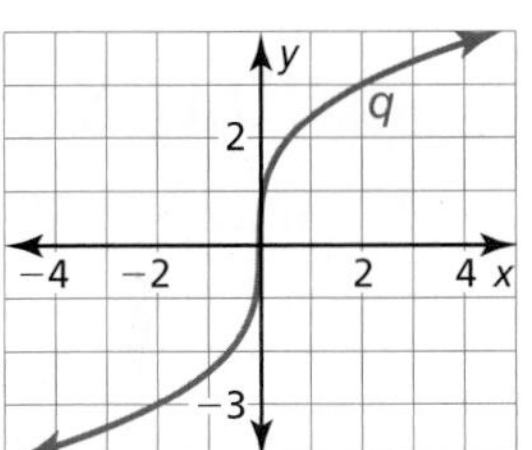

31. **MODELING REAL LIFE** The radius *r* of a sphere is given by $r = \sqrt[3]{\frac{3}{4\pi}V}$, where *V* is the volume of the sphere. Estimate the volume of a spherical head of brain coral with a radius of 1.5 feet. *Example 5*

32. **MODELING REAL LIFE** For a drag race car that weighs 1600 kilograms, the velocity v (in kilometers per hour) reached by the end of a drag race can be modeled by the function $v = 23.8\sqrt[3]{p}$, where p is the car's power (in horsepower). Estimate the power of a 1600-kilogram car that reaches a velocity of 220 kilometers per hour.

33. **MAKING AN ARGUMENT** Your friend says that all cube root functions are odd functions. Is your friend correct? Explain.

34. **HOW DO YOU SEE IT?**
The graph represents the cube root function $f(x) = \sqrt[3]{x}$.

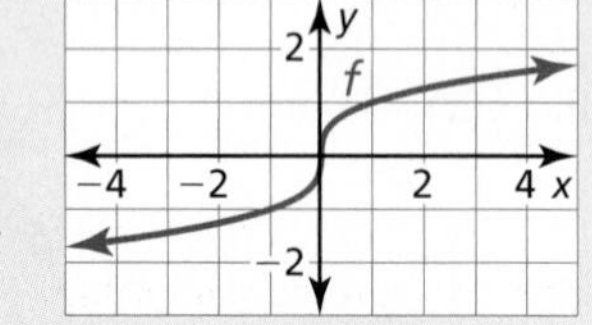

   a. On what interval is f negative? positive?
   b. On what interval, if any, is f decreasing? increasing?
   c. Does f have a maximum or minimum value? Explain.
   d. Describe the end behavior of f.
   e. Find the average rate of change of f over the interval $x = -1$ to $x = 1$.

35. **MP REASONING** Can a cube root function be increasing on part of its domain and decreasing on a different part of its domain? Explain your reasoning.

36. **COLLEGE PREP** Which of the following describes the transformations from the graph of $f(x) = \sqrt[3]{x+5} + 2$ to the graph of $g(x) = \sqrt[3]{x-1} - 2$?
   (A) a translation 1 unit right and 2 units down
   (B) a translation 1 unit left and 2 units down
   (C) a translation 6 units right and 4 units down
   (D) a translation 6 units left and 4 units down

37. **MP REASONING** Write the cube root function represented by the graph.

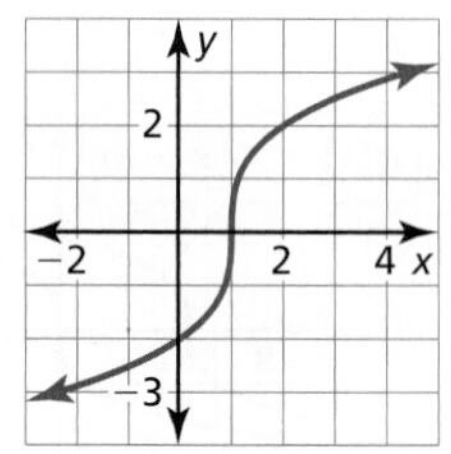

38. **THOUGHT PROVOKING**
Write a cube root function that passes through the point (3, 4) and has an average rate of change of −1 over the interval $x = -5$ to $x = 2$.

REVIEW & REFRESH

In Exercises 39–42, factor the polynomial.

39. $x^2 - 20x + 75$
40. $3x^2 + 12x - 36$
41. $2x^2 - 11x + 9$
42. $4x^2 + 7x - 15$

In Exercises 43 and 44, find the domain of the function.

43. $f(x) = 15\sqrt{x}$
44. $y = \sqrt{3 - x}$

45. Determine whether the graph represents a function. Explain.

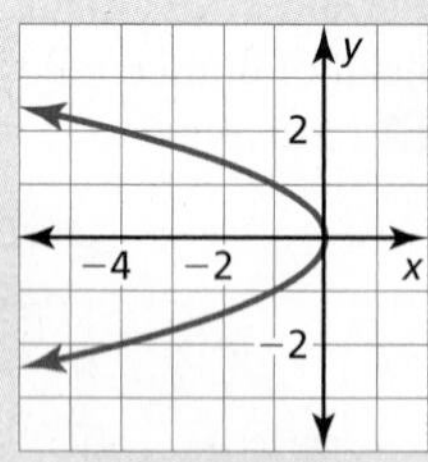

46. **MODELING REAL LIFE** You can use at most 5 gigabytes of data per month on your cell phone. Your data usage so far for the month is 1.24 gigabytes. What are the possible amounts of data you can use for the remainder of the month?

47. **MP REASONING** A quadratic equation has 1 real solution. What do you know about the value of the discriminant?

In Exercises 48–51, solve the equation.

48. $x^2 - 36 = 0$
49. $5x^2 + 20 = 0$
50. $(x + 4)^2 = 81$
51. $25(x - 2)^2 = 9$

In Exercises 52 and 53, graph the function. Compare the graph to the graph of $f(x) = \sqrt[3]{x}$.

52. $g(x) = \sqrt[3]{x + 7}$
53. $h(x) = -\sqrt[3]{x} - 6$

54. Write a cubic function represented by the table in standard form.

x	−3	−2	0	1
y	0	−18	0	0

In Exercises 55 and 56, solve the equation. Round your solution(s) to the nearest hundredth.

55. $0.5(4)^x + 1 = -x^2 + 6x$
56. $x^2 - 3x - 4 = 5^x - 2$

10.3 Solving Radical Equations

Learning Target Solve radical equations and identify any extraneous solutions.

Success Criteria
- I can identify radical equations.
- I can solve radical equations.
- I can identify extraneous solutions of radical equations.
- I can solve real-life problems involving radical equations.

EXPLORE IT! Solving Radical Equations

Work with a partner.

a. A student solves the radical equations below as shown. Justify each solution step and describe the method the student used.

i. $\sqrt{x+1} - 7 = -5$ **ii.** $\sqrt{x+1} + 7 = 5$

i.

$\sqrt{x+1} - 7 = -5$	Write the equation.
$\sqrt{x+1} = 2$	______
$(\sqrt{x+1})^2 = 2^2$	______
$x + 1 = 4$	______
$x = 3$	______

ii.

$\sqrt{x+1} + 7 = 5$	Write the equation.
$\sqrt{x+1} = -2$	______
$(\sqrt{x+1})^2 = (-2)^2$	______
$x + 1 = 4$	______
$x = 3$	______

b. Check each solution. What do you notice? Why do you think this happened?

c. Explain how to solve each equation using the method shown above. Check your solutions and analyze your results.

i. $\sqrt{x} = 4$ **ii.** $\sqrt{x} = -10$

iii. $-5 = \sqrt{x+20}$ **iv.** $4 = \sqrt{x-18}$

v. $\sqrt{x} + 2 = 3$ **vi.** $-3 = -2\sqrt{x}$

d. Write a radical equation that has an extraneous solution. Explain how you found your answer.

Math Practice

Consider Similar Problems

How can you use your knowledge of extraneous solutions of absolute value equations to reason about extraneous solutions of radical equations?

Solving Radical Equations

GO DIGITAL

Vocabulary 

radical equation, *p. 562*

A **radical equation** is an equation that contains a radical expression with a variable in the radicand. To solve a radical equation involving a square root, first use properties of equality to isolate the radical on one side of the equation, if necessary. Then use the following property to eliminate the radical and solve for the variable.

KEY IDEA

Squaring Each Side of an Equation

Words If two expressions are equal, then their squares are also equal.

Algebra If $a = b$, then $a^2 = b^2$.

EXAMPLE 1 Solving Radical Equations 

Solve each equation.

a. $\sqrt{x} + 5 = 13$ **b.** $3 - \sqrt{x} = 0$ **c.** $4\sqrt{x+2} + 3 = 19$

SOLUTION

a. $\sqrt{x} + 5 = 13$ Write the equation.

$\sqrt{x} = 8$ Subtract 5 from each side.

$(\sqrt{x})^2 = 8^2$ Square each side of the equation.

$x = 64$ Simplify.

▶ The solution is $x = 64$.

b. $3 - \sqrt{x} = 0$ Write the equation.

$3 = \sqrt{x}$ Add $\sqrt{x}$ to each side.

$3^2 = (\sqrt{x})^2$ Square each side of the equation.

$9 = x$ Simplify.

▶ The solution is $x = 9$.

c. $4\sqrt{x+2} + 3 = 19$ Write the equation.

$4\sqrt{x+2} = 16$ Subtract 3 from each side.

$\sqrt{x+2} = 4$ Divide each side by 4.

$(\sqrt{x+2})^2 = 4^2$ Square each side of the equation.

$x + 2 = 16$ Simplify.

$x = 14$ Subtract 2 from each side.

▶ The solution is $x = 14$.

Check

$4\sqrt{x+2} + 3 = 19$

$4\sqrt{14+2} + 3 \stackrel{?}{=} 19$

$4\sqrt{16} + 3 \stackrel{?}{=} 19$

$4(4) + 3 \stackrel{?}{=} 19$

$19 = 19$ ✓

SELF-ASSESSMENT 1 I do not understand. 2 I can do it with help. 3 I can do it on my own. 4 I can teach someone else.

Solve the equation. Check your solution.

1. $\sqrt{x} = 6$ **2.** $\sqrt{x} - 7 = 3$ **3.** $\sqrt{y} + 15 = 22$

4. $1 - \sqrt{c} = -2$ **5.** $\sqrt{x+4} + 7 = 11$ **6.** $15 = 6 + \sqrt{3w - 9}$

EXAMPLE 2 Solving an Equation with Radicals on Both Sides

Solve $\sqrt{2x-1} = \sqrt{x+4}$.

SOLUTION

Method 1

$\sqrt{2x-1} = \sqrt{x+4}$	Write the equation.
$\left(\sqrt{2x-1}\right)^2 = \left(\sqrt{x+4}\right)^2$	Square each side of the equation.
$2x - 1 = x + 4$	Simplify.
$x = 5$	Solve for x.

▶ The solution is $x = 5$.

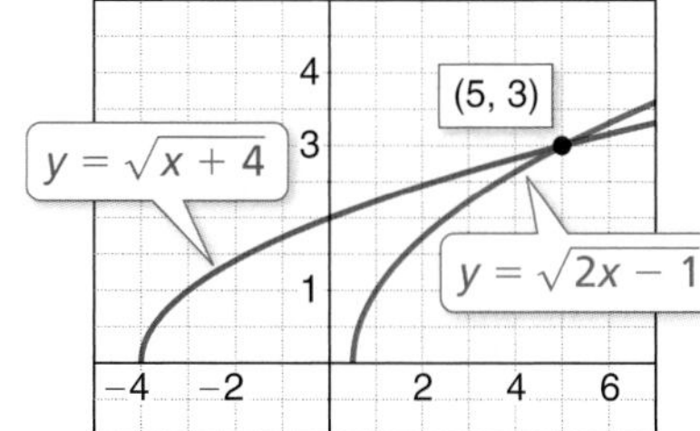

Method 2 Graph each side of the equation, as shown. Use technology to find the coordinates of the point of intersection. The two graphs intersect at (5, 3).

▶ So, the solution is $x = 5$.

EXAMPLE 3 Solving a Radical Equation Involving a Cube Root

Solve each equation.

a. $\sqrt[3]{x} + 7 = -1$ **b.** $\sqrt[3]{5x-2} = 12$

SOLUTION

a.

$\sqrt[3]{x} + 7 = -1$	Write the equation.
$\sqrt[3]{x} = -8$	Subtract 7 from each side.
$\left(\sqrt[3]{x}\right)^3 = (-8)^3$	Cube each side of the equation.
$x = -512$	Simplify.

▶ The solution is $x = -512$.

Math Practice

Consider Similar Problems

Compare solving a radical equation involving a cube root to solving a radical equation involving a square root. How can you solve a radical equation involving an *n*th root?

b.

$\sqrt[3]{5x-2} = 12$	Write the equation.
$\left(\sqrt[3]{5x-2}\right)^3 = 12^3$	Cube each side of the equation.
$5x - 2 = 1728$	Simplify.
$x = 346$	Solve for x.

▶ The solution is $x = 346$.

Check

$$\sqrt[3]{5x-2} = 12$$
$$\sqrt[3]{5(346)-2} \stackrel{?}{=} 12$$
$$\sqrt[3]{1728} \stackrel{?}{=} 12$$
$$12 = 12 \checkmark$$

SELF-ASSESSMENT

1 I do not understand. 2 I can do it with help. 3 I can do it on my own. 4 I can teach someone else.

Solve the equation. Check your solution.

7. $\sqrt{3x+1} = \sqrt{4x-7}$ **8.** $\sqrt{n} = \sqrt{5n-1}$ **9.** $\sqrt{\frac{w}{4} - 5} = \sqrt{w-20}$

10. $\sqrt[3]{x} = -6$ **11.** $\sqrt[3]{y} - 4 = 1$ **12.** $\sqrt[3]{3c+7} = 10$

13. WHICH ONE DOESN'T BELONG? Which equation does *not* belong with the other three? Explain your reasoning.

$\sqrt{x} + 6 = 10$ $2\sqrt{x+3} = 32$ $x\sqrt{3} - 5 = 4$ $\sqrt{x-1} = 16$

GO DIGITAL

Math Practice

Consider Simpler Forms

To understand how extraneous solutions can be introduced, consider the equation $\sqrt{x} = -2$. This equation has no real solution, however, you obtain $x = 4$ after squaring each side.

Identifying Extraneous Solutions

Squaring each side of an equation can sometimes introduce an extraneous solution.

EXAMPLE 4 Identifying an Extraneous Solution

Solve $x = \sqrt{x + 6}$.

SOLUTION

$x = \sqrt{x+6}$	Write the equation.
$x^2 = \left(\sqrt{x+6}\right)^2$	Square each side of the equation.
$x^2 = x + 6$	Simplify.
$x^2 - x - 6 = 0$	Subtract x and 6 from each side.
$(x-3)(x+2) = 0$	Factor.
$x - 3 = 0$ *or* $x + 2 = 0$	Zero-Product Property
$x = 3$ *or* $x = -2$	Solve for x.

Check Check each solution in the original equation.

$3 \stackrel{?}{=} \sqrt{3+6}$	Substitute for x.	$-2 \stackrel{?}{=} \sqrt{-2+6}$
$3 \stackrel{?}{=} \sqrt{9}$	Simplify.	$-2 \stackrel{?}{=} \sqrt{4}$
$3 = 3$ ✓	Simplify.	$-2 \neq 2$ ✗

▶ Because $x = -2$ does not satisfy the original equation, it is an extraneous solution. The only solution is $x = 3$.

EXAMPLE 5 Identifying an Extraneous Solution

Solve $13 + \sqrt{5n} = 3$.

SOLUTION

$13 + \sqrt{5n} = 3$	Write the equation.
$\sqrt{5n} = -10$	Subtract 13 from each side.
$\left(\sqrt{5n}\right)^2 = (-10)^2$	Square each side of the equation.
$5n = 100$	Simplify.
$n = 20$	Divide each side by 5.

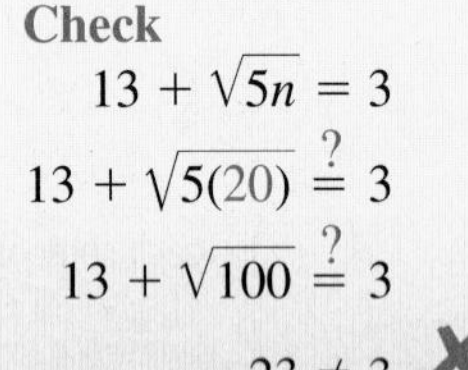

▶ Because $n = 20$ does not satisfy the original equation, it is an extraneous solution. So, the equation has no real solution.

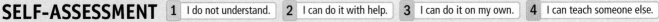

1 I do not understand. 2 I can do it with help. 3 I can do it on my own. 4 I can teach someone else.

Solve the equation. Check your solution(s).

14. $\sqrt{4 - 3x} = x$ **15.** $\sqrt{3m} + 10 = 1$ **16.** $p + 1 = \sqrt{7p + 15}$

17. WRITING Why should you check every solution of a radical equation?

Solving Real-Life Problems

EXAMPLE 6 Modeling Real Life

The period of a pendulum is the amount of time it takes for it to swing back and forth once. The period P (in seconds) of a pendulum is given by the function $P = 2\pi\sqrt{\frac{L}{32}}$, where L is the pendulum length (in feet).

A pendulum has a period of 4 seconds. Another pendulum has a period of 2 seconds. Is one pendulum twice as long as the other? Explain your reasoning.

SOLUTION

1. **Understand the Problem** You are given a function that represents the period P of a pendulum based on its length L. You need to find and compare the values of L for two values of P.
2. **Make a Plan** Substitute $P = 2$ and $P = 4$ into the function and solve for L. Then compare the values.
3. **Solve and Check**

$P = 2\pi\sqrt{\frac{L}{32}}$	Write the function.	$P = 2\pi\sqrt{\frac{L}{32}}$
$2 = 2\pi\sqrt{\frac{L}{32}}$	Substitute for P.	$4 = 2\pi\sqrt{\frac{L}{32}}$
$\frac{1}{\pi} = \sqrt{\frac{L}{32}}$	Divide each side by 2π.	$\frac{2}{\pi} = \sqrt{\frac{L}{32}}$
$\frac{1}{\pi^2} = \frac{L}{32}$	Square each side and simplify.	$\frac{4}{\pi^2} = \frac{L}{32}$
$\frac{32}{\pi^2} = L$	Multiply each side by 32.	$\frac{128}{\pi^2} = L$
$3.24 \approx L$	Use technology.	$12.97 \approx L$

▶ No, the length of the pendulum with a period of 4 seconds is $\frac{128}{\pi^2} \div \frac{32}{\pi^2} = 4$ times longer than the length of a pendulum with a period of 2 seconds.

Check Use technology to check your solutions.

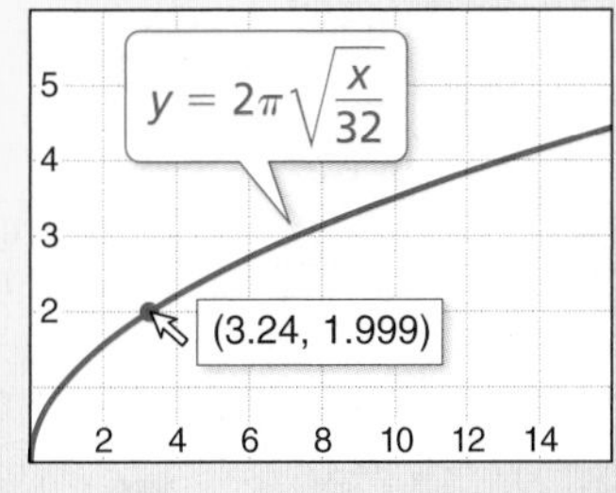

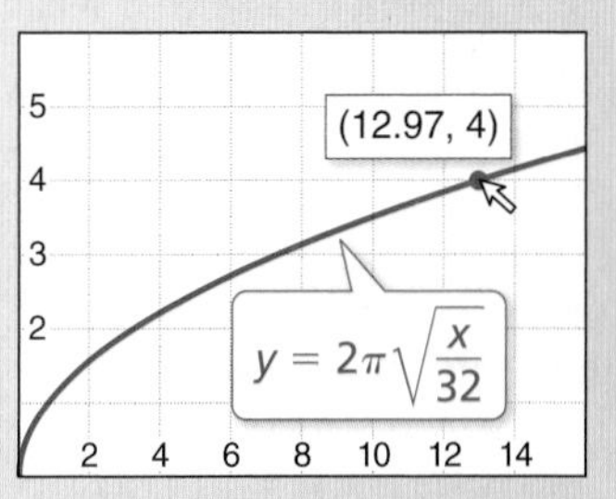

SELF-ASSESSMENT 1 I do not understand. 2 I can do it with help. 3 I can do it on my own. 4 I can teach someone else.

18. The pendulum on a grandfather clock has a period of 2.25 seconds. The pendulum on a cuckoo clock has a period of 1 second. Which clock has a longer pendulum? How much longer is it?

10.3 Practice WITH CalcChat® AND CalcView®

In Exercises 1–18, solve the equation. Check your solution. *Example 1*

1. $\sqrt{x} = 9$
2. $\sqrt{y} = 4$
3. $7 = \sqrt{m} - 5$
4. $\sqrt{p} - 7 = -1$
5. $\sqrt{c} + 12 = 23$
6. $\sqrt{x} + 6 = 8$
7. $4 - \sqrt{a} = 2$
8. $-8 = 7 - \sqrt{r}$
9. $3\sqrt{y} - 18 = -3$
10. $2\sqrt{q} + 5 = 11$
11. $\sqrt{a - 3} + 5 = 9$
12. $\sqrt{b + 7} - 5 = -2$
13. $2\sqrt{x + 4} = 16$
14. $5\sqrt{y - 2} = 10$
15. $-1 = \sqrt{5r + 1} - 7$
16. $2 = \sqrt{4s - 4} - 4$
17. $7 + 3\sqrt{3p - 9} = 25$
18. $19 - 4\sqrt{3c - 11} = 11$

19. **MODELING REAL LIFE** The Cave of Swallows is a natural open-air pit cave in Mexico. The 1220-foot-deep cave, which is open at the surface, is a popular destination for BASE jumpers. The function $t = \frac{1}{4}\sqrt{d}$ represents the time t (in seconds) that it takes a BASE jumper to fall d feet. How far does a BASE jumper fall in 3 seconds?

20. **MODELING REAL LIFE** The edge length s of a cube with a surface area of A is given by $s = \sqrt{\frac{A}{6}}$. What is the surface area of a puzzle cube with an edge length of 4 inches?

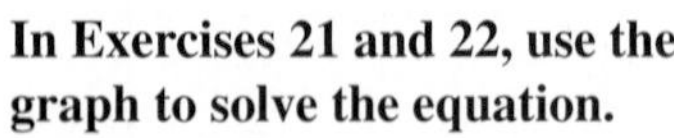

In Exercises 21 and 22, use the graph to solve the equation.

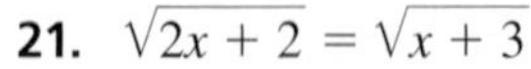

21. $\sqrt{2x + 2} = \sqrt{x + 3}$

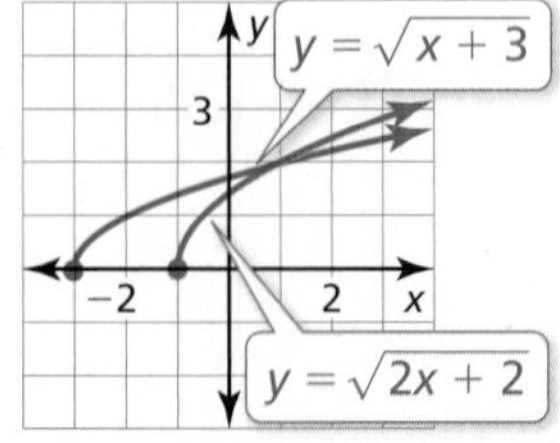

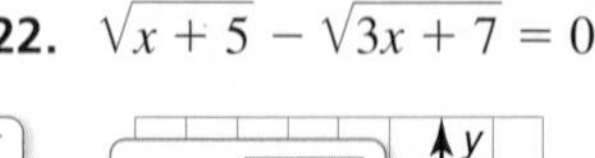

22. $\sqrt{x + 5} - \sqrt{3x + 7} = 0$

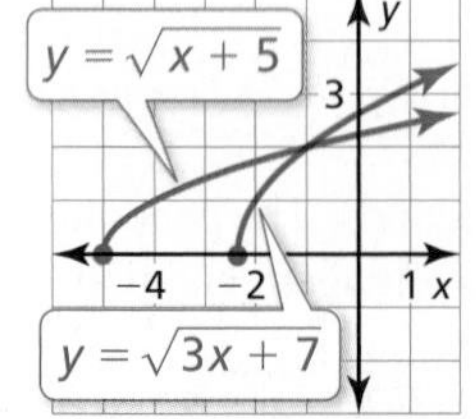

In Exercises 23–30, solve the equation. Check your solution. *Example 2*

23. $\sqrt{2x - 9} = \sqrt{x}$
24. $\sqrt{y + 1} = \sqrt{4y - 8}$
25. $\sqrt{3g + 1} = \sqrt{7g - 19}$
26. $\sqrt{8h - 7} = \sqrt{6h + 7}$
27. $\sqrt{\frac{p}{2} - 2} = \sqrt{p - 8}$
28. $\sqrt{2v - 5} = \sqrt{\frac{v}{3} + 5}$
29. $\sqrt{2c + 1} - \sqrt{4c} = 0$
30. $\sqrt{5r} - \sqrt{8r - 2} = 0$

In Exercises 31–38, solve the equation. Check your solution. *Example 3*

31. $\sqrt[3]{x} = 4$
32. $\sqrt[3]{y} = 2$
33. $6 = \sqrt[3]{8g}$
34. $\sqrt[3]{r + 19} = 3$
35. $\sqrt[3]{2s + 9} = -3$
36. $-5 = \sqrt[3]{10x + 15}$
37. $\sqrt[3]{y + 6} = \sqrt[3]{5y - 2}$
38. $\sqrt[3]{7j - 2} = \sqrt[3]{j + 4}$

39. **WRITING** Explain why the x-coordinate of the points where the graphs of the equations $y = \sqrt{2x - 9}$ and $y = \sqrt{x}$ intersect is the solution of the equation in Exercise 23.

40. **WRITING** Explain how you can solve $\sqrt[4]{m + 4} - \sqrt[4]{3m} = 0$.

In Exercises 41–44, determine which solution, if any, is an extraneous solution.

41. $\sqrt{6x - 5} = x$; $x = 5, x = 1$
42. $\sqrt{2y + 3} = y$; $y = -1, y = 3$
43. $\sqrt{12p + 16} = -2p$; $p = -1, p = 4$
44. $-3g = \sqrt{-18 - 27g}$; $g = -2, g = -1$

In Exercises 45–54, solve the equation. Check your solution(s). *Examples 4 and 5*

45. $y = \sqrt{5y - 4}$
46. $\sqrt{-14 - 9x} = x$
47. $\sqrt{1 - 3a} = 2a$
48. $2q = \sqrt{10q - 6}$
49. $9 + \sqrt{5p} = 4$
50. $\sqrt{3n} - 11 = -5$
51. $\sqrt{2m + 2} - 3 = 1$
52. $15 + \sqrt{4b - 8} = 13$
53. $r + 4 = \sqrt{-4r - 19}$
54. $\sqrt{3 - s} = s - 1$

ERROR ANALYSIS In Exercises 55 and 56, describe and correct the error in solving the equation.

55.

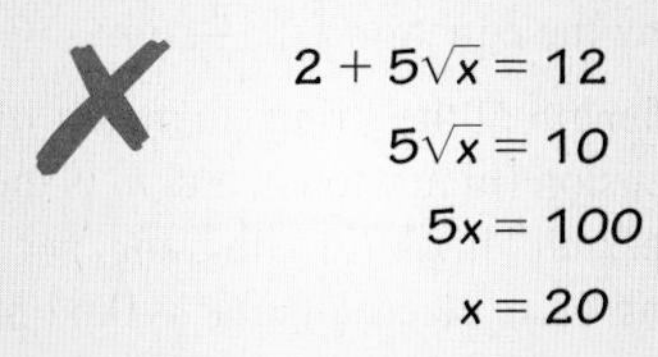

56.

$$x = \sqrt{12 - 4x}$$
$$x^2 = 12 - 4x$$
$$x^2 + 4x - 12 = 0$$
$$(x - 2)(x + 6) = 0$$
$$x = 2 \quad \text{or} \quad x = -6$$

The solutions are $x = 2$ and $x = -6$.

57. **MP REASONING** Explain how to determine that the equation in Example 5 has no real solution without completely solving the equation.

58. **COMPARING METHODS** Solve the equation $x + 2 = \sqrt{2x - 3}$ graphically and algebraically. Describe each process. Which method do you prefer? Explain your reasoning.

59. **MODELING REAL LIFE** The formula $V = \sqrt{PR}$ relates the voltage V (in volts), power P (in watts), and resistance R (in ohms) of an electrical circuit. A 1875-watt hair dryer is on a 120-volt circuit. Is the resistance of the hair dryer $\frac{1}{4}$ as much as the resistance of the same hair dryer on a 240-volt circuit? Explain your reasoning. *Example 6*

60. **MODELING REAL LIFE** The time t (in seconds) it takes a trapeze artist to swing back and forth is represented by the function $t = 2\pi\sqrt{\frac{r}{32}}$, where r is the rope length (in feet). It takes the trapeze artist 6 seconds to swing back and forth. Is this rope $\frac{3}{2}$ as long as the rope used when it takes the trapeze artist 4 seconds to swing back and forth? Explain your reasoning.

MP REASONING In Exercises 61–64, determine whether the statement is *true* or *false*. If it is false, explain why.

61. If $\sqrt{a} = b$, then $a = b^2$.

62. If $\sqrt{a} = \sqrt{b}$, then $a = b$.

63. If $a^2 = b^2$, then $a = b$.

64. If $a^2 = \sqrt{b}$, then $a^4 = b$.

65. **COLLEGE PREP** Find the solution(s) of the system of equations shown. Select all that apply.

$$y = 2x - 1$$
$$y = \sqrt{4x + 1}$$

Ⓐ (0, −1) Ⓑ (0, 1)

Ⓒ (2, 3) Ⓓ no real solution

66. **HOW DO YOU SEE IT?**
The graph shows two radical functions.

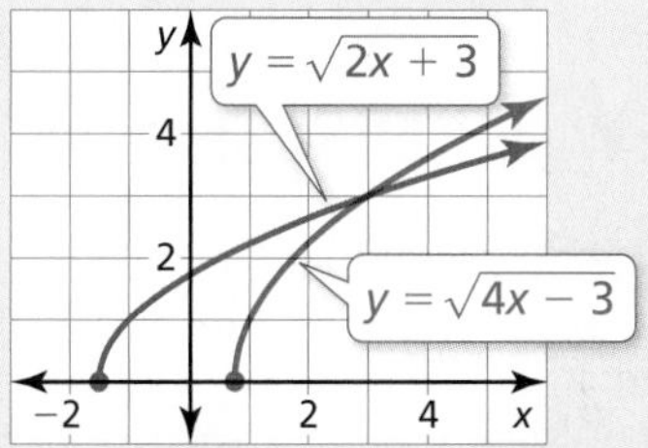

a. Write an equation whose solution is the x-coordinate of the point of intersection of the graphs.

b. Use the graph to solve the equation.

67. **CONNECTING CONCEPTS** The slant height s of a cone with a radius of r and a height of h is given by $s = \sqrt{r^2 + h^2}$. The slant heights of the two cones are equal. Find the radius of each cone.

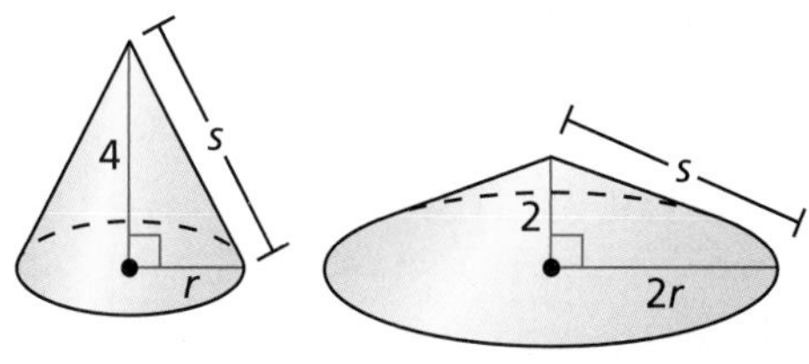

68. **MP PRECISION** Explain how squaring $\sqrt{x + 2}$ is different from squaring $\sqrt{x} + 2$.

MP STRUCTURE In Exercises 69–74, solve the equation. Check your solution.

69. $\sqrt{m + 15} = \sqrt{m} + \sqrt{5}$

70. $2 - \sqrt{x + 1} = \sqrt{x + 2}$

71. $\sqrt{5y + 9} + \sqrt{5y} = 9$

72. $\sqrt{2c - 8} - \sqrt{2c} - 4 = 0$

73. $2\sqrt{1 + 4h} - 4\sqrt{h} - 2 = 0$

74. $\sqrt{20 - 4z} + 2\sqrt{-z} = 10$

75. **OPEN-ENDED** Write a radical equation that has a solution of $x = 5$.

76. **OPEN-ENDED** Write a radical equation that has $x = 3$ and $x = 4$ as solutions.

77. **MAKING AN ARGUMENT** Your friend says the equation $\sqrt{(2x + 5)^2} = 2x + 5$ is always true, because after simplifying the left side of the equation, the result is an equation with infinitely many solutions. Is your friend correct? Explain.

78. **THOUGHT PROVOKING** Solve the equation $\sqrt[3]{x + 1} = \sqrt{x - 3}$. Show your work and explain your steps.

79. **DIG DEEPER** The frequency f (in cycles per second) of a string of an electric guitar is given by the equation $f = \frac{1}{2\ell}\sqrt{\frac{T}{m}}$, where ℓ is the length of the string (in meters), T is the string's tension (in newtons), and m is the string's mass per unit length (in kilograms per meter). The high E string of an electric guitar is 0.64 meter long with a mass per unit length of 0.000401 kilogram per meter.

a. How much tension is required to produce a frequency of about 330 cycles per second?

b. Do you need more or less tension to create the same frequency on a string with greater mass per unit length? Explain.

GO DIGITAL

REVIEW & REFRESH

WATCH

In Exercises 80–83, find the product.

80. $4y(-2y^2 + 5)$

81. $(x + 8)(x - 2)$

82. $(3p - 1)(4p + 5)$

83. $(s + 2)(s^2 + 3s - 4)$

84. Use the graph to solve $\sqrt{x + 2} - \sqrt{2x} = 0$.

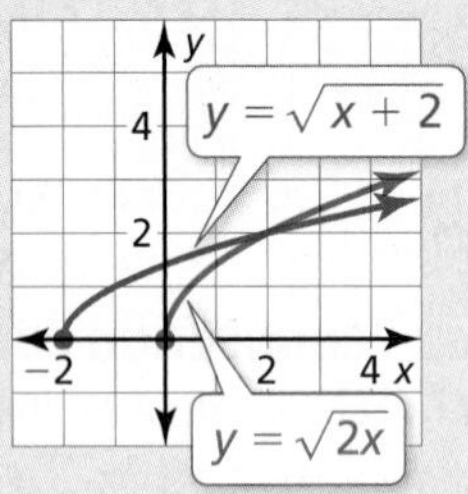

In Exercises 85–88, graph the function. Compare the graph to the graph of $f(x) = x^2$.

85. $g(x) = \frac{3}{4}x^2$

86. $h(x) = -5x^2$

87. $r(x) = 3x^2 - 1$

88. $v(x) = -\frac{1}{2}(x - 4)^2 + 3$

In Exercises 89 and 90, solve the equation. Check your solution(s).

89. $\sqrt{3y - 11} + 8 = 3$

90. $2z = \sqrt{4z + 15}$

91. The points represented by the table lie on a line. Find the slope of the line.

x	−3	0	3	6
y	8	6	4	2

In Exercises 92 and 93, graph the function. Compare the graph to the graph of $f(x) = \sqrt[3]{x}$.

92. $g(x) = \sqrt[3]{x - 8}$

93. $h(x) = -\frac{1}{3}\sqrt[3]{x + 4}$

In Exercises 94 and 95, find the domain of the function.

94. $y = \sqrt{-2x}$

95. $m(x) = \sqrt{x - 1} + 6$

96. **MODELING REAL LIFE** The graph represents the number y (in hundreds) of visitors to a new skate park after x months. Write an exponential function that represents this situation. Then approximate the number of visitors after 5 months.

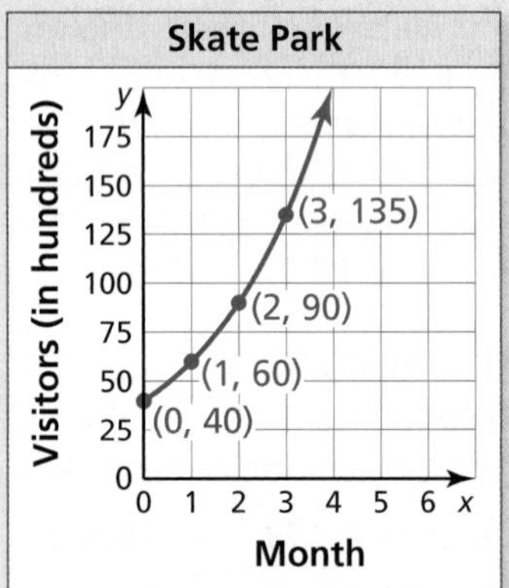

In Exercises 97 and 98, solve the system using any method. Explain your choice of method.

97. $y = 2x + 3$
$y = -x^2 + 4x + 2$

98. $y + x = 7$
$y - 2x = x^2 - 3$

In Exercises 99–102, simplify the expression.

99. $\sqrt{\frac{15}{4}}$

100. $\sqrt{\frac{3y^2}{7}}$

101. $2\sqrt{6} - 9\sqrt{24}$

102. $\sqrt[3]{-9}\left(\sqrt[3]{3} - \sqrt[3]{81}\right)$

10.4 Inverse of a Function

Learning Target Understand the relationship between inverse functions.

Success Criteria
- I can explain what inverse functions are.
- I can find inverses of functions algebraically.
- I can determine if the inverse of a function is also a function.

EXPLORE IT! Describing Inverse Functions

Work with a partner.

x	-1	-0.5	0	0.5	1	1.5	2	2.5
$f(x)$	-2	-1	0	1	2	3	4	5

x	-2	-1	0	1	2	3	4	5
$g(x)$	-1	-0.5	0	0.5	1	1.5	2	2.5

a. Compare the functions represented by the tables. How are the functions related?

b. Graph the functions represented by the tables. Connect each set of points and describe the relationship between the graphs.

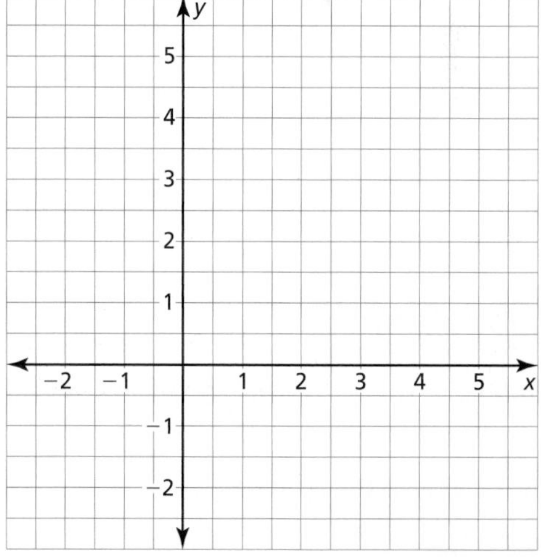

c. Write an equation that represents each function. What do you notice about the operation in each equation?

d. The functions f and g are *inverses* of each other. Describe how a function and its inverse are related in your own words.

e. MP **CHOOSE TOOLS** Graph $h(x) = x + 4$ and its inverse in the same coordinate plane. Write an equation of the inverse of h. What do you notice about the operations in each equation? Explain your reasoning.

Math Practice

Analyze Relationships
Compare the graphs in part (b). Then compare the graphs in part (e). How are the pairs of graphs similar? How are they different?

Finding Inverses of Relations

Recall that a relation pairs inputs with outputs. An **inverse relation** switches the inputs and outputs of the original relation.

> **WORDS AND MATH**
>
> The word *inverse* is related to the word *invert*. When you invert something, you reverse its order, turn it upside down, or turn it inside out. When you invert a relation, you obtain its inverse.

> **Vocabulary** 
>
> inverse relation, *p. 570*
> inverse function, *p. 571*

KEY IDEA

Inverse Relation

When a relation contains (a, b), the inverse relation contains (b, a).

EXAMPLE 1 Finding Inverses of Relations 

Find the inverse of each relation.

a. $(-4, 7), (-2, 4), (0, 1), (2, -2), (4, -5)$ — Switch the coordinates of each ordered pair.

$(7, -4), (4, -2), (1, 0), (-2, 2), (-5, 4)$ — Inverse relation

b.

Input	−1	0	1	2	3	4
Output	5	10	15	20	25	30

Inverse relation:

Input	5	10	15	20	25	30
Output	−1	0	1	2	3	4

Switch the inputs and outputs.

c. 
Input Output

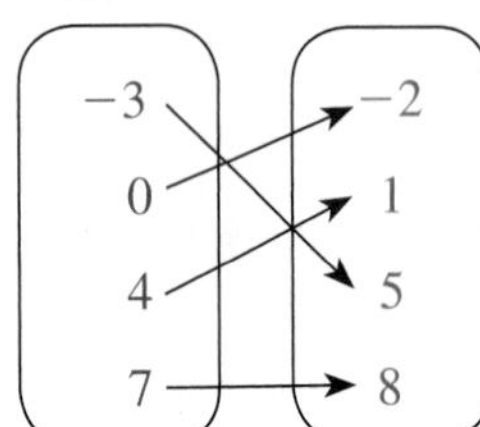

Inverse relation: Input Output

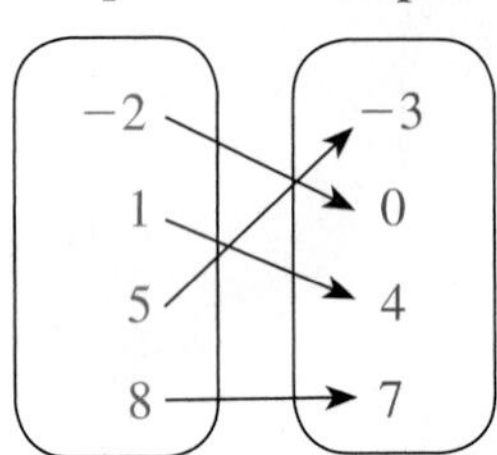

Switch the inputs and outputs.

SELF-ASSESSMENT

1 I do not understand. 2 I can do it with help. 3 I can do it on my own. 4 I can teach someone else.

1. **COMPLETE THE SENTENCE** A relation contains the point $(-3, 10)$. The ____________ contains the point $(10, -3)$.

Find the inverse of the relation.

2. $(-3, -4), (-2, 0), (-1, 4), (0, 8), (1, 12), (2, 16), (3, 20)$

3.

Input	−2	−1	0	1	2
Output	4	1	0	1	4

4. **Input** **Output**

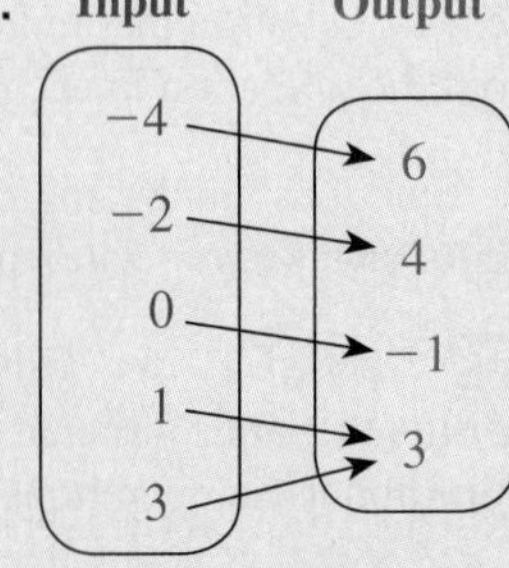

Exploring Inverses of Functions

You can solve equations of the form $y = f(x)$ for x to obtain an equation that gives the input for a specific output of f.

EXAMPLE 2 Writing an Equation for the Input of a Function

Let $f(x) = 2x + 1$. Solve $y = f(x)$ for x. Then find the input when the output is -3.

SOLUTION

$y = 2x + 1$ — Set y equal to $f(x)$.

$y - 1 = 2x$ — Subtract 1 from each side.

$\frac{y-1}{2} = x$ — Divide each side by 2.

Find the input when $y = -3$.

$x = \frac{-3-1}{2}$ — Substitute -3 for y.

$= \frac{-4}{2}$ — Subtract.

$= -2$ — Divide.

Check

$f(-2) = 2(-2) + 1$

$= -4 + 1$

$= -3$ ✓

▶ So, the input is -2 when the output is -3.

SELF-ASSESSMENT 1 I do not understand. 2 I can do it with help. 3 I can do it on my own. 4 I can teach someone else.

Solve $y = f(x)$ for x. Then find the input(s) when the output is 4.

5. $f(x) = x - 6$

6. $f(x) = \frac{1}{2}x + 3$

7. $f(x) = 4x^2$

Math Practice

Communicate Precisely
The term *inverse functions* does not refer to a new type of function. It describes any pair of functions that are inverses.

In Example 2, notice the operations in the equations $y = 2x + 1$ and $x = \frac{y-1}{2}$.

$y = 2x + 1$ $\qquad$ $x = \frac{y-1}{2}$

Multiply by 2. → Subtract 1.

Add 1. → Divide by 2.

inverse operations in the reverse order

These operations *undo* each other. **Inverse functions** are functions that undo each other. In Example 2, use the equation solved for x to write the inverse of f by switching x and y.

$$x = \frac{y-1}{2} \xrightarrow{\text{switch } x \text{ and } y} y = \frac{x-1}{2}$$

Because an inverse function switches the input and output values of the original function, the domain and range are also switched.

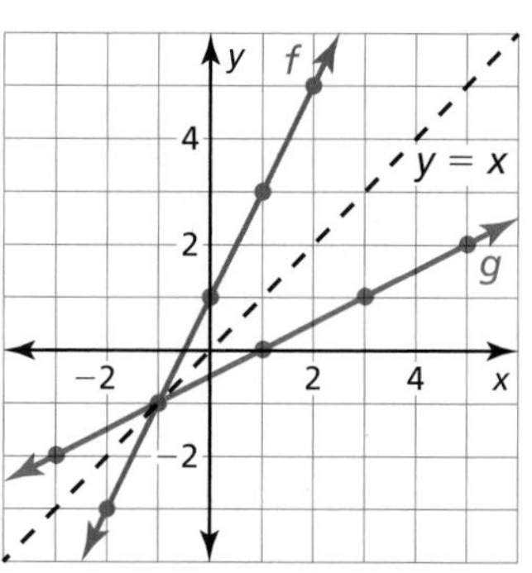

Original function: $f(x) = 2x + 1$

Inverse function: $g(x) = \frac{x-1}{2}$

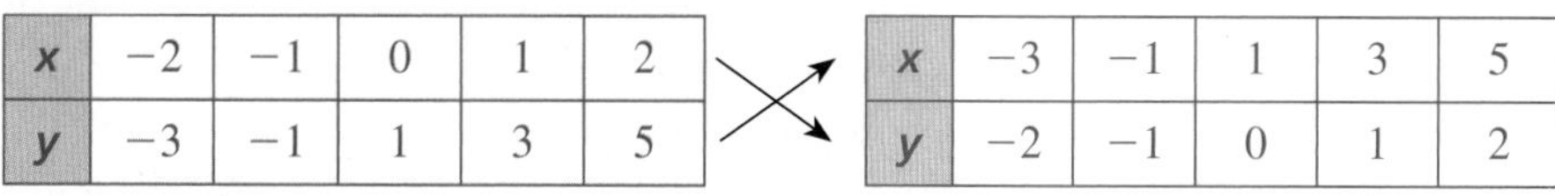

x	−2	−1	0	1	2
y	−3	−1	1	3	5

x	−3	−1	1	3	5
y	−2	−1	0	1	2

The graph of g is a *reflection* of the graph of f. The *line of reflection* is $y = x$. This is true for all inverse functions.

Finding Inverses of Functions Algebraically

On the previous page, you solved a function for x and switched x and y to find the inverse function. You can also find the inverse function by switching x and y first, and then solving for y.

KEY IDEA

Finding Inverses of Functions Algebraically

Step 1 Set y equal to $f(x)$.

Step 2 Switch x and y in the equation.

Step 3 Solve the equation for y.

EXAMPLE 3 Finding the Inverse of a Linear Function

Find the inverse of $f(x) = 4x - 9$.

SOLUTION

Method 1 Find the inverse of f algebraically.

	$f(x) = 4x - 9$	Write the function.
Step 1	$y = 4x - 9$	Set y equal to $f(x)$.
Step 2	$x = 4y - 9$	Switch x and y in the equation.
Step 3	$x + 9 = 4y$	Add 9 to each side.
	$\dfrac{x+9}{4} = y$	Divide each side by 4.

▶ The inverse of f is $g(x) = \dfrac{x+9}{4}$, or $g(x) = \dfrac{1}{4}x + \dfrac{9}{4}$.

Check

The graph of g appears to be a reflection of the graph of f in the line $y = x$.

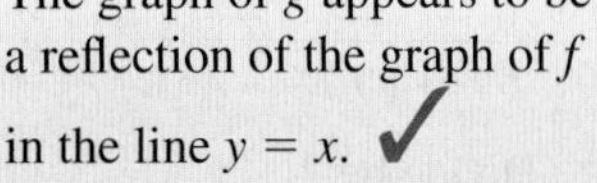

Method 2 Use inverse operations in the reverse order.

$f(x) = 4x - 9$ — Multiply the input x by 4 and then subtract 9.

To find the inverse, apply inverse operations in the reverse order.

$g(x) = \dfrac{x+9}{4}$ — Add 9 to the input x and then divide by 4.

▶ The inverse of f is $g(x) = \dfrac{x+9}{4}$, or $g(x) = \dfrac{1}{4}x + \dfrac{9}{4}$.

Finding Inverses of Nonlinear Functions

The inverse of a linear function is always a function, as shown in Example 3. However, inverses of functions are *not* always functions. The graph of $f(x) = x^2$ is shown along with its reflection in the line $y = x$. Notice that the graph of the inverse of $f(x) = x^2$ does not pass the Vertical Line Test. So, the inverse is *not* a function.

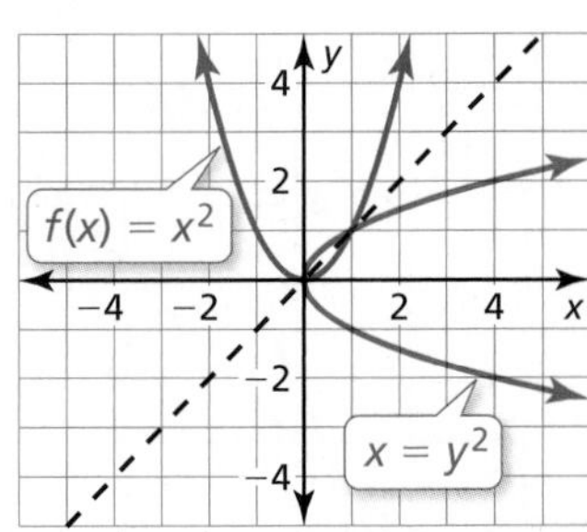

When the domain of $f(x) = x^2$ is *restricted* to only nonnegative real numbers, the inverse of f *is* a function, as shown in the next example.

EXAMPLE 4 Finding the Inverse of a Quadratic Function

Find the inverse of $f(x) = x^2$, $x \geq 0$. Then graph the function and its inverse.

SOLUTION

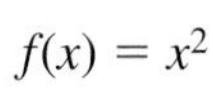

$f(x) = x^2$	Write the function.
$y = x^2$	Set y equal to $f(x)$.
$x = y^2$	Switch x and y in the equation.
$\pm\sqrt{x} = y$	Take square root of each side.

▶ Because the domain of f is restricted to nonnegative values of x, the range of the inverse must also be restricted to nonnegative values. So, the inverse of f is $g(x) = \sqrt{x}$.

You can use the graph of a function f to determine whether the inverse of f is a function by applying the *Horizontal Line Test*.

KEY IDEA

Horizontal Line Test

The inverse of a function f is also a function if and only if no horizontal line intersects the graph of f more than once.

EXAMPLE 5 Finding the Inverse of a Radical Function

Consider the function $f(x) = \sqrt{x + 2}$. Determine whether the inverse of f is a function. Then find the inverse.

SOLUTION

Graph the function f. Because no horizontal line intersects the graph more than once, the inverse of f is a function. Find the inverse.

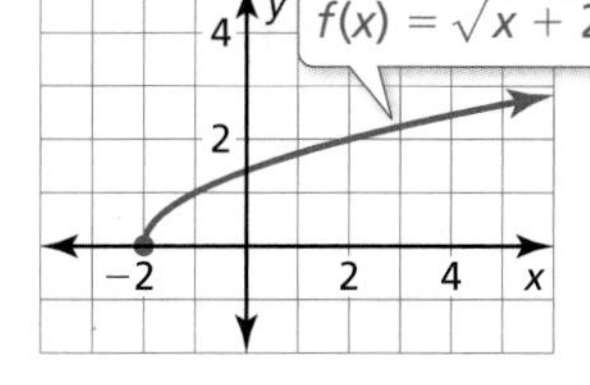

$y = \sqrt{x + 2}$	Set y equal to $f(x)$.
$x = \sqrt{y + 2}$	Switch x and y in the equation.
$x^2 = \left(\sqrt{y + 2}\right)^2$	Square each side.
$x^2 = y + 2$	Simplify.
$x^2 - 2 = y$	Subtract 2 from each side.

Check

▶ Because the range of f is $y \geq 0$, the domain of the inverse must be restricted to $x \geq 0$. So, the inverse of f is $g(x) = x^2 - 2$, where $x \geq 0$.

SELF-ASSESSMENT

1 I do not understand. 2 I can do it with help. 3 I can do it on my own. 4 I can teach someone else.

Find the inverse of the function. Then graph the function and its inverse.

8. $f(x) = 6x$

9. $f(x) = -x + 5$

10. $f(x) = \frac{1}{4}x - 1$

11. $f(x) = -x^2, x \leq 0$

12. $f(x) = 4x^2 + 3, x \geq 0$

13. $f(x) = -\frac{1}{2}x^2 - 1, x \leq 0$

14. Is the inverse of $f(x) = \sqrt{2x - 1}$ a function? Find the inverse.

15. WRITING Explain why you can use horizontal lines to determine whether the inverse of a function is also a function.

10.4 Practice WITH CalcChat® AND CalcView®

In Exercises 1–6, find the inverse of the relation. *Example 1*

1. (1, 0), (3, −8), (4, −3), (7, −5), (9, −1)

2. (2, 1), (4, −3), (6, 7), (8, 1), (10, −4)

3.

Input	−10	−5	0	5	10
Output	8	6	0	6	8

4.

Input	−12	−8	−5	−3	−2
Output	2	5	−1	10	−2

5. 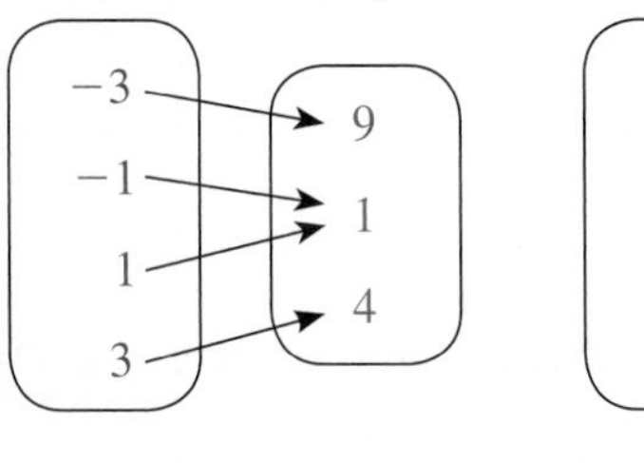

6. 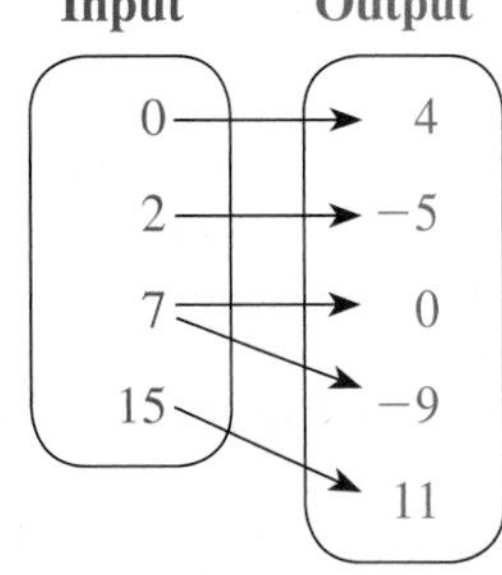

In Exercises 7–12, solve $y = f(x)$ for x. Then find the input(s) when the output is 2. *Example 2*

7. $f(x) = x + 11$

8. $f(x) = 2x - 3$

9. $f(x) = \frac{1}{4}x - 5$

10. $f(x) = \frac{2}{3}x + 4$

11. $f(x) = 9x^2$

12. $f(x) = \frac{1}{2}x^2 - 7$

In Exercises 13 and 14, graph the inverse of the function by reflecting the graph in the line $y = x$. Find the domain and range of the inverse.

13. 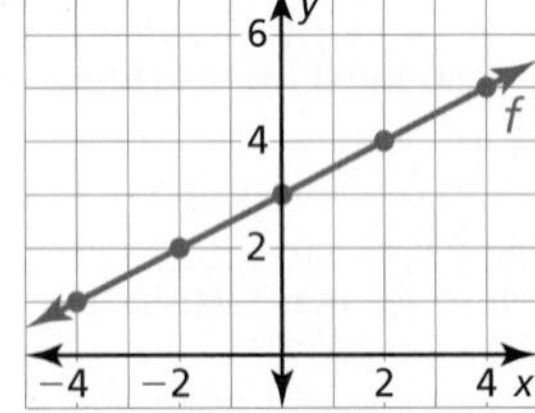

14. 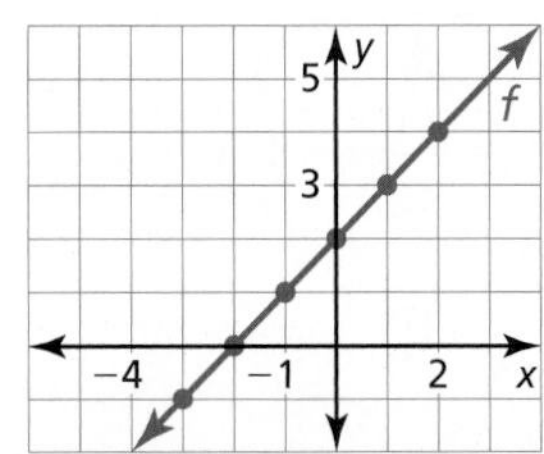

In Exercises 15–20, find the inverse of the function. Then graph the function and its inverse. *Example 3*

15. $f(x) = 4x - 1$

16. $f(x) = -2x + 5$

17. $f(x) = -3x - 2$

18. $f(x) = 2x + 3$

19. $f(x) = \frac{1}{3}x + 8$

20. $f(x) = -\frac{3}{2}x + \frac{7}{2}$

In Exercises 21–26, find the inverse of the function. Then graph the function and its inverse. *Example 4*

21. $f(x) = 4x^2, x \geq 0$

22. $f(x) = -\frac{1}{25}x^2, x \leq 0$

23. $f(x) = -x^2 + 10, x \leq 0$

24. $f(x) = 2x^2 + 6, x \geq 0$

25. $f(x) = \frac{1}{9}x^2 + 2, x \geq 0$

26. $f(x) = -4x^2 - 8, x \leq 0$

In Exercises 27–30, use the Horizontal Line Test to determine whether the inverse of f is a function.

27. 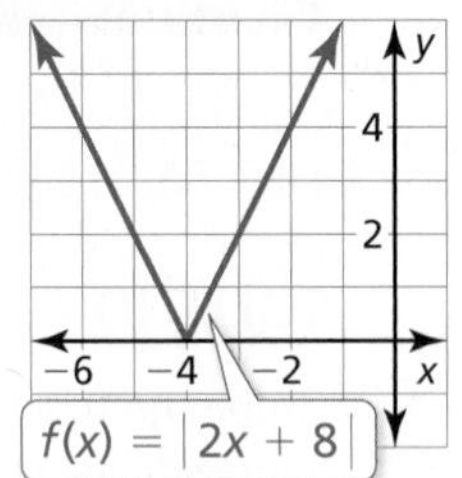

28. 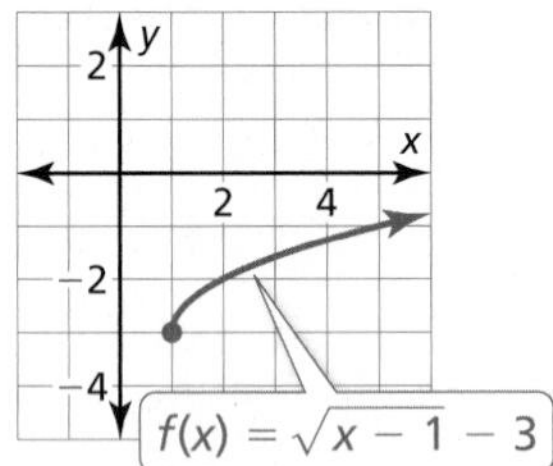

29. 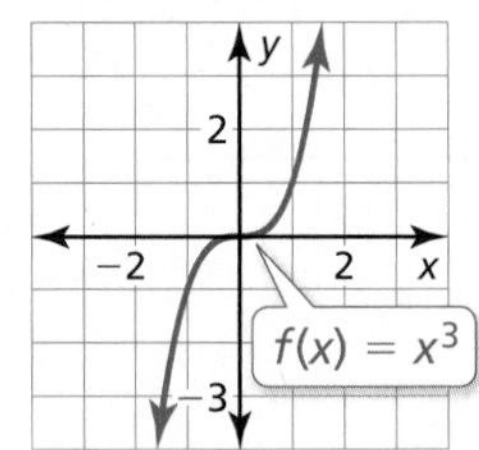

30. 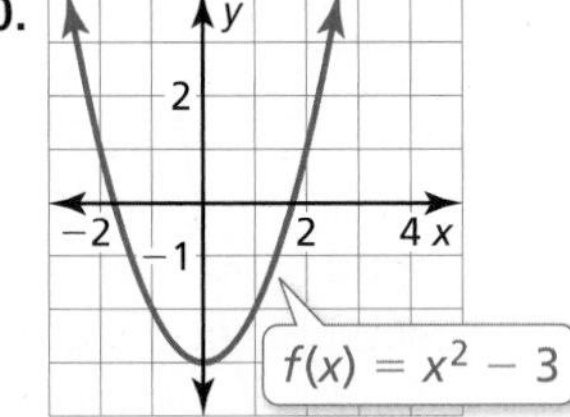

In Exercises 31–40, determine whether the inverse of f is a function. Then find the inverse. *Example 5*

31. $f(x) = \sqrt{x + 3}$

32. $f(x) = \sqrt{x - 5}$

33. $f(x) = \sqrt{2x - 6}$

34. $f(x) = \sqrt{4x + 1}$

35. $f(x) = 3\sqrt{x - 8}$

36. $f(x) = -\frac{1}{4}\sqrt{5x + 2}$

37. $f(x) = -\sqrt{3x + 5} - 2$

38. $f(x) = 2\sqrt{x - 7} + 6$

39. $f(x) = 2x^2$

40. $f(x) = |x|$

41. ERROR ANALYSIS Describe and correct the error in finding the inverse of the function $f(x) = 3x + 5$.

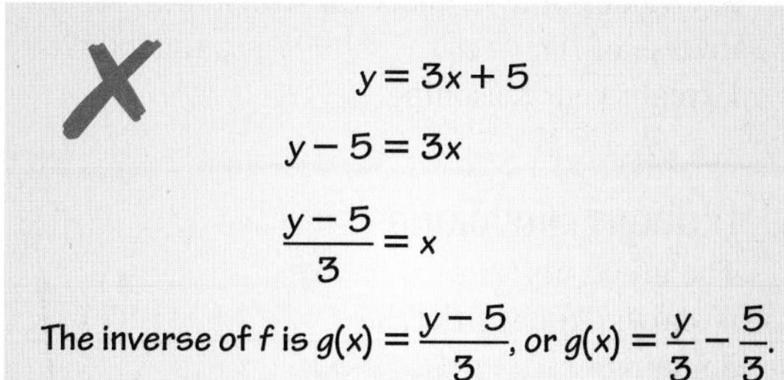

$y = 3x + 5$
$y - 5 = 3x$
$\frac{y-5}{3} = x$
The inverse of f is $g(x) = \frac{y-5}{3}$, or $g(x) = \frac{y}{3} - \frac{5}{3}$.

42. ERROR ANALYSIS Describe and correct the error in finding the inverse of the function $f(x) = \sqrt{x - 3}$.

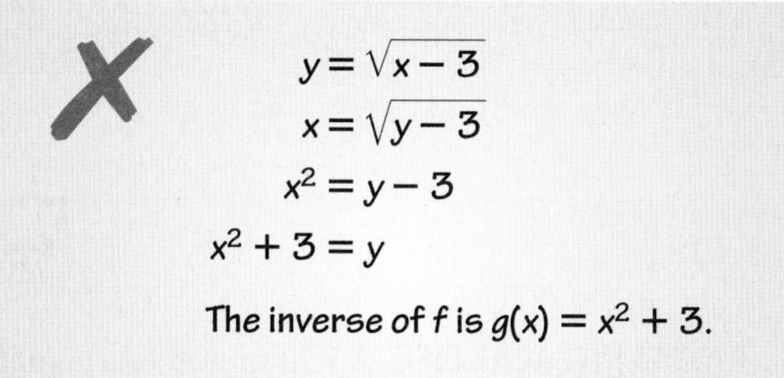

43. MODELING REAL LIFE The euro is the unit of currency for the European Union. On a certain day, the number E of euros that could be obtained for D U.S. dollars was represented by the formula shown.

$$E = 0.8809D$$

Solve the formula for D. Then find the number of U.S. dollars that could be obtained for 250 euros on that day.

44. MODELING REAL LIFE A crow is flying at a height of 50 feet when it drops a walnut to break it open. The height h (in feet) of the walnut above ground can be modeled by $h = -16t^2 + 50$, where t is the time (in seconds) since the crow dropped the walnut. Solve the equation for t. After how many seconds will the walnut be 15 feet above the ground?

45. CONNECTING CONCEPTS The height h of an equilateral triangle is given by $h = \frac{\sqrt{3}s}{2}$, where s is the side length of the triangle. Solve the formula for s. Then find the side length of an equilateral triangle with a height of 16 inches.

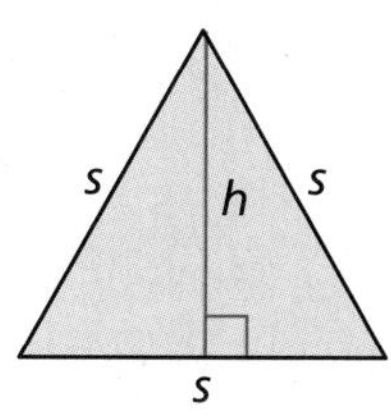

46. CRITICAL THINKING A linear function f has the values $f(-3) = 4$ and $f(3) = 12$. Write a function for the inverse of f.

In Exercises 47–52, find the inverse of the function. Then graph the function and its inverse.

47. $f(x) = 2x^3$

48. $f(x) = x^3 - 4$

49. $f(x) = (x - 5)^3$

50. $f(x) = 8(x + 2)^3$

51. $f(x) = 4\sqrt[3]{x}$

52. $f(x) = -\sqrt[3]{x - 1}$

53. MAKING AN ARGUMENT Is the inverse of a function of the form $f(x) = b$, where b is any real number, a function? Explain your reasoning.

54. HOW DO YOU SEE IT?
Pair the graph of each function with the graph of its inverse.

A.
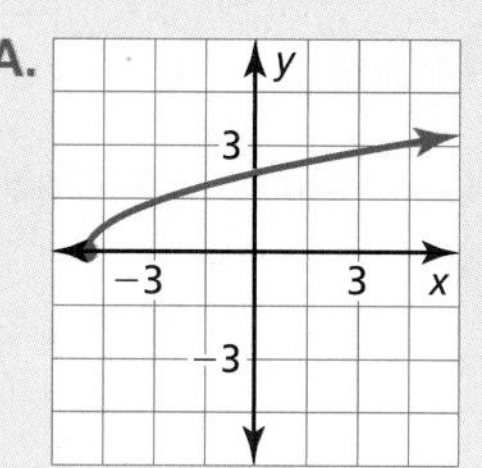

B.
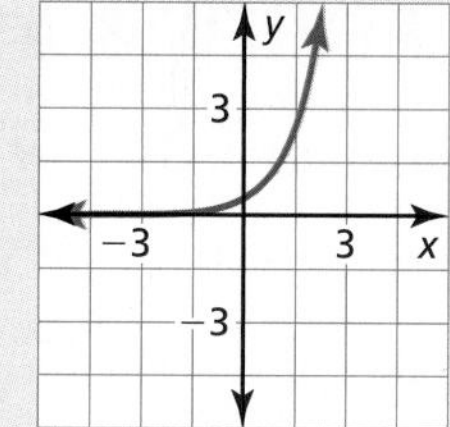

C.
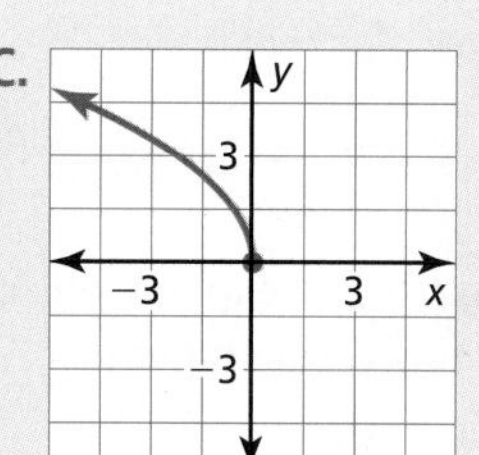

D.
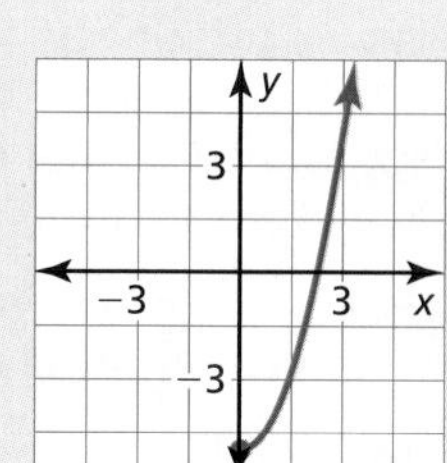

E.
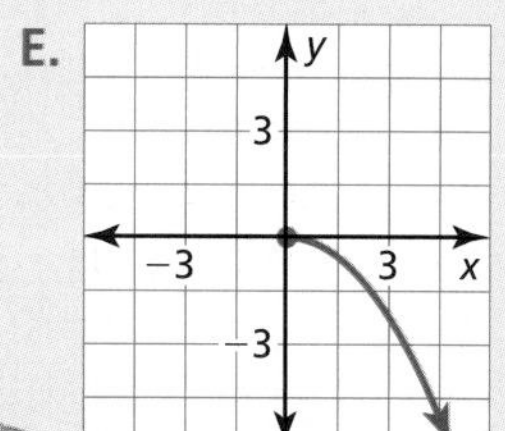

F.
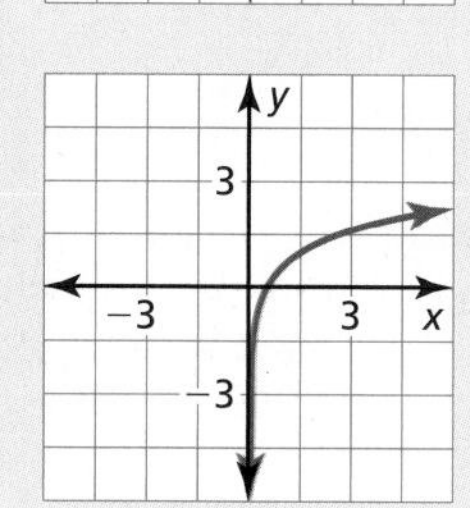

55. COLLEGE PREP For what values of p and q is f a function but the inverse of f *not* a function? Select all that apply.

x	-4	-2	1	3	p
$f(x)$	5	2	0	-7	q

Ⓐ $p = -2, q = 4$

Ⓑ $p = -1, q = 2$

Ⓒ $p = 2, q = -5$

Ⓓ $p = 6, q = 5$

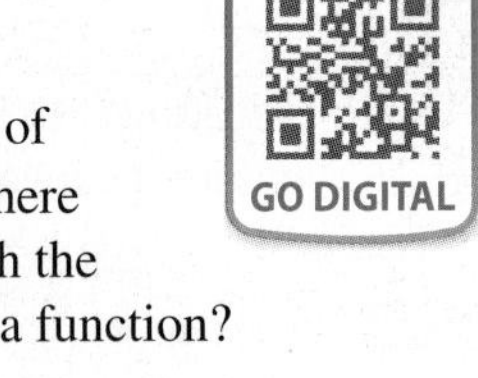

56. OPEN-ENDED Write a function such that the graph of its inverse is a line with a slope of 4.

57. MP REPEATED REASONING Consider the function $g(x) = -x$.

a. Graph $g(x) = -x$ and explain why it is its own inverse.

b. Graph other linear functions that are their own inverses. Write equations of the lines you graph.

c. Use your results from part (b) to write a general equation that describes the family of linear functions that are their own inverses.

58. DIG DEEPER Show that the inverse of any linear function $f(x) = mx + b$, where $m \neq 0$, is also a linear function. Write the slope and y-intercept of the graph of the inverse in terms of m and b.

59. MP REASONING Is the inverse of $f(x) = 2|x + 1|$ a function? Are there any values of a, h, and k for which the inverse of $f(x) = a|x - h| + k$ is a function? Explain your reasoning.

60. THOUGHT PROVOKING
The graph of $f(x) = x^3 - 3x$ is shown. You restrict the domain of f to $-a \leq x \leq a$ so that the inverse of f is a function. What is the greatest possible value of a? Write an equation of the inverse function.

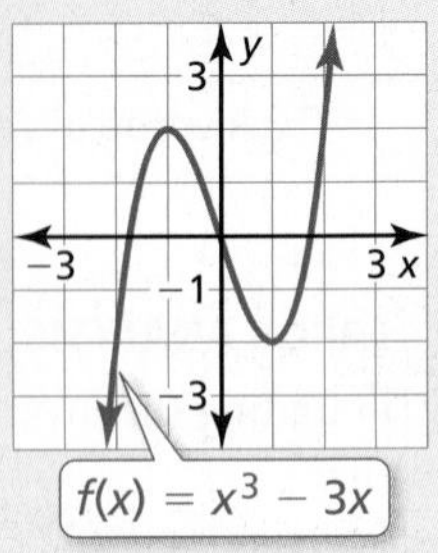

REVIEW & REFRESH

WATCH

In Exercises 61–64, find the sum or difference.

61. $(2x - 9) - (6x + 5)$

62. $(8y + 1) + (-y - 12)$

63. $(t^2 - 4t - 4) + (7t^2 + 12t + 3)$

64. $(-3d^2 + 10d - 8) - (7d^2 - d - 6)$

In Exercises 65–68, simplify the expression. Write your answer using only positive exponents.

65. $7a^{-10}b^0$

66. $(-5x^6)^4$

67. $\dfrac{y^{-8} \cdot y^{17}}{y^3}$

68. $\left(\dfrac{2}{r^{-7}}\right)^{-5}$

69. Compare the graph of g to the graph of f. Find the value of h.

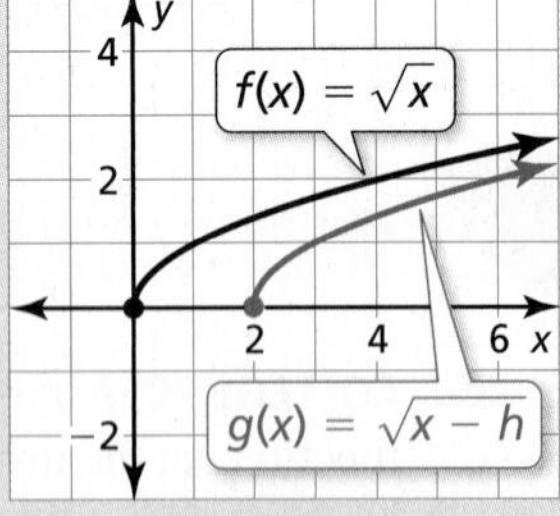

70. Graph $y = \begin{cases} x + 1, & \text{if } x \leq -2 \\ -2x - 1, & \text{if } x > -2 \end{cases}$. Find the domain and range.

In Exercises 71 and 72, find the inverse of the function. Then graph the function and its inverse.

71. $f(x) = 5x - 15$

72. $f(x) = \frac{1}{4}x^2, x \leq 0$

73. MODELING REAL LIFE A badminton tournament begins with 64 teams. After the first round, 32 teams remain. After the second round, 16 teams remain. How many teams remain after the third, fourth, and fifth rounds?

In Exercises 74–77, solve the equation. Check your solution(s).

74. $\sqrt{b} + 2 = 10$

75. $\sqrt[3]{x - 12} = -5$

76. $-3 = \sqrt{3t + 4} - 8$

77. $p = \sqrt{4p + 5}$

78. Tell whether the table of values represents a *linear*, an *exponential*, or a *quadratic* function.

x	−3	−2	−1	0	1
y	6	1	−2	−3	−2

In Exercises 79 and 80, solve the system. Explain your choice of method.

79. $-3x + 2y = 4$
$x = -6y + 2$

80. $2x + 5y = 25$
$7x + 4y = -7$

In Exercises 81–84, graph the function. Compare the graph to the graph of $f(x) = x^2$.

81. $g(x) = x^2 + 6$

82. $h(x) = -x^2 - 2$

83. $p(x) = -4x^2 + 5$

84. $q(x) = \frac{1}{3}x^2 - 1$

85. Graph $h(x) = \frac{1}{2}\sqrt[3]{x} - 3$. Describe the transformations from the graph of $f(x) = \sqrt[3]{x}$ to the graph of h.

10 Chapter Review WITH CalcChat®

Chapter Learning Target Understand radical functions and equations.

Chapter Success Criteria
- ◆ I can identify domains and ranges of radical functions.
- ◆ I can graph square root and cube root functions.
- ■ I can solve radical equations.
- ■ I can find inverses of relations and functions.

◆ Surface
■ Deep

SELF-ASSESSMENT 1 I do not understand. 2 I can do it with help. 3 I can do it on my own. 4 I can teach someone else.

10.1 Graphing Square Root Functions (pp. 547–554)

Learning Target: Graph and describe square root functions.

Vocabulary AZ VOCAB
square root function
radical function

Graph the function. Find the domain and range. Compare the graph to the graph of $f(x) = \sqrt{x}$.

1. $g(x) = \sqrt{x} + 7$
2. $h(x) = \sqrt{x - 6}$
3. $r(x) = -\sqrt{x + 3} - 1$
4. $p(x) = 3\sqrt{x - 4} + 1$
5. Graph $g(x) = \frac{1}{4}\sqrt{x - 6} + 2$. Describe the transformations from the graph of $f(x) = \sqrt{x}$ to the graph of g.
6. Match each function with its graph. Explain your reasoning.

   a. $y = \sqrt{x - 2}$ **b.** $y = -\sqrt{x + 2}$

   c. $y = -\sqrt{x} - 2$ **d.** $y = \sqrt{x} + 2$

   A.
   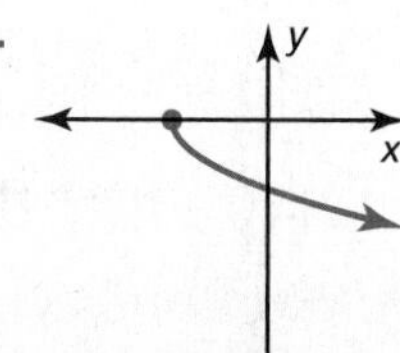

   B.
   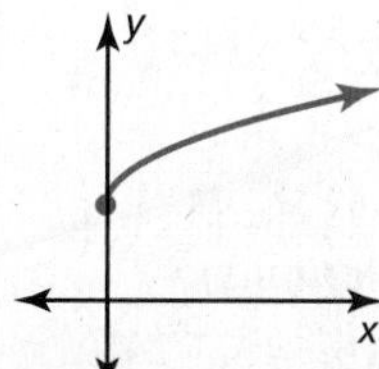

   C.
   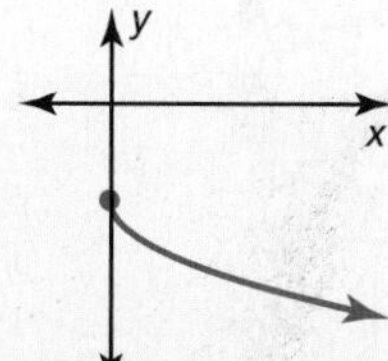

   D.
   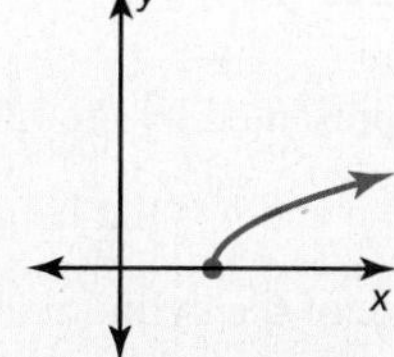

7. The time t (in seconds) it takes a dropped object to fall h feet is represented by $t = \frac{1}{4}\sqrt{h}$.

   a. Graph the function. Find the domain and range.

   b. It takes about 7.4 seconds for a stone dropped from the New River Gorge Bridge in West Virginia to reach the water below. About how high is the bridge above the New River?

10.2 Graphing Cube Root Functions (pp. 555–560)

Learning Target: Graph and describe cube root functions.

Vocabulary

cube root function

Graph the function. Compare the graph to the graph of $f(x) = \sqrt[3]{x}$.

8. $g(x) = \sqrt[3]{x} + 4$

9. $h(x) = -8\sqrt[3]{x}$

10. $s(x) = \sqrt[3]{-2(x-3)}$

11. $k(x) = \frac{1}{2}\sqrt[3]{x+1} - 5$

12. Graph $g(x) = -3\sqrt[3]{x+2} - 1$. Describe the transformations from the graph of $f(x) = \sqrt[3]{x}$ to the graph of g.

13. The graph of cube root function r is shown. Compare the average rate of change of r to the average rate of change of $p(x) = \sqrt[3]{\frac{1}{2}x}$ over the interval $x = 0$ to $x = 8$.

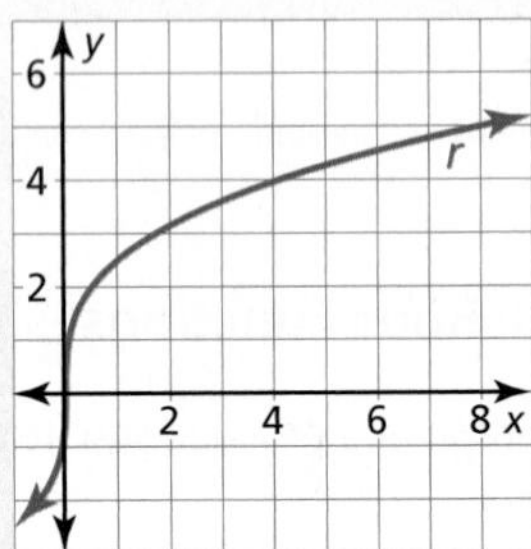

10.3 Solving Radical Equations (pp. 561–568)

Learning Target: Solve radical equations and identify any extraneous solutions.

Vocabulary

radical equation

Use the graph to solve the equation.

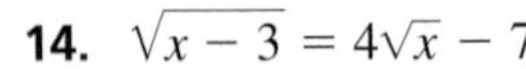

14. $\sqrt{x-3} = 4\sqrt{x} - 7$

15. $\sqrt{8x} - \left(\sqrt{x+2} + 2\right) = 0$

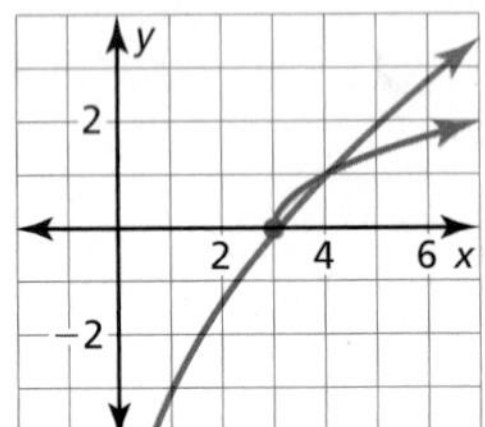

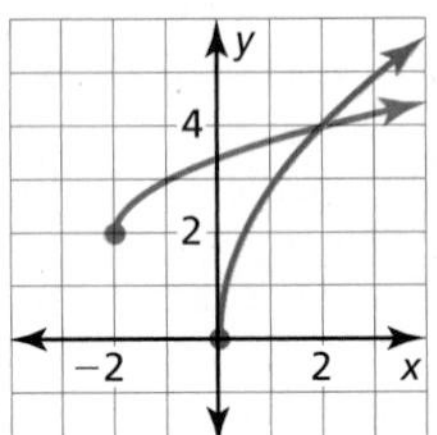

Solve the equation. Check your solution(s).

16. $8 + \sqrt{x} = 18$

17. $\sqrt[3]{x-1} = 3$

18. $\sqrt{5x-9} = \sqrt{4x}$

19. $x = \sqrt{3x+4}$

20. $8\sqrt{x-5} + 34 = 58$

21. $\sqrt{5x} + 6 = 5$

22. The radius r of a cylinder is represented by the function $r = \sqrt{\frac{V}{\pi h}}$, where V is the volume and h is the height of the cylinder. What is the volume of the cylindrical can?

23. You drop snowballs from two bridges. The velocity v (in meters per second) of each snowball after falling h meters is represented by $v = \sqrt{19.6h}$. Is the second bridge 9 times taller than the first bridge? Justify your answer.

	Velocity when hitting the ground
First snowball	5 meters per second
Second snowball	15 meters per second

10.4 Inverse of a Function (pp. 569–576)

Learning Target: Understand the relationship between inverse functions.

Vocabulary

inverse relation
inverse function

Find the inverse of the relation.

24. (1, −10), (3, −4), (5, 4), (7, 14), (9, 26)

25.

Input	−4	−2	0	2	4
Output	6	3	0	−3	−6

Solve $y = f(x)$ for x. Then find the input(s) when the output is 3.

26. $f(x) = x - 11$

27. $f(x) = \frac{1}{4}x + 2$

28. $f(x) = \sqrt{7x - 5}$

29. $f(x) = -x^2 + 12$

Find the inverse of the function. Then graph the function and its inverse.

30. $f(x) = -5x + 10$

31. $f(x) = 3x^2 - 1, x \geq 0$

32. $f(x) = \frac{1}{2}\sqrt{2x + 6}$

33. Consider the function $f(x) = x^2 + 4$. Use the Horizontal Line Test to determine whether the inverse of f is a function.

34. Compare the domains and ranges of the inverses of f and g.

$$f(x) = (x + 3)^2 - 2, x \geq -3$$

$$g(x) = (x + 3)^2 - 2, x \leq -3$$

35. In golf, a handicap is an adjustment to a golfer's score to even out differences in ability levels. On a particular course, you can find a golfer's handicap h by using the formula $h = \dfrac{113(a - 69.6)}{125}$, where a is the golfer's average score. Write an equation that represents the inverse of h. What does the inverse represent in this context?

Mathematical Practices

Reason Abstractly and Quantitatively

Mathematically proficient students bring two complementary abilities to bear on problems involving quantitative relationships: the ability to decontextualize and the ability to contextualize.

1. When solving Exercise 32 on page 560, explain how it can be helpful to focus on the variables and the given values in the problem apart from their context.
2. In real-life situations, why is it sometimes necessary to restrict the domain or range of a function and its inverse? Give an example to support your answer.

10 Practice Test WITH CalcChat®

Graph the function f. Find the domain and range. Compare the graph of f to the graph of g.

1. $f(x) = -\sqrt{x+6}$; $g(x) = \sqrt{x}$
2. $f(x) = \sqrt{x-3} + 2$; $g(x) = \sqrt{x}$
3. $f(x) = \sqrt[3]{x} - 5$; $g(x) = \sqrt[3]{x}$
4. $f(x) = -2\sqrt[3]{x+1}$; $g(x) = \sqrt[3]{x}$

Solve the equation. Check your solution(s).

5. $9 - \sqrt{x} = 3$
6. $\sqrt[3]{2x-8} - 3 = -1$
7. $\sqrt{8x-21} = \sqrt{18-5x}$
8. $x + 5 = \sqrt{7x+53}$

Find the inverse of the function.

9. $f(x) = 5x - 8$
10. $f(x) = 2\sqrt{x+3} - 1$
11. $f(x) = -\frac{1}{3}x^2 + 4, x \geq 0$

12. When solving the equation $x - 5 = \sqrt{ax+b}$, you obtain $x = 3$ and $x = 8$. Explain why at least one of these solutions must be extraneous.

Compare the graphs. Find the value of h, k, or a.

13.

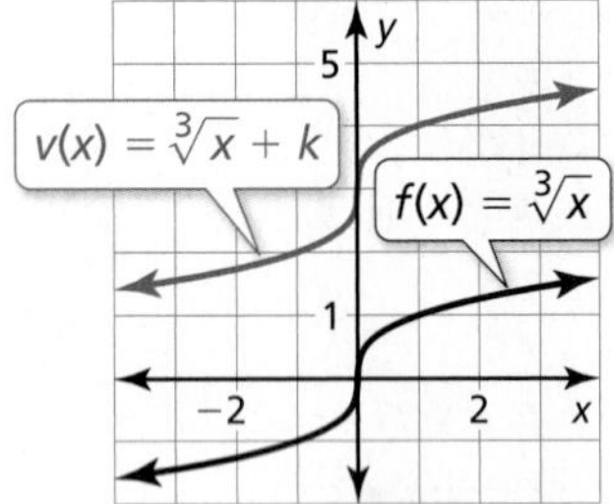

14.

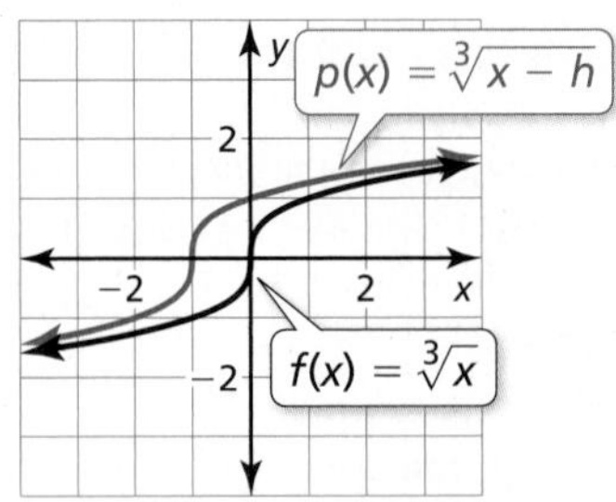

15.

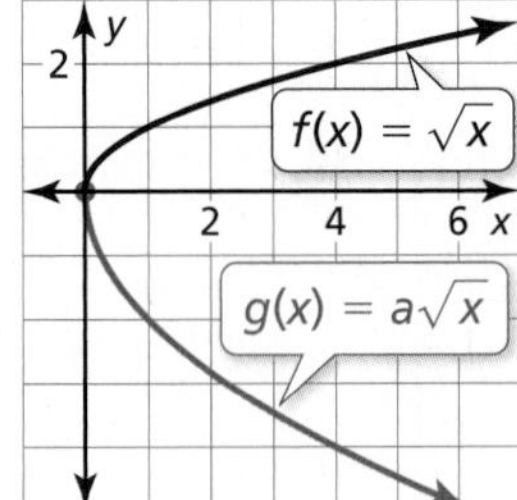

16. The velocity v (in meters per second) of a roller coaster after descending h meters from the top of a hill is represented by $v = \sqrt{18.4h}$.
    a. Use technology to graph the function.
    b. The velocity of the roller coaster at the bottom of the hill is 41.5 meters per second. How tall is the hill?
    c. Compare the average rate of change of the velocity over the interval $h = 0$ to $h = 10$, to the average rate of change over the interval $h = 10$ to $h = 20$.

17. The speed s (in meters per second) of sound through air is given by $s = 20\sqrt{T + 273}$, where T is the temperature (in degrees Celsius). How long does it take you to hear the wolf howl when the temperature is $-17°C$?

18. Solve the system algebraically.

$$y = \frac{1}{2}x + 4$$
$$y = 2\sqrt{x+5}$$

10 Performance Task
Health of Coral Reefs

When a coral reef is damaged, two components are critical to reestablish the health of the ecosystem.

RECOVERY: The return of hard and soft coral coverage to pre-disturbance levels.

REASSEMBLY: The return of coral composition to pre-disturbance levels.

THREATS TO CORAL REEFS INCLUDE:

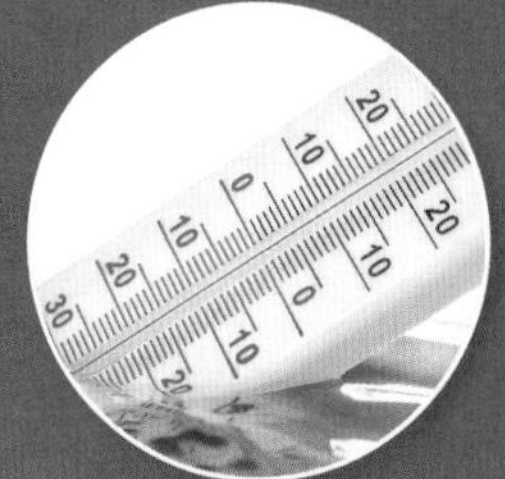

WARMING WATERS

Leads to coral bleaching

OVERFISHING

Removes fish that are benefical to the health of the reef

EXTREME WEATHER

Produces powerful waves that break apart coral

POLLUTION

Interferes with coral's ability to feed, grow, and reproduce

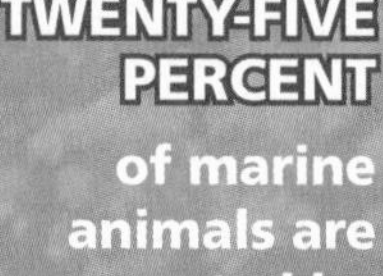

TWENTY-FIVE PERCENT of marine animals are supported by coral reefs.

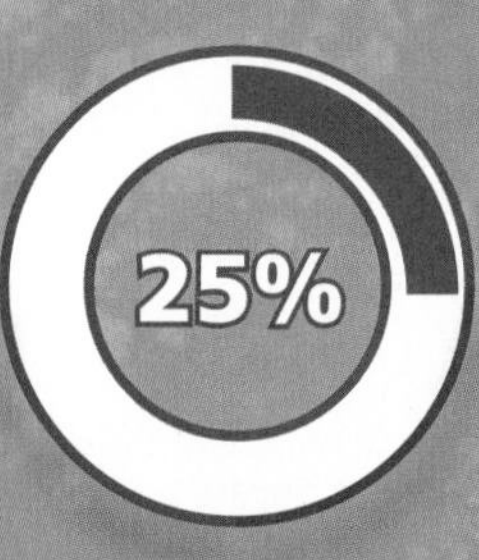

CORAL HEALTH CHECKUP

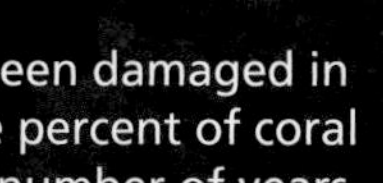

You are a biologist studying a coral reef that has been damaged in a storm. You use the functions below to model the percent of coral recovery and reassembly over time, where x is the number of years since the reef was damaged.

$$\text{Recovery: } f(x) = 0.7x^2 + 6.3x$$

$$\text{Reassembly: } g(x) = 8.5\sqrt{x} + 42$$

Write a brief report detailing the projected percents of recovery and reassembly over time. Include a graph of each function in your report.

Due to frequent natural variations in the composition of the

10 College and Career Readiness WITH CalcChat®

Tutorial videos are available for each exercise.

1. Use the graph to complete the function.

$f(x) = \square\sqrt{x - \square} + \square$

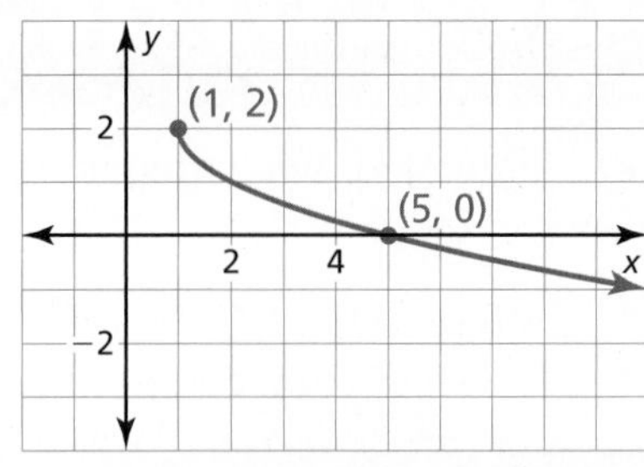

2. Consider the equation $y = mx + b$. Find values of m and b so that each statement is true.

a. When $m =$ ______ and $b =$ ______, the graph of the equation passes through the points $(-1, 4)$ and $(11, 2)$.

b. When $m =$ ______ and $b =$ ______, the graph of the equation is parallel to the graph of $y = \frac{1}{2}x + 9$ and passes through the point $(-2, -5)$.

c. When $m =$ ______ and $b =$ ______, the graph of the equation is perpendicular to the graph of $y = 4x - 3$ and passes through the point $(1, 6)$.

3. Which graph represents the inverse of the function $f(x) = 2x + 4$?

Ⓐ
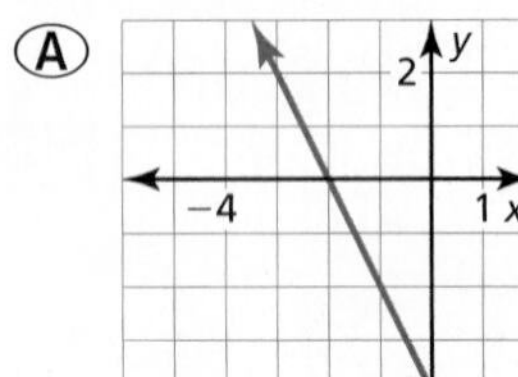

Ⓑ
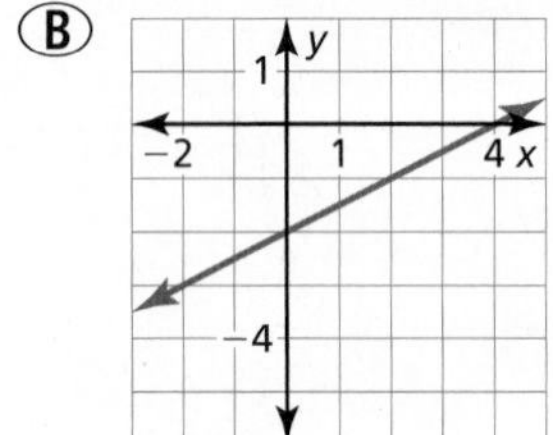

Ⓒ
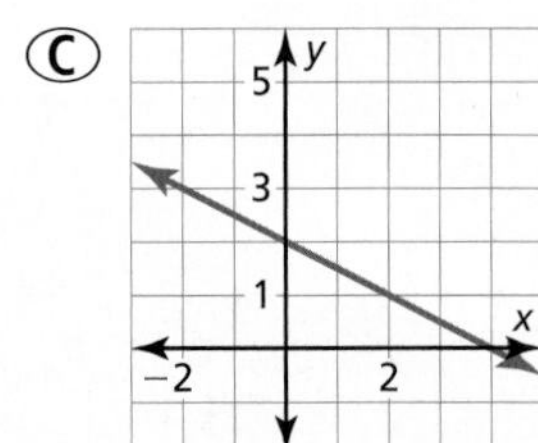

Ⓓ
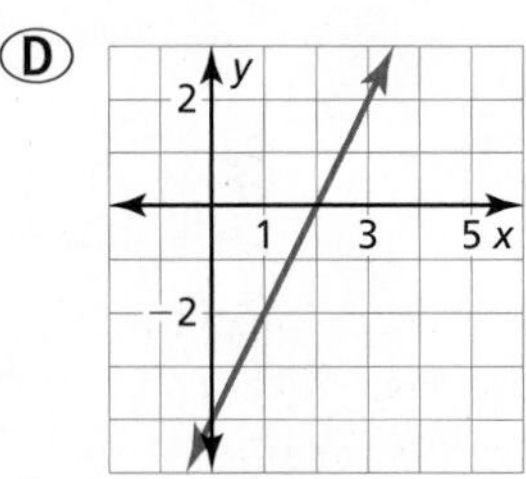

4. Which equation represents the nth term of the sequence 3, 12, 48, 192, . . .?

Ⓐ $a_n = 3(4)^{n-1}$

Ⓑ $a_n = 3(9)^{n-1}$

Ⓒ $a_n = 9n - 6$

Ⓓ $a_n = 9n + 3$

5. Which of the following are zeros of $f(x) = 2x^2 - 6x - 36$? Select all that apply.

−7	−6	−5	−4	−3	−2	−1	0
1	2	3	4	5	6	7	

6. Consider the function $f(x) = \frac{1}{2}\sqrt[3]{x + 3}$. The graph represents function g. Which statements are true? Select all that apply.

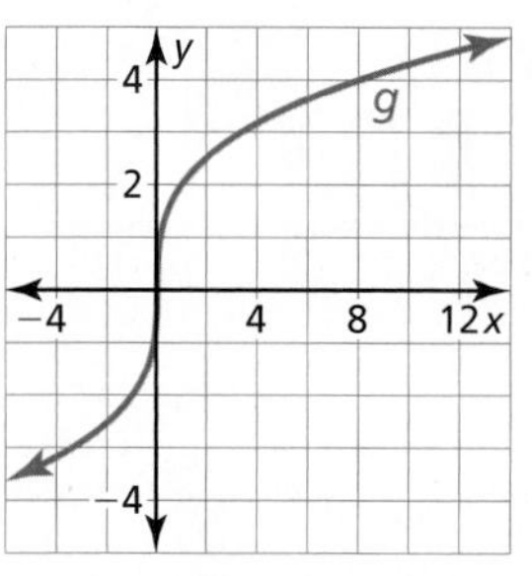

The x-intercept of the graph of f is greater than the x-intercept of the graph of g.

The graph of g is always increasing.

The average rate of change of g decreases as x increases.

The average rate of change of f increases as x increases.

The average rate of change of g is greater than the average rate of change of f over the interval $x = 0$ to $x = 8$.

7. You are making a tabletop with a tiled center and a uniform mosaic border.

x in. x in. x in. 12 in. 16 in. x in.

a. Write the polynomial in standard form that represents the perimeter of the tabletop.

b. Write the polynomial in standard form that represents the area of the tabletop.

c. The perimeter of the tabletop is less than 80 inches, and the area of tabletop is at least 252 square inches. Select all the possible values of x.

8. Solve $x - 4 = \sqrt{3x + 6}$.

Ⓐ $x = -10$ Ⓑ $x = -1$

Ⓒ $x = 1$ Ⓓ $x = 10$

Ⓔ A and B Ⓕ C and D

9. The table shows the average number of daily campsite reservations at a park x years after the park opened. Write an equation of a line of fit that models the average number of reservations as a function of the number of years since the park opened. Interpret the slope and y-intercept of the line of fit.

Year, *x*	0	1	2	3	4	5	6	7
Campsites, *y*	113	128	134	139	155	167	183	192

10. Identify the percent rate of change of $y = 0.4(0.85)^t$.

Ⓐ 15% Ⓑ 40%

Ⓒ 60% Ⓓ 85%

11 Data Analysis and Displays

NATIONAL GEOGRAPHIC EXPLORER

Chadwicke Jenkins

Dr. Chadwicke Jenkins explores topics related to human-robot interaction and robot learning, with a specific focus on robot learning from human demonstration and on robot software systems. Dr. Jenkins specializes in "Learning from Demonstration" (LfD). His goal is to create robots that are smart enough to learn tasks by simply observing the tasks being performed.

- Name some forms of life that learn from demonstration. Name some forms of life that are unable to learn from demonstration.
- Do you learn mathematics best from demonstration or by discovering concepts yourself?
- What is the definition of a robot? Do you own any robots?

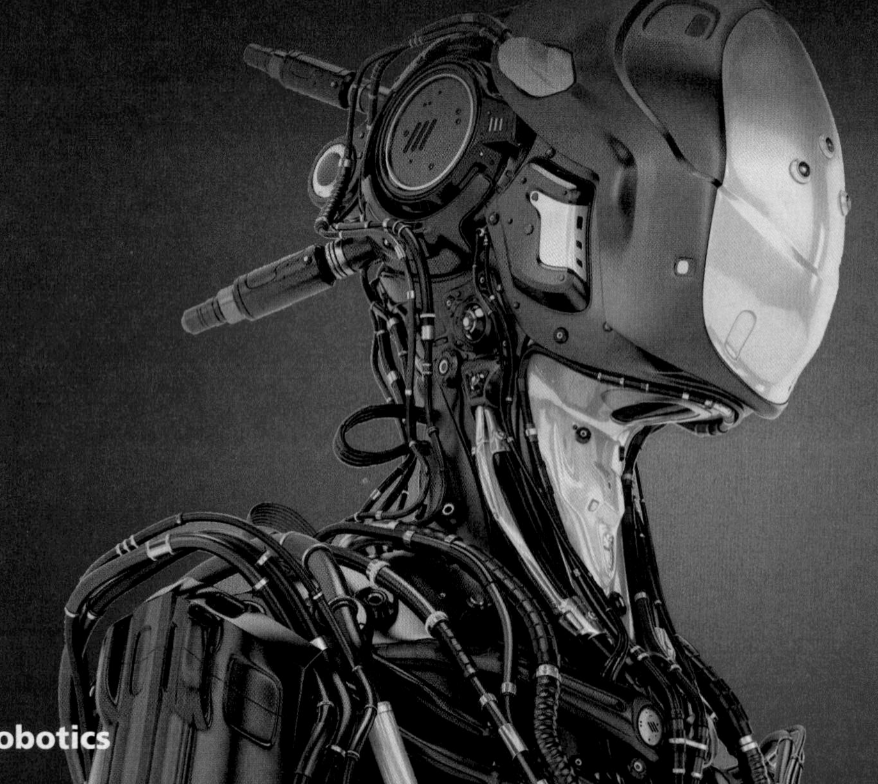

STEM

Robotics are used all around us. In the Performance Task, you will conduct a survey about the use of robotics in everyday life, analyze the data, and use data displays to create a presentation of your findings.

Robotics

Preparing for Chapter 11

Chapter Learning Target	Understand data.
Chapter Success Criteria	◆ I can interpret data displays. ◆ I can describe the shapes of data distributions. ■ I can represent data in different ways. ■ I can analyze data.

◆ Surface
■ Deep

Chapter Vocabulary

Work with a partner. Discuss each of the vocabulary terms.

measure of center	range	qualitative data
median	standard deviation	quantitative data
outlier	data transformation	misleading graph
measure of variation	two-way table	

Mathematical Practices

Model with Mathematics

Mathematically proficient students identify important quantities in practical situations and map their relationships using such tools as diagrams, two-way tables, graphs, flowcharts, and formulas. They analyze those relationships mathematically to draw conclusions.

Displaying Data Graphically

When solving a problem involving data, it is helpful to display the data graphically. This can be done in a variety of ways.

Pictograph 

Bar Graph 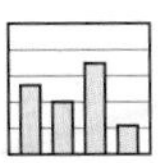

Circle Graph 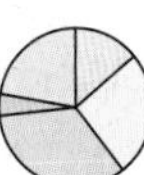

Line Graph 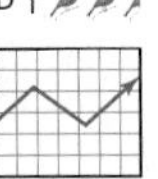

Histogram 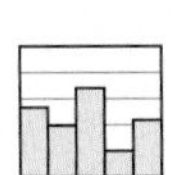

Stem-and-Leaf Plot 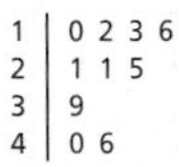

Box-and-Whisker Plot 

Dot Plot 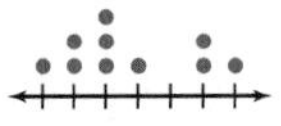

Scatter Plot 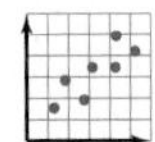

Work with a partner. The table shows the numbers of male and female participants by age at a robotics competition.

1. Use technology to make two different displays for the data.
2. Explain why you chose each type of data display. What conclusions can you draw from your data displays?

Participants by Age and Gender		
Ages	**Males**	**Females**
12–13	864	896
14–15	1238	1153
16–17	1654	1030
18–19	1521	936
20–21	1118	442

11 Prepare WITH CalcChat®

Making Histograms

Example 1 **The frequency table shows the numbers of books that 12 people read last month. Display the data in a histogram.**

Number of books	Frequency
0–1	6
2–3	4
4–5	0
6–7	2

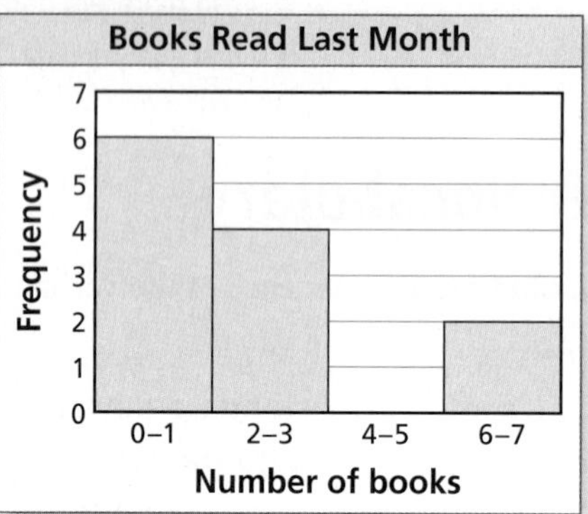

The table shows the results of a survey. Display the data in a histogram.

1.

After-school activities	Frequency
0–1	11
2–3	8
4–5	6
6–7	1

2.

Pets	Frequency
0–1	10
2–3	18
4–5	2

Solving Percent Problems

Example 2 **What percent of 20 is 12?**

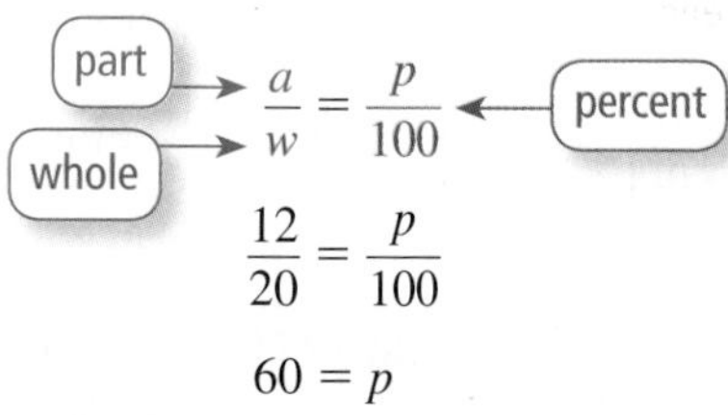

$\frac{a}{w} = \frac{p}{100}$ Write the percent proportion.

$\frac{12}{20} = \frac{p}{100}$ Substitute 12 for *a* and 20 for *w*.

$60 = p$ Simplify.

▶ So, 60% of 20 is 12.

Solve the percent problem.

3. What percent of 45 is 18?

4. 45% of what number is 36?

5. What number is 80% of 120?

6. What percent of 56 is 112?

7. **MP STRUCTURE** A number x is 75% of a number y. What percent of x is y? Explain your reasoning.

11.1 Measures of Center and Variation

Learning Target Find measures of center and variation of a data set.

Success Criteria

- I can find and compare the measures of center of a data set.
- I can find measures of variation of a data set.
- I can describe effects of data transformations.

EXPLORE IT! Describing the Variation of Data

Math Practice

Analyze Givens
What does one rectangle represent in each graph?

Work with a partner. The graphs show the weights and positions of the players on a professional football team and a professional baseball team.

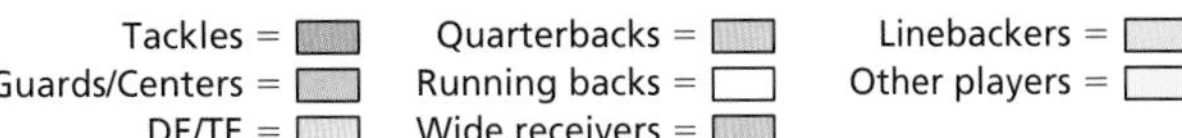

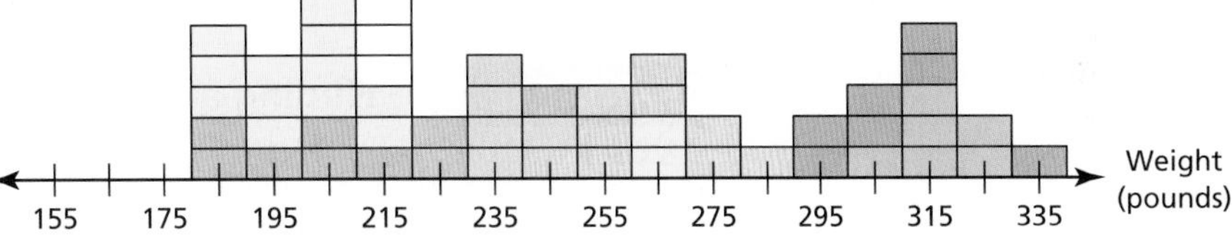

Weights of Players on a Baseball Team

Pitchers =
Catchers =
Infielders =
Outfielders =
Designated hitters =

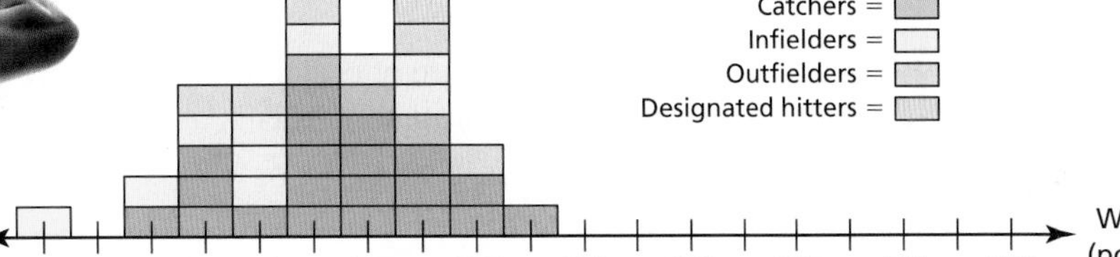

a. Describe the data in each graph in terms of how much the weights vary from the mean. Explain your reasoning.

b. Compare how much the weights of the players on the football team vary from the mean to how much the weights of the players on the baseball team vary from the mean.

c. Does there appear to be a correlation between the body weights and the positions of players in professional football? in professional baseball? Explain.

d. The weights (in pounds) of the players on a professional basketball team by position are as follows.

Power forwards: 235, 255, 295, 245
Centers: 255, 245, 325
Shooting guards: 205, 215, 185
Small forwards: 235, 235
Point guards: 205, 185, 205

Make a graph that represents the weights and positions of the players. Does there appear to be a correlation between the body weights and the positions of players in professional basketball? Explain your reasoning.

e. How can you describe the *variation* of a data set?

GO DIGITAL

Comparing the Mean, Median, and Mode

A **measure of center** is a measure that represents the center, or typical value, of a data set. The *mean*, *median*, and *mode* are measures of center.

Vocabulary

measure of center, *p. 588*
mean, *p. 588*
median, *p. 588*
mode, *p. 588*
outlier, *p. 589*
measure of variation, *p. 589*
range, *p. 589*
standard deviation, *p. 590*
data transformation, *p. 591*

KEY IDEAS

Mean

The **mean** of a numerical data set is the sum of the data divided by the number of data values. The symbol $\overline{x}$ represents the mean. It is read as "x-bar."

Median

The **median** of a numerical data set is the middle number when the values are written in numerical order. When a data set has an even number of values, the median is the mean of the two middle values.

Mode

The **mode** of a data set is the value or values that occur most often. There may be one mode, no mode, or more than one mode.

STUDY TIP

The only measure of center that can represent a nonnumerical data set is the mode.

EXAMPLE 1 Finding and Comparing Measures of Center

WATCH

An amusement park hires students for the summer. The students' hourly wages are shown in the table.

a. Find the mean, median, and mode of the hourly wages.

b. Which measure of center best represents the data? Explain.

Students' Hourly Wages	
\$16.50	\$8.25
\$8.75	\$8.45
\$8.65	\$8.25
\$9.10	\$9.25

SOLUTION

a. Mean $\overline{x} = \dfrac{16.5 + 8.75 + 8.65 + 9.1 + 8.25 + 8.45 + 8.25 + 9.25}{8} = 9.65$

Median 8.25, 8.25, 8.45, 8.65, 8.75, 9.10, 9.25, 16.50 — Order the data.

$\dfrac{17.4}{2} = 8.7$ — Mean of two middle values

Mode 8.25, 8.25, 8.45, 8.65, 8.75, 9.10, 9.25, 16.50 — 8.25 occurs most often.

▶ The mean is \$9.65, the median is \$8.70, and the mode is \$8.25.

b. The median best represents the data. The mode is less than most of the data, and the mean is greater than most of the data.

SELF-ASSESSMENT

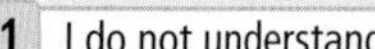

1 I do not understand. 2 I can do it with help. 3 I can do it on my own. 4 I can teach someone else.

1. **VOCABULARY** In a data set, what does a measure of center represent?
2. **WHAT IF?** The park hires another student at an hourly wage of \$8.45.
   a. How does this additional value affect the mean, median, and mode? Explain.
   b. Which measure of center best represents the data? Explain.

An **outlier** is a data value that is much greater than or much less than the other values in a data set.

EXAMPLE 2 Removing an Outlier 

Students' Hourly Wages	
\$16.50	\$8.25
\$8.75	\$8.45
\$8.65	\$8.25
\$9.10	\$9.25

Consider the data in Example 1.

a. Identify the outlier. How does the outlier affect the mean, median, and mode?

b. Describe one possible explanation for the outlier.

SOLUTION

a. The value \$16.50 is much greater than the other wages. It is the outlier. Find the mean, median, and mode without the outlier.

STUDY TIP
Outliers usually have the greatest effect on the mean.

Mean $\bar{x} = \frac{8.75 + 8.65 + 9.1 + 8.25 + 8.45 + 8.25 + 9.25}{7} \approx 8.67$

Median 8.25, 8.25, 8.45, 8.65, 8.75, 9.10, 9.25 — The middle value is 8.65.

Mode 8.25, 8.25, 8.45, 8.65, 8.75, 9.10, 9.25 — The mode is 8.25.

▶ When you remove the outlier, the mean decreases \$9.65 − \$8.67 = \$0.98, the median decreases \$8.70 − \$8.65 = \$0.05, and the mode is the same.

b. The outlier could be a student who is hired to maintain the park's website, while the other students could be game attendants.

SELF-ASSESSMENT 1 I do not understand. 2 I can do it with help. 3 I can do it on my own. 4 I can teach someone else.

3. The table shows the annual salaries of the employees of an auto repair service.

a. Identify the outlier. How does the outlier affect the mean, median, and mode?

b. Describe one possible explanation for the outlier.

Annual Salaries	
\$32,000	\$42,000
\$41,000	\$38,000
\$38,000	\$45,000
\$72,000	\$35,000

Finding the Range and Standard Deviation

A **measure of variation** is a measure that describes the spread, or distribution, of a data set. One measure of variation is the *range*. The **range** of a data set is the difference of the greatest value and the least value.

EXAMPLE 3 Finding a Range 

Ages for Show A	
20	29
19	22
25	27
27	29
30	20
21	31

Ages for Show B	
25	19
20	27
22	25
27	22
48	21
32	24

Two reality cooking shows select 12 contestants each. The ages of the contestants are shown in the tables. Find the range of the ages for each show. Compare your results.

SOLUTION

Show A 19, 20, 20, 21, 22, 25, 27, 27, 29, 29, 30, 31 — Order the data.

So, the range is 31 − 19, or 12 years.

Show B 19, 20, 21, 22, 22, 24, 25, 25, 27, 27, 32, 48 — Order the data.

So, the range is 48 − 19, or 29 years.

▶ The range of the ages for Show A is 12 years, and the range of the ages for Show B is 29 years. So, the ages for Show B are more spread out.

A disadvantage of using the range to describe the spread of a data set is that it uses only two data values. A measure of variation that uses all the values of a data set is the *standard deviation*.

KEY IDEA

Standard Deviation

REMEMBER

An ellipsis " . . . " indicates that a pattern continues.

The **standard deviation** of a numerical data set is a measure of how much a typical value in the data set differs from the mean. The symbol σ represents the standard deviation. It is read as "sigma." It is given by

$$\sigma = \sqrt{\frac{(x_1 - \overline{x})^2 + (x_2 - \overline{x})^2 + \cdots + (x_n - \overline{x})^2}{n}}$$

where n is the number of values in the data set. The *deviation* of a data value x is the difference of the data value and the mean of the data set, $x - \overline{x}$.

Step 1 Find the mean, $\overline{x}$.

Step 2 Find the deviation of each data value, $x - \overline{x}$.

Step 3 Square each deviation, $(x - \overline{x})^2$.

Step 4 Find the mean of the squared deviations. This is called the *variance*.

Step 5 Take the square root of the variance.

A small standard deviation means that the data are clustered around the mean. A large standard deviation means that the data are more spread out.

EXAMPLE 4 Finding a Standard Deviation

Find the standard deviation of the ages for Show A in Example 3. Use a table to organize your work. Interpret your result.

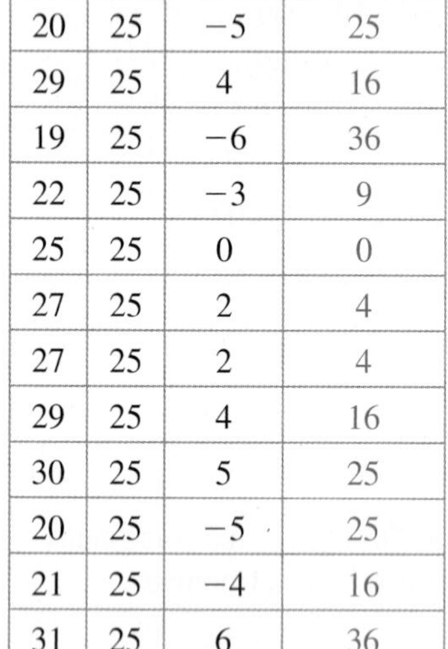

x	$\overline{x}$	$x - \overline{x}$	$(x - \overline{x})^2$
20	25	−5	25
29	25	4	16
19	25	−6	36
22	25	−3	9
25	25	0	0
27	25	2	4
27	25	2	4
29	25	4	16
30	25	5	25
20	25	−5	25
21	25	−4	16
31	25	6	36

SOLUTION

Step 1 Find the mean, $\overline{x}$. $\quad \overline{x} = \dfrac{20 + 29 + 19 + \cdots + 31}{12} = \dfrac{300}{12} = 25$

Step 2 Find the deviation of each data value, $x - \overline{x}$, as shown in the table.

Step 3 Square each deviation, $(x - \overline{x})^2$, as shown in the table.

Step 4 Find the mean of the squared deviations, or variance.

$$\frac{(x_1 - \overline{x})^2 + (x_2 - \overline{x})^2 + \cdots + (x_n - \overline{x})^2}{n} = \frac{25 + 16 + \cdots + 36}{12} = \frac{212}{12}$$

Step 5 Use technology to take the square root of the variance.

$$\sqrt{\frac{(x_1 - \overline{x})^2 + (x_2 - \overline{x})^2 + \cdots + (x_n - \overline{x})^2}{n}} = \sqrt{\frac{212}{12}} \approx 4.2$$

▶ The standard deviation is about 4.2. This means that the typical age of a contestant on Show A differs from the mean by about 4.2 years.

SELF-ASSESSMENT

1 I do not understand. 2 I can do it with help. 3 I can do it on my own. 4 I can teach someone else.

4. After the first week, the 25-year-old is voted off Show A and the 48-year-old is voted off Show B in Example 3. How does this affect the range of the ages of the remaining contestants on each show? Explain.

5. Find the standard deviation of the ages for Show B in Example 3. Interpret your result. Then compare the standard deviations for Show A and Show B. What can you conclude?

Effects of Data Transformations

A **data transformation** is a procedure that uses a mathematical operation to change a data set into a different data set.

KEY IDEAS

Data Transformations Using Addition

When a real number k is added to each value in a numerical data set

- the measures of center of the new data set can be found by adding k to the original measures of center.
- the measures of variation of the new data set are the *same* as the original measures of variation.

STUDY TIP

The standard deviation stays the same because the amount by which each data value deviates from the mean stays the same.

Data Transformations Using Multiplication

When each value in a numerical data set is multiplied by a real number k, where $k > 0$, the measures of center and variation can be found by multiplying the original measures by k.

EXAMPLE 5 Modeling Real Life

Students' Hourly Wages	
\$16.50	\$8.25
\$8.75	\$8.45
\$8.65	\$8.25
\$9.10	\$9.25

Consider the data in Example 1. A manager considers increasing all hourly wages by either \$1.25 or 10%. Which increase results in a greater mean hourly wage? Which increase results in a greater range of hourly wages?

SOLUTION

In Example 1, you found that the mean hourly wage is \$9.65. The range of the original data set is \$16.50 − \$8.25 = \$8.25. Find the mean and the range after each wage increase.

\$1.25 increase

Add \$1.25 to the mean. The range is the same as the original range.

Mean: \$9.65 + \$1.25 = \$10.90

Range: \$8.25

10% increase

To increase by 10%, multiply by 110%, or 1.1. Multiply the mean and range by 1.1.

Mean: \$9.65(1.1) ≈ \$10.62

Range: \$8.25(1.1) ≈ \$9.08

▶ Because \$10.90 > \$10.62, the \$1.25 increase results in a greater mean hourly wage. Because \$9.08 > \$8.25, the 10% increase results in a greater range of hourly wages.

SELF-ASSESSMENT 1 I do not understand. 2 I can do it with help. 3 I can do it on my own. 4 I can teach someone else.

6. Each airplane increases in altitude. Which increase results in a greater mean altitude, an increase of $1\frac{1}{2}$ miles or a 50% increase? Explain your reasoning.

7. **WRITING** When you add a real number k to each value in a numerical data set, explain why the measures of variation stay the same while the measures of center change. When you multiply each value in a numerical data set by a real number k, explain why the measures of center and variation change.

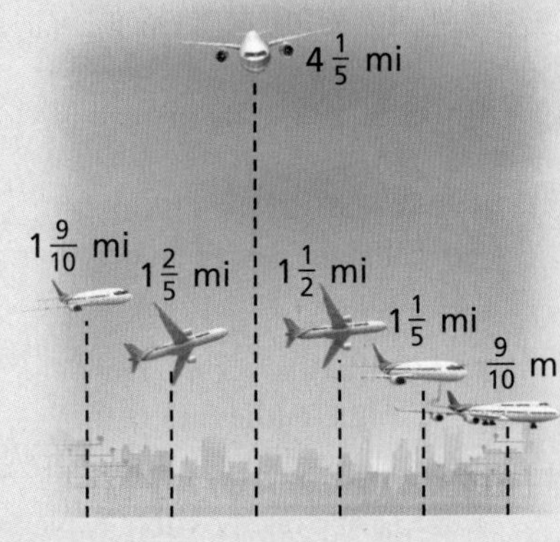

11.1 Practice WITH CalcChat® AND CalcView®

In Exercises 1–4, (a) find the mean, median, and mode of the data set and (b) determine which measure of center best represents the data. Explain. *Example 1*

1. 3, 5, 1, 5, 1, 1, 2, 3, 15

2. 12, 9, 17, 15, 10

3. 13, 30, 16, 19, 20, 22, 25, 31

4. 14, 15, 3, 15, 14, 14, 18, 15, 8, 16

5. ANALYZING DATA The table shows the lengths of nine movies.

Movie Lengths (hours)		
$1\frac{1}{3}$	$1\frac{2}{3}$	2
3	$2\frac{1}{3}$	$1\frac{2}{3}$
2	2	$1\frac{2}{3}$

a. Find the mean, median, and mode of the lengths.

b. Which measure of center best represents the data? Explain.

6. ANALYZING DATA The table shows the daily changes in the value of a stock over 12 days.

Changes in Stock Value (dollars)		
1.05	2.03	−13.78
−2.41	2.64	0.67
4.02	1.39	0.66
−0.28	−3.01	2.20

a. Find the mean, median, and mode of the changes in stock value.

b. Which measure of center best represents the data? Explain.

c. On the 13th day, the value of the stock increases by \$4.28. How does this additional value affect the mean, median, and mode? Explain.

In Exercises 7–10, find the value of x.

7. 2, 8, 9, 7, 6, x; The mean is 6.

8. 12.5, −10, −7.5, x; The mean is 11.5.

9. 9, 10, 12, x, 20, 25; The median is 14.

10. 30, 45, x, 100; The median is 51.

11. ANALYZING DATA The table shows the masses of eight polar bears. *Example 2*

Masses (kilograms)	
455	262
471	358
364	553
62	351

a. Identify the outlier. How does the outlier affect the mean, median, and mode?

b. Describe one possible explanation for the outlier.

12. ANALYZING DATA The sizes of emails (in kilobytes) in your inbox are 2, 3, 5, 2, 1, 46, 3, 7, 2, and 1.

a. Identify the outlier. How does the outlier affect the mean, median, and mode?

b. Describe one possible explanation for the outlier.

13. ANALYZING DATA The scores of two golfers are shown. Find the range of the scores for each golfer. Compare your results. *Example 3*

Golfer A		Golfer B	
83	88	89	87
84	95	93	95
91	89	92	94
90	87	88	91
98	95	89	92

14. ANALYZING DATA The graph shows a player's monthly home run totals in two seasons. Find the range of the number of home runs for each season. Compare your results.

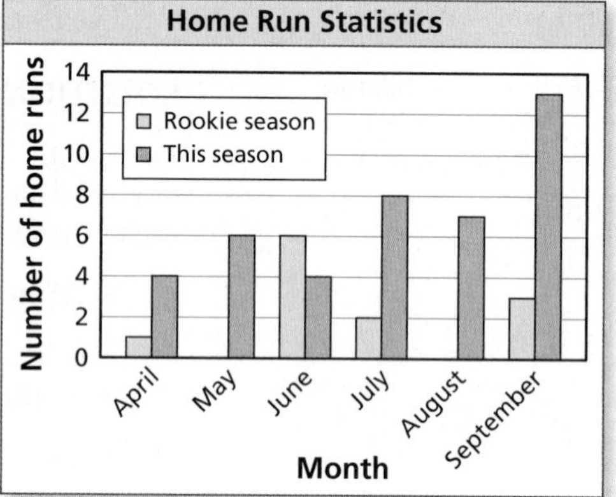

In Exercises 15–18, find the (a) range and (b) standard deviation of the data set.

15. 40, 35, 45, 55, 60

16. 141, 116, 117, 135, 126, 121

17. 0.5, 2.0, 2.5, 1.5, 1.0, 1.5

18. 8.2, 10.1, 2.6, 4.8, 2.4, 5.6, 7.0, 3.3

19. ANALYZING DATA Consider the data in Exercise 13. *Example 4*

a. Find the standard deviation of the scores for Golfer A. Interpret your result.

b. Find the standard deviation of the scores for Golfer B. Interpret your result.

c. Compare the standard deviations for Golfer A and Golfer B. What can you conclude?

20. **ANALYZING DATA** Consider the data in Exercise 14.

a. Find the standard deviation of the monthly home run totals in the player's rookie season. Interpret your result.

b. Find the standard deviation of the monthly home run totals in this season. Interpret your result.

c. Compare the standard deviations for the rookie season and this season. What can you conclude?

21. **TRANSFORMING DATA** Find the values of the measures shown when each value in the data set increases by 14.

Mean: 62 Median: 55 Mode: 49

Range: 46 Standard deviation: 15.5

22. **TRANSFORMING DATA** Find the values of the measures shown when each value in the data set is multiplied by 0.5.

Mean: 320 Median: 300 Mode: none

Range: 210 Standard deviation: 70.6

MODELING REAL LIFE In Exercises 23 and 24, the prices of wireless headphones at a store have the given median and range. Which price change will result in a lesser median price? a lesser range of prices? *Example 5*

Median: \$149.99 Range: \$330

23. increasing all prices by either \$10 or 7%

24. decreasing all prices by either \$5 or 3%

25. **ERROR ANALYSIS** Describe and correct the error in finding the range of the data set when each value in the set increases by 20.

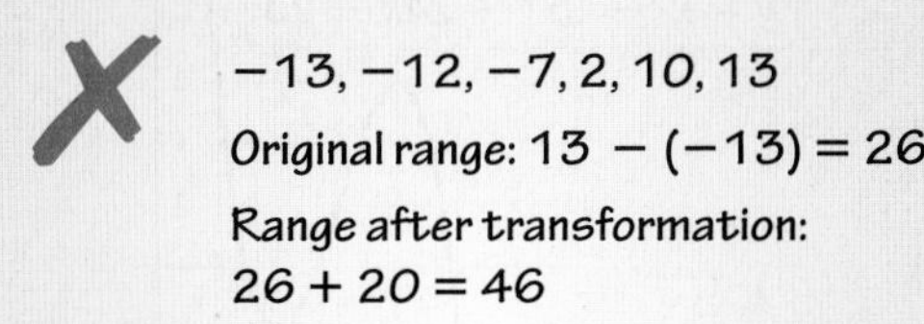

26. **ANALYZING DATA** The table shows the results of a survey that asked 12 students to name their favorite meal. Which measure of center can be used to describe the data? Explain.

Favorite Meal			
spaghetti	pizza	steak	hamburger
steak	taco	pizza	chili
pizza	chicken	fish	spaghetti

27. **CONNECTING CONCEPTS** Compare the process of finding the mean absolute deviation of a data set with the process of finding the standard deviation of a data set.

GO DIGITAL

28. **MP PROBLEM SOLVING** In a bowling match, the team with the greater mean score wins. The scores of the members of two bowling teams are shown.

Team A: 172, 130, 173, 212

Team B: 136, 184, 168, 192

a. Which team wins the match? If the team with the greater median score wins, is the result the same? Explain.

b. Which team is more consistent? Explain.

c. In another match between the two teams, all the members of Team A increase their scores by 15 and all the members of Team B increase their scores by 12.5%. Which team wins this match? Explain.

29. **MP REASONING** A data set is described by the measures shown.

Mean: 27 Median: 32 Mode: 18

Range: 41 Standard deviation: 9

Find the mean, median, mode, range, and standard deviation of the data set when each data value is multiplied by 3 and then increased by 8.

30. **HOW DO YOU SEE IT?** The dot plots show the ages of the members of three different adventure clubs. Without performing calculations, which data set has the greatest standard deviation? Which has the least standard deviation? Explain your reasoning.

Ⓐ

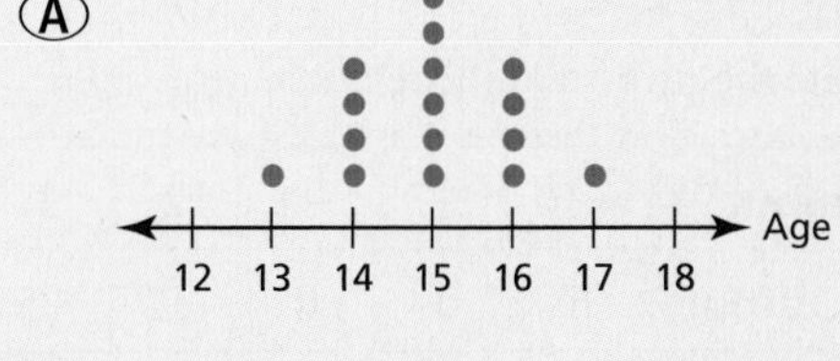

Ⓑ

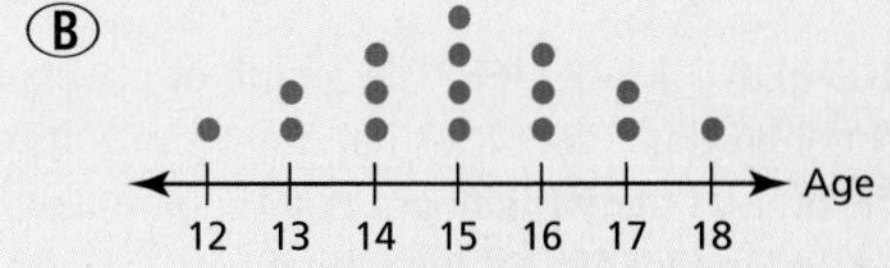

Ⓒ

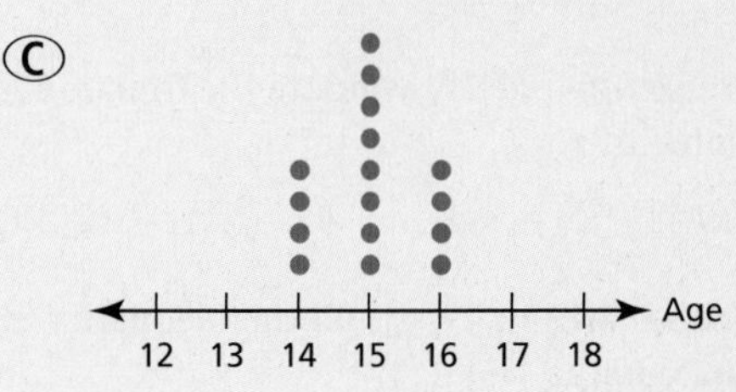

31. COLLEGE PREP In the data set 8, 4, 13, 21, 9, and 11, the least value increases by 1 and the greatest value decreases by 1. Select each measure that changes.

Ⓐ mean Ⓑ median

Ⓒ range Ⓓ standard deviation

32. THOUGHT PROVOKING
Write two data sets with 7 different numbers that have (a) the same mean but different standard deviations and (b) the same standard deviation but different means.

33. MP USING TOOLS Measure the heights (in inches) of the students in your class.

a. Find the mean, median, mode, range, and standard deviation of the heights.

b. A new student who is 7 feet tall joins your class. How would you expect this student's height to affect the measures in part (a)? Verify your answer.

34. CRITICAL THINKING Can the standard deviation of a data set be 0? Can it be negative? Explain.

35. 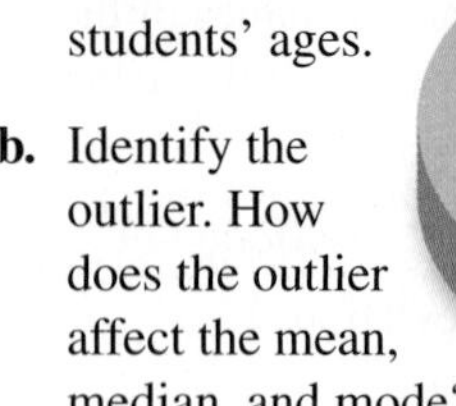 The circle graph shows the distribution of the ages of 50 students enrolled in a lifeguard training course.

a. Find the mean, median, and mode of the students' ages.

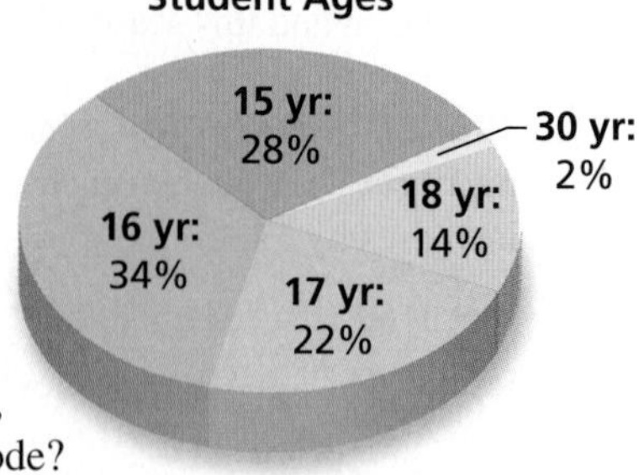

b. Identify the outlier. How does the outlier affect the mean, median, and mode?

c. All 50 students take a review course exactly 2 years later to extend their certification. Find the mean, median, and mode of the students' ages.

REVIEW & REFRESH

WATCH

In Exercises 36–39, solve the inequality. Graph the solution, if possible.

36. $6x + 1 \leq 4x - 9$ **37.** $-3(3y - 2) < 7 - 9y$

38. $2(5c - 4) \geq 5(2c + 8)$

39. $4(3 - w) > 3(4w - 4)$

In Exercises 40–43, graph the linear equation.

40. $x = 10$ **41.** $-4x + 3y = 18$

42. $y = -\frac{3}{5}x + 1$ **43.** $y + 2 = 5x$

44. Find the inverse of the relation.

Input	−10	−7	−1	2	3
Output	6	1	0	−2	−5

45. MODELING REAL LIFE The length of a rectangular whiteboard is 2 feet less than three times its width. The area of the whiteboard is 40 square feet. What are the dimensions of the whiteboard?

In Exercises 46 and 47, evaluate the function for the given value of *x*.

46. $f(x) = 7^x; x = -2$ **47.** $f(x) = -2(3)^x; x = 4$

In Exercises 48 and 49, graph the inequality in a coordinate plane.

48. $y > -5.5$ **49.** $y \leq 3x - 6$

50. MP STRUCTURE Write a function that is a horizontal translation and a reflection in the *x*-axis of the graph of $f(x) = \sqrt[3]{x}$.

In Exercises 51 and 52, find the mean, median, mode, range, and standard deviation of the data set.

51. 104, 103, 100, 108, 110

52. 21, 32, 41, 21, 36, 44

53. Approximate when the function is positive, negative, increasing, or decreasing. Then describe the end behavior of the function.

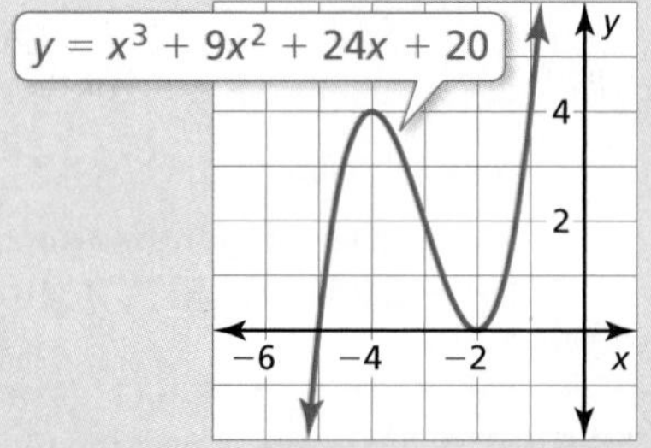

In Exercises 54 and 55, solve the equation.

54. $5\sqrt{x - 3} - 7 = 23$ **55.** $8 = \sqrt{3c + 1} + 12$

56. Determine which of the lines, if any, are parallel or perpendicular. Explain.

Line *a*: $y = -7x + 11$, Line *b*: $-7x + y = 8$, Line *c*: $7y = x - 14$

11.2 Box-and-Whisker Plots

Learning Target Make and interpret box-and-whisker plots for data sets.

Success Criteria
- I can use box-and-whisker plots to represent data sets.
- I can interpret box-and-whisker plots.
- I can use box-and-whisker plots to compare data sets.
- I can explain how to identify outliers in a data set.

EXPLORE IT! Making and Interpreting Box-and-Whisker Plots

Numbers of Photos Shared Online			
3	10	18	8
9	3	0	32
23	19	13	8
6	3	3	10
12	45	1	5
13	24	16	14

Work with a partner. The numbers of photos shared online by students in a class during spirit week are shown.

a. Order the data on a strip of grid paper that has 24 equally spaced boxes. Fold the paper in half.

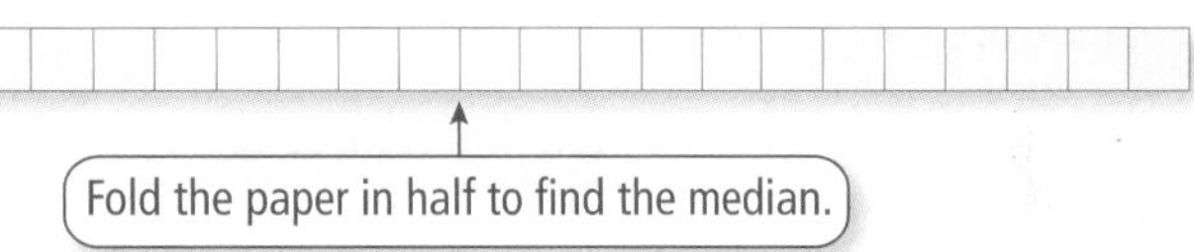

b. Fold the paper in half again. Explain how this divides the data. Find the least value, the greatest value, the median, the median of the lower half of the data, and the median of the upper half of the data.

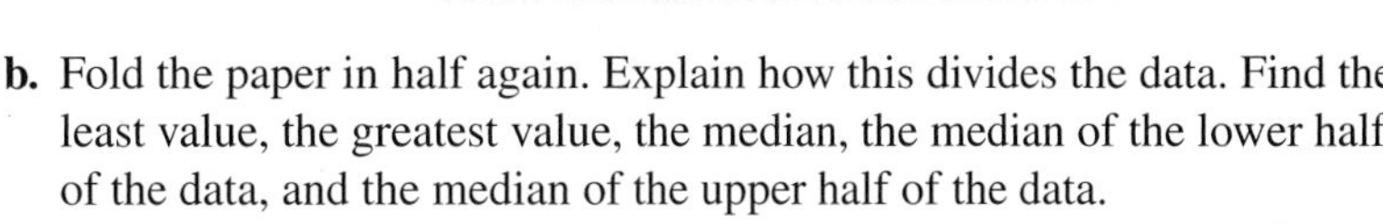

c. A *box-and-whisker plot* is one way to represent the data visually. Explain how the box-and-whisker plot shown represents the data set.

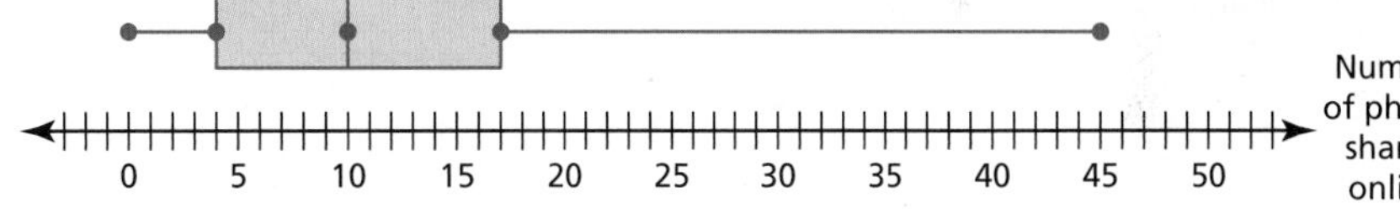

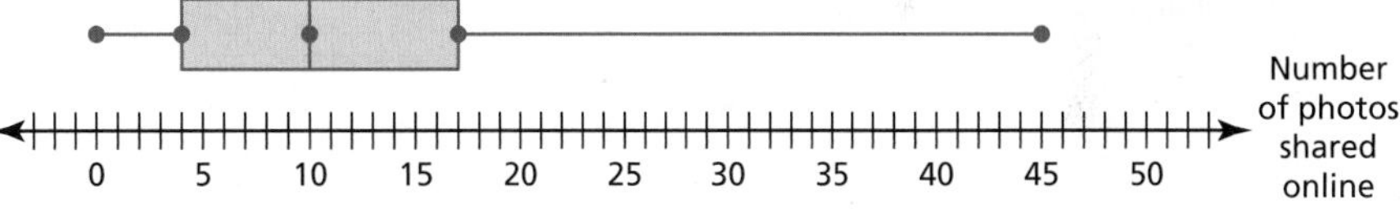

d. Do you think any of the data values are outliers? How can you tell? Explain your reasoning.

e. Interpret each box-and-whisker plot. How would you describe the shape of the box-and-whisker plot?

i. body mass indices (BMI) of students in a ninth-grade class

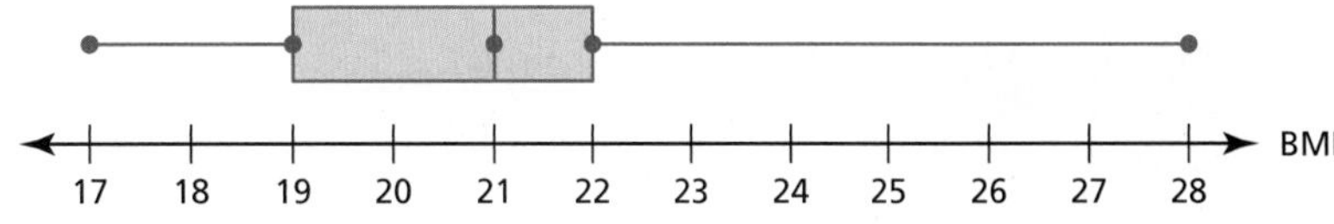

ii. heights of roller coasters at an amusement park

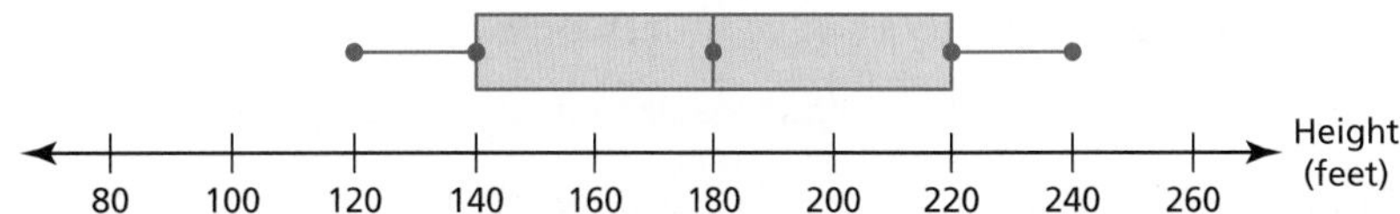

f. Do you think the data sets in part (e) include any outliers? Explain your reasoning.

Math Practice

View as Components
What does the box and its length represent in a box-and-whisker plot? What does each whisker and its length represent?

Using Box-and-Whisker Plots to Represent Data Sets

Vocabulary 

box-and-whisker plot, *p. 596*
quartile, *p. 596*
five-number summary, *p. 596*
interquartile range, *p. 597*

KEY IDEA

Box-and-Whisker Plot

A **box-and-whisker plot** shows the variability of a data set along a number line using the least value, the greatest value, and the *quartiles* of the data. **Quartiles** divide the data set into four equal parts. The median (second quartile, Q2) divides the data set into two halves. The median of the lower half is the first quartile, Q1. The median of the upper half is the third quartile, Q3.

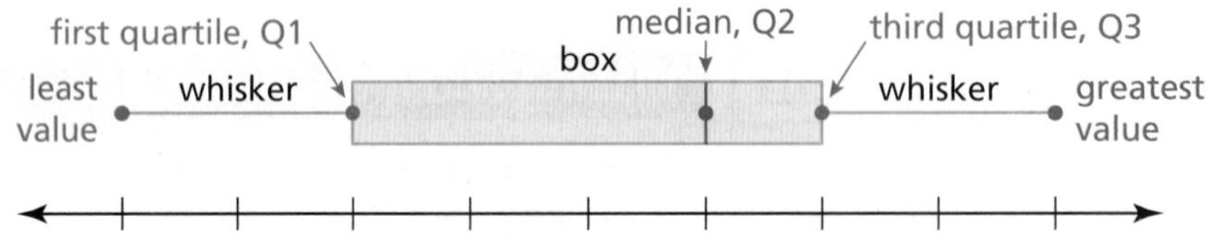

The five numbers that make up a box-and-whisker plot are called the **five-number summary** of the data set.

STUDY TIP

Sometimes, the first quartile is called the *lower quartile* and the third quartile is called the *upper quartile*.

EXAMPLE 1 Making a Box-and-Whisker Plot 

Make a box-and-whisker plot that represents the ages of the members of a backpacking expedition.

24, 30, 30, 22, 25, 22, 18, 25, 28, 30, 25, 27

SOLUTION

Step 1 Order the data. Find the median and the quartiles.

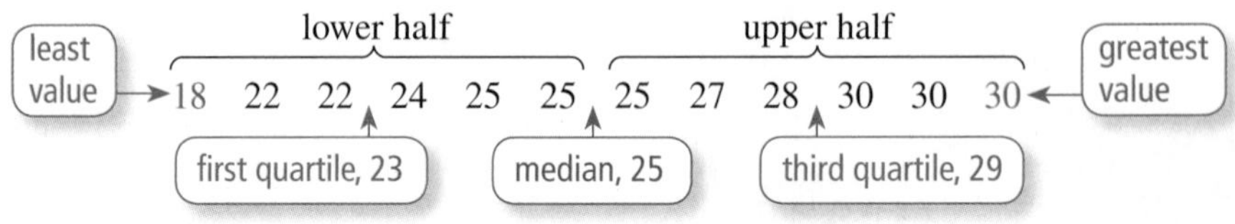

Step 2 Draw a number line that includes the least and greatest values. Graph points above the number line for the five-number summary.

Step 3 Draw a box using Q1 and Q3. Draw a line through the median. Draw whiskers from the box to the least and greatest values.

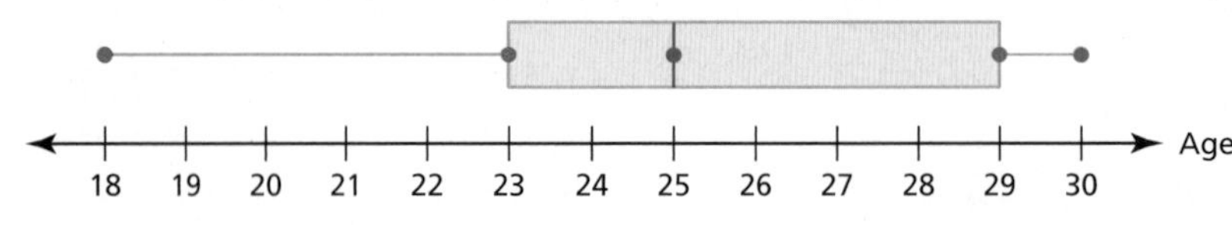

SELF-ASSESSMENT 1 I do not understand. 2 I can do it with help. 3 I can do it on my own. 4 I can teach someone else.

1. **VOCABULARY** How is a box-and-whisker plot different from a dot plot?
2. **WRITING** Describe how to find the first quartile of a data set.
3. A basketball player scores 14, 16, 20, 5, 22, 30, 16, and 28 points during a tournament. Make a box-and-whisker plot that represents the data.
4. MP **REASONING** Is it possible to have a box-and-whisker plot with no whisker(s)? Explain.

Interpreting Box-and-Whisker Plots

The figure shows how data are distributed in a box-and-whisker plot.

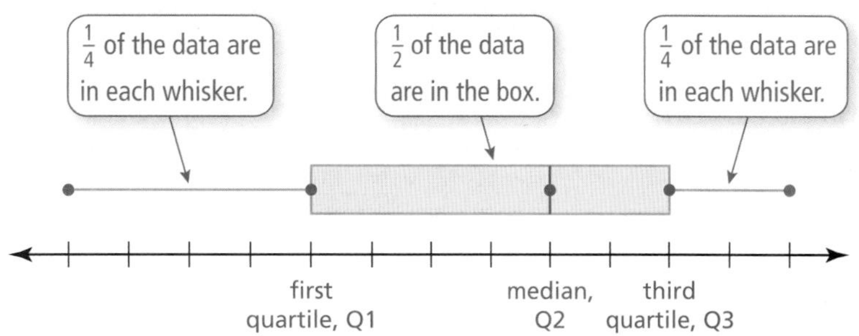

$\frac{1}{4}$ of the data are in each whisker.
$\frac{1}{2}$ of the data are in the box.
$\frac{1}{4}$ of the data are in each whisker.
first quartile, Q1
median, Q2
third quartile, Q3

STUDY TIP

A longer whisker or box indicates that the data are more spread out within that portion of the data.

Another measure of variation for a data set is the **interquartile range** (IQR), which is the difference of the third quartile, Q3, and the first quartile, Q1. It represents the range of the middle half of the data.

EXAMPLE 2 Interpreting a Box-and-Whisker Plot

WATCH

The box-and-whisker plot represents the lengths (in seconds) of the songs played by a rock band at a concert.

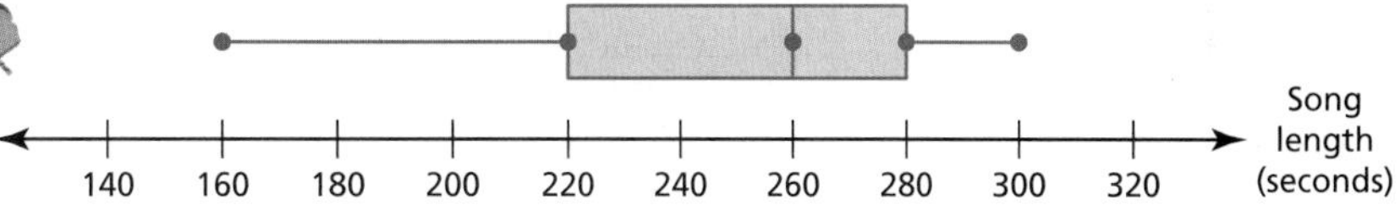

140
160
180
200
220
240
260
280
300
320
Song length (seconds)

a. Find and interpret the range of the data.

b. Describe the distribution of the data.

c. Find and interpret the interquartile range of the data.

d. Are the data more spread out below Q1 or above Q3? Explain.

SOLUTION

a. The least value is 160. The greatest value is 300.

▶ So, the range is $300 - 160 = 140$ seconds. This means that the song lengths vary by no more than 140 seconds.

b. Each whisker represents 25% of the data. The box represents 50% of the data. So,

- 25% of the song lengths are between 160 and 220 seconds.
- 50% of the song lengths are between 220 and 280 seconds.
- 25% of the song lengths are between 280 and 300 seconds.

c. The first quartile is 220. The third quartile is 280.

$$\text{IQR} = \text{Q3} - \text{Q1} = 280 - 220 = 60$$

▶ So, the interquartile range is 60 seconds. This means that the middle half of the song lengths vary by no more than 60 seconds.

d. The left whisker is longer than the right whisker.

▶ So, the data below Q1 are more spread out than the data above Q3.

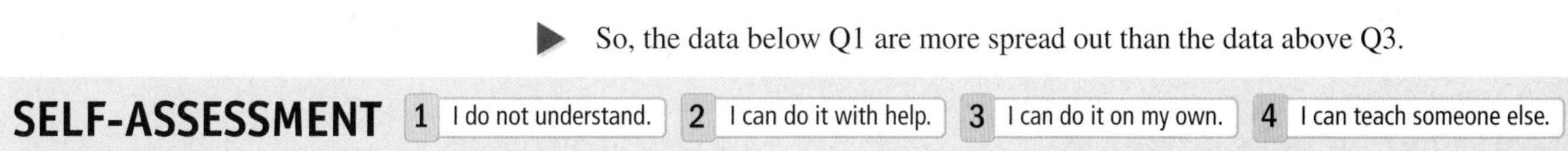

SELF-ASSESSMENT
1 I do not understand.
2 I can do it with help.
3 I can do it on my own.
4 I can teach someone else.

Use the box-and-whisker plot in Example 1.

5. Find and interpret the range and interquartile range of the data.

6. Describe the distribution of the data.

GO DIGITAL

Using Box-and-Whisker Plots to Compare Data Sets

A box-and-whisker plot shows the shape of a distribution.

KEY IDEA

Shapes of Box-and-Whisker Plots

Skewed left	Symmetric	Skewed right
• The left whisker is longer than the right whisker. • Most of the data are on the right side of the plot.	• The whiskers are about the same length. • The median is in the middle of the plot.	• The right whisker is longer than the left whisker. • Most of the data are on the left side of the plot.

STUDY TIP

If you can draw a line through the median of a box-and-whisker plot, and each side is approximately a mirror image of the other, then the distribution is symmetric.

EXAMPLE 3 Comparing Box-and-Whisker Plots

The double box-and-whisker plot represents the test scores for your class and your friend's class.

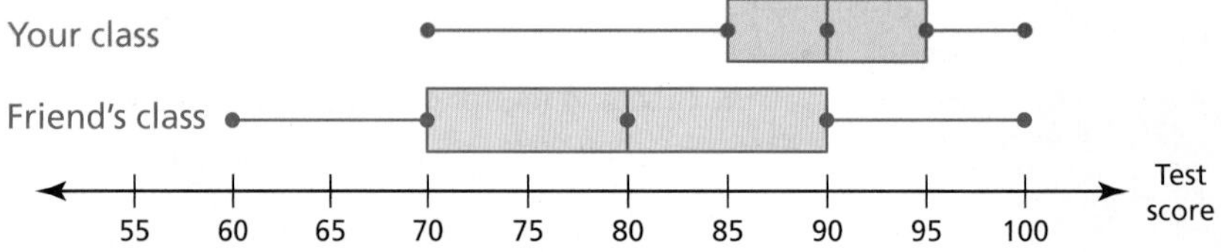

a. Identify the shape of each distribution.

b. Which class's test scores are more spread out? Explain.

SOLUTION

a. For your class, the left whisker is longer than the right whisker, and most of the data are on the right side of the plot. For your friend's class, the whisker lengths are equal, and the median is in the middle of the plot.

▶ So, the distribution for your class is skewed left, and the distribution for your friend's class is symmetric.

b. The range and interquartile range of the test scores for your friend's class are greater than the range and interquartile range for your class.

▶ So, the test scores for your friend's class are more spread out.

SELF-ASSESSMENT 1 I do not understand. 2 I can do it with help. 3 I can do it on my own. 4 I can teach someone else.

7. The double box-and-whisker plot represents the surfboard prices at Shop A and Shop B.

   a. Identify the shape of each distribution.

   b. Which shop's prices are more spread out? Which shop has cheaper prices? Explain your reasoning.

Shop A

Shop B

0 100 200 300 400 500 600 700 800 900

Surfboard price (dollars)

GO DIGITAL

Identifying Outliers

You can use quartiles and the interquartile range to check a data set for outliers.

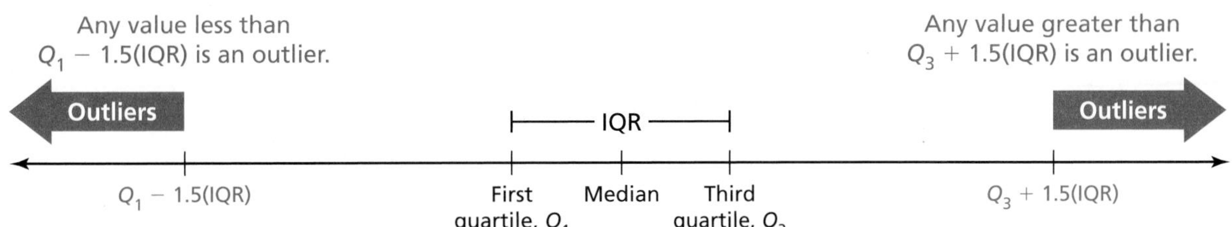

EXAMPLE 4 Modeling Real Life

	Batting Average
Mike	0.276
Albert	0.210
Cole	0.260
Dave	0.311
Juan	0.174
Felix	0.290
Lou	0.280
Don	0.295
Ryan	0.406
Carlos	0.325
Aaron	0.380
Ty	0.264

A manager makes a list that shows the batting averages for players on a baseball team.

a. Make a box-and-whisker plot that represents the data. Describe the shape of the distribution.

b. Does the data set contain any outliers?

SOLUTION

a. Find the five-number summary of the data set. Then make the box-and-whisker plot.

Least value: 0.174
First quartile: 0.262
Median: 0.285
Third quartile: 0.318
Greatest value: 0.406

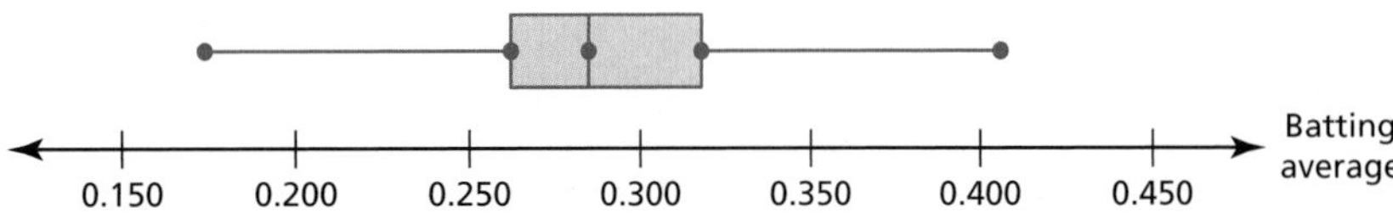

▶ The whisker lengths are equal, and the median is about in the middle of the plot. So, the distribution is symmetric.

b. Find the IQR, which is Q3 − Q1 = 0.318 − 0.262 = 0.056. Use the IQR to find the outlier boundaries.

Q1 − 1.5(IQR) = 0.262 − 1.5(0.056) = 0.178

Q3 + 1.5(IQR) = 0.318 + 1.5(0.056) = 0.402

▶ Yes, the only data value less than 0.178 is 0.174. The only data value greater than 0.402 is 0.406. So, the outliers are 0.174 and 0.406.

SELF-ASSESSMENT

1 I do not understand. 2 I can do it with help. 3 I can do it on my own. 4 I can teach someone else.

8. **WHAT IF?** In Example 4, the manager realizes that he entered Cole's batting average incorrectly. His average should be 0.206. How does this affect the results?

9. The weights (in milligrams) of several flying microrobots are shown.

   110, 85, 95, 90, 80, 85, 90, 120, 100, 110, 175

   a. Make a box-and-whisker plot that represents the data. Describe the shape of the distribution.

   b. Does the data set contain any outliers? If so, does the shape of the distribution change when you remove the outliers from the data set? Explain.

11.2 Practice WITH CalcChat® AND CalcView®

In Exercises 1–6, use the box-and-whisker plot to find the given measure.

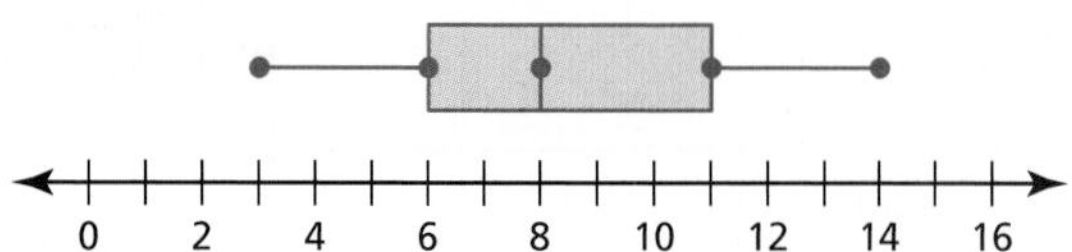

1. least value
2. greatest value
3. third quartile
4. first quartile
5. median
6. range

In Exercises 7–12, make a box-and-whisker plot that represents the data. *Example 1*

7. Hours of television watched: 0, 3, 4, 5, 2, 4, 6, 5
8. Cat lengths (in inches): 16, 18, 20, 25, 17, 22, 23, 21
9. Elevations (in feet): −2, 0, 5, −4, 1, −3, 2, 0, 2, −3, 6
10. Activity tracker prices (in dollars): 124, 95, 105, 110, 95, 124, 300, 190, 114
11. Puppy weights (in pounds): 5, 4, 8, 4, 7, 9, 3, 6, 6, 10
12. Ages of professional basketball players: 23, 26, 21, 24, 25, 36, 28, 31, 33, 21, 34, 27
13. **MULTIPLE REPRESENTATIONS** The dot plot represents the numbers of hours students spent studying for an exam. Make a box-and-whisker plot that represents the data.

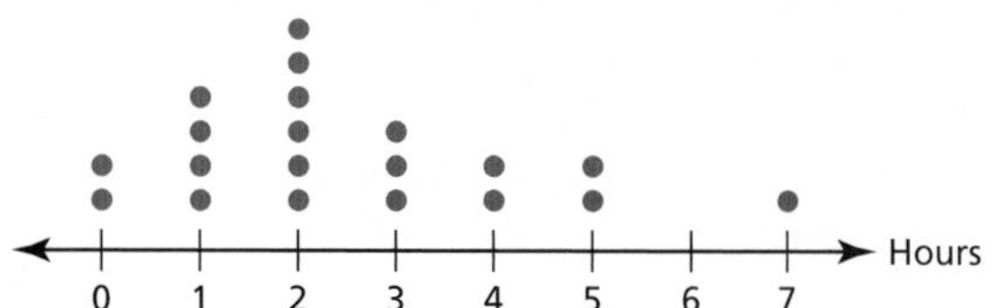

14. **MULTIPLE REPRESENTATIONS** The stem-and-leaf plot represents the lengths (in inches) of the fish caught on a fishing trip. Make a box-and-whisker plot that represents the data.

Stem	Leaf
0	6 7 8 8 9
1	0 0 2 2 3 4 4 7
2	1 2

Key: 1 | 0 = 10 inches

15. **ANALYZING DATA** The box-and-whisker plot represents the prices (in dollars) of the entrées at a restaurant. *Example 2*

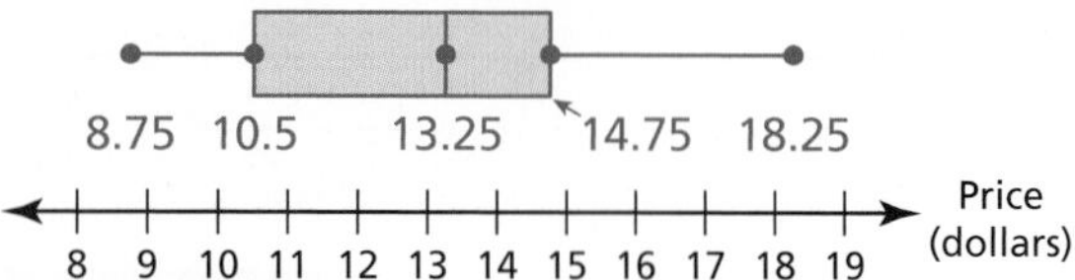

a. Find and interpret the range of the data.

b. Describe the distribution of the data.

c. Find and interpret the interquartile range of the data.

d. Are the data more spread out below Q1 or above Q3? Explain.

16. **ANALYZING DATA** The box-and-whisker plot represents the lengths (in minutes) of the movies at a theater.

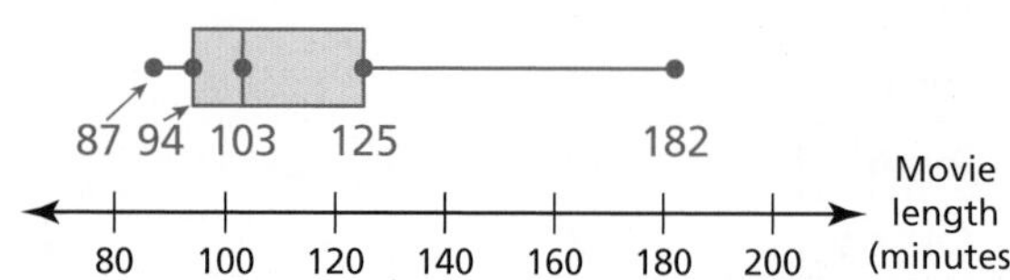

a. Find and interpret the range of the data.

b. Describe the distribution of the data.

c. Find and interpret the interquartile range of the data.

d. Are the data more spread out between Q1 and Q2 or between Q2 and Q3? Explain.

17. **ANALYZING DATA** The double box-and-whisker plot represents the monthly car sales for a year for two sales representatives. *Example 3*

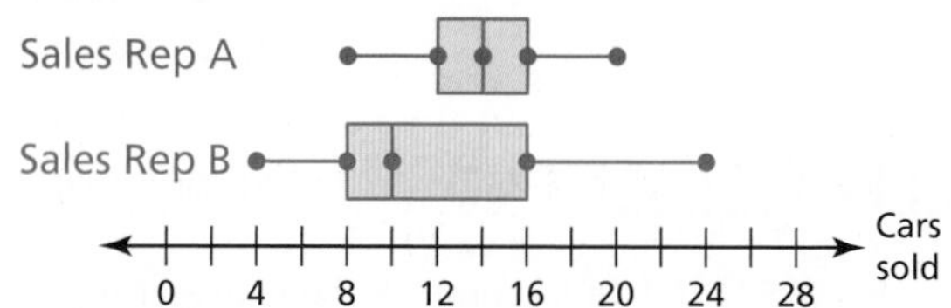

a. Identify the shape of each distribution.

b. Which representative's sales are more spread out? Explain.

c. Which representative had the single worst sales month during the year? Explain.

18. ANALYZING DATA The double box-and-whisker plot represents the toy drone prices at Store A and Store B.

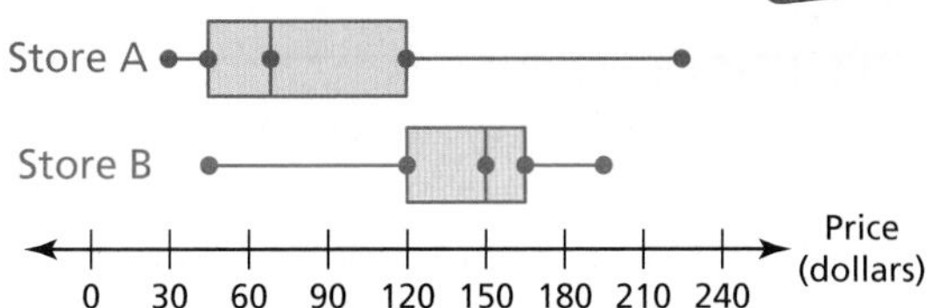

a. Identify the shape of each distribution.

b. Which store's prices are more spread out? Explain.

c. Which store has more expensive drones? Explain.

19. ERROR ANALYSIS Describe and correct the error in making a box-and-whisker plot for the data shown.

10, 16, 12, 12, 20, 17, 13, 20, 19, 14, 11, 13

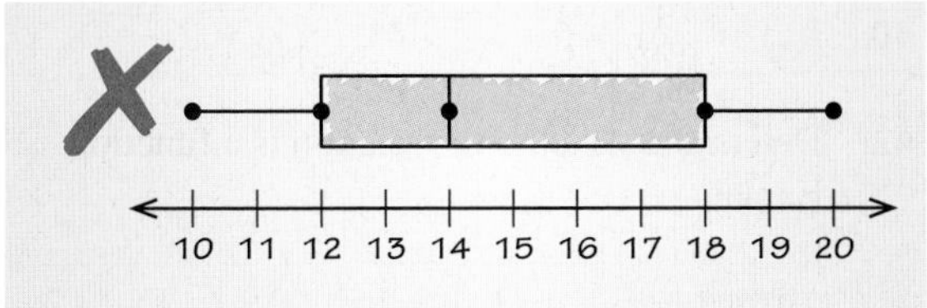

20. ERROR ANALYSIS Describe and correct the error in describing the box-and-whisker plot.

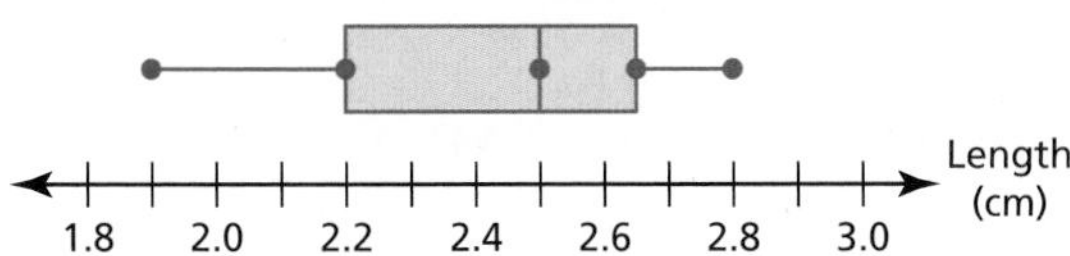

The distribution is skewed left. So, most of the data are on the left side of the plot.

21. WRITING The numbers 36 and 12 describe two measures of variation of a data set. Identify which number is the range and which number is the interquartile range. Explain.

22. COLLEGE PREP Which number is *not* part of the five-number summary of the data shown? Explain.

69, 51, 64, 75, 67, 54, 83, 64, 59, 82

Ⓐ 51 Ⓑ 59

Ⓒ 64 Ⓓ 65.5

Ⓔ 75 Ⓕ 83

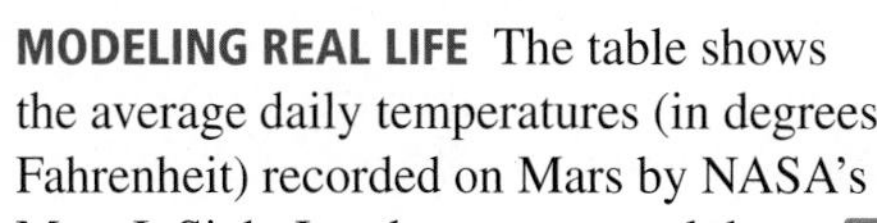

23. MODELING REAL LIFE The table shows the average daily temperatures (in degrees Fahrenheit) recorded on Mars by NASA's Mars InSight Lander over several days. ▶ *Example 4*

Day	Temperature (°F)
124	−86.6
125	−85.9
126	−85.2
127	−86.0
128	−85.6
129	−86.6
130	−67.7
131	−86.7
132	−86.7

a. Make a box-and-whisker plot that represents the data. Describe the shape of the distribution.

b. Identify any outliers.

24. MODELING REAL LIFE The prices (in dollars) of several smart speakers are shown.

49.99, 399.99, 34.99, 39.00, 199.99, 99.99, 99.99, 149.99, 129.99, 124.99, 79.99

a. Make a box-and-whisker plot that represents the data. Describe the shape of the distribution.

b. Does the data set contain any outliers? If so, explain how the outlier(s) affect the mean and five-number summary.

25. MP PROBLEM SOLVING The double box-and-whisker plot represents the battery lives (in hours) of two brands of cell phones.

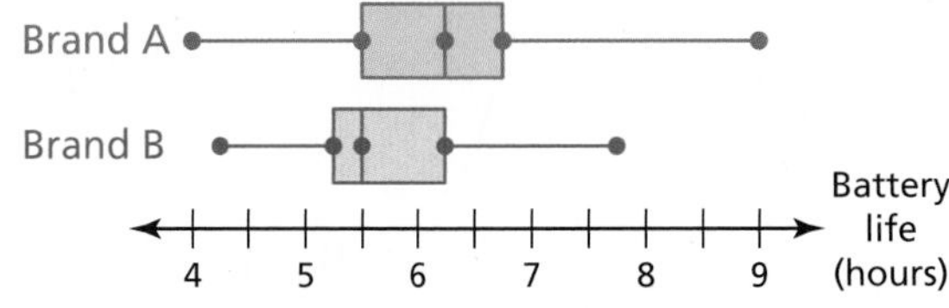

a. Identify the shape of each distribution.

b. What is the range of the battery lives for the upper 75% of each brand?

c. Compare the interquartile ranges of the data sets.

d. Which brand do you think has a greater standard deviation? Explain.

e. You need a cell phone that has a battery life of at least 5.5 hours most of the time. Which brand should you buy? Explain.

26. **HOW DO YOU SEE IT?** The box-and-whisker plot represents a data set. Determine whether each statement is always true. Explain your reasoning.

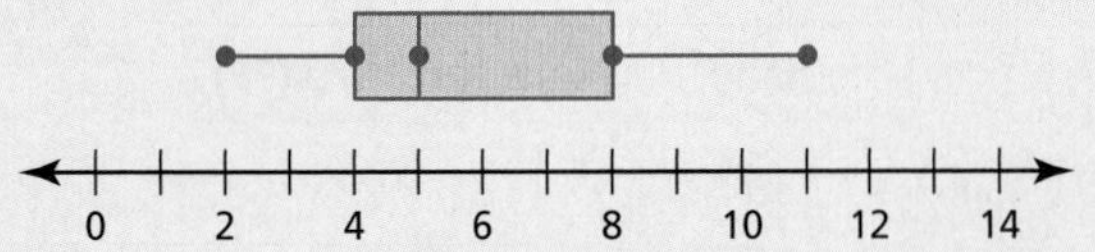

a. The data set contains the value 11.

b. The data set contains the value 6.

c. The distribution is skewed right.

d. The mean of the data is 5.

27. **CRITICAL THINKING** Two data sets have the same median, the same interquartile range, and the same range. Is it possible for the box-and-whisker plots of the data sets to be different? Justify your answer.

28. **THOUGHT PROVOKING** Create a data set that can be represented by the box-and-whisker plot shown. Justify your answer.

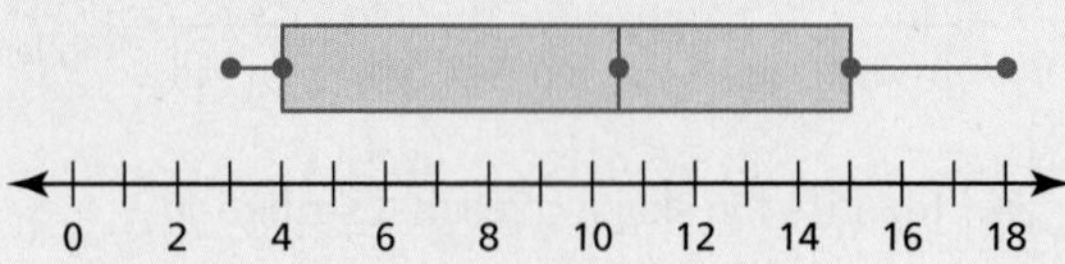

REVIEW & REFRESH

In Exercises 29–32, solve the equation.

29. $\sqrt{y} + 7 = 13$

30. $\sqrt{3z - 1} = \sqrt{6z - 5}$

31. $\sqrt[3]{2n - 5} = -3$

32. $2p = \sqrt{p + 3}$

In Exercises 33 and 34, graph the function.

33. $f(x) = -2(x + 9)(x - 3)$

34. $y = 4x^2 - 16x - 48$

MP STRUCTURE In Exercises 35–38, match the function with its graph.

35. $y = -(x + 1)^2 - 3$

36. $y = -\frac{1}{2}(x - 1)^2 + 3$

37. $y = \frac{1}{3}(x - 1)^2 + 3$

38. $y = 2(x + 1)^2 - 3$

A.
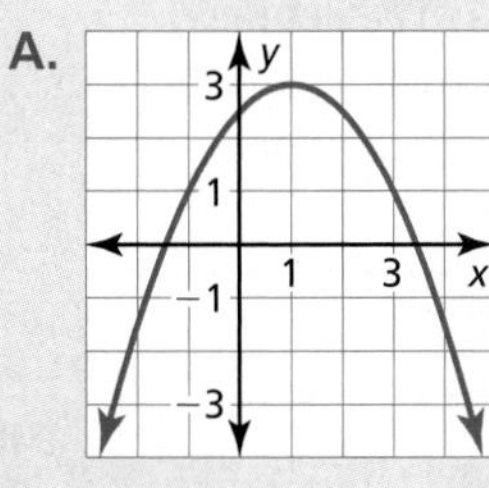

B.
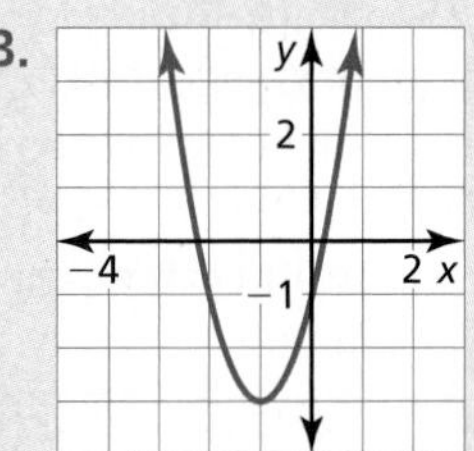

C.
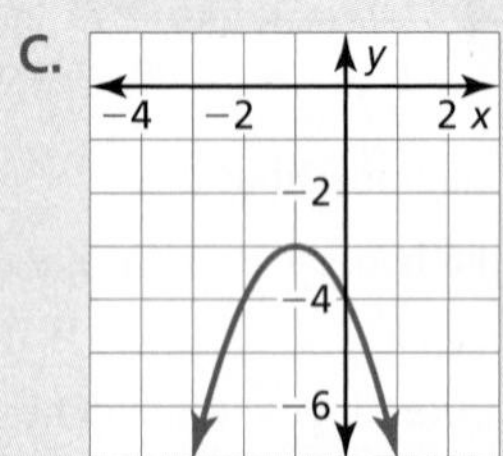

D.
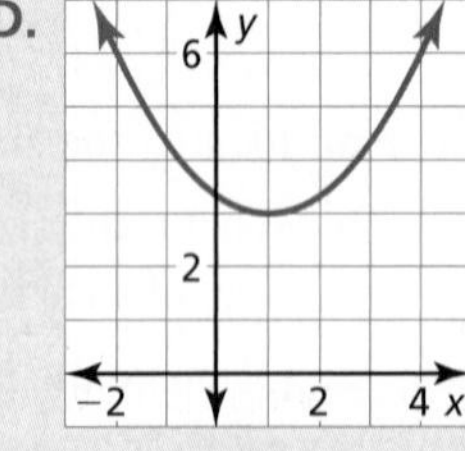

39. Find the mean, median, and mode of the data set shown. Then determine which measure of center best represents the data.

52, 80, 62, 54, 75, 73, 76, 68, 54

In Exercises 40 and 41, find the inverse of the function. Then graph the function and its inverse.

40. $f(x) = -\frac{1}{4}x + 6$

41. $f(x) = 2x^2 - 8, x \geq 0$

42. Determine whether the relation is a function. Explain.

Input, x	−2	−1	0	1	2
Output, y	5	2	1	2	5

In Exercises 43 and 44, solve the inequality. Graph the solution.

43. $k - 7 \leq -1$

44. $3z < 12$

45. **MODELING REAL LIFE** The times (in minutes) several students spend on a school bus on a given morning are shown.

35, 24, 30, 16, 36, 57, 26, 19, 33, 23, 42

a. Make a box-and-whisker plot that represents the data. Describe the shape of the distribution.

b. Does the data set contain any outliers?

In Exercises 46–49, simplify the expression.

46. $\sqrt{\dfrac{16}{x^2}}$

47. $\dfrac{1}{\sqrt{3}}$

48. $\sqrt[3]{\dfrac{27a^7b^3}{343}}$

49. $\dfrac{\sqrt{11}}{4 + \sqrt{3}}$

In Exercises 50 and 51, find the sum or difference.

50. $(3d + 4) + (-d^2 + 8d - 1)$

51. $(5g^3 + 9g^2 - 12) - (3g + 7g^2 + 6)$

11.3 Shapes of Distributions

Learning Target Describe and compare shapes of distributions.

Success Criteria

- I can describe the shape of a distribution.
- I can determine which measures of center and variation best represent a data set.
- I can compare data sets.

EXPLORE IT! Analyzing Symmetric Distributions

Work with a partner.

Math Practice

Evaluate Results
How should your percents change as the number of standard deviations increases? Do they change as you expect?

a. A famous data set, collected in Scotland in the mid-1800s, contains the chest sizes (in inches) of 5738 men in the Scottish Militia. Estimate the percent of chest sizes that lie within 1 standard deviation of the mean, 2 standard deviations of the mean, and 3 standard deviations of the mean. Explain your reasoning.

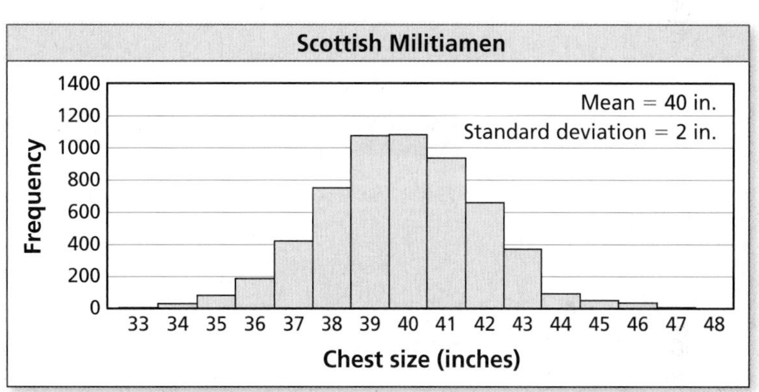

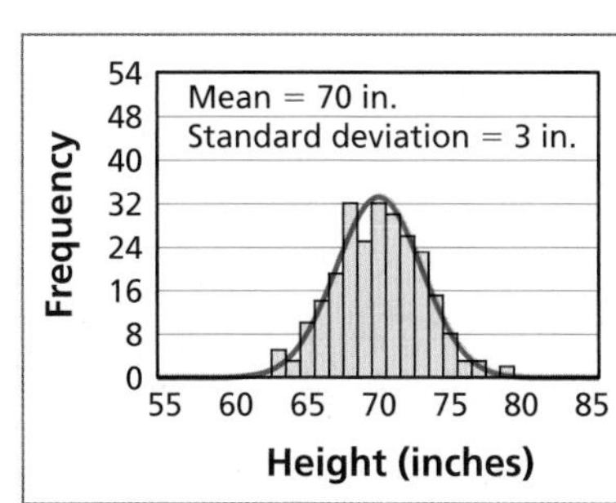

Mean = 64 in.
Standard deviation = 2.5 in.
Frequency
56 48 40 32 24 16 8 0
55 60 65 70 75 80 85
Height (inches)

b. The graphs at the left show the distributions of the heights of 250 adult American males and 250 adult American females.

i. Which graph represents the males? the females? Explain your reasoning.

ii. Which data set has a lesser standard deviation? Explain what this means in the context of the problem.

iii. Estimate the percent of male heights between 67 inches and 73 inches. Explain your reasoning. Does this agree with your answer in part (a)?

c. All three distributions in parts (a) and (b) are roughly symmetric. The histograms are called "bell-shaped."

i. What are the characteristics of a symmetric distribution?

ii. Why is a symmetric distribution called "bell-shaped?"

iii. Give two other real-life examples of symmetric distributions.

Describing the Shapes of Data Distribution

Recall that a histogram is a bar graph that shows the frequencies of data values in intervals of the same size. A histogram is another useful data display that shows the shape of a distribution.

KEY IDEA

Symmetric and Skewed Distributions

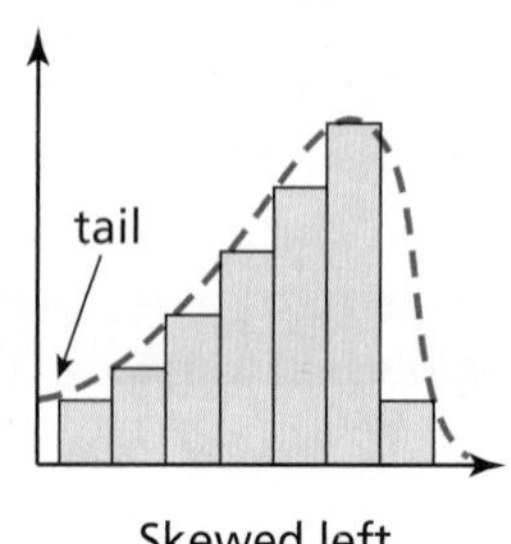

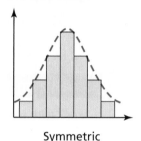

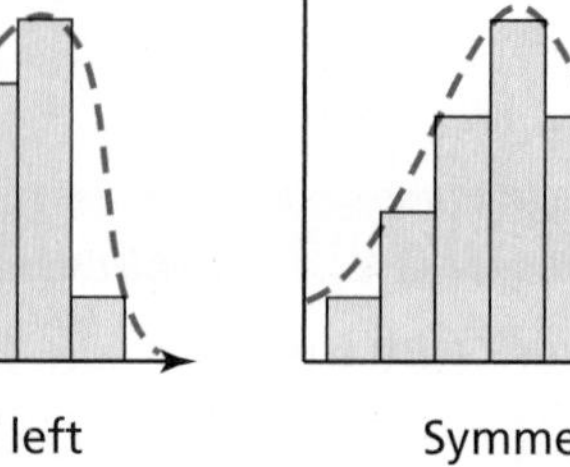

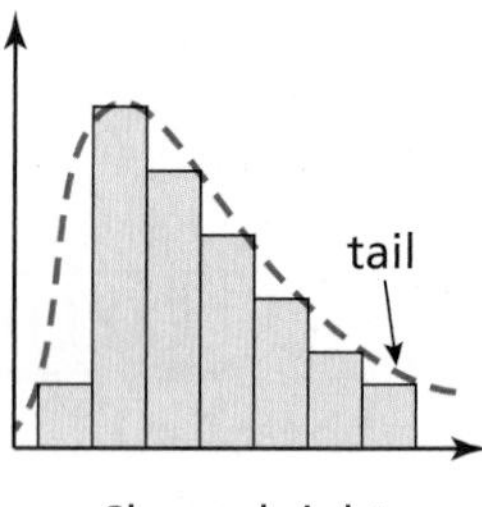

Skewed left
- The "tail" of the graph extends to the left.
- Most of the data are on the right.

Symmetric
- The data on the right of the distribution are approximately a mirror image of the data on the left of the distribution.

Skewed right
- The "tail" of the graph extends to the right.
- Most of the data are on the left.

WORDS AND MATH

The word *symmetry* comes from Latin and Greek word parts—*syn-* meaning "together," and *metron* meaning "measure." It is used in science to describe types of plant and animal life whose two sides mirror each other.

EXAMPLE 1 Describing the Shape of a Distribution

The frequency table shows the numbers of raffle tickets sold by students in your grade. Display the data in a histogram. Describe the shape of the distribution.

Number of tickets sold	Frequency
1–8	5
9–16	9
17–24	16
25–32	25
33–40	20
41–48	8
49–56	7

SOLUTION

Step 1 Draw and label the axes.

Step 2 Draw a bar to represent the frequency of each interval.

The data on the right of the distribution are approximately a mirror image of the data on the left of the distribution.

▶ So, the distribution is symmetric.

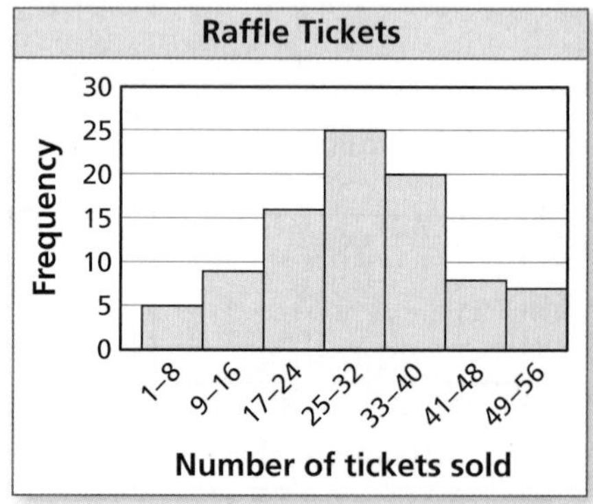

SELF-ASSESSMENT 1 I do not understand. 2 I can do it with help. 3 I can do it on my own. 4 I can teach someone else.

1. **VOCABULARY** Describe how data are distributed in a symmetric distribution, a distribution that is skewed left, and a distribution that is skewed right.

2. The frequency table shows the numbers of pounds of aluminum cans collected by classes for a fundraiser. Display the data in a histogram. Describe the shape of the distribution.

Number of pounds	Frequency
1–10	7
11–20	8
21–30	10
31–40	16
41–50	34
51–60	15

Choosing Appropriate Measures

Use the shape of a distribution to choose the most appropriate measure of center and measure of variation to describe the data set.

STUDY TIP

When a distribution is symmetric, the mean and median are about the same. When a distribution is skewed, the mean will be in the direction in which the distribution is skewed while the median will be less affected.

KEY IDEA

Choosing Appropriate Measures

When a data distribution is symmetric,

- use the mean to describe the center and
- use the standard deviation to describe the variation.

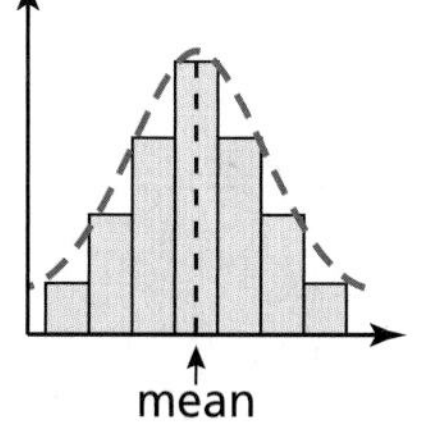

When a data distribution is skewed,

- use the median to describe the center and
- use the five-number summary to describe the variation.

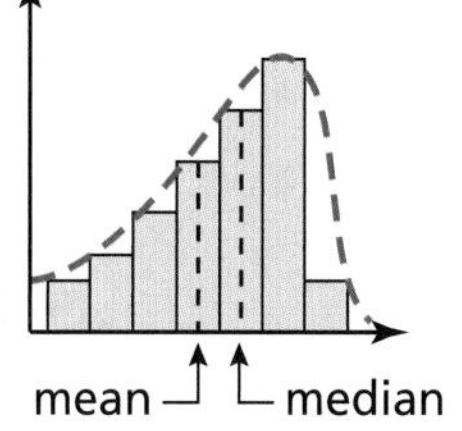

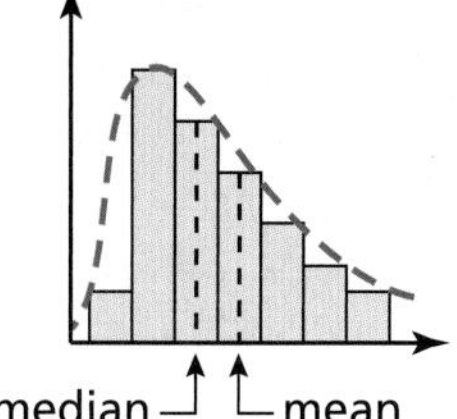

EXAMPLE 2 Choosing Appropriate Measures

Speeds (mi/h)		
32	44	39
53	38	48
56	41	42
50	50	55
55	45	49
51	53	52
54	60	55
52	50	52
55	40	60
45	58	47

You measure the speeds (in miles per hour) of 30 motorists. The results are shown in the table at the left. (a) Display the data in a histogram using six intervals beginning with 31–35. (b) Which measures of center and variation best represent the data?

SOLUTION

a. Make a frequency table using the described intervals. Then use the frequency table to make a histogram.

Speed (mi/h)	Frequency
31–35	1
36–40	3
41–45	5
46–50	6
51–55	11
56–60	4

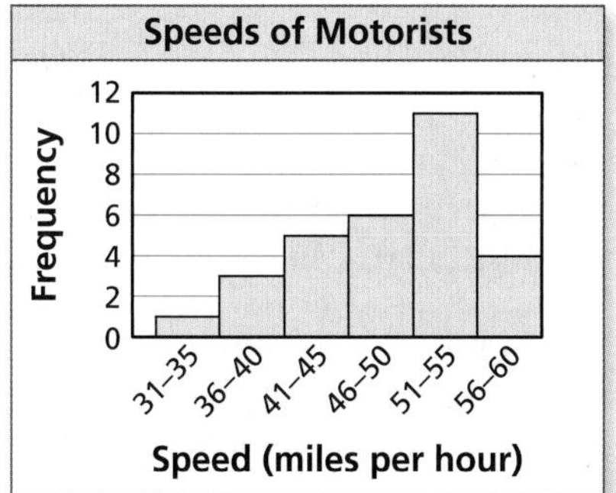

b. Because most of the data are on the right and the tail of the graph extends to the left, the distribution is skewed left. So, use the median to describe the center and the five-number summary to describe the variation.

SELF-ASSESSMENT

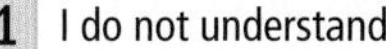

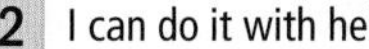

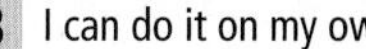

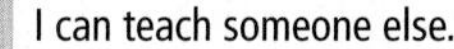

3. You record the number of "likes" for each of the last 30 photos you posted. The results are shown in the table. (a) Display the data in a histogram using six intervals beginning with 1–20. (b) Which measures of center and variation best represent the data? Explain.

Number of "Likes"									
74	105	98	68	64	85	75	60	48	51
65	55	58	45	64	52	65	30	38	72
5	45	77	70	83	42	25	95	16	120

Comparing Data Distributions

EXAMPLE 3 Comparing Data Distributions

The double histogram shows the distributions of messages with emojis sent by a group of female students and a group of male students during 1 week. Compare the distributions using their shapes and appropriate measures of center and variation.

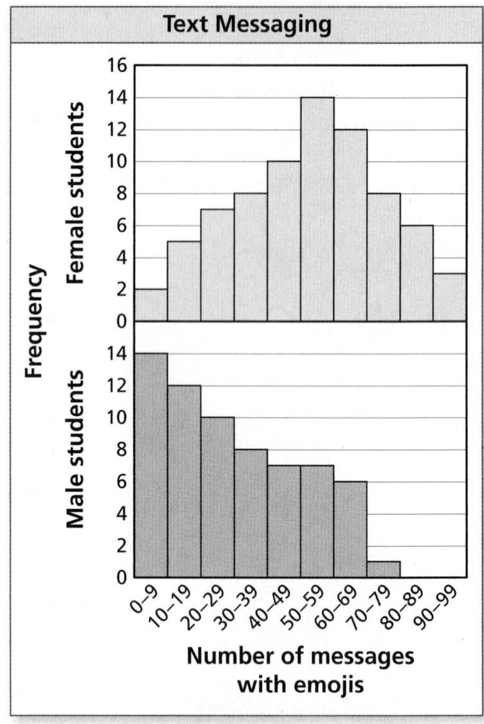

SOLUTION

Because the data on the right of the distribution for the female students are approximately a mirror image of the data on the left of the distribution, the distribution is symmetric. So, the mean and standard deviation best represent the distribution for female students.

Because most of the data are on the left of the distribution for the male students and the tail of the graph extends to the right, the distribution is skewed right. So, the median and five-number summary best represent the distribution for male students.

The mean of the female data set is probably in the 50–59 interval, while the median of the male data set is in the 20–29 interval. So, a typical female student is much more likely to use emojis than a typical male student.

The data for the female students are more variable than the data for the male students. This means that the use of emojis tends to differ more from one female student to the next.

SELF-ASSESSMENT

1 I do not understand. 2 I can do it with help. 3 I can do it on my own. 4 I can teach someone else.

4. Compare the distributions using their shapes and appropriate measures of center and variation.

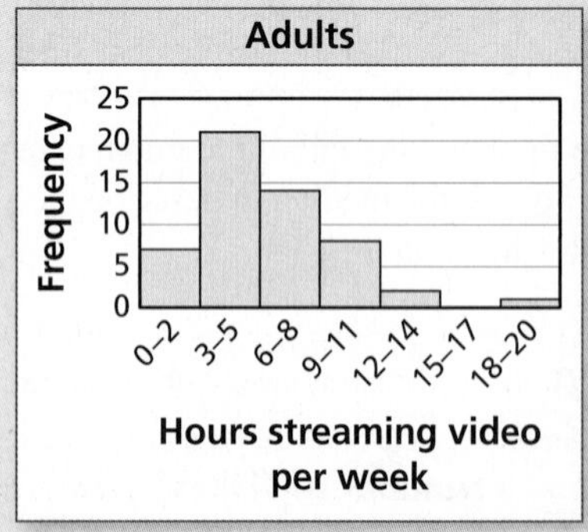

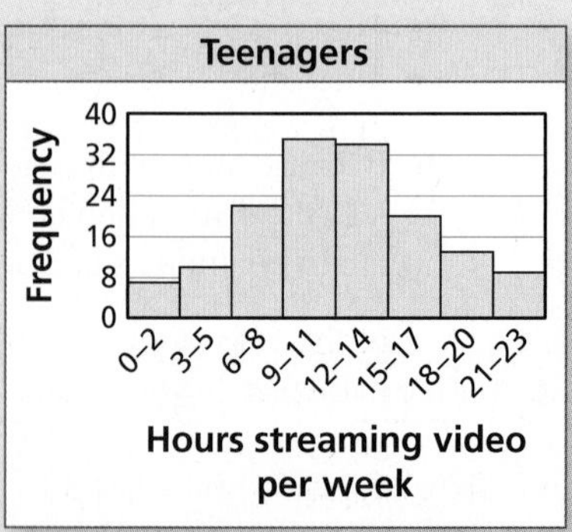

5. WRITING How does the shape of a distribution help you decide which measures of center and variation best describe the data?

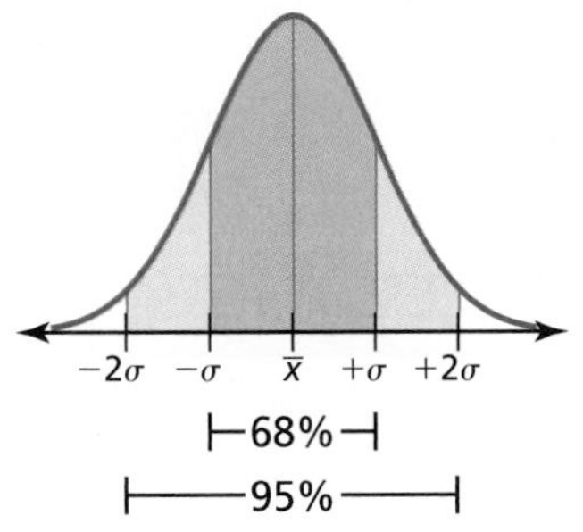

Many real-life data sets have distributions that are bell-shaped and approximately symmetric about the mean. In a future course, you will study this type of distribution in detail. For now, the following rules can help you see how valuable the standard deviation can be as a measure of variation.

- About 68% of the data lie within 1 standard deviation of the mean.
- About 95% of the data lie within 2 standard deviations of the mean.
- Data values that are more than 2 standard deviations from the mean are considered unusual.

Because the data are symmetric, you can deduce that 34% of the data lie within 1 standard deviation to the left of the mean, and 34% of the data lie within 1 standard deviation to the right of the mean.

EXAMPLE 4 Comparing Data Distributions

The table shows the results of a survey that asked men and women how many pairs of shoes they own.

a. Make a double box-and-whisker plot that represents the data. Describe the shape of each distribution.

b. Compare the number of pairs of shoes owned by men to the number of pairs of shoes owned by women.

c. About how many of the women surveyed would you expect to own between 10 and 18 pairs of shoes?

	Men	Women
Survey size	35	40
Least value	2	5
Greatest value	17	24
First quartile	5	12
Median	7	14
Third quartile	10	17
Mean	8	14
Standard deviation	3	4

SOLUTION

a.

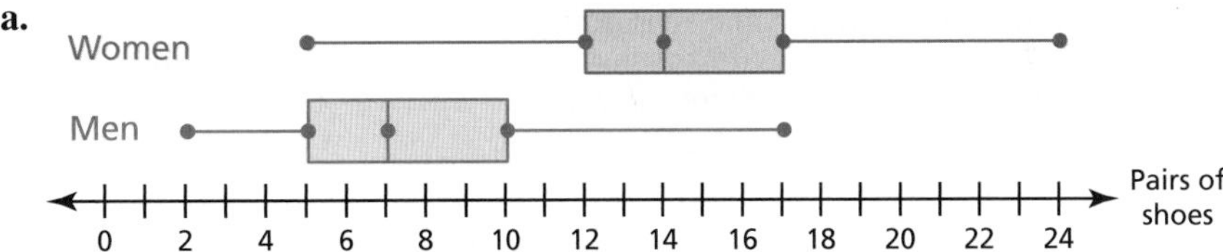

▶ The distribution for men is skewed right, and the distribution for women is symmetric.

b. The centers and spreads of the two data sets are quite different from each other. The mean for women is twice the median for men, and there is more variability in the number of pairs of shoes owned by women.

c. Assuming the symmetric distribution is bell-shaped, you know about 68% of the data lie within 1 standard deviation of the mean. Because the mean is 14 and the standard deviation is 4, the interval from 10 to 18 represents about 68% of the data. So, you would expect about $0.68 \cdot 40 \approx 27$ of the women surveyed to own between 10 and 18 pairs of shoes.

SELF-ASSESSMENT

1 I do not understand. 2 I can do it with help. 3 I can do it on my own. 4 I can teach someone else.

6. Why is the mean greater than the median for the men?

7. If 50 more women are surveyed, about how many more would you expect to own between 10 and 18 pairs of shoes?

11.3 Practice WITH CalcChat® AND CalcView®

1. **DESCRIBING DISTRIBUTIONS** The frequency table shows the numbers of hours that students volunteer per month. Display the data in a histogram. Describe the shape of the distribution. *Example 1*

Number of volunteer hours	1–2	3–4	5–6	7–8	9–10	11–12	13–14
Frequency	1	5	12	20	15	7	2

2. **DESCRIBING DISTRIBUTIONS** The frequency table shows the results of a survey that asked people how many hours they spend online per week. Display the data in a histogram. Describe the shape of the distribution.

Hours online	Frequency
0–3	5
4–7	7
8–11	12
12–15	14
16–19	26
20–23	45
24–27	33

In Exercises 3 and 4, describe the shape of the distribution of the data. Explain your reasoning.

3.

Stem	Leaf
1	1 1 3 4 8
2	2 3 4 7 8
3	1 2 4 9
4	0 3 2
5	7 9
6	6

Key: 3 | 1 = 31

4.

Stem	Leaf
5	0 0 1
6	3 6 7 9
7	1 4 5 8 9
8	2 4 5 5 7
9	4 6 8 9
10	1 3 4

Key: 6 | 3 = 63

In Exercises 5 and 6, determine which measures of center and variation best represent the data. Explain your reasoning.

5.

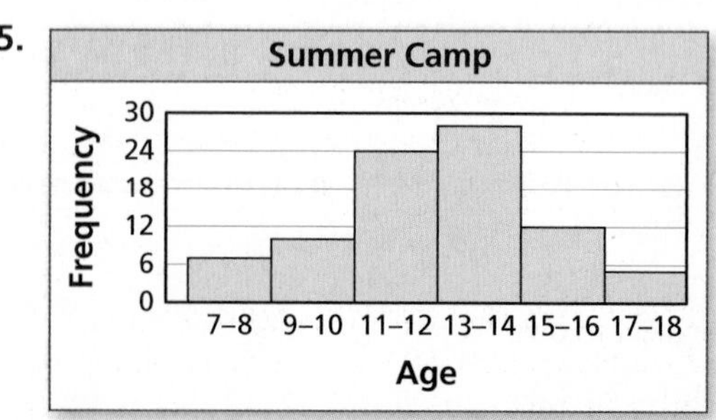

6.

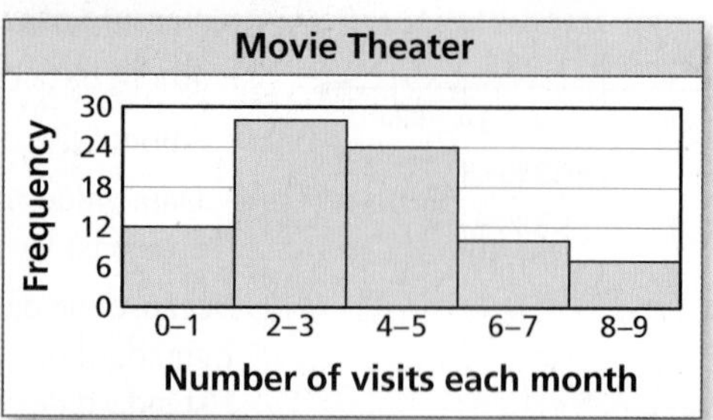

7. **ANALYZING DATA** The table shows the last 24 money transfer amounts made on an app. *Example 2*

Money Transfer Amounts (dollars)		
120	100	70
60	40	80
150	80	50
120	60	175
30	50	50
60	200	30
100	150	110
70	40	100

a. Display the data in a histogram using seven intervals beginning with 26–50.

b. Which measures of center and variation best represent the data? Explain.

8. **ANALYZING DATA** Measuring an IQ is an inexact science. However, IQ scores have been around for years in an attempt to measure human intelligence. The table shows some of the greatest known IQ scores.

IQ Scores		
170	190	180
160	180	210
154	170	180
195	230	160
170	186	180
225	190	170

a. Display the data in a histogram using five intervals beginning with 151–166.

b. Which measures of center and variation best represent the data? Explain.

c. The distribution of IQ scores for the human population is symmetric. What happens to the shape of the distribution in part (a) as you include more and more IQ scores from the human population in the data set?

9. **MP CHOOSE TOOLS** For a large data set, would you use a stem-and-leaf plot or a histogram to show the distribution of the data? Explain.

10. **MP PRECISION** For a symmetric distribution, why is the mean used to describe the center and the standard deviation used to describe the variation? For a skewed distribution, why is the median used to describe the center and the five-number summary used to describe the variation?

ERROR ANALYSIS **In Exercises 11 and 12, describe and correct the error in the statement(s) about the data displayed in the histogram.**

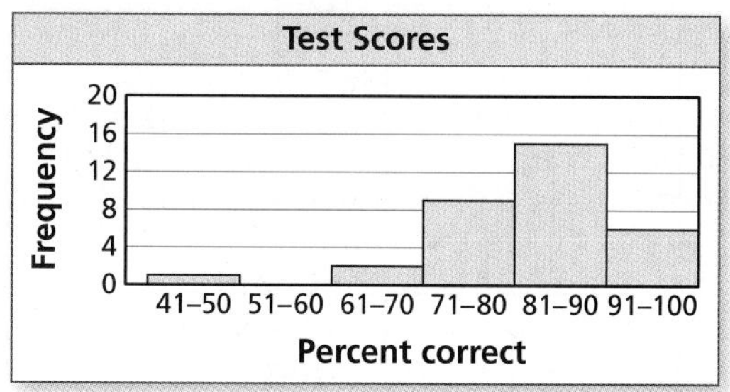

11.  Most of the data are on the right. So, the distribution is skewed right.

12.  Because the distribution is skewed, use the standard deviation to describe the variation of the data.

OPEN-ENDED **In Exercises 13 and 14, describe a real-life data set that has a distribution with the given shape.**

13. skewed right

14. skewed left

15. **COMPARING DATA SETS** The double histogram shows the distributions of daily high temperatures for two towns over a 50-day period. Compare the distributions using their shapes and appropriate measures of center and variation. *Example 3*

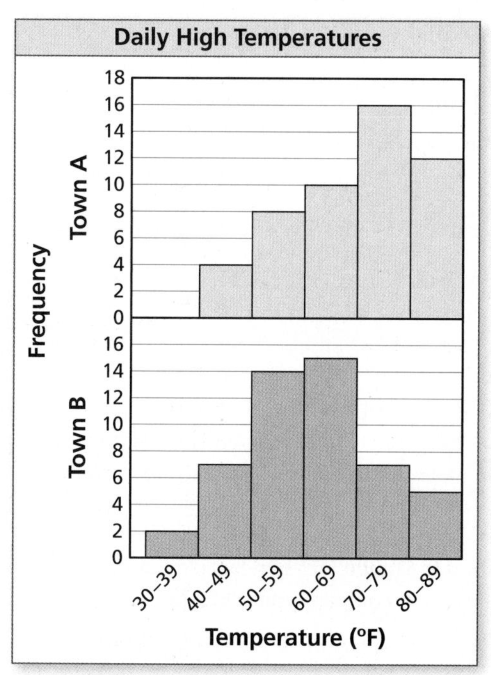

16. **COMPARING DATA SETS** The frequency tables show the numbers of patients in certain age groups at two different medical clinics over four hours. Display the data in a double histogram. Compare the distributions using their shapes and appropriate measures of center and variation.

GO DIGITAL

Clinic A	
Age	**Frequency**
0–14	9
15–29	12
30–44	5
45–59	4
60–74	3
75–89	0

Clinic B	
Age	**Frequency**
0–14	0
15–29	2
30–44	5
45–59	7
60–74	8
75–89	6

17. **COMPARING DATA SETS** The table shows the results of a survey that asked teenagers and adults the amounts of storage on their cell phones (in megabytes, MB) used by apps. *Example 4*

	Teenagers	Adults
Survey size	45	54
Least value	250	360
Greatest value	2150	2400
First quartile	800	780
Median	1200	2000
Third quartile	1600	2200
Mean	1150	1650
Standard deviation	420	480

a. Make a double box-and-whisker plot of the data. Describe the shape of each distribution.

b. Compare the amount of storage teenagers use for apps to the amount of storage adults use for apps.

c. About how many of the teenagers surveyed would you expect to use between 730 and 1570 MB for apps? If you survey 100 more teenagers, about how many would you expect to use between 310 and 1990 MB for apps?

18. **COMPARING DATA SETS** You conduct the same survey as in Exercise 17 but use a different group of teenagers. The results are as follows.

Survey size: 60; least value: 200; greatest value: 2400; first quartile: 640; median: 1670; third quartile: 2150; mean: 1480; standard deviation: 500

a. Compare the app storage of this group of teenagers to the app storage of adults.

b. Why is the median greater than the mean for this group of teenagers?

19. **MP REASONING** A data set has a symmetric distribution. Every value in the data set is doubled. Describe the shape of the new distribution. Are the measures of center and variation affected? Explain.

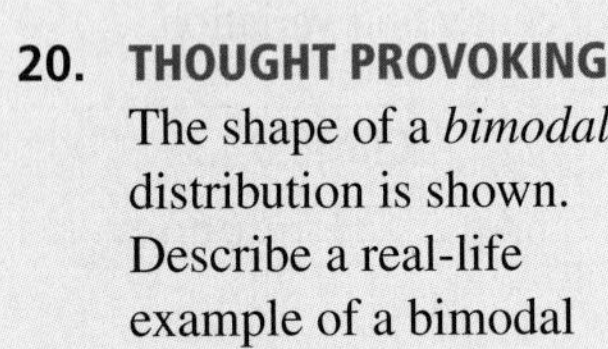

20. **THOUGHT PROVOKING** The shape of a *bimodal* distribution is shown. Describe a real-life example of a bimodal distribution.

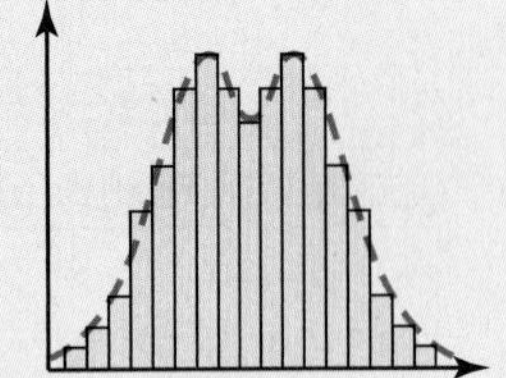

21. **MP REASONING** The wait times (in minutes) for the roller coasters at an amusement park are shown.

    26, 38, 15, 8, 22, 42, 25, 20, 17, 18, 40, 35, 24, 31, 42, 29, 25, 0, 30, 13

    a. Display the data in a histogram using five intervals beginning with 0–9. Describe the shape of the distribution.

    b. Display the data in a histogram using 10 intervals beginning with 0–4. What happens when the number of intervals is increased?

    c. Which histogram best represents the data? Explain your reasoning.

22. **HOW DO YOU SEE IT?** Match the distribution with the corresponding box-and-whisker plot.

a.

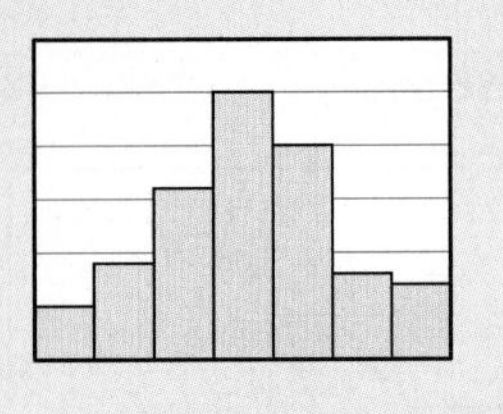

b.

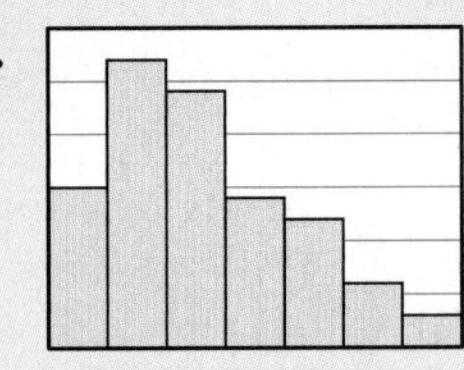

c.

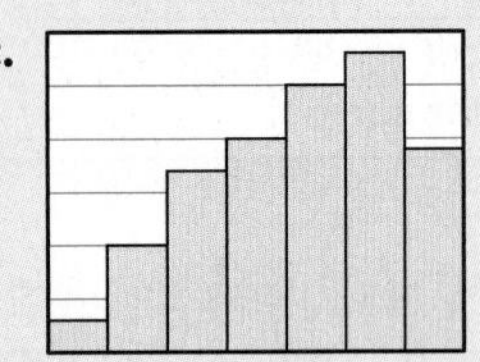

A.

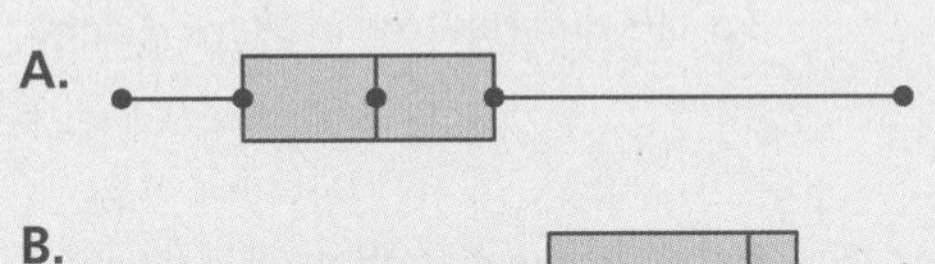

B.

C.

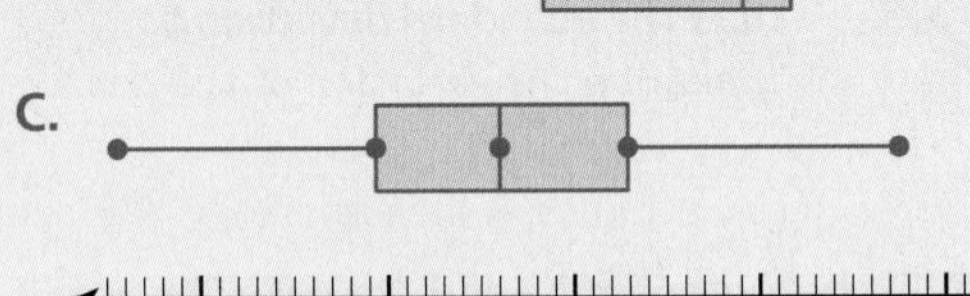

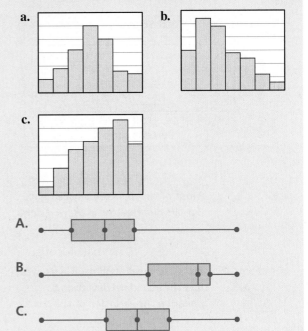

REVIEW & REFRESH

In Exercises 23 and 24, find the domain of the function.

23. $f(x) = \sqrt{x+6}$

24. $f(x) = -\sqrt{\frac{1}{2}x} + 5$

25. **MODELING REAL LIFE** The function $h(t) = -16t^2 + 32t + 2$ models the height (in feet) of a softball t seconds after it is pitched in an underhand motion. Find the domain and range of the function. Then find the maximum height of the softball.

26. The frequency table shows the numbers of books students in your class read over the summer. Display the data in a histogram. Describe the shape of the distribution.

Number of books	0–3	4–7	8–11	12–15	16–19	20–23
Frequency	7	8	4	2	2	0

In Exercises 27–30, simplify the expression. Write your answer using only positive exponents.

27. $(-5)^2 \bullet (-5)^3$

28. $(3z^8)^4$

29. $\dfrac{n^7 \bullet n^6}{n^{10}}$

30. $\dfrac{a^0b^{-3}}{4c^2d^{-5}}$

31. Make a box-and-whisker plot that represents the data.

    Minutes of violin practice: 20, 50, 60, 40, 40, 30, 60, 40, 50, 20, 20, 35

32. Find the inverse of the relation.

Input	−3	−1	1	3	5
Output	9	8	7	6	5

In Exercises 33–36, solve the equation.

33. $9g + 4 = 3(3g + 1)$

34. $|7k - 5| - 10 = -1$

35. $3^{x-1} = 9^x$

36. $\left(\frac{1}{4}\right)^x = 64$

37. Is there a correlation between time spent practicing an instrument and the length of a school concert? If so, is there a causal relationship? Explain your reasoning.

38. Find the range and standard deviation of each data set. Then compare your results.

    Absent students during a week of school

    Female: 6, 2, 4, 3, 4 Male: 5, 3, 6, 6, 9

GO DIGITAL

11.4 Two-Way Tables

Learning Target Use two-way tables to represent data.

Success Criteria
- I can find and interpret marginal frequencies.
- I can make two-way tables.
- I can find and interpret relative frequencies and conditional relative frequencies.
- I can recognize associations and trends in data using two-way tables.

EXPLORE IT! Completing and Using a Two-Way Table

Work with a partner. A survey of 616 students at a high school asks whether they have ever visited a national park. Some of the results are shown in the double bar graph.

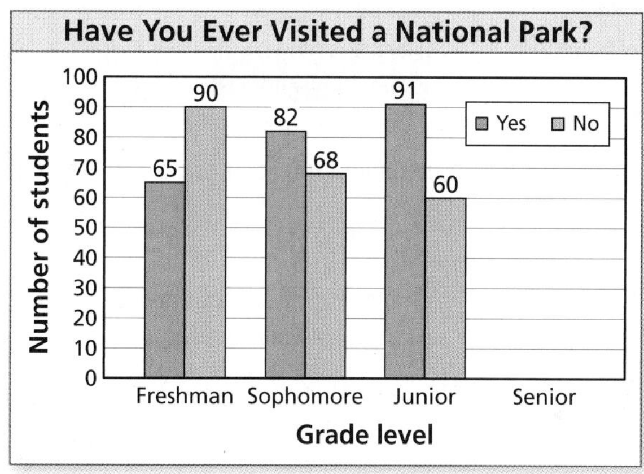

a. Show how you can represent the data in the double bar graph using a single table. Complete as much of the table as possible.

b. You know that 269 students responded "no" in the survey. Do you have enough information to complete the double bar graph and the table? If so, complete each data representation.

c. Use the table to answer each question.

- What percent of students in the survey responded "yes?"
- What percent of students in the survey are seniors?
- What percent of sophomores in the survey responded "no?"
- What percent of students who responded "yes" in the survey are juniors?

d. Write several other observations you can make from the table.

Math Practice

Analyze Givens
How did you use the given information to complete the table?

Finding and Interpreting Marginal Frequencies

Vocabulary 

two-way table, *p. 612*
joint frequency, *p. 612*
marginal frequency, *p. 612*
joint relative frequency, *p. 613*
marginal relative frequency, *p. 613*
conditional relative frequency, *p. 614*

A **two-way table** is a frequency table that displays data collected from one source that belong to two different categories. One category of data is represented by rows, and the other is represented by columns. For instance, the two-way table below shows the results of a survey that asked freshmen and sophomores whether they have ever ridden an electric bicycle.

The two categories of data are *class* and *ridden an electric bicycle*. Class is further divided into *freshman* and *sophomore*, and ridden an electric bicycle is further divided into *yes* and *no*.

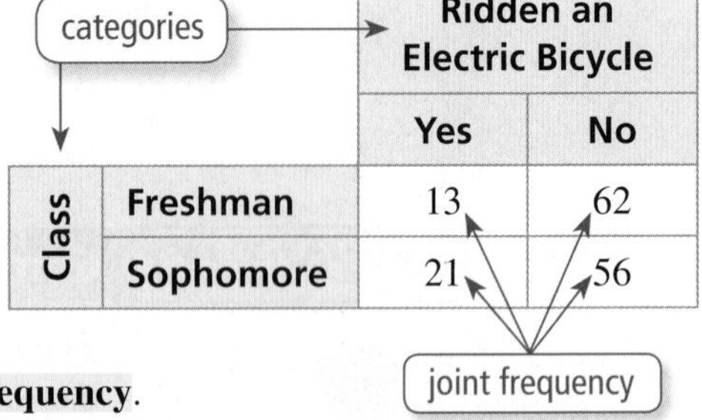

		Ridden an Electric Bicycle	
		Yes	No
Class	Freshman	13	62
	Sophomore	21	56

The *frequency* of an event is the number of times the event occurs. Each entry in the table is called a **joint frequency**. The sums of the rows and columns in a two-way table are called **marginal frequencies**.

EXAMPLE 1 Finding and Interpreting Marginal Frequencies

Find and interpret the marginal frequencies for the two-way table above.

SOLUTION

Create a new column and a new row for the marginal frequencies. Then add the entries in each row and column.

		Ridden an Electric Bicycle		
		Yes	No	Total
Class	Freshman	13	62	75
	Sophomore	21	56	77
	Total	34	118	152

75 freshmen responded.
77 sophomores responded.
152 students were surveyed.
34 students have ridden an electric bicycle.
118 students have not ridden an electric bicycle.

STUDY TIP

The sum of the "total" row should be equal to the sum of the "total" column.

SELF-ASSESSMENT

1 I do not understand. 2 I can do it with help. 3 I can do it on my own. 4 I can teach someone else.

1. **VOCABULARY** Explain the difference between joint frequencies and marginal frequencies.
2. You conduct a technology survey to publish on your school's website. You survey students in the school cafeteria about the technological devices they use. The results are shown in the two-way table.
   a. What does 124 represent? What does 18 represent?
   b. Find and interpret the marginal frequencies.

		Tablet	
		Yes	No
Laptop	Yes	34	124
	No	18	67

3. **MP REASONING** You switch the two categories of data in the two-way table in Exercise 2. Do you need to switch any of the joint frequencies? Explain.

GO DIGITAL

Making Two-Way Tables

EXAMPLE 2 Making a Two-Way Table

You conduct a survey that asks 286 students in your class whether they play a sport or a musical instrument. One hundred eighteen of the students play a sport, and 64 of those students play an instrument. Ninety-three of the students do not play a sport or an instrument. Organize the results in a two-way table. Include the marginal frequencies.

SOLUTION

Step 1 Determine the two categories for the table: *sport* and *instrument*.

Step 2 Use the given joint and marginal frequencies to fill in parts of the table.

		Instrument		
		Yes	No	Total
Sport	Yes	64		118
	No		93	
	Total			286

Step 3 Use reasoning to find the missing joint and marginal frequencies. For instance, you can conclude that there are $286 - 118 = 168$ students who do not play a sport, and $118 - 64 = 54$ students who play a sport but do not play an instrument.

		Instrument		
		Yes	No	Total
Sport	Yes	64	54	118
	No	75	93	168
	Total	139	147	286

SELF-ASSESSMENT 1 I do not understand. 2 I can do it with help. 3 I can do it on my own. 4 I can teach someone else.

4. **WRITING** When is it appropriate to use a two-way table to organize data?
5. You survey students about whether they are getting a summer job. Seventy-five males respond, with 18 of them responding "no." Fifty-seven females respond, with 45 of them responding "yes." Organize the results in a two-way table. Include the marginal frequencies.

Finding Relative and Conditional Relative Frequencies

STUDY TIP
When finding relative frequencies in a two-way table, you can use the corresponding decimals or percents.

You can display entries of a two-way table as frequency counts (as in Examples 1 and 2) or as *relative frequencies*.

KEY IDEA

Relative Frequencies

A **joint relative frequency** is the ratio of a joint frequency to the total number of values or observations.

A **marginal relative frequency** is the sum of the joint relative frequencies in a row or a column.

EXAMPLE 3 Finding Relative Frequencies

The two-way table shows the results of a survey that asked college-bound high school students whether they plan to major in a medical field. Make a two-way table that shows the joint and marginal relative frequencies.

		Major in Medical Field	
		Yes	No
Class	Junior	124	219
	Senior	101	236

SOLUTION

There are $124 + 219 + 101 + 236 = 680$ students in the survey. To find the joint relative frequencies, divide each frequency by 680. Then find the sum of each row and each column to find the marginal relative frequencies.

		Major in Medical Field		
		Yes	No	Total
Class	Junior	$\frac{124}{680} \approx 0.18$	$\frac{219}{680} \approx 0.32$	0.50
	Senior	$\frac{101}{680} \approx 0.15$	$\frac{236}{680} \approx 0.35$	0.50
	Total	0.33	0.67	1

About 50% of the students are juniors.

About 35% of the students are seniors who are not planning to major in a medical field.

STUDY TIP

The sum of the marginal relative frequencies in the "total" row and the "total" column should each be equal to 1.

KEY IDEA

Conditional Relative Frequencies

A **conditional relative frequency** is the ratio of a joint relative frequency to the marginal relative frequency. You can find a conditional relative frequency using a row total or a column total of a two-way table.

EXAMPLE 4 Finding Conditional Relative Frequencies

Use the survey results in Example 3 to make a two-way table that shows the conditional relative frequencies based on the column totals.

SOLUTION

Use the marginal relative frequency of each *column* to calculate the conditional relative frequencies.

		Major in Medical Field	
		Yes	No
Class	Junior	$\frac{0.18}{0.33} \approx 0.55$	$\frac{0.32}{0.67} \approx 0.48$
	Senior	$\frac{0.15}{0.33} \approx 0.45$	$\frac{0.35}{0.67} \approx 0.52$

Given that a student is not planning to major in a medical field, the conditional relative frequency that he or she is a junior is about 48%.

STUDY TIP

The sum of the conditional relative frequencies for each column should be equal to 1.

SELF-ASSESSMENT

1 I do not understand. 2 I can do it with help. 3 I can do it on my own. 4 I can teach someone else.

6. Use the survey results in Exercise 5 to make a two-way table that shows the joint and marginal relative frequencies. What percent of students are not getting a summer job?

7. Use the survey results in Example 3 to make a two-way table that shows the conditional relative frequencies based on the row totals. Given that a student is a senior, what is the conditional relative frequency that he or she is planning to major in a medical field?

Recognizing Associations in Data

EXAMPLE 5 Recognizing Associations in Data

You survey students and find that 40% exercise regularly, 35% eat fruits and vegetables each day, and 52% do not exercise and do not eat fruits and vegetables each day. Is there an association between exercising regularly and eating fruits and vegetables each day?

SOLUTION

Make a two-way table. Use reasoning to find the missing joint and marginal relative frequencies.

		Exercise Regularly		
		Yes	No	Total
Eat Fruits/ Vegetables	Yes	27%	8%	35%
	No	13%	52%	65%
	Total	40%	60%	100%

Use conditional relative frequencies based on the column totals to determine whether there is an association. Of the students who exercise regularly, 67.5% eat fruits and vegetables each day. Of the students who do not exercise regularly, only about 13% eat fruits and vegetables each day. It appears that students who exercise regularly are more likely to eat more fruits and vegetables than students who do not exercise regularly.

		Exercise Regularly	
		Yes	No
Eat Fruits/ Vegetables	Yes	$\frac{0.27}{0.4} = 0.675$	$\frac{0.08}{0.6} \approx 0.133$
	No	$\frac{0.13}{0.4} = 0.325$	$\frac{0.52}{0.6} \approx 0.867$

▶ So, there is an association between exercising regularly and eating fruits and vegetables each day.

You can also find the conditional relative frequencies by dividing each joint frequency by its corresponding column total or row total, as shown in Example 6.

EXAMPLE 6 Recognizing Associations in Data

The two-way table shows the results of a survey that asked students whether they use public transportation. Is there an association between age and using public transportation?

		Age		
		14–15	16–17	18–19
Use Public Transportation	Yes	22	47	40
	No	34	25	10

SOLUTION

Use conditional relative frequencies based on column totals to determine whether there is an association. Based on this sample, only 39% of students ages 14–15 use public transportation and 80% of students ages 18–19 use public transportation as shown.

		Age		
		14–15	16–17	18–19
Use Public Transportation	Yes	$\frac{22}{56} \approx 0.39$	$\frac{47}{72} \approx 0.65$	$\frac{40}{50} = 0.8$
	No	$\frac{34}{56} \approx 0.61$	$\frac{25}{72} \approx 0.35$	$\frac{10}{50} = 0.2$

▶ The table shows that as age increases, students are more likely to use public transportation. So, there is an association.

SELF-ASSESSMENT 1 I do not understand. 2 I can do it with help. 3 I can do it on my own. 4 I can teach someone else.

8. Using the results of the survey in Exercise 2, is there an association between using a tablet and using a laptop? Explain your reasoning.

11.4 Practice WITH CalcChat® AND CalcView®

You conduct a survey that asks 346 students whether they pack their lunch. In Exercises 1–4, use the results of the survey shown in the two-way table.

		Pack Lunch	
		Yes	No
Class	Freshman	86	92
	Sophomore	52	116

1. How many freshmen were surveyed?

2. How many sophomores were surveyed?

3. How many students pack their lunch?

4. How many students do not pack their lunch?

In Exercises 5 and 6, the two-way table shows the results of a survey. Find and interpret the marginal frequencies. *Example 1*

5.

		Set Academic Goals	
		Yes	No
Gender	Male	168	64
	Female	142	54

6.

		Own a Cat	
		Yes	No
Own a Dog	Yes	104	208
	No	186	98

7. **USING TWO-WAY TABLES** You conduct a survey that asks students how they would rate a television series finale. The results are shown in the two-way table. Find and interpret the marginal frequencies.

		Rating		
		Good	Fair	Poor
Gender	Male	124	42	58
	Female	120	48	62

8. **USING TWO-WAY TABLES** You conduct a survey that asks students whether they plan to participate in school spirit week. The results are shown in the two-way table. Find and interpret the marginal frequencies.

		Participate in Spirit Week		
		Yes	No	Undecided
Class	Freshman	112	56	54
	Sophomore	92	68	32

MP STRUCTURE In Exercises 9 and 10, complete the two-way table that shows survey results.

9.

		Traveled on an Airplane		
		Yes	No	Total
Age Group	Teenager		62	
	Adult	184		
	Total	274		352

10.

		Plan to Attend School Dance		
		Yes	No	Total
Gender	Male	38		
	Female		24	112
	Total			196

11. **MAKING TWO-WAY TABLES** You conduct a survey that asks 245 students in your school whether they have taken a Spanish or a French class. One hundred nine of the students have taken a Spanish class, and 45 of those students have taken a French class. Eighty-two of the students have not taken a Spanish or a French class. Organize the results in a two-way table. Include the marginal frequencies. *Example 2*

12. **MAKING TWO-WAY TABLES** A county has a total of 165,557 registered Democratic and Republican voters. There are 96,759 registered Democrats, and 24,532 of those Democrats voted in the last primary election. There are 51,489 registered Republicans who did not vote in the last primary election. Organize this information in a two-way table. Include the marginal frequencies.

In Exercises 13 and 14, the two-way table shows the results of a survey. Make a two-way table that shows the joint and marginal relative frequencies. *Example 3*

13.

		Exercise Preference	
		Aerobic	Anaerobic
Gender	Male	88	108
	Female	94	60

14.

		Hip Hop Music	
		Like	Dislike
Pop Music	Like	133	25
	Dislike	31	36

15. USING TWO-WAY TABLES Refer to Exercise 13. What percent of students prefer aerobic exercise? What percent of students are males who prefer anaerobic exercise?

16. USING TWO-WAY TABLES Refer to Exercise 14. What percent of students dislike pop music? What percent of students like both hip hop and pop music?

17. ERROR ANALYSIS Describe and correct the error in interpreting the survey results.

		Participate in Fundraiser	
		Yes	No
Class	Freshman	187	85
	Sophomore	123	93

✗ *One hundred eighty-seven freshmen responded to the survey.*

18. ERROR ANALYSIS Describe and correct the error in finding the joint relative frequencies in the two-way table in Exercise 17.

✗

		Participate in Fundraiser	
		Yes	No
Class	Freshman	$\frac{187}{272} \approx 0.69$	$\frac{85}{272} \approx 0.31$
	Sophomore	$\frac{123}{216} \approx 0.57$	$\frac{93}{216} \approx 0.43$

19. USING TWO-WAY TABLES Refer to Exercise 13. *Example 4*

a. Make a two-way table that shows the conditional relative frequencies based on the row totals.

b. Given that a student is female, what is the conditional relative frequency that she prefers aerobic exercise?

20. USING TWO-WAY TABLES Refer to Exercise 14.

a. Make a two-way table that shows the conditional relative frequencies based on the column totals.

b. Given that a student dislikes hip hop music, what is the conditional relative frequency that he or she likes pop music?

21. ANALYZING TWO-WAY TABLES You survey college students and find that 79% live on campus, 38% have a car while at college, and 3% live off campus and do not have a car. Is there an association between living on campus and having a car at college? Explain. *Example 5*

22. ANALYZING TWO-WAY TABLES You survey students and find that 70% watch sports on TV, 48% participate in a sport, and 16% do not watch sports on TV and do not participate in a sport. Is there an association between participating in a sport and watching sports on TV? Explain.

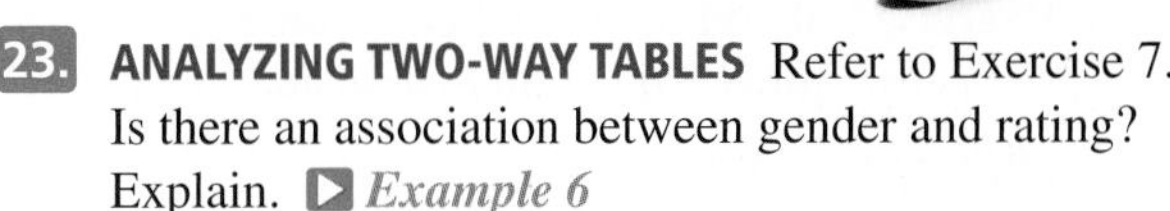

23. ANALYZING TWO-WAY TABLES Refer to Exercise 7. Is there an association between gender and rating? Explain. *Example 6*

24. ANALYZING TWO-WAY TABLES The two-way table shows the results of a survey that asked adults whether they participate in recreational skiing. Is there an association between age and recreational skiing?

		Age				
		21–30	31–40	41–50	51–60	61–70
Ski	Yes	87	93	68	37	20
	No	165	195	148	117	125

25. OPEN-ENDED Collect data from a random sample of at least 30 people on two categories of your choice. Display your results in a two-way table and in another data display using technology. Then determine whether there is an association between the two categories.

26. HOW DO YOU SEE IT?
The graph shows the results of a survey that asked students about their favorite movie genre. Display the given information in a two-way table. Which data display do you prefer? Explain.

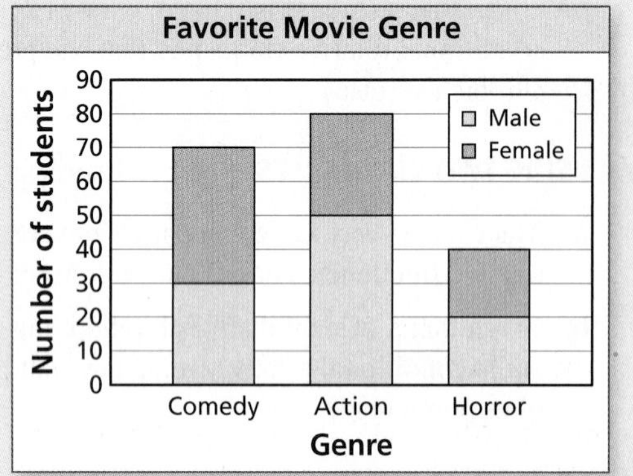

27. DIG DEEPER A box office sells 1809 tickets to a play, 800 of which are for the main floor. The tickets consist of $2x + y$ adult tickets for the main floor, $x - 40$ child tickets for the main floor, $x + 2y$ adult tickets for the balcony, and $3x - y - 80$ child tickets for the balcony. Organize this information in a two-way table. What percent of tickets are adult tickets? What percent of child tickets are balcony tickets?

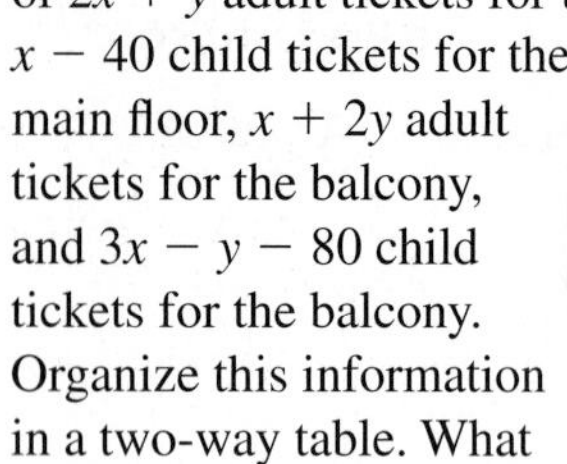

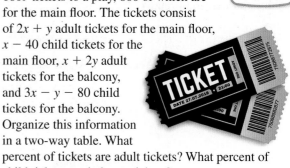

28. THOUGHT PROVOKING
Is it possible to have a "three-way table?" If so, give an example of a three-way table.

REVIEW & REFRESH

WATCH

29. The box-and-whisker plot represents the wait times (in minutes) for rides at an amusement park.

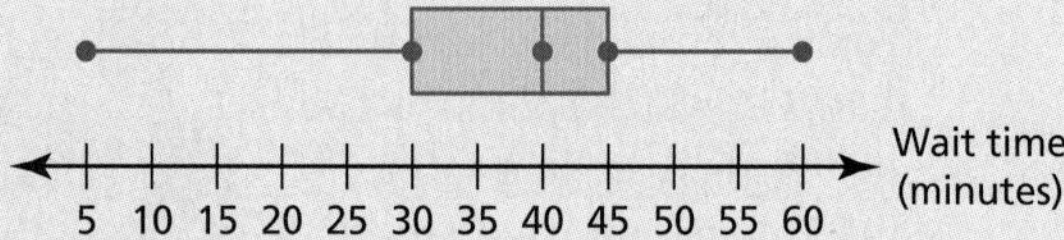

a. Find and interpret the range of the data.

b. Find and interpret the interquartile range of the data.

c. Are the data more spread out below Q1 or above Q3? Explain.

In Exercises 30 and 31, tell whether the table of values represents a *linear*, an *exponential*, or a *quadratic* function.

30.

x	0	1	2	3	4
y	144	24	4	$\frac{2}{3}$	$\frac{1}{9}$

31.

x	−1	0	1	2	3
y	3	0	−1	0	3

32. MP **REASONING** A data set is described by the measures shown.

Mean: 12 Median: 10 Mode: 8

Range: 18 Standard deviation: 6

Find the mean, median, mode, range, and standard deviation of the data set when each data value is increased by 40% and then increased by 5.

In Exercises 33 and 34, determine the number of real solutions of the equation.

33. $x^2 + 6x - 2 = 0$ **34.** $4x^2 + 8x = -5$

35. Display the data in a histogram. Describe the shape of the distribution.

Quiz score	0–2	3–5	6–8	9–11	12–14
Frequency	1	3	6	16	4

36. Solve $(13 - h)(3h + 4) = 0$.

In Exercises 37 and 38, write an equation for the *n*th term of the arithmetic sequence. Then find a_{12}.

37. 36, 23, 10, −3, . . . **38.** −12, −5, 2, 9, . . .

39. The two-way table shows the results of a survey. Find and interpret the marginal frequencies. Then make a two-way table that shows the joint and marginal relative frequencies.

		Visited a Foreign Country	
		Yes	No
Age	14–15	10	60
	16–17	18	62

In Exercises 40 and 41, solve the equation by graphing.

40. $\frac{3}{4}x - 5 = -2x + 6$ **41.** $|x + 5| = |3x + 3|$

11.5 Choosing a Data Display

Learning Target Use appropriate data displays to represent situations.

Success Criteria

- I can classify data as qualitative or quantitative.
- I can create an appropriate data display and explain the choice of display.
- I can identify misleading data displays.

EXPLORE IT! Displaying Data

MP **CHOOSE TOOLS** **Work with a partner.** Analyze the data and then create a display that best represents the data. Explain your choice of data display.

a. The Montana Department of Fish, Wildlife & Parks reported the following numbers of claims made to retrieve elk killed on roadways.

adult male: 69 adult female: 178 calf: 52

b. The data below show the numbers of deer killed on roads in one region of Colorado from 2007 to 2018.

OBSERVED DEER FATALITIES

2007: 352	2011: 315	2015: 159
2008: 348	2012: 275	2016: 301
2009: 264	2013: 139	2017: 291
2010: 336	2014: 116	2018: 220

c. A yearlong study by volunteers in California reported the following numbers of animals killed by motor vehicles.

gray squirrels: 715
cottontail rabbits: 629
barn owls: 486
jackrabbits: 466
gopher snakes: 363

Math Practice

Use Other Resources
In what other resources would you expect to find different types of data displays?

d. Use the Internet or some other resource to find examples of the following types of data displays. Then choose two of the displays and write several conclusions that you can make from the displays.

bar graph	circle graph	scatter plot
stem-and-leaf plot	pictograph	line graph
box-and-whisker plot	histogram	dot plot

Classifying Data

Data sets can consist of two types of data: *qualitative* or *quantitative.*

GO DIGITAL

Vocabulary 

qualitative (categorical) data, *p. 620*
quantitative data, *p. 620*
misleading graph, *p. 622*

KEY IDEA

Types of Data

Qualitative data, or **categorical data**, consist of labels or nonnumerical entries that can be separated into different categories. When using qualitative data, operations such as adding or finding a mean do not make sense.

Quantitative data consist of numbers that represent counts or measurements.

STUDY TIP

Just because a frequency count can be shown for a data set does not make it quantitative. A frequency count can be shown for both qualitative and quantitative data.

EXAMPLE 1 Classifying Data

Tell whether the data are *qualitative* or *quantitative*.

a. prices of used cars at a dealership

b. jersey numbers for a basketball team

c. lengths of songs played at a concert

d. zodiac signs of students in your class

SOLUTION

a. Prices are numerical entries. So, the data are quantitative.

b. Jersey numbers are numerical, but they are labels. It does not make sense to compare them, and you cannot measure them. So, the data are qualitative.

c. Song lengths are numerical measurements. So, the data are quantitative.

d. Zodiac signs are nonnumerical entries that can be separated into different categories. So, the data are qualitative.

Qualitative and quantitative data can be collected from the same data source, as shown below. You can use these types of data together to obtain a more accurate description of a population.

Data Source	Quantitative Data	Qualitative Data
a student	How much do you earn per hour at your job? \$10.50	What is your occupation? painter
a house	How many square feet of living space is in the house? 2500 ft^2	In what city is the house located? Chicago

SELF-ASSESSMENT 1 I do not understand. 2 I can do it with help. 3 I can do it on my own. 4 I can teach someone else.

Tell whether the data are *qualitative* or *quantitative*. Explain your reasoning.

1. telephone numbers in a directory
2. ages of patients at a hospital
3. lengths of videos on a website
4. types of flowers at a florist
5. **WHICH ONE DOESN'T BELONG?** Which data set does *not* belong with the other three? Explain your reasoning.

ages of people attending a concert	heights of skyscrapers in a city
populations of counties in a state	breeds of dogs at a pet store

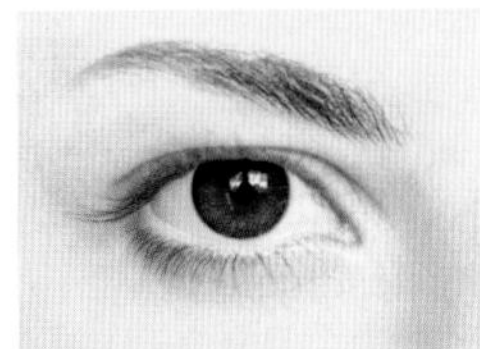
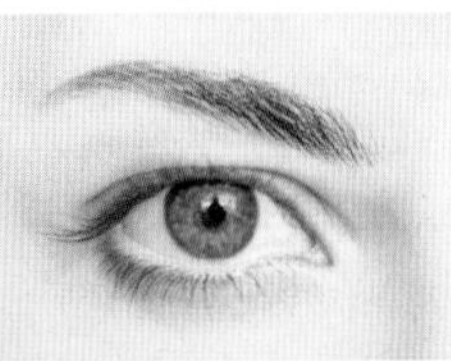
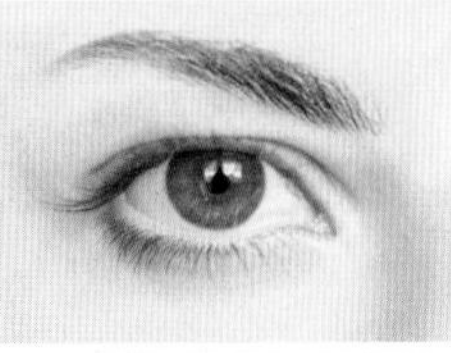
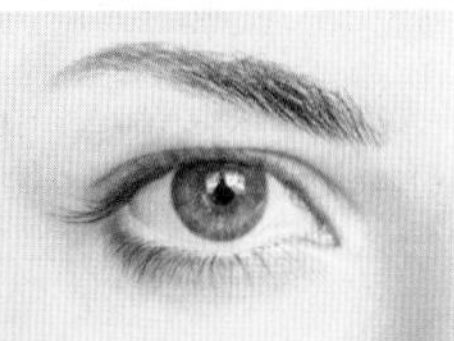
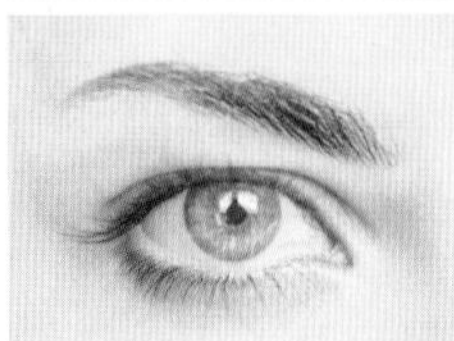
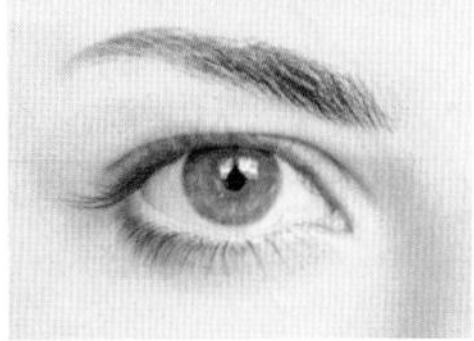

Choosing and Creating Appropriate Data Displays

As shown on page 585, you have learned a variety of ways to display data sets graphically. Choosing an appropriate data display can depend on whether the data are qualitative or quantitative.

EXAMPLE 2 Choosing and Creating Data Displays

Analyze the data and then create a display that best represents the data. Explain your reasoning.

a.

Eye Color Survey	
Color	**Number of students**
brown	63
blue	37
hazel	25
green	10
gray	3
amber	2

b.

Speeds of Vehicles (mi/h)			
Interstate A		**Interstate B**	
65	67	67	72
68	71	70	78
72	70	65	71
68	65	71	80
65	68	84	81
75	82	77	79
68	59	69	70
62	68	66	69
75	80	73	75
77	75	84	79

SOLUTION

a. A circle graph is one appropriate way to display the qualitative data. It shows data as parts of a whole.

Step 1 Find the angle measure for each section of the circle graph by multiplying the fraction of students who have each eye color by 360°. Notice that there are $63 + 37 + 25 + 10 + 3 + 2 = 140$ students in the survey.

Brown: $\frac{63}{140} \cdot 360° = 162°$ **Blue:** $\frac{37}{140} \cdot 360° \approx 95°$ **Hazel:** $\frac{25}{140} \cdot 360° \approx 64°$

Green: $\frac{10}{140} \cdot 360° \approx 26°$ **Gray:** $\frac{3}{140} \cdot 360° \approx 8°$ **Amber:** $\frac{2}{140} \cdot 360° \approx 5°$

Step 2 Use a protractor to draw the angle measures found in Step 1 on a circle. Then label each section and title the circle graph, as shown.

Eye Color Survey

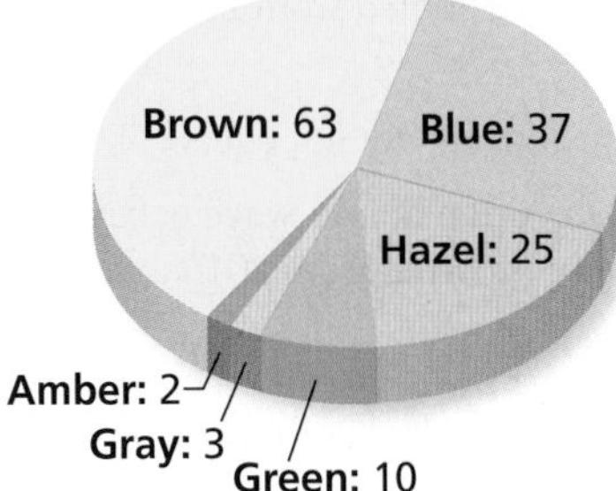

b. A double box-and-whisker plot is one appropriate way to display the quantitative data. Use the five-number summary of each data set to create a double box-and-whisker plot.

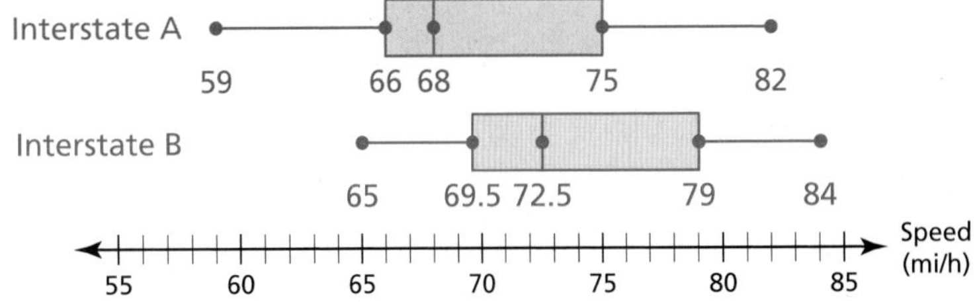

SELF-ASSESSMENT

1 I do not understand. 2 I can do it with help. 3 I can do it on my own. 4 I can teach someone else.

6. Display the data in Example 2(a) in another way.
7. Display the data in Example 2(b) in another way.

Analyzing Misleading Graphs

GO DIGITAL

Data displays can be misleading. A **misleading graph** is a statistical graph that is not drawn appropriately. This may cause viewers to misinterpret the graph. Below are some questions you can ask yourself when analyzing a statistical graph that will help you recognize when a graph may be misleading.

- Does the graph have a title?
- Are the numbers of the scale evenly spaced?
- Does the scale begin at zero? If not, is there a break?
- Does the graph need a key?
- Are all the axes or sections of the graph labeled?
- Are all the components of the graph, such as the bars, the same size?

EXAMPLE 3 Analyzing Misleading Graphs

Describe how each graph is misleading. Then explain how someone might misinterpret the graph.

a.

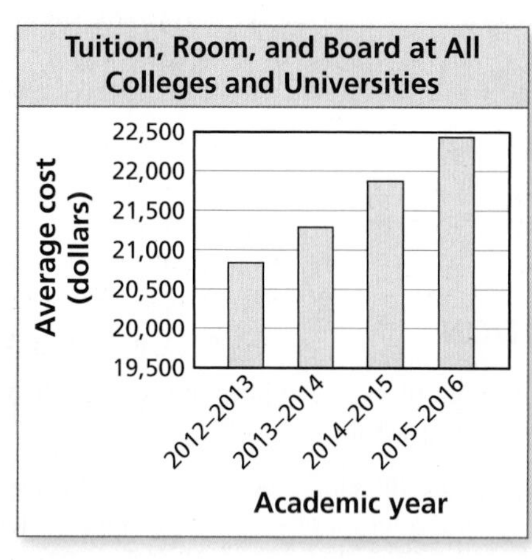

b.

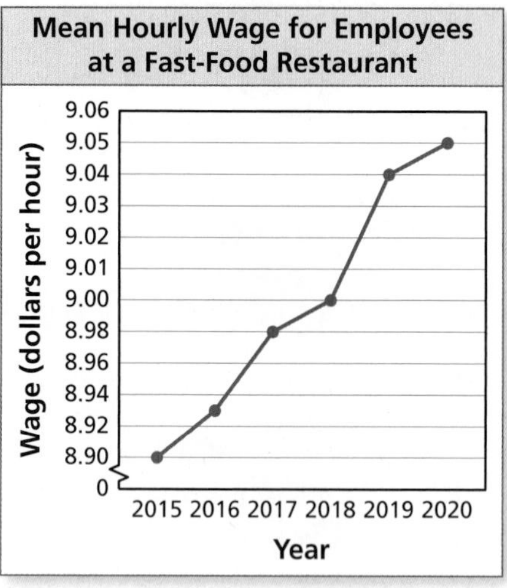

SOLUTION

a. The scale on the vertical axis of the graph starts at $19,500 and does not have a break. This makes it appear that the average cost increased rapidly for the years given.

Someone might believe that the average cost more than doubled from 2012 to 2016, when actually, it increased by only about $1500.

b. The scale on the vertical axis has very small increments that are not equal.

Someone might believe that the greatest increase in the mean hourly wage occurred from 2018 to 2019, when the greatest increase actually occurred from 2016 to 2017.

SELF-ASSESSMENT

1 I do not understand. 2 I can do it with help. 3 I can do it on my own. 4 I can teach someone else.

8. Describe how the graph is misleading. Then explain how someone might misinterpret the graph.

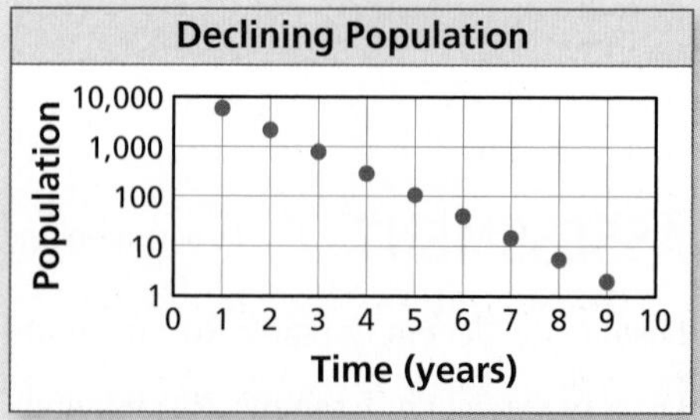

9. Redraw the graphs in Example 3 so they are not misleading.

10. **OPEN-ENDED** Describe two ways that a line graph can be misleading.

11.5 Practice WITH CalcChat® AND CalcView®

In Exercises 1–6, tell whether the data are *qualitative* or *quantitative*. Explain your reasoning. *Example 1*

1. brands of cars in a parking lot
2. weights of bears at a zoo
3. budgets of feature films
4. file formats of documents on a computer
5. shoe sizes of students in your class
6. street addresses in a phone book

In Exercises 7–10, choose an appropriate data display for the situation. Explain your reasoning.

7. the number of students in a marching band each year
8. a comparison of students' grades (out of 100) in two different classes
9. the favorite sports of students in your class
10. the distribution of teachers by age

In Exercises 11–14, analyze the data and then create a display that best represents the data. Explain your reasoning. *Example 2*

11.

Ages of Olympic Gold Medalists	
2016 Women's Basketball (USA)	2016 Men's Basketball (USA)
32 35 37 27 26 30 25 29 29 21 34 34	32 24 26 26 27 27 26 26 24 28 30 26

12.

Average Precipitation (inches)			
January	1.1	July	4.0
February	1.5	August	4.4
March	2.2	September	4.2
April	3.7	October	3.5
May	5.1	November	2.1
June	5.5	December	1.8

13.

Grades (out of 100) on a Test						
96	74	97	80	62	84	88
53	77	75	89	81	52	85
63	87	95	59	83	100	

14.

Colors of Cars that Drive Past			
white	25	green	3
red	12	silver/gray	27
yellow	1	blue	6
black	21	brown/beige	5

15. **DISPLAYING DATA** Display the data in Exercise 11 in another way.
16. **DISPLAYING DATA** Display the data in Exercise 12 in another way.
17. **DISPLAYING DATA** Display the data in Exercise 13 in another way.
18. **DISPLAYING DATA** Display the data in Exercise 14 in another way.

In Exercises 19 and 20, describe how the graph is misleading. Then explain how someone might misinterpret the graph. *Example 3*

19.

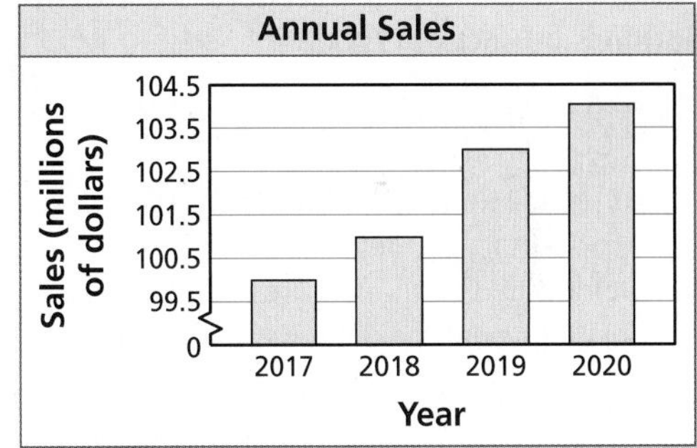

20.

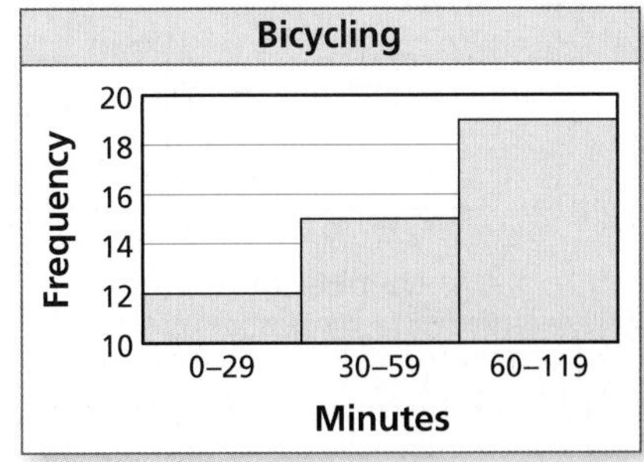

21. **DISPLAYING DATA** Redraw the graph in Exercise 19 so it is not misleading.
22. **DISPLAYING DATA** Redraw the graph in Exercise 20 so it is not misleading.

23. **MAKING AN ARGUMENT** A data set gives the ages of voters for a city election. Would the data be better displayed in a bar graph or in a histogram? Explain your reasoning.

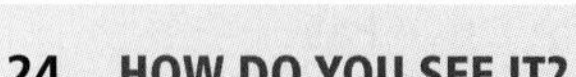

24. **HOW DO YOU SEE IT?**
The manager of a company sees the graph shown and concludes that the company is experiencing a decline. What is missing from the graph? Explain why the manager may be mistaken.

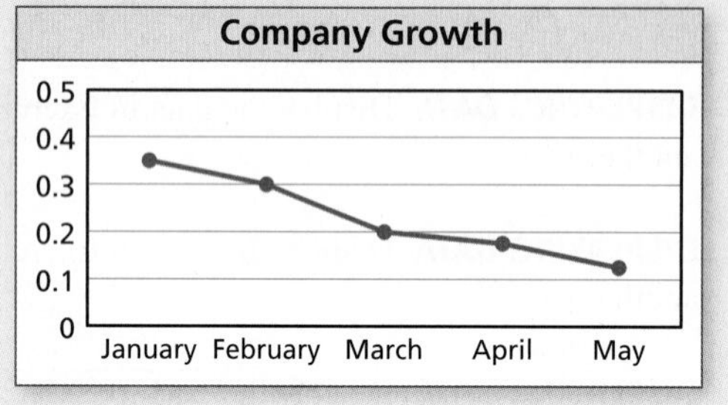

25. **MP REASONING** What types of data displays show the mode of a data set?

26. **THOUGHT PROVOKING**
Use technology to create a type of data display that is not listed on page 585.

27. **DIG DEEPER** A company creates a commercial advertisement for a product aimed at viewers ages 16–25. The company needs to decide whether to run the advertisement during a certain television show. The results of a random sample of 40 viewers of the show are shown in the table. Create a data display that will help the company decide. Should the company run the advertisement during this show? Explain your reasoning.

Viewer Ages							
31	12	26	9	32	19	33	17
36	28	22	16	24	12	13	10
23	7	18	28	45	14	39	23
15	20	16	29	39	19	31	23
27	27	20	25	19	24	42	35

REVIEW & REFRESH

In Exercises 28 and 29, determine whether the relation is a function. Explain.

28. $(-5, -1), (-6, 0), (-5, 1), (-2, 2), (3, 3)$

29. $(0, 1), (4, 0), (8, 1), (12, 2), (16, 3)$

30. Determine which measures of center and variation best represent the data. Explain your reasoning.

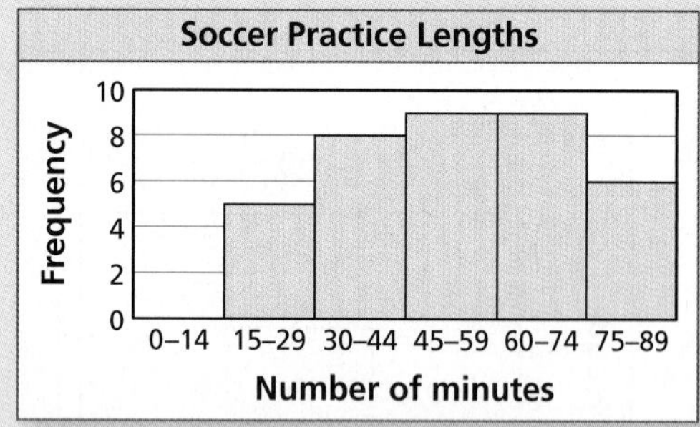

In Exercises 31–34, factor the polynomial completely.

31. $x^2 - 7x - 30$

32. $x^2 - 16x + 64$

33. $4x^2 + 27x - 7$

34. $x^3 - 9x^2 - 2x + 18$

35. **MP REASONING** Is it possible to determine the number of values in a data set from a box-and-whisker plot? Explain your reasoning.

36. **MODELING REAL LIFE** You survey students about which of two candidates they will vote for in a school election. Fifty freshmen respond, with 23 of them responding "Candidate A." Seventy sophomores respond, with 41 of them responding "Candidate B." Organize the results in a two-way table. Include the marginal frequencies.

In Exercises 37 and 38, solve the system using any method. Explain your choice of method.

37. $y = -5x + 10$
$-3x + y = -6$

38. $6x + y = -7$
$6x + y = 9$

In Exercises 39 and 40, use the graphs of *f* and *g* to describe the transformation from the graph of *f* to the graph of *g*.

39. $f(x) = \frac{3}{2}x - 8;\ g(x) = f(x) + 4$

40. $f(x) = -5x + 2;\ g(x) = f(-x)$

41. Analyze the data and then create a display that best represents the data. Explain your reasoning.

Hurricane Wind Speeds (miles per hour)				
90	85	88	105	112
95	80	82	94	100
75	115	90	87	79

11 Chapter Review WITH CalcChat®

Chapter Learning Target Understand data.

Chapter Success Criteria
- ◆ I can interpret data displays.
- ◆ I can describe the shapes of data distributions.
- ■ I can represent data in different ways.
- ■ I can analyze data.

◆ Surface
■ Deep

SELF-ASSESSMENT 1 I do not understand. 2 I can do it with help. 3 I can do it on my own. 4 I can teach someone else.

11.1 Measures of Center and Variation *(pp. 587–594)*

Learning Target: Find measures of center and variation of a data set.

Vocabulary

measure of center
mean
median
mode
outlier
measure of variation
range
standard deviation
data transformation

Find the mean, median, and mode of the data.

1.

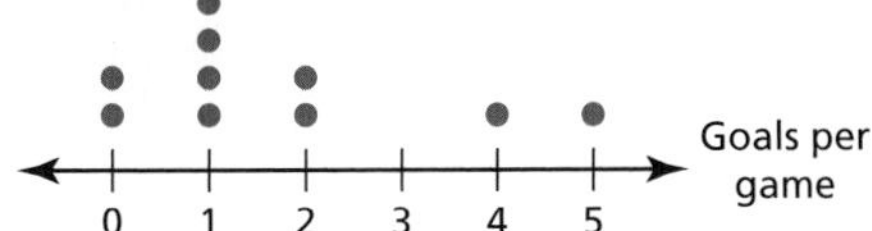

2.

Ski Resort Temperatures (°F)		
11	3	3
0	−9	−2
10	10	10

3. The table shows the numbers (in thousands) of times that ten podcast episodes were downloaded.

a. Find the mean, median, and mode of the data.

b. Identify the outlier. How does the outlier affect the mean, median, and mode?

Downloads	
3.5	4.1
4.0	4.3
4.4	2.5
3.9	1.0
4.3	5.0

Find the range and standard deviation of each data set. Then compare your results.

4.

Bowling Scores			
Player A		Player B	
205	190	228	205
185	200	172	181
210	219	154	240
174	203	235	235

5.

Fitness Tracker Prices			
Store A		Store B	
\$140	\$180	\$225	\$310
\$200	\$250	\$260	\$190
\$150	\$190	\$190	\$285
\$250	\$160	\$160	\$240

Find the values of the measures shown after the given transformation.

Mean: 109 **Median: 104** **Mode: 96** **Range: 45** **Standard deviation: 3.6**

6. Each value in the data set increases by 25.

7. Each value in the data set is multiplied by 0.6.

11.2 Box-and-Whisker Plots (pp. 595–602)

Learning Target: Make and interpret box-and-whisker plots for data sets.

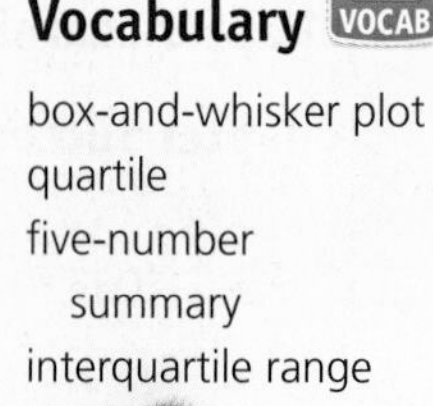

Make a box-and-whisker plot that represents the data. Identify the shape of the distribution.

8. Masses (in kilograms) of lions:

120, 230, 180, 210, 200, 200, 230, 160

9. Ages of volunteers at a hospital:

14, 17, 20, 16, 17, 14, 21, 18, 22

10. The box-and-whisker plot represents the weights (in pounds) of Australian Terriers owned by a dog breeder.

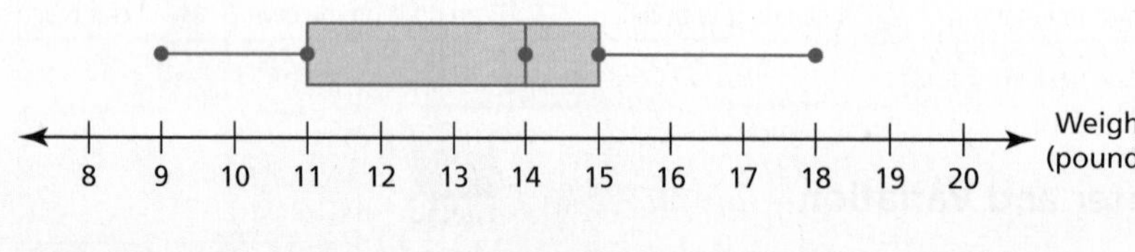

a. Find and interpret the range of the data.

b. Describe the distribution of the data.

c. Find and interpret the interquartile range of the data.

d. Are the data more spread out below Q1 or above Q3? Explain.

11.3 Shapes of Distributions (pp. 603–610)

Learning Target: Describe and compare shapes of distributions.

11. The frequency table shows the amounts of money students in a class have in their pockets.

Amount of money (dollars)	0–0.99	1–1.99	2–2.99	3–3.99	4–4.99	5–5.99
Frequency	9	10	9	7	4	1

a. Display the data in a histogram and describe the shape of the distribution. Which measures of center and variation best represent the data?

b. The histogram shown represents the amounts of money a group of adults have in their pockets. Compare the distributions for students and adults using their shapes and appropriate measures of center and variation.

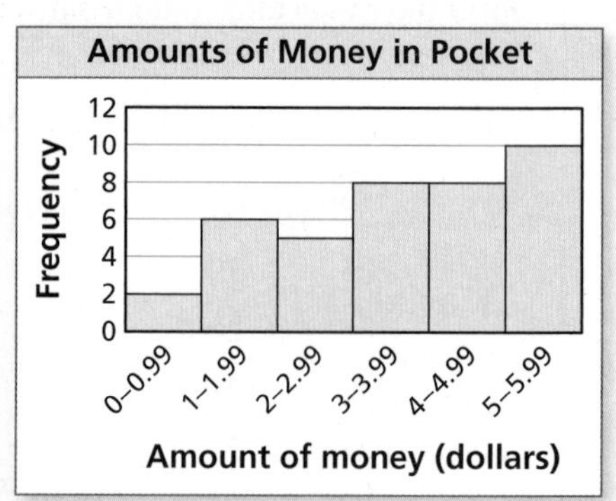

12. A distribution is bell-shaped. The interval from 24 to 40 represents about 95% of the data. Find the mean and standard deviation of the data. Explain your reasoning.

13. For each distribution, determine whether the mean is *less than* or *greater than* the median. Explain your reasoning.

a.

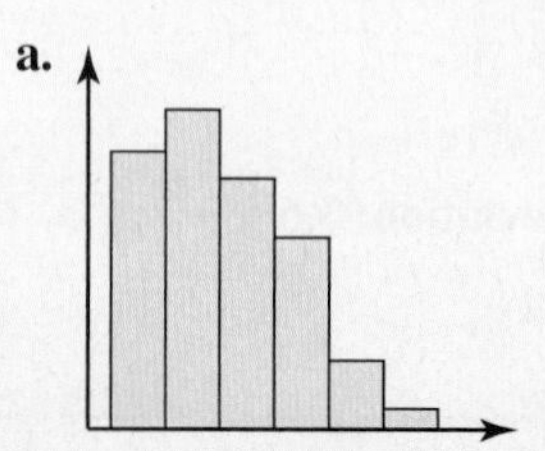

b.

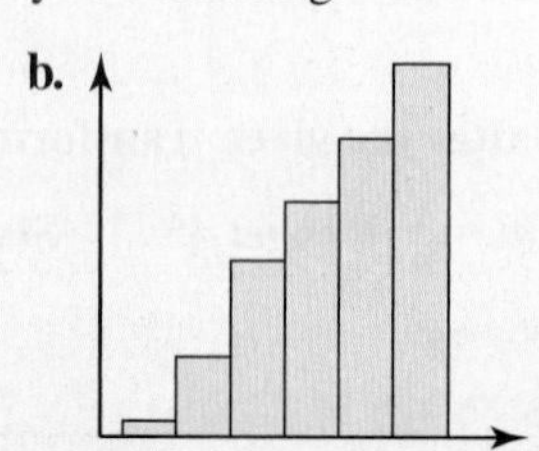

11.4 Two-Way Tables (pp. 611–618)

GO DIGITAL

Learning Target: Use two-way tables to represent data.

Vocabulary
two-way table
joint frequency
marginal frequency
joint relative frequency
marginal relative frequency
conditional relative frequency

You conduct a survey that asks 200 shoppers at a mall whether they like the new food court. One hundred seventeen of the shoppers like the new food court, 96 of whom are teenagers. Seventy-nine adults dislike the new food court.

14. Organize the results in a two-way table. Include the marginal frequencies.

15. Make a two-way table that shows the joint and marginal relative frequencies.

16. Make a two-way table that shows the conditional relative frequencies based on the column totals.

17. The two-way table shows the results of a survey that asked adults whether they have seen the latest superhero movie. Is there an association between age and seeing the movie? Explain.

		Age			
		15–24	**25–34**	**35–44**	**45–54**
Seen Movie	**Yes**	58	23	19	23
	No	18	18	21	79

11.5 Choosing a Data Display (pp. 619–624)

Learning Target: Use appropriate data displays to represent situations.

Vocabulary
qualitative (categorical) data
quantitative data
misleading graph

18. Analyze the data in the table and then create a display that best represents the data. Explain your reasoning.

Perfect Attendance	
Class	**Number of students**
freshman	84
sophomore	42
junior	67
senior	31

Choose an appropriate data display for the situation. Explain your reasoning.

19. the heights of the members of a basketball team

20. the grade levels of students in an elementary school

Mathematical Practices

Model with Mathematics

Mathematically proficient students identify important quantities in practical situations and map their relationships using such tools as diagrams, two-way tables, graphs, flowcharts, and formulas. They analyze those relationships mathematically to draw conclusions.

1. In Exercise 8 on page 616, compare the data for the freshman class with the data for the sophomore class. What conclusions can you draw?

2. Name two data displays that would be appropriate to show the numbers of books read each year by students in your school. Describe the benefits of each display.

11 Practice Test WITH CalcChat®

Describe the shape of the data distribution. Then determine which measures of center and variation best represent the data.

1. 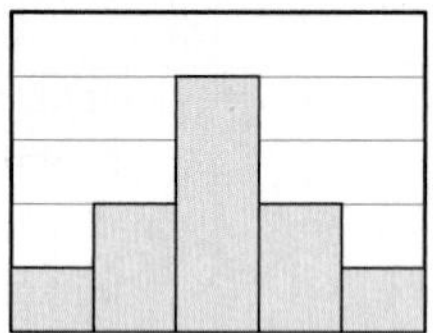

2. 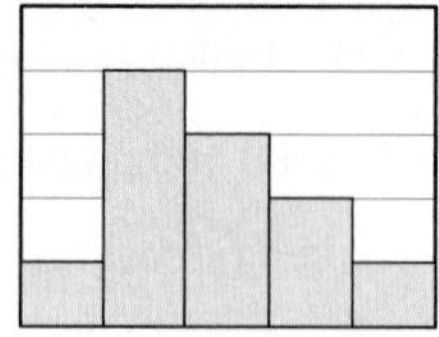

3. 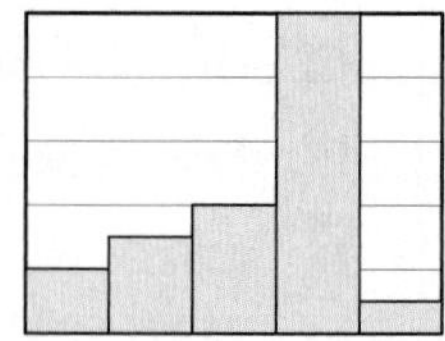

4. Determine whether each statement is *always*, *sometimes*, or *never* true. Explain your reasoning.

   a. The sum of the marginal relative frequencies in the "total" row and the "total" column of a two-way table should each be equal to 1.

   b. In a box-and-whisker plot, the length of the box to the left of the median and the length of the box to the right of the median are equal.

   c. Qualitative data are numerical.

5. Find the mean, median, mode, range, and standard deviation of the prices.

Prices of Shirts at a Clothing Store			
\$15.50	\$18.90	\$10.60	\$12.25
\$7.80	\$23.50	\$9.75	\$21.70

6. Repeat Exercise 5 when all the shirts are 20% off.

7. The tables show the battery lives (in hours) of two brands of laptops.

   a. Make a double box-and-whisker plot that represents the data.

   b. Identify the shape of each distribution.

   c. Which brand's battery lives are more spread out? Explain.

   d. Compare the distributions using their shapes and appropriate measures of center and variation.

Brand A	
20.75	18.5
13.5	16.25
8.5	13.5
14.5	15.5
11.5	16.75

Brand B	
10.5	12.5
9.5	10.25
9.0	9.75
8.5	8.5
9.0	7.0

Preferred method of exercise	Number of students
walking	20
jogging	28
biking	17
swimming	11
lifting weights	10
dancing	14

8. The table shows the results of a survey that asked students their preferred method of exercise. Analyze the data and then create a display that best represents the data. Explain your reasoning.

9. You conduct a survey that asks 271 students in your class whether they are attending the class field trip. One hundred twenty-one males respond, 92 of which are attending the field trip. Thirty-one females are not attending the field trip.

   a. Organize the results in a two-way table. Find and interpret the marginal frequencies.

   b. What percent of females are attending the class field trip?

10. The recursive rule $a_1 = 2.5$, $a_n = a_{n-1} + 1.25$ represents a sequence, where $n \leq 9$. Find the mean and standard deviation of the terms of the sequence.

GO DIGITAL

11 Performance Task

Robotics

Modern Applications of Robotics

Cleaning

Manufacturing

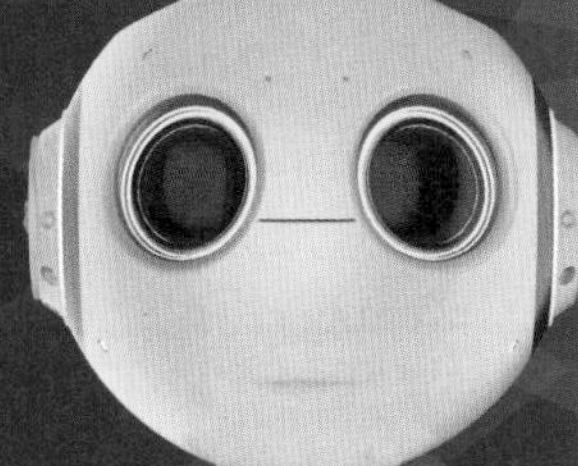

Computing

Entertainment

Transportation

Space Exploration

350 BC
The Flying Pigeon
Archytas, a Greek mathematician, creates a flying wooden pigeon powered by steam.

270 BC
Water Clock
Ctesibius, a Greek inventor and mathematician, invents a water clock with moveable figurines.

1921
The Word "Robot"
The word "Robot" is first used in Karel Capek's play, "R.U.R.," or "*Rossum's Universal Robots*."

1939
Elektro
Westinghouse builds a 7-foot-tall mechanical man named Elektro, who debuts at the New York World's Fair.

1942
The Three Laws of Robotics
Science fiction writer Isaac Asimov writes three rules to govern robotic behavior in his short story, "Runaround."

1948
Elmer and Elsie
William Grey Walter creates two machines named Elmer and Elsie that mimic lifelike behavior.

1950
The Turing Test
Alan Turing develops a test to determine whether a machine can think for itself.

1954
Unimate
George Devol and Joseph Engelberger design a robotic arm called Unimate for industrial use.

1966
Shakey
The Stanford Research Institute creates Shakey, a robot that can reason about its surroundings.

1973
The First Full-Scale Robot
Built at Waseda University in Japan, this robot can communicate, walk, and grip objects with its hands.

1985
Robot-Assisted Surgery
The PUMA 560 robotic arm is used in the first robot-assisted surgical procedure.

1997
Mission to Mars
The robotic rover Sojourner collects data on the Mars Pathfinder mission.

Check Mate
Deep Blue, a supercomputer developed by IBM, wins a chess match against grand champion chess player Garry Kasparov.

1999
Aibo
Sony releases a toy dog named Aibo that reacts to its surroundings.

2002
Roomba
The Roomba autonomous vacuum is released by iRobot.

2011
Watson wins *Jeopardy!*
Watson, a computer system invented by IBM, beats Ken Jennings and Brad Rutter on the popular TV trivia show, *Jeopardy!*

2012
Self-Driving Vehicles
The first driverless car is licensed in Nevada.

2016
Industrial Robots
Approximately 1.8 million robots are used in manufacturing.

INFO

CONDUCT A SURVEY

Create a survey of at least four questions that involves both qualitative and quantitative data about the use of robotics in everyday life. Then survey a random sample of at least 50 people and record the results. Analyze the data using measures and methods from this chapter and create a presentation of your findings. Include several different data displays in your presentation.

11 College and Career Readiness with CalcChat®

Tutorial videos are available for each exercise.

1. You ask all the students in your grade whether they have a cell phone. The results are shown in the two-way table. Which of the following statements are true? Select all that apply.

		Cell Phone	
		Yes	No
Gender	Male	33	6
	Female	32	8

Ⓐ A greater percent of males in your grade have a cell phone than females in your grade.

Ⓑ More males were surveyed than females.

Ⓒ Less than 15% of males in your grade do not have a cell phone.

Ⓓ Most students in your grade have a cell phone.

2. In the graph shown, f is a quadratic function, g is an exponential function, and h is a linear function.

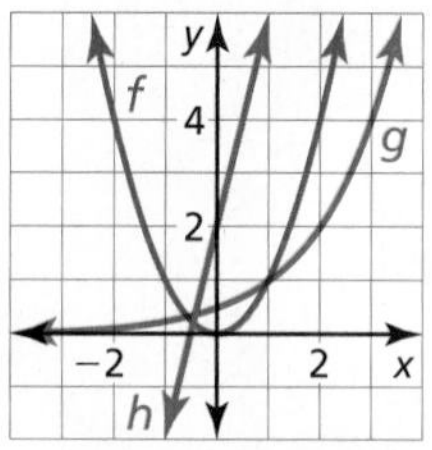

a. Are there any values of x greater than 0 where $f(x) > h(x)$? Explain.

b. Are there any values of x greater than 1 where $g(x) > f(x)$? Explain.

c. Are there any values of x greater than 0 where $g(x) > h(x)$? Explain.

3. Find the first quartile for the data set shown.

12, 8, 2, 14, 10, 19, 6, 8, 11, 3, 20, 16

Ⓐ 7 Ⓑ 8

Ⓒ 10.5 Ⓓ 15

4. Scores in a video game can be between 0 and 100. For each statement, use the data set shown to find a value for x so that the statement is true.

a. When $x =$ _____, the mean of the scores is 45.5.

b. When $x =$ _____, the median of the scores is 47.

c. When $x =$ _____, the mode of the scores is 63.

d. When $x =$ _____, the range of the scores is 71.

Video Game Scores	
36	28
48	x
42	57
63	52

5. Match each function with its inverse.

$y = -3x^2, x \geq 0$	$y = -x + 7$	$y = 2x - 4$	$y = \sqrt{-\frac{1}{3}x}$
$y = \frac{1}{2}x + 2$	$y = x^2 - 5, x \geq 0$	$y = \sqrt{x + 5}$	$y = -x + 7$

6. Complete the equation so that the solutions of the system of equations are $(-2, 4)$ and $(1, -5)$.

$$y = \square x + \square$$
$$y = 2x^2 - x - 6$$

7. The box-and-whisker plot represents the lengths (in minutes) of project presentations at a science fair. Find the interquartile range of the data. What does this represent in the context of the situation?

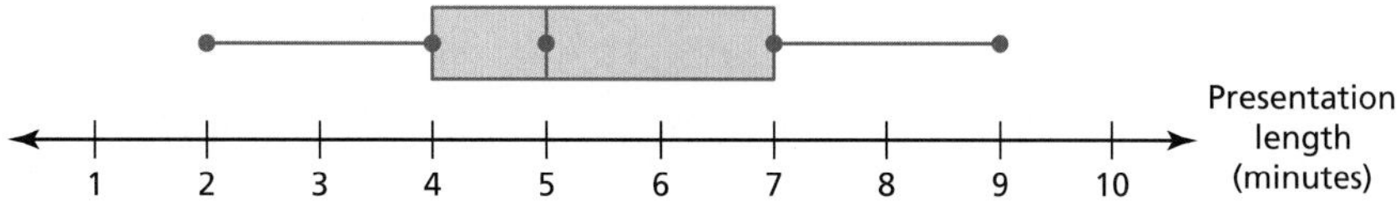

Ⓐ 7; The middle half of the presentation lengths vary by no more than 7 minutes.

Ⓑ 3; The presentation lengths vary by no more than 3 minutes.

Ⓒ 3; The middle half of the presentation lengths vary by no more than 3 minutes.

Ⓓ 7; The presentation lengths vary by no more than 7 minutes.

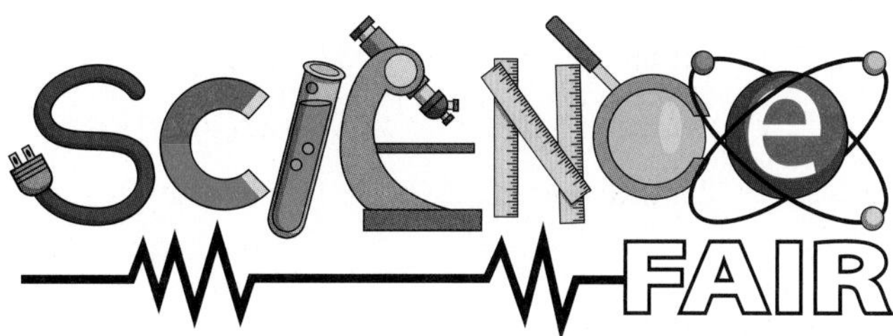

8. Which of the following numbers are in the range of the function shown? Select all that apply.

$$y = \begin{cases} x^2 + 4x + 7, & \text{if } x \leq -1 \\ \frac{1}{2}x + 2, & \text{if } x > -1 \end{cases}$$

Ⓐ $\frac{1}{2}$ Ⓑ 1 Ⓒ $1\frac{1}{2}$ Ⓓ 2

Ⓔ $2\frac{1}{2}$ Ⓕ 3 Ⓖ $3\frac{1}{2}$ Ⓗ 4

9. Which expression is equivalent to $8x^{2/3}$?

Ⓐ $4\sqrt[3]{x^2}$ Ⓑ $8\sqrt[3]{x^2}$ Ⓒ $8\sqrt{x^3}$ Ⓓ $\sqrt[3]{8x^2}$

10. A traveler walks and takes a shuttle bus to get to a terminal of an airport. The function $y = D(x)$ represents the traveler's distance (in feet) after x minutes.

a. Estimate and interpret $D(2)$.

b. Use the graph to find the solution of the equation $D(x) = 3500$. Explain the meaning of the solution.

c. How long does the traveler wait for the shuttle bus?

d. How far does the traveler ride on the shuttle bus?

e. What is the total distance that the traveler walks before and after riding the shuttle bus?

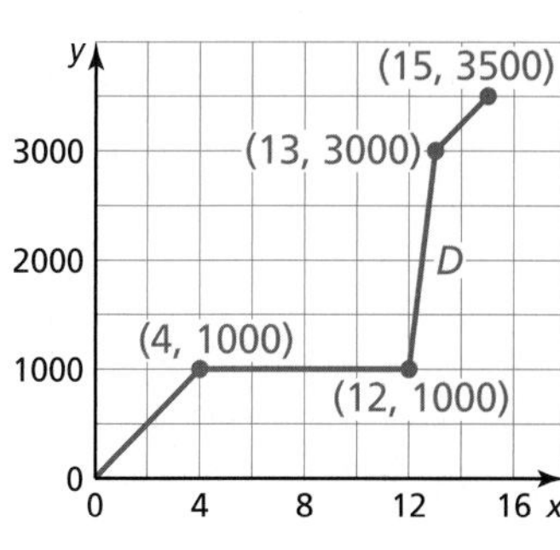

Selected Answers

Chapter 1

Chapter 1 Prepare

1. -7
2. -13
3. 8
4. 4.9
5. -2
6. 1.6
7. $\frac{11}{10}$
8. $\frac{7}{3}$
9. 6
10. -24
11. 63
12. -28
13. $\frac{1}{24}$
14. -0.8
15. -0.4
16. $\frac{3}{8}$
17. 3
18. 14.875

19. a. Both numbers are positive or the number with the greater absolute value is positive; *Sample answer:* 2 and 5, or 6 and -2

b. Both numbers have the same sign; *Sample answer:* 3 and 5, or -2 and -7

c. Both numbers have the same sign; *Sample answer:* 10 and 2, or -8 and -4

1.1 Practice

1. $x = 3$; Subtract 5 from each side.
3. $y = 7$; Add 4 to each side.
5. $w = -7$; Subtract 3 from each side.
7. $a = 5.6$
9. $t = -1$
11. $p - 12.95 = 44$; \$56.95
13. $g = 4$; Divide each side by 5.
15. $p = 15$; Multiply each side by 5.
17. $s = -6$; Divide each side by 9.
19. $x = -8.4$; Multiply each side by -6.
21. $r = -12$; Divide each side by 9π.
23. $p = -3$; Add 11 to each side.
25. $r = -8$; Divide each side by -8.
27. $m = 14$
29. $d = -5.7$
31. $f = 4\pi$
33. Subtract -0.8 from each side, not add; $r = 12.6 - (-0.8)$; $r = 13.4$
35. $x + 100 + 120 + 100 = 360$; $x = 40$
37. C; Multiplying the number of eggs in each carton by the number of cartons will give the total number of eggs; 9 cartons.
39. $24.76s = 50$; 2.02 yd/sec
41. $-5 = 20 - T$; 25°F
43. no; 12 cans cost $8.64 \div 0.80 = \$10.80$ and $\$10.80 > \$10$.
45. $B = 12\pi \text{ in.}^2$
47. $B = 9\pi \text{ m}^2$
49. a. 5; 10
b. -2; 9
51. 71; Because $\frac{1}{6}$ of the girls is 6, there are 36 girls. Because $\frac{2}{7}$ of the boys is 10, there are 35 boys; $36 + 35 = 71$
53. $x = -\frac{7}{b}$; $b < 0$
55. $x = -6.5c$; $c < 0$
57. a. 132 hits
b. no; Player B has $132 - 33 = 99$ hits. $\frac{99}{x} = 0.296$, $x \approx 334$ at-bats, and $334 < 446$

1.1 Review & Refresh

59. $\frac{4}{15}$
60. $1\frac{5}{12}$
61. $\frac{5}{6}$
62. $3\frac{2}{21}$
63. 7
64. 150, 2, $\frac{1}{4}$; $50:\frac{1}{2}$, $150:\frac{3}{2}$, $200:2$, $25:\frac{1}{4}$
65. $-3.6x - 10$
66. $-24m + 28$
67. $2y + 4$
68. 9 arrangements
69. $0.\overline{7}$, $77.\overline{7}\%$
70. $10.99 + 1.5n$; \$15.49
71. $4x + 5$
72. $x = -12$; Subtract 7 from each side.
73. $b = -27$; Multiply each side by -9.
74. $t = 2.5$; Divide each side by -1.8.
75. $w = -\frac{7}{12}$; Add $\frac{1}{4}$ to each side.
76. 3.2

1.2 Practice

1. $w = 4$
3. $q = 1$
5. $z = -32$
7. $h = 4$
9. $v = 3$
11. $y = 0.5$
13. 6 min
15. $z = 3$
17. $m = 3$
19. $x = -\frac{27}{2}$
21. $c = 5.5$
23. $2n + 13 = 75$; $n = 31$
25. $8 + \frac{n}{3} = -2$; $n = -30$
27. $6(n + 15) = -42$; $n = -22$
29. $x = 125$; 120°, 100°, 120°, 135°, 120°, 125°
31. When using the Distributive Property in the second step, the second term should be positive; $-14 + 2y + 4 = -4$; $-10 + 2y = -4$; $2y = 6$; $y = 3$
33. $30(8.75) + 11t = 400$; 12.5 h
35. 3.6 MB
37. 30 in. by 45 in.
39. Add 1 to each side; Multiply each side by -2; Add 8 to each side; Divide each side by 5.
41. $x = \frac{15}{16}$; *Sample answer:* Distributive Property; There are no fractions until the last step.
43. 6 tickets
45. $x = \frac{12.5 + b}{a}$; $a > b + 12.5$
47. $x = -\frac{8}{b}$; $b > 0$
49. 16, 18, 20; The next consecutive even integers after $2n$ are $2n + 2$ and $2n + 4$. Solve the equation $2n + (2n + 2) + (2n + 4) = 54$. Then substitute the solution into the expressions for the integers.

1.2 Review & Refresh

51. 0.765
52. $\frac{1}{2}$
53. 27.4
54. $-\frac{11}{4}$
55. 77.6 times
56. 49%, 0.5, $\frac{11}{20}$
57. 30 m; 54 m^2
58. $n = \frac{15}{2}$
59. $x = -2$
60. $z = 12.4$
61. $r = \frac{4}{3}$
62. $p = 4$
63. $A'(-2, 1), B'(0, 3), C'(1, -1)$
64. $162.50
65. $8(3x + 4)$

1.3 Practice

1. $x = 5$
3. $p = \frac{52}{5}$
5. yes
7. *Sample answer:* School A has fewer students per teacher. School B has more support staff per teacher.
9. 5
11. 1.21, 1.22, or 1.24
13. 0.47
15. roller coaster B
17. $3.28 \frac{\text{m}}{\text{ft}}$ should be $\frac{1 \text{ m}}{3.28 \text{ ft}}$; 106.71 cm
19. no; *Sample answer:* One meter is longer than one yard, so the number of yards would be greater than the number of meters.
21. no; $\left(\frac{1 \text{ yd}}{36 \text{ in.}}\right)^2 = \frac{1 \text{ yd}^2}{1296 \text{ in.}^2}$,

$3240 \text{ in.}^2 \times \frac{1 \text{ yd}^2}{1296 \text{ in.}^2} = 2.5 \text{ yd}^2 < 3 \text{ yd}^2$

23. *Sample answer:* 100 people; The distance between two people standing in a line is about 2 feet.
25. **a–c.** Answers will vary.

1.3 Review & Refresh

26. 18 m^2
27. 105 cm^2
28. 100π in.^{2}
29. $m = 8$
30. $a = -0.6$
31. $x = 14$
32. increase; 50%
33. decrease; 25%
34. 7.55, 7.58, 7.6, or 7.69
35. 720, 724.48, 727.27, or 731.43
36. 10 sec
37. $\frac{27}{50}$, or 54%

1.4 Practice

1. 30 in.^{3}
3. $27,000
5. 10 bags
7. D
9. 1.01 lb
11. *Sample answer:* To obtain accurate measurements, the unit of measure used should be decided based on the size of the object.
13. **a.** Ultra: 3.8 fl oz, Regular: 6.8 fl oz, Concentrated: 10.0 fl oz; *Sample answer:* Because the concentration is measured to the nearest tenth of a percent, the same level of accuracy was used.

b. regular; concentrated;
Ultra: $2.49/3.8 \approx \$0.66$ per fl oz,
Regular: $3.99/6.8 \approx \$0.59$ per fl oz,
Concentrated: $\$6.99/10.0 \approx \$0.70$ per fl oz

1.4 Review & Refresh

14. 9.64×10^7
15. 3.5×10^{-4}
16. 44
17. $3n + 12 = 45; n = 11$
18. $9 - \frac{n}{7} = -5; n = 98$
19. 580 trips
20. $z = 1.8$
21. $t = \frac{2}{7}$
22. 30 mi/h; about 5.2 mi/h, or about 8.4 km/h
23.

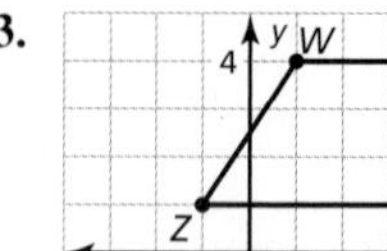

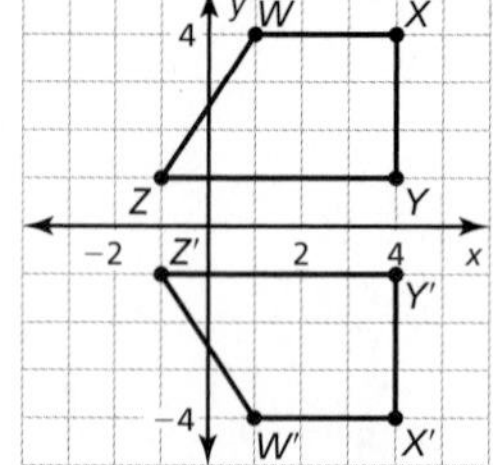

$W'(1, -4), X'(4, -4), Y'(4, -1), Z'(-1, -1)$

1.5 Practice

1. $x = 3$
3. $p = 7$
5. $t = -1$
7. $x = \frac{1}{2}$
9. $g = -4$
11. $x = -3$
13. $y = 1.2$
15. no solution
17. $h = 3$
19. $w = \frac{1}{4}$
21. all real numbers
23. 2 h
25. 4 sec
27. **a.** 3 h; The cost at Studio A is $10.49 + 8h$ and the cost at Studio B is $14.99 + 6.5h$. To find when the costs are the same, set these two expressions equal and solve for the time.

b. The costs will never be the same; *Sample answer:* The cost for Studio B changes to $14.99 + 8h$, and the new equation has no solution.

29. $a = 5$; Both sides simplify to $10x + 15$.
31. 11, 12
33. no solution; 5 more than a number will never be equal to 5 less than the same number.
35. C, D

1.5 Review & Refresh

37. 8.0 cm^2
38. $v = 5$
39. $k = -9$
40. $x = -\frac{3}{5}$
41. $n = 31.5$
42. $t = -2$
43. $c = \frac{1}{3}$
44. 27 yd^2
45. 48 words per minute
46. $-|21|, -16, |-10|, 22, |-32|$
47. 140 ft

1.6 Practice

1. 9
3. 0
5. −35
7. 9
9. no solution
11. $m = -10, m = 4$

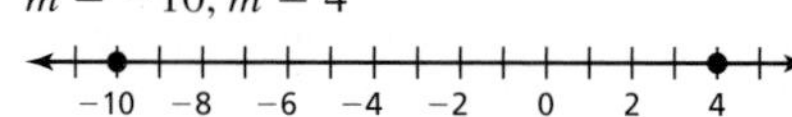

13. $t = -12, t = 12$

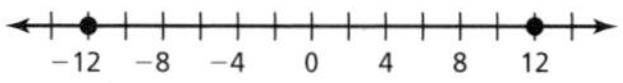

15. $b = -3.5, b = 6$

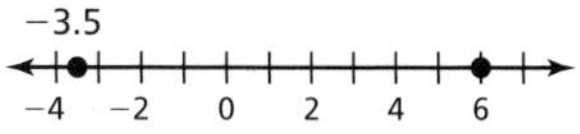

17. $w = -4, w = 5.5$

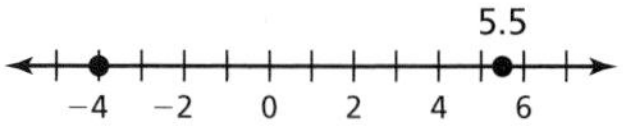

19. no solution

21. $s = 20$

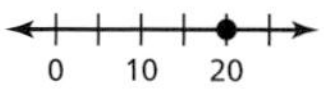

23. $|d - 92.95| = 1.55$; 91.4 million mi, 94.5 million mi

25. B

27. C

29. $n = 3, n = 5$

31. $k = -0.4, k = 6$

33. $p = \frac{2}{3}, p = 10$

35. $h = 0.25$

37. $f = \frac{7}{12}$

39. $|x - 13| = 5$

41. $|x - 5| = 3.5$

43. The absolute value cannot be negative. So, there is no solution.

45. **a.** the distance the car travels after t seconds

b. 5 sec, 7.5 sec

47. no; The absolute value has to be isolated first, which makes the constant on the right positive.

49. always; Square roots of the same number have the same absolute value.

51. sometimes; The equation will only have two solutions if p is positive.

53. Absolute value equations will have no solution when the absolute value is equal to a negative number, one solution when the absolute value is equal to zero, and two solutions when the absolute value is equal to a positive number; *Sample answer:* $|x + 12| = -2$ has no solution, $|x + 12| = 0$ has one solution, and $|x + 12| = 2$ has two solutions.

55. A, E

57. *Sample answer:* In a round of a trivia game, you lose 5 points for an incorrect answer and win 5 points for a correct answer. You have 67 points. x represents your score after your next answer.

59. $|x - 84.5| = 14.5$

1.6 Review & Refresh

61. $c = 0$

62. no solution

63. all real numbers

64. $y = -3$

65. 300 sections

66. $13h + 8.5$

67. 0.00000007

68. 2590

69. 2144.7 cm^3

70. 1900.7 ft^3

71. Addition Property of Equality

72. Division Property of Equality

73. 6 in.

74. 12 ft

75. 27 min, 33 min

76. $2\frac{3}{4}$

77. 8000

78. 10,849.06, or 10,925

79. 1.61, 1.63, or 1.65

1.7 Practice

1. $y = 13 + 3x$

3. $y = -13 + 9x$

5. $y = 9x - 45$

7. $y = x - 3$

9. $y = 18x + 12$

11. $x = \frac{1}{12}y$

13. $x = \frac{a}{2 + 6z}$

15. $x = \frac{y - 6}{4 + r}$

17. $x = \frac{r}{s + t}$

19. $x = \frac{y - 12}{-5 - 4k}$

21. **a.** $x = \frac{C - 60}{85}$

b. 3 trips; 5 trips

23. The equation is not solved for x because there is still a term with x on both sides; $x = y - x + 6$; $2x = y + 6$; $x = \frac{y + 6}{2}$

25. $C = R - P$

27. $b_2 = \frac{2A}{h} - b_1$

29. $C = A\left(\frac{R}{5} + 0.3\right)$

31. **a.** $r = \frac{L - S}{L}$

b. 20%

33. no; 70°F is about 21.1°C, which is greater than 20°C.

35. 2.5 h; 2.3 h; $\frac{d}{460}$ represents the original trip time, and $\frac{d}{500}$ represents the return trip time. Add these expressions and solve for the one-way distance. Substituting the distance into each of the expressions gives the time for each flight.

37. **a.** $d = 55t$; $d = 20g$

b. $55t = 20g$; $g = \frac{11t}{4}$

c. 16.5 gal; 330 mi; The amount of gasoline used can be found using the formula from part (b). Either of the original formulas can be used to find the distance.

39. $a = \frac{b + c}{bx - 1}$

41. **a.** 1.1 ft; 1.3 ft; 1.4 ft

b. *Sample answer:* It is easier to find the radius when the circumference formula is rewritten for r.

43. $A = \frac{5}{2}bh$; $h = \frac{2A}{5b}$

1.7 Review & Refresh

45. 37

46. 14

47. $\frac{7}{4}$

48. 93

49. $y = 6x - 12$

50. 90π in.^{2}

51. no

52. **a.** $h = \frac{231G}{\ell w}$

b. about 16 in.

53. $x = 8, x = -2$

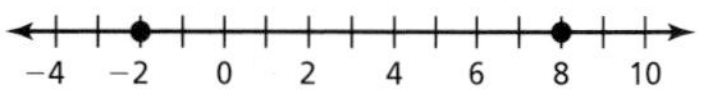

54. $y = 1, y = 7$

55. no solution

56. $s = -15; s = -3$

57. yes

58. 3 h

59. $z = 30$

60. $t = -3$

61. $y = -\frac{3}{2}$

Chapter 1 Review

1. $z = -9$; Subtract 3 from each side.

2. $t = -13$; Divide each side by -0.2.

3. $n = 10$; Multiply each side by -5.

4. $y = 8.6$; Add 2.7 to each side.

5. $b = -\dfrac{1}{9\pi}$; Divide each side by π.

6. $w = 1\frac{1}{2}$; Subtract each side by $1\frac{4}{5}$.

7. Subtraction Property of Equality; Because a and b are negative numbers, $\dfrac{a}{b}$ is positive and the inverse operation is subtraction.

8. \$25.95

9. $y = -9$

10. $b = -5$

11. $n = 6$

12. $z = -5$

13. $x = 18$

14. $w = \frac{25}{4}$

15. decreases; The equation can be rewritten as $x = 7b$, so when the value of b decreases, the value of $7b$ also decreases.

16. 23, 25, 27

17. $d = 4$

18. $m = 4$

19. $b = 32$

20. 7647.5 m, or 7661.29 m

21. *Sample answer:* Concert A had more merchandise sales per person that attended. Concert B had more social media posts per ticket sold.

22. 24 in.^{2}

23. 150 people

24. $n = -4$

25. $y = 9$

26. all real numbers

27. no solution

28. 2475 mi

29. **a.** sometimes

b. sometimes

c. always

30. $y = 14, y = -20$

31. $k = 12, k = -6$

32. $g = \frac{5}{2}$

33. no solution

34. $w = 3, w = -\frac{1}{5}$

35. $x = -1$

36. $|v - 84.5| = 10.5$

37. $y = \frac{1}{2}x - 5$

38. $y = 2x - 2$

39. $y = -\frac{5}{2}x$

40. $y = \dfrac{a}{9 + 3x}$

41. **a.** $K = \frac{5}{9}(F - 32) + 273.15$

b. 355.37 K

Chapter 1 Mathematical Practices (Chapter Review)

1. The two equations were written in terms of the distance d, so you can use substitution to equate the equations.

2. no; By the Multiplication Property of Equality, each term of Equation 2 should be multiplied by 4, not just the variable terms.

3. *Sample answer:* Use the Addition and Subtraction Properties of Equality to rewrite the equation with the variable terms and constant terms on different sides of the equation. Then use the Multiplication and Division Properties of Equality to isolate the given variable.

Chapter 1 Practice Test

1. $x = 22$

2. $x = -3$

3. $x = -3, x = 9$

4. $x = 3$

5. all real numbers

6. no solution

7. $c \neq 5$; If c is 5, then the equation is an identity. For all other values of c, subtracting $3x$ from each side will give a statement that is always false.

8. $c < 0$; An absolute value cannot be negative.

9. $|h - 34| = 4$

10. skateboard

11. **a.** $w = \dfrac{P - 2\ell}{2}$

b. 65 yd

c. 4.8%

12. **a.** 2.1 h; The cost at the dealership is $24 + 99t$ and the cost at the local mechanic is $45 + 89t$. Set these two expressions equal and solve for the time.

b. time is less than 2.1 h; time is greater than 2.1 h; Because the expressions are equal for 2.1 hours, that is the cutoff point from the dealership being less expensive to the local mechanic being less expensive.

13. 8.3 min

14. It will give a negative value on the right and absolute value cannot be negative.

Chapter 1 College and Career Readiness

1. D

2. B

3. 18 beginner, 15 intermediate, 15 expert

4. **a.** $<$

b. $<$

c. $>$

d. $<$

e. $=$

f. $=$

5. $8x + 6 = -2x - 14$ and $5x + 3 = -7$

6. **a.** $24x + 28(5 - x) = 132$ or $24(5 - x) + 28x = 132$

b. \$4; *Sample answer:* Switching gives a total cost of \$128, which is \$4 less than \$132.

7. A

8. yes; Because the expenses are equal for month 11, any time after that satellite TV will be less expensive.

9. B

10. no solution: $12x - 2x = 10x - 8$, $0 = |x + 13| + 2$, $3x - 12 = 3(x - 4) + 1$

one solution: $|8x + 3| = 0$, $-2x + 4 = 2x + 4$, $-6 = 5x - 9$

two solutions: $9 = 3|2x - 11|$

infinitely many solutions: $-4(x + 4) = -4x - 16$, $7 - 2x = 3 - 2(x - 2)$

11. C

Chapter 2

Chapter 2 Prepare

1. 6

−8 −4 0 4 8

2. −5

−6 −4 −2 0 2 4 6

3. $-\frac{1}{4}$

−1 $-\frac{1}{2}$ 0 $\frac{1}{2}$ 1

4. −4 −2 0 2 4

5. 1

−4 −2 0 2 4

6. −2.2

−2.4 −1.6 −0.8 0 0.8 1.6 2.4

7. $<$ **8.** $<$

9. $>$ **10.** $>$

11. $=$ **12.** $<$

13. $-b < -a$

2.1 Practice

1. $x > 3$ **3.** $15 \leq \frac{t}{5}$

5. $v + 6.2 \geq -4.7$ **7.** $3k - \frac{5}{3} \leq \frac{4}{9}$

9. no **11.** yes

13. yes **15.** yes

17. yes

19. $\ell < 4800$

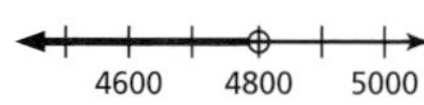

21. *Sample answer:* You ride your bike 12 miles each day for x days, and you ride at least 60 miles.

23. −2 0 2 4

25. −1

−4 −2 0 2

27. −5.4 −5.2 −5.0 −4.8 −4.6 −4.4

29. $\frac{1}{4}$

$-\frac{1}{2}$ 0 $\frac{1}{2}$ 1 $1\frac{1}{2}$

31. The arrow should point to the left.

−3

−6 −4 −2 0 2

33. $x < 7$

7

0 2 4 6 8 10

35. $1.3 \leq z$ **37.** $k \leq \frac{9}{5}$

1.3

1.0 1.2 1.4 1.6

1 $\frac{7}{5}$ $\frac{9}{5}$ $\frac{11}{5}$

39. $x \leq 4$

41. $m \geq 9.25$; The state requires that employees earn at least \$9.25 per hour.

43. C; The temperature must be at least 2°F warmer, so the increase is represented by $x \geq 2$.

45. Because $Y < X$, $2Y < X + Y$; not true

47. Because $X > Y$, $\frac{Y}{X+Y} < 1$ and $\frac{X}{Y} > 1$, so $\frac{Y}{X+Y} < \frac{X}{Y}$; true

49. $\leq$ **51.** $x < 3$

53. yes; You ride the bus about $2 \times 5 \times 4 = 40$ times per month and spend $40(1.65) = \$66 > \$52$.

55. a. $r > 5.71$

5.71

5.68 5.70 5.72 5.74

b. The graph includes speeds that are faster than a runner can run.

c. *Sample answer:* $r > 5.71$ and $r < 10$

2.1 Review & Refresh

56. $x = 1$ **57.** $y = -1$

58. $z = 8$ **59.** $w = 4$

60. $v = 3$ **61.** $s = -8$

62. not similar

63. *Sample answer:* (a) $5x - 3 = 7$ (b) $2(2x - 3) = 4x - 8$ (c) $2x + 6 = 2(x + 3)$

64. $a = -6, a = 9$ **65.** no solution

66. $g = 4$ **67.** $h = -1$

68. \$118.75 **69.** 5.25

70. 3600 **71.** $x = \frac{v}{yz}$

72. $x = \frac{s - 2r}{3}$ **73.** $x = \frac{w - 2}{3}$

74. $x = n - \frac{1}{2}$ **75.** laser measure 1

76.

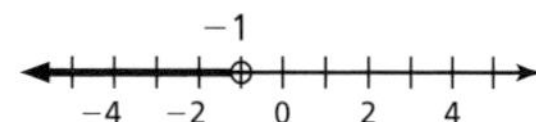

77. 1

0 2 4 6

78. a. $h < 107.1$

b. no; A height of 9 feet is equal to 108 inches, which is not less than 107.1 inches.

79. 24, 18, 36; 12 : 3, 24 : 6, 72 : 18, 36 : 9

80. $8 \leq z$ **81.** $p - 1 > 6$

2.2 Practice

1. $x < -1$

−1

−4 −2 0 2 4

3. $m \leq 7$

7

0 2 4 6 8 10

5. $r < 1$

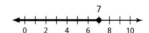

1

−4 −2 0 2 4

7. $w > -2$

−4 −2 0 2 4

9. $h \geq 8$

8

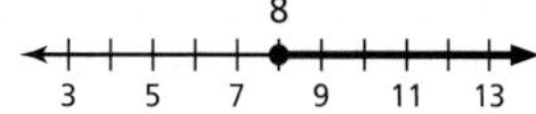

SELECTED ANSWERS

11. $j < -3.8$

−4.4 −4.2 −4.0 −3.8 −3.6

13. $p \le -\frac{2}{5}$

$-\frac{4}{5}$ $-\frac{3}{5}$ $-\frac{2}{5}$ $-\frac{1}{5}$ 0

15. $n + 8 > 11; n > 3$

17. $n - 9 < 4; n < 13$

19. more than 33 goals

21. 10 should have been added to each side of the inequality, not just the left.

$$-10 + x \ge -9$$
$$-10 + 10 + x \ge -9 + 10$$
$$x \ge 1$$

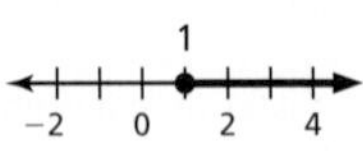

23. hair dryer and souvenir, or souvenir and boots

25. $14.2 + 14.2 + x < 51.3; x < 22.9$

27. **a.** score greater than 117.4 points

b. they both are; Both scores are greater than 117.4 points.

29. **a.** $x \ge 6$

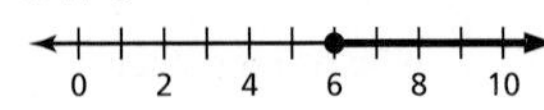

b. $x < 17.7$

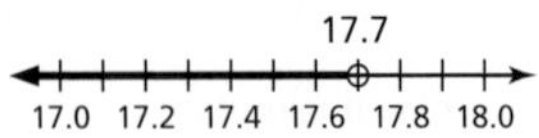

31. A; Subtract 3 from each side; D; order of inequality reverses for opposites

33. *Sample answer:* $x + 33.2 \le 50$; A shelf can safely support up to 50 pounds. The combined weight of items on the shelf is 33.2 pounds. x represents the possible weights of items that can be put on the shelf safely.

2.2 Review & Refresh

34. −63

35. 132

36. 9

37. −4

38. $y = 6$

39. $n = -29.2$

40. $x \ge 16$; You must be 16 years or older to obtain a driver's license.

41. $x = -\frac{8}{5}, x = 12$

42. $a < -10$

43. $\frac{3}{7}$, or 42.9%

44. $w \le -5$

−5
−8 −6 −4 −2 0

45. $x > 2.7$

2.5 2.7 2.9 3.1 3.3

46. 2 h 30 min there, 2 h 45 min back

47. 11

48. $-\frac{2}{9}$

2.3 Practice

1. $y \le -3$

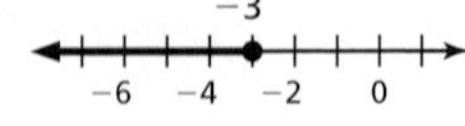

3. $c \le 5$

5
0 2 4 6 8

5. $n \ge -2$

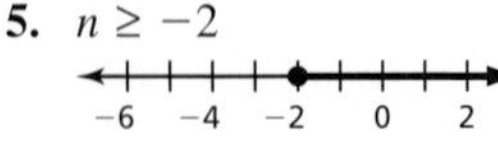

7. $t > 4$

0 2 4 6 8

9. $x > -4$

−6 −4 −2 0 2

11. $t \ge -6$

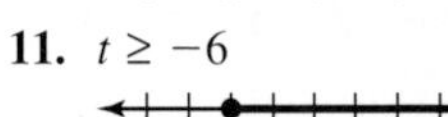

13. $w \le \frac{55}{2}$

$\frac{55}{2}$
25 26 27 28 29

15. $n \le -2.25$

−2.25
−3.5 −3.0 −2.5 −2.0 −1.5

17. 4.5 h

19. The inequality should not be reversed when multiplying each side by $\frac{3}{2}$; $\frac{3}{2} \cdot (-6) > \frac{3}{2} \cdot \frac{2}{3}x$; $-\frac{18}{2} > x$; $-9 > x$; $x < -9$; The solution is $x < -9$.

21. $y > 12$

23. $n > -16$

25. more than 50 million bills

27. **a.** at least 2000 glass bottles

b. at least 1000 plastic bottles

c. $0.05g + 0.10p \ge 100$

29. no; The distance you run in 4 hours would be no more than 25.2 miles, which is less than the distance required for a marathon.

31. Because x may represent a positive or negative number, the inequality may need to be reversed when multiplying by x.

33. less than 13.5 mi

2.3 Review & Refresh

35. $x = 2$

36. $y = -4$

37. no solution

38. $x = -3$

39. $x = 5.5$

40. 2.5 years

41. $d > -4.5$

42. $c \le 21$

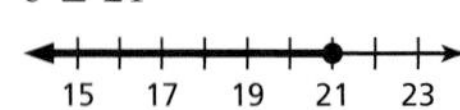

43. $2^3 \cdot 3^2$

44. 85%

45. 25%

46. 120%

47. $\frac{2}{3}$

48. at most $8.01

49. $A'(-1, -4), B'(-3, -1), C'(4, -1), D'(3, -4)$

50. 24, 25

51.

−4 −2 0 2 4

52.

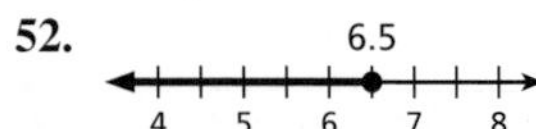

53.

$\frac{3}{8}$
0 $\frac{1}{4}$ $\frac{1}{2}$ $\frac{3}{4}$ 1

54.

55. **a.** $\frac{1}{20}$, or 5%

b. $\frac{9}{20}$, or 45%

c. $\frac{1}{4}$, or 25%

2.4 Practice

1. $x > 5$

5
0 2 4 6 8

3. $v \le \frac{1}{2}$

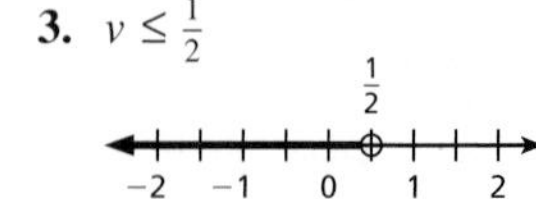

5. $w > 2$

−4 −2 0 2 4

7. $p < -16$

−20 −18 −16 −14 −12

9. $a \ge -4.1$

−4.5 −4.3 −4.1 −3.9 −3.7 −3.5

11. $m > 3$

3
2 4 6 8 10

13. $d > -2$

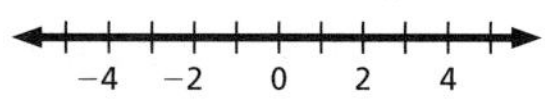

15. all real numbers

17. no solution

19. no solution

21. all real numbers

23. In the first step, you need to use the Distributive Property on the left side; $x + 24 \geq 12$; $x \geq -12$

25. at least 40 active min

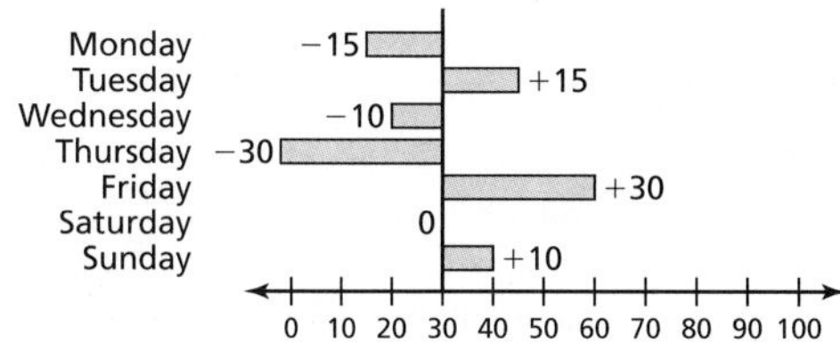

27. $x > 4$

29. $a = 4$

31. *Sample answer:* $-2, -4, -3$

33. 7 stories; Using the Pythagorean Theorem, the 74-foot ladder can reach at most 70 feet. Solving the inequality $10n - 8 \leq 70$ gives $n \leq 7.8$, so the ladder cannot quite reach the 8th story.

2.4 Review & Refresh

35. $y = -3x - 1$

36. $x = 8$

37. $n \geq -7$

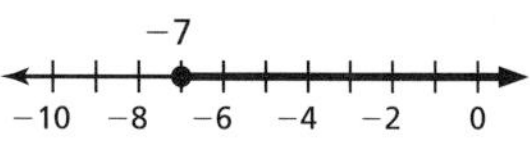

38. $b < -15.2$

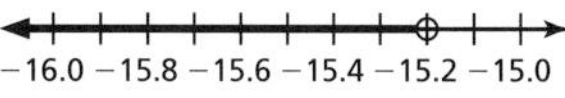

39. $x < -\frac{1}{7}$

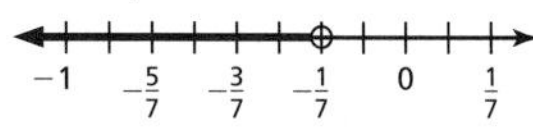

40. all real numbers

41. a. 3 months

b. The number of weeks is reduced; $20w + 50 \geq 229.95$, $w \geq 9$ weeks

42. yes

43. $6y \leq 10$

44. $p + 7 > 24.8$

45. $z = -1$

46. no solution

47. 25 students; 40%

2.5 Practice

1. $2 < p < 6$

3. $m > -7\frac{2}{3}$ *or* $m \leq -10$

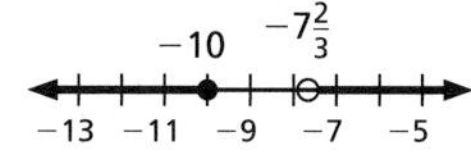

5. $1 < x \leq 6$

7. $v < -5$ *or* $v > 5$

9. $r < -\frac{5}{2}$ *or* $r \geq \frac{3}{8}$

11. $-10 < x < 5$

13. a. *Sample answer:* $1700 < h \leq 2500$

b. *Sample answer:* $4000 < h \leq 14{,}410$

15. $-4 \leq F \leq 5$

17. no solution

19. $y > 7$

21. all real numbers

23. $h < 50.4$ in. *or* $h > 74.0$ in., or $h < 50.9$ in. *or* $h > 74.7$ in.

25. $k = 8.5$

27. $7.3 + 5.5 > x$, $7.3 + x > 5.5$, $5.5 + x > 7.3$; no; $5.5 + 1.5 \not> 7.3$

2.5 Review & Refresh

29. $d = 54, d = -54$

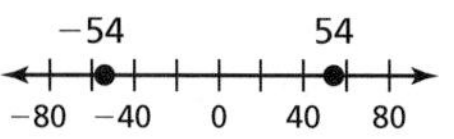

30. no solution

31. $r = -11.4, r = 7.4$

32. $w = -26, w = -\frac{2}{3}$

33. 2.8; The data values are clustered close together.

34. 5 quarters, 3 dimes, 6 nickels

35. $-3 < x \leq 2$

36. $x \leq \frac{1}{3}$ *or* $x > \frac{5}{3}$

37. 83% or higher

38. $q \leq 5.8$

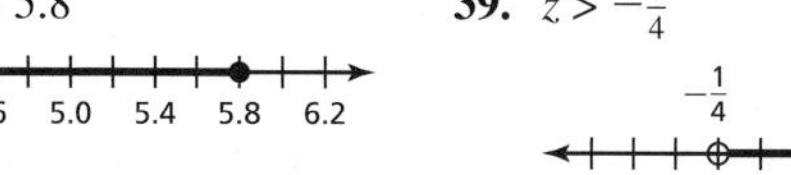

39. $z > -\frac{1}{4}$

40. $x \leq -9$

41. $x \geq \frac{3}{8}$

42. *Sample answer:* The probability of spinning a 4 is about $\frac{1}{6}$, so you can predict you will spin a 4 about $\frac{1}{6} \cdot 50 = 8\frac{1}{3}$, or about 8 times.

2.6 Practice

1. $-3 < x < 3$

3. $d < -12$ *or* $d > -6$

5. all real numbers

7. no solution

9. $t \leq -\frac{2}{3}$ *or* $t \geq 3$

11. $m > 20$ *or* $m < 8$

13. $-4 \leq w \leq -\frac{4}{3}$

15. $f < 12$ *or* $f > 12$

17. $|n| < 6$; $-6 < n < 6$

19. $|w - 500| \leq 30$; 470 to 530 words

21. The absolute value inequality should be written as a compound inequality; $-20 < x - 5 < 20$; $-15 < x < 25$

23. the gasket with a weight of 0.53 lb; $|0.6 - w| > 0.06$, $w < 0.54$ *or* $w > 0.66$

25. $\left|\frac{1}{2} \cdot 4(x + 6) - 2 \cdot 6\right| < 2$; $-1 < x < 1$

27. $d = 0.86$

29. true

31. false; It has to be a solution of $x + 3 \leq -8$ *or* $x + 3 \geq 8$.

33. no; If n is 0, the statement is false.

35. $6 < x < 7$; *Sample answer:* Solve each inequality, then draw a sketch of the 2 solutions on the same number line to see where they intersect.

2.6 Review & Refresh

36–39.

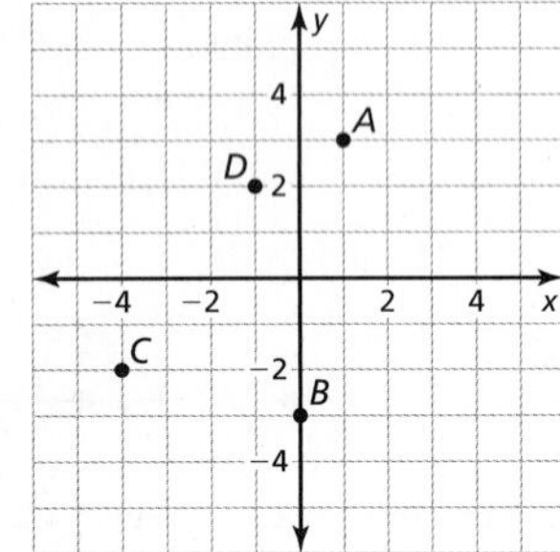

36. Quadrant I

37. y-axis

38. Quadrant III

39. Quadrant II

40. yes; Because the absolute value must be positive, all values will be greater than -6.

41. 1, 6, 11, 16, 21

42. $m = -\frac{3}{4}$

43. $x = -5, x = -2$

44. all real numbers

45. $x < -4$

46. $x > -7c$

47. $x \leq -\dfrac{10.5}{c}$

48. -6

49. $\frac{2}{5}$

50. you bike faster

51. $t \leq -18.5$

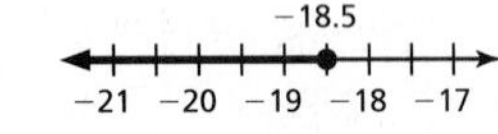

52. $x > -3$

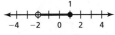

−3
−6 −4 −2 0 2

53. $-2 < y \leq 1$

1
−4 −2 0 2 4

54. $x < -4$ *or* $x > \frac{8}{3}$

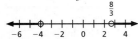

$\frac{8}{3}$
−6 −4 −2 0 2 4

55. $b \leq \frac{4}{3}$ *or* $b \geq 2$

$\frac{4}{3}$
0 1 2 3 4

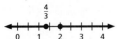

56. 81

57. -100

Chapter 2 Review

1. $d - 2 < -1$

2. $5h \leq 10$

3. no

4. yes

5. yes

6. 0 2 4 6 8

7. −4 −2 0 2 4

8. −1.5
−3 −2 −1 0

9. $\frac{2}{3}$
−1 0 1

10. $y > 2$

11. $y \leq -0.06$

12. a. $s \geq 100$

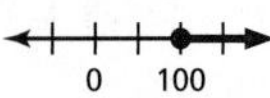

$t \geq 5$

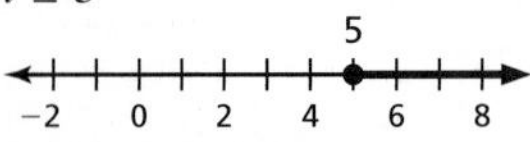

$u \geq 10$

0 10 20

b. no; One of the requirements is to swim 100 yards, which is equal to 300 feet. If you only swim 250 feet you do not meet this requirement.

13. sometimes; If $M > 0$ and $N > 0$, then $\frac{M}{N} > 1$ and $\frac{N}{M} < 1$, so $\frac{M}{N} > \frac{N}{M}$. If $M < 0$ and $N < 0$, then $\frac{M}{N} < 1$ and $\frac{N}{M} > 1$, so $\frac{M}{N} < \frac{N}{M}$.

14. $p < 6$

0 2 4 6 8

15. $r > -2$

−4 −2 0 2 4

16. $m \leq 8.8$

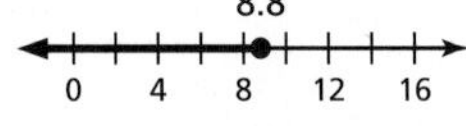

17. $x \leq -10.5$

−10.5
−13 −12 −11 −10

18. *Sample answer:* $-1 > b - \frac{1}{3}$

19. more than 1.18 m

20. $x > -7$

−7
−8 −6 −4 −2 0

21. $g \geq -20$

−20 −10 0 10

22. $n \geq -4$

−8 −6 −4 −2 0

23. $s \leq -88$

−88
−160 −120 −80 −40 0

24. $q > 18$

18
0 8 16 24 32

25. $k < -5$

−5
−8 −6 −4 −2 0

26. *Sample answer:* $3h \geq 9.75$

27. $x > 5$

5
0 2 4 6 8

28. $b > -26$

−26
−32 −24 −16 −8 0

29. $n \geq 2.25$

2.25
1.5 2.0 2.5 3.0 3.5

30. $s \leq \frac{14}{3}$

$\frac{14}{3}$
0 2 4 6 8

31. no solution

32. $r > 2.8$

2.6 2.8 3.0 3.2 3.4

33. 16 or more months

34. $-6 < x \leq 8$

−6
−8 −4 0 4 8

35. $-2 \leq z \leq 6$

−2 6
−8 −4 0 4 8

36. $p \leq 2$ *or* $p > 3$

3
0 2 4 6

37. $r < -20$ *or* $r \geq -5$

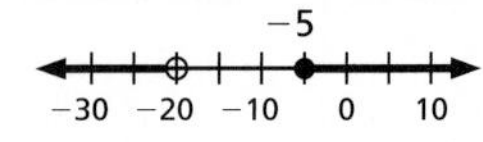

38. $-\frac{3}{2} < d \le 4$

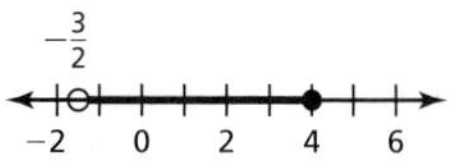

39. $8000 < x \le 8850$

40. $45 \le 1.61k \le 70$, $27.95 \le k \le 43.48$, or $45 \le \dfrac{k}{0.62} \le 70$, $27.9 \le k \le 43.4$

41. $m \ge 10$ *or* $m \le -10$

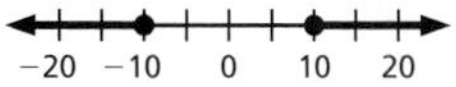

42. no solution

43. $-\frac{14}{3} < g < 2$

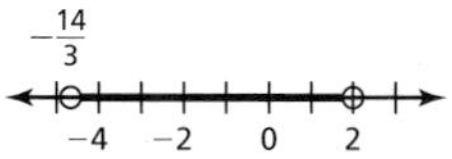

44. all real numbers

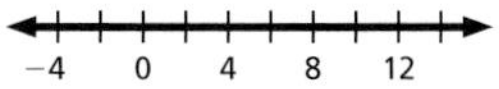

45. $|h - 106| \le 7$; 99 cm to 113 cm

Chapter 2 Mathematical Practices (Chapter Review)

1. The temperature needs to increase at least two degrees, so the graph should start at 2 and point to the right.
2. *Sample answer:* If the right side is equivalent to the left side, then the inequality would have no solution. So, the expression on the right was written to be equivalent to the left side.
3. It is a compound inequality using "and" and the graph has 2 endpoints with a line segment between the open or closed endpoints.

Chapter 2 Practice Test

1. $y + 9 \ge -1$
2. $|k - 10| < 3$
3. $m \le -7$

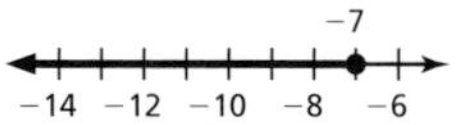

4. $x \ge -8$

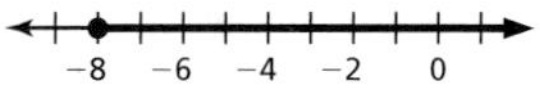

5. all real numbers

6. $-3 \le a \le 2$

7. $h < 9.5$ *or* $h > 11$

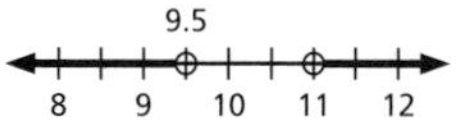

8. $\frac{1}{3} < b < 3$

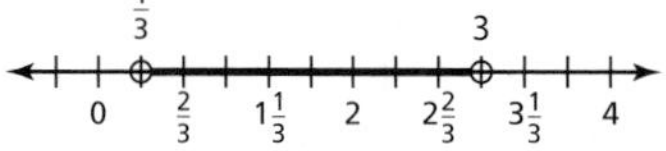

9. at least \$405
10. $|w - 0.3| \le 0.0003$; between 0.2997 in. and 0.3003 in.
11. $-3 < x \le 2$

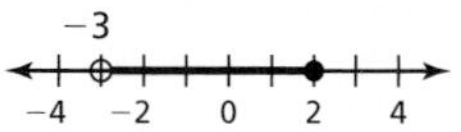

The values between −3 and 2, including 2, are not solutions.

12. scores greater than 6
13. $8.8t < 6.6t + 55$, $t < 25$ sec
14. **a.** 6.25%
    b. $175 + 1.0625(p - 175) \le 430$; $p \le 415$
    c. $1.05p < 175 + 1.0625(p - 175)$; $p > 875$; *Sample answers:* \$900, \$950, \$1000

Chapter 2 College and Career Readiness

1. A
2. **a.** −2
   b. 3; *Sample answer:* 10
   c. 3; *Sample answer:* 0
3. D
4. −2, −1, 0, 1
5. B, E
6. C
7. <; ≤
8. A
9. **a.** $160 + 12x \le 250$; no; 8 is not a solution of the inequality.
   b. the possible number of pairs of sneakers you can buy when you buy 5 pairs of socks
10. **a.** *Sample answer:* 1; 2; 3; 4
    b. *Sample answer:* 2; 3; 2; 4
    c. *Sample answer:* 6; 5; 6; 5

Chapter 3

Chapter 3 Prepare

1–6.

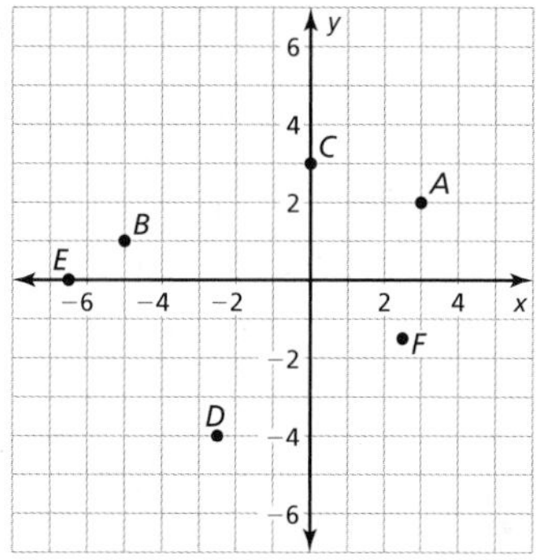

1. in Quadrant I
2. in Quadrant II
3. on positive y-axis
4. in Quadrant III
5. on negative x-axis
6. in Quadrant IV
7. 17
8. −7
9. 20
10. 34
11. 42
12. $\frac{15}{2}$
13. Start at the origin. Move a units right and b units up. Plot the point; Start at the origin. Move a units left and b units up. Plot the point; Start at the origin. Move a units right and b units down. Plot the point; Start at the origin. Move a units left and b units down. Plot the point.

3.1 Practice

1. function; Every input has exactly one output.
3. not a function; The input 2 has two outputs, 3 and 2.
5. not a function; The input 16 has two outputs, −2 and 2, and the input 1 has two outputs, −1 and 1.
7. function; No vertical line can be drawn through more than one point on the graph.
9. not a function; A vertical line can be drawn through more than one point on the graph in many places, such as (4, 0) and (4, 6).
11. domain: −2, −1, 0, 1, 2; range: −2, 0, 2
13. domain: $-4 \le x \le 2$; range: $2 \le y \le 6$

15. The amount of time is the dependent variable and the number of quarters is the independent variable.

17. a. yes; The total cost of the cell phone plan is the dependent variable and the number of cell phone lines is the independent variable.

b. domain: 1, 2, 3, 4; range: 30, 60, 90, 120

19. A function can have one output paired with two inputs, but cannot have one input paired with more than one output; The relation is a function. No input is paired with more than one output.

21. *Sample answer:* The balance of the savings account is \$100 in month 0 and increases by \$25 per month through month 4.

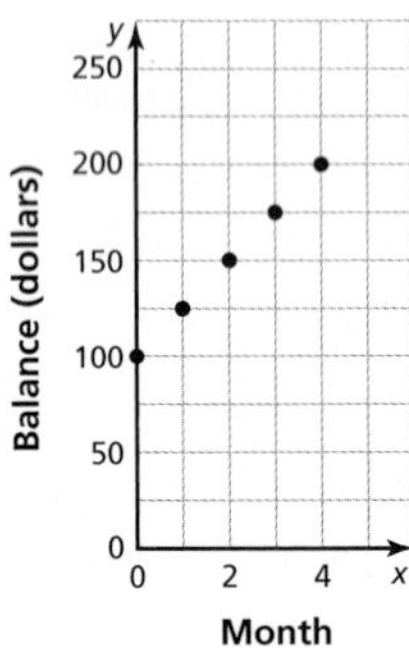

yes; No vertical line can be drawn through more than one point on the graph.

23. -2

25. no; A vertical line does not represent a function.

27. no; Items that cost the same to make could be sold for different prices.

29. yes; Each student has exactly one homeroom teacher.

31. true

33. false; More than one input can have the same output in a function, so reversing the values may not produce a function.

35. A, C, and D

37. domain: all real numbers; range: $y \geq 0$

39. domain: all real numbers; range: $y \geq -6$

41. domain: $3 < h < 23$; range: $26 < P < 46$

3.1 Review & Refresh

42. no

43. 21

44. 36%

45. $n = -2.1$

46. $x = 5$

47. $c = 7$

48. $h = -10$

49. function; Every input has exactly one output.

50. $7 \leq \dfrac{d}{-5}$

51. \$31.80

52. $z < -4$

53. $y \leq 5.5$

54. $x \geq -14$

55. $w > -3$

56. $t \leq 2$ *or* $t \geq 8$

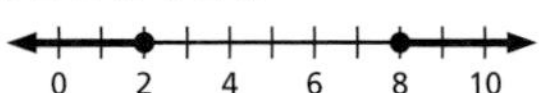

57. $-10 \leq m < -2$

58. domain: $-3 \leq x \leq 2$; range: $-2 \leq y \leq 1$

59. $a = -3$

60. $x < -1$ *or* $x \geq 2$

61. 12 points

62. $y = \frac{1}{2}x - 3$

63. 1278 ft^2

3.2 Practice

1. x-intercept: about -3, y-intercept: about 1

3. x-intercept: about 5, y-intercept: about -10

5. positive: $x < -2$; negative: $x > -2$; decreasing: for all real numbers; $y \to -\infty$ as $x \to +\infty$ and $y \to +\infty$ as $x \to -\infty$

7. positive: $1 < x < 5$, negative: $x < 1$ and $x > 5$, increasing: $x < 3$, decreasing: $x > 3$; $y \to -\infty$ as $x \to +\infty$ and $y \to -\infty$ as $x \to -\infty$

9. positive: $x > 2$, negative: $x < -1$ and $-1 < x < 2$, increasing: $x < -1$ and $x > 1$, decreasing: $-1 < x < 1$; $y \to +\infty$ as $x \to +\infty$ and $y \to -\infty$ as $x \to -\infty$

11. *Sample answer:*

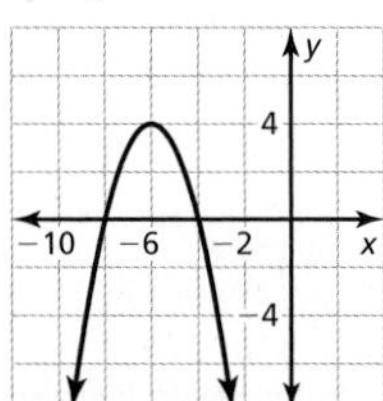

13. The initial speed of the blue car is 5 mi/h greater. The stopping time for the red car is about 1 second longer.

15. The function is not positive when $x = 3$; The function is positive when $x < 3$ and $x > 3$.

17. B and C

19. *Sample answer:*

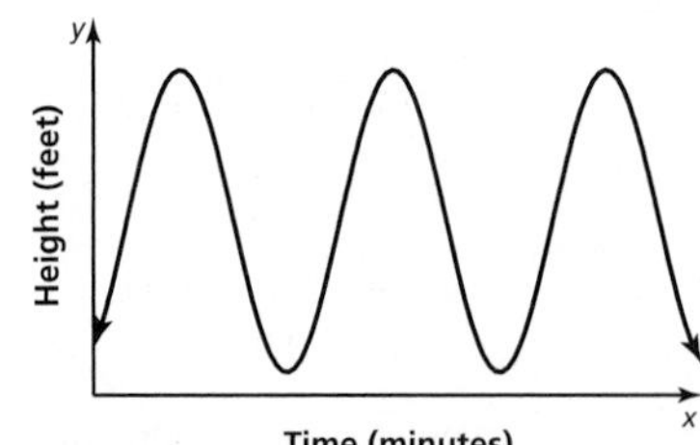

As time increases, your height will oscillate between the maximum height at the top of the Ferris wheel to the minimum height at the bottom of the Ferris wheel.

3.2 Review & Refresh

21. $-5 \leq n < -1$

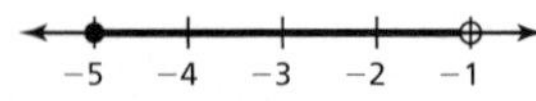

22. $k \leq -\frac{1}{2}$ *or* $k \geq 2\frac{1}{2}$

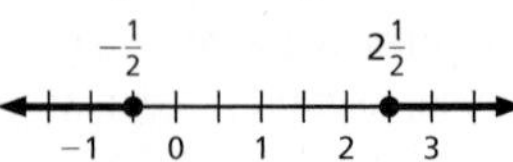

23. $b = -28$

24. $x = -5$

25. $t = \frac{1}{3}$

26. $m = -3$

27. coffee and muffin, coffee and bagel

28. 6

29. x-intercepts: about -3.5 and -1.5, y-intercept: about -3

30. $a > 4$

31. $r \geq -10$

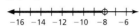

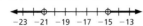

−12 −10 −8 −6 −4 −2

32. $x < -8$

−16 −14 −12 −10 −8 −6

33. $x < -21$ *or* $x > -15$

−23 −21 −19 −17 −15 −13

34. (a) *Sample answer:* (4, 3); Each input has exactly one output. (b) *Sample answer:* (2, 3); The input 2 has two outputs, 2 and 3.

3.3 Practice

1. nonlinear; The graph is not a line.

3. linear; The graph is a line.

5. nonlinear; The graph is not a line.

7. linear; As x increases by 1, y increases by 5. The rate of change is constant.

9. nonlinear; As x increases by 4, y decreases by different amounts. The rate of change is not constant.

11. The graph is not a line.

13. The increase in y needs to be done by adding or subtracting the same amount to be linear, not multiplying; As x increases by 2, y increases by different amounts. The rate of change is not constant. So, the function is nonlinear.

15. nonlinear; It cannot be rewritten in the form $y = mx + b$.

17. linear; It can be rewritten as $y = -1x + 2$.

19. linear; It can be rewritten as $y = 18x + 12$.

21. linear; It can be rewritten as $y = 9x - 13$.

23. A, C, F; None of these can be rewritten in the form $y = mx + b$.

25. 2, 4, 6; discrete; The graph consists of individual points.

27. continuous; The time can be any value greater that or equal to 0.

29. **a.** 10 represents the amount of money you can spend, $1.44p$ represents the cost of printing photographs, and 1.44 represents the price per photograph.

b. the set of all integers between 0 and 6; discrete; The number of photographs must be a whole number.

c.

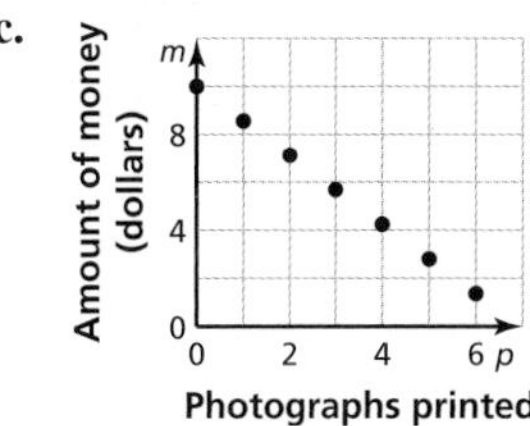

31. **a.** yes; As the number of minutes increase by 1, the number of gallons increase by 17. The rate of change is constant, so the situation represents a linear function.

b. $m \geq 0$; continuous; Because it is possible to have a portion of a minute, the number of minutes can be any value greater than or equal to 0.

c.

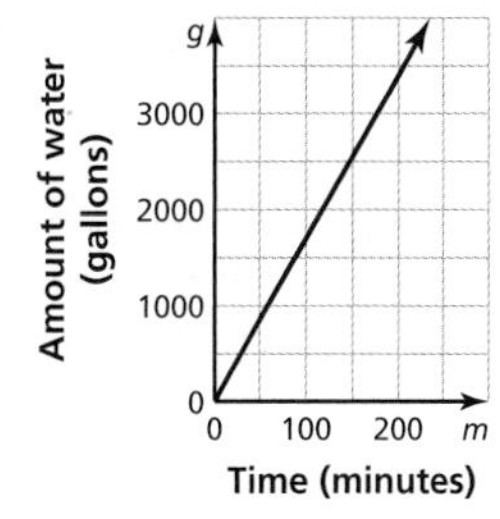

33. 2, 5, 8

35. linear; As x increases by 1, y increases by 4. The rate of change is constant.

37. *Sample answer:* The number of hours on a parking meter is a function of the number of tokens used. 4 tokens for 1 hour and a maximum time of 2 hours; discrete; The number of tokens used must be 0, 4, or 8.

39. **a.** \$10.20

b. domain: $0 \leq x \leq 18$; range: $0 \leq y \leq 183.60$

41. **a.** the total gallons of water in one jug of each type; continuous

b. the total number of jugs of both types; discrete

c. the total gallons of water in all the jugs of the first types; continuous

d. the total gallons of water in all the jugs of both types; continuous

43. Check students' work. Simple Tees when $x \leq 26$ and T-shirts Unlimited when $27 \leq x \leq 200$

45. no; A linear function can be constant.

47. The range is discrete because each value of the domain maps to exactly one value of the range; The range is discrete or continuous because each value of the domain maps to either certain values or all of the values in the range.

49. *Sample answer:* profit (or loss) on the sale of x units at \$1 each that cost \$0.75 to make, plus \$50 in fixed costs

3.3 Review & Refresh

50. $h = -13$

51. $y = 3$

52. $g = 4$

53. $w = -12, w = 6$

54. $\frac{6}{7}$

55. $8\frac{3}{4}$

56. 14

57. $\frac{2}{9}$

58. no; The graph does not pass through the origin.

59. $n + 12 \geq 35$

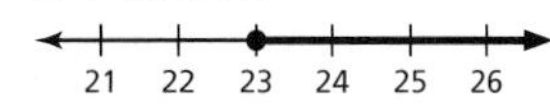

60. not a function

61. function

62. discrete; The number of stories must be a whole number.

63. *Sample answer:* $-5x \geq 25$

64. **a.** yes; Profit is the dependent variable, and the number of tickets sold is the independent variable.

b. domain: the set of integers between 0 and 9350; range: $0 \leq p \leq 560{,}532.50$; discrete; You cannot buy part of a ticket.

65. positive: $0.7 < x < 4.3$, negative: $x < 0.7$ and $x > 4.3$, increasing: $x < 2.5$, decreasing: $x > 2.5$; $y \to -\infty$ as $x \to +\infty$; $y \to -\infty$ as $x \to -\infty$

66. $-\frac{23}{2} \leq x < \frac{13}{2}$

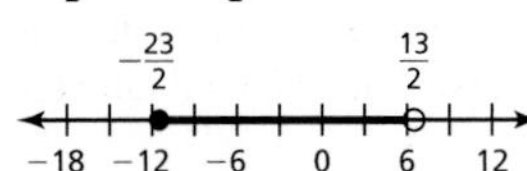

67. $q < -6$ *or* $q \geq 5$

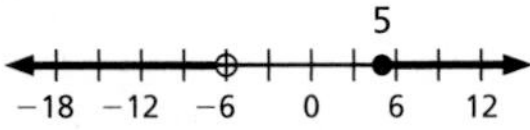

68. all real numbers

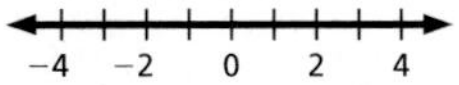

69. $0 \leq z \leq 3$

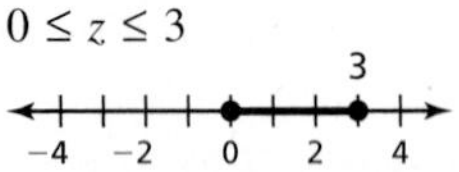

70. linear; The rate of change is constant.

71. 1.07×10^8 **72.** 2.0×10^{-6}

3.4 Practice

1. 4; 6; 11 **3.** 13; 9; −1

5. $-\frac{7}{2}$; −3; $-\frac{7}{4}$ **7.** 10.2; 6.2; −3.8

9. **a.** There are no customers in the restaurant at 8 A.M.

b. There are the same number of customers in the restaurant at 11 A.M. as there are at 4 P.M.

c. There are 29 customers in the restaurant *n* hours after 8 A.M.

d. There are fewer customers in the restaurant at 9:30 P.M. than there are at 8 P.M.

11. $x = -9$ **13.** $x = -2$

15. $x = -2$ **17.** $x = 5$

19. $77.50

21.

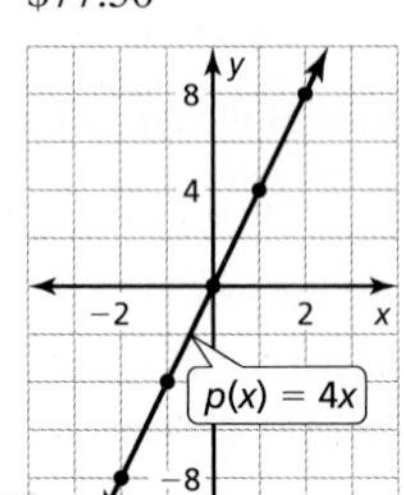

23.

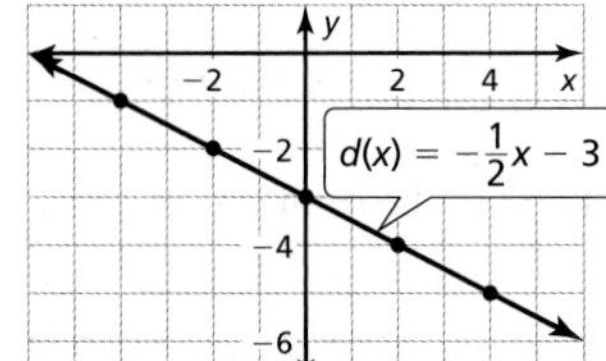

25.

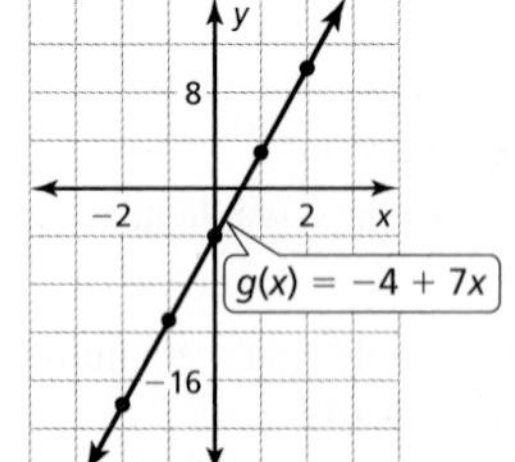

27. tablet; $f(x) = 0$ when $x = 6$ hours and $g(x) = 0$ when $x = 5$ hours.

29. **a.** (5, 9)

b. (5, −3)

31. **a.** the student's height at age 14; no; The units for height are not given.

b. The height of the student is 58 inches at age 15; The only reasonable units are inches.

33. false; The function could include operations that would not give the same result. For example, if $f(x) = x^2$, $f(3 + 4) \neq f(3) + f(4)$.

3.4 Review & Refresh

35. *Sample answer:*

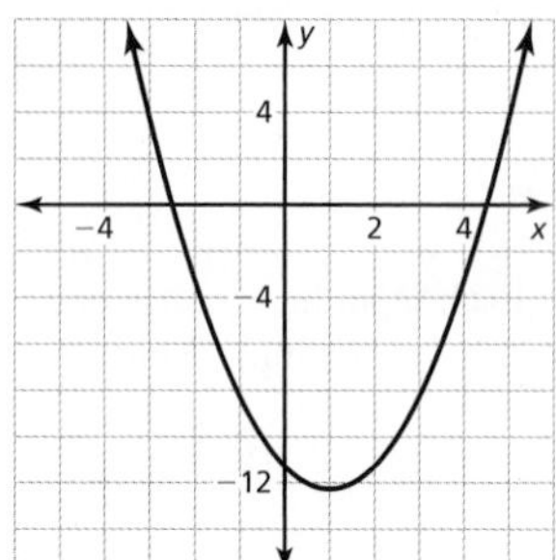

36. $a < -7$ *or* $a > 15$

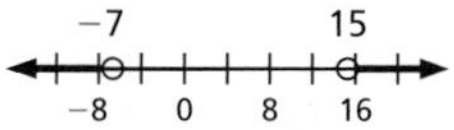

37. $-3 \leq k < -\frac{1}{3}$

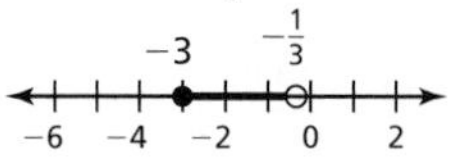

38. function; Each input has exactly one output.

39. $4n - 10.5 \geq -1.5$ **40.** $x = -4$

41. $x = \dfrac{m}{5 + 6y}$ **42.** $2.00

43. nonlinear; The graph is not a line.

44. −9 and −7 **45.** $1.\overline{27}$

46.

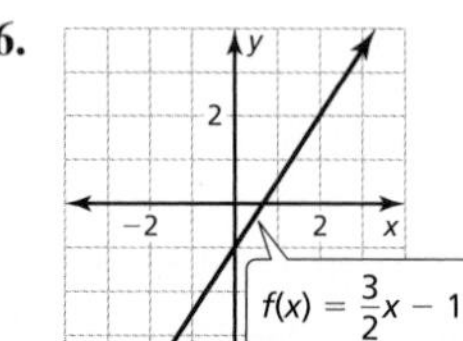

3.5 Practice

1.

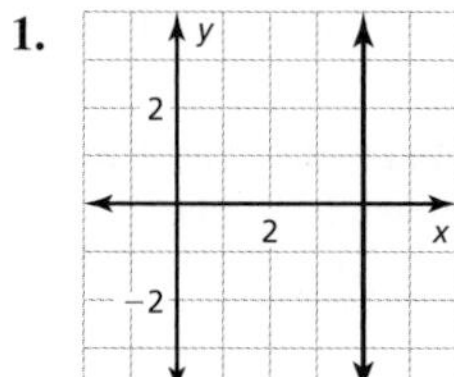

3.

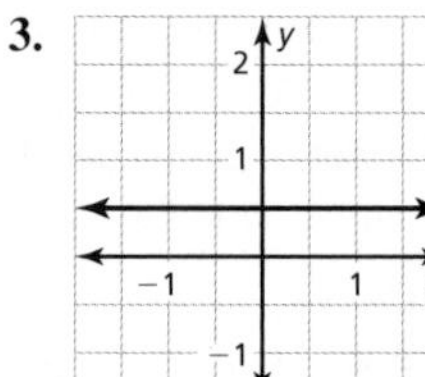

5. 6; 4 **7.** $\frac{2}{3}$; $-\frac{1}{3}$

9. 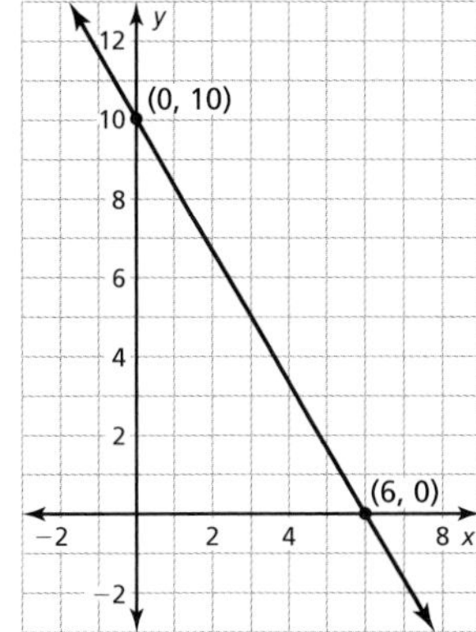

11. 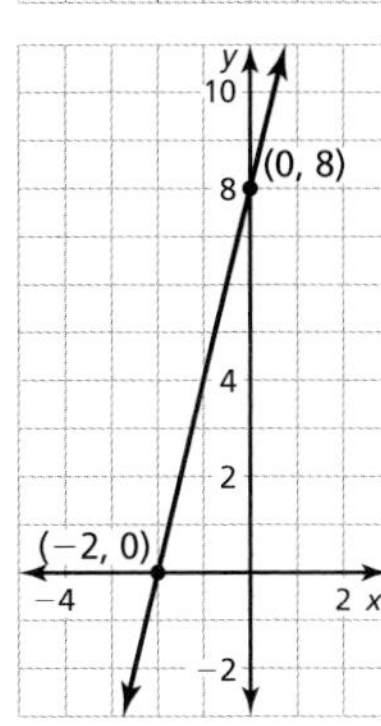

13. 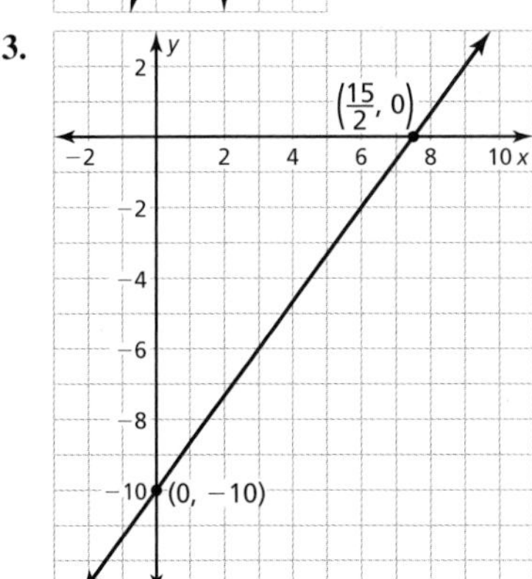

15. 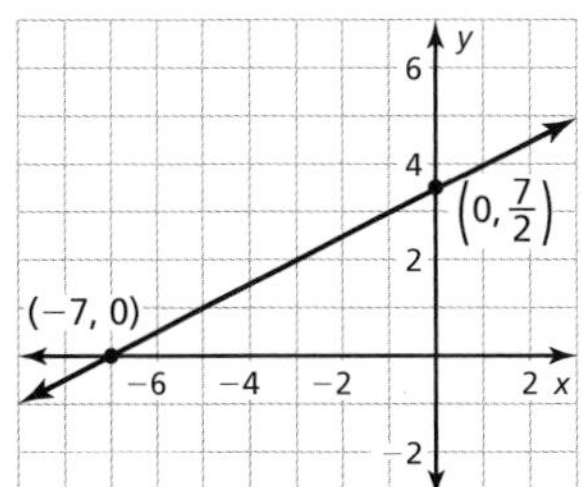

17. 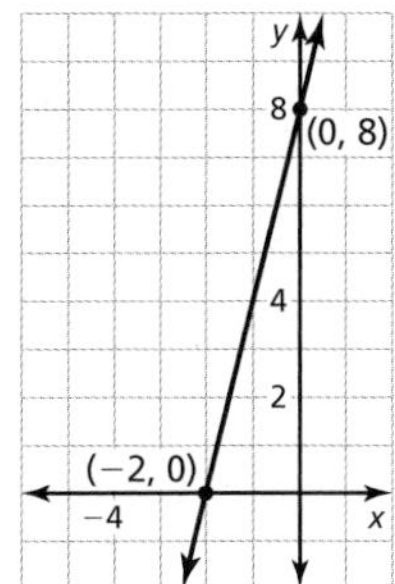

19. A

21. D

23. **a.** $10x$ represents the total cost of short-sleeved shirts at \$10 a shirt. $12y$ represents the total cost of long-sleeved shirts at \$12 a shirt. 300 represents the total amount you can spend on shirts.

b. 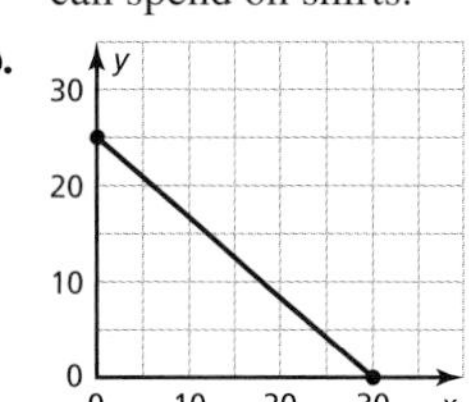

The x-intercept shows that you can buy 30 short-sleeved shirts and 0 long-sleeved shirts. The y-intercept shows that you can buy 25 long-sleeved shirts and 0 short-sleeved shirts.

c. 30 short-sleeved and 0 long-sleeved, 0 short-sleeved and 25 long-sleeved, 18 short-sleeved and 10 long-sleeved

25. The x- and y-intercepts are switched.

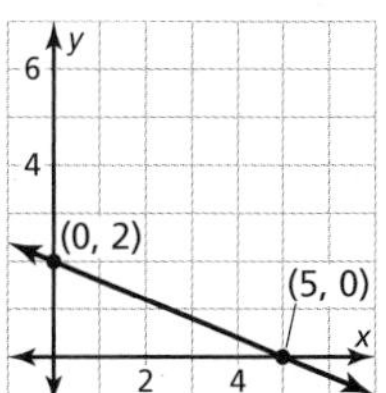

27. *Sample answer:* $x = -1, y = 5, x = 2, y = 1$

29. *Sample answer:* $x = 2, y = 1, y = -\frac{3}{2}x + 7$

31. yes; $x = a$ can be written as $1x + 0y = a$, and $y = b$ can be written as $0x + 1y = b$.

33. B

35. **a.** $11x + 7.5y = 99$; no; You need to buy both stamps and envelopes. The intercepts represent when you do not buy either stamps or envelopes.

b. no; When $x = 5$ and $y = 2$, the number of stamps and envelopes are the same, but you only spend \$70.

3.5 Review & Refresh

36. **a.** 48

b. 250 min, or 4 h 10 min

37. x-intercept: 1, y-intercept: -1

38. The graph of a linear function is a line, a nonlinear function does not form a line.

39. nonlinear; It cannot be written in the form $y = mx + b$.

40. $b \leq -17$

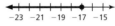

−23 −21 −19 −17 −15

41. $c < 45$

39 41 43 45 47

42. $-3; 6$

43. $g = 7.3$

44. $h = 4$

45. all real numbers

46. $n = \frac{2}{3}, n = \frac{7}{3}$

47. 45

48. $x = -12$

49. 4, 2

3.6 Practice

1. negative; $-\frac{3}{5}$

3. positive; 3

5. -5

7. $\frac{1}{2}$

9. undefined

11. $m = 60$; The bus is traveling at a speed of 60 miles per hour.

13. slope: -3; y-intercept: 2

15. slope: 6; y-intercept: 0

17. slope: 0.75; y-intercept: 4 **19.** slope: $-\frac{1}{6}$; y-intercept: $\frac{1}{3}$

21. To be in slope-intercept form, the equation needs to be solved for y, not x; $y = -\frac{1}{4}x$; The slope is $-\frac{1}{4}$ and the y-intercept is 0.

23.

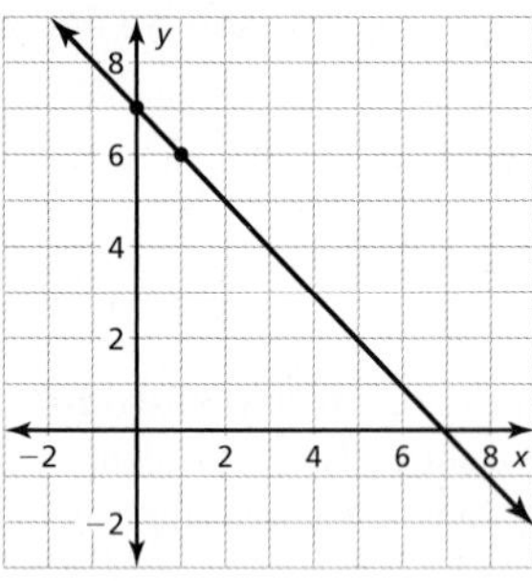

x-intercept: 7

25.

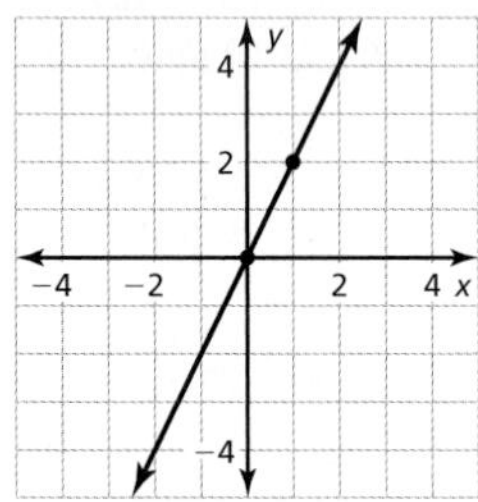

x-intercept: 0

27.

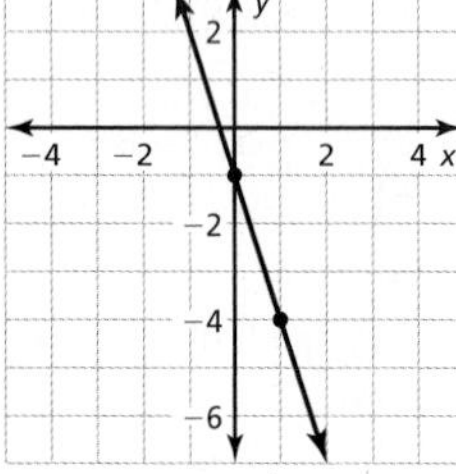

x-intercept: $-\frac{1}{3}$

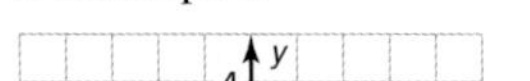

29.

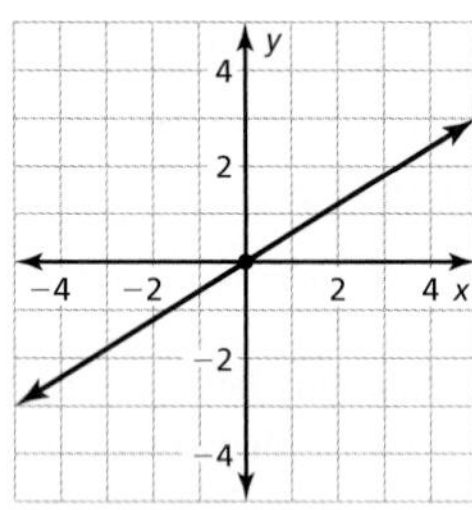

x-intercept: 0

31.

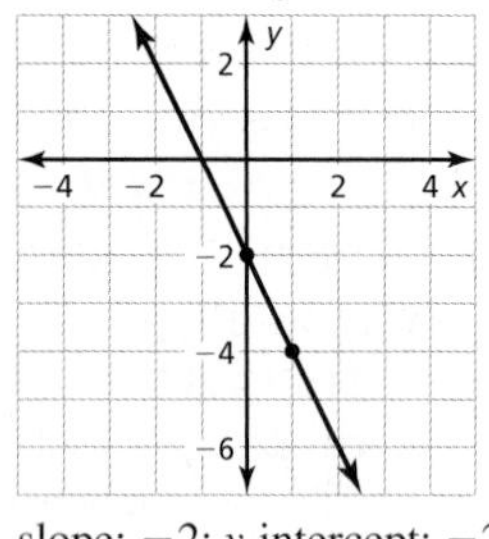

slope: -2; y-intercept: -2; x-intercept: -1

33.

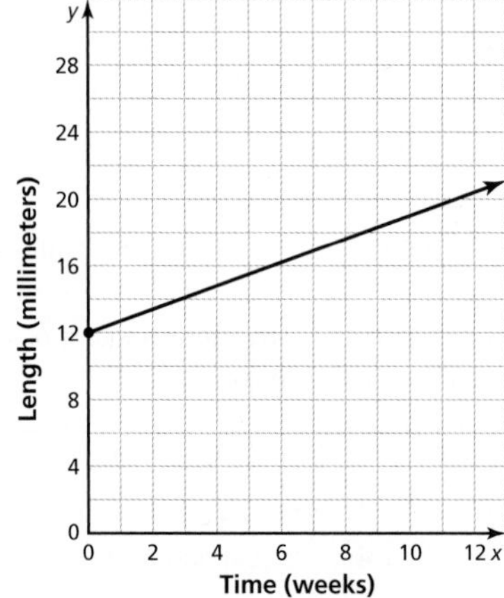

slope: $\frac{7}{10}$; y-intercept: 12; So, the right index fingernail is initially 12 millimeters long.

35. The slope is 3, but the graph shows a slope of $\frac{1}{3}$.

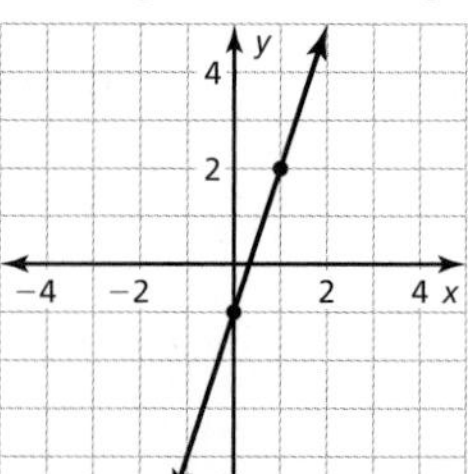

37. a.

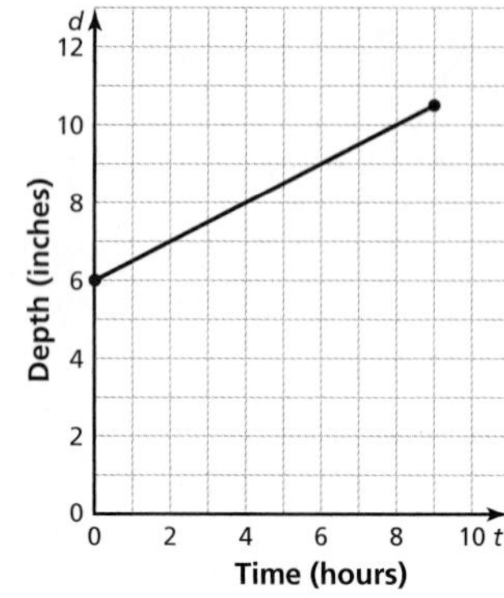

domain: $0 \leq t \leq 9$; range: $6 \leq d \leq 10\frac{1}{2}$

b. $\frac{1}{2}t$ represents the number of inches of snow that has fallen after t hours at a rate of $\frac{1}{2}$ in./h. 6 represents the snow on the ground before the snowfall.

39. Find and plot the intercepts, then draw a line through the intercepts. Or, rewrite the equation in slope-intercept form, plot the slope and the y-intercept, then draw a line through the points; *Sample answer:* standard form; It requires less steps.

41. A and D

43. a.

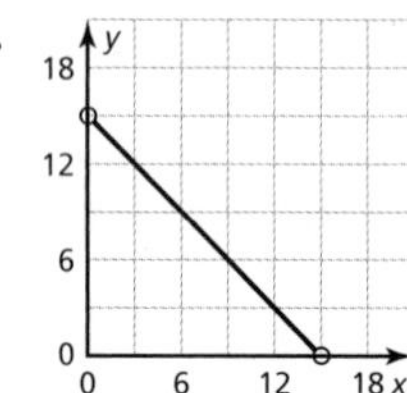

b. The slope of each graph is the same. The open circles in the graph in part (a) are closer to the origin.

45.

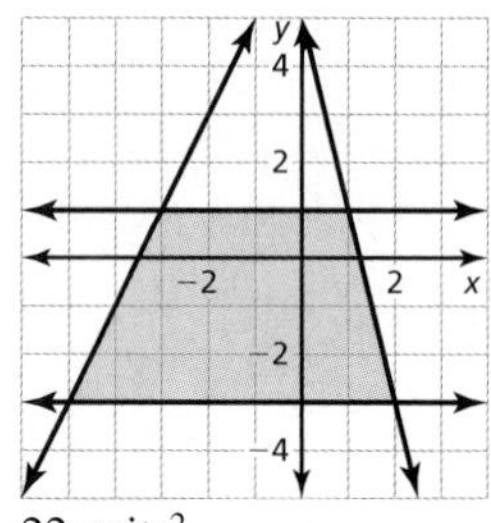

22 units^2

47. a. $y = \frac{1}{3}x + 5$

b. $y = \frac{7}{4}x - \frac{1}{4}$; $y = 2x - 4$

c. $y = -3x + 8$

d. $y = -4x - 9$; $y = -x - \frac{4}{3}$

49. $k = \frac{1}{8}$

51. $\dfrac{y_2 - y_1}{x_2 - x_1} = \dfrac{(mx_2 + b) - (mx_1 + b)}{x_2 - x_1}$

$= \dfrac{mx_2 + b - mx_1 - b}{x_2 - x_1}$

$= \dfrac{mx_2 - mx_1}{x_2 - x_1}$

$= \dfrac{m(x_2 - x_1)}{x_2 - x_1}$

$= m$

53. $g(p + 2)$; 8 units greater; The value of $g(x)$ will increase 12 units when moving 2 units right, the value of $h(x)$ will increase 4 units when moving 2 units right, and $12 - 4 = 8$.

3.6 Review & Refresh

54. $Q'(-1, 4), R'(1, 2), S'(1, -1), T'(-1, -3)$

55. $Q'(-2, 2), R'(-1, 1), S'\left(-1, -\frac{1}{2}\right), T'\left(-2, -\frac{3}{2}\right)$

56. $Q'(4, 4), R'(2, 2), S'(2, -1), T'(4, -3)$

57. $x = -17.5$

58. all real numbers

59. $a = \frac{3}{2}$

60. $q = -1$

61. slope: $\frac{7}{4}$; y-intercepts: $-\frac{5}{2}$

62. $r \geq 7$

63. a. $(3, -8)$

b. $\left(-1, \frac{3}{4}\right)$

64.

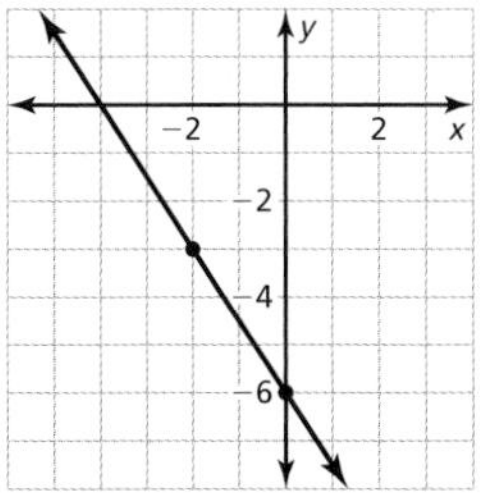

x-intercept: -4

65. nonlinear; The rate of change is not constant.

66. linear; It can be rewritten as $y = -3x + 12$.

67. B or D; $|0.80p - 30| \leq 5$, $31.25 \leq p \leq 43.75$

68.

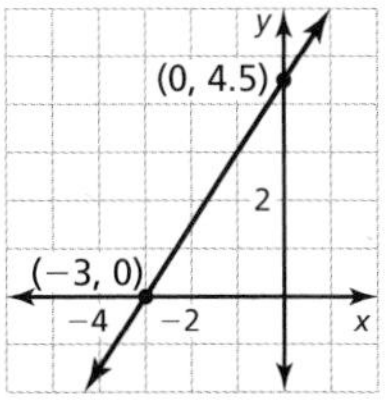

69.

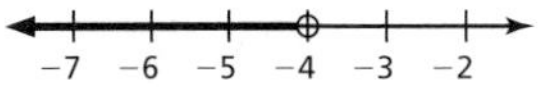

70.

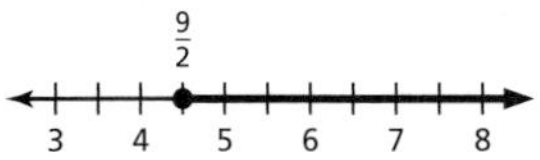

3.7 Practice

1. The graph of g is a vertical translation 2 units up of the graph of f.

3. The graph of g is a vertical translation 3 units down of the graph of f.

5. The graph of g is a horizontal translation 5 units left of the graph of f.

7. The graph of f is a horizontal translation 5 units right of the graph of d.

9. The graph of h is reflection in the x-axis of the graph of f.

11. The graph of h is reflection in the y-axis of the graph of f.

13. The graph of r is a vertical stretch of the graph of f by a factor of 2.

15. The graph of r is a horizontal stretch of the graph of f by a factor of 2.

17. The graph of r is a vertical stretch of the graph of f by a factor of 3.

19. The graph of h is a horizontal shrink of the graph of f by a factor of $\frac{1}{3}$.

21. The graph of h is a vertical shrink of the graph of f by a factor of $\frac{1}{6}$.

23. The graph of h is a horizontal shrink of the graph of f by a factor of $\frac{1}{5}$.

25. The graph of d is reflection in the y-axis of the graph of t.

27. The graph of g is a horizontal translation 4 units left of the graph of f.

29. The graph of g is a horizontal translation 2 units right of the graph of f.

31. The graph of g is a vertical stretch of the graph of f by a factor of 6.

33. $g(x) = f(x - 2)$

35. $g(x) = f(x) + 4$

37. $f(x - 2)$ is a translation to the right, not to the left.

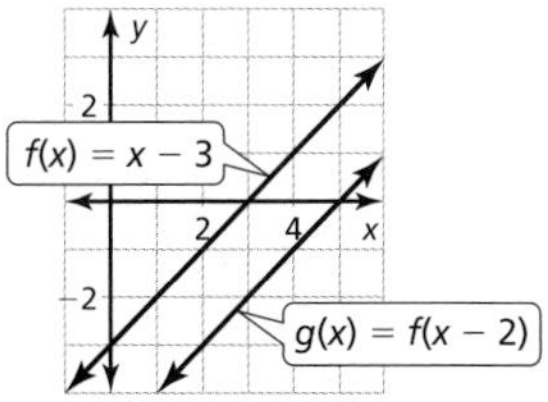

39.

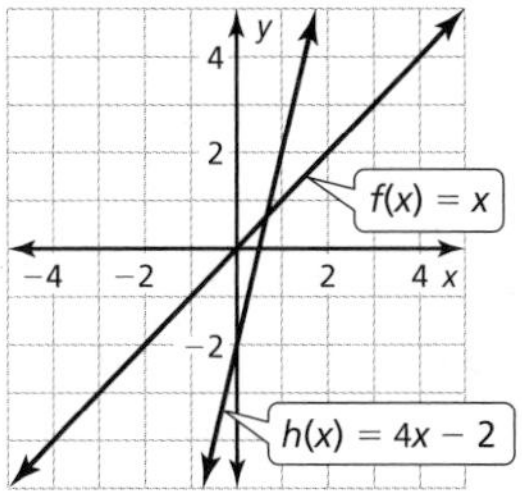

The transformations are a vertical stretch by a factor of 4, then a vertical translation 2 units down.

41.

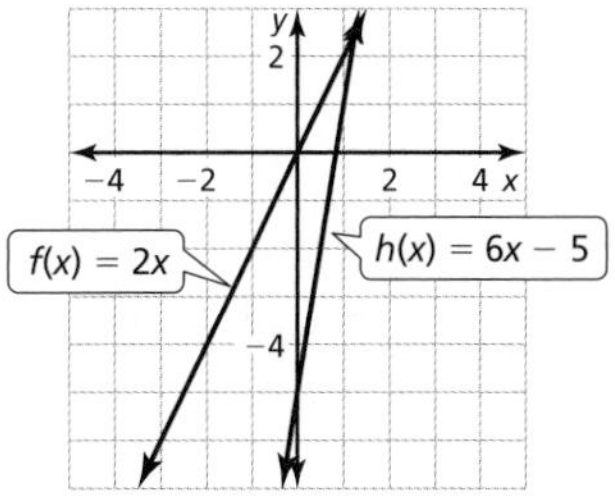

The transformations are a vertical stretch by a factor of 3, then a vertical translation 5 units down.

43. The graph of $y = g(x) + p$ is a vertical translation p units up or down of the graph of $y = g(x)$. The graph of $y = g(x + p)$ is a horizontal translation p units left or right of the graph of $y = g(x)$.

45. $a = \frac{2}{3}$, vertical shrink by a factor of $\frac{2}{3}$; $b = 45$, vertical translation 45 units up

47. B and C, A and F; Adding 4 to the y-coordinate of each point on B gives the corresponding y-coordinate on C. Adding 2 to the y-coordinate of each point of F gives you the corresponding y-coordinate on A.

49. *Sample answer:* $g(x) = \frac{1}{4}f(x) + 1$

51. *Sample answer:* $g(x) = f(x) + 2$

53. a. The new graph is a horizontal shrink of the old graph by a factor of $\frac{3}{4}$.

b. The new graph is a vertical translation of 2000 units up of the old graph.

55. $r = 2$

57. $r = 2$

59.

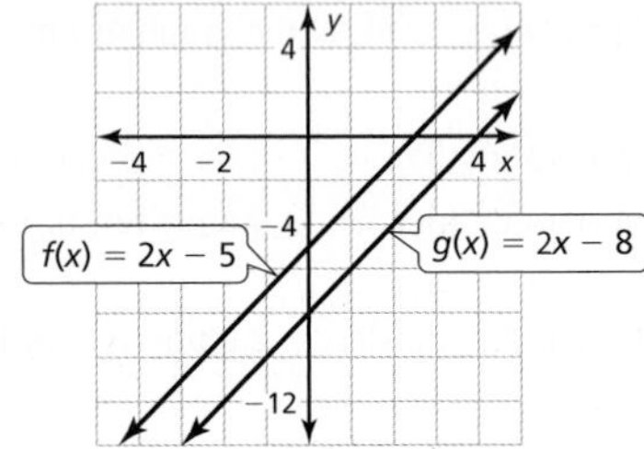

$g(x) = f(x) - 3$; The graph of g is a vertical translation 3 units down of the graph of f.

61.

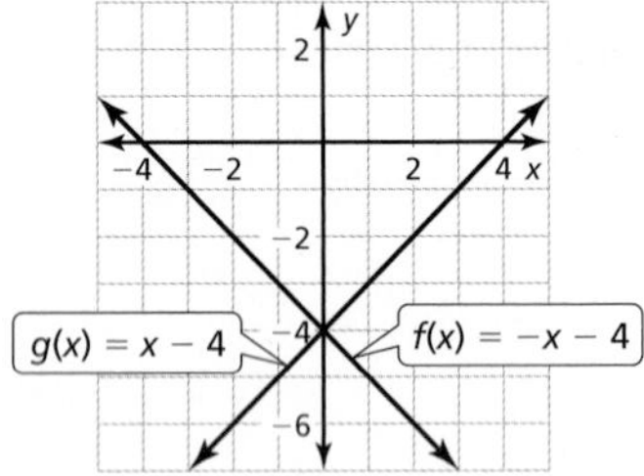

$g(x) = f(-x)$; The graph of g is a reflection in the y-axis of the graph of f.

63. no; Let $f(x) = 2x + 4$. $f\left(\frac{1}{2}x\right) = x + 4$ is a horizontal stretch by a factor of 2. $\frac{1}{2} \cdot f(x) = x + 2$ is a vertical shrink by a factor of $\frac{1}{2}$. Because $x + 4 \neq x + 2$, $f\left(\frac{1}{2}x\right) \neq \frac{1}{2} \cdot f(x)$. So, $f(cx) \neq \frac{1}{c} \cdot f(x)$.

3.7 Review & Refresh

65. Dilate the blue triangle by using a scale factor of 2 and then reflect in the x-axis.

66. $-12 < x < -2$

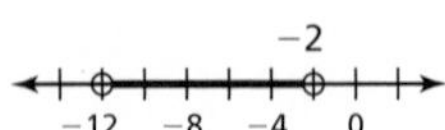

67. no solution

68. $\geq$

69. -2; $-\frac{11}{2}$

70. a.

domain: $0 \leq t \leq 31.25$; range: $0 \leq h(t) \leq 250$

b. $-8t$ represents the distance the elevator descends after t seconds at a rate of 8 m/sec. 250 represents the height at the top floor. The t-intercept shows it takes 31.25 seconds to reach the ground floor.

71. $b = 4$

72. $c = -15$

73. $q = \frac{7}{2}$

74. $r = -3, r = 6$

75. a. 0, 1, 2, 3, 4, 5, 6; discrete; The number of books must be a whole number.

b.

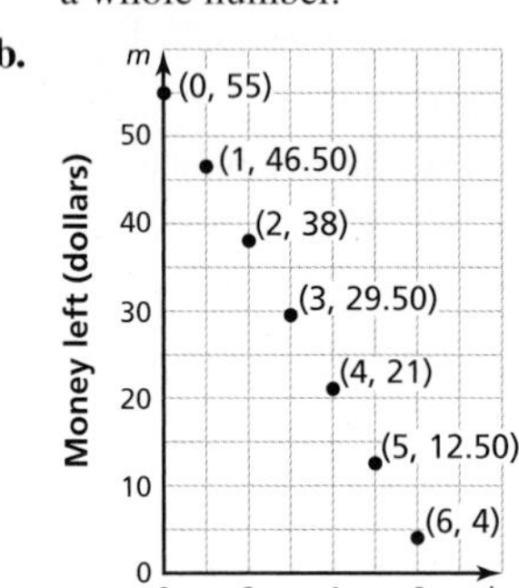

76.

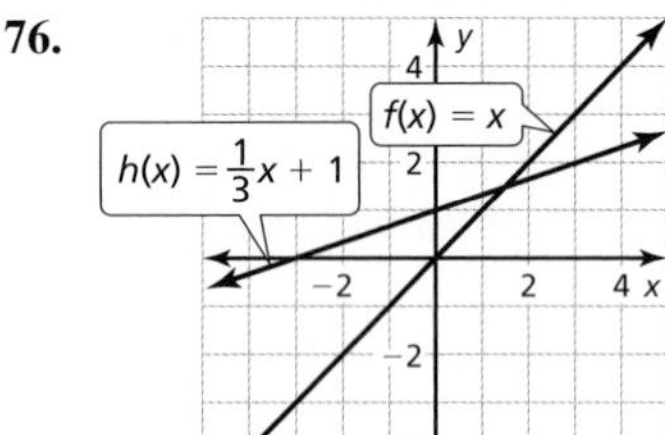

The transformations are a vertical shrink by a factor of $\frac{1}{3}$ then a vertical translation 1 unit up.

77.

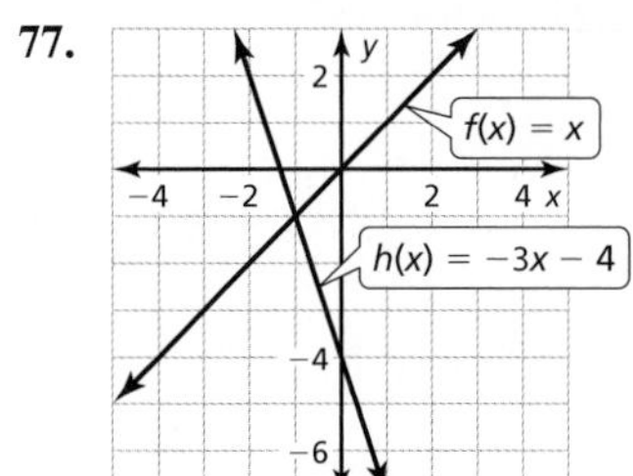

The transformations are a vertical stretch by a factor of 3, then a reflection in the x-axis, then a vertical translation 4 units down.

78. $A = 3$, $B = -\frac{3}{2}$

79. not a function; The input -10 has two outputs, 2 and 6, and the input -8 has two outputs, 3 and 8.

80. $h = \frac{V}{\pi r^2}$

81. $x < -\frac{1}{10}$

3.8 Practice

1.

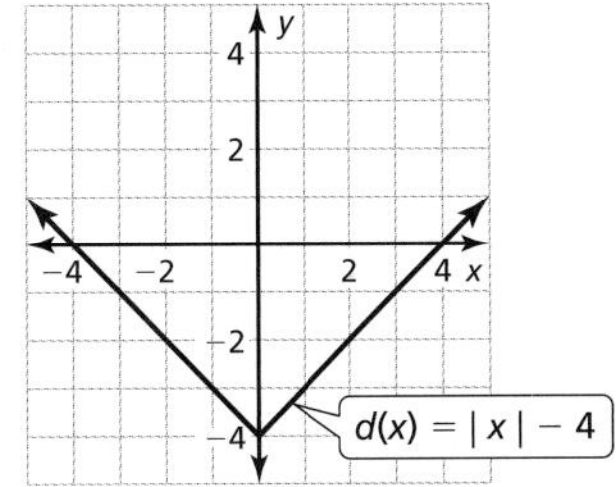

The graph of d is a vertical translation 4 units down of the graph of f; domain: all real numbers; range $y \geq -4$

3.

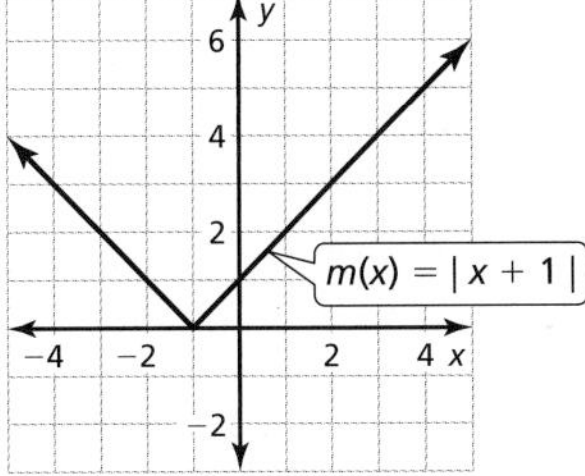

The graph of m is a horizontal translation 1 unit left of the graph of f; domain: all real numbers; range $y \geq 0$

5.

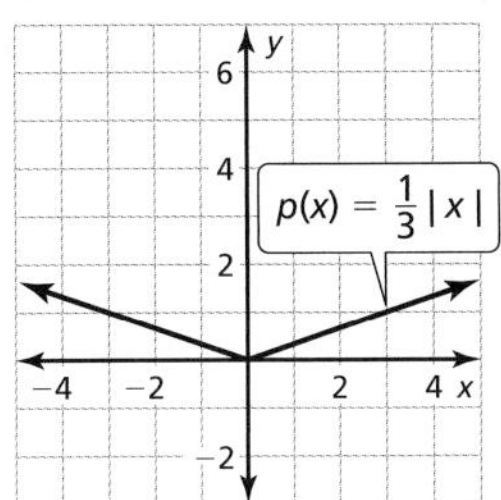

The graph of p is a vertical shrink of the graph of f by a factor of $\frac{1}{3}$; domain: all real numbers; range $y \geq 0$

7.

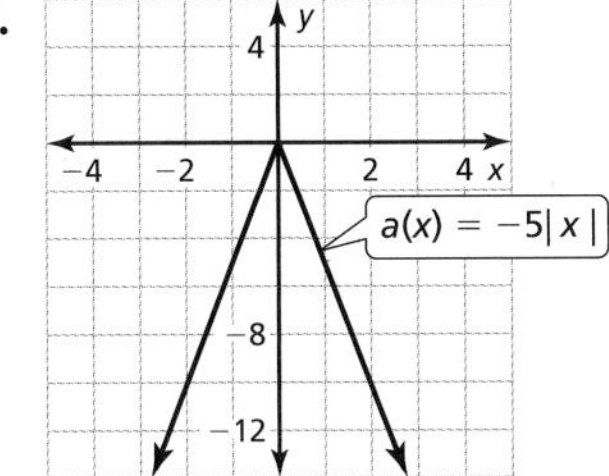

The graph of a is a vertical stretch of the graph of f by a factor of 5 and a reflection in the x-axis; domain: all real numbers; range $y \leq 0$

9. $h(x) = |x| - 7$

11. $h(x) = \frac{1}{4}|x|$

13.

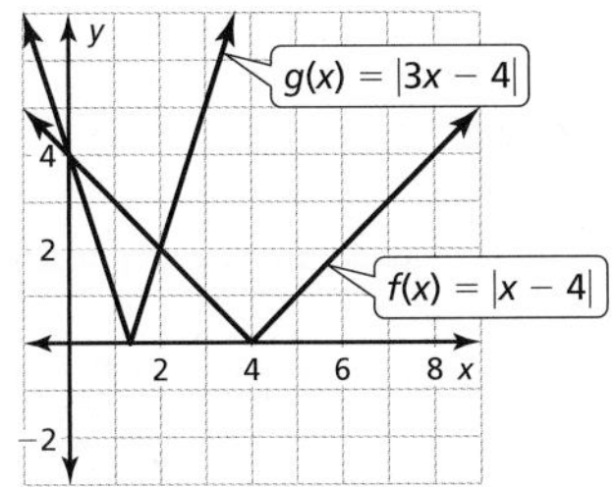

The graph of g is a horizontal shrink of the graph of f by a factor of $\frac{1}{3}$.

15.

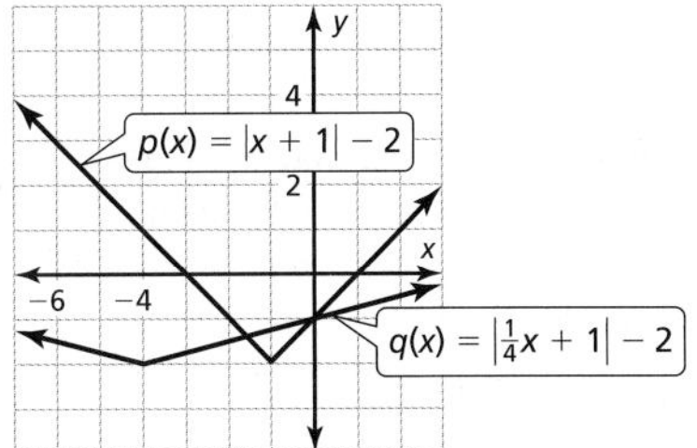

The graph of q is a horizontal stretch of the graph of p by a factor of 4.

17.

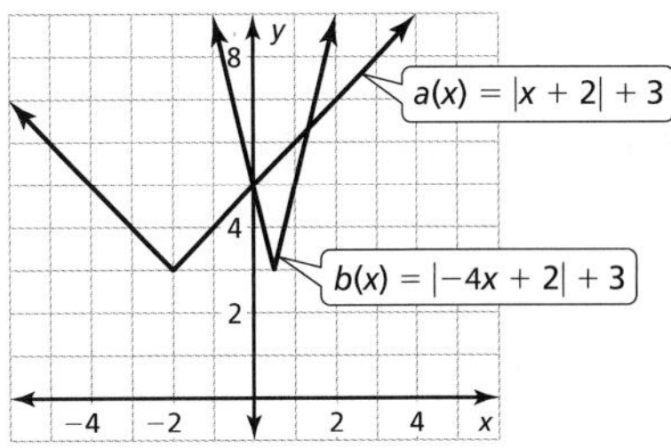

The graph of b is a horizontal shrink of the graph of a by a factor of $\frac{1}{4}$ and a reflection in the y-axis.

19. The graph of g is a vertical translation 3 units down of the graph of f; $k = -3$

21. The graph of p is a vertical stretch of the graph of f by a factor of 3 and a reflection in the x-axis; $a = -3$

23.

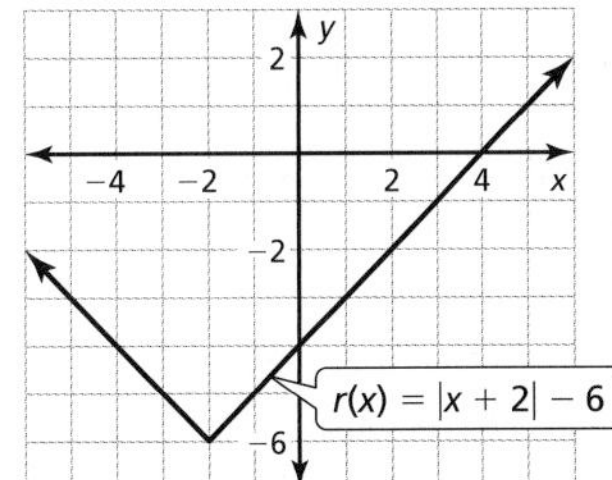

The graph of r is a horizontal translation 2 units left, then a vertical translation 6 units down of the graph of f.

25.

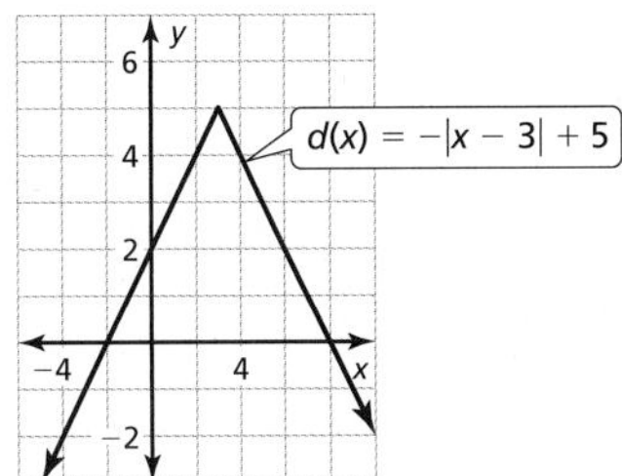

The graph of d is a horizontal translation 3 units right, then a reflection in the x-axis, then a vertical translation 5 units up of the graph of f.

27.

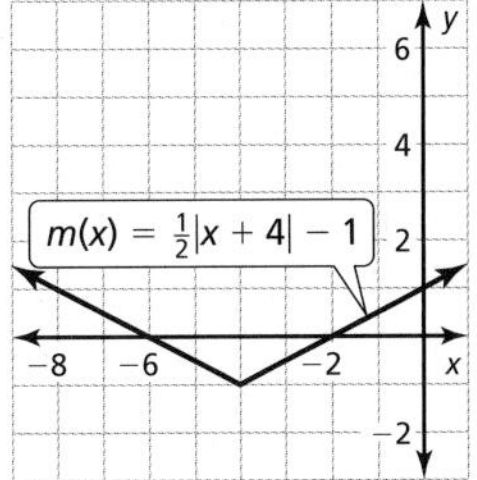

The graph of m is a horizontal translation 4 units left, then a vertical shrink by a factor of $\frac{1}{2}$, then a vertical translation 1 unit down of the graph of f.

29. 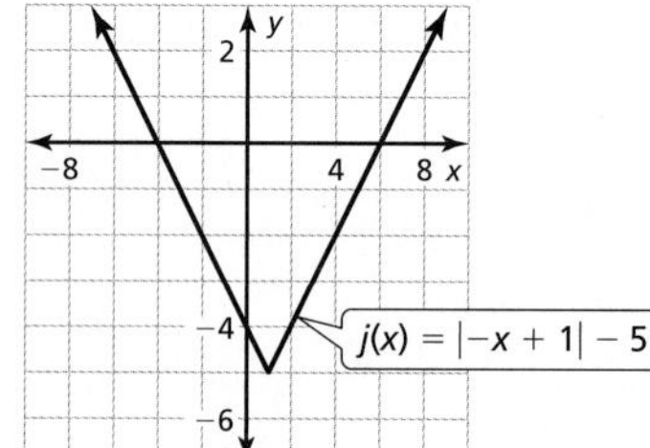

The graph of j is a horizontal translation 1 unit left, then a reflection in the y-axis, then a vertical translation 5 units down of the graph of f.

31. **a.** $\left(\frac{5}{4}, 0\right)$

b. yes; The location of the pocket (5, 5) is a solution of p.

33. none

35. **a.** $A'\left(-\frac{1}{2}, -2\right)$; $B'(1, -5)$; $C'(-4, -7)$

b. $A'\left(\frac{5}{2}, 3\right)$; $B'(4, 0)$; $C'(-1, -2)$

c. $A'\left(-\frac{1}{2}, -3\right)$; $B'(1, 0)$; $C'(-4, 2)$

d. $A'\left(-\frac{1}{2}, 12\right)$; $B'(1, 0)$; $C'(-4, -8)$

37. *Sample answer:* $f(x) = -|x| + 2$

39. no; no; Because the graph is V-shaped, half of the graph is decreasing and the other half is increasing.

41. 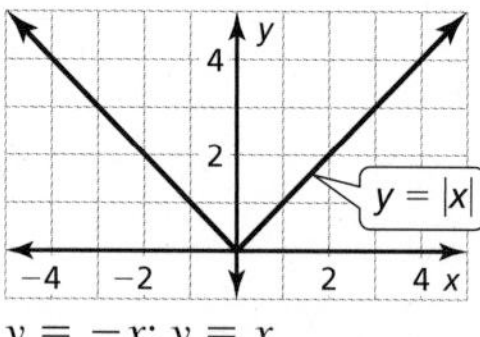

$y = -x$; $y = x$

43. 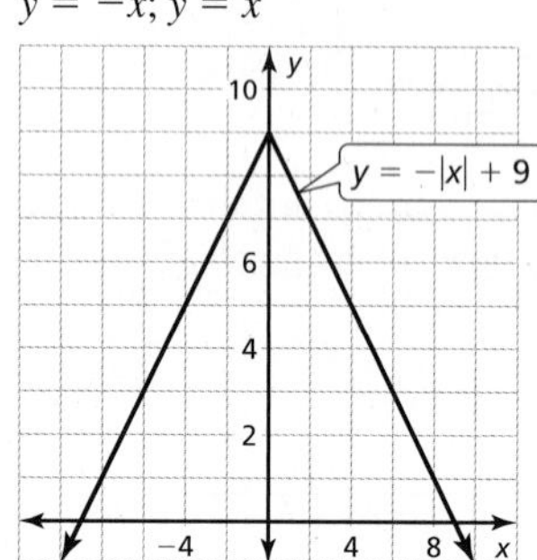

$y = x + 9$; $y = -x + 9$

45. 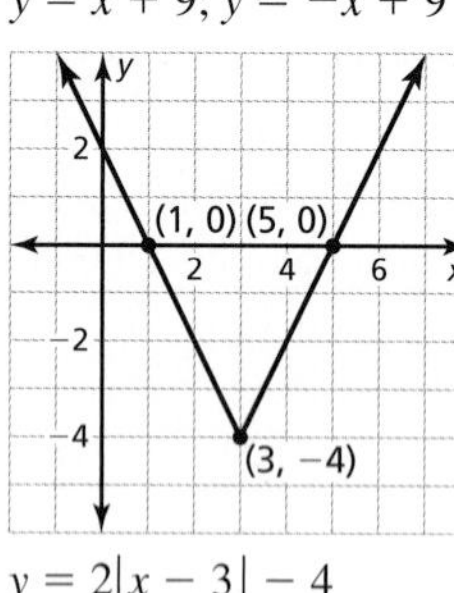

$y = 2|x - 3| - 4$

47. 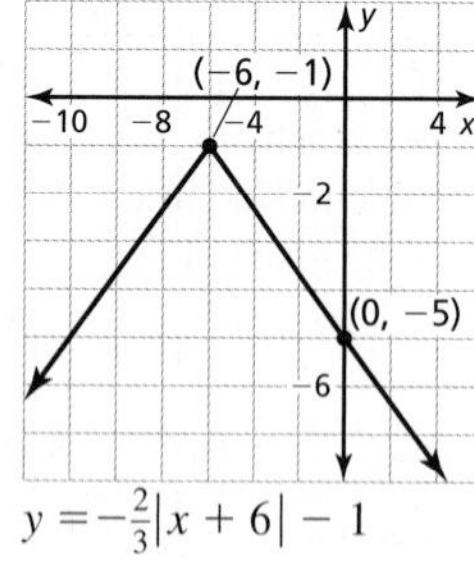

$y = -\frac{2}{3}|x + 6| - 1$

49. A, C, and D

51. 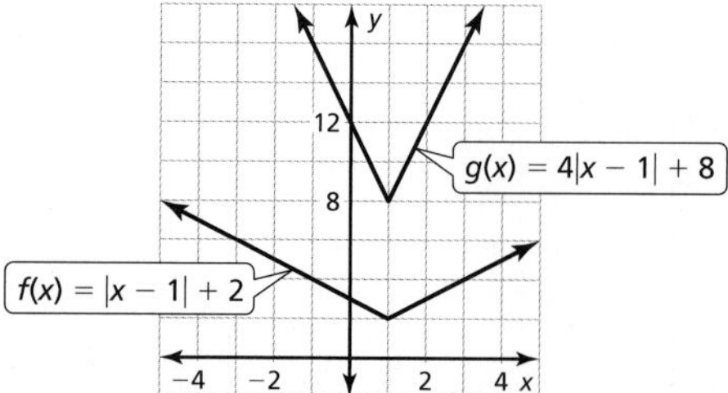

The graph of g is a vertical stretch by a factor of 4 of the graph of f.

53. 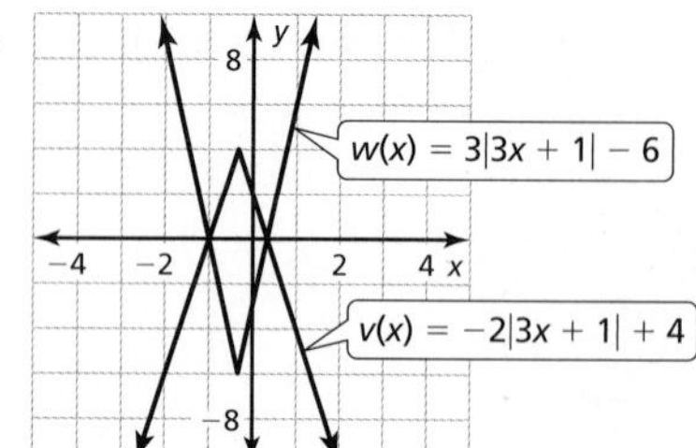

The graph of w is a vertical stretch of the graph of v by a factor of $\frac{3}{2}$ and a reflection in the x-axis.

55. 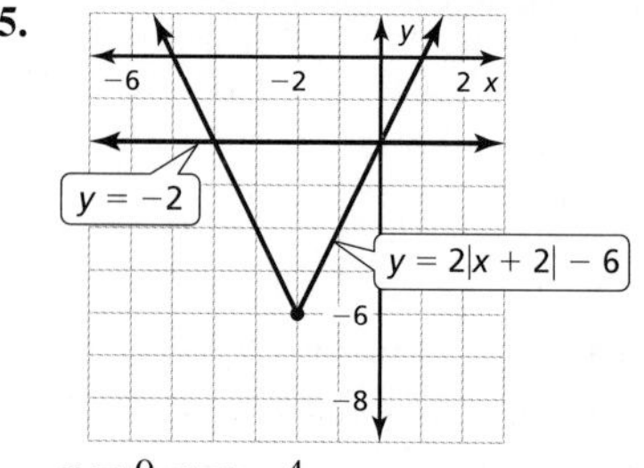

$x = 0, x = -4$

57. no; The form of a horizontal translation of $y = f(x)$ is $y = f(x - h)$. So, if p is positive, the graph of $y = |x + p|$ is a horizontal translation in the negative direction.

3.8 Review & Refresh

59. $-\frac{5}{4}$

60. **a.** At 1 P.M., the temperature is 30°C.

b. m hours after 9 A.M., the temperature is 28.9°C.

c. The temperature is the same at 11 A.M. and 6 P.M.

d. The temperature is higher at 3:30 P.M. than at 9 A.M.

61. $a \leq \frac{5}{2}$

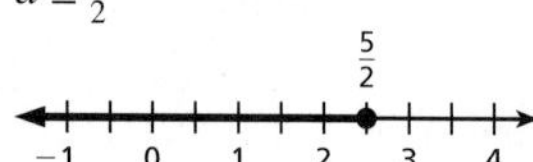

62. no solution

63. all real numbers

64. $x > -\frac{3}{4}$

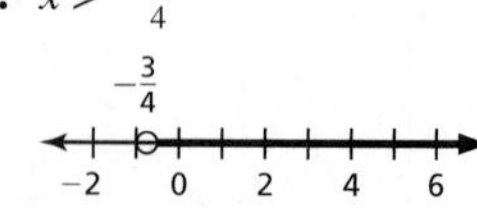

65. The graph of g is a horizontal translation 2 units left of the graph of f.

66. The graph of g is a reflection in the x-axis of the graph of f.

67. **a.** $12x$ represents the total you spend on pecans at \$12/lb; $7.5y$ represents the total you spend on walnuts at \$7.50/lb.

b. 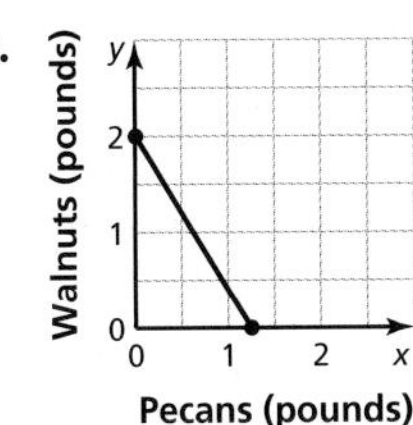

The y-intercept shows you can buy 2 pounds of walnuts when you do not buy any pecans. The x-intercept shows you can buy 1.25 pounds of pecans when you do not buy any walnuts.

68. $x = -1, x = 4$ **69.** $x = -1, x = \frac{1}{2}$

70. *Sample answer:*

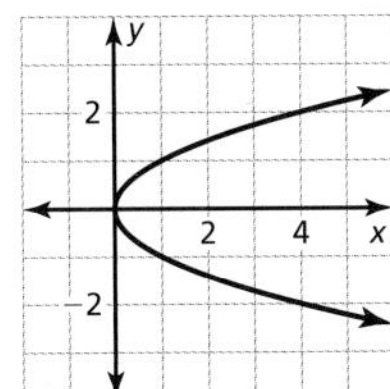

71. 8.75 ft/sec, or 8.89 ft/sec

72. The graph of g is a vertical translation 2 units up and a horizontal translation 3 units left of the graph of f; $h = -3$, $k = 2$

Chapter 3 Review

1. function; Every input has exactly one output.

2. not a function; The input 5 has two outputs, 11 and 3.

3. function; domain: 0, 1, 2, 3, 4, 5, 6, 7; range: 1, 4, 6

4. not a function; domain: $x \leq 6$; range: all real numbers

5. function; domain: $-3 \leq x \leq 3$; range: $-1 \leq y \leq 3$

6. not a function; domain: $-1, 0, 1$; range: $-3, -2, -1, 0$

7. **a.** yes; The amount of money you have is the dependent variable, and the number of hours you work is the independent variable.

b. domain: $0 \leq x \leq 4$; range: $170 \leq y \leq 204$

8. *Sample answer:* (1, 3), (2, −1), (3, 3), (4, −2), (5, 3)

9. positive: $-1 < x < 1$; negative: $x < -1$ and $x > 1$; increasing: $x < 0$; decreasing: $x > 0$; $y \to -\infty$ as $x \to +\infty$ and $y \to -\infty$ as $x \to -\infty$

10. positive: $x > 1.6$; negative: $x < 1.6$; increasing: for all real numbers; $y \to +\infty$ as $x \to +\infty$ and $y \to -\infty$ as $x \to -\infty$

11. The second kick has a greater horizontal distance and the first kick has a greater maximum height.

12. *Sample answer:*

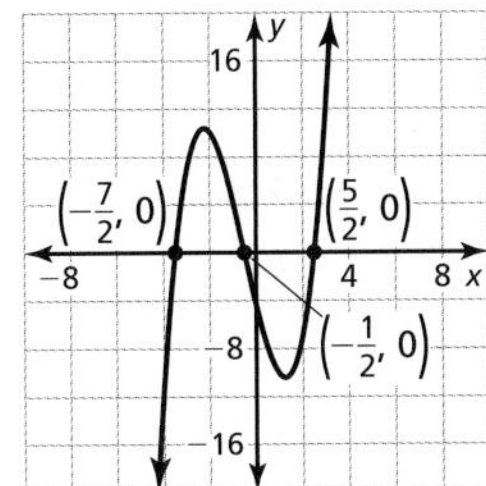

13. linear; As x increases by 5, y decreases by 3. The rate of change is constant.

14. nonlinear; The graph is not a line.

15. linear; $y = 4x + 12$ is written in the form $y = mx + b$.

16. nonlinear; $xy = 9$ cannot be written in the form $y = mx + b$.

17. 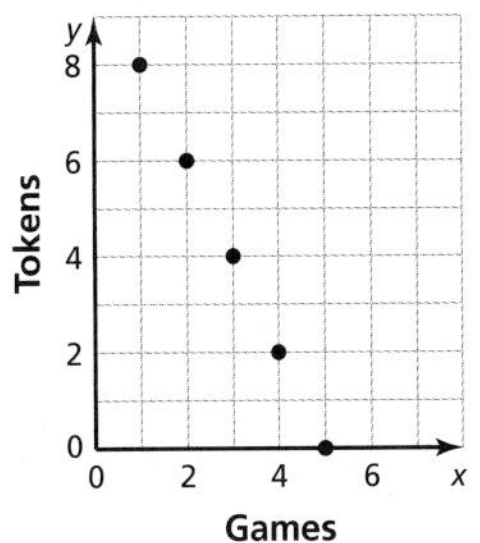

Because it is not possible to play part of a game, the domain is discrete.

18. 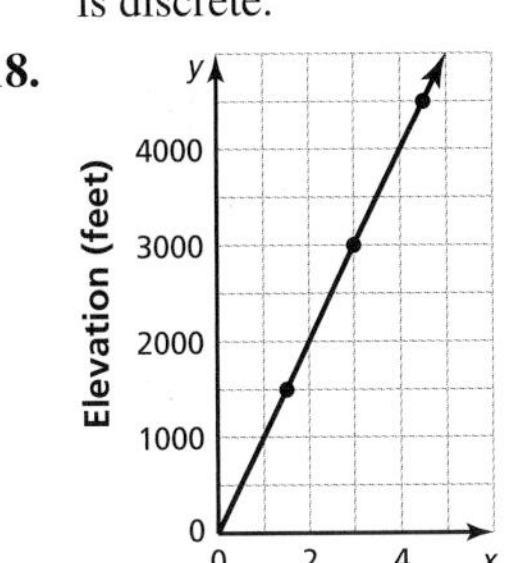

Because the elevation can change for part of a minute, the domain is continuous.

19. **a.** 0, 1, 2, 3, 4, 5, 6, 7; discrete; The number of tickets bought must be a whole number.

b. 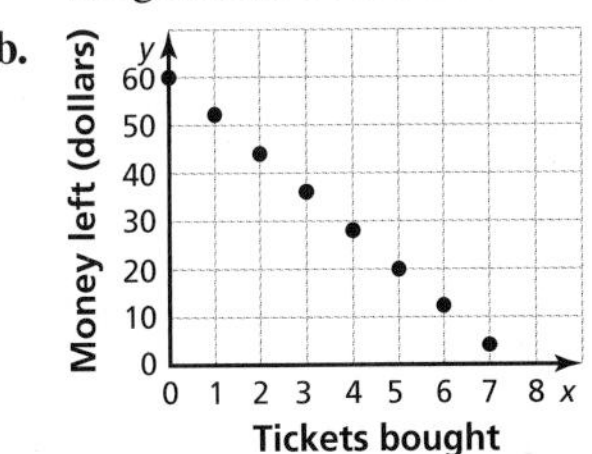

20. 5, 8, 13 **21.** −18, −9, 6

22. **a.** There is the same number of people in the stadium at 2:00 P.M. and 4:00 P.M.

b. There are less people in the stadium at 5:00 P.M. than at 1:30 P.M.

23. $x = 7$ **24.** $x = -4$

25. 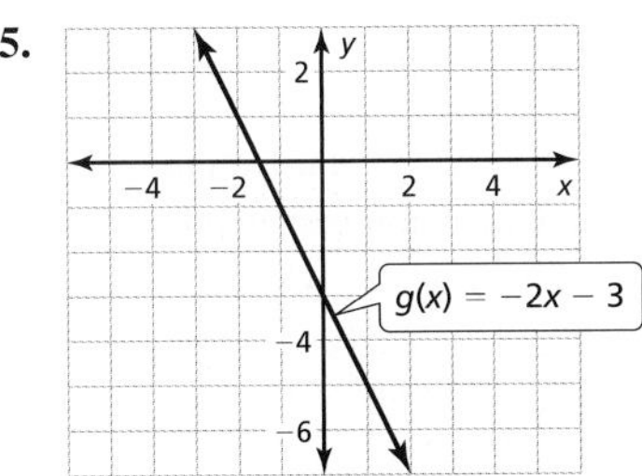

26. 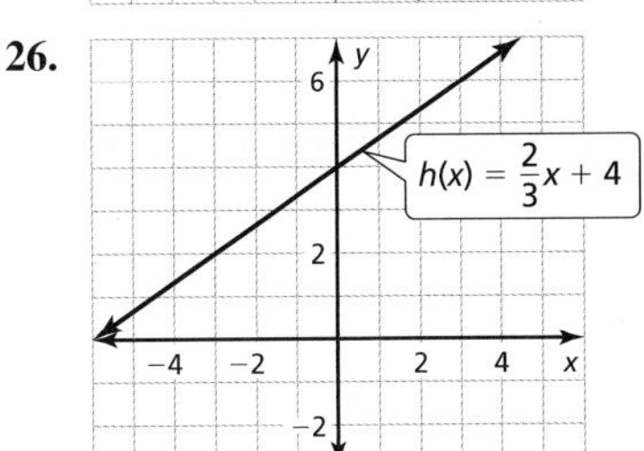

27. **a.** 495 mi

b. 12.5 h

28.

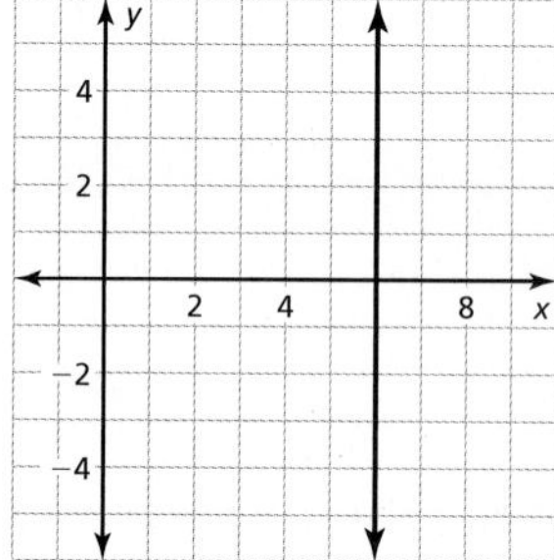

29.

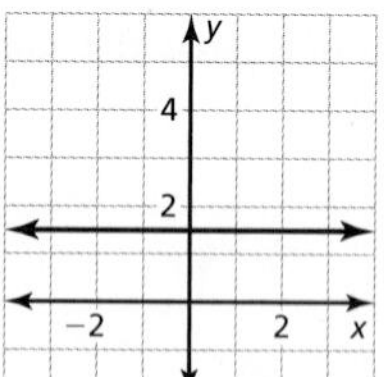

30.

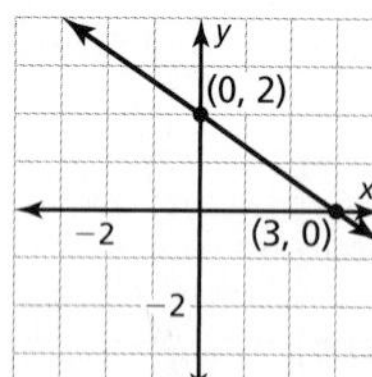

31.

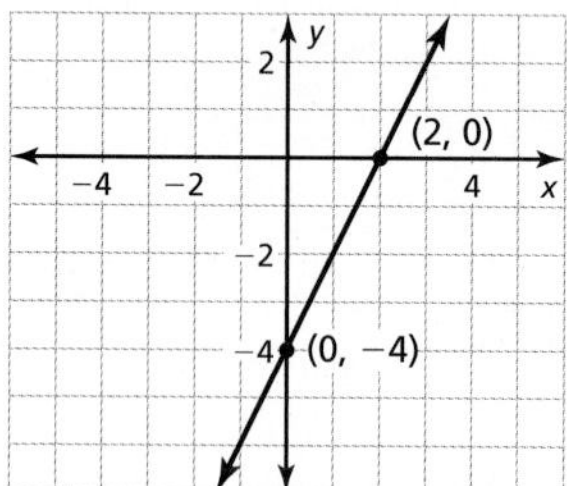

32.

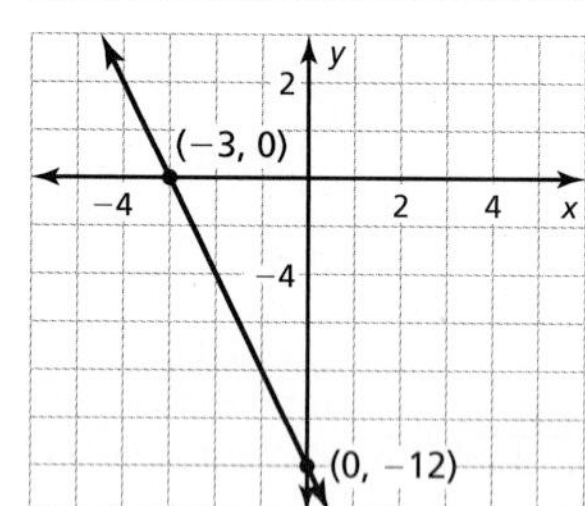

33.

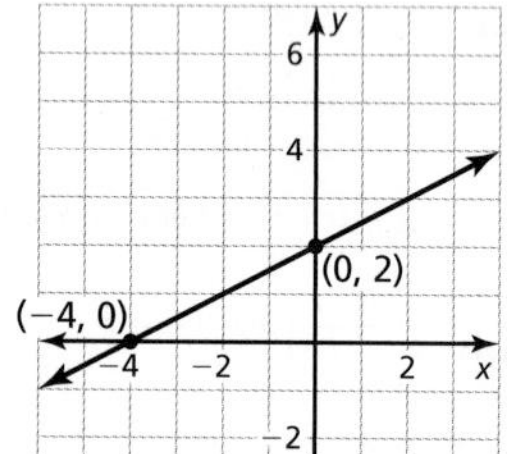

34.

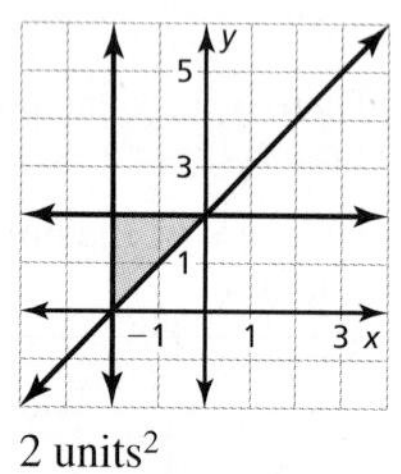

2 units^2

35. a. $2x$ represents the total points scored by 2-point baskets; $3y$ represents the total points scored by 3-point baskets. The x-intercept indicates 27 two-point baskets were made if there were no three-point baskets. The y-intercept indicates 18 three-point baskets were made if there were no two-point baskets.

b. no; If y is odd, then $3y$ will also be odd. Subtracting an odd number from 54 will also be odd, so dividing this result by 2 to find x will never give a whole number.

c.

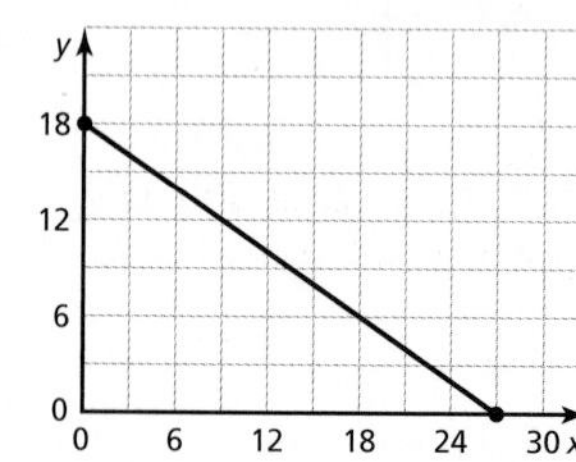

d. *Sample answer:* 24 two-point baskets and 2 three-point baskets; 9 two-point baskets and 12 three-point baskets; 6 two-point baskets and 14 three-point baskets; 12 two-point baskets and 10 three-point baskets

36. positive; $\frac{2}{3}$

37. $\frac{6}{5}$

38. undefined

39. 0

40.

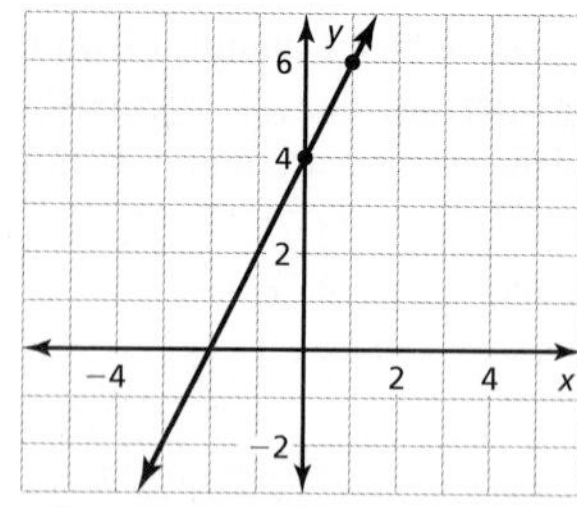

x-intercept: −2

41.

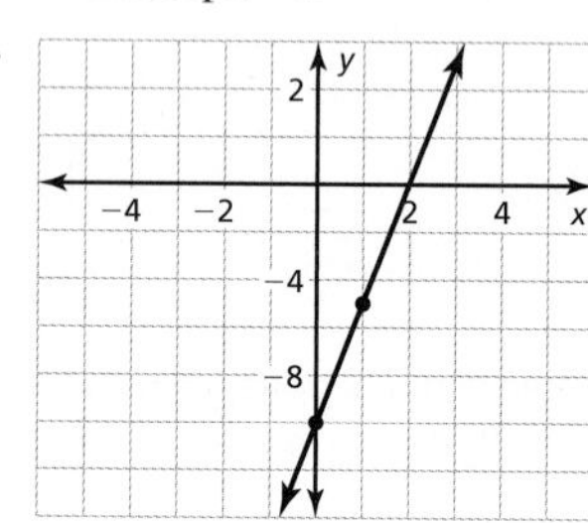

x-intercept: 2

42.

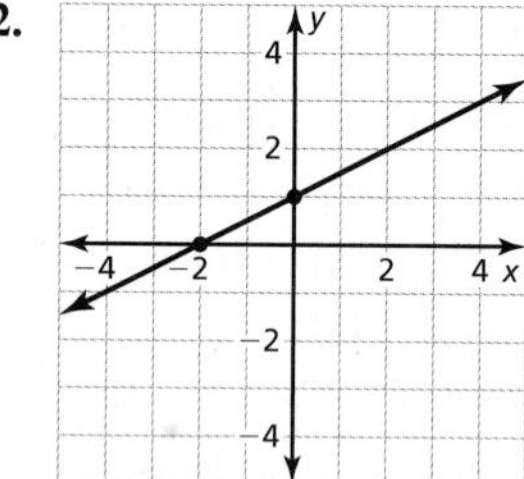

x-intercept: −2

43.

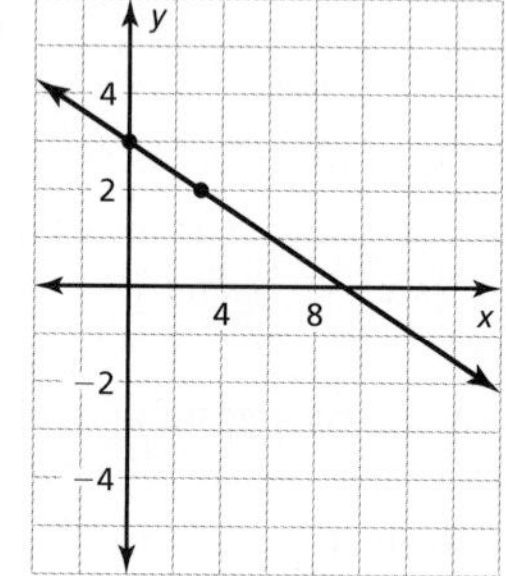

x-intercept: 9

44.

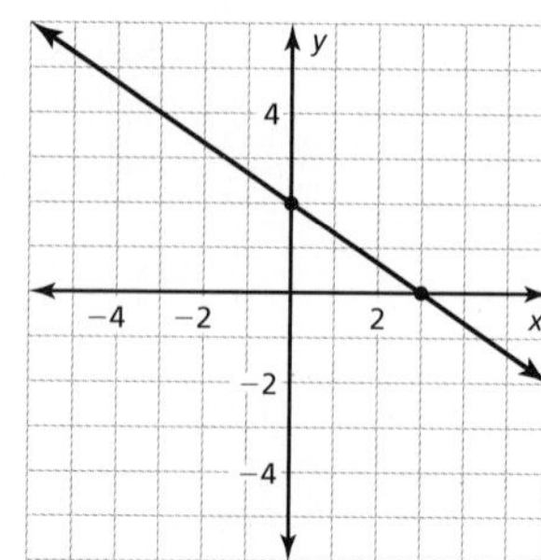

slope: $-\frac{2}{3}$; y-intercept: 2; x-intercept: 3

45. 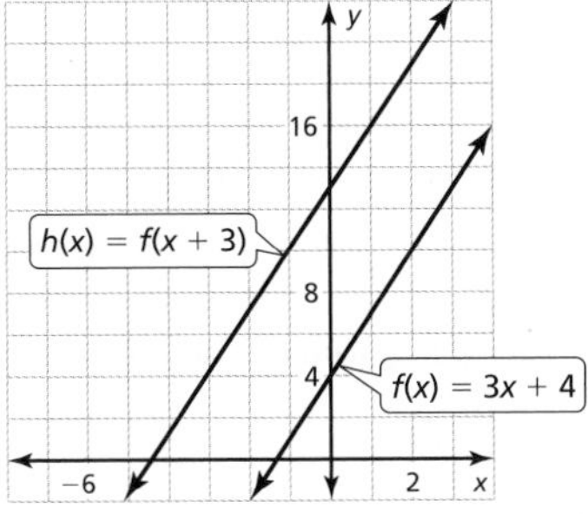

The graph of h is a horizontal translation 3 units left of the graph of f.

46. 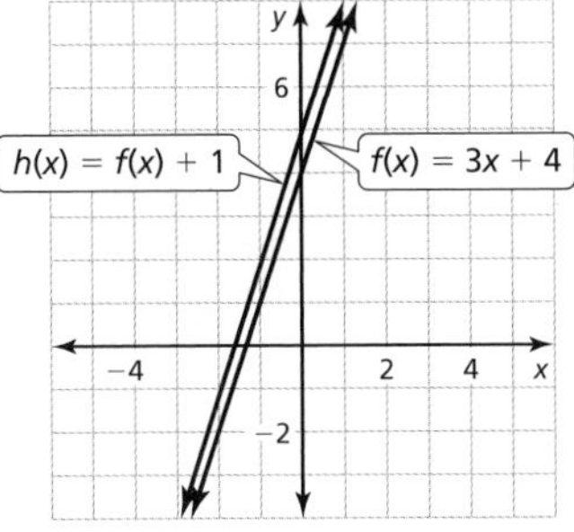

The graph of h is a vertical translation 1 unit up of the graph of f.

47. 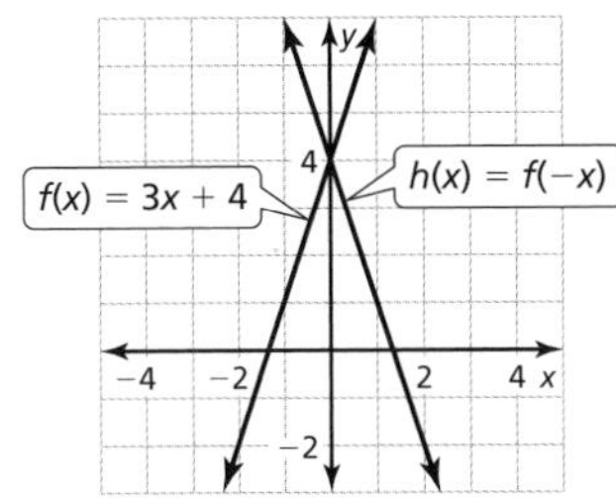

The graph of h is a reflection in the y-axis of the graph of f.

48. 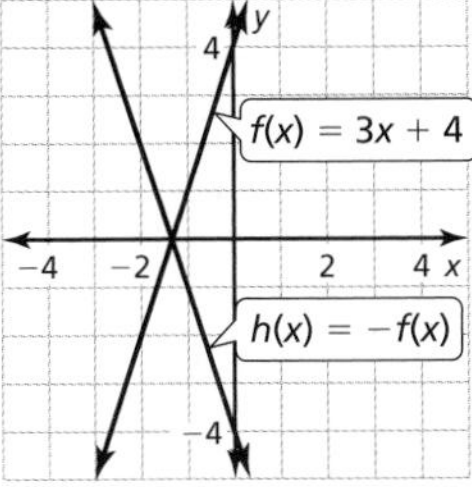

The graph of h is a reflection in the x-axis of the graph of f.

49. 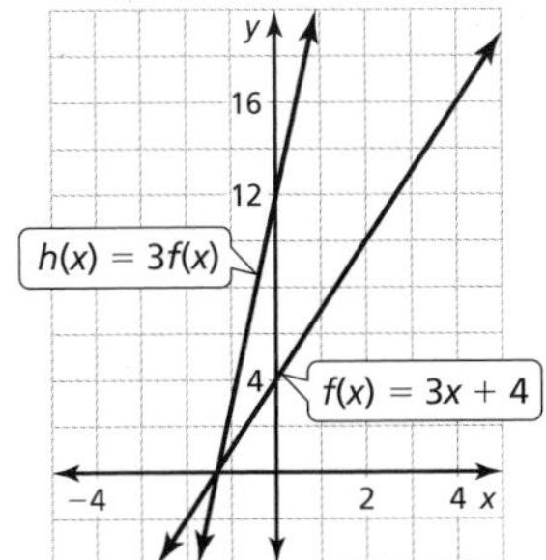

The graph of h is a vertical stretch of the graph of f by a factor of 3.

50. 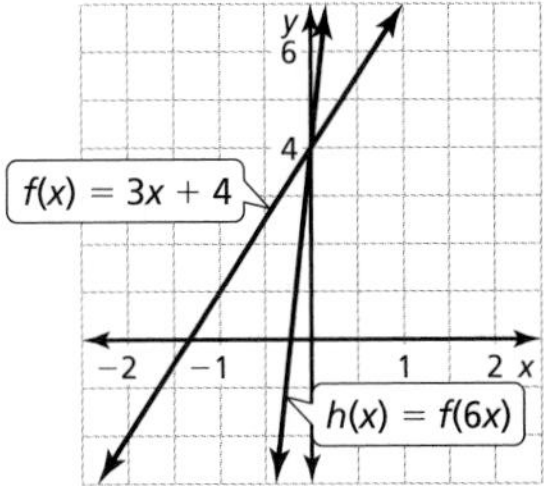

The graph of h is a horizontal shrink of the graph of f by a factor of $\frac{1}{6}$.

51. 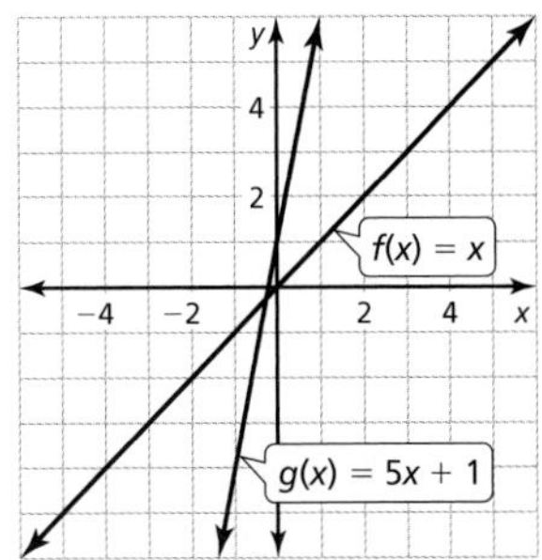

The transformations are a vertical stretch by a factor of 5, then a vertical translation 1 unit up.

52. 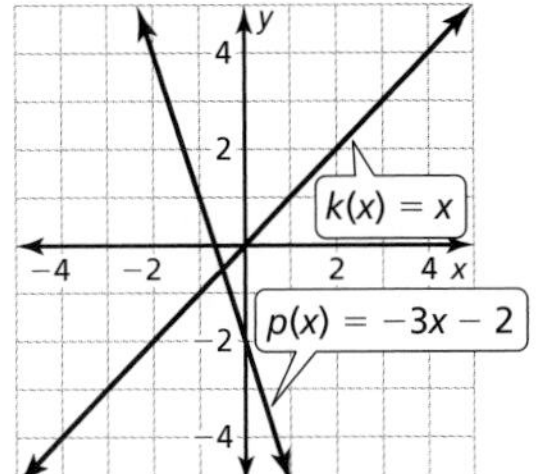

The graph of p is a reflection in the x-axis, a vertical stretch by a factor of 3, and a vertical translation 2 units down of the graph of k.

53. $n = -1, p = 18$

54. 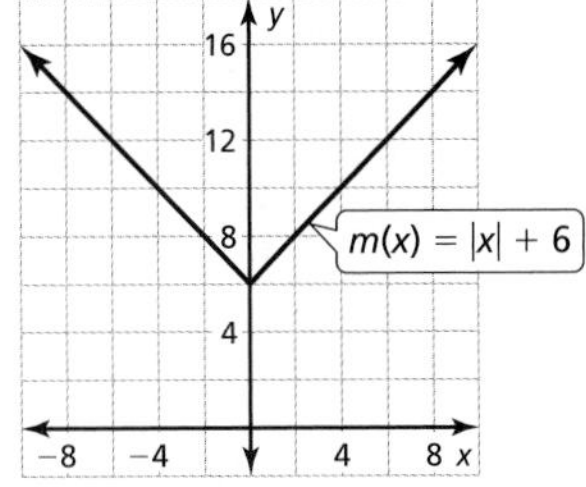

The graph of m is a vertical translation 6 units up of the graph of f; domain: all real numbers; range $y \geq 6$

55. 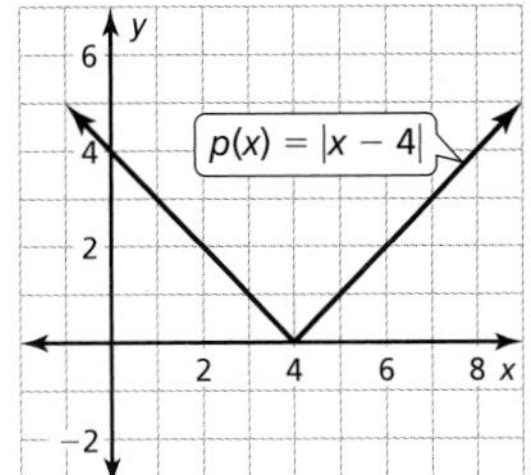

The graph of p is a horizontal translation 4 units right of the graph of f; domain: all real numbers; range $y \geq 0$

56. 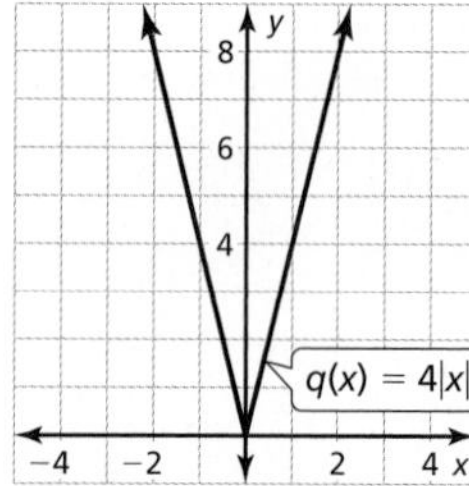

The graph of q is a vertical stretch of the graph of f by a factor of 4; domain: all real numbers; range $y \geq 0$

57. 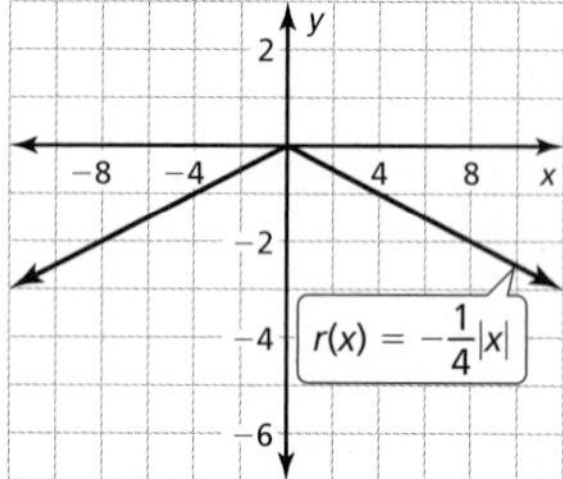

The graph of r is a vertical shrink of the graph of f by a factor of $\frac{1}{4}$ and a reflection in the x-axis; domain: all real numbers; range $y \leq 0$

58. $f(x) = |x - 9|$

59. $f(x) = \frac{1}{6}|x|$

60. $f(x) = -5|x|$

61. 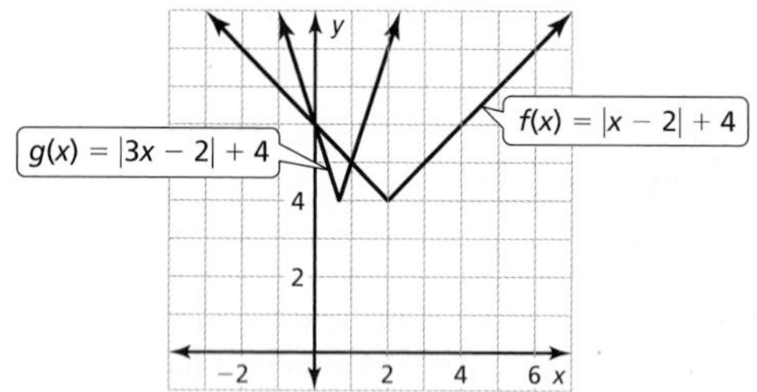

The graph of g is a horizontal shrink of the graph of f by a factor of $\frac{1}{3}$.

62. The graph of p is a horizontal translation 2 units left of the graph of f; $h = 2$

63. The graph of d is a horizontal stretch by a factor of 3 of the graph of f; $a = 3$

64. $g(x) = 2|3x - 3| - 2$

65. **a.** 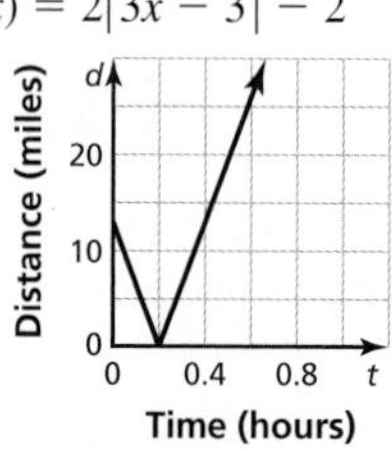

The t-intercept shows it takes 0.2 hour to reach the exit; The d-intercept shows you start 13 miles from the exit.

b. 1 h

Chapter 3 Mathematical Practices (Chapter Review)

1. *Sample answer:* A graphing calculator can be used to explore the effects of transformations on a parent function.
2. *Sample answer:* spreadsheet; List multiple values for x in one column, then use the function $f(x) = 3x + 8$ for a second column to find the output values.

Chapter 3 Practice Test

1. function; Every input has exactly one output; not linear; As x increases by 1, y changes by different amounts. The rate of change is not constant.
2. function; Every input has exactly one output; linear; It is in the form $y = mx + b$.
3. not a function; The input -2 has infinite output values.

4. 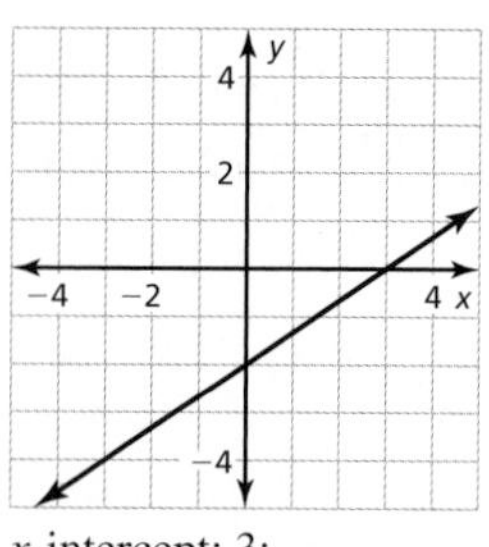

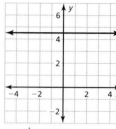

x-intercept: 3;
y-intercept: -2; slope: $\frac{2}{3}$

5. no x-intercept;
y-intercept: 4.5; slope: 0

6. 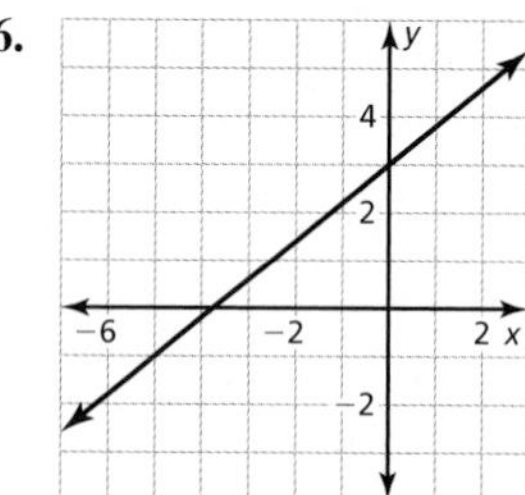

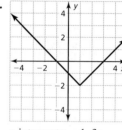

x-intercept: -3.75;
y-intercept: 3; slope: $\frac{4}{5}$

7. x-intercepts: -1, 3;
y-intercept: -1

8. domain: all real numbers; range: $y \geq -2$; continuous; Because the domain is all real numbers, the domain is continuous.
9. positive: $x < -3$ and $x > 1$; negative: $-3 < x < 1$; decreasing: $x < -1$; increasing: $x > -1$; $y \to +\infty$ as $x \to +\infty$ and $y \to +\infty$ as $x \to -\infty$

10. 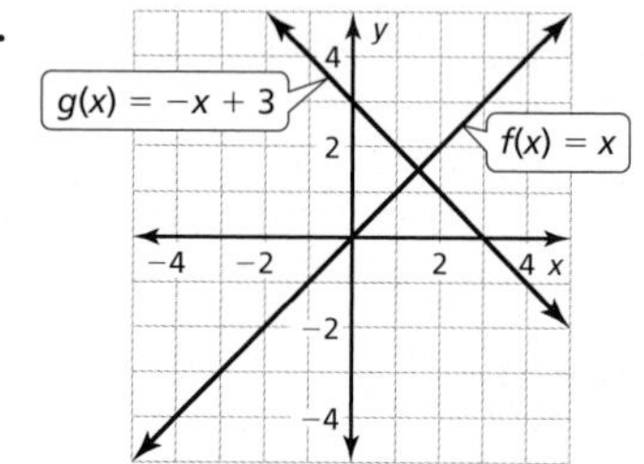

The graph of g is a reflection in the x-axis then a vertical translation 3 units up of the graph of f.

11. 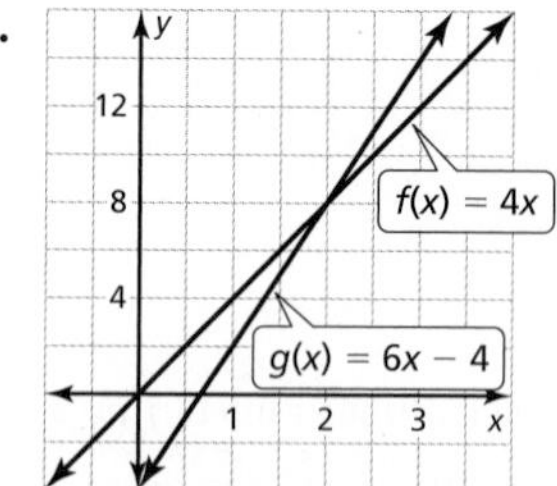

The graph of g is a vertical stretch by a factor of $\frac{3}{2}$ and a vertical translation 4 units up of the graph of f.

12. 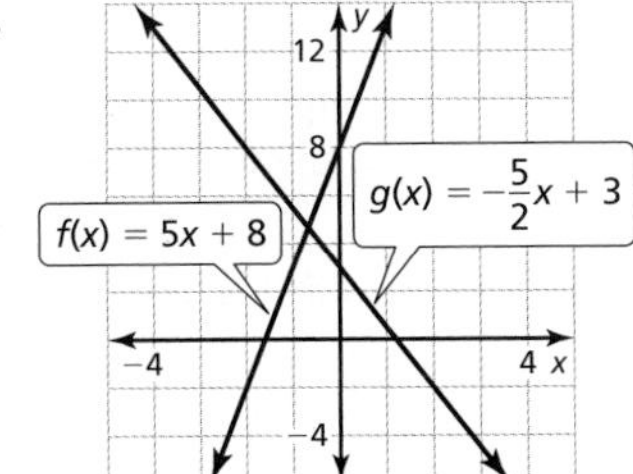

The graph of g is a reflection in the y-axis, a vertical shrink by a factor of $\frac{1}{2}$, and a vertical translation 1 unit down.

13. 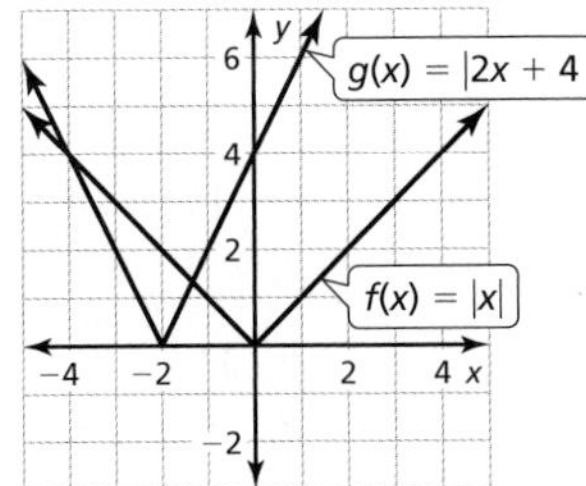

The graph of g is a horizontal translation 4 units left, then a horizontal shrink by a factor of $\frac{1}{2}$ of the graph of f.

14. **a.** m is the dependent variable and r is the independent variable.

b. domain: 0, 1, 2, 3, 4, 5, 6, 7, 8, 9, 10; range: 0, 3, 6, 9, 12, 15, 18, 21, 24, 27, 30; discrete; The number of video games rented must be a whole number.

c.

Money left (dollars)

(0, 30) (1, 27) (2, 24) (3, 21) (4, 18) (5, 15) (6, 12) (7, 9) (8, 6) (9, 3) (10, 0)

Videos rented

15. **a.** The slope is 125, so the climber ascends at a rate of 125 feet per hour; The y-intercept is 50, so the climber began the ascent at 50 feet above sea level.

b. 3.6 h; At the top, $f(x) = 500$. Setting 500 equal to $125x + 50$ and solving for x gives the time it takes to reach the top.

16. 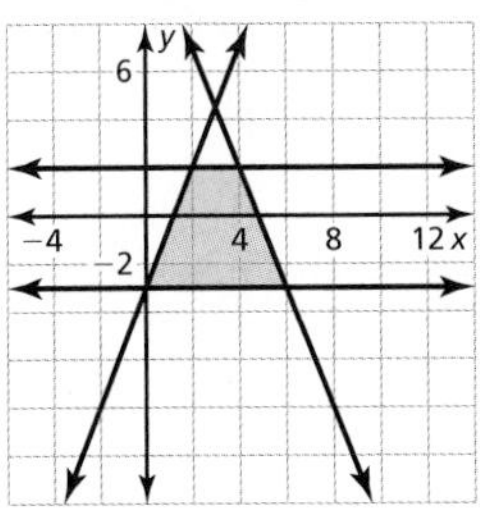

20 units^2

17. **a.** The number of downloads (in thousands) is the dependent variable and time is the independent variable.

b. 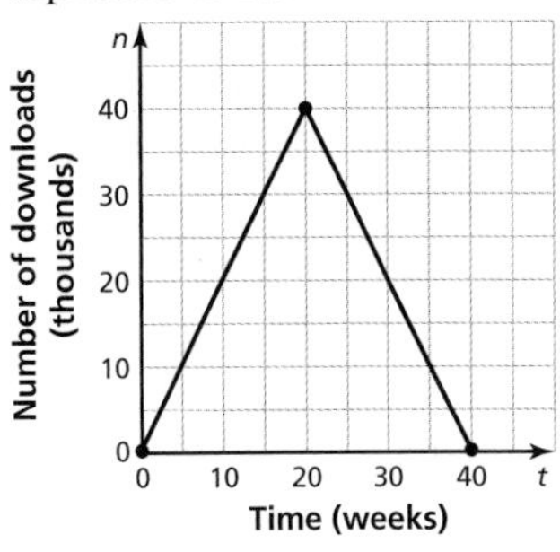

The transformations are a horizontal translation 20 units right, then a vertical stretch by a factor of 2, then a reflection in the t-axis, then a vertical translation 40 units up.

Chapter 3 College and Career Readiness

1. *Sample answer:* x: −4, −3, −2, −1 and y: 1, 2, 3, 4; x: −4, −3, −2, −1 and y: 0, 1, 3, 5
2. 8 days
3. A
4. D
5. C
6. $\leq$
7. yes; domain: $h \geq 0$; range: $p \geq 0$
8. C
9. A, B, D, E
10. 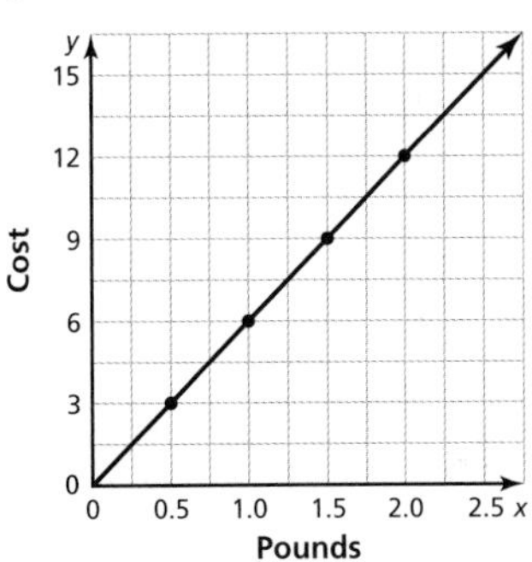

yes; The pounds can be any value, so the domain is continuous.

11. $a = -4$
12. B
13. D
14. **a.** 3 months; $3000 - 625m \geq 700$, so $m \leq 3.68$

b. June, July, August, September

Chapter 4

Chapter 4 Prepare

1. $(-5, -2)$
2. $(2, 0)$
3. C
4. E
5. $y = -5 + x$
6. $y = -\frac{1}{3} - 2x$
7. $y = 4x - 5$
8. $y = \frac{1}{4}x + 7$
9. $y = 4x - \frac{1}{2}$
10. $y = -\frac{3}{4}x - 1$

11. Points in Quadrant I move to Quadrant III, points in Quadrant II move to Quadrant IV, points in Quadrant III move to Quadrant I, points in Quadrant IV move to Quadrant II, points on the positive x- or y-axis move to the negative x- or y-axis respectively, points on the negative x- or y-axis move to the positive x- or y-axis respectively, and a point on the origin stays at the origin.

4.1 Practice

1. $y = 2x + 9$
3. $y = -3x$
5. $y = \frac{2}{3}x - 8$
7. $y = \frac{1}{3}x + 2$
9. $y = -\frac{4}{3}x$
11. $y = -3x + 10$
13. $y = -4$
15. $y = 2.8x + 5.2$
17. $f(x) = x + 2$
19. $f(x) = -\frac{1}{4}x - 2$
21. $f(x) = -10x - 4$
23. $f(x) = -2x + 1$
25. The slope and the y-intercept were substituted incorrectly: $y = 2x + 7$
27. \$12,260
29. your friend; If f is a function, then the line is not vertical.
31. $y = \frac{5}{3}x - 1$
33. $f(x) = mx + b$; b is the y-intercept. m is the slope.

4.1 Review & Refresh

34. $y = \frac{1}{4}$
35. no solution
36. all real numbers
37. $y = -\frac{1}{3}x + 5$
38.

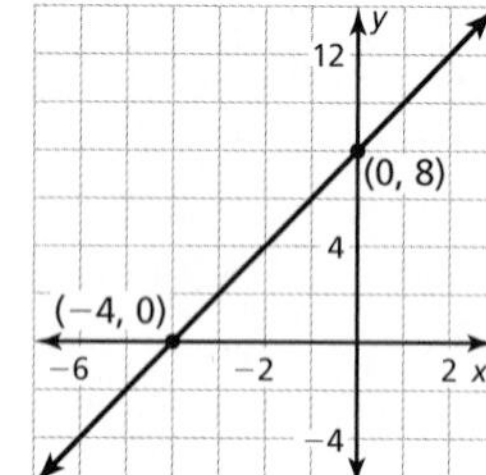

39. a. The graph of g is a reflection in the x-axis, a vertical shrink by a factor of $\frac{1}{2}$, a horizontal translation 2 units left, and then a vertical translation 4 units down of the graph of f.

b.

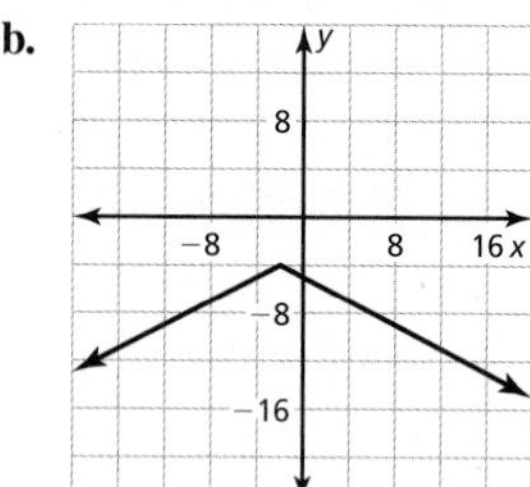

40. $\frac{1}{2}$
41. slope: 0; y-intercept: 9.5
42. slope: -10; y-intercept: -7
43. not a solution
44. $a = 1.25$ represents the factor that your weekly earnings increase by; $k = 120$ represents a \$120 one-time bonus.

4.2 Practice

1. $y - 1 = 2(x - 2)$
3. $y + 4 = -6(x - 7)$
5. $y = -3\left(x - \frac{5}{6}\right)$
7. $y + 12 = -\frac{2}{5}(x - 5)$
9. $y = 2x - 5$
11. $y = -\frac{1}{2}x + 1$
13. $y = -2x + 16$
15. $y = -9$
17. $y = \frac{2}{3}x + 7$
19. $f(x) = -3x + 4$
21. $f(x) = -\frac{1}{2}x$
23. $f(x) = \frac{1}{4}x + \frac{7}{4}$
25. no; y does not increase at a constant rate.
27. a. yes; The total cost increases at a constant rate.
    b. \$49; \$104.50
    c. 11 days
29. The coordinates substituted into the point-slope form were not from the same point; $y - 2 = \frac{1}{3}(x - 1)$ or $y - 3 = \frac{1}{3}(x - 4)$
31. The graph of $y - 1 = 2(x + 3)$ is a horizontal translation 3 units left and a vertical translation 1 unit up of the graph of $y = 2x$; The graph of $y - k = m(x - h)$ is a translation h units vertically and k units horizontally of the graph of $y = n$.
33. a. Account B; Account A
    b. Account B; Account A
    c. Account C; Account A

4.2 Review & Refresh

35. $\frac{1}{5}$
36. $-\frac{1}{8}$
37. $-\frac{7}{2}$
38. $\frac{2}{3}$
39. $y - 1 = \frac{2}{3}(x + 9)$
40. The graph of p is a horizontal translation 6 units right of the graph of $f(x) = |x|$. The graph of q is a vertical translation 6 units down of the graph of $f(x) = |x|$.
41. continuous; The number of years can be any value greater than or equal to 0.
42. $f(x) = -x + 2$
43. The graph of T is a vertical translation 25 units up of the graph of C.
44. $r < 2$ or $r \geq 7$

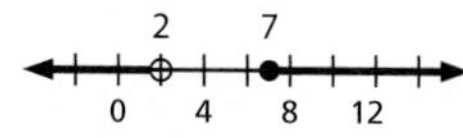

45.

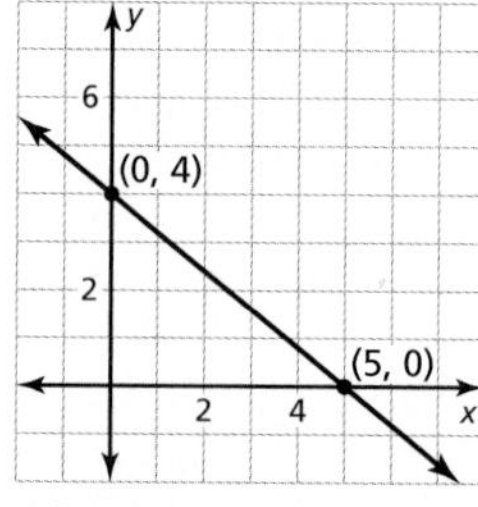

x-intercept: 5;
y-intercept: 4

46.

x-intercept: 6;
y-intercept: -3

4.3 Practice

1. lines a and b; They have the same slope.
3. lines a and c; They have the same slope.
5. none; None of the lines have the same slope.
7. $y = -3x$
9. $y = \frac{1}{3}x + 2$
11. None are parallel or perpendicular; None of the lines have the same slope or slopes that are negative reciprocals of each other.

13. None are parallel; Lines b and c are perpendicular; None of the lines have the same slope and the slope of line b is the negative reciprocal of the slope of line c.

15. Lines a and b are parallel; Line c is perpendicular to lines a and b; Lines a and b have the same slope and the slope of line c is the negative reciprocal of the slopes of lines a and b.

17. $y = 5x - 25$

19. $y = -\frac{1}{4}x + \frac{9}{4}$

21. $(-1, 1)$

23. Perpendicular lines have negative reciprocal slopes, not just reciprocal slopes; $y - (-5) = -3(x - 4)$; $y + 5 = -3x + 12$; $y = -3x + 7$

25. yes; no; Opposite sides are parallel but adjacent sides are not perpendicular, so it is a parallelogram but not a rectangle.

27. never; Perpendicular lines have opposite reciprocal slopes, so one must be positive and the other must be negative.

29. sometimes; They are perpendicular when the slopes are negative reciprocals, otherwise they will not be perpendicular.

31. no; The lines that form the angle are not perpendicular.

4.3 Review & Refresh

32. not a function; The input values of -1 and 1 are each paired with more than one output value.

33. 100 gal

34. 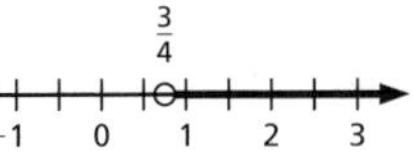

35. 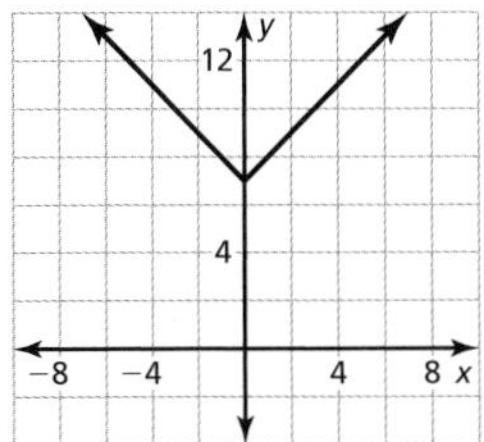

The graph of g is a vertical translation 7 units up of the graph of f; domain: all real numbers; range: $y \geq 7$

36. 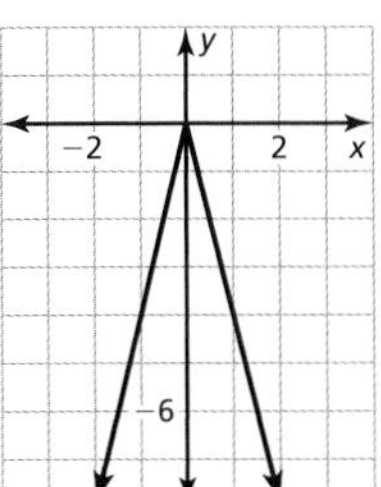

The graph of h is a reflection in the x-axis, and a vertical stretch by a factor of 4 of the graph of f; domain: all real numbers; range: $y \leq 0$

37. 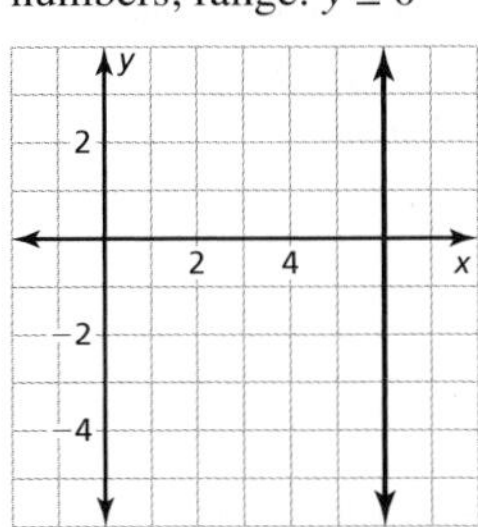

38. 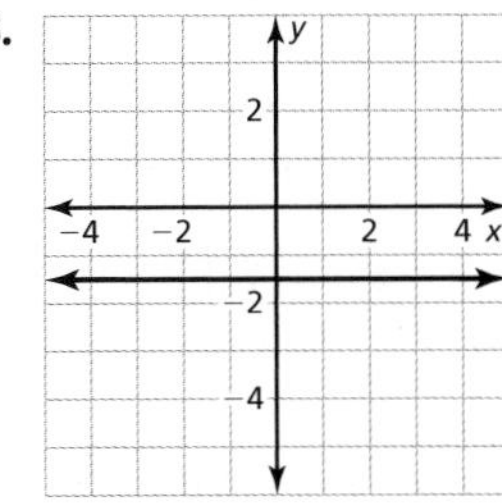

39. 1.41 kg, 1.42 kg, or 1.43 kg

40. a. $y = -4x + 19$

b. $y = \frac{1}{4}x + 2$

41. $y = -1.8x - 4.5$

42. $a = -\frac{2}{3}$; $a = 6$

43. 279 in.^{2}

4.4 Practice

1. a. \$800

b. 16 GB

c. increases

3. positive linear correlation

5. no correlation

7. 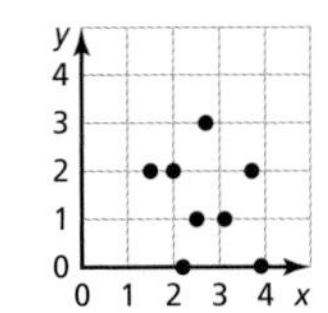

no correlation

9. a. $y = 1.55x - 12$

b. The slope of 1.55 means a homeowner saves about \$1550 on electric bills each year after installing solar panels. The y-intercept of -12 represents the total cost to install the solar panels was about \$12,000.

11. no; A line of fit should have about as many points above the line as below it, but does not have to pass through any data points.

13. a. *Sample answer:*

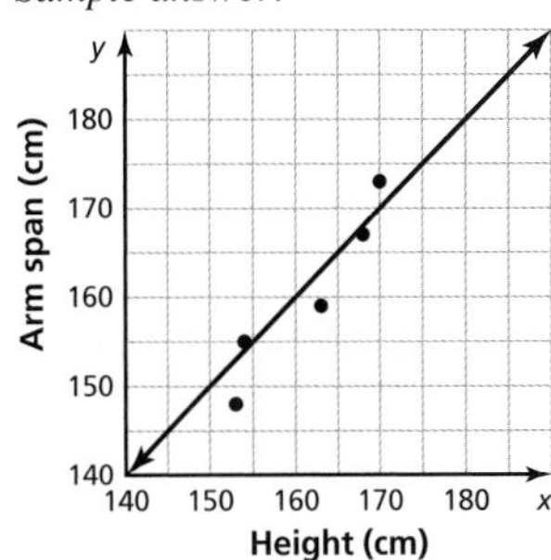

b. $y = x$ is the equation of the line of fit, where y is the length, in centimeters, of a person's arm span and x is the height, in centimeters, of the person. The coefficient of 1 means a person's arm span increases by about 1 centimeter for every 1 centimeter increase in height.

15. no; The data points do not have a linear trend.

4.4 Review & Refresh

17. no; The data points do not have a linear trend.

18. a. $y = -4x - 16$

b. $y = \frac{1}{4}x + 1$

19. 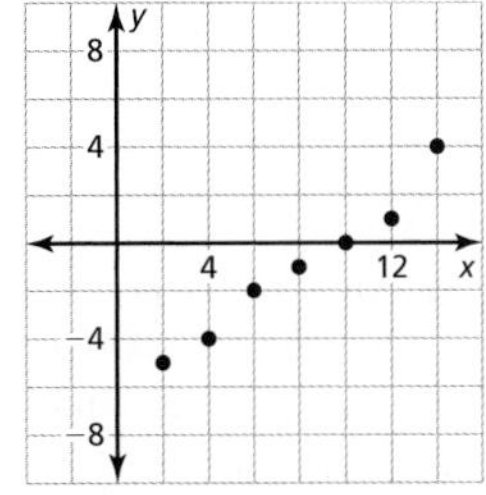

positive linear correlation

SELECTED ANSWERS

20. 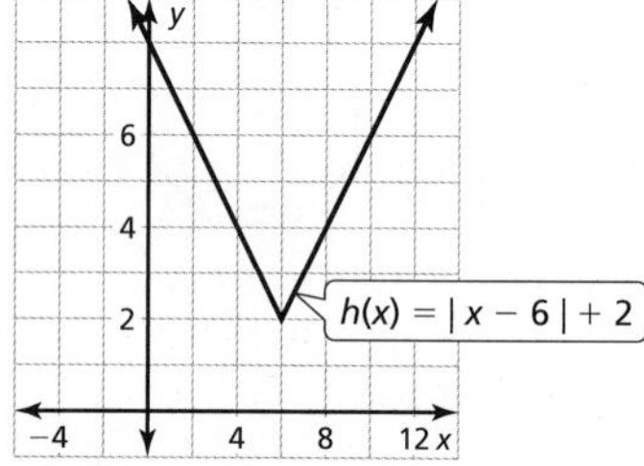

The graph of h is a vertical translation 2 units up of the graph of f.

21. 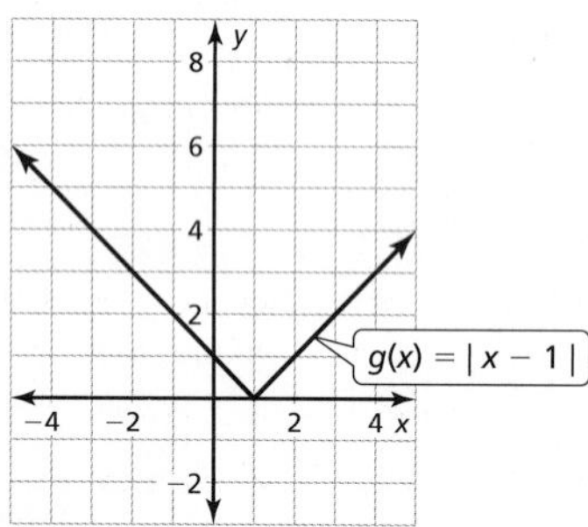

The graph of g is a horizontal translation 5 units left of the graph of f.

22. Company A; You can keep the site running for 13 months at Company A. You can keep the site running for 10 months at Company B.

23. yes; y decreases at a constant rate; $y = -2.25x + 9.25$

24. $w = \dfrac{P - 2\ell}{2}$, or $w = \frac{1}{2}P - \ell$

25. 40%

4.5 Practice

1. no; The residual points are not evenly dispersed about the horizontal axis.

3. yes; The residual points are evenly dispersed about the horizontal axis.

5. yes; The residual points are evenly dispersed about the horizontal axis.

7. $y = 1.4x + 16$; $r = 0.999$; strong positive correlation

9. **a.** $y = x + 7$

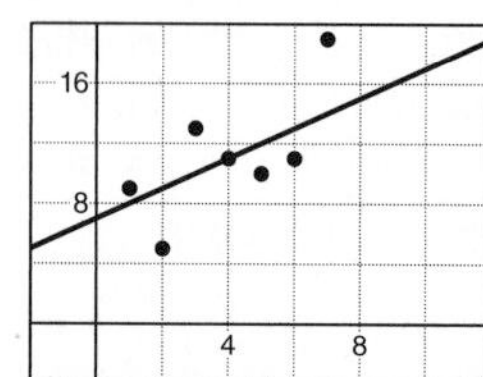

b. $r = 0.619$; weak positive correlation

c. The slope of 1 means the number of people who volunteer increases by about 1 each day. The y-intercept of 6.75 has no meaning in this context because there is no day 0.

11. **a.** $y = -0.2x + 20$

b. $r = -0.968$; strong negative correlation

c. The slope of -0.2 means the selling price decreases by about \$200 for every increase in mileage of 1000 miles. The y-intercept of 19.7 has no meaning in this context because a used car cannot have 0 milage.

d. \$15,000

e. \$18,800

13. The data do not have a strong positive correlation; The data have a strong negative correlation.

15. There is a negative correlation and a casual relationship because the more time you spend talking on the phone, the less charge there is left in the battery.

17. A correlation is unlikely. The number of hats you own is not related to the size of your head.

19. *Sample answer:* ACT math score and SAT math score

21. **a.** $y = 513.5x - 298$; $r = 0.993$; strong positive correlation

b. no; The year does not determine the number of text messages sent.

c. 25.5; -128; 117.5; 50; -63.5

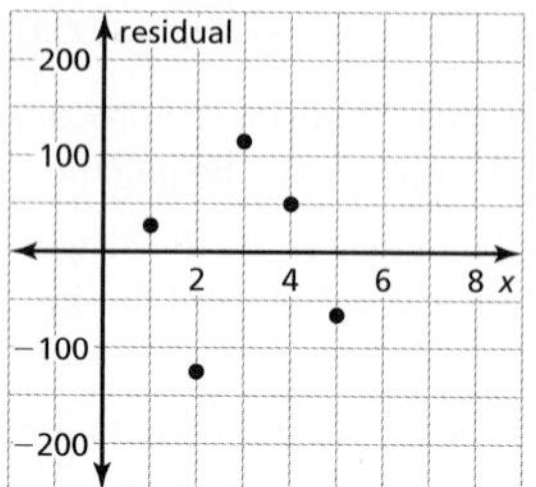

The equation $y = 513.5x - 298$ is a good fit.

d. *Sample answer:* part(a); The correlation coefficient is a single value, which is easily interpreted where as interpreting the scatter plot of the residuals is more subjective.

23. your cousin; The point (5, 8.5) is not close to the other data values, so there is no correlation.

4.5 Review & Refresh

25. $w \le 25$

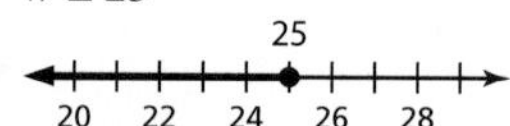

26. $y > -\frac{8}{3}$

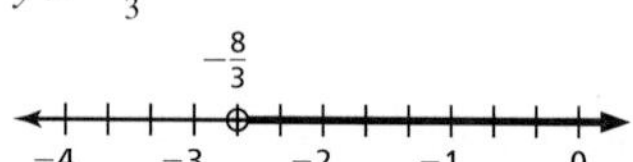

27. yes; no; There may be other factors that can cause an illness.

28. \$25

29. linear; The rate of change is constant.

30. $y = \frac{1}{2}x - 7$

31. positive linear correlation

32. Interpolation is using a graph or its equation to approximate a value between two known values, and extrapolation is using a graph or its equation to predict a value outside the range of known values.

33. $y = -2x - 6$

34. None are parallel; Lines a and b are perpendicular; None of the lines have the same slope and the slope of line a is the negative reciprocal of the slope of line b.

35. $d = -5, d = 5$

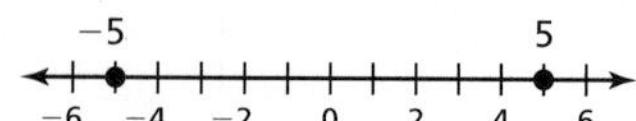

36. $b = \frac{31}{8}$

37. $y = 2.1x - 8$; $r = 0.980$; strong positive correlation

38. $y = -1.3x + 8$; $r = -0.886$; strong negative correlation

4.6 Practice

1. 15, 28, 41
3. 5
5. $-\frac{1}{3}$
7. 31, 34, 37
9. 36, 41, 46
11. 0.1, −0.2, −0.5
13. 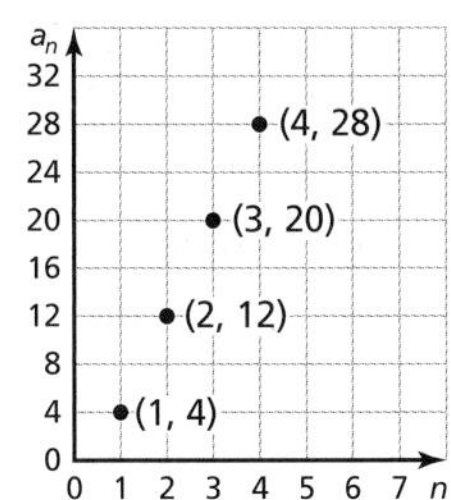

15. 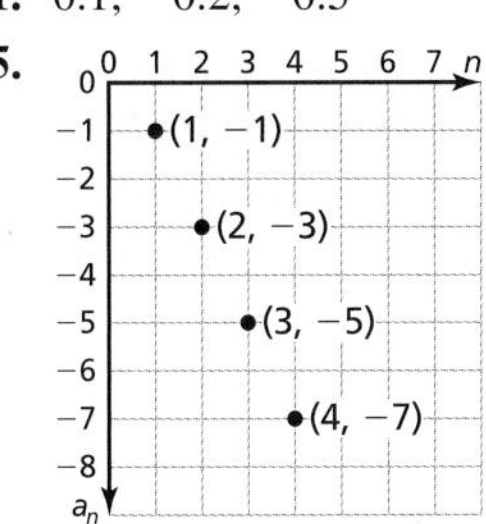

17. 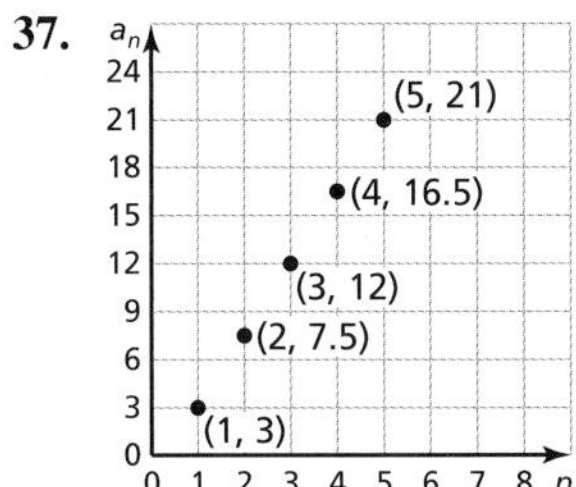

19. not an arithmetic sequence; Consecutive terms do not have a common difference.
21. arithmetic sequence; Consecutive terms have a common difference of −15.
23. arithmetic sequence; 13
25. not an arithmetic sequence
27. 4, 6, 8, 10; yes; Consecutive terms have a common difference of 2.
29. $a_n = n - 6$; 4
31. $a_n = \frac{1}{2}n$; 5
33. $a_n = -10n + 20$; −80
35. −1 is added each time, not 1; The common difference is −1.
37. 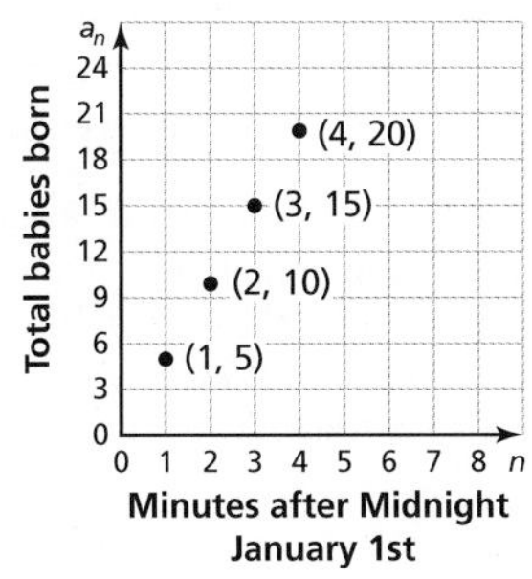

39. a. $f(n) = 5n$

    b. 20 min
41. B
43. a. 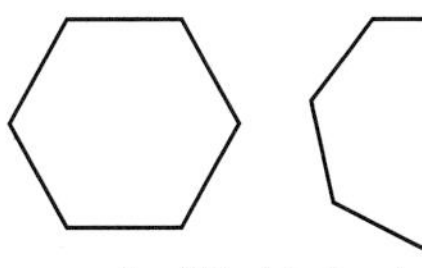 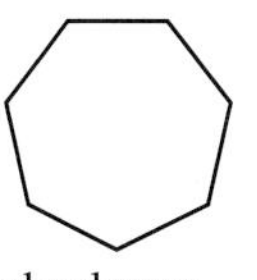 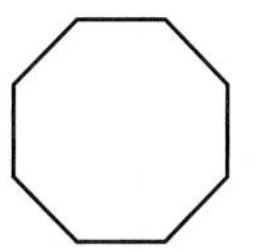

    b. a regular 22-sided polygon
45. the number of dots in each figure: 1, 3, 6, 10, 15, …; the number of dots in the bottom row: 1, 2, 3, 4, 5, …
47. 119 logs
49. 7 min
51. a. arithmetic sequence; Consecutive terms have a common difference of $2x$.

    b. not an arithmetic sequence; Consecutive terms have a common difference.

4.6 Review & Refresh

52. Lines a and b have the same slope, so they are parallel. The slope of line c is the negative reciprocal of the slope of lines a and b, so line c is perpendicular to both lines a and b.
53. The graph of g is a horizontal shrink by a factor of $\frac{1}{5}$ and a vertical translation 2 units down of the graph of f.
54. The graph of g is a reflection in the x-axis and a vertical translation 3 units up of the graph of f.
55. $f(n) = 6n + 17$
56. a. 357 shoppers

    b. 297 shoppers
57. rational; $\dfrac{9}{13}$ is written as $\dfrac{a}{b}$, where a and b are integers, and $b \neq 0$.
58. irrational; 7 is not a perfect square.
59. rational; 49 is a perfect square.
60. irrational; The decimal form of π neither terminates nor repeats.
61. a. 65°F

    b. 53°F
62. not an arithmetic sequence
63. arithmetic sequence; 5

4.7 Practice

1. −21; −11; 2; $\frac{7}{2}$; 5
3. 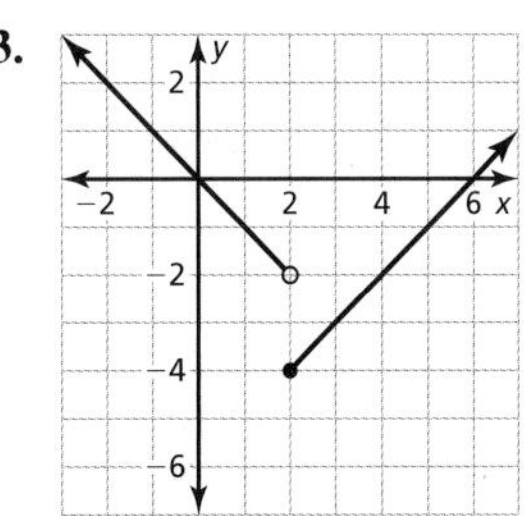

   domain: all real numbers; range: $y \geq -4$
5. 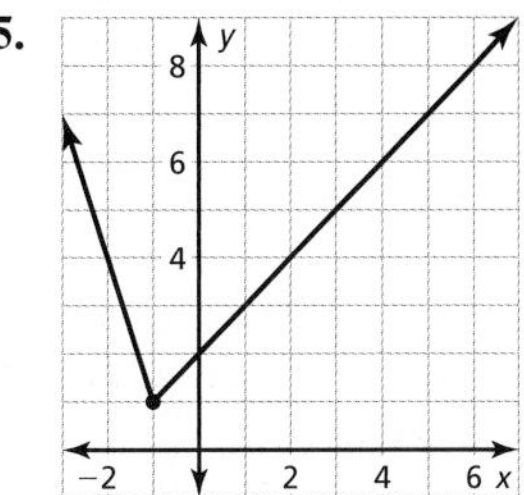

   domain: all real numbers; range: $y \geq 1$

7.

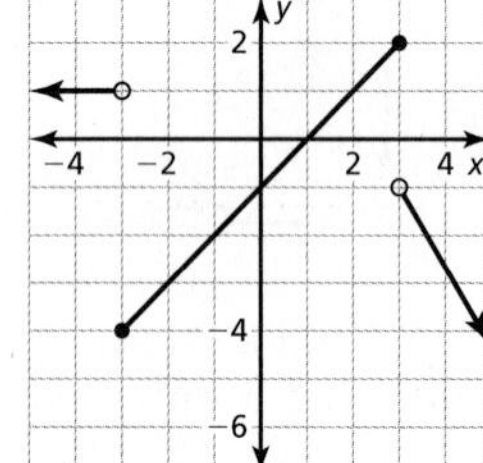

domain: all real numbers; range: $y \leq 2$

9. 240 mi

11. $f(x) = \begin{cases} x + 2, & \text{if } x < 0 \\ 2, & \text{if } x \geq 0 \end{cases}$

13. $f(x) = \begin{cases} -x, & \text{if } x < 4 \\ -x + 1, & \text{if } x \geq 4 \end{cases}$

15. $f(x) = \begin{cases} 1, & \text{if } x \leq -2 \\ 2x, & \text{if } 2 < x \leq 0 \\ -\frac{1}{2}x + 2, & \text{if } x > 0 \end{cases}$

17. *Sample answer:* A piecewise function contains pieces of more than one function, and a linear function is a line for the entire domain.

19.

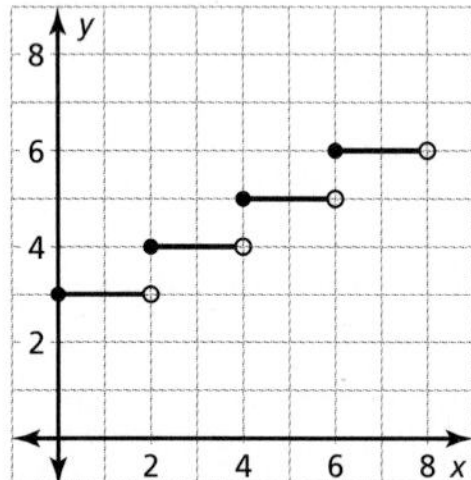

domain: $0 \leq x < 8$; range: 3, 4, 5, 6

21. $f(x) = \begin{cases} 40, & \text{if } 0 < x \leq 10 \\ 70, & \text{if } 10 < x \leq 20 \\ 120, & \text{if } 20 < x \leq 30 \\ 200, & \text{if } x > 30 \end{cases}$

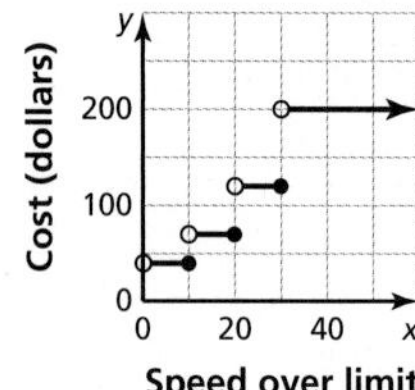

23. $y = \begin{cases} -x + 1, & \text{if } x < 0 \\ x + 1, & \text{if } x \geq 0 \end{cases}$

25. $y = \begin{cases} -4x + 4, & \text{if } x < 1 \\ 4x - 4, & \text{if } x \geq 1 \end{cases}$

27. $y = \begin{cases} x - 1, & \text{if } x < 3 \\ -x + 5, & \text{if } x \geq 3 \end{cases}$

29. **a.** $f(x) = 2|x - 3|$

b. $f(x) = \begin{cases} -2x + 6, & \text{if } x < 3 \\ 2x - 6, & \text{if } x \geq 3 \end{cases}$

31. B, C, D

33. **a.** The open circle at (2, 4) changes to a closed circle and the closed circle at (2, −3) changes to an open circle; The domain does not change. The range changes from $y < 4$ to $y \leq 4$.

b. It does not change; The domain and range do not change; Because the value of each expression at $x = 1$ is 2, the two pieces of the function have the same endpoint. So, the graph does not change.

35. no; The input value of 3 has two outputs.

37. Answers will vary. *Sample answer:*

$f(x) = \begin{cases} 10\%, & \text{if } 0 < x < 50 \\ 20\%, & \text{if } 50 \leq x < 75 \\ 30\%, & \text{if } 75 \leq x < 100 \\ 40\%, & \text{if } x \geq 100 \end{cases}$

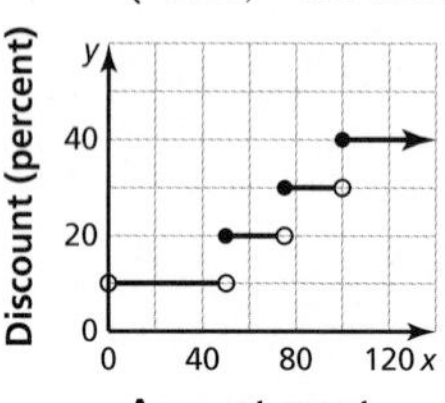

Answers will vary.

39. $f(x) = \begin{cases} x, & \text{if } 0 \leq x \leq 2 \\ 2x - 2, & \text{if } 2 < x \leq 8 \\ x + 6, & \text{if } 8 < x \leq 9 \end{cases}$

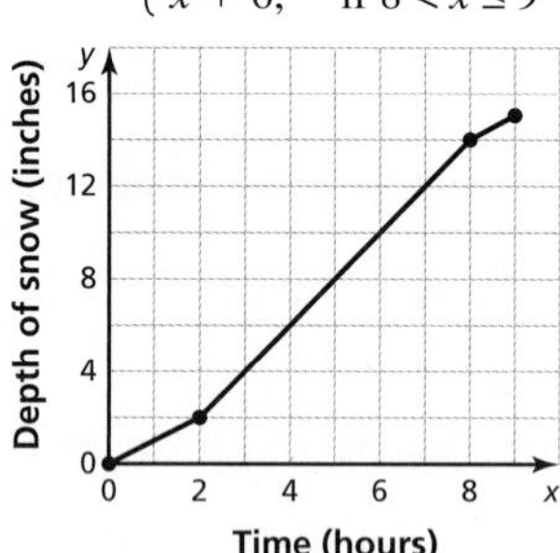

15 in.

4.7 Review & Refresh

40.

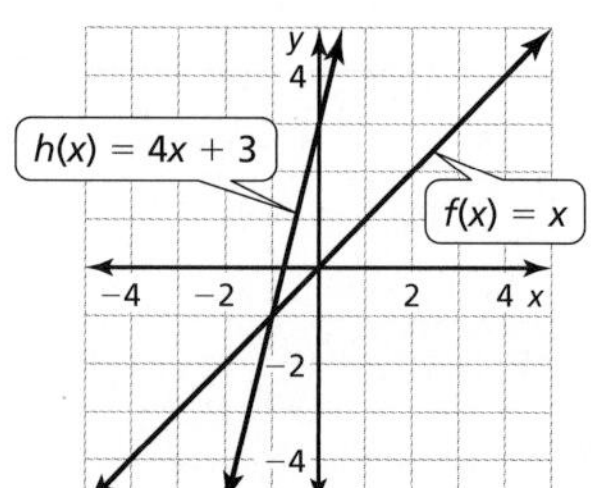

The graph of h is a vertical stretch by a factor of 4 and a vertical translation 3 units up of the graph of f.

41.

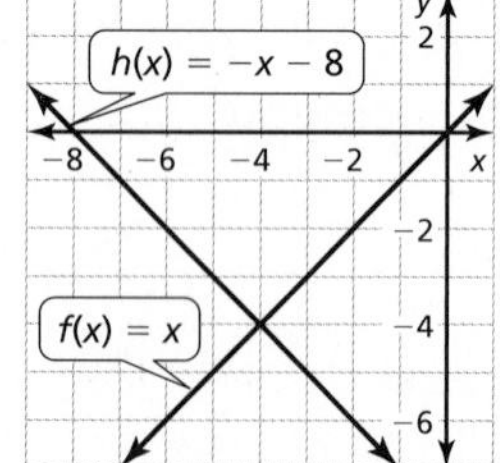

The graph of h is a reflection in the x-axis and a vertical translation 8 units down of the graph of f.

42. 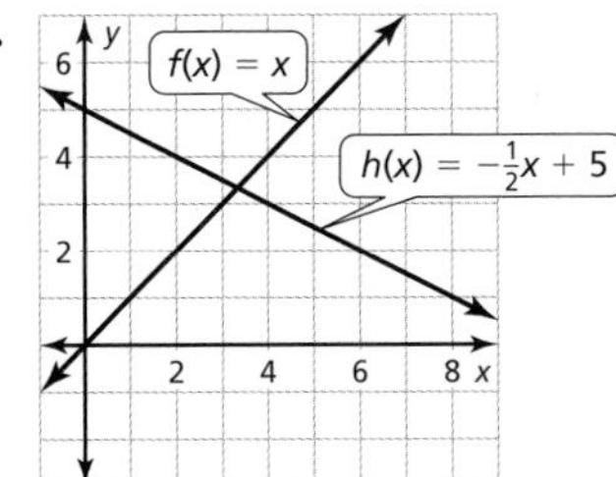

The graph of h is a vertical shrink by a factor of $\frac{1}{2}$, a reflection in the x-axis, and a vertical translation 5 units up of the graph of f.

43. negative linear correlation

44. $x = 8$

45. $x = -3$

46. 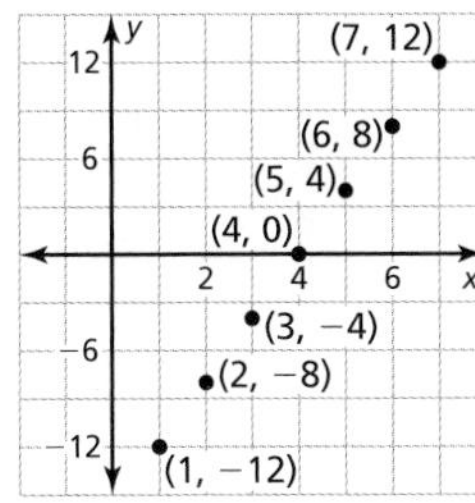

47. undefined

48. 16 chaperones

49. 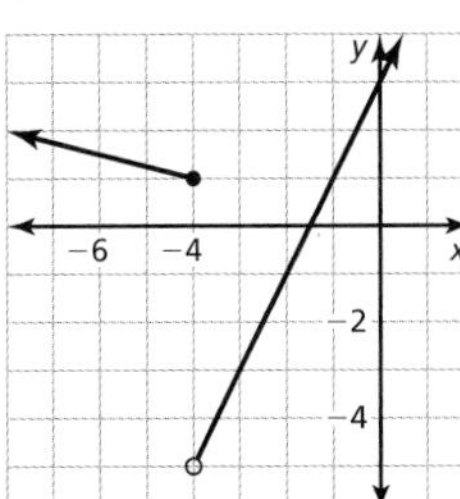

domain: all real numbers; range: $y > -5$

50. $f(x) = -x + 3$

51. $f(x) = -\frac{4}{5}x - 4$

52. There may be a positive correlation but not a causal relationship. An increase in your quiz score will not cause your test score to increase.

53. -4; 6

Chapter 4 Review

1. $y = -\frac{1}{2}x + 1$

2. $y = \frac{2}{3}x + 3$

3. \$1140

4. $y - 7 = -(x - 4)$

5. $f(x) = x - 5$

6. $f(x) = -4$

7. $f(x) = -\dfrac{5}{3}x + 18$

8. $y - \dfrac{C}{B} = -\dfrac{A}{B}(x - 0)$

9. \$22.25

10. Lines a and b are parallel; None of the lines are perpendicular; Lines a and b have the same slope and none of them have negative reciprocal slopes.

11. None of the lines are parallel; Lines b and c are perpendicular; None of the lines have the same slope and the slope of line b is the negative reciprocal of the slope of line c.

12. $y = -4x + 9$

13. $y = \frac{1}{2}x - 4$

14. 4 h

15. positive linear correlation

16. $y = 10.89x + 54.6$; The slope of 10.89 shows that the salary cap increases by about \$10.89 million each year. The y-intercept of 54.6 represents the salary cap at the beginning of the season in 2013, in millions of dollars.

17. a. $y = 0.50x - 23.5$; $r \approx 0.974$; strong positive correlation

b. 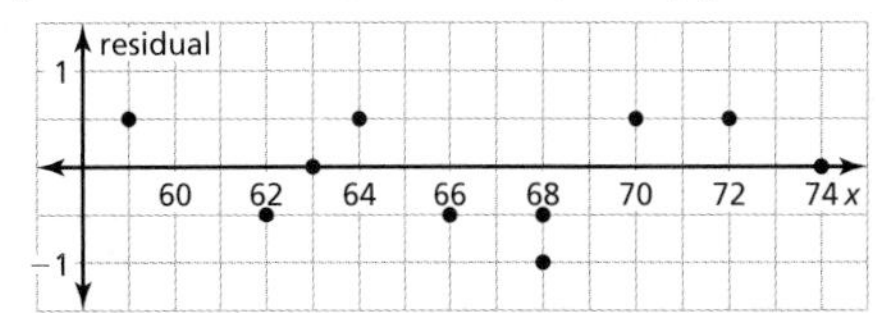

c. *Sample answer:* no; Height does not determine shoe size.

18. $a_n = 6n$; 180

19. $a_n = 3n - 12$; 78

20. yes; The points lie on a line.

21. Each molecule added to the group increases the number of atoms by 3; 69 atoms

22. a. 3

b. -10

23. 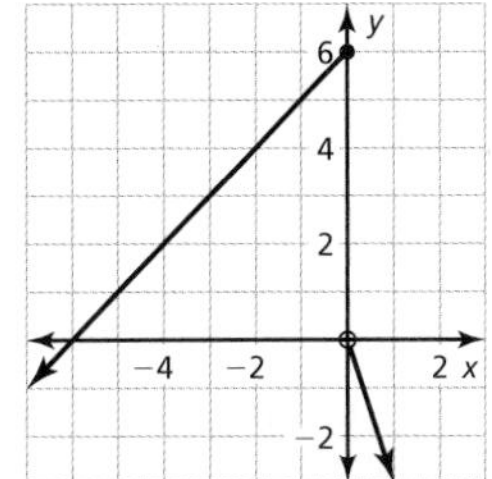

domain: all real numbers; range: $y \le 6$

24. 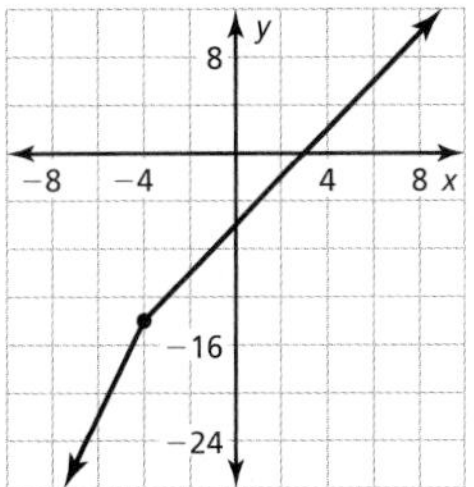

domain: all real numbers; range: all real numbers

25. $y = \begin{cases} -x + 15, & \text{if } x < 0 \\ x + 15, & \text{if } x \ge 0 \end{cases}$

26. $y = \begin{cases} -4x - 20, & \text{if } x < -5 \\ 4x + 20, & \text{if } x \ge -5 \end{cases}$

27. $y = \begin{cases} -2x - 7, & \text{if } x < -2 \\ 2x + 1, & \text{if } x \ge -2 \end{cases}$

28. $f(x) = \begin{cases} 65, & \text{if } 0 < x \le 1 \\ 100, & \text{if } 1 < x \le 2 \\ 135, & \text{if } 2 < x \le 3 \end{cases}$

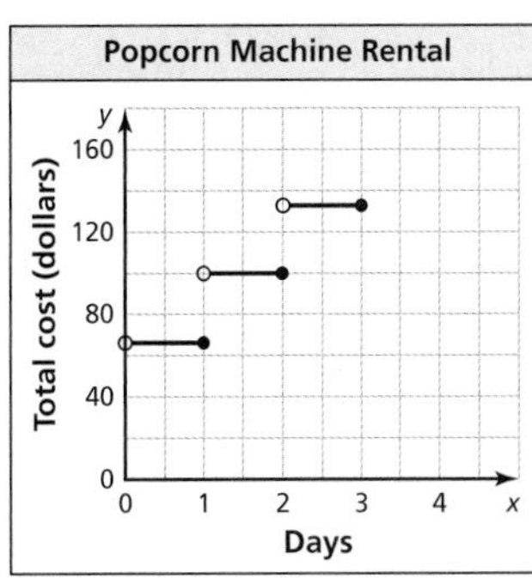

Chapter 4 Mathematical Practices (Chapter Review)

1. the first graph; the total amount you have paid after each month

2. *Sample answer:* Test two consecutive integer values represented by two different functions, such as $x = 10$ and $x = 11$.

Chapter 4 Practice Test

1. 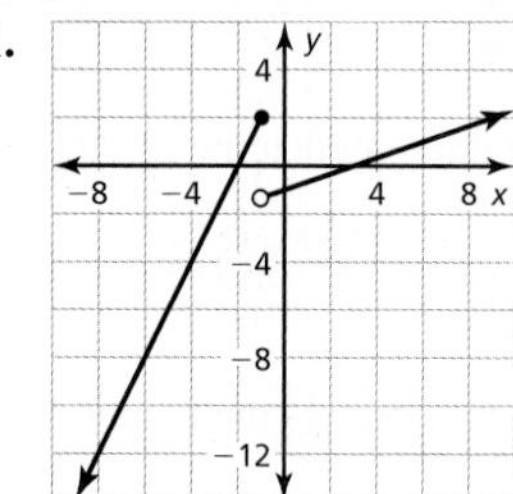

domain: all real numbers; range: all real numbers

2. $y = \frac{2}{5}x - 7$
3. $y = -3x + 6$
4. $y = 3x - 2$
5. $y = -4x + 5$
6. $y - 2 = 10(x - 6)$
7. $y - 2 = -\frac{1}{3}(x + 3)$ or $y + 1 = -\frac{1}{3}(x - 6)$
8. $f(x) = 3x + 6$
9. None of the lines are parallel; Lines 1 and 2 are perpendicular; None of the lines have the same slope, but the slope of line 1 is the negative reciprocal of the slope of line 2.
10. **a.** 114
    b. row 17
11. $g(x) = -\frac{6}{5}(x - 3) + \frac{34}{5} = -\frac{6}{5}x + \frac{52}{5}$
12. **a.** *Sample answer:* $y = \frac{1}{5}x + 300$; The slope of $\frac{1}{5}$ means the attendance increases by about 1 person for every additional \$5 spent on advertising. The intercept of 300 means that if no money is spent on advertising, about 300 people attend the festival.
    b. more or less evenly dispersed about the horizontal axis; The line of best fit models the data well.
    c. There may be a casual relationship in the data but the correlation may be caused by other factors, such as the quality of the attractions each year.
    d. 2000 people
13. *Sample answer:* $y = \begin{cases} 0, & \text{if } x \le -3 \\ x, & \text{if } -3 < x \le 1 \\ 1, & \text{if } x > 1 \end{cases}$

Chapter 4 College and Career Readiness

1. C
2. A, B, C, F
3. D
4. **a.** discrete; The number of new players must be a whole number.
   b. 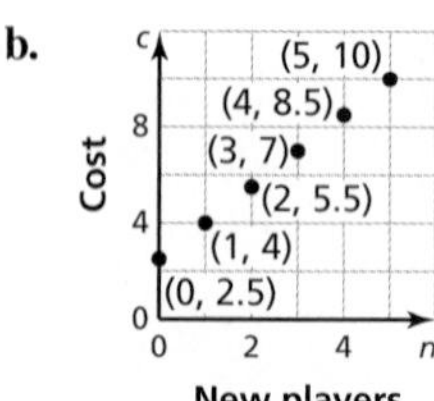

5. C
6. +; <; −; ≥
7. A
8. B

9. **a.** (92, −6), (78, 96), (60, −10), (84, 58), (98, −64), (72, 94), (54, −72), (68, 26)
   b. no; The residuals form a ∩-shaped pattern.

Chapter 5

Chapter 5 Prepare

1. 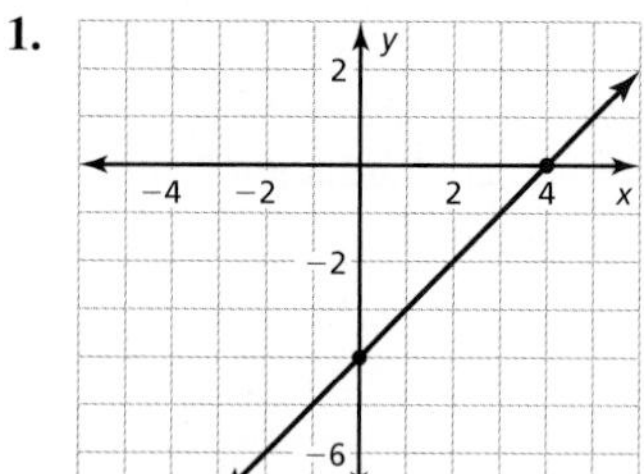

2. 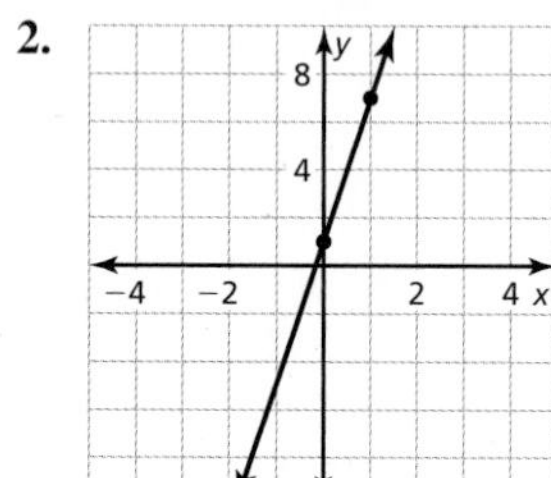

3. 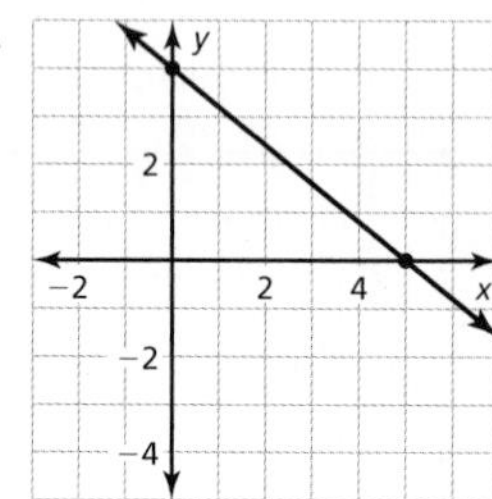

4. 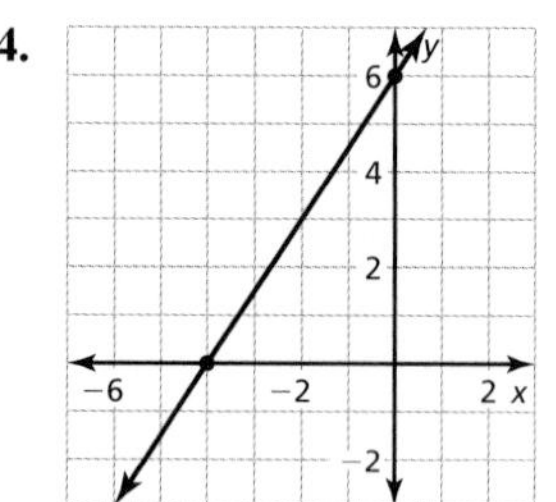

5. $m > 5$
6. $t \le -4$

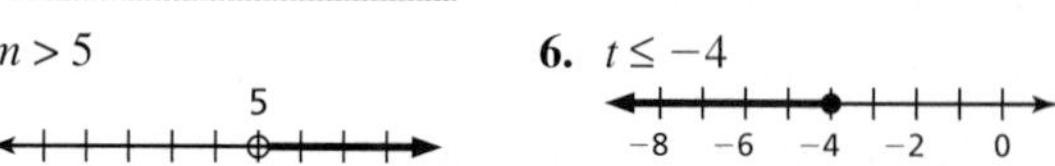

7. $a \le 9$

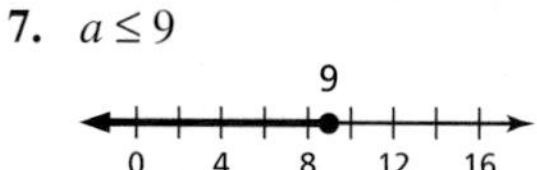

8. $z > 12$

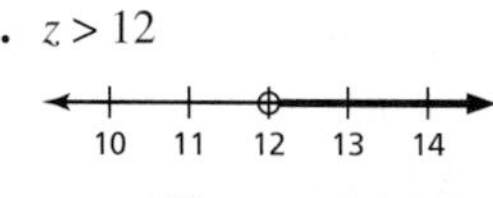

9. $k < 6$

10. $w \ge -\frac{12}{5}$

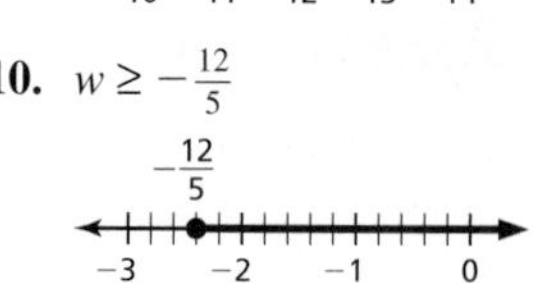

11. The two lines intersect.

5.1 Practice

1. yes
3. no
5. no
7. (1, −3)
9. (3, 4)
11. (−9, −1)
13. (−1, 2)
15. (0, −5.5)
17. (10, 5)
19. (1.2, 1.4)
21. The solution needs to be an ordered pair; (2, 3)
23. 30 min on the elliptical trainer, 10 min on the stationary bike
25. $m\angle X = 32°$, $m\angle Y = 58°$
27. **a.** yes; Because $y = 4.5x$ and $y = 3x + 1.5$ intersect at (1, 4.5), after one hour, you and your friend will be 4.5 miles from the trailhead.
    b. you; 1.5 h; It will take you $18 \div 4.5 = 4$ hours, and your friend $(18 - 1.5) \div 3 = 5.5$ hours.

5.1 Review & Refresh

29. $y = 2x + 3$

30. $y = -3x + 20$

31. *Sample answer:* $y + 5 = \frac{2}{5}(x - 12)$; $y = \frac{2}{5}x - \frac{49}{5}$

32. $n = 5$

33. $r = -12$

34. $p = 8$

35. $k = 23$

36. arithmetic sequence; Consecutive terms have a common difference.

37. $(-4, 0)$

38. The model is a good fit. The absolute values of the residuals are relatively small.

39. x-intercept: $\frac{15}{2}$; y-intercept: 3

40. $$f(x) = \begin{cases} 350, & \text{if } 0 < x \leq 7 \\ 360, & \text{if } 7 < x \leq 8 \\ 370, & \text{if } 8 < x \leq 9 \\ 380, & \text{if } 9 < x \leq 10 \end{cases}$$

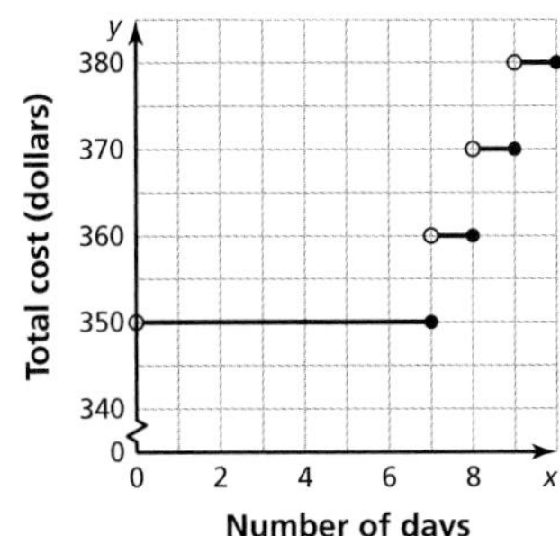

41. $y = -\frac{3}{4}x + 2$

42. all real numbers

5.2 Practice

1. *Sample answer:* Substitute $2y$ for x into $x + 4y = 30$.

3. *Sample answer:* Substitute $x - 15$ for $12y$ into $-3x + 12y = 3$.

5. *Sample answer:* Solve $x - y = -3$ for x then substitute that expression for x into $4x + 3y = -5$.

7. $(5, 3)$

9. $(-4, 5)$

11. $\left(4, \frac{3}{2}\right)$

13. $(6, 7)$

15. $(-9, 2)$

17. In Step 2, parenthesis should be used when substituting $3x + 4$ for $2y$. Because $4x - 4 = 12$, $x = 4$. The solution is $(4, 8)$.

19. 8 five-point problems, 30 two-point problems

21. *Sample answer:* $2x + y = 5$ and $2x - y = 55$

23. yes; Both equations have the term $-7x$, so you can substitute $42 - y$ for $-7x$ into the first equation and solve for y.

25. $x = 67$, $y = 23$

27. $a = 4$, $b = 5$

29. 47

5.2 Review & Refresh

31. $3x - 11$

32. $3d + 5$

33. $64v$

34. $\left(3, -\frac{1}{2}\right)$

35. a. 24 marbles
    b. 32 times

36. $$f(x) = \begin{cases} -3x + 2, & \text{if } x < 1 \\ x + 1, & \text{if } x \geq 1 \end{cases}$$

37. $a = -2$

38. $a_n = 9n - 23$; $a_{15} = 112$

39.

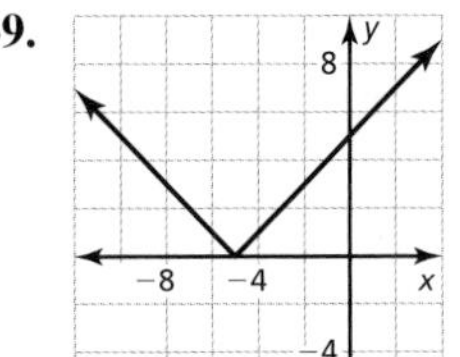

The graph of g is a horizontal translation 5 units left of the graph of f; domain: all real numbers; range: $y \geq 0$

40.

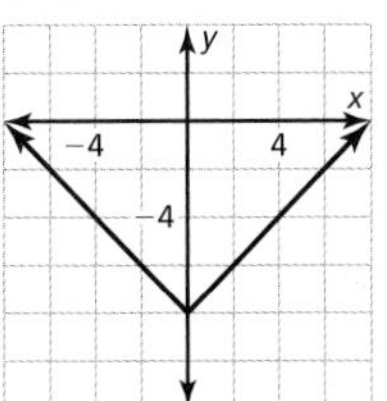

The graph of p is a vertical translation 8 units down of the graph of f; domain: all real numbers; range: $y \geq -8$

41. $(-3, 2)$

42. $x < \frac{1}{2}$ *or* $x > \frac{13}{2}$

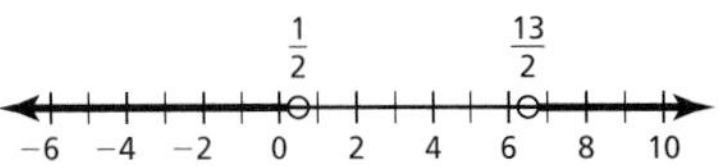

43. 80 shares of Stock A, 120 shares of Stock B

5.3 Practice

1. $(1, 6)$

3. $(4, 5)$

5. $(-1, 2)$

7. $(0, -10)$

9. $(1, 1)$

11. $(8, 3)$

13. $(-7, -12)$

15. $(5, -3)$

17. \$14.95, \$4.50

19. $5x + x \neq 4x$; $6x = 24$, $x = 4$

21. $(2, -1)$; *Sample answer:* elimination because y has the same coefficient in both equations

23. $(4, 6)$; *Sample answer:* substitution because the second equation is already solved for y

25. $(-5, 3)$; *Sample answer:* elimination because multiplying the first equation by 2 creates two equations with the same coefficient for x

27. *Sample answer:* $3x + 4y = 12$ and $3x - 4y = 6$

29. C, D; C because the result is $5x = 2$, D because the result is $-x - 2(-3x + 7) = 16$

31. 4.5 qt of 100% fruit juice, 1.5 qt of 20% fruit juice

33. Equation 1 can be rewritten as Equation 3 by adding $2(x + y)$ to the left and $2(6)$ to the right, and Equation 3 can be rewritten as Equation 1 by subtracting $2(x + y)$ from the left and $2(6)$ from the right. Because either system can be rewritten as the other. System 1 and System 2 have the same solution.

35. $(-5, 4, 2)$; *Sample answer:* Subtract Equation 2 from Equation 1. The resulting equation only has 1 variable, y, so use it to solve for y. Substitute this result in Equation 3 and solve for x. Substitute the values of x and y in Equation 2 and solve for z.

5.3 Review & Refresh

36. no solution

37. $t = \frac{3}{8}$

38. *Sample answer:* Multiply each side of Equation 1 by 3. Add the equations to eliminate y. Solve the resulting equation for x. Substitute the value of x into one of the original equations and solve for y.

39. a. $y = \frac{2}{3}x + \frac{4}{3}$

b. $y = -\frac{3}{2}x - \frac{19}{2}$

40. $(-8, -30)$

41. $(0, -2)$

42. no; A vertical line can be drawn through more than one point on the graph.

43. not a solution

44.

domain: all real numbers; range: $y \geq 1$

45. ★ = 2, ■ = 7

46. $d(5) = -1$

47. $c \leq -22$

48. $y > -\frac{3}{2}$

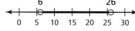

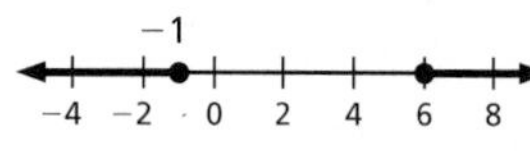

49. $z > 3$

50. all real numbers

51. $6 < g < 26$

52. $r \leq -1$ *or* $r \geq 6$

53.

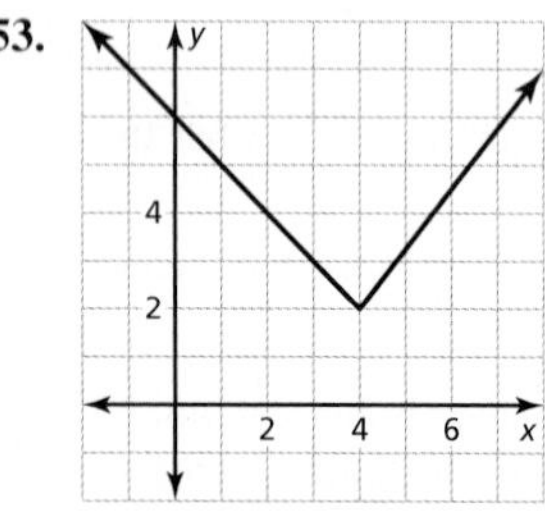

The graph of f is a horizontal translation 5 units right and a vertical translation 1 unit down of the graph of g.

5.4 Practice

1. $(0, -4)$; Explanations will vary.
3. infinitely many solutions; Explanations will vary.
5. infinitely many solutions; Explanations will vary.
7. no solution; Explanations will vary.
9. $\left(\frac{2}{3}, -9\right)$; Explanations will vary.
11. infinitely many solutions; The lines have the same slope and the same y-intercept, so they are the same line.
13. one solution; The lines have different slopes, so they will intersect.
15. no solution; The lines have the same slope but different y-intercepts, so they are parallel.
17. The lines are not parallel, so they must intersect.

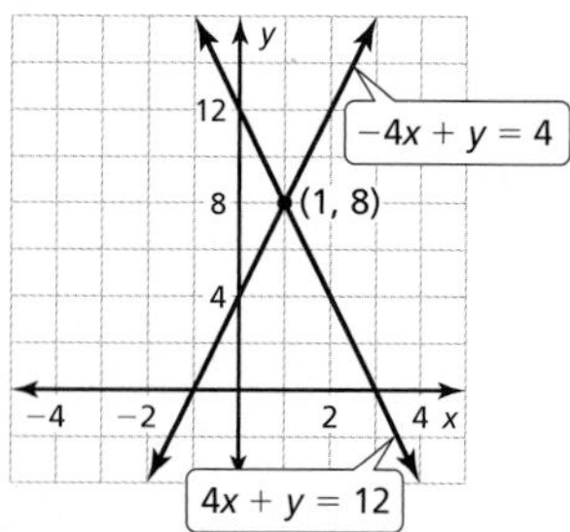

$(1, 8)$

19. There is not enough information to determine the price of 1 cup of dried fruit and 1 cup of almonds.
21. yes; The system $150c + 80b = 22{,}860$ and $170c + 100b = 27{,}280$ has a solution.
23. one; The lines have different slopes, so they will intersect at exactly one point.
25. a. *Sample answer:* $3x - 8y = 7$ and $5x - 4y = 9$

b. *Sample answer:* $3x - 8y = 7$ and $3x - 8y = 10$

c. *Sample answer:* $3x - 8y = 7$ and $6x - 16y = 14$

27. a. never; The intercepts are different, so they can never be equations for the same line.

b. sometimes; When $a = b$, the lines are parallel and there is no solution.

c. always; When $a > b$, the slopes are different and the lines intersect at one point.

5.4 Review & Refresh

29. $(-2, -2)$
30. $x = 3$
31. $x = 12, x = 2$
32. $(4, -1)$
33. $x = \dfrac{y + 8}{5z + 7}$
34. nonlinear; The rate of change is not constant.
35. linear; The rate of change is constant.
36. no solution; The slopes are the same, but y-intercepts are different, so the lines are parallel.
37. infinitely many solutions; The slopes and y-intercepts are the same, so they are the same line.
38. $-\frac{1}{4}$; *Sample answer:* $(8, -10)$
39. $g(12) = -7$
40. $(-22, -26)$
41. $d > 18.5$; Distances greater than 18.5 feet would break the women's long jump record.

5.5 Practice

1. $x = -1$
3. $x = -2$
5. $x = 2$
7. $x = 3$
9. $x = 2$
11. $x = \frac{1}{4}$; one solution
13. all real numbers; infinitely many solutions
15. $x = 3, x = -1$
17. $x = 2, x = -2$
19. $x = 0, x = 6$
21. $x = -5, x = -1$
23. $x = -3, x = 1$
25. $x = -3$
27. $x = -5, x = -1$
29. $x = -2$
31. about 13 months
33. no; Only the x-coordinate is the solution, so the solution is $x = 4$.
35. *Sample answer:* $m = 1, b = 8$

37. **a.** 30 sec

b. you; 5 sec; When $d = 100$, $t = 40$ for you and $t = 45$ for your friend, and $45 - 40 = 5$ sec.

5.5 Review & Refresh

39. The graph of g is a vertical translation 2 units up of the graph of f.

40. The graph of g is a horizontal translation 1 unit right of the graph of f.

41. *Sample answer:*

Weight of car (pounds), x	2400	2500	2900	3000
Gas mileage (mi/gal), y	39	38	25	32

Weight of car (pounds), x	3400	3500	3700	5100
Gas mileage (mi/gal), y	30	24	21	16

42. $x = -2, x = 1$

43. yes

44. 9

0 4 8 12 16

45. −6

−16 −12 −8 −4 0

46. 12 small candles, 16 large candles

47. (4, 4); Explanations will vary.

48. infinitely many solutions; Explanations will vary.

49. $\left(-\frac{19}{2}, 2\right)$; Explanations will vary.

50. (4, 7); Explanations will vary.

51. $x = 2$; one solution

52. $y + 2 = -\frac{2}{3}(x - 9)$

53. nonlinear; It cannot be written in the form $y = mx + b$.

5.6 Practice

1. yes

3. no

5. yes

7. no

9. no

11. yes

13. no

15.

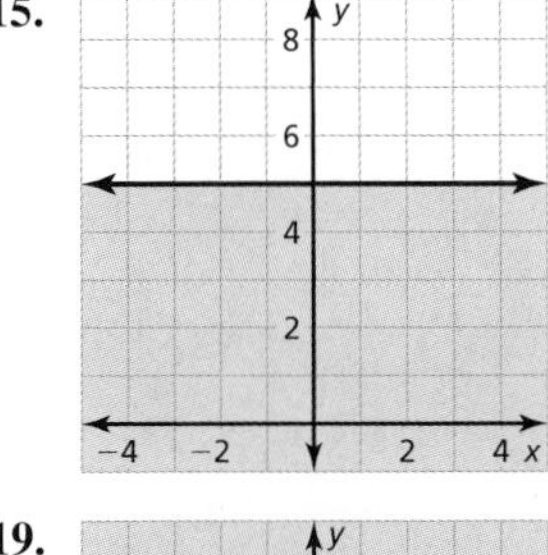

17.

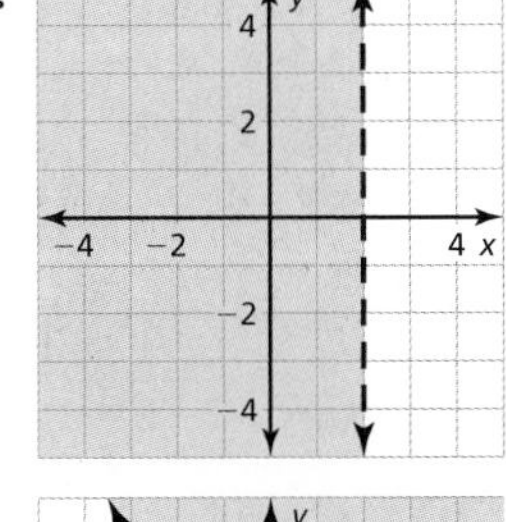

19.

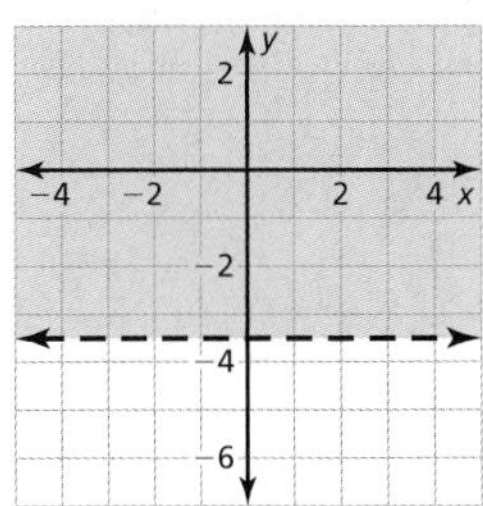

21.

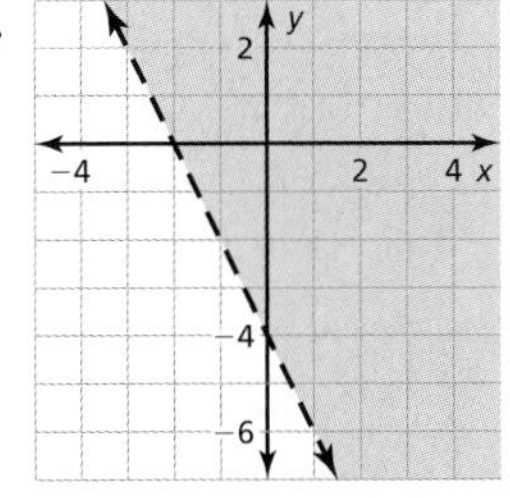

23.

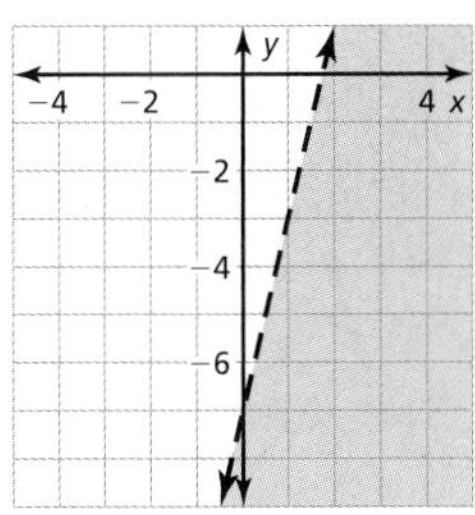

25.

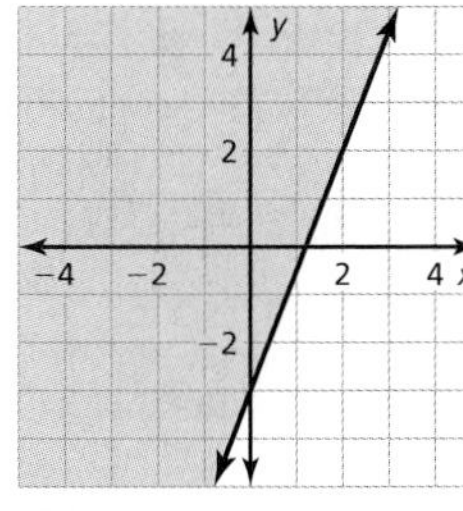

27.

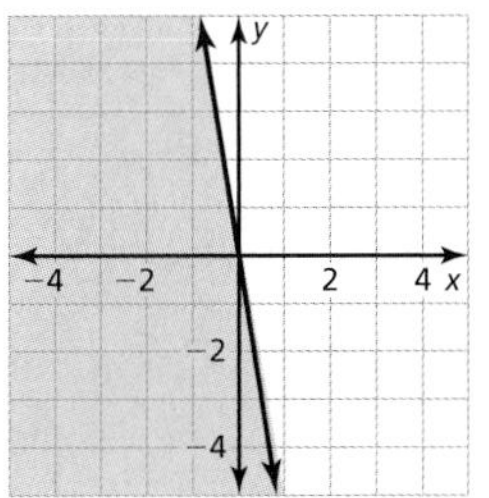

29. The line should be dashed.

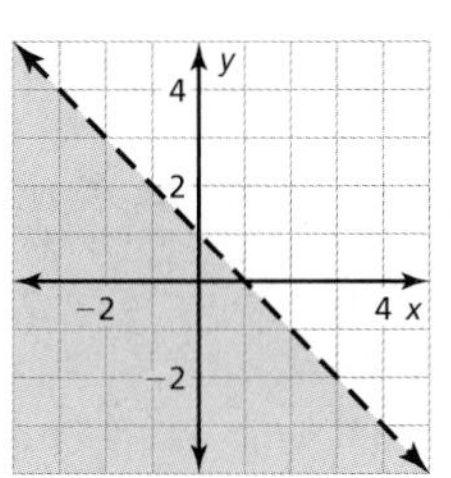

31. no; (12, 14) is not a solution of the inequality.

33. $y > 2x + 1$

35. $x + 5y \le 25$

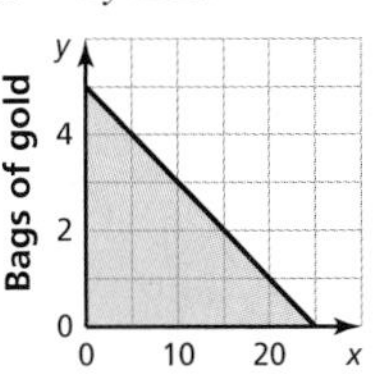

Sample answer: (15, 2), You can buy 15 sets of extra lives and 2 bags of gold; (8, 3), You can buy 8 sets of extra lives and 3 bags of gold.

37. <

39. yes; The graph of a proportional relationship passes through (0, 0) and a test point cannot be on the boundary line.

41. $y \le 2x + 1$

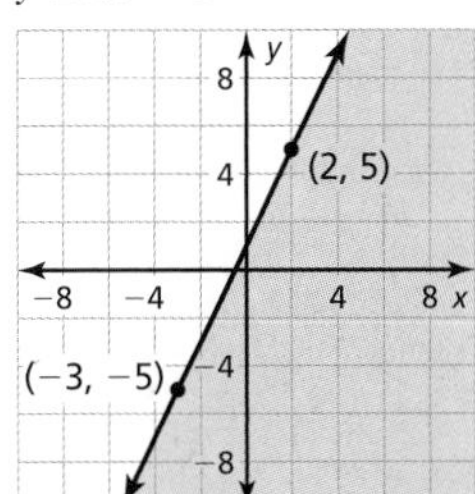

43. **a.** $75x + 40y \le 1800$

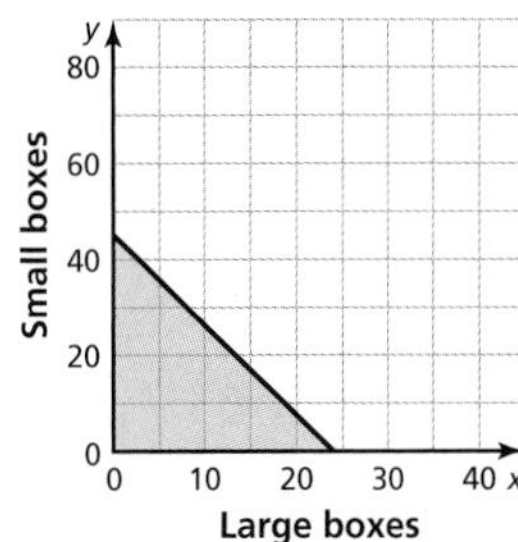

b. *Sample answer:* The number of boxes must be a positive whole number. It is also unlikely for 1 person to carry 45 boxes onto an elevator.

5.6 Review & Refresh

44. infinitely many solutions; Explanations will vary.

45. positive: $x < -3$ and $x > 1$; negative: $-3 < x < 1$; increasing: $x > -1$; decreasing: $x < -1$; As $x \to -\infty$, $y \to +\infty$ and as $x \to +\infty$, $y \to +\infty$.

46.

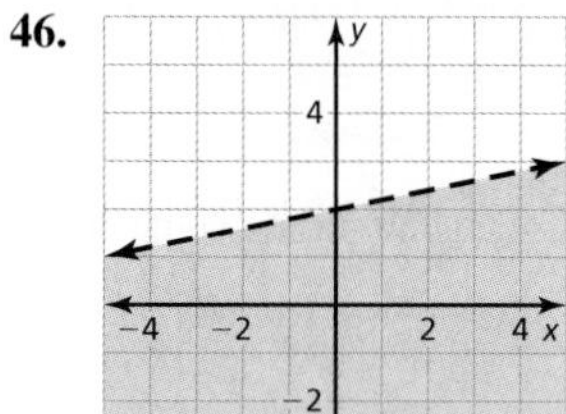

47. $-20, -23, -26$

48. $\frac{7}{2}, \frac{9}{2}, \frac{11}{2}$

49. $b = 3$ or $b = -3$; The coefficients of the y-terms should be the same or opposites to eliminate the variable y after addition or subtraction.

50. 32,600,000

51. $x = 3$

52. $x = -2, x = 4$

53. $y > \frac{1}{2}x + 2$

54. $y \leq 3x - 3$

55. no; The input -5 has two outputs, 2 and 4.

5.7 Practice

1. yes

3. no

5. no

7. no

9.

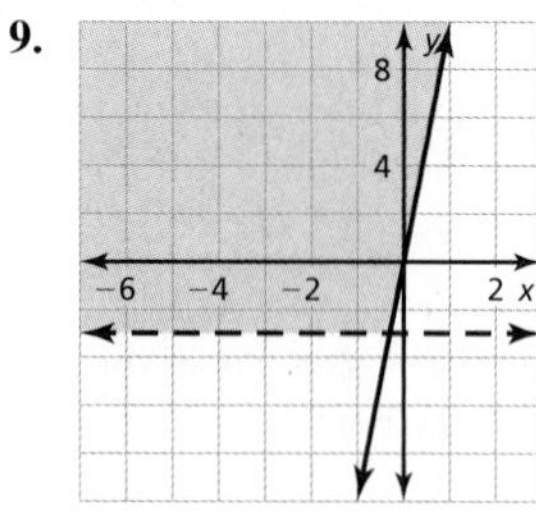

Sample answer: $(-2, 2)$

11. no solution

13.

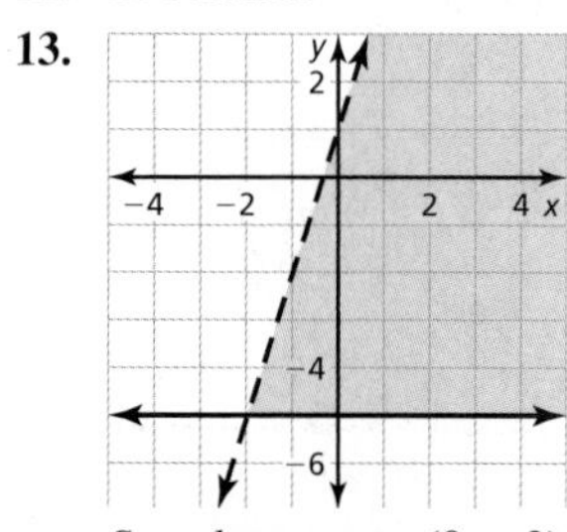

Sample answer: $(0, -3)$

15.

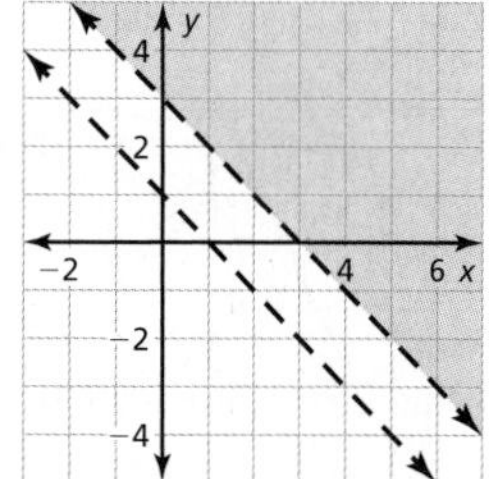

Sample answer: $(4, 3)$

17.

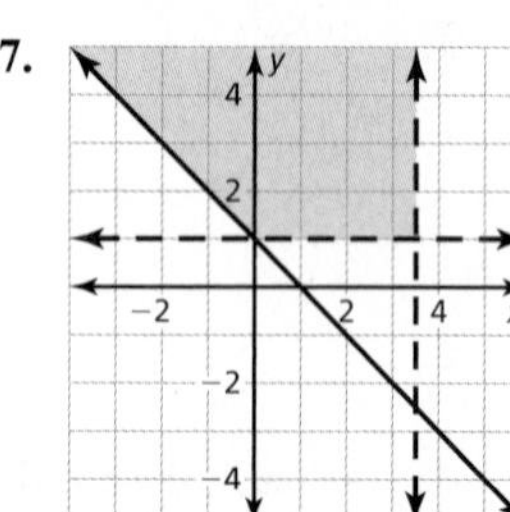

Sample answer: $(1, 3)$

19. $x \geq -1$ and $y < 3$

21. $y \geq \frac{2}{3}x - 2$ and $y \geq -3x + 2$

23. $y < -2x - 1$ and $y > -2x - 3$

25. The wrong region is shaded for $y > \frac{1}{2}x + 2$.

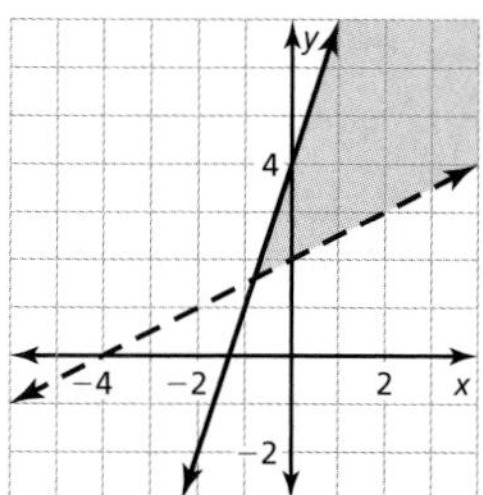

27. $x > 3$, $y \geq 2.5$, and $x + y \leq 7$

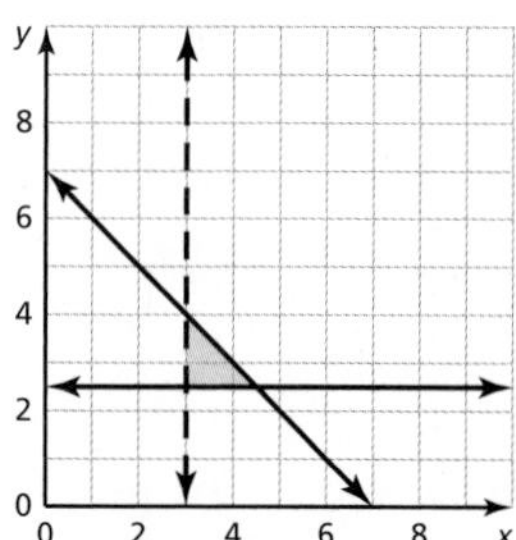

Sample answer: 3.5 hours traveling, 3 hours exploring

29. **a.** $x \leq 15$, $y \leq 10$, and $x + y \leq 20$; You can catch no more than 15 surfperch per day, no more than 10 rockfish per day, and no more than 20 total surfperch and rockfish per day.

b. yes; The point (11, 9) is a solution of the system of linear inequalities.

31. *Sample answer:* \$300 on savings, \$500 on housing; $x + y < 1000$, $x \geq 200$, and $y \leq 600$

33. **a.** $x \geq -1$, $x \leq 6$, $y \geq -3$, and $y \leq 1$

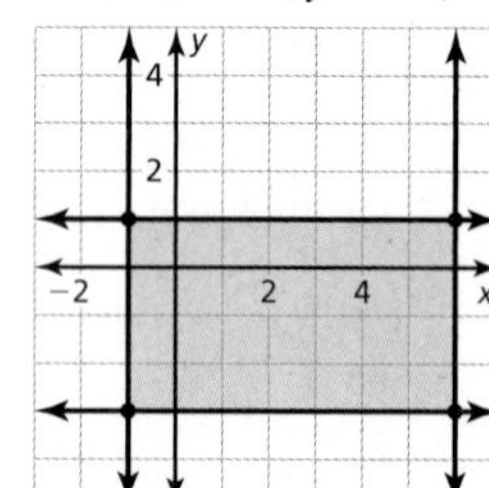

b. 28 square units

35. $y > -x$; $y < x$; and $x > 0$

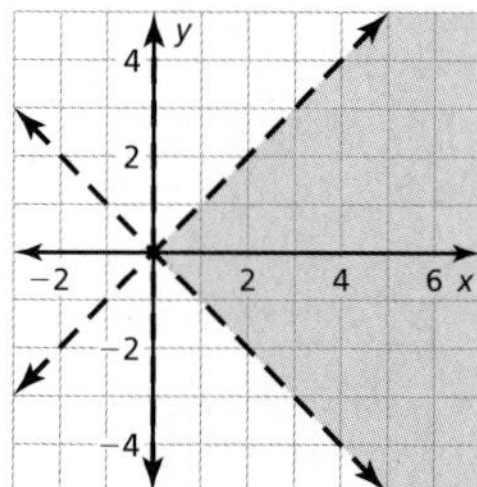

37. no; The half-planes could overlap depending on which side of the boundaries they are on.

39. *Sample answer:* $x > 2$ and $y > 3$

41. *Sample answer:* $y > 2$ and $y < -2$

43. a.

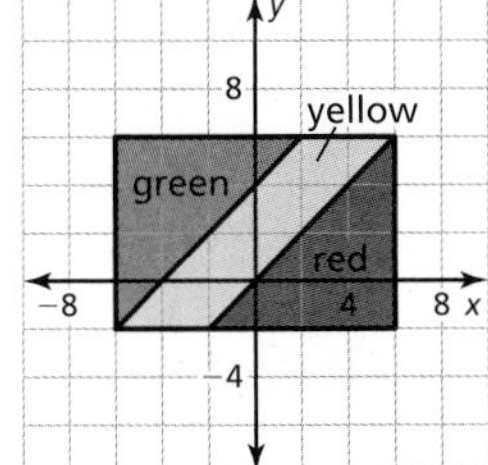

b. The Republic of Congo

c. Answers will vary.

45. a. *Sample answer:* 20 necklaces, 20 key chains; 10 necklaces, 30 key chains; 15 necklaces, 25 key chains; $0.5x + 0.25y \le 20$, $2x + 3y \le 120$

b. 30 necklaces, 20 key chains; \$460

5.7 Review & Refresh

46.

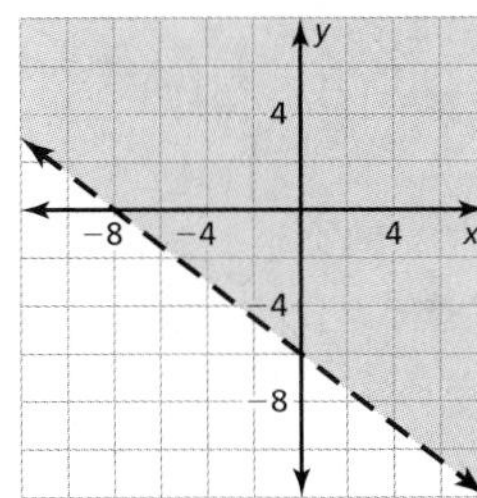

47. $(-13)^3$

48. x^6

49. $y \le \frac{1}{3}x - 1$ and $y < -2x + 3$

50. $y = -\frac{1}{4}x - 1$

51. $x = 12$

52. $x = -\frac{1}{4}$

53. no solution; Explanations will vary.

54. $(-2, -5)$; Explanations will vary.

55. $-2500 \le e \le -100$

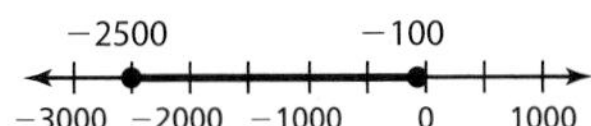

56. $x = -3$

57. *Sample answer:* $|x - 5| + 3 = 3$

58.

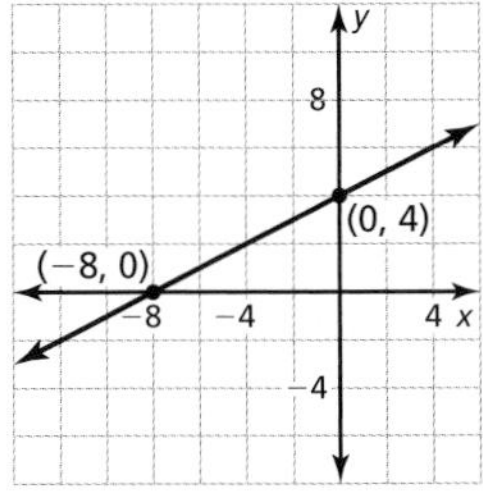

59.

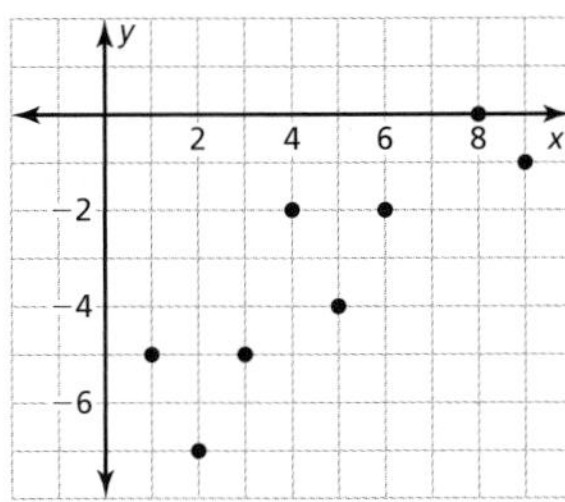

positive correlation

60.

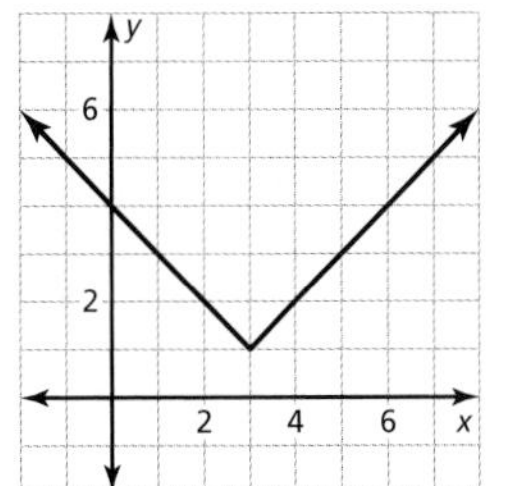

The graph of g is a vertical translation 1 unit up of the graph of f.

Chapter 5 Review

1. $(2, -5)$

2. $(1, -1)$

3. $(4, -1)$

4. $(3, 4)$

5. *Sample answer:* $y = 1.5x - 8.8$ and $y = -0.75x + 0.65$

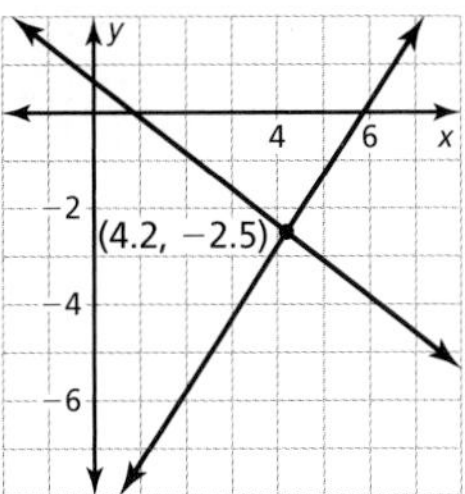

6. $(5a, 0)$

7. 3 years

8. $(-2, -3)$

9. $(2, 1)$

10. $(2, 0)$

11. 8 brushes, 4 tubes of paint

12. $(2, -8)$

13. $(-2, 5)$

14. $\left(-\frac{9}{4}, -\frac{5}{2}\right)$

15. 2 touchdowns, 4 field goals

16. one solution; $x + (x + 2) = 2$, $x = 0$, and $y = 0 + 2 = 2$

17. no solution; $-x + (x + 2) = 1$, and $2 \ne 1$ is not true.

18. infinitely many solutions; $-2x + 2(x + 2) = 4$ and $4 = 4$ is true.

19. no solution; Explanations will vary.

20. $(0, 1)$; Explanations will vary.

21. infinitely many solutions; Explanations will vary.

22. $x = -3$

23. $x = -5$

24. $x = 13$, $x = 1$

25. 2073

26.

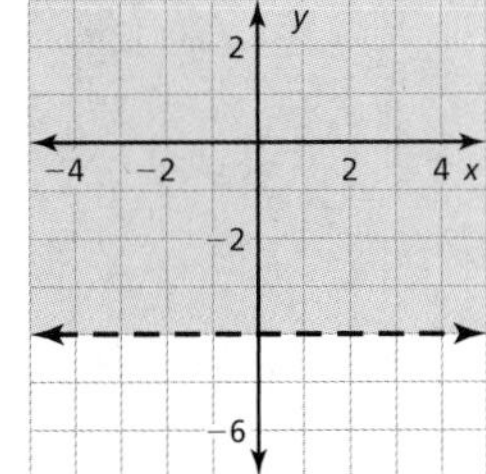

27.

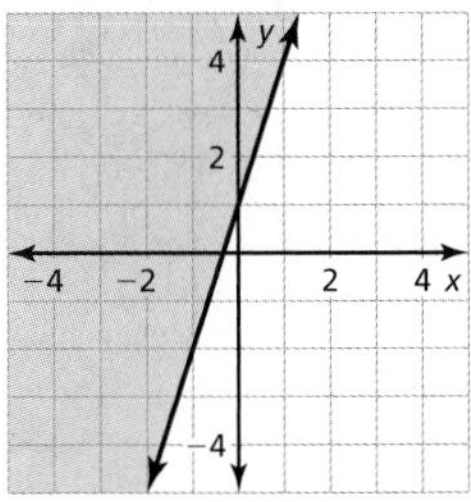

28.

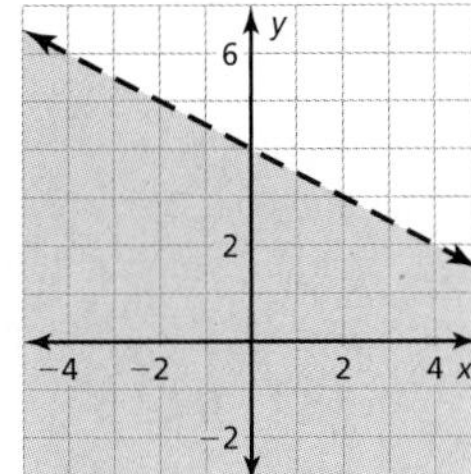

29. $y < -\frac{5}{4}x - 3$

30. $y \ge \frac{2}{3}x + \frac{4}{3}$

31. no solution

32. 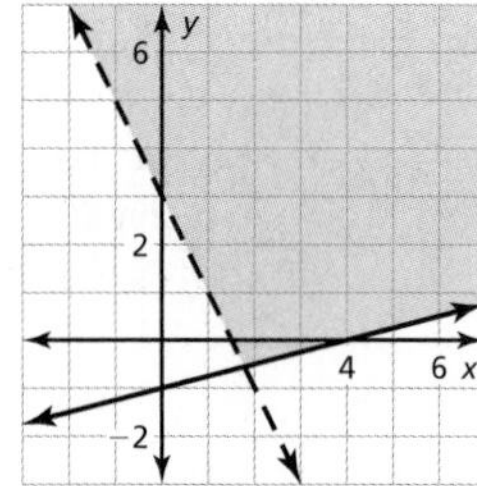

33. 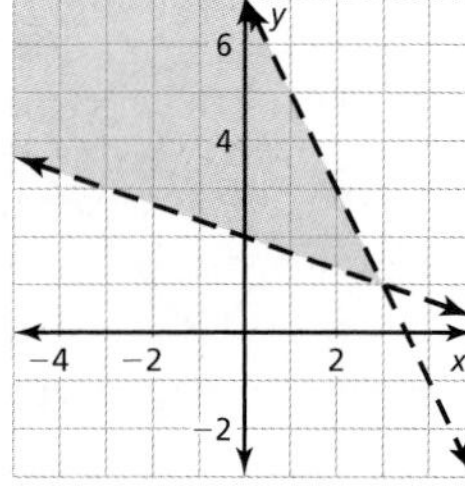

34. C

35. B

36. A

Chapter 5 Mathematical Practices (Chapter Review)

1. *Sample answer:* A graphing calculator can be used to explore the effects different inequality symbols have on graphs.
2. *Sample answer:* Technology can be useful when graphing a system of linear equations that may be too difficult to graph by hand, or when the solution of a system is an approximation and the point of intersection is found using the *trace* feature.

Chapter 5 Practice Test

1. $(-3, 5)$; Explanations will vary.
2. $(-10, -1)$; Explanations will vary.
3. infinitely many solutions; Explanations will vary.
4. $(-17, -6)$; Explanations will vary.
5. no solution; Explanations will vary.
6. $(6, 23)$; Explanations will vary.
7. $y < -\frac{1}{3}x + 3$
8. $y \geq 2x - 1$
9. no solution
10. 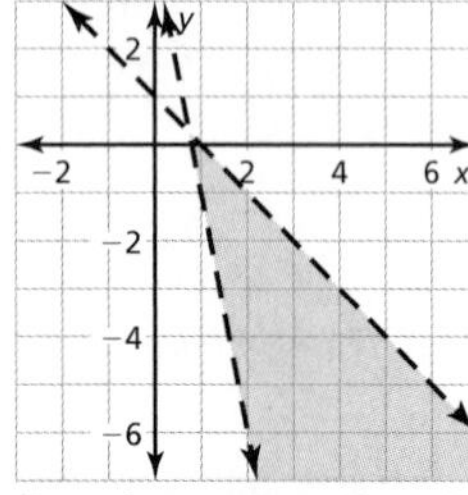

    Sample answer: $(3, -4)$
11. 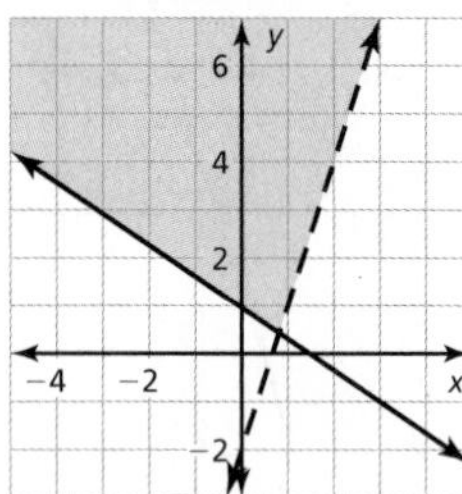

    Sample answer: $(-2, 5)$
12. $x = 1$ and $x = 5$
13. **a.** no; The system $10g + 2q = 45.50$ and $5g + q = 22.75$ represents the situation and has infinitely many solutions.

    b. yes; The solution of the system $10g + 2q = 45.50$ and $8g + 2q = 38.40$ is $(3.55, 5)$. So, gasoline is \$3.55 per gallon and oil is \$5 per quart.
14. 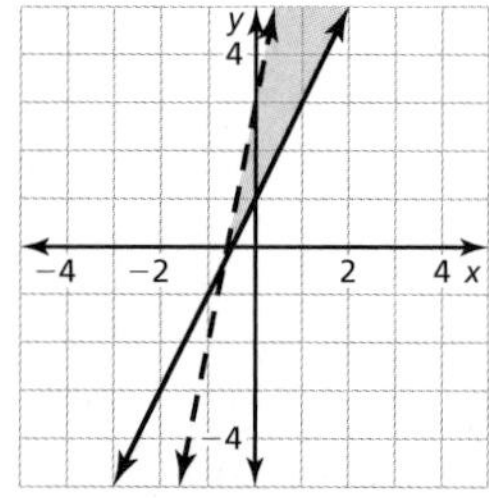

    $2x + 1 \leq y < 5x + 3$
15. **a.** $12x + 3y \leq 60$

    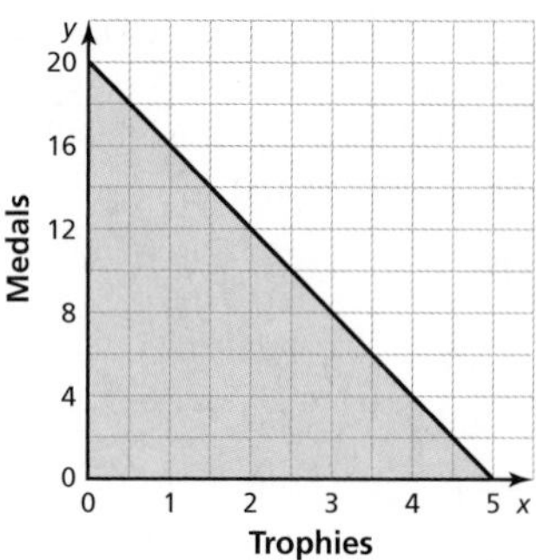

    Sample answer: $(2, 8)$; You can buy 2 trophies and 8 medals.

    b. $12x + 3y \leq 60$ and $x + y \geq 6$

    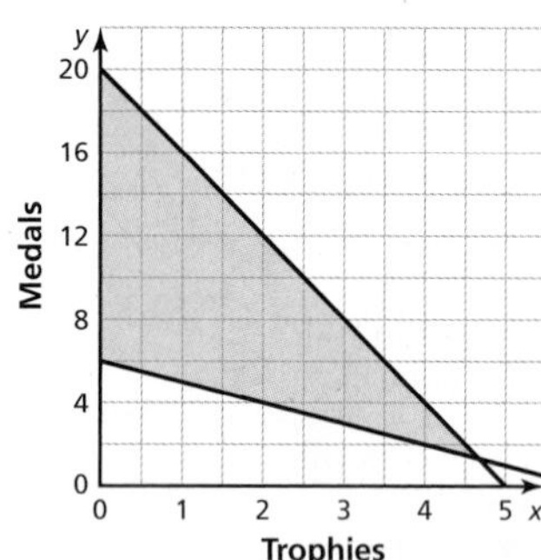

    Sample answer: 2 trophies, 6 medals

Chapter 5 College and Career Readiness

1. D
2. A, B, D, F
3. $\geq$; $>$
4. A
5. $y = 3x + 2$; $y = 3x + \frac{1}{2}$
6. **a.** -7

   b. 0

   c. 3
7. B
8. $4x - 5y = 3$
   $2x + 15y = -1$;
   $4x - 5y = 3$
   $-4x - 30y = 2$;
   $12x - 15y = 9$
   $2x + 15y = -1$
9. $P > 38$; If $x > 9$, then $P > 9 + 13 + 16$, so $P > 38$.
10. C

Chapter 6

Chapter 6 Prepare

1. -9
2. 106
3. $-\frac{11}{8}$
4. 8
5. -2
6. $-\frac{5}{7}$
7. ± 11
8. $a_n = 2n + 10$
9. $a_n = -3n + 9$
10. $a_n = -1.75n + 10.75$
11. yes; no; The product of two perfect squares can be represented by $m^2n^2 = (mm)(nn) = (mn)(mn) = (mn)^2$. If m and n are integers, their product is also an integer, so $(mn)^2$ is an integer. There are many counterexamples illustrating that the quotient of two perfect squares does not have to be a perfect square, such as $9 \div 4$.

6.1 Practice

1. 1
3. $\frac{1}{625}$
5. $\frac{1}{64}$
7. $-\frac{4}{3}$
9. $\frac{1}{x^7}$
11. $\frac{9}{y^3}$
13. $\frac{1}{4m^3}$
15. $\frac{b^7}{64}$
17. $\frac{32x^7}{y^6}$
19. 625
21. 6561
23. p^{24}
25. $\frac{1}{6^5}$
27. x^2
29. 10^{-2} m
31. The product has a base of 2, not $2 \cdot 2$; $2^4 \cdot 2^5 = 2^9$
33. $-125z^3$
35. $\frac{n^2}{36}$
37. $\frac{1}{243s^{40}}$
39. $\frac{81}{w^6}$
41. A, C, D, F
43. $\frac{16y^{28}}{81x^{12}}$
45. $\frac{n^{10}}{144m^4}$
47. 4.5×10^{-3}; 0.0045
49. 4×10^2; 400
51. 1.2×10^8
53. $(7 \cdot 7)^{-8}, (7 \cdot 7)^0, (7 \cdot 7)^5$; $(7 \cdot 7)^{-8} = \frac{1}{(7 \cdot 7)^8} < 1$, $(7 \cdot 7)^0 = 1$, and $(7 \cdot 7)^5 > 1$.
55. a. 2^{30} kilobytes
    b. 2^{14} megabytes
    c. Multiply each number in the table by 8; yes; The number 8 can be expressed as 2^3, so multiply each number in the table by 2^3. Because the values have a common base of 2, they can be simplified using the Product of Powers Property.
57. $(2ab)^3$
59. $(2w^3z^2)^6$
61. -3; 18
63. *Sample answer:* $\frac{(xy^2x^2)^3}{(x^3y^2)^2}$; Product of Powers Property, Power of a Power Property, Quotient of Powers Property
65. $x = 8, y = -1$; Using the Quotient of Powers Property, you can conclude from the first equation that $x - y = 9$. Using the Product of Powers Property and the Quotient of Powers Property, you can conclude from the second equation that $x + 2 - 3y = 13$. Use the equations to solve a system of linear equations.

6.1 Review & Refresh

67. natural number, whole number, integer, rational number, real number
68. rational number, real number
69. irrational number, real number
70. integer, rational number, real number
71.

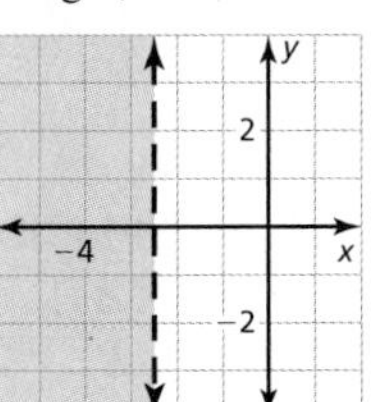

72. Lines a and c are perpendicular; The slopes are negative reciprocals.
73. $\frac{x^4}{4y^8}$
74. $y = -\frac{5}{2}x - 4$
75. $x = 0, x = 6$
76. 5
77. -10
78. $\pm\frac{1}{8}$
79. -1.2
80. all real numbers except $a = 15$; $a = 15$
81. $4x + 3y \le 21$ and $x + y \ge 3$

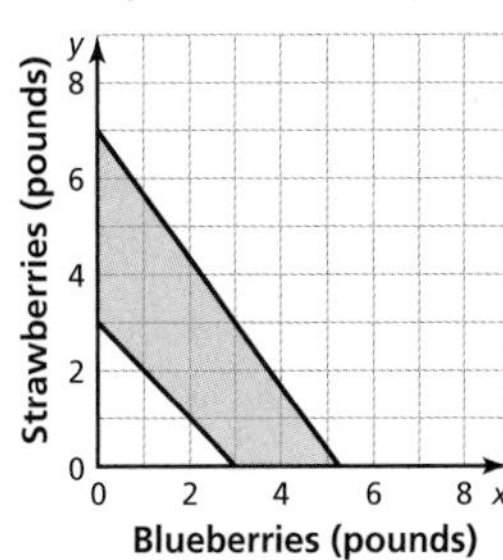

Sample answer: (2, 4); You can buy 2 pounds of blueberries and 4 pounds of strawberries.

82. mean: 55, median: 55, mode: 54, range: 14

6.2 Practice

1. $10^{1/2}$
3. $\sqrt[3]{15}$
5. ± 6
7. 10
9. $s = 4$ in.
11. 4
13. -7
15. 2
17. $8^{4/5}$
19. $(\sqrt[7]{-4})^2$ or $\sqrt[7]{(-4)^2}$
21. 8
23. not a real number
25. -32
27. The numerator and denominator are reversed: $(\sqrt[3]{2})^4 = 2^{4/3}$
29. $\frac{1}{10}$
31. $\frac{1}{9}$
33. about 1 in.
35. about 5.5%
37. $(\sqrt[4]{16})^5$; $\sqrt[4]{16}$ is easier to evaluate using mental math than 16^5.

39. Because $b^n = a$, $(b^n)^{1/n} = a^{1/n}$. By the Power of a Power Property $(b^n)^{1/n} = b^{n \cdot 1/n} = b^1 = b$. Because $b = a^{1/n}$ and $b = \sqrt[n]{a}$, $a^{1/n} = \sqrt[n]{a}$.

41. $(xy)^{1/2}$

43. $2xy^2$

45. -1, 0, and 1

47. no; If n is odd and a is negative, $\sqrt[n]{a}$ will be negative, and $-\sqrt[n]{a}$ will be positive.

49. sometimes; true when $x = 1$, otherwise false

51. sometimes; true when $x = 0$ or $x = 1$, otherwise false

53. sometimes; true when $x = 0$ or $x = 1$, otherwise false

6.2 Review & Refresh

54. $w(-3) = 14$; $w(0) = -1$; $w\left(\frac{4}{5}\right) = -5$

55.

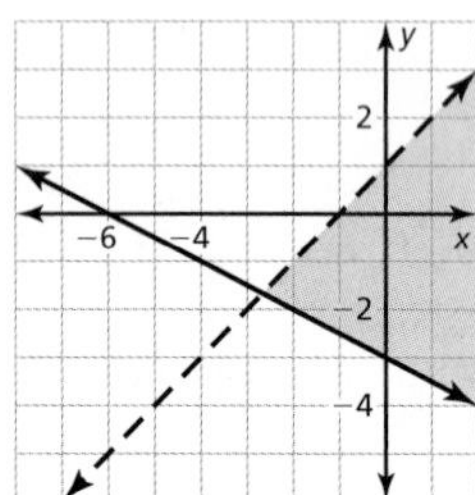

56. $(3, -5)$; Explanations will vary.

57. $(2, 3)$; Explanations will vary.

58. **a.** *Sample answer:* $y = 20x$

b. *Sample answer:* The slope of 20 means the server's earnings increase by about \$20 per hour. The y-intercept of 0 means the server makes \$0 if he doesn't work.

59. $\frac{1}{6^6}$

60. 3^2z^{16}

61.

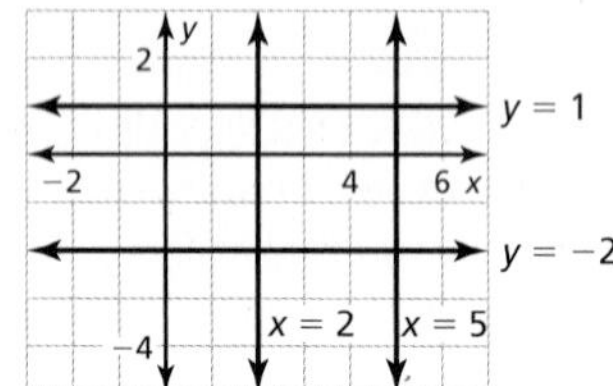

9 units^2

62. $f(x) = \begin{cases} -2x - 2, & \text{if } x \le -3 \\ \frac{1}{3}x + 3, & \text{if } -3 < x \le 0 \\ x + 1, & \text{if } x > 0 \end{cases}$

63. -9

64. 64

65. yes

6.3 Practice

1. yes; It fits the pattern $y = ab^x$.

3. no; The exponent is a constant.

5. no; Although it fits the pattern $y = ab^x$, b cannot be negative.

7. linear; As x increases by 1, y increases by 2. The rate of change is constant.

9. exponential; As x increases by 1, y is multiplied by 4.

11. 9

13. -100

15. 72

17.

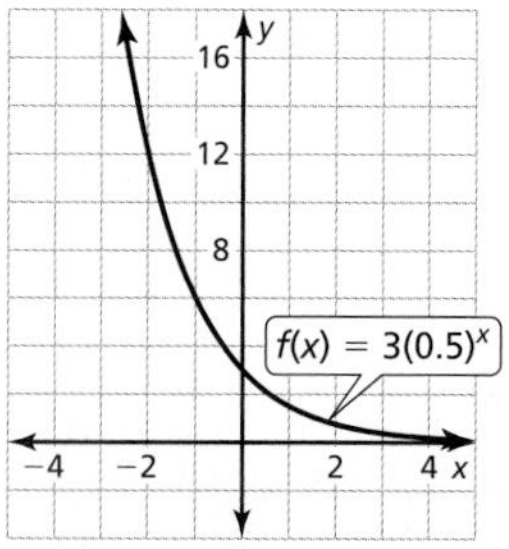

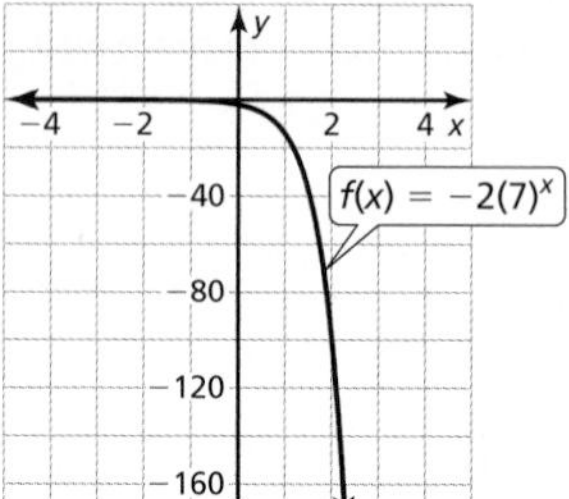

The graph of f is a vertical stretch by a factor of 3 of the graph of $g(x) = 0.5^x$. For f, the y-intercept is 3, and the asymptote is $y = 0$. For g, the y-intercept is 1, and the asymptote is $y = 0$; domain: all real numbers, range: $y > 0$

19.

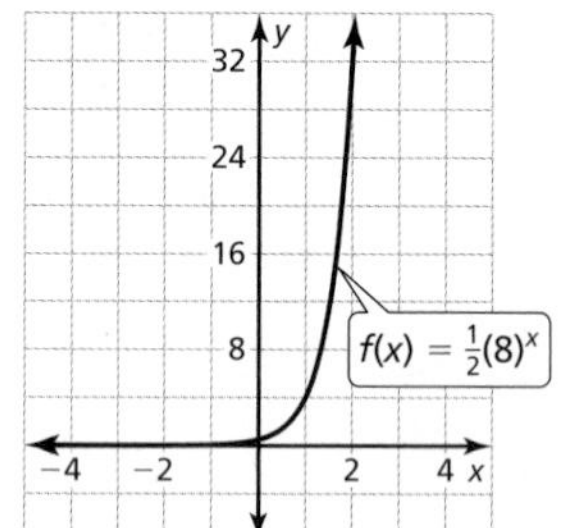

The graph of f is a vertical stretch by a factor of 2 and a reflection in the x-axis of the graph of $g(x) = 7^x$. For f, the y-intercept is -2, and the asymptote is $y = 0$. For g, the y-intercept is 1, and the asymptote is $y = 0$; domain: all real numbers, range: $y < 0$

21.

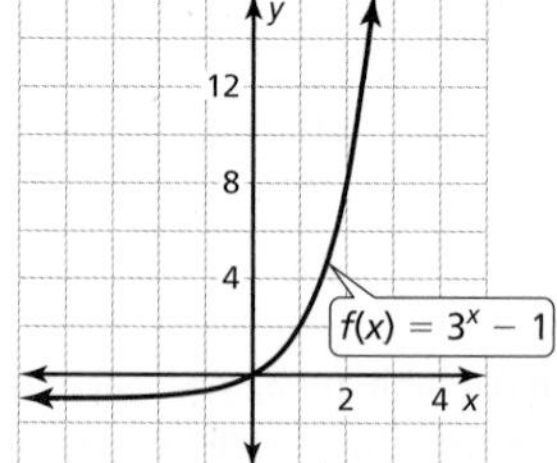

The graph of f is a vertical shrink by a factor of $\frac{1}{2}$ of the graph of $g(x) = 8^x$. For f, the y-intercept is $\frac{1}{2}$, and the asymptote is $y = 0$. For g, the y-intercept is 1, and the asymptote is $y = 0$; domain: all real numbers, range: $y > 0$

23.

f(x) = 3^x − 1

asymptote: $y = -1$; domain: all real numbers, range: $y > -1$

25.

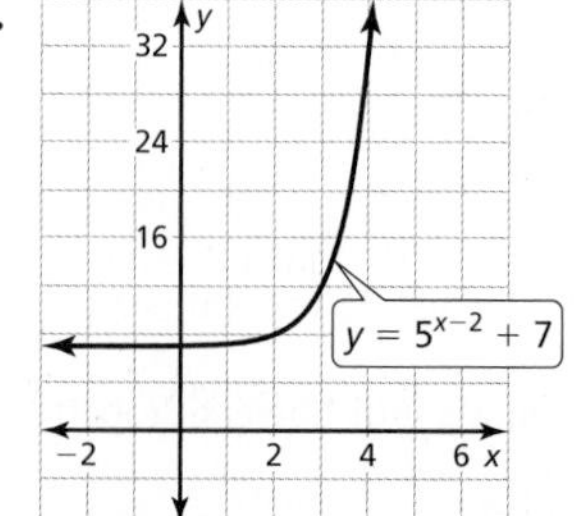

asymptote: $y = 7$; domain: all real numbers, range: $y > 7$

27. 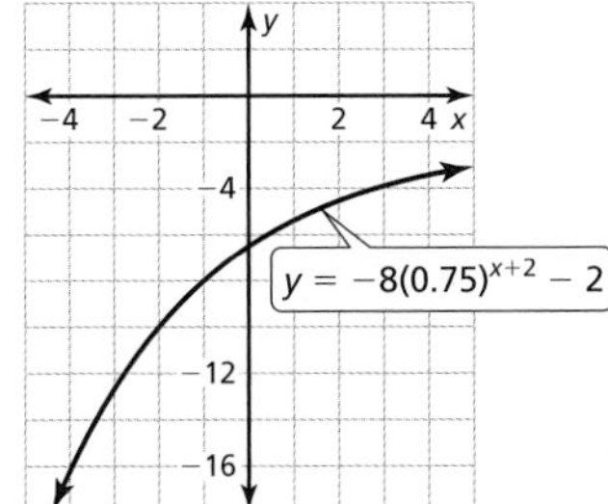

asymptote: $y = -2$; domain: all real numbers, range: $y < -2$

29. The graph of g is a vertical shrink by a factor of $\frac{1}{2}$ of the graph of f; $a = \frac{1}{2}$

31. The graph of g is a horizontal translation 4 units right of the graph of f; $h = 4$

33. The graph approaches the line $y = -1$, not $y = 0$; The range is $y < -1$.

35. 8; 4096

37. The y-intercept occurs when $x = 0$. So, $y = ab^0 = a \cdot 1 = a$.

39. 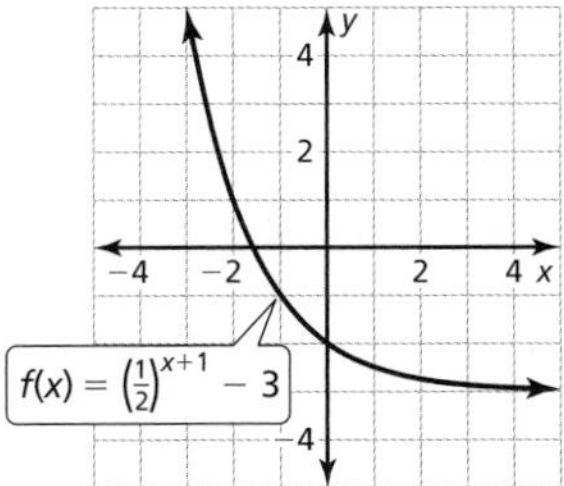

decreasing: for all real numbers; $y \to -3$ as $x \to +\infty$ and $y \to +\infty$ as $x \to -\infty$.

41. 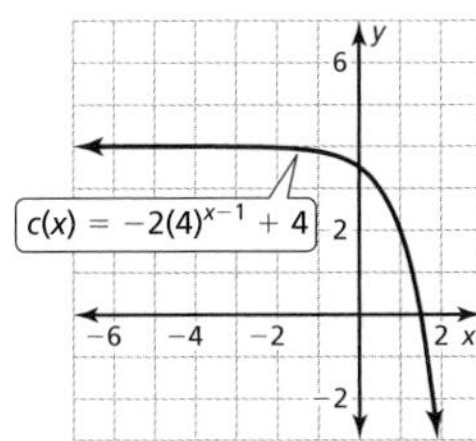

decreasing: for all real numbers; $y \to 4$ as $x \to -\infty$ and $y \to -\infty$ as $x \to +\infty$.

43. $y = 11(7.1)^x$; about 10.1 million views

45. The graph of g is a vertical translation 3 units down of the graph of f; The y-intercept of g is 3 units below the y-intercept of f. The domain of both functions is all real numbers. The range of g is $y < -3$ and the range of f is $y < 0$.

47. *Sample answer:* $f(x) = 4^{x-2}$

49. −192

51. yes; Because as x changes by a constant amount, y increases or decreases by a constant factor.

53. $g(x) = 5(2)^x$

6.3 Review & Refresh

55. 0.04

56. 1.28

57. $y > 4$ and $y \le \frac{3}{2}x + 7$

58. The graph of g is a vertical translation 4 units down of the graph of f.

59. The graph of g is a horizontal translation 2 units left of the graph of f.

60. $y = -\frac{3}{4}x + 6$

61. $\frac{1}{2}$

62. −243

63. $7 < x < 14$

64. 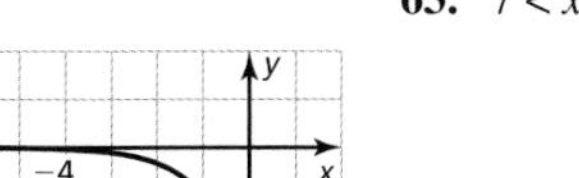
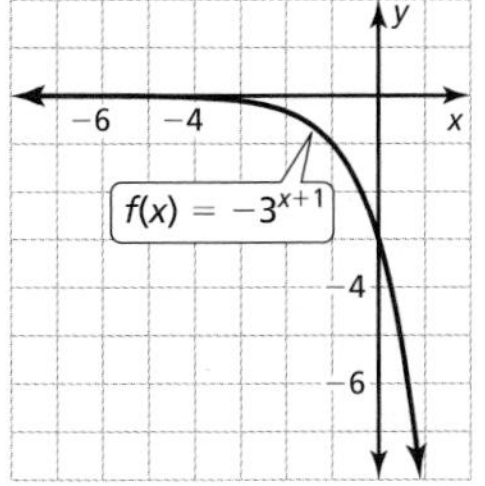

The graph of f is a reflection in the x-axis and a horizontal translation 1 unit left of the graph of $g(x) = 3^x$. For f, the y-intercept is -3, and the asymptote is $y = 0$. For g, the y-intercept is 1, and the asymptote is $y = 0$; domain: all real numbers, range: $y < 0$

65. 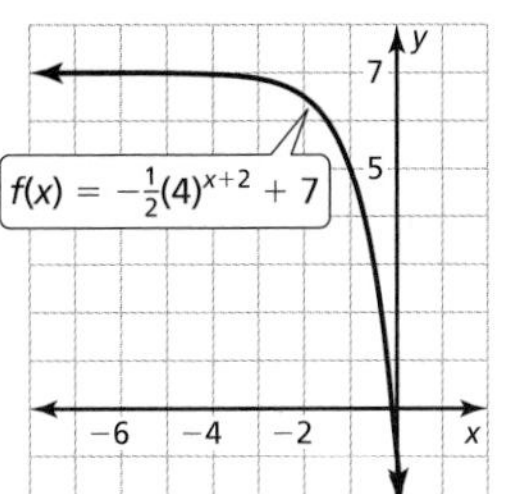

The graph of f is a vertical shrink by a factor of $\frac{1}{2}$, a reflection in the x-axis, a horizontal shift 2 units left, and a vertical shift 7 units up of the graph of $g(x) = 4^x$. For f, the y-intercept is -1, and the asymptote is $y = 7$. For g, the y-intercept is 1, and the asymptote is $y = 0$; domain: all real numbers, range: $y < 7$

66. no

67. $x \le 170$

68. a. $f(4) = 5$
   b. $f(-8) = 8$

69. When a is positive, it causes a vertical stretch or shrink on the graph. When a is negative, it causes a vertical stretch or shrink and a reflection in the x-axis on the graph.

70. $-\frac{5^3d^{12}}{9^3}$

71. $\frac{y^4}{16x^{12}}$

6.4 Practice

1. $a = 350$, $r = 75\%$; about 5744.6

3. $a = 25$, $r = 20\%$; about 62.2

5. $a = 1500$, $r = 7.4\%$; about 2143.4

7. $a = 6.72$, $r = 100\%$; about 215.0

9. $y = 10{,}000(1.65)^t$

11. $y = 210{,}000(1.125)^t$

13. a. $y = 315{,}000(1.02)^t$
   b. about 468,000

15. $a = 575$, $r = 60\%$; about 36.8

17. $a = 240$, $r = 25\%$; about 101.3

19. $a = 700$, $r = 0.5\%$; about 689.6

21. $a = 1$, $r = 12.5\%$; about 0.7

23. $y = 100{,}000(0.98)^t$

25. $y = 100(0.905)^t$

27. The growth rate is $1 + 1.5$, not just 1.5; $b(t) = 10(2.5)^t$; $b(8) = 10(2.5)^8 \approx 15{,}258.8$; After 8 hours, there are about 15,259 bacteria in the culture.

29. exponential decay; As x increases by 1, y is multiplied by $\frac{1}{5}$.

31. neither; As x increases by 1, y decreases by 6.

33. exponential growth; As x increases by 5, y is multiplied by 4.

35. exponential decay; 20%

37. exponential decay; 5%

39. exponential growth; 6%

41. exponential growth; 25%

43. $y \approx 1.52(0.9)^t$; exponential decay

45. $y \approx 2(1.69)^t$; exponential growth

47. $x(t) \approx (1.20)^t$; exponential growth

49. $b(t) \approx 0.67(0.55)^t$; exponential decay

51. *Sample answer:*

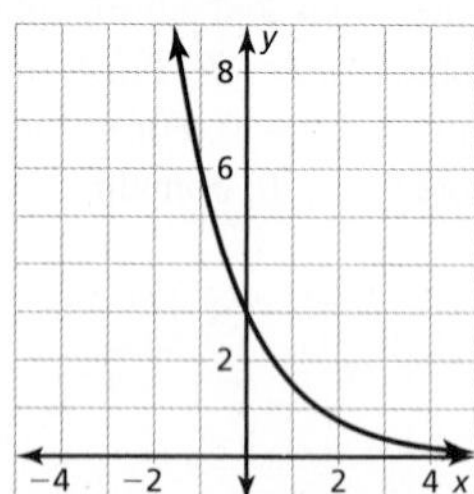

53. $y = 2000(1.0125)^{4t}$

55. $y = 6200(1.007)^{12t}$

57. a. $s(t) = 9000(1.003)^{12t}$

b. $B(t) = 9000(1.003)^{12t} + 40(12)t$; $B(3) = \$11,464.81$

59. a. $y = 25,000(1.055)^t$

b. 0.45%

c. 30,971 people

61. a. $y \approx 800(0.9943)^{60t} \approx 800(0.9943^{60})^t \approx 800(0.7097)^t$; $y \approx 800(0.843)^{2t} \approx 800(0.843^2)^t \approx 800(0.7106)^t$

b. All three functions indicate the initial amount of ibuprofen in a person's bloodstream is 800 mg. The first function indicates the amount of ibuprofen in a person's bloodstream decreases by about 29% each hour. The second function indicates the amount of ibuprofen in a person's bloodstream decreases by about 0.57% each minute. The third function indicates the amount of ibuprofen in a person's bloodstream decreases by about 15.7% each half-hour.

63. 200%; The growth factor is 3, which is also $r + 1$, so r, the growth rate, is 2, or 200%.

65. no; The discount is 20% of the preceding day's price, not always the original price, so the amount of the discount is less each day.

67. a.

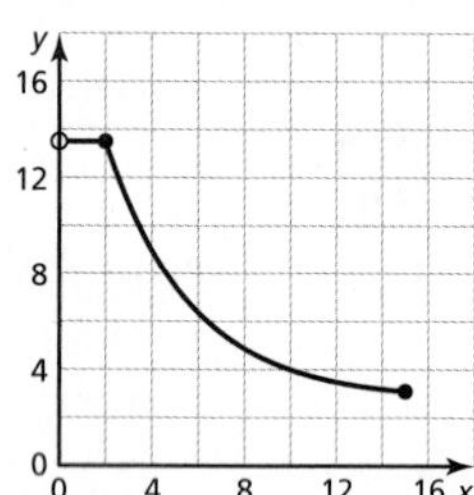

domain: $0 < x \leq 15$; range: $2.8 < y < 13.5$

b. 56°F; 39°F

69. *Sample answer:* account 1: 4% compounded annually, account 2: 8% compounded quarterly; $y = 1000(1.04)^t$; $y = 1000(1.02)^{4t}$; account 2; Graphing both functions shows the balance is always greater in account 2.

6.4 Review & Refresh

70. (6, 0); Explanations will vary.

71. (−4, −6); Explanations will vary.

72. no solution; Explanations will vary.

73. (1, 2); Explanations will vary.

74. a. exponential growth; As t increases by 1, y is multiplied by 4.

b.

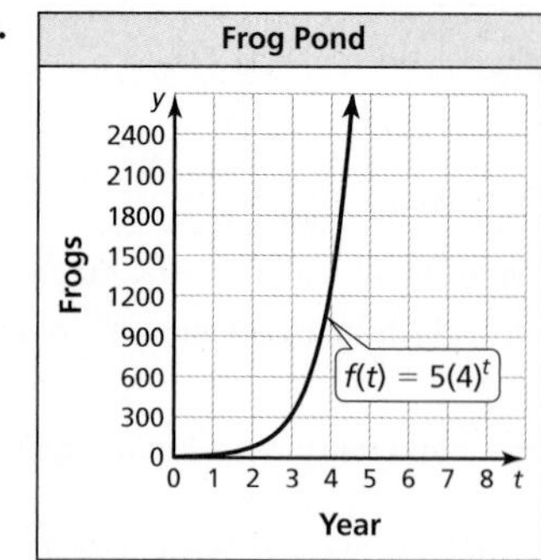

domain: $t \geq 0$, range: $y \geq 5$

c. 300%; about 12%

d. 1280 frogs

75. no correlation

76. *Sample answer:* 8

77. $\frac{1}{k^{12}}$

78. $\frac{64r^6}{27s^{15}}$

79. exponential growth; 26%

80. exponential decay; 40%

81. $y = 4x - 3$

82. $y = -\frac{4}{3}x + 1$

83. linear; The rate of change is constant.

84. slope: $\frac{1}{4}$; y-intercept: 7

85. slope: 2; y-intercept: −4

86. $\frac{1}{2}$

87. 64

88. linear; The formula can be written in the form $V = 6b + 0$.

89. $x = -3$

90. $t = -2$

91. infinitely many solutions

92. no solution

6.5 Practice

1. $x = 2$

3. $x = 4$

5. $x = 6$

7. $x = -5$

9. $x = 3$

11. $x = -3$

13. $x = -2$

15. $x = 3$

17. The exponents are not equal because there is not a common base; $5^{3x+2} = (5^2)^{x-8}$; $5^{3x+2} = 5^{2x-16}$; $3x + 2 = 2x - 16$; $x = -18$

19. $x = 6$

21. $x = -4$

23. $x = -2, x = 0$

25. $x = 1$

27. no solution

29. $x \approx -1.77$

31. $x = -2$

33. $x = -3$

35. 4 years

37. all real numbers

39. no solution

41. Any number to the zero power is 1, so $x - 4 = 0$, and $x = 4$.

43. about 7 years

45. C

47. $x = \frac{5}{2}$

49. $x = -\frac{5}{3}$

51. $x = 18$

53. yes; If x was 0, b would equal 1. By the definition of negative exponents, $\left(\frac{1}{a}\right)^x = (a^{-1})^x$. By the Power of a Power Property, $(a^{-1})^x = a^{-x}$. a must be raised to a positive exponent to stay positive. So, x must be negative.

6.5 Review & Refresh

55. yes, -6

56. no

57. exponential growth; As x increases by 1, y is multiplied by 3.

58. no solution

59. $-1 \le t \le \frac{3}{5}$

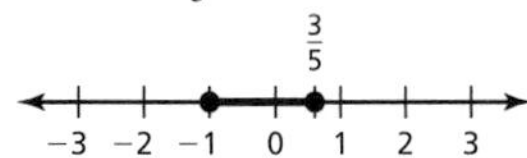

60. $x = 5$

61. $x = -1$

62.

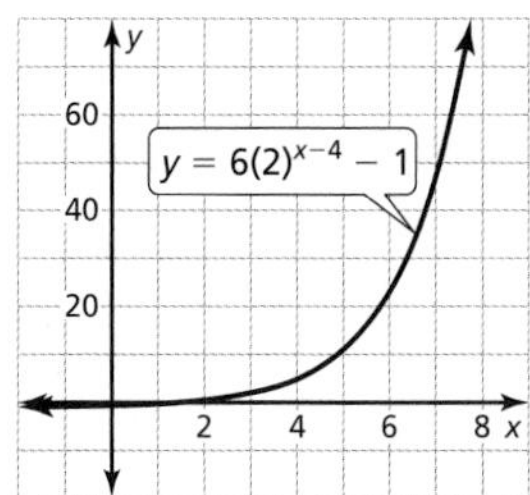

asymptote: $y = -1$; domain: all real numbers, range: $y > -1$

63. no; The input 5 has two outputs, 1 and 4.

64. *Sample answer:* 400 cars; The length of a car plus the space between is about 20 feet; 1.5 mi = 7920 ft and $7920 \div 20 = 396 \approx 400$

65. $70^{5/6}$

66. $y = -5x + 12$

67. $y = \frac{3}{4}x - 10$

68. -3; 4

6.6 Practice

1. 3

3. -8

5. $\frac{3}{4}$

7. arithmetic; There is a common difference of 8.

9. neither; There is no common difference or common ratio.

11. geometric; There is a common ratio of $\frac{1}{8}$.

13. geometric; There is a common ratio of 5.

15. neither; There is no common difference or common ratio.

17. 1280; 5120; 20,480

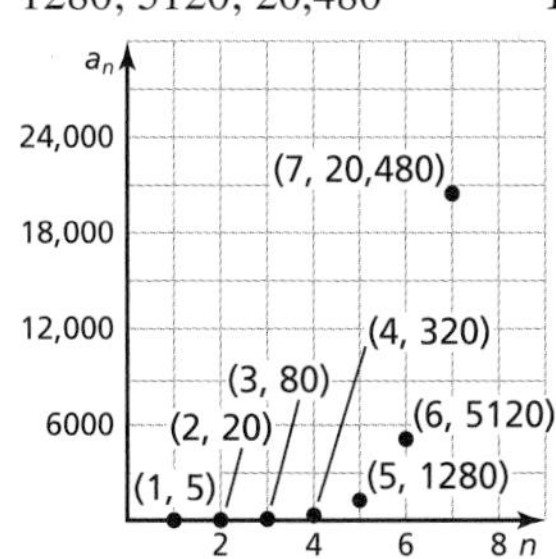

19. $1, -\frac{1}{3}, \frac{1}{9}$

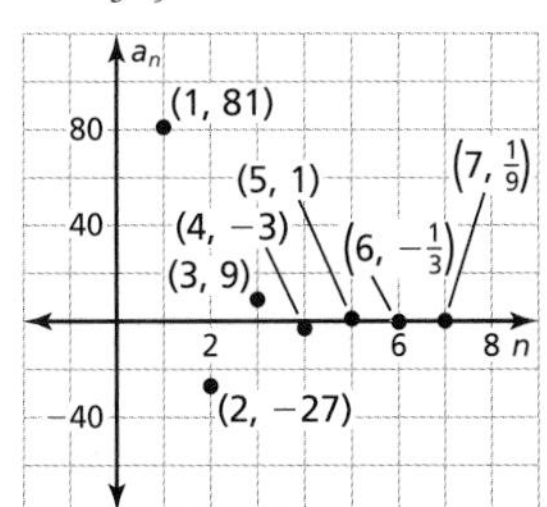

21. $\frac{1}{8}, \frac{1}{32}, \frac{1}{128}$

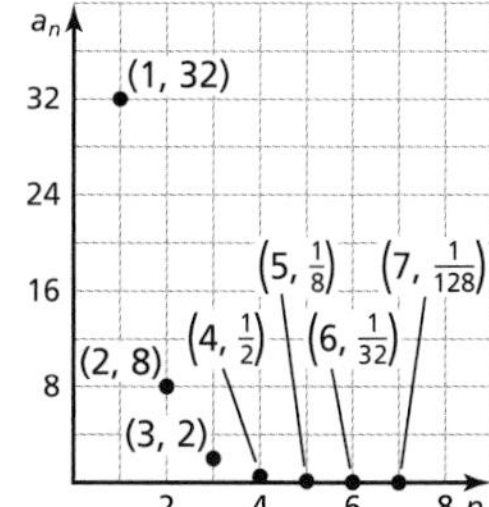

23. $a_n = 2(4)^{n-1}$; 2048

25. $a_n = -\frac{1}{8}(2)^{n-1}$; -4

27. $a_n = 7640(0.1)^{n-1}$; 0.0764

29. $a_n = 0.5(-6)^{n-1}$; -3888

31. The common factor is $\frac{1}{2}$, not -2;

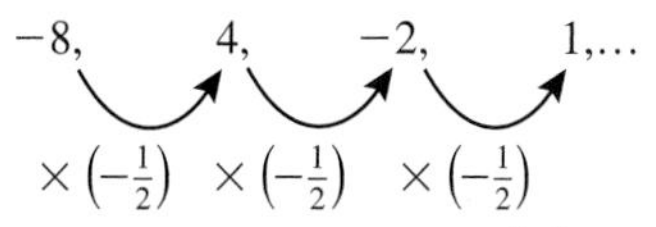

The next three terms are $-\frac{1}{2}$, $\frac{1}{4}$, and $-\frac{1}{8}$.

33. Graphs of arithmetic sequences form a linear pattern. Graphs of geometric sequences form an exponential pattern when the common ratio is positive, and a pattern of points alternating between Quadrants I and IV when the common ratio is negative.

35. a. $a_n = 625\left(\frac{4}{5}\right)^{n-1}$
b. the fifth swing

37. a large square containing 387,420,489 small squares

39. D

41. your friend; The only way to get 0 as a term would be with a common ratio of 0. If the common ratio is 0, then there is no possible previous term that would result in -8 as the next term.

43. 59,049

45. Option 2; \$60.24; After 10 hours, Option 1 will earn \$235, Option 2 will earn \$295.24, and $295.24 - 235 = 60.24$.

47. $a_n = 2(3)^{n-1}$; $b_n = 5^{n-1}$
a. no
b. yes; It is the quotient of the common ratios of each sequence.

6.6 Review & Refresh

48. yes; The residual points are evenly dispersed about the horizontal axis.

49. geometric; The common ratio is $\frac{2}{3}$.

50. arithmetic; The common difference is 13.

51.

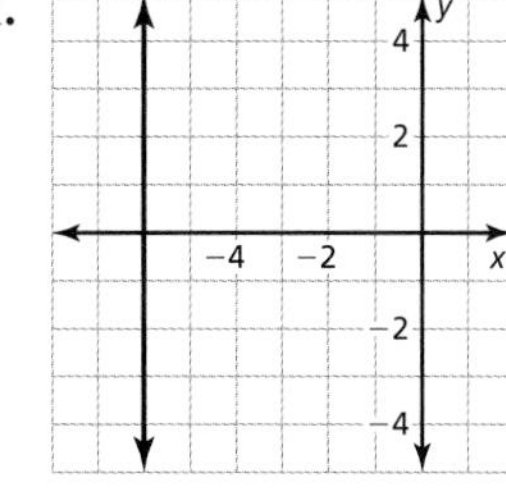

52.

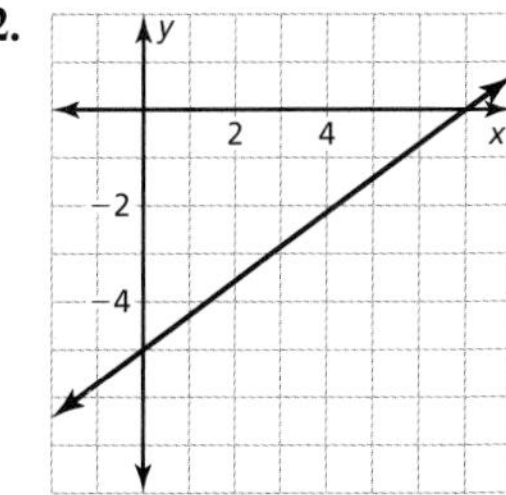

53. $\frac{n}{8} \ge -3.5$

54. $81n^{20}$

55. $\frac{x^6}{144}$

56. dependent; Each term is calculated from the preceding term.

57. $x = -2$

58. $f(t) = 750(0.8)^t$

59. $f(t) = 8000(1.025)^t$

60. $y < \frac{2}{3}x + 2$ and $y \ge -2x - 3$

61. $x = -3$

62. $x = 1$

63. $g(x) = 4^{x+2} - 7$

64. $-\frac{5}{6}$

6.7 Practice

1. arithmetic

3. geometric

5. 0, 2, 4, 6, 8, 10

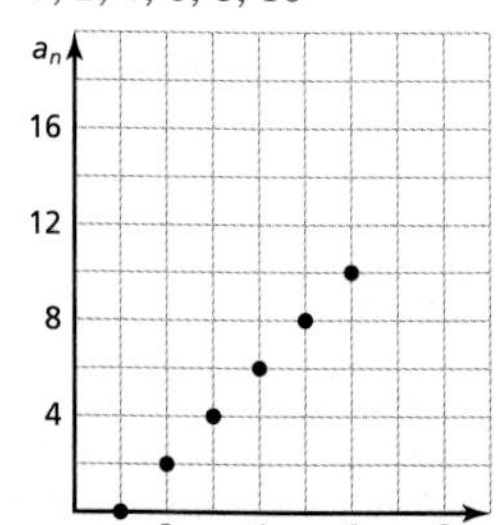

7. 2, 6, 18, 54, 162, 486

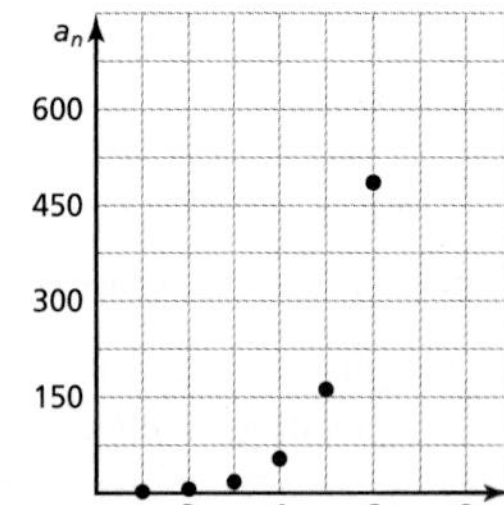

9. 80, −40, 20, −10, 5, $-\frac{5}{2}$

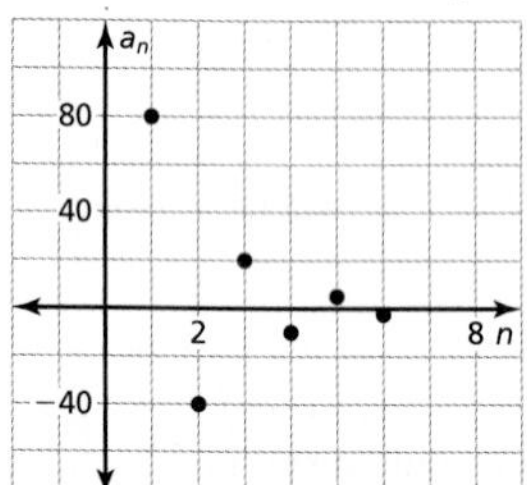

11. $a_1 = 7, a_n = a_{n-1} + 9$ **13.** $a_1 = 3, a_n = a_{n-1} + 8$

15. $a_1 = 243, a_n = \frac{1}{3}a_{n-1}$ **17.** $a_1 = 35, a_n = a_{n-1} - 11$

19. $a_1 = 1$ cell, $a_n = (2a_{n-1})$ cells

21. $a_n = 3n - 6$ **23.** $a_n = -2(9)^{n-1}$

25. $a_n = 1.75n + 2.25$ **27.** $a_1 = 8, a_n = 2a_{n-1}$

29. $a_1 = -14, a_n = a_{n-1} + 6$

31. $a_1 = 1, a_n = 9a_{n-1}$ **33.** $a_1 = -\frac{1}{16}, a_n = \frac{1}{2}a_{n-1}$

35.

$a_1 = 5, a_n = a_{n-1} + 15; a_n = 15n - 10$

37.

$a_1 = 16, a_n = \frac{1}{2}a_{n-1}; a_n = 16\left(\frac{1}{2}\right)^{n-1}$

39. $a_1 = 1, a_2 = 3, a_n = a_{n-2} + a_{n-1}$; 18, 29

41. $a_1 = 2, a_2 = 4, a_n = a_{n-1} - a_{n-2}$; 2, 4

43. $a_1 = 1, a_2 = 3, a_n = (a_{n-1})(a_{n-2})$; 243, 6561

45. The common difference is −12, not 12;
$a_n = 6 + (n - 1)(-12); a_n = 6 - 12n + 12; a_n = 18 - 12n$

47. 10; 31; 66 **49.** 5; 23; 254

51. 5, 19, 61, 187, 565; neither; There is no common difference or common ratio.

53. a. Substituting $n - 1$ for n in the explicit rule that defines an arithmetic sequence results in this expression.

b. Write the equation; Identity Property of Addition; Additive Inverse Property; Associative Property of Addition; Distributive Property; Substitution Property of Equality

55. yes; The sequence is a geometric sequence with a common factor of −1, so it can be represented by $a_1 = -5$, $a_n = -a_{n-1}$.

57. $a_1 = 3, a_n = a_{n-1} + 2^n$

6.7 Review & Refresh

58. infinitely many solutions; Explanations will vary.

59. neither; As x increases by 1, y decreases by 6.

60. exponential growth; As x increases by 1, y is multiplied by 4.

61. a. $y = \frac{1}{4}x - \frac{1}{2}$

b. $y = -4x + 25$

62. $x = -3$ **63.** $x = -3$

64. $x = -\frac{5}{3}$ **65.** $x \approx 9.7$

66. yes; no; A proportional relationship has a constant rate of change.

67. $f(x) = -3x - 6$

68. 54, 324, 1944

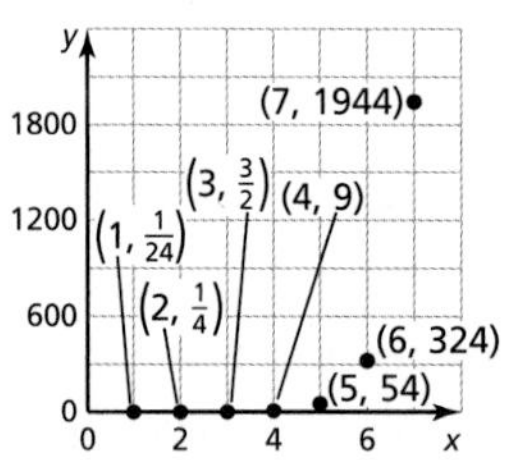

69. $a_1 = 2, a_n = 4a_{n-1}$ **70.** $a_1 = 17, a_n = a_{n-1} - 3$

71. $-8 < x \leq -1$

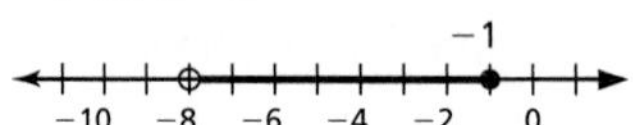

72. The graph of g is a horizontal shrink by a factor of $\frac{1}{4}$ and a vertical translation 9 units down of the graph of f. Or, the graph of g is a vertical stretch by a factor of 4 and a vertical translation 12 units down of the graph of f.

Chapter 6 Review

1. $\frac{1}{y^2}$ **2.** $\frac{1}{x^3}$

3. y^6 **4.** $\frac{25y^8}{4x^4}$

5. a. 10^{12}

b. 1000 dg; 10,000 mg = 10 g, 1000 dg = 100g

6. 2 **7.** −3

8. 125 **9.** not a real number

10. 1.7 m² **11.** 48 ft³

12.

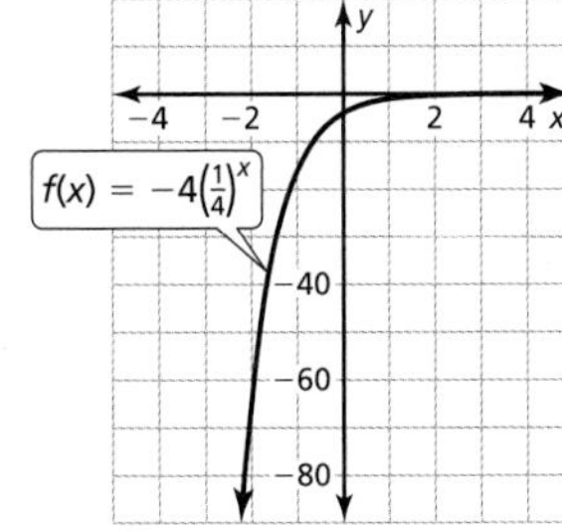

asymptote: $y = 0$; domain: all real numbers, range: $y < 0$

13.

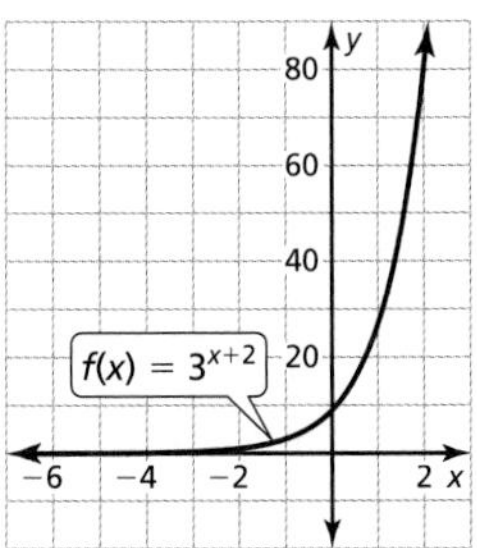

asymptote: $y = 0$; domain: all real numbers, range: $y > 0$

14.

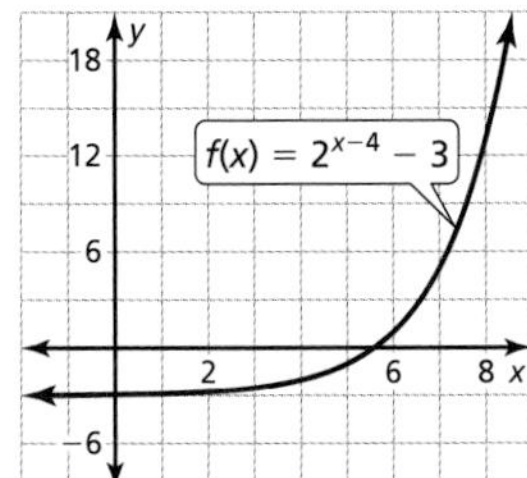

asymptote: $y = -3$; domain: all real numbers, range: $y > -3$

15. $f(x) = 2\left(\frac{1}{2}\right)^x$

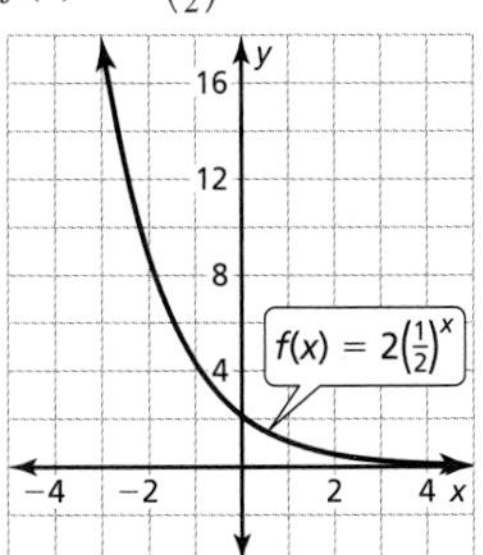

The graph of f is a vertical stretch by a factor of 2 of the graph of g.

16. *Sample answer:* $f(x) = 3^{x+1} - 2$

17. exponential growth; As x increases by 1, y is multiplied by 2.

18. exponential decay; As x increases by 1, y is multiplied by $\frac{2}{3}$.

19. exponential growth; 25%

20. exponential growth; about 59%

21. exponential decay; 16%

22. **a.** $y = 750(1.0125)^{4t}$
b. \$914.92

23. **a.** $y = 1500(0.86)^t$
b. about 1.2%
c. about \$950

24. $x = 1$ **25.** $x = 5$

26. $x = 2$ **27.** no solution

28. $x \approx -2.23$ **29.** $x = -3$

30. **a.** never; The graph of a linear equation with a negative slope will intersect the graph of an exponential function.
b. sometimes; The graph of a linear equation with a positive slope can intersect the graph of an exponential function zero, one, or two times.
c. always; The graph of a linear equation with a slope y-intercept greater than 1 will intersect the graph of an exponential function two times.

31. geometric; There is a common ratio of 4; 768, 3072, 12,288

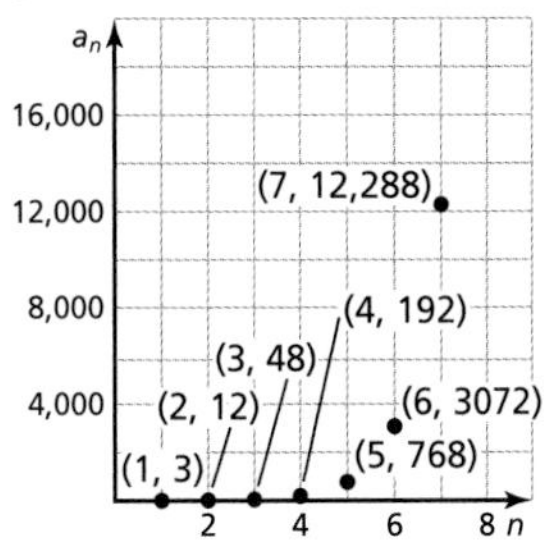

32. neither; There is no common difference or common ratio.

33. geometric; There is a common ratio of $-\frac{1}{5}$; $\frac{3}{5}, -\frac{3}{25}, \frac{3}{125}$

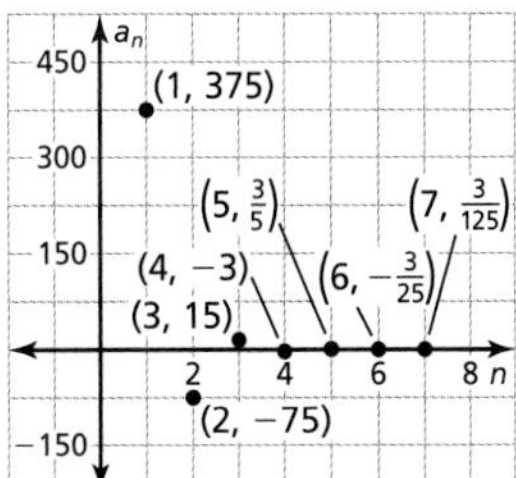

34. $a_n = 4^{n-1}$; 65,536 **35.** $a_n = 5(-2)^{n-1}$; 1280

36. $a_n = 486\left(\frac{1}{3}\right)^{n-1}$; $\frac{2}{27}$ **37.** $a_{12} = -19{,}683$

38. 0.75 mm

39. 4, 9, 14, 19, 24, 29

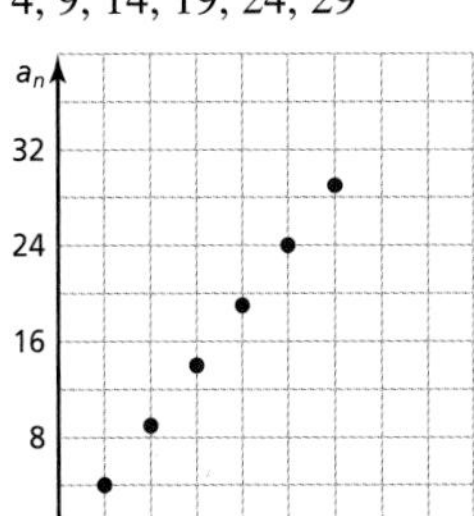

40. 32, −8, 2, $-\frac{1}{2}, \frac{1}{8}, -\frac{1}{32}$

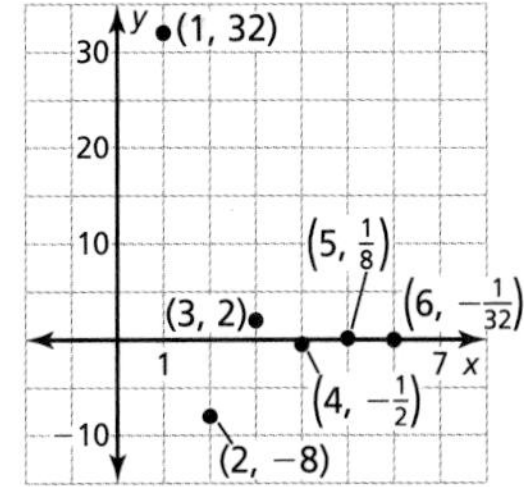

41. $a_1 = 3, a_n = a_{n-1} + 5$ **42.** $a_1 = 3, a_n = 2a_{n-1}$

43. $a_1 = 7, a_2 = 6, a_n = a_{n-2} + a_{n-1}$

44.

$a_1 = 8, a_n = 5a_{n-1}; a_n = 8(5)^{n-1}$

Chapter 6 Mathematical Practices (Chapter Review)

1. Use the properties of exponents to rewrite the expression as factors of $3x$. Then factor $3x$ from each term.

2. A triangle is drawn on the inside of each triangle from the previous stage. This means, the number of triangles is 4 times greater than the number of triangles in the previous stage.

Chapter 6 Practice Test

1. z^2
2. b^3
3. $\frac{125}{8c^{12}}$
4. -2
5. 3
6. -128
7. \$1142.33
8. $a_n = 2187\left(\frac{1}{3}\right)^{n-1}$; $a_1 = 2187$, $a_n = \frac{1}{3}a_{n-1}$; $a_{10} = \frac{1}{9}$
9. $x = -7$
10. $x = 5$
11. **a.** 1; 0.99988; 0.012%

    b. about 0.549 atmosphere

12. 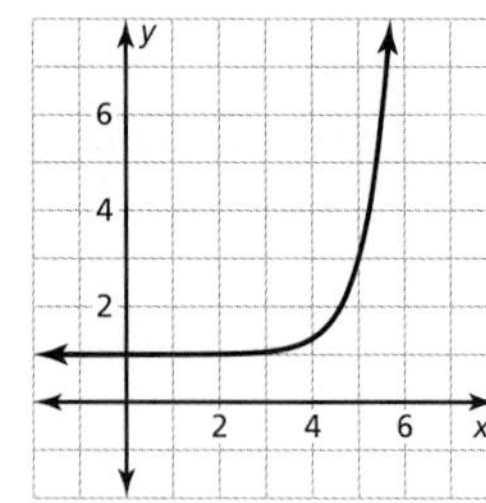

The graph of f is a vertical stretch by a factor of 2, then a horizontal translation 5 units right, and a vertical translation 1 unit up of the graph of $g(x) = 6^x$. For f, the y-intercept is about 1, and the asymptote is $y = 1$. For g, the y-intercept is 1, and the asymptote is $y = 0$; domain: all real numbers, range: $y > 1$

13. **a.** less than; By the Quotient of Powers Property, $a - b = -3$, so $a < b$.

    b. equal to; By the Product of Powers Property, $a + (-b) = 0$, so $a = b$.

14. *Sample answer:* $\frac{3}{4}(4)^x = 9x - 6$; Use the points (1, 3) and (2, 12) to write a linear equation using the point-slope form $y - y_1 = m(x - x_1)$, where $m = \frac{12-3}{2-1} = 9$ and $(x_1, y_1) = (1, 3)$, on one side of the exponential equation. Then use the same points to write an exponential equation $y = ab^x$, where $a = 3 \div 4 = \frac{3}{4}$ and $b = 12 \div 3 = 4$, on the other side of the equation.

15. *Sample answer:* The account offering 3.5% annual interest compounded monthly will have a greater balance after about 7.5 years; The account offering 4% simple interest will have a greater balance up to 7.5 years.

Chapter 6 College and Career Readiness

1. D
2. -2.5
3. C
4. B
5. B, D
6. F
7. C
8. 128
9. $<$
10. B

Chapter 7

Chapter 7 Prepare

1. $5x - 7$
2. $-5r + 5$
3. $2t - 1$
4. $3s + 2$
5. $9.25m - 21.75$
6. $\frac{13}{4}h + \frac{51}{2}$
7. 4
8. 21
9. 27
10. 12
11. 4
12. 1
13. no; The GCF of two prime numbers is 1.

7.1 Practice

1. 1
3. 2
5. 9
7. 11
9. $3t^8$; 8; 3; monomial
11. $3p^2 + 7$; 2; 3; binomial
13. $2c^4 + 6c^2 - c$; 4; 2; trinomial
15. $3z^4 + 2z^3 + 5z$; 4; 3; trinomial
17. It is the product of a number, $\frac{4}{3}\pi$, and a variable with a whole number exponent, r^3; 3
19. $3y + 10$
21. $n^2 - 8n + 5$
23. $6g^2 - 9g + 4$
25. $a^3 - \frac{1}{2}a^2 + \frac{1}{4}a + 5$
27. $-2d - 8$
29. $-2y^2 + 2y + 18$
31. $k^3 - k^2 - 7k + 14$
33. $t^4 + 8t^2 + 8t - 12$
35. When writing the subtraction as addition, the last term of the polynomial was not multiplied by -1;
    $= (x^2 + x) + (-2x^2 + 3x) = (x^2 - 2x^2) + (x + 3x)$
    $= -x^2 + 4x$
37. $3b + 2$
39. $s^2 - 12st$
41. $2c^2 - 2cd - 4d^2$
43. **a.** $10t + 6$

    b. 10 shows that the distance between the two water rockets changes by 10 feet per second; 6 represents the distance in feet between the water rockets when they were launched.

45. The sum and difference of two polynomials is always a monomial or sum of monomials, which is a polynomial.
47. always; A polynomial is a monomial or a sum of monomials, and each monomial is a term of the polynomial.
49. sometimes; The two terms in the binomial can be of any degree.
51. $12x - 3$
53. no; Addition is commutative and associative, so you can add in any order.
55. yes; The sum of two negative integers is always a negative integer; no; The difference of two negative integers is sometimes a positive integer; no; The product of two negative integers is always a positive integer.
57. **a.** $x^2 + 1$

    b. yes; *Sample answer:* $h(x) = x^4 - 2x^2 + 6 \geq 0$ for all values of x and has a negative coefficient.

    c. no; The leading coefficient must be positive and the constant term must be non-negative.

7.1 Review & Refresh

58. $x = 2$
59. $x = 7$
60. $x = -3$
61. $x = -\frac{1}{2}$
62. $k = 45$; 45°, 90°, 45°
63. geometric
64. neither
65. arithmetic
66. geometric
67. \$11.95; \$3.50
68. $2x^3 - x^2 + x - 16$
69. $2y^3 + 4y^2 + 2y + 8$

70. $b^4 + b^2 - 2b + 4$ **71.** $6d^3 - d^2 + 3d - 12$

72. yes; The rate of change is constant; $y = -\frac{3}{2}x + 10$

73. $a_1 = \frac{3}{2}, a_n = a_{n-1} + \frac{1}{2}$ **74.** $a_1 = -3, a_n = 5a_{n-1}$

75. linear; The graph is a line. **76.** $22r - 1$

77. $\frac{8}{3}c + 3$

7.2 Practice

1. $10c^3$ **3.** $-36r^3 - 24r^2$

5. $7w^5 - 28w^4 - 7w^3$ **7.** $-24g^7 + 120g^5$

9. $n^2 + 4n - 10$ **11.** $-x^4 + 4x^2 + 7x$

13. 7 **15.** $5p - 15$

17. $x^2 + 4x + 3$ **19.** $z^2 - 2z - 15$

21. $g^2 - 2g + \frac{3}{4}$ **23.** $3m^2 + 28m + 9$

25. $x^2 + 5x + 6$ **27.** $12k^2 + 23k - 9$

29. $8j^2 - 26j + 21$ **31.** $b^2 + 10b + 21$

33. $k^2 + 4k - 5$ **35.** $q^2 - \frac{1}{2}q - \frac{3}{16}$

37. $3r^2 - 29r + 18$ **39.** $w^3 + 8w^2 + 15w$

41. t also should be multiplied by $t + 5$; $= t(t + 5) - 2(t + 5) = t^2 + 5t - 2t - 10 = t^2 + 3t - 10$

43. $2x^2 + x - 45$ **45.** $\frac{1}{2}x^2 + \frac{11}{2}x + 15$

47. $x^3 + 7x^2 + 14x + 8$ **49.** $y^3 + 11y^2 + 22y - 6$

51. $-5b^3 + 15b^2 + 24b - 16$ **53.** $18e^3 - 27e^2 + 37e + 7$

55. a. $(4x^2 + 84x + 400)$ in.^{2}

b. 840 in.^{2}

57. *Sample answer:* Distribute one of the binomials over each term in the other binomial and simplify; Write each binomial as a sum of terms and make a table of products; Answers will vary.

59. yes; You are both multiplying the same binomials, and neither the order in which you multiply nor the method used will make a difference.

61. The degree of the product is the sum of the degrees of each binomial.

63. A

65. a. $(2x - 4)$ cm

b. 20 cm

67. *Sample answer:* $(2x - 6)(x^2 + 3x + 4)$

69. a. They have the same signs.

b. They have opposite signs.

7.2 Review & Refresh

70. $y = \begin{cases} -x + 4, & \text{if } x < 0 \\ x + 4, & \text{if } x \geq 0 \end{cases}$

71. $y = \begin{cases} -6x + 18, & \text{if } x < 3 \\ 6x - 18, & \text{if } x \geq 3 \end{cases}$

72. $-1, -2, -4, -8, -16, -32$

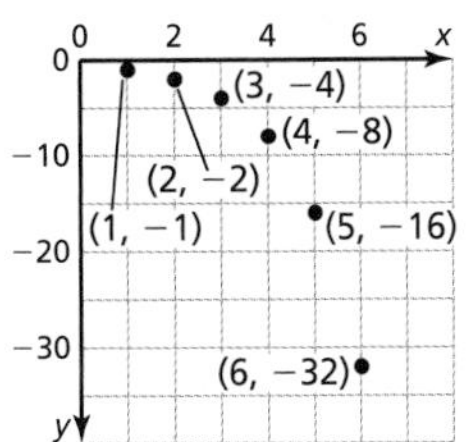

73. $3x^3 - 14x^2 + 23x - 14$ **74.** $s^4 + 7s^2 - 5s + 3$

75. $(-2, 6)$ **76.** 10^{11}

77. $\frac{1}{x^2}$ **78.** $\frac{1}{27z^{18}}$

79. $\frac{1}{4y^2}$ **80.** $a_n = 256\left(\frac{1}{2}\right)^{n-1}; \frac{1}{2}$

81. $x < 0$ or $x \geq 5$

82. no; The input 8 has more than one output, -1 and 2.

83. $8y^3 + y^2 + 3y + 8$ **84.** $z^2 + 9$; 2; 1; binomial

85. $-6d^6 + 3d^4$; 6; -6; binomial

86. $-4c^3 + c^2 - 2c$; 3; -4; trinomial

87. $7w^8 + \frac{1}{2}w^5 + 5w^3$; 8; 7; trinomial

88. The points on the graph of an arithmetic sequence lie on a line, and the points on the graph of a geometric sequence lie on an exponential curve.

89. $-8a^3 - 18a^2$ **90.** $b^2 - 9b + 18$

91. $2g^3 + 5g^2 + 16g + 40$ **92.** $-6v^3 - 30v^2 - 14v + 40$

93. $w \geq 1.7$

7.3 Practice

1. $x^2 + 16x + 64$ **3.** $4f^2 - 4f + 1$

5. $49t^2 - 56t + 16$ **7.** $4a^2 + 4ab + b^2$

9. $x^2 + 8x + 16$ **11.** $49n^2 - 70n + 25$

13. $t^2 - 49$ **15.** $16x^2 - 1$

17. $\frac{1}{4} - c^2$ **19.** $p^2 - 100q^2$

21. $y^2 - 16z^2$ **23.** 384

25. 1764 **27.** 930.25

29. The middle term in the square of a binomial pattern was not included; $= k^2 + 2(k)(4) + 4^2 = k^2 + 8k + 16$

31. a. 25%

b. $(N + n)^2 = N^2 + 2Nn + n^2$

33. $(x + 11)(x - 11)$; $x^2 - 121$ fits the product side of the sum and difference pattern, so working backwards, a and b are the square roots of a^2 and b^2.

35. $4m^4 - 20m^2n^2 + 25n^4$ **37.** $k = 64$

39. 760 people

7.3 Review & Refresh

40.

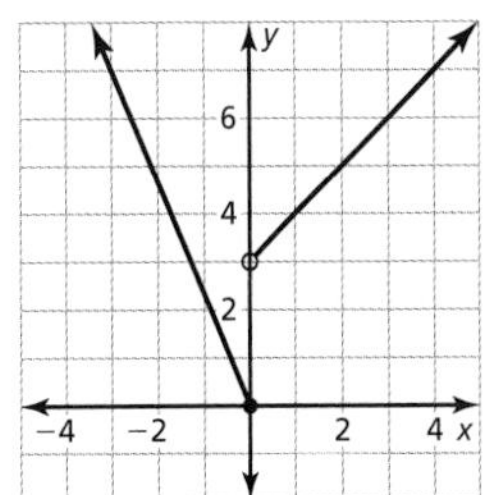

domain: all real numbers; range: $y \geq 0$

41.

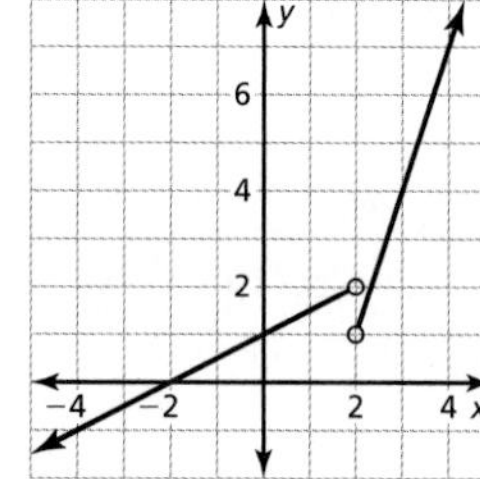

domain: all real numbers except $x = 2$; range: all real numbers

42. 37, 129.5, 5; 18.5 : 1; 37 : 2; 92.5 : 5; 129.5 : 7

43. $-2k + 7$ **44.** $7g^2 + 3g - 20$

45. $\frac{1}{4}d^2 - \frac{3}{2}d + 5$

46. $y = 180{,}000(1.035)^x$; \$253,908

47. $x^2 + 2x - 15$ **48.** $y^3 - 3y^2 - 19y + 6$

49. $x^2 - 12x + 36$ **50.** $4n^2 + 36ny + 81y^2$

51. $p^2 - 16$ **52.** $w^2 - 25z^2$

53. $4p^4 + 5p^2 - 3 - \dfrac{2}{p}$ **54.** $24h - 32$

55. small: \$5, large: \$8.50

56. $a_n = 1.5(-2)^{n-1}$; $a_1 = 1.5$, $a_n = -2a_{n-1}$

7.4 Practice

1. $x = 0, x = -7$ **3.** $t = 0, t = 5$

5. $s = 9, s = 1$ **7.** $a = 3, a = -5$

9. $g = \frac{3}{2}, g = 7$ **11.** $h = 8$

13. $r = 4, r = -8$ **15.** $z = 0, z = -2, z = 1$

17. $c = 3, c = -1, c = 6$ **19.** $x = 8, x = -8$

21. $5z(z + 9)$ **23.** $3y^2(y - 3)$

25. $n^5(5n + 2)$ **27.** $p = 0, p = \frac{1}{4}$

29. $c = 0, c = -\frac{5}{2}$ **31.** $n = 0, n = 5$

33. $6x$ is also a factor, so you need to set $6x = 0$ and solve; $6x = 0$ or $x + 5 = 0$; $x = 0$ or $x = -5$; The roots are $x = 0$ and $x = -5$.

35. 20 ft

37. $x = 0, x = 0.3$ sec; The roots represent the times when the penguin is at water level. $x = 0$ is when it leaves the water, and $x = 0.3$ sec is when it returns to the water after the leap.

39. no; If $a = b$, then there is a repeated root and the graph will only have one x-intercept.

41. no; Roots will occur if $x^2 + 3 = 0$ or $x^4 + 1 = 0$. However, solving these equations results in $x^2 = -3$ or $x^4 = -1$, and even powers of any number cannot be negative.

43. a. $x = -y, x = \frac{1}{2}y$

b. $x = \pm y, x = -4y$

7.4 Review & Refresh

45. 1, 48; 2, 24; 3, 16; 4, 12; 6, 8

46. $-8d^2 + 26d - 15$ **47.** $9z^2 - 25$

48. $y^3 + 11y^2 + 15y - 27$ **49.** $t^2 + 10t + 25$

50. $2x^3 - x^2 + 4$ **51.** 5

52. -14

53. linear; The rate of change is constant.

54. nonlinear; The rate of change is not constant.

55. $3z^4 + 7.4z^2 - 1.3z$; 4; 3; trinomial

56. $25x + 15y \geq 300$

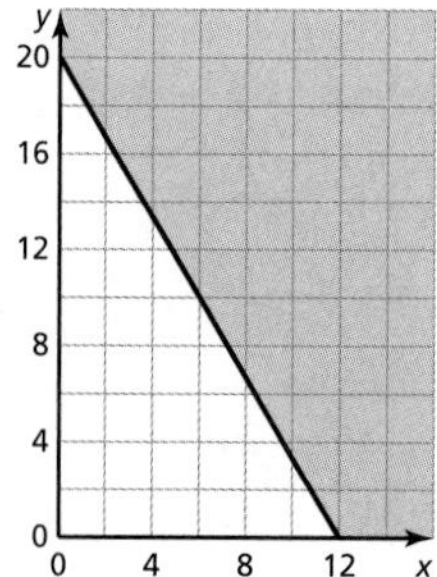

Sample answer: (12, 16) represents selling 12 coupon books and 16 candles; (14, 2) represents selling 14 coupon books and 2 candles.

57. $9x^2(2x^3 - 7)$

58. $-3 < x \leq 6$

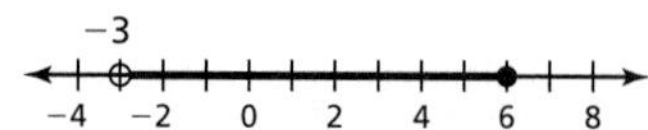

59. $x < 4$ *or* $x \geq 8$

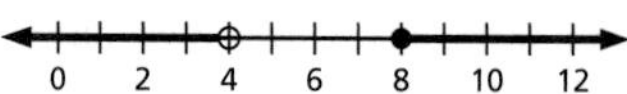

60. The graph of g is a vertical translation 2 units down of the graph of f; $k = -2$

61. $n = 0, n = \frac{2}{5}$

7.5 Practice

1. $(x + 1)(x + 7)$ **3.** $(n + 4)(n + 5)$

5. $(h + 2)(h + 9)$ **7.** $(v - 1)(v - 4)$

9. $(d - 2)(d - 3)$ **11.** $(w - 8)(w - 9)$

13. $(x - 1)(x + 4)$ **15.** $(n - 2)(n + 6)$

17. $(y - 6)(y + 8)$ **19.** $(x + 4)(x - 5)$

21. $(t + 2)(t - 8)$

23. $4 + 12$ is not 14; $= (x + 6)(x + 8)$

25. a. $(x - 5)$ ft

b. 16 ft

27. $m = -1, m = -2$ **29.** $v = 1, v = -26$

31. $n = -3, n = 8$ **33.** $a = 5, a = -10$

35. $m = 4, m = 11$ **37.** 100 in.^{2}

39. base: 10 m, height: 7 m

41. yes; p and q must be factors of -12 that have a sum of b, and -12 has 6 sets of integer factors, -1 and 12, -2 and 6, -3 and 4, -4 and 3, -6 and 2, and -12 and 1.

43. $(x + 2y)(x + 4y)$ **45.** $(a - 4b)(a + 15b)$

47. 10 m **49.** $(7n - 20)(7n + 9)$

7.5 Review & Refresh

50. $p = 9$ **51.** $z = -17$

52. $c = -42$ **53.** $k = 0$

54. $-18x^5 - 42x^3 + 6x^2$ **55.** $25w^2 - 16x^2$

56. $k = -\frac{1}{3}$ **57.** $k = 14$

58. $a_1 = 85$, $a_n = a_{n-1} - 25$

59. $p = -\frac{6}{5}, p = 2$ **60.** $x = 0, x = \frac{2}{3}$

61. $m > -7$

−7

−10 −8 −6 −4 −2 0

62. $t \leq 3$

63. $-2p^2 + 7p - 15$
64. $-2ab + 2b^2$
65. 11 bills
66. $(d + 2)(d + 14)$
67. $(x - 9)(x + 4)$

7.6 Practice

1. $3(x - 1)(x + 2)$
3. $4(k + 3)(k + 4)$
5. $7(b - 4)(b - 5)$
7. $(3h + 2)(h + 3)$
9. $(2x - 1)(3x - 1)$
11. $(n + 2)(3n - 1)$
13. $2(g - 2)(4g + 3)$
15. $-(t - 3)(3t - 2)$
17. $-(c - 5)(4c + 1)$
19. $-(3w - 4)(5w + 7)$
21. need to factor 2 out of every term; $= 2(x^2 - x - 12) = 2(x + 3)(x - 4)$
23. a. $(5x - 2)$ ft
    b. Substitute 3 for x into the expression for the area $15x^2 - x - 2$, then simplify; Substitute 3 for x into the expressions for the length $(5x - 2)$ and width $(3x + 1)$, simplify each, then multiply these two numbers.
25. $x = -2, x = 3$
27. $n = -\frac{5}{3}, n = \frac{3}{4}$
29. $x = -\frac{7}{2}, x = 5$
31. length: 70 m, width: 31 m
33. when no combination of factors of a and c produce the correct middle term; *Sample answer:* $2x^2 + x + 1$
35. $\pm 9, \pm 12, \pm 21$
37. 3.5 in.
39. $-2x - 10$
41. $(k + 2j)(4k - j)$
43. $-(a - 2b)(6a - 7b)$

7.6 Review & Refresh

45. ± 8
46. 2
47. -15
48. $\pm\frac{3}{7}$
49. $(-1, -4)$; Explanations will vary.
50. $(4, 6)$; Explanations will vary.
51. $y = -3x - 9$
52. a. exponential growth function
    b. about 17,716 people
53. $n = 0, n = 2$
54. $p = -7, p = 3$
55. $q = -6$
56. $r = 0, r = 12$
57. Factor out the GCF, 3, from each term; It is easier to factor $y^2 - 7y + 12$ than the original trinomial.
58. yes; No vertical line can be drawn through more than one point on the graph.
59. $(z + 7)(z + 4)$
60. $(v - 6)(v + 9)$
61. $(7x + 5)(2x + 3)$
62. $-(y + 1)(2y + 3)$
63. $t \leq 32$

26 28 30 32 34 36

64. $4x^2 - 9$

7.7 Practice

1. $(m + 7)(m - 7)$
3. $(8 + 9d)(8 - 9d)$
5. $9(5a + 2b)(5a - 2b)$
7. 63
9. 900
11. 600
13. $(h + 6)^2$
15. $(y - 11)^2$
17. $(a - 14)^2$
19. $(5n + 2)^2$
21. should follow the difference of two squares pattern; $= (n + 8)(n - 8)$
23. $(4d + 16)$ cm
25. $z = -2, z = 2$
27. $k = 8$
29. $n = 3$
31. $y = -\frac{1}{4}$
33. 1.25 sec
35. $3(z + 3)(z - 3)$
37. $2(5y + 6)^2$
39. a. no; $w^2 + 18w + 81$
    b. no; $y^2 - 10y + 25$
41. Square each binomial, then combine like terms; Use the difference of two squares pattern with each binomial as one of the terms, then simplify; *Sample answer:* The difference of two squares pattern; You do not need to square any binomials.
43. $x = 3$

7.7 Review & Refresh

44. $x = -5, x = 5$
45. $x = -\frac{3}{2}, x = \frac{3}{2}$
46.

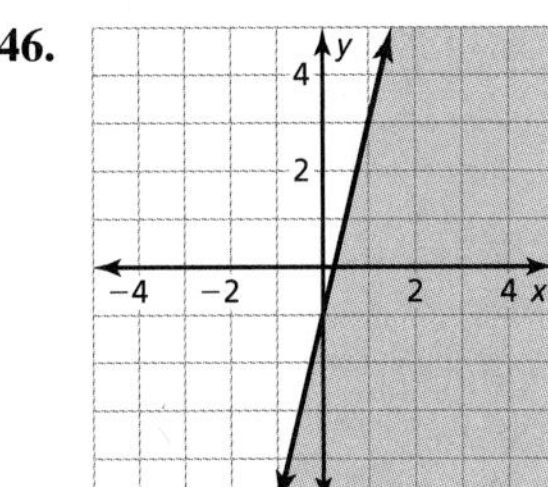

47.

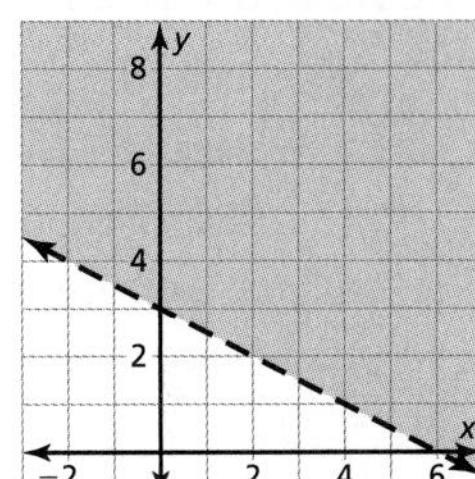

48.

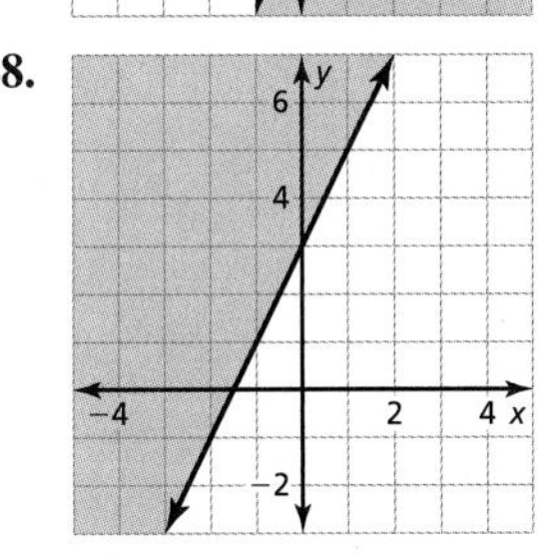

49.

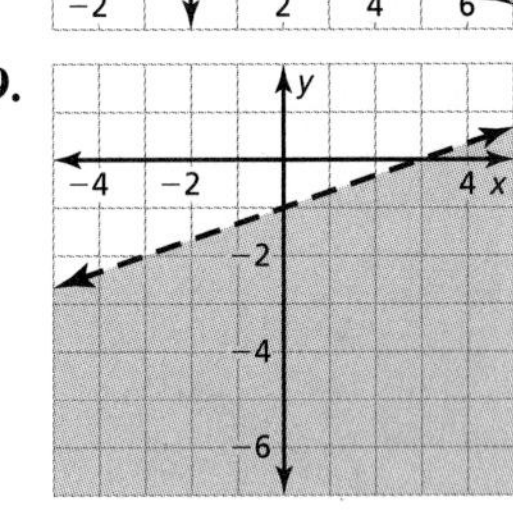

50. arithmetic; $a_1 = 4x + 9, a_n = a_{n-1} + (-3x + 6)$
51. $(x + 3)(x - 1)$
52. $(w - 7)(w + 3)$
53. $(3h - 4)(h + 2)$
54. $2(p - 8)(p + 5)$
55. exponential; As x increases by 1, y increases by a factor of 3.
56. a. $x = 20; \frac{3}{4}(x - 12) = 6, \frac{3}{4}x - 9 = 6, \frac{3}{4}x = 15, x = 20$
    b. $x = 20; \frac{3}{4}(x - 12) = 6, x - 12 = 8, x = 20$
57. $(x + 12)(x - 12)$
58. $(x - 4)^2$
59. $\left(x + \frac{2}{3}\right)^2$
60. $(2x + 9)^2$
61. a. $y = 0.174x - 0.24$
    b. \$2.37
    c. about \$4.11

7.8 Practice

1. $(x + 1)(x^2 + 2)$
3. $(z - 4)(3z^2 + 2)$
5. $(x + y)(x + 8)$
7. $(m - 3)(m + n)$
9. $2x(x + 1)(x - 1)$
11. unfactorable
13. $6g(g - 2)^2$
15. $3r^3(r + 6)(r - 5)$
17. $-4c^2(c^2 - 2c + 7)$
19. $(b - 5)(b + 2)(b - 2)$
21. $n = 0, n = 2, n = 4$
23. $x = -1, x = -2, x = 2$
25. $s = 0, s = -7, s = 7$
27. $x = 0, x = -9, x = 9$

29. $x = 0, x = 4$

31. In the second group, factor out -6 instead of 6; $= a^2(a + 8) - 6(a + 8) = (a + 8)(a^2 - 6)$

33. length: 4 in., width: 4 in., height: 8 in.

35. $(x + 2y)(x + 1)(x - 1)$

37. $(4s - 1)(s + 3t)$

39. B, C, D

41. no; The factors of the polynomial are $x^2 + 3$ and $x + 2$. Using the Zero-Product Property, $x + 2 = 0$ will give 1 real solution, but $x^2 + 3 = 0$ has no real solutions.

43. radius: 5, height: 8

45. a. *Sample answer:* $w = 40$; When $w = 40$, factoring out $5x$ will leave a perfect square trinomial, so there will be 2 factors.

b. *Sample answer:* $w = 50$; When $w = 50$, factoring out $5x$ will leave a factorable trinomial that is not a perfect square, so there will be 3 factors.

7.8 Review & Refresh

47. (2, 3); Explanations will vary.

48. (4, 8); Explanations will vary.

49. $(-6, -2)$; Explanations will vary.

50. no solution; Explanations will vary.

51. yes; Each input has exactly one output.

52. $3(y - 7)(y + 3)$

53. $(z + 2)(z + 10)(z - 10)$

54. a. \$16.50

b. \$17.25

55.

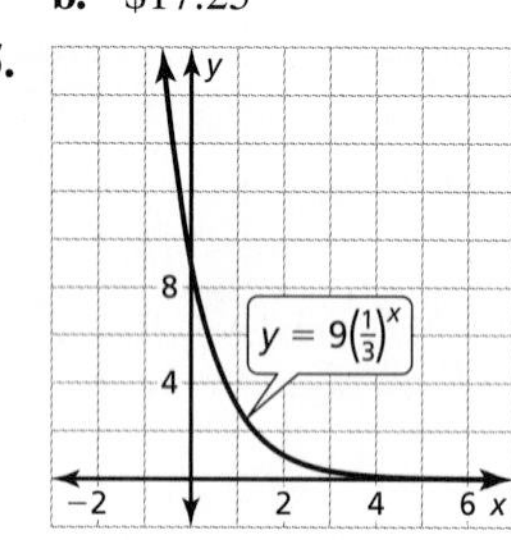

domain: all real numbers, range: $y > 0$

56.

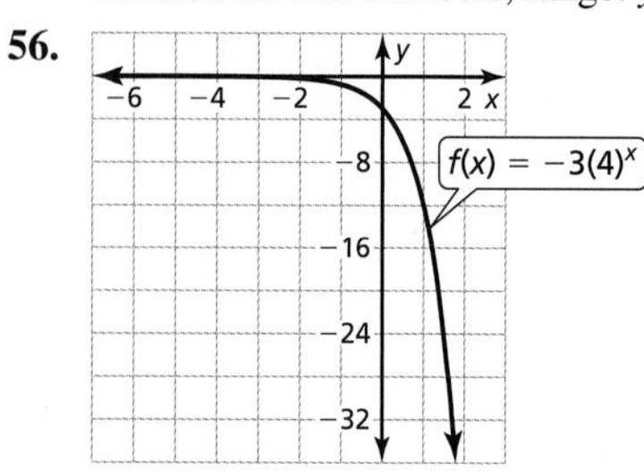

domain: all real numbers, range: $y < 0$

57. <

58. $n = -\frac{9}{5}, n = \frac{9}{5}$

59. $x = -\frac{5}{3}, x = \frac{1}{2}$

60. $h = 6, h = 9$

61. $x = 0, x = -5$

62. $y = -\frac{3}{4}x - 2$

63. $x = \dfrac{p + r}{1 - q}$

Chapter 7 Review

1. $5p^6 - 3p^3 - 4$; 6; 5; trinomial

2. $9x^7 + 13x^5 - 6x^2$; 7; 9; trinomial

3. $4a + 6$

4. $3x^2 + 6x + 10$

5. $-2y^2 + 6y + 4$

6. $-6p^2 - 12p + 7$

7. $x^2 + 2x - 24$

8. $-12y^3 + 7y^2 + 20y - 7$

9. $3n + 24$

10. $3x + 3$; no solution; When $x = 5$, the denominator of the original expression is 0, and division by 0 is undefined.

11. $x^2 - 81$

12. $4y^2 - 16$

13. $p^2 + 8p + 16$

14. $4d^2 - 4d + 1$

15. x^2 in.^{2}; The area of the new quilt is $(72 + x)(72 - x) = 5184 - x^2$ and $72^2 - (5184 - x^2) = x^2$.

16. $z = -3, z = 7$

17. $b = -13$

18. $y = 0, y = 9, y = -4$

19. $x = 0, x = -5$

20. 144 in.

21. $x = 0, x = \dfrac{b}{a}$

22. $(p + 7)(p - 5)$

23. $(b + 8)(b + 10)$

24. $(z + 3)(z - 7)$

25. $(x - 7)(x - 4)$

26. 324 ft^2

27. $q > p$; $p + (-q) = -b$, so q must be greater.

28. $(t + 6)(3t - 2)$

29. $-(y + 4)(5y + 2)$

30. $(2x + 1)(3x + 7)$

31. $-(y - 2)(2y - 3)$

32. $(z + 9)(3z - 1)$

33. $(2a - 3)(5a + 1)$

34. 12, 13, 15, 20, 37; The two binomial factors are $(2x + c)(x + d)$, where c and d are factor pairs of 18 and $2d + c = k$.

35. $(x + 3)(x - 3)$

36. $(y + 10)(y - 10)$

37. $(z - 3)^2$

38. $(m + 8)^2$

39. $-20, 20$

40. 30 m

41. $n(n + 3)(n - 3)$

42. $(x - 3)(x + 4a)$

43. $2x^2(x^2 + x - 10)$

44. $x = 0, x = 6, x = -3$

45. $x = -\frac{3}{2}, x = \frac{3}{2}$

46. $z = -3, z = 5, z = -5$

47. length: 12 ft, width: 4 ft, height: 2 ft

Chapter 7 Mathematical Practices (Chapter Review)

1. The terms can be grouped in pairs so the GCF can be factored out of each pair of terms of the polynomial.

2. *Sample answer:* When like terms of two trinomials have the same coefficient, the difference of the trinomials will have less than three terms.

3. If $a = 0$, then b is any real number because $0 \cdot b = 0$. If $a \neq 0$, then $b = 0$ because $b = \dfrac{0}{a} = 0$.

Chapter 7 Practice Test

1. $6s^4 - 3t$; 4; binomial

2. $-p^2 + 4p - 4$; 2; trinomial

3. $h^2 - 25$

4. $6w^2 + w - 15$

5. $p^3 - 3p^2 - 6$

6. 7

7. Check the first and last terms to verify they are perfect squares. If they are, find 2 times the product of their square roots. If this matches the middle term, or the opposite of the middle term, it is a perfect square trinomial.

8. yes; A monomial is a type of polynomial, and a number is a type of monomial.

9. $(s - 5)(s - 10)$

10. $(h + 2)(h + 3)(h - 3)$

11. $-(5k - 3)(k + 5)$

12. $n = 1, n = -6, n = -5$

13. $d = -7$

14. $x = 0, x = \frac{1}{3}, x = 4$

15. $x = 5, x = -4, x = 4$

16. $\pi r^2 - 6\pi r + 9\pi$

17. **a.** $(x + 11)$ ft

b. yes; The area of the stage is 234 square feet, and twenty times the area of the trap door is 200 square feet, so the area of the stage is greater than twenty times the area of the trap door.

18. $0 \leq t \leq 1.5$; You are in the air for 1.5 seconds.

19. length: 10 in., width: 2 in., height: 3 in.

Chapter 7 College and Career Readiness

1. B
2. C
3. B, C, F
4. $y = 61x + 1$
5. 1.2 cups per sec
6. A
7. 250 adult tickets, 350 child tickets
8. D
9. $h = 3$
10. 68 ft
11. C

Chapter 8

Chapter 8 Prepare

1.

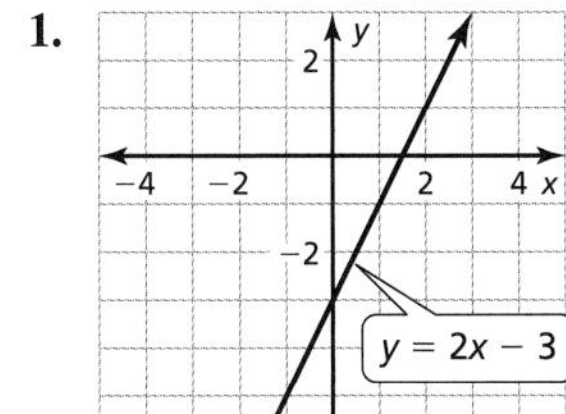

2.

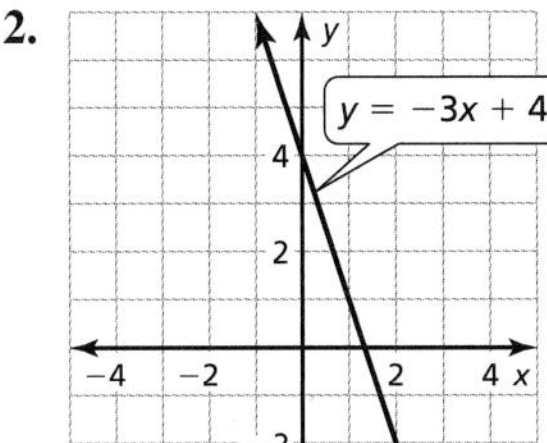

3.

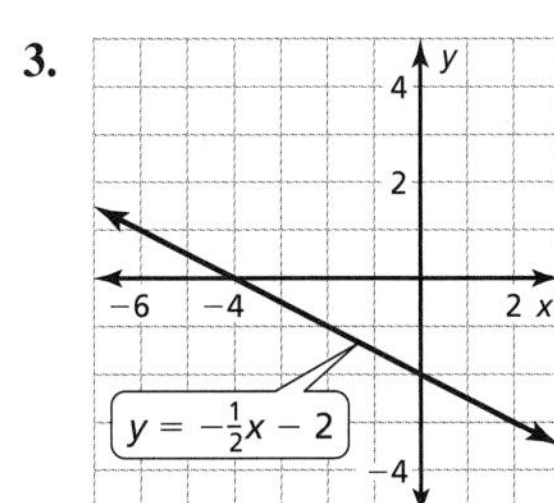

4.

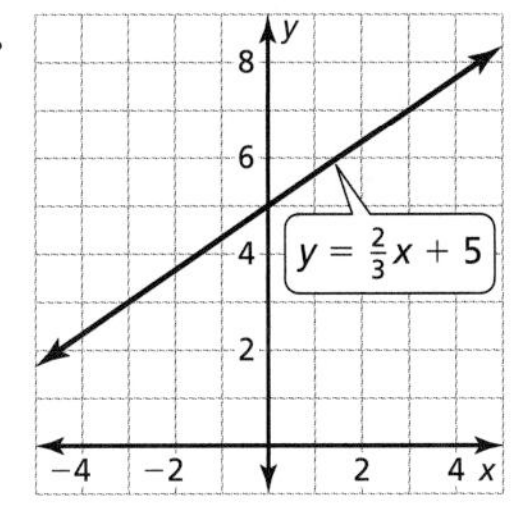

5. 11
6. 8
7. -11
8. -7
9. 9
10. $-\frac{47}{2}$
11. a, $4a$, $9a$, $16a$, $25a$; The differences of consecutive values increase by 2; $36a$, $49a$, $64a$

8.1 Practice

1. The vertex is $(1, -1)$. The axis of symmetry is $x = 1$. The domain is all real numbers. The range is $y \leq -1$. The function is increasing when $x < 1$ and decreasing when $x > 1$. The y-intercept is -2. The function is negative for all real numbers. $y \to -\infty$ as $x \to -\infty$ and $y \to -\infty$ as $x \to +\infty$.

3. The vertex is $(0, -8)$. The axis of symmetry is $x = 0$. The domain is all real numbers. The range is $y \geq -8$. The function is decreasing when $x < 0$ and increasing when $x > 0$. The y-intercept is -8. The x-intercepts are -4 and 4. The function is positive when $x < -4$ and $x > 4$, and negative when $-4 < x < 4$. $y \to +\infty$ as $x \to -\infty$ and $y \to +\infty$ as $x \to +\infty$.

5.

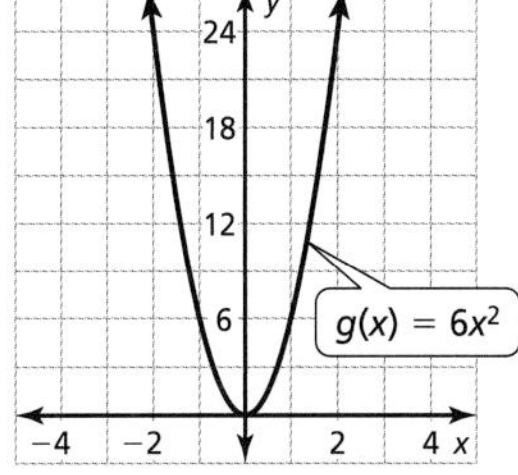

Both graphs have the same vertex, $(0, 0)$, and axis of symmetry, $x = 0$. The graph of g is a vertical stretch by a factor of 6 of the graph of f.

7.

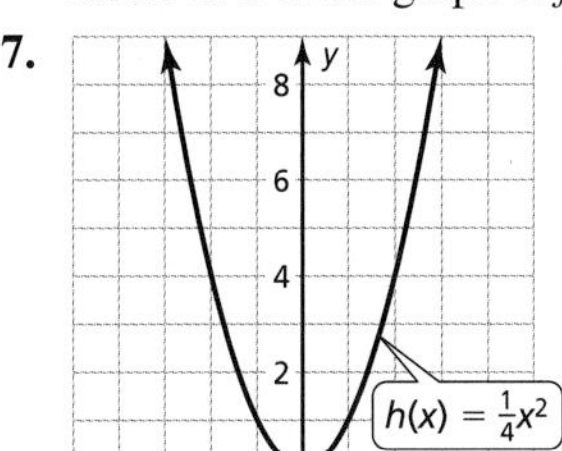

Both graphs have the same vertex, $(0, 0)$, and axis of symmetry, $x = 0$. The graph of h is a vertical shrink by a factor of $\frac{1}{4}$ of the graph of f.

9.

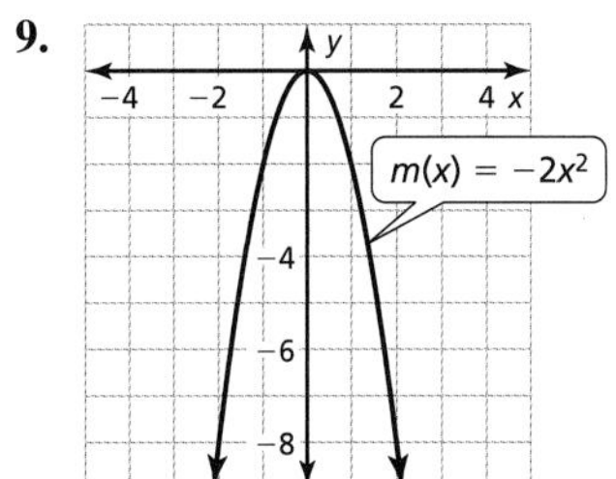

Both graphs have the same vertex, $(0, 0)$, and axis of symmetry, $x = 0$. The graph of m is a vertical stretch by a factor of 2 and a reflection in the x-axis of the graph of f.

11.

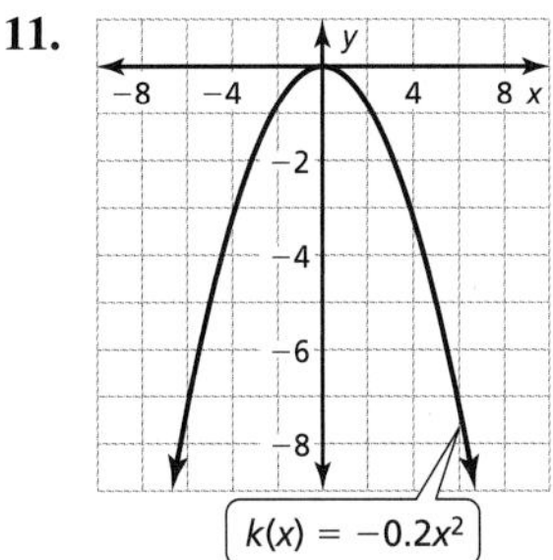

Both graphs have the same vertex, $(0, 0)$, and axis of symmetry, $x = 0$. The graph of k is a vertical shrink by a factor of 0.2 and a reflection in the x-axis of the graph of f.

13.

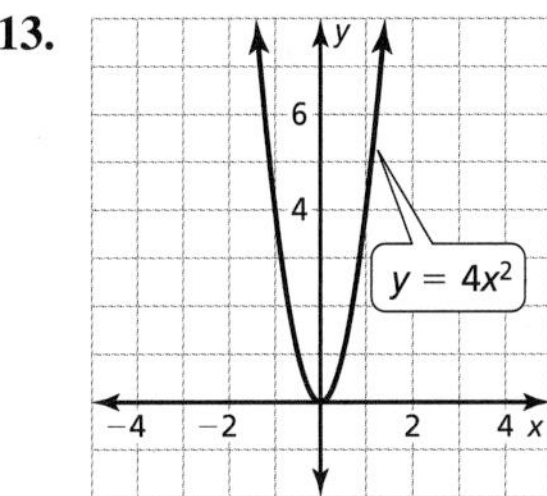

Both graphs have the same vertex, $(0, 0)$, and axis of symmetry, $x = 0$. The graph of $y = 4x^2$ is a reflection in the x-axis of the graph of $y = -4x^2$.

15. height: 300 ft, width: 1000 ft

17. The graph of g is a vertical shrink by a factor of 0.5 of the graph of f.

19. f is increasing when $x > 0$. g is increasing when $x < 0$.; f is decreasing when $x < 0$. g is decreasing when $x > 0$.

21. f; $a = \frac{3}{4}$

23. *Sample answer:* The vertex of a parabola that opens up is the minimum point, so its y-coordinate is the minimum value of y. The graph passes through $(6, -3)$, so 2 is not the minimum value of y.

25. sometimes; *Sample answer:* The graph of f will be narrower than the graph of g when $a > 1$, but it will be wider when $0 < a < 1$.

27. always; *Sample answer:* When $0 < |a| < 1$, the graph of f will be a vertical shrink of the graph of g, so it will be wider.

29. **a.** 8 cm

b. decrease; As the rotational speed decreases, the depth of the parabola decreases.

8.1 Review & Refresh

30. *Sample answer:*

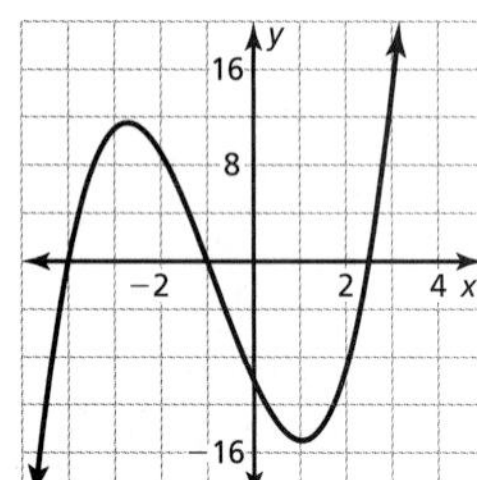

31. -25

32. 11

33. $(11 - 2h)(11 + 2h)$

34. $-(4t + 7)(t - 1)$

35. $(x + 5)(x - 11)$

36. $5r^2(r - 3)(r + 2)$

37. principal: 500; annual interest rate: 3%; compounded 4 times per year

38. $a_n = -11n + 36$; $a_{13} = -107$

39.

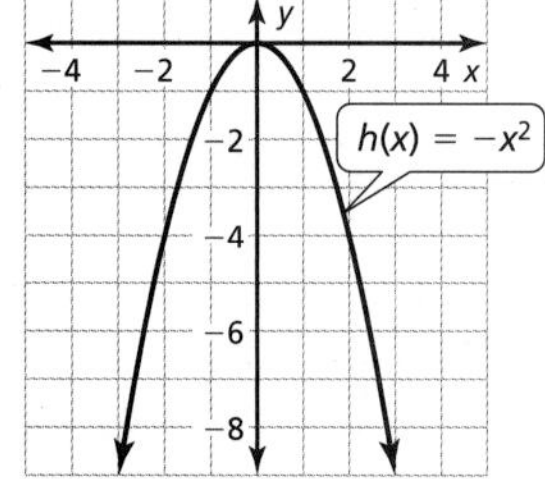

Both graphs have the same vertex, $(0, 0)$, and axis of symmetry, $x = 0$. The graph of h is a reflection in the x-axis of the graph of f.

40.

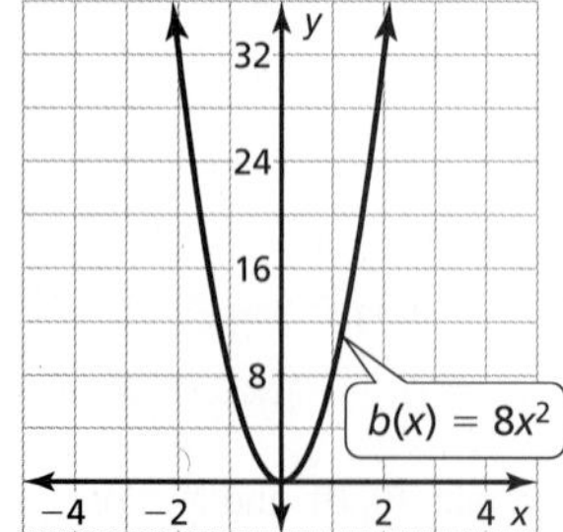

Both graphs have the same vertex, $(0, 0)$, and axis of symmetry, $x = 0$. The graph of b is a vertical stretch by a factor of 8 of the graph of f.

41. 3 spools of ribbon, 20 pieces of scrapbook paper

42. negative; $-\frac{5}{3}$

43.

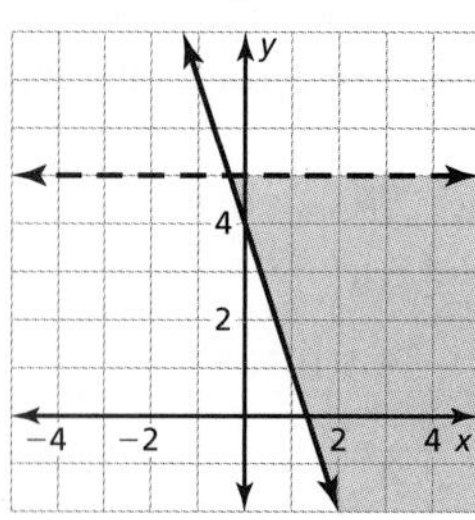

Sample answer: (2, 2)

44.

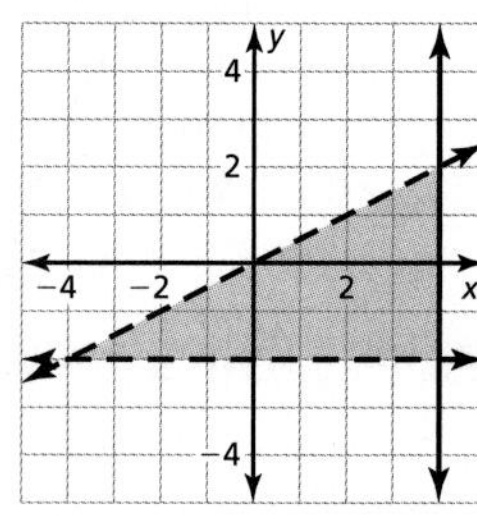

Sample answer: (3, 0)

8.2 Practice

1.

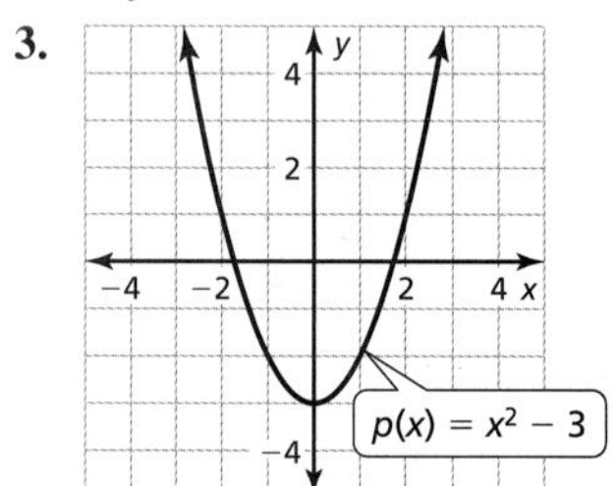

The graph of g is a vertical translation 6 units up of the graph of f.

3.

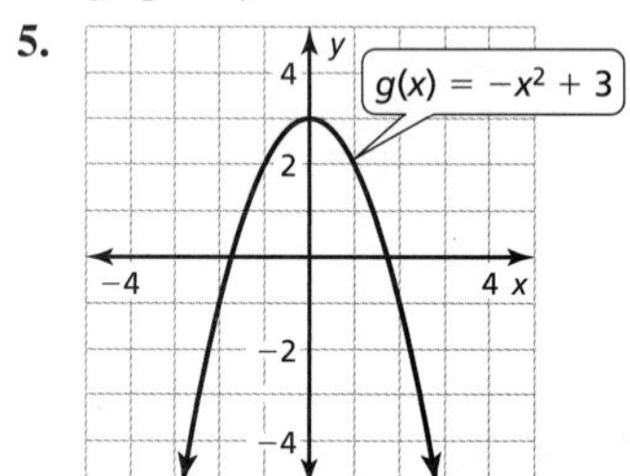

The graph of p is a vertical translation 3 units down of the graph of f.

5.

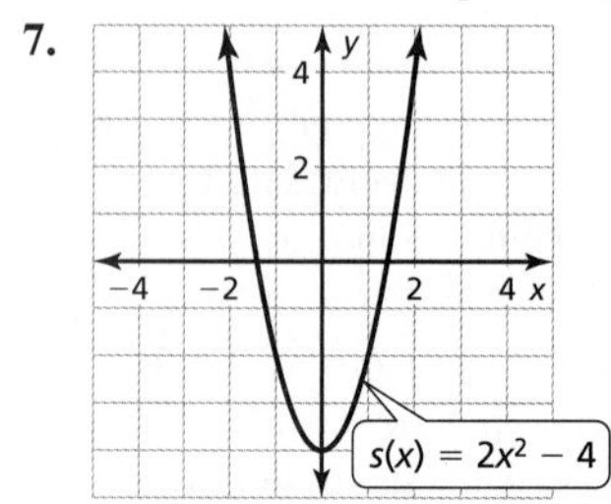

The graph of g is a reflection in the x-axis, and a vertical translation 3 units up of the graph of f.

7.

The graph of s is a vertical stretch by a factor of 2, and a vertical translation 4 units down of the graph of f.

9. 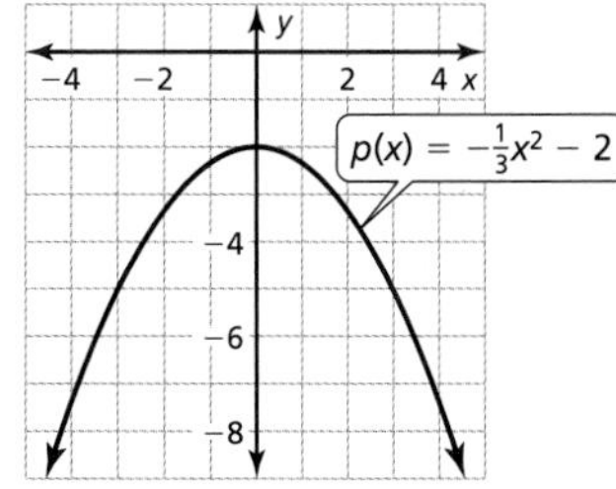

The graph of p is a vertical stretch by a factor of $\frac{1}{3}$, a reflection in the x-axis, and a vertical translation 2 units down of the graph of f.

11. The graph of g is a vertical translation 2 units up of the graph of f.

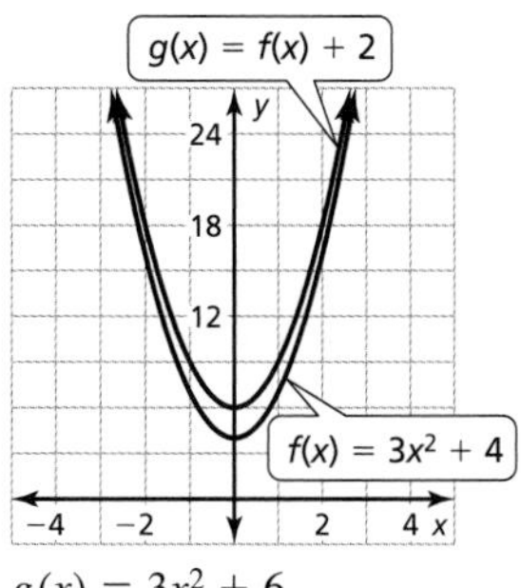

$g(x) = 3x^2 + 6$

13. The graph of g is a vertical translation 3 units down of the graph of f.

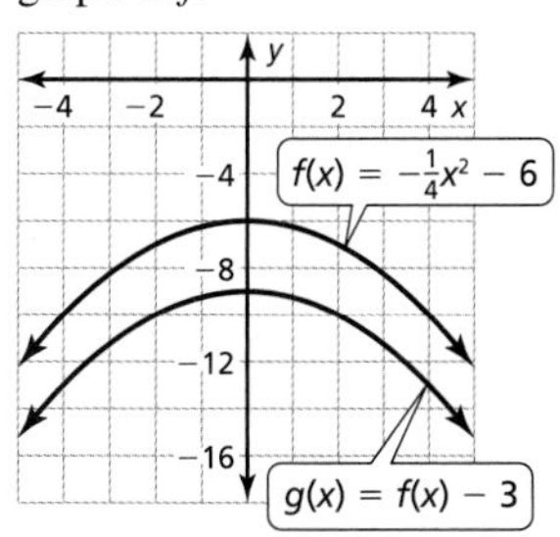

$g(x) = -\frac{1}{4}x^2 - 9$

15. $x = 1, x = -1$

17. $x = 5, x = -5$

19. $x = 2, x = -2$

21. $x = \frac{1}{2}, x = -\frac{1}{2}$

23. **a.** the height of the balloon after t seconds

b. 3 sec

25. The zeros of a function are the x-intercepts, not the y-intercept; The x-intercepts of the graph of f are -8 and 8. So, the zeros are -8 and 8.

27. *Sample answer:*

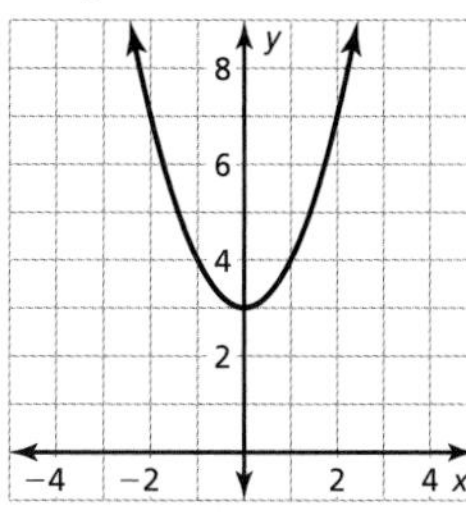

29. *Sample answer:*

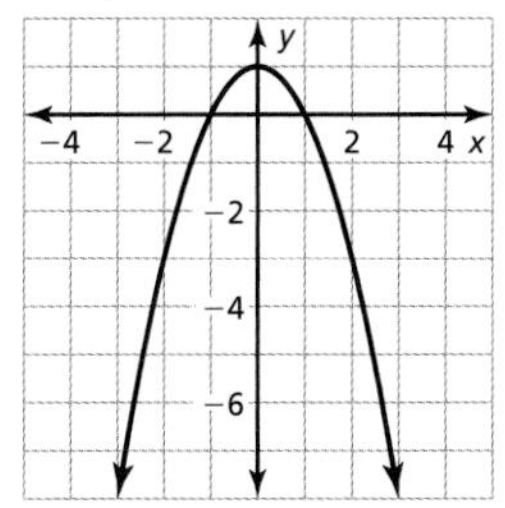

31. no; *Sample answer:* Changing a causes a vertical stretch or shrink, which does not change the vertex.

33. Graph the function and determine the x-intercepts; Set the function equal to 0, factor $-16t^2 + 400$, and apply the Zero-Product Property.

35. **a.** waterfall 1

b. waterfall 2

c. waterfall 1

37. (0, 5.8); *Sample answer:* The outer edges are located 40 feet from the center. Substituting this into $y = 0.012x^2$ indicates they are 19.2 feet above the x-axis. To be 25 feet above the x-axis, they must be vertically translated up 5.8 feet.

8.2 Review & Refresh

39. $\frac{3}{8}$

40. $\frac{7}{9}$

41. $x = \frac{10}{3}, x = -\frac{10}{3}$

42. $h = 0, h = -3$

43. **a.** $y = 3x + 8$

b. $y = -\frac{1}{3}x - 2$

44. -4; 15

45. $\frac{1}{b^4}$

46. $\frac{1}{144m^2}$

47. 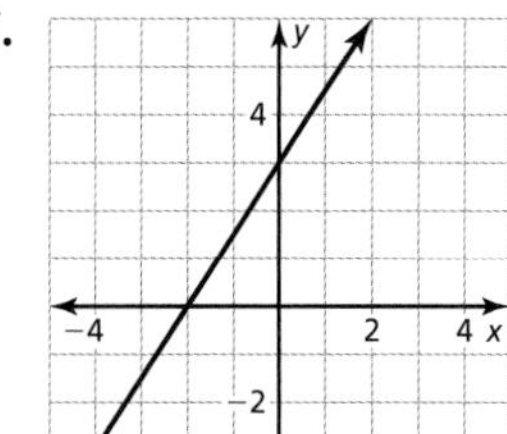

48.

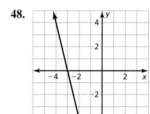

49. The vertex is $(-2, 4)$. The axis of symmetry is $x = -2$. The domain is all real numbers. The range is $y \geq 4$. The function is decreasing when $x < -2$ and increasing when $x > -2$. The y-intercept is 8. The function is positive for all real numbers. $y \to +\infty$ as $x \to -\infty$ and $y \to +\infty$ as $x \to +\infty$.

50. $0 \leq s \leq 13$

51. 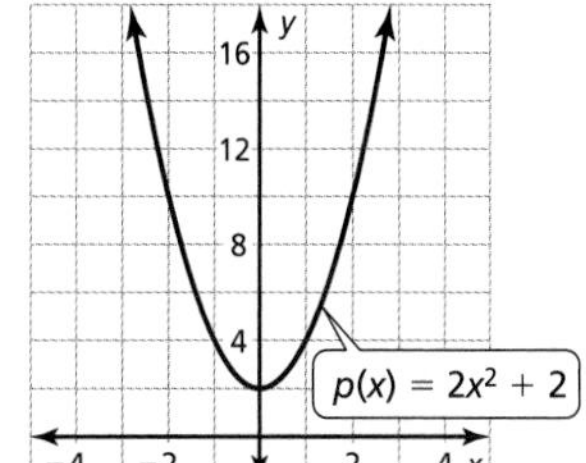

The graph of p is a vertical stretch by a factor of 2 and a vertical translation 2 units up of the graph of f.

52. 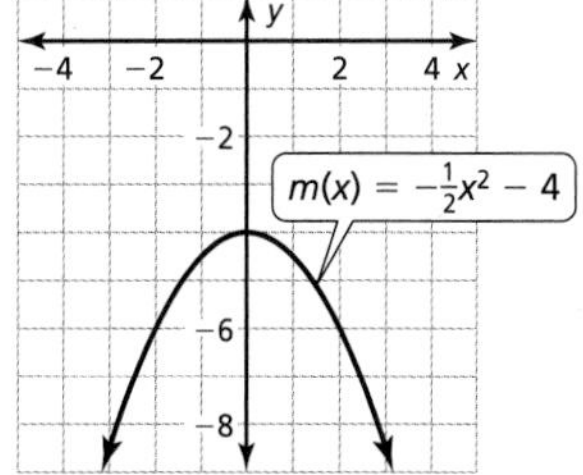

The graph of m is a vertical shrink by a factor of $\frac{1}{2}$, a reflection in the x-axis, and a vertical translation 4 units down of the graph of f.

8.3 Practice

1. $(2, -1)$; $x = 2$; 1

3. **a.** $x = 1$

b. $(1, -2)$

5. **a.** $x = -1$

b. $(-1, 8)$

7. **a.** $x = 5$

b. $(5, 4)$

9\. 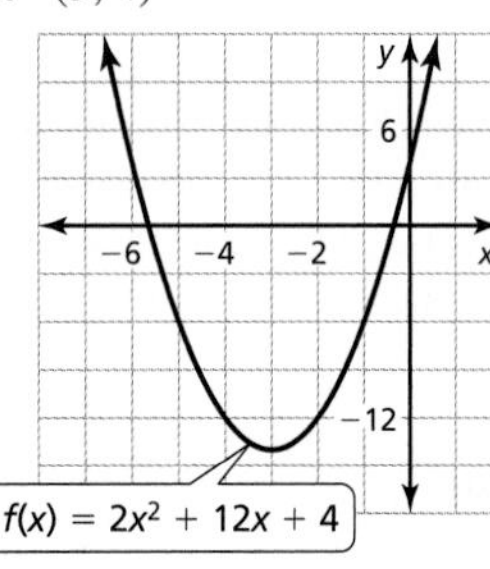

domain: all real numbers, range: $y \geq -14$

11\. 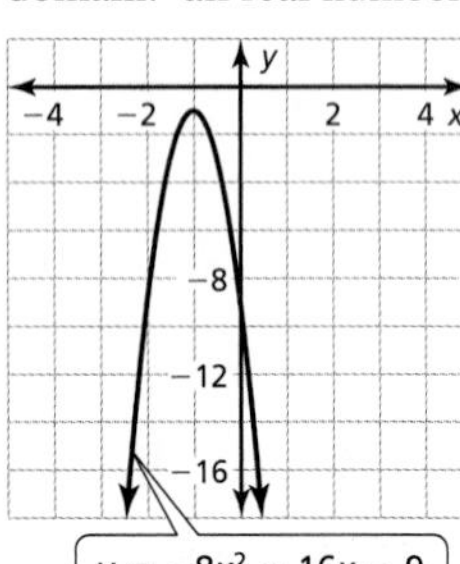

domain: all real numbers, range: $y \leq -1$

13\. 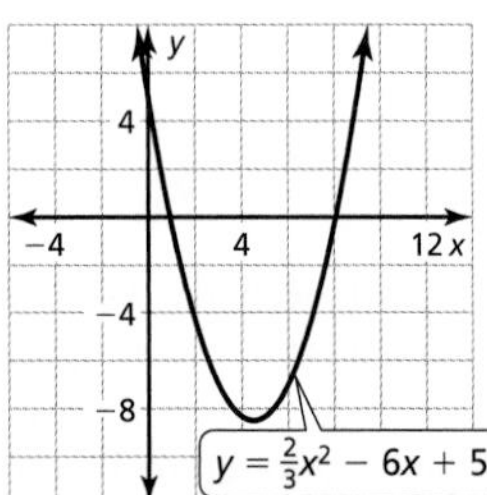

domain: all real numbers, range: $y \geq -\frac{17}{2}$

15\. There should be two negatives in the substitution, one from the formula and one because b is -12;

$x = -\frac{b}{2a} = -\frac{-12}{2(3)} = 2$; The axis of symmetry is $x = 2$.

17\. minimum value; -12

19\. maximum value; -1

21\. maximum value; $66\frac{1}{2}$

23\. 110; The javelin reaches a maximum height of about 110 feet.

25\. *Sample answer:* $(0, 8)$; Because the axis of symmetry is $x = 3$, the point $(0, 8)$ would also lie on the graph.

27\. $(-1.41, -4)$

29\. $(0.48, 0.72)$

31\. **a.** second aircraft hangar

b. first aircraft hangar

33\. $x = 0$; no; *Sample answer:* If $a = 0$, the equation is linear, not quadratic, so it has no axis of symmetry.

35\. **a.** $x = 4.5$

b. 20.25 in.^{2}

37\. The graph of g is a reflection in the y-axis of the graph of h.

39\. $f(x) = 2x^2 - 6x + 2$

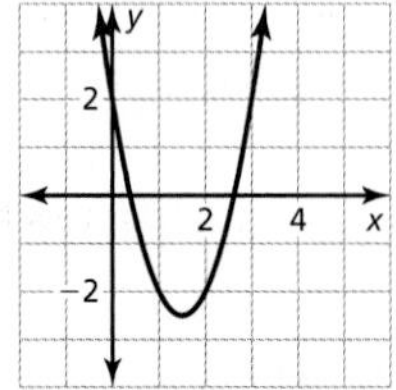

41\. **a.** not possible; Two points is not enough to graph a parabola.

b. The vertex is $(3, -4)$. The axis of symmetry is $x = 3$. The domain is all real numbers. The range is $y \geq -4$. The function is decreasing when $x < 3$ and increasing when $x > 3$. The y-intercept is 14. $y \to +\infty$ as $x \to -\infty$ and $y \to +\infty$ as $x \to +\infty$.

43\. 14 ft

45\. Answers will vary. Check students' work.

47\. $\frac{k^2}{8}$ ft^2

8.3 Review & Refresh

48\. The graph of q is a horizontal translation 6 units left of the graph of f.

49\. The graph of h is a vertical shrink by a factor of 0.5, and a reflection in the x-axis of the graph of f.

50\. The graph of g is a horizontal translation 2 units right, and a vertical translation 5 units up of the graph of f.

51\. The graph of p is a vertical stretch by a factor of 3, and a horizontal translation 1 unit left of the graph of f.

52\. geometric sequence; Consecutive y-values have a common ratio of 2.

53\. 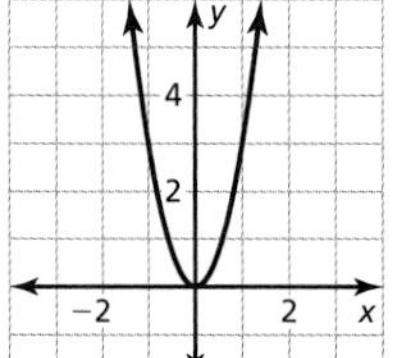

Both graphs have the same vertex, $(0, 0)$, and axis of symmetry, $x = 0$. The graph of g is a vertical stretch by a factor of 3 of the graph of f.

54\. 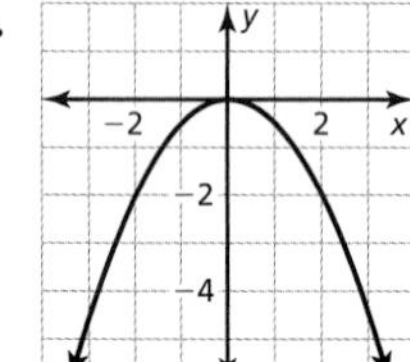

Both graphs have the same vertex, $(0, 0)$, and axis of symmetry, $x = 0$. The graph of h is a reflection in the x-axis, and a vertical shrink by a factor of $\frac{1}{2}$ of the graph of f.

55\. 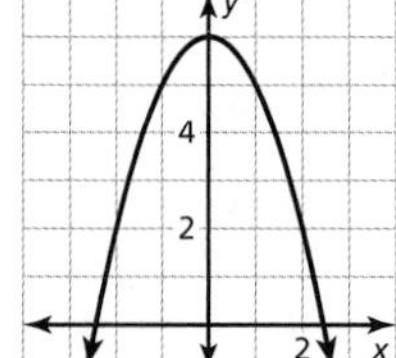

Both graphs have the same axis of symmetry, $x = 0$, and the vertex of d, $(0, 6)$, is above the vertex of f, $(0, 0)$. The graph of d is a reflection in the x-axis, and a vertical translation 6 units up of the graph of f.

56. 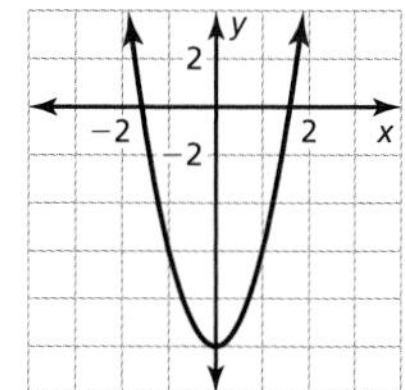

Both graphs have the same axis of symmetry, $x = 0$, and the vertex of p, (0, 10), is below the vertex of f, (0, 0). The graph of p is a vertical stretch by a factor of 4 and a vertical translation 10 units down of the graph of f.

57. when $0 < b < 1$ and x represents time

58. $y^2 + 3y - 21$

59. $4k^3 + 5k^2 - 10k + 10$

60. 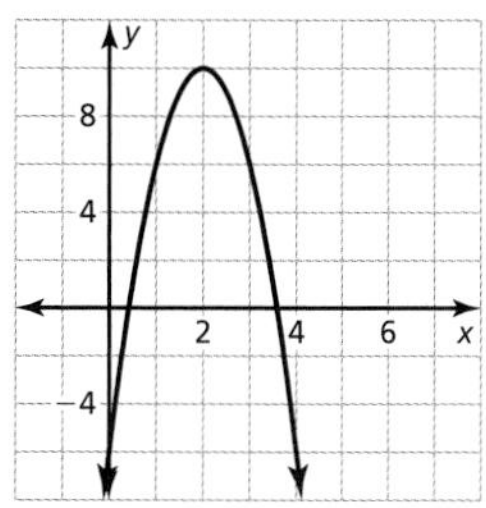

domain: all real numbers, range: $y \leq 10$

61. a. integers between 0 and 15; discrete

b. 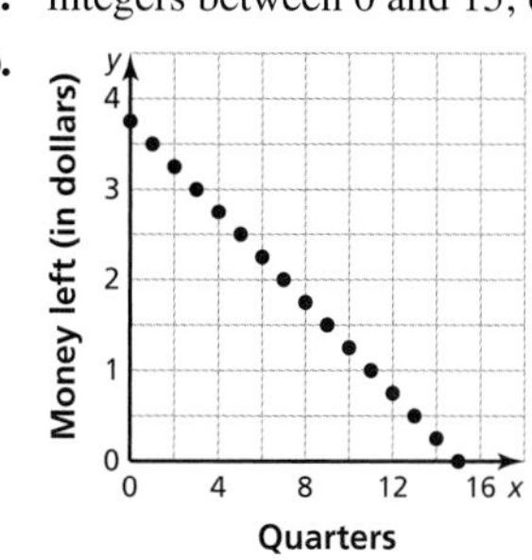

62. $(z + 7)(z - 7)$

63. $(w + 1)^2$

64. $(n + 3)(n + 8)$

65. $(q - 1)(q + 5)$

66. $(2s - 3)(s - 9)$

67. $-3(3r - 2)(r + 2)$

68. $(b + 1)(b + 2)(b - 2)$

69. $2c(c + 4)(c - 3)$

70. $y = \dfrac{x}{4 - k}$

71. $(-2, 0)$; $x = -2$; -3

72. $(-1, 1)$; $x = -1$; 5

8.4 Practice

1. neither

3. neither

5. even

7. neither

9. even

11. neither

13. $(-1, 0)$; $x = -1$

15. $(4, 0)$; $x = 4$

17. 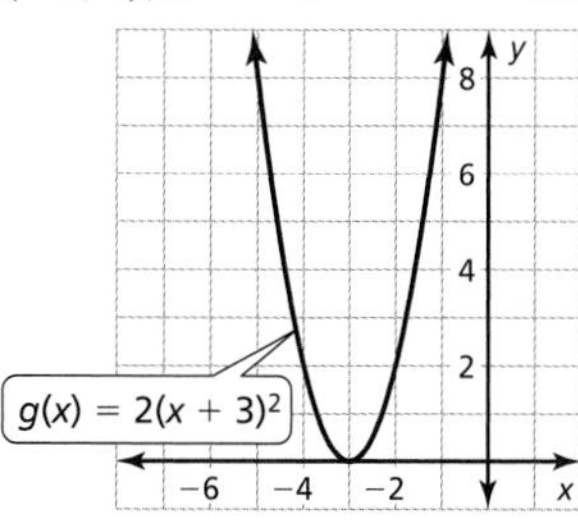

The graph of g is a horizontal translation 3 units left, and a vertical stretch by a factor of 2 of the graph of f.

19. 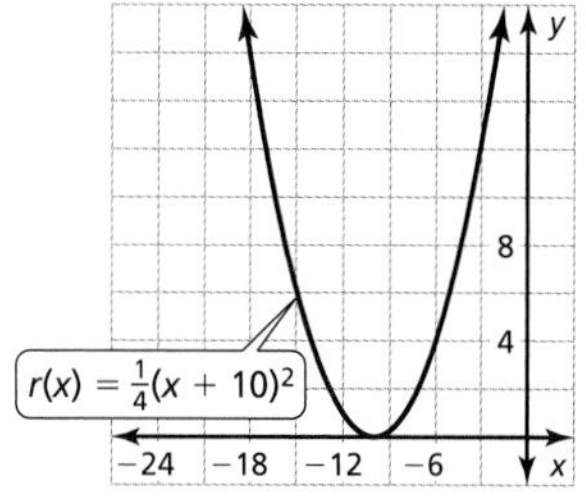

The graph of r is a horizontal translation 10 units left, and a vertical shrink by a factor of $\frac{1}{4}$ of the graph of f.

21. 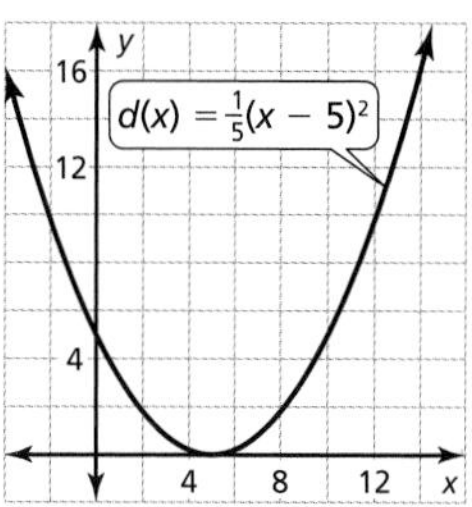

The graph of d is a horizontal translation 5 units right, and a vertical shrink by a factor of $\frac{1}{5}$ of the graph of f.

23. $(-4, -3)$; $x = -4$

25. $(-3, 1)$; $x = -3$

27. 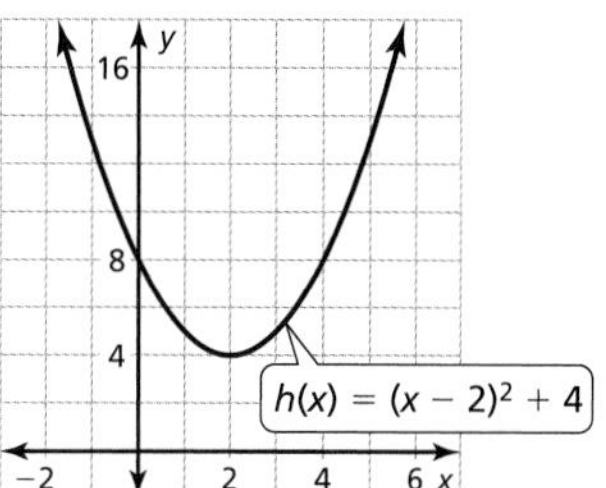

The graph of h is a translation 2 units right and 4 units up of the graph of f.

29. 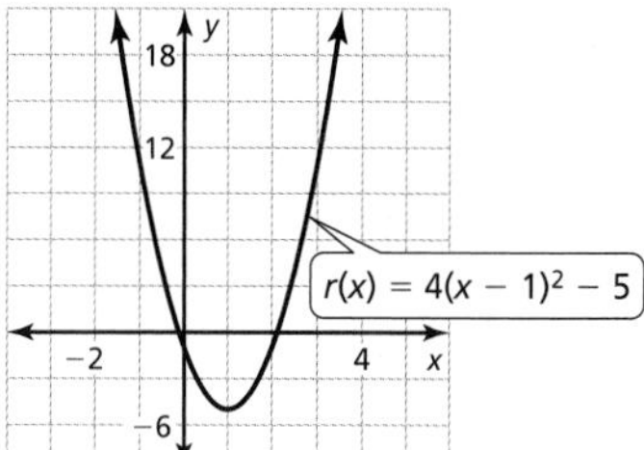

The graph of r is a vertical stretch by a factor of 4, and a translation 1 unit right and 5 units down of the graph of f.

31. 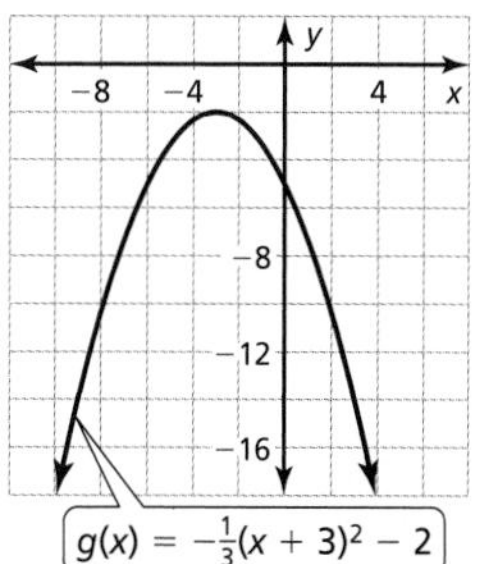

The graph of g is a vertical shrink by a factor of $\frac{1}{3}$, a reflection in the x-axis, and a translation 3 units left and 2 units down of the graph of f.

33. If $f(-x) = f(x)$ the function is even; So, f is an even function.

35. A

37. B

39. 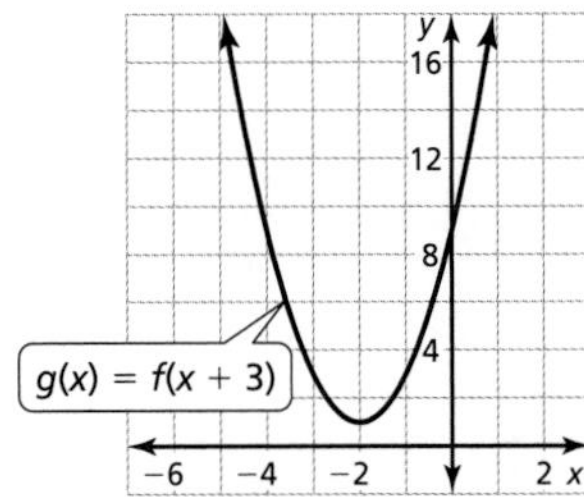

41. 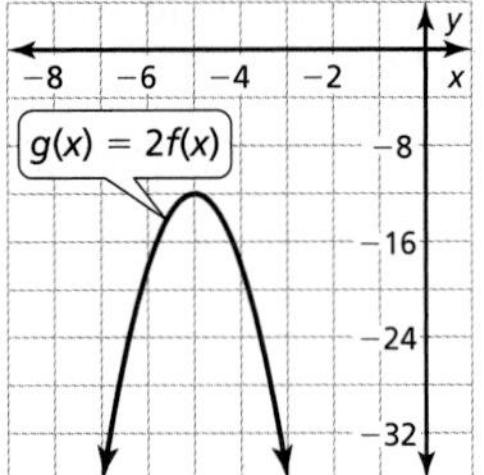

43. 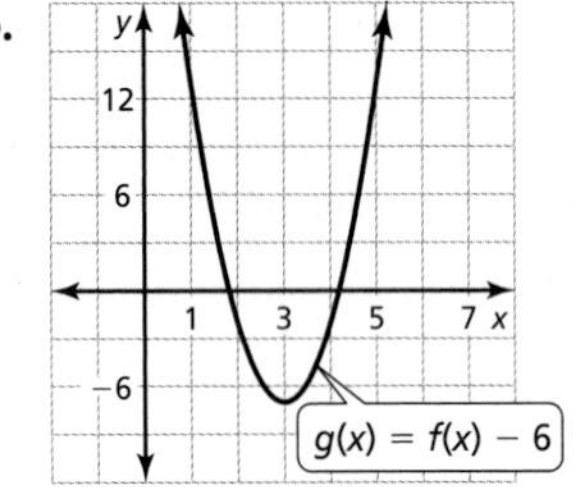

45. 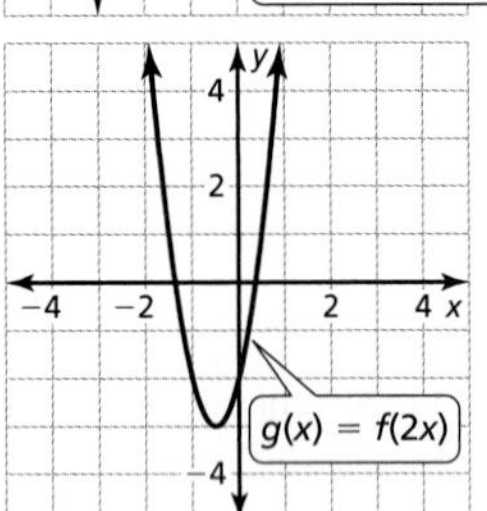

47. a. 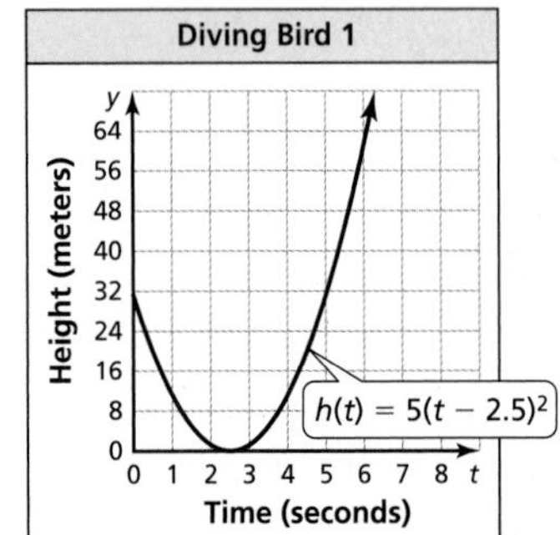

b. 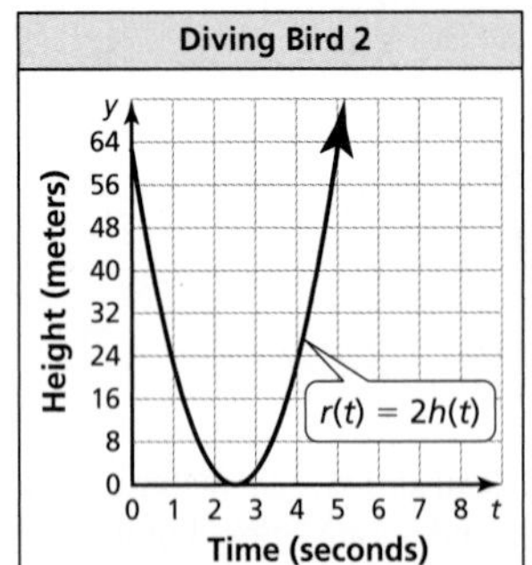

c. The graph of r is a vertical stretch by a factor of 2 of the graph of h; the second bird; *Sample answer:* Because $r(t)$ is twice $h(t)$, the second bird starts at a height twice as high as the first bird.

49. $f(x) = 2(x - 1)^2 + 2$

51. $f(x) = -2(x + 2)^2 - 4$

53. $f(x) = -\frac{18}{125}(x - 25)^2 + 90$

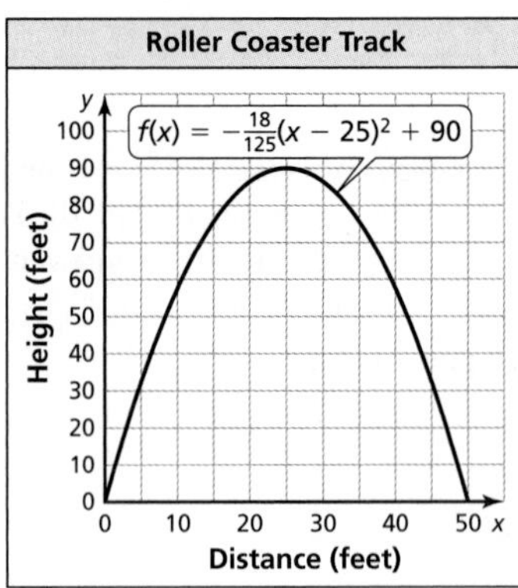

55. D

57. The graph of h is a vertical translation 4 units up of the graph of f; $h(x) = -(x + 1)^2 + 2$

59. The graph of h is a vertical stretch by a factor of 2 of the graph of f; $h(x) = 8(x - 2)^2 + 6$

61. $y = (x - 2)^2 - 5$; $y = x^2 - 4x - 1$; *Sample answer:* The vertex, $(2, -5)$, can be quickly determined from the vertex form; The y-intercept, -1, can be quickly determined from the standard form.

63. $y = 2(x - 2)^2 - 4$

65. $f(x) = -(x + 2)^2 + 6$

67. yes; Because the axis of symmetry of $y = a(x - 0)^2 + c$ is $x = 0$, the graph is symmetric about the y-axis.

8.4 Review & Refresh

69. The vertex is $(1, 4)$. The axis of symmetry is $x = 1$. The domain is all real numbers. The range is $y \leq 4$. The function is increasing when $x < 1$ and decreasing when $x > 1$. The y-intercept is 3, and the x-intercepts are -1 and 3. The function is negative when $x < -1$ and $x > 3$, and positive when $-1 < x < 3$. $y \to -\infty$ as $x \to -\infty$ and $y \to -\infty$ as $x \to +\infty$.

70. The graph of g is a horizontal translation h units right if h is positive or $|h|$ units left if h is negative, and a vertical translation k units up if k is positive or $|k|$ units down if k is negative of the graph of f.

71. $t \geq 3$

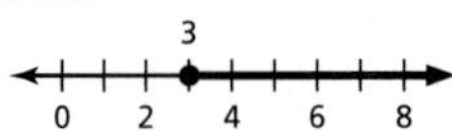

72. $-8 < v \leq 8$

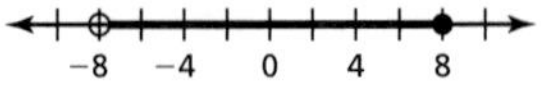

73. minimum value; -8

74. maximum value; 16

75. no solution

76. exponential function; The common factor is $\frac{1}{4}$.

77. The graph g is a vertical translation 6 units down of the graph of f.

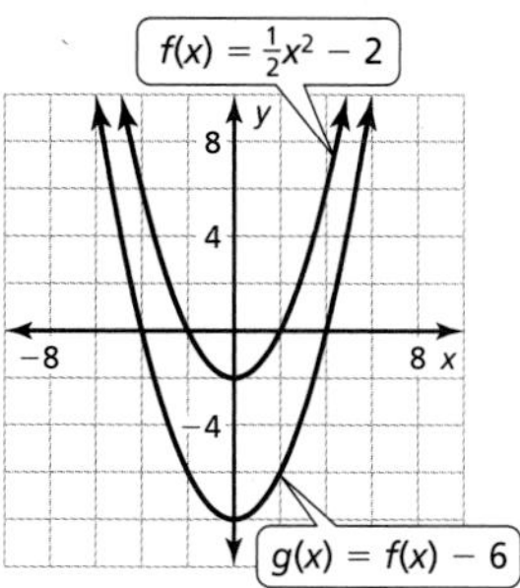

$g(x) = \frac{1}{2}x^2 - 8$

78.

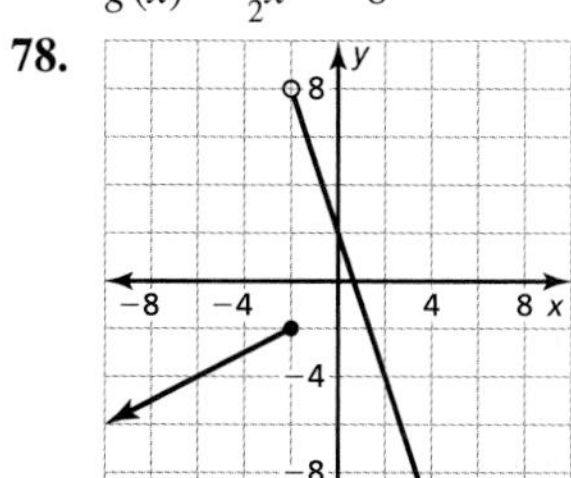

domain: all real numbers, range: $y < 8$

79.

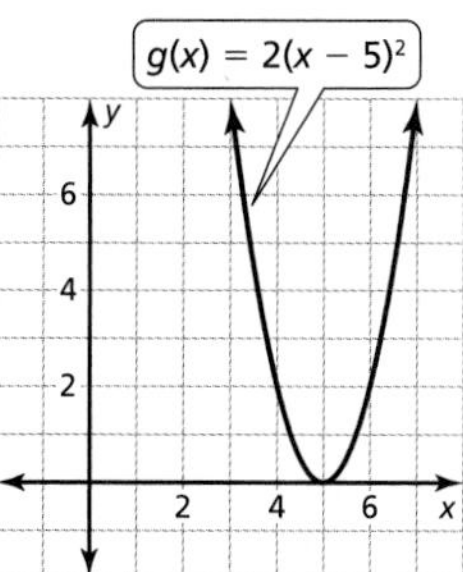

The graph of g is a vertical stretch by a factor of 2, and a horizontal translation 5 units right of the graph of f.

80.

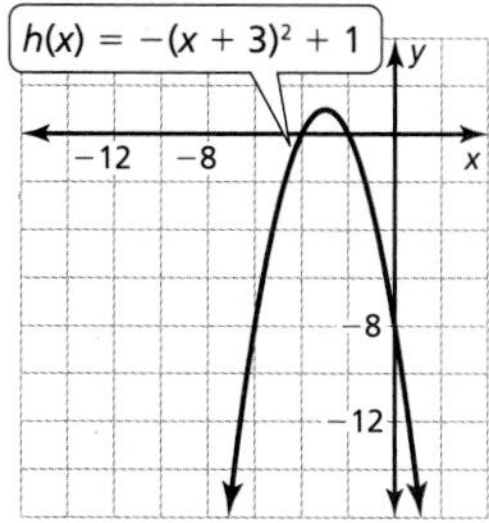

The graph of h is a reflection in the x-axis, and a translation 3 units left and 1 unit up of the graph of f.

81.

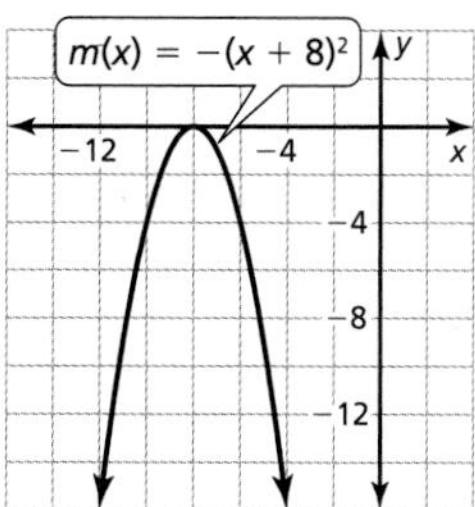

The graph of m is a reflection in the x-axis, and a horizontal translation 8 units left of the graph of f.

82.

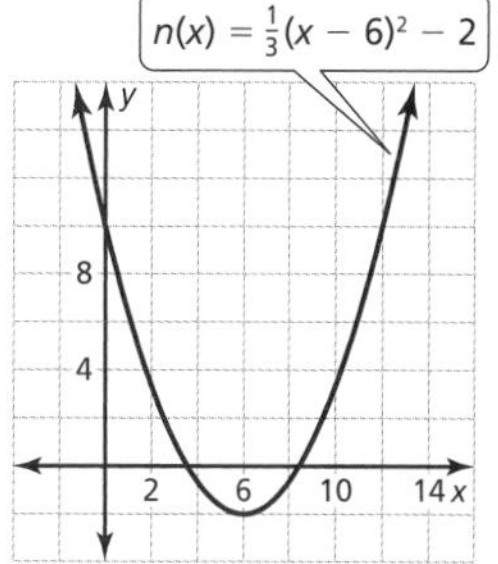

The graph of n is a vertical shrink by a factor of $\frac{1}{3}$, and a translation 6 units right and 2 units down of the graph of f.

83. $a_n = 2^n$; $a_{10} = 1024$

84. 15 standard and 3 tandem bicycles

85. $x = 0, x = 1$ **86.** $x = -3, x = 8$

87. $x = \frac{3}{2}$ **88.** $x = 3, x = -\frac{1}{4}$

8.5 Practice

1. $-3, 1; x = -1$ **3.** $-7, 5; x = -1$

5.

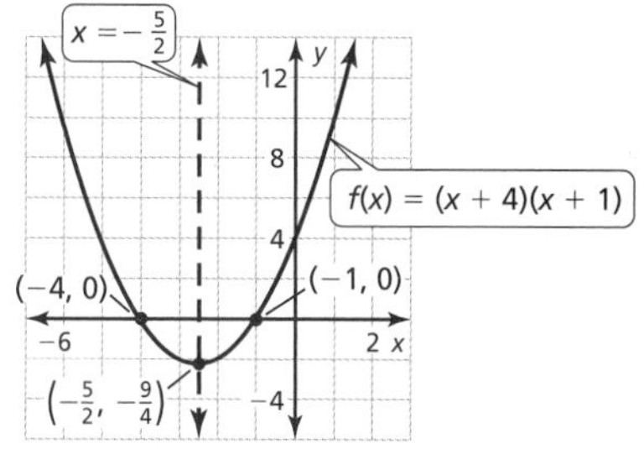

domain: all real numbers, range: $y \geq -\frac{9}{4}$

7.

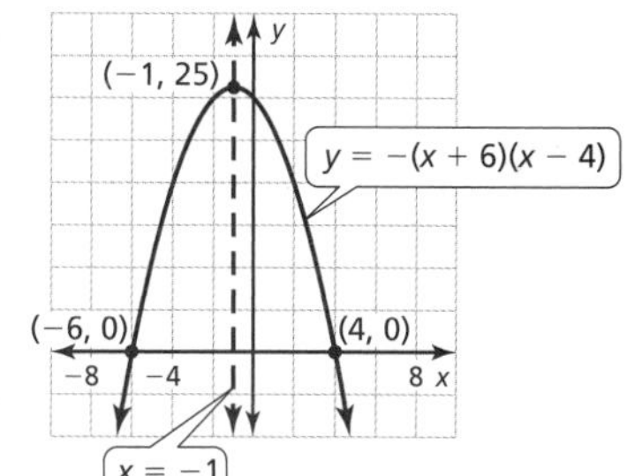

domain: all real numbers, range: $y \leq 25$

9.

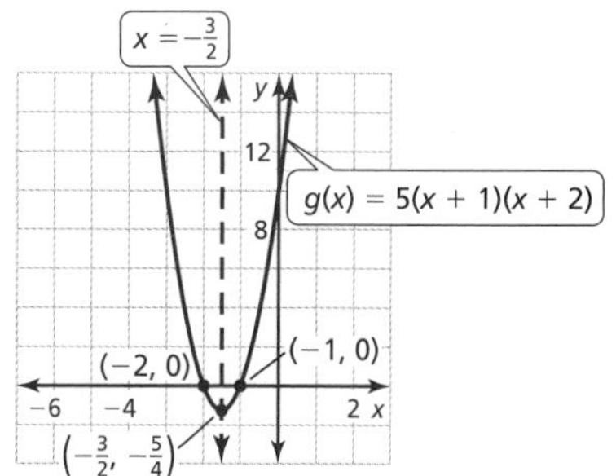

domain: all real numbers, range: $y \geq -\frac{5}{4}$

11.

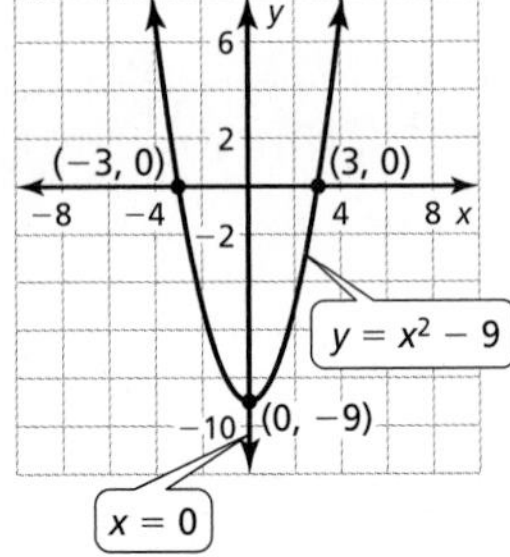

domain: all real numbers, range: $y \geq -9$

13.

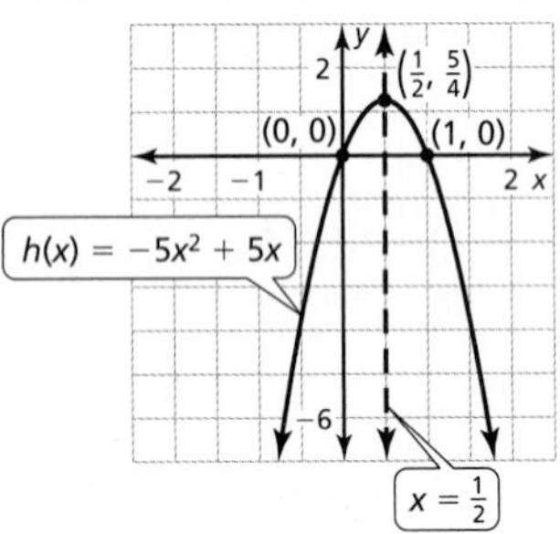

domain: all real numbers, range: $y \leq \frac{5}{4}$

15.

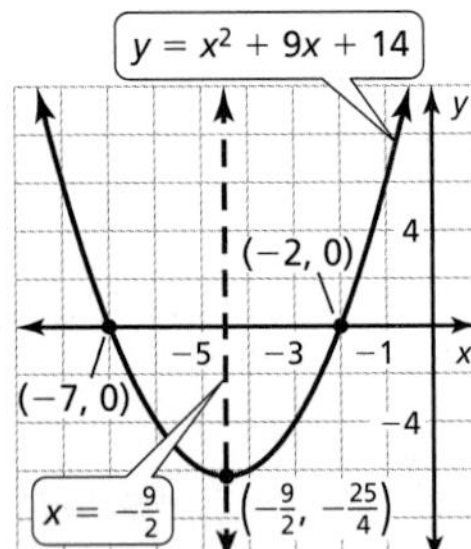

domain: all real numbers, range: $y \geq -\frac{25}{4}$

17.

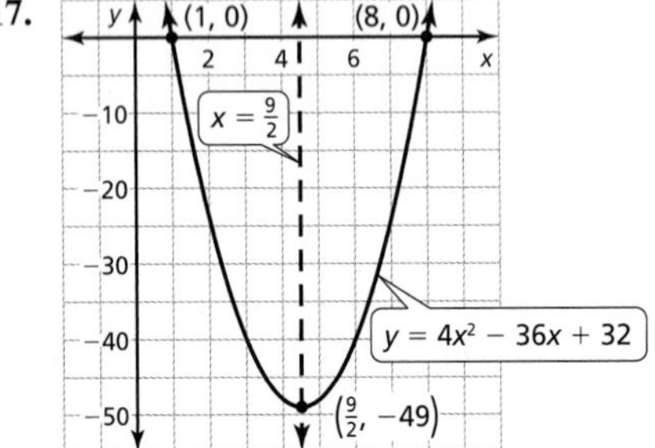

domain: all real numbers, range: $y \geq -49$

19. 2, 10

21. −8, 3

23. −2, 7

25. −5, −2

27. −7, 0, 7

29. The factors need to be set equal to 0 and solved to find the zeros; $x + 3 = 0$ or $x - 2 = 0$; $x = -3$ or $x = 2$; The zeros of the function are −3 and 2.

31. C

33. B

35.

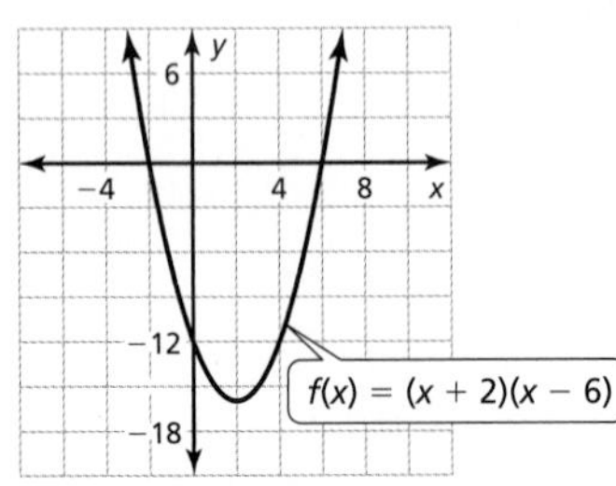

37.

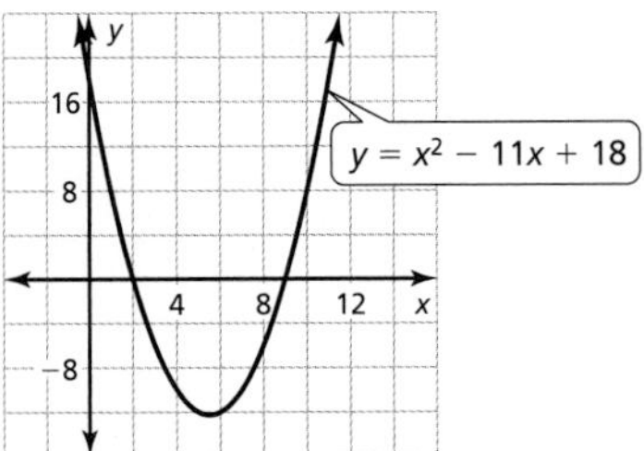

39.

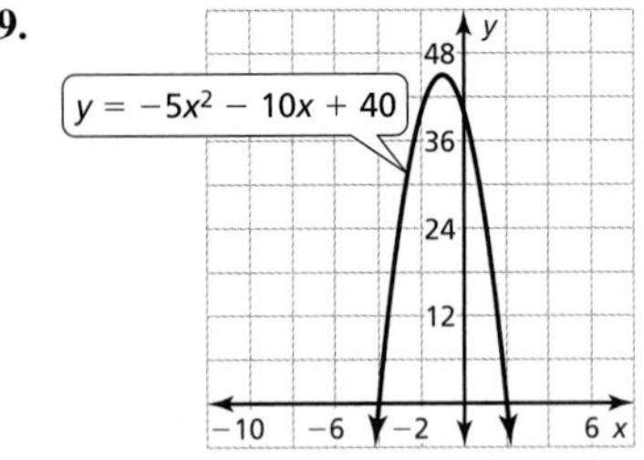

41. *Sample answer:* $f(x) = x^2 - 14x + 46$

43. *Sample answer:* $f(x) = x^2 - 10x + 9$

45. $f(x) = 3x^2 + 3x - 36$

47. *Sample answer:* $f(x) = -x^2 + 8x - 16$

49. *Sample answer:* $f(x) = x^2 - 3$

51. *Sample answer:* $f(x) = x^2 + 10x + 25$

53.

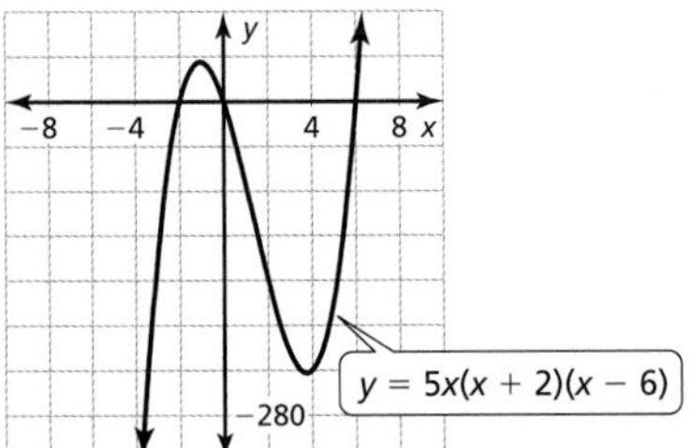

55.

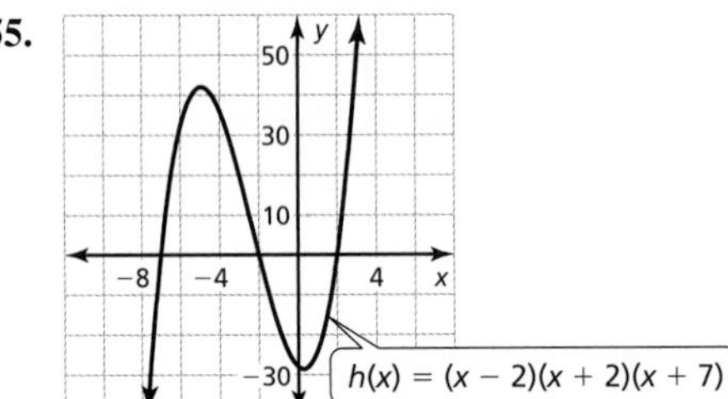

57.

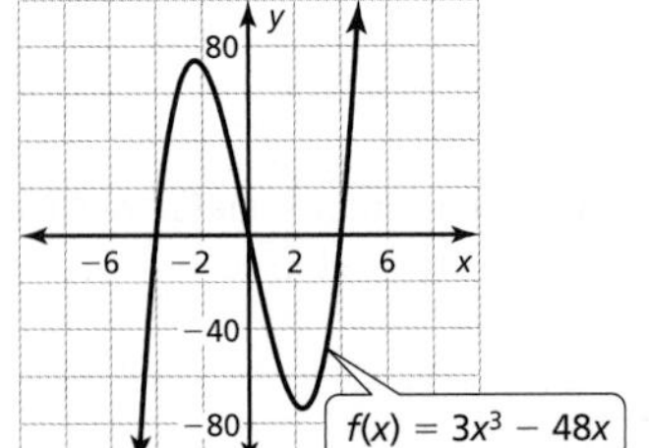

59.

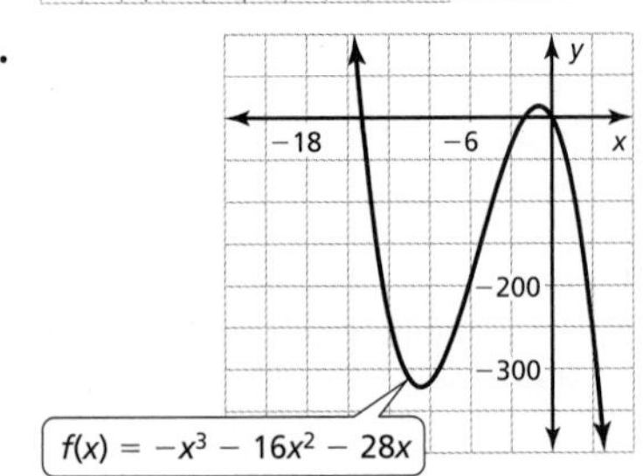

61. $f(x) = 4x^3 - 12x^2 - 16x$

63. $f(x) = -2x^3 - 22x^2 - 56x$

65. *Sample answer:* $f(x) = x^3 - 9x^2 + 2x + 48$

67. *Sample answer:* $f(x) = x^3 - 8x^2 + 7x$

69. $f(x) = -3x^2 + 21x$

71.

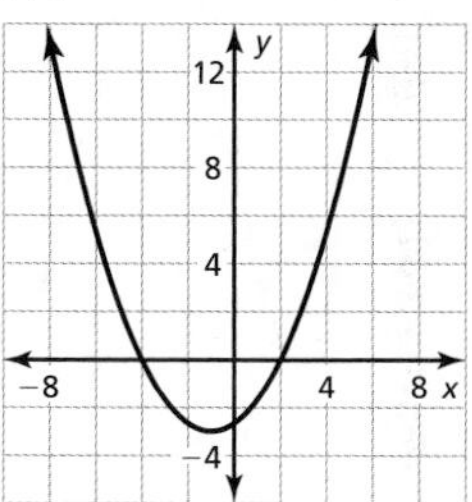

73. *Sample answer:*

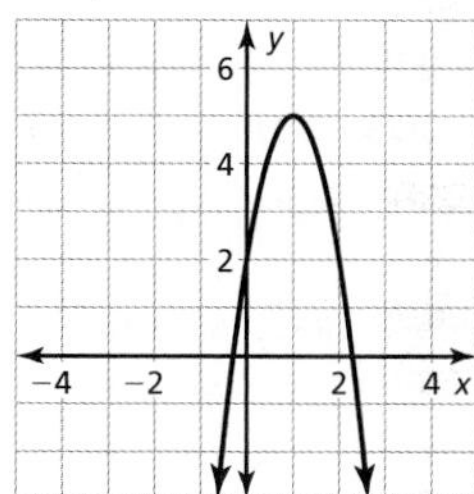

75. **a.** 4 ft

b. $\frac{1}{2}$ ft

c. $y = \frac{1}{6}x^2 - \frac{3}{2}$

77. B, F

79. **a.** $f(x) = -3(x + 4)(x - 2)$

b.

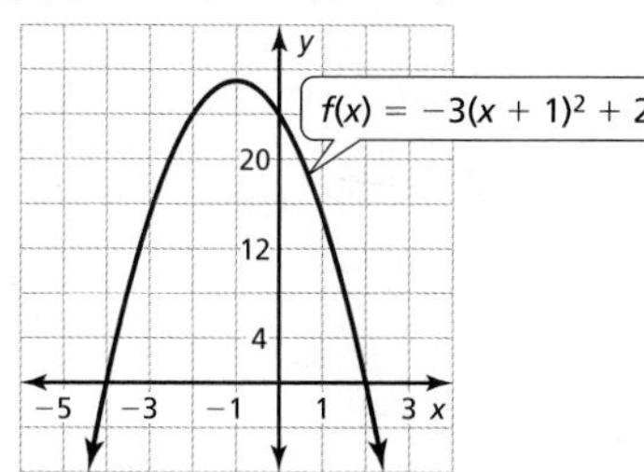

Sample answer: Plot the vertex $(-1, 27)$, which can be determined from the vertex form. Then plot the x-intercepts $(-4, 0)$ and $(2, 0)$, which can be determined from the intercept form. Draw a smooth curve through these points.

81. yes; *Sample answer:* Let p and q be real zeros of a quadratic function. When $p = q$, the function has exactly one real zero and can be written as $y = a(x - p)(x - p)$.

83. no; *Sample answer:* Because -5 and 1 are the x-intercepts, the axis of symmetry is $x = -2$. The points $(-3, 12)$ and $(-1, 4)$ are the same horizontal distance from the axis of symmetry, so for both of them to lie on the parabola they would have to have the same y-coordinate.

85. *Sample answer:* $y = (x + 4)(x - 2)$ and $y = 2(x + 4)(x - 2)$; The two given points are x-intercepts, so the graphs of any two quadratic equations having these two intercepts would intersect at these points.

87. $f(x) = \frac{1}{10}(x + 5)(x + 2)(x - 1)(x - 4)(x - 8)$

89. Check students' work; One end of the graph will approach positive infinity and the other end will approach negative infinity.

8.5 Review & Refresh

91. neither; There is no common difference or common ratio.

92. geometric; There is a common ratio of 3.

93. arithmetic; There is a common difference of -8.

94. $y \geq -1, y > -3x + 4$

95. $-6, 9$

96. $x \geq -2$

97. $x > 3$

98.

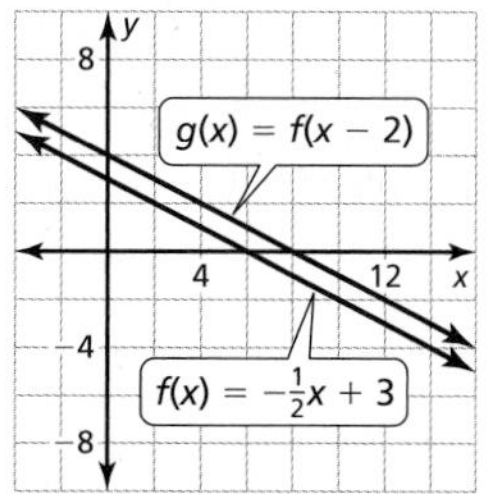

The graph of g is a horizontal translation 2 units right of the graph of f.

99. $y = \frac{1}{3}x - 2$

100. $y = -4x + 7$

101. $(1, 7); x = 1$

102. $(-3, -5); x = -3$

103. $(-3, -13); x = -3$

104. $(2, 10); x = 2$

105. $a_1 = \frac{1}{3}, a_n = 3a_{n-1}$

106. **a.** intercept form; The x-intercepts are the values of p and q.

b. standard form; The y-intercept is the value of c.

c. vertex form; The axis of symmetry is $x = h$.

d. vertex form; The vertex is (h, k).

e. vertex form; The maximum or minimum value is k.

107. $(3x - 4)(2x + 5)$

108.

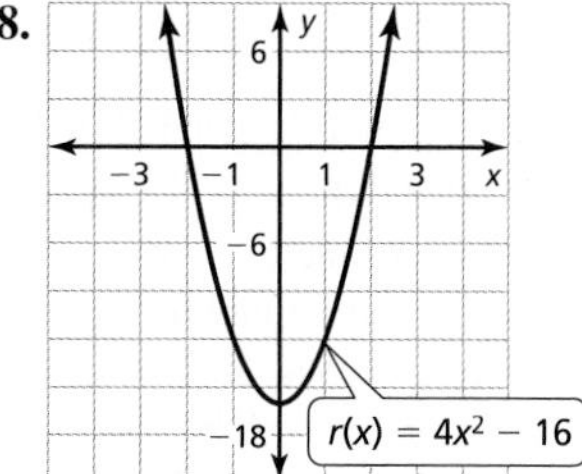

The graph of r is a vertical stretch by a factor of 4 and a vertical translation 16 units down of the graph of f.

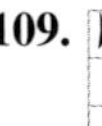

109.

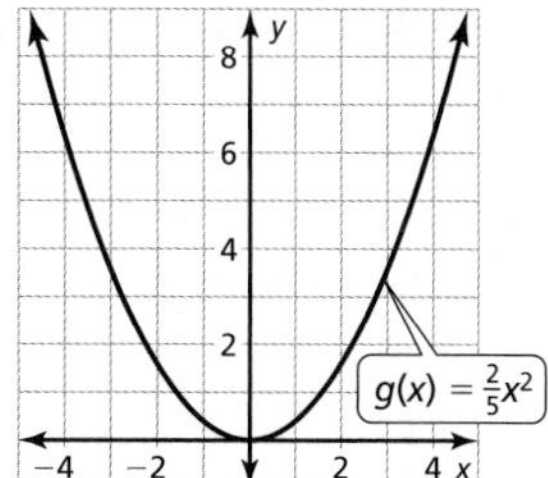

The graph of g is a vertical shrink by a factor of $\frac{2}{5}$ of the graph of f.

110. $f(x) = -4x^2 + 8x + 32$

8.6 Practice

1. quadratic

3. exponential

5. 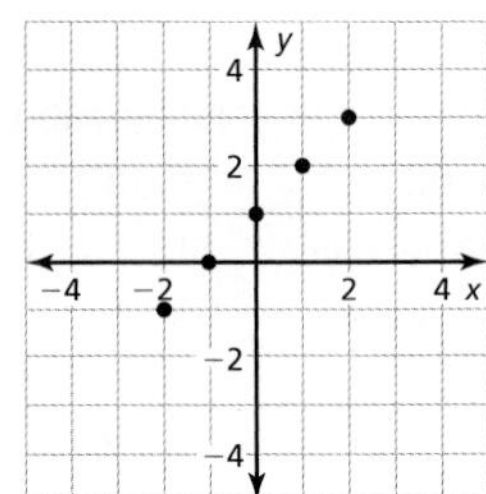
linear

7. 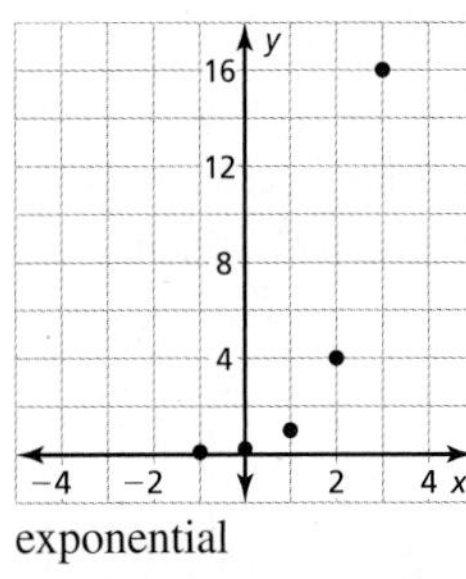
exponential

9. linear
11. exponential
13. linear; The first differences are constant.
15. $y = 2x^2 - 2x - 4$
17. $y = -3x - 2$
19. $y = -3x^2$
21. a. $f(x) = -0.5x + 1050$
    b. 975; The central air pressure of a hurricane at a sustained wind speed of 150 km/h is about 975 millibars.
23. $f(0) = 3, f(n) = 2 \cdot f(n - 1)$
25. $f(0) = 2, f(n) = f(n - 1) + 2n - 3$
27. $f(0) = -\frac{7}{3}, f(n) = f(n - 1) - \frac{2}{3}$
29. Consecutive y-values have a constant ratio. They do not change by a constant amount; Consecutive y-values change by a constant ratio. So, the table represents an exponential function.
31. From 2000 to 2020, the population of Town A increased at an average rate of about 950 people per decade and the population of Town B increased at an average rate of 660 people per decade. So, the population of Town A is growing faster.
33. a. Oak Hill
    b. Poplar Grove; Poplar Grove's population can be modeled by an increasing exponential function.
35. The average rate of change of a linear function is constant because the dependent variable of a linear function increases by the same amount for each constant change in the independent variable. The average rate of change of a quadratic or exponential function is not constant because the dependent variable of a quadratic or exponential function changes by a different amount for each constant change in the independent variable.
37. none; The points do not appear to follow the shape of a linear, an exponential, nor a quadratic function.
39. *Sample answer:* $y = 1.5x^2$
41. quadratic; The second differences have a constant value of $9n - 5$.

8.6 Review & Refresh

43. 11
44. 5
45. 8
46. 3
47. $y = 3\left(\frac{1}{3}\right)^x$
48. $y = x^2 - 7x + 4$
49. $x^2 - 64$
50. $16y^2 - 4$
51. $9a^2 - 25b^2$
52. $4r^2 - 36s^2$
53. $f(x) = x^3 - 7x + 6$
54. $f(x) = \frac{1}{4}x^3 - \frac{1}{2}x^2 - 2x$

55. 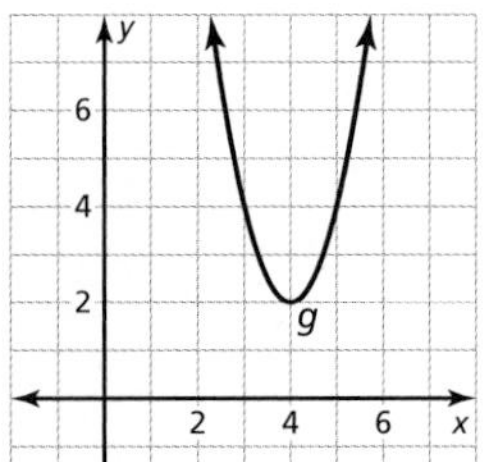

56. 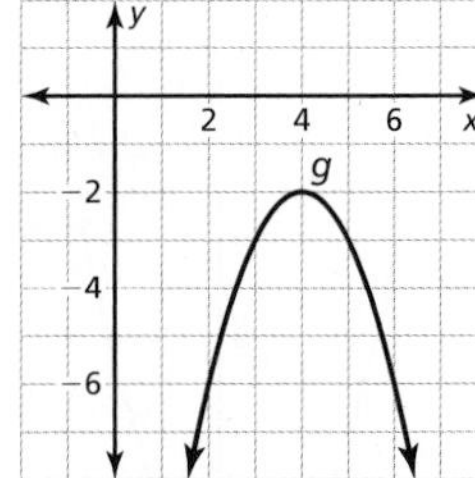

57. $x = -1$; one solution
58. $x = 2$; one solution
59. no solution
60. infinitely many solutions
61. a. \$450
    b. 0.3-carat
62. minimum; 0
63. minimum; -2
64. minimum; $-\frac{1}{4}$
65. maximum; $\frac{7}{2}$
66. a. two solutions; The absolute value expression is equal to a positive number.
    b. no solution; The absolute value expression cannot be negative.

Chapter 8 Review

1. The vertex is $(-1, -8)$. The axis of symmetry is $x = -1$. The domain is all real numbers. The range is $y \geq -8$. The function is decreasing when $x < -1$ and increasing when $x > -1$. The y-intercept is -6. The x-intercepts are -3 and 1. The function is positive when $x < -3$ and $x > 1$, and negative when $-3 < x < 1$; $y \to +\infty$ as $x \to -\infty$ and $y \to +\infty$ as $x \to +\infty$.
2. The vertex is $(-1, 3)$. The axis of symmetry is $x = -1$. The domain is all real numbers. The range is $y < 3$. The function is increasing when $x < -1$ and decreasing when $x > -1$. The y-intercept is 0. The x-intercepts are -2 and 0. The function is negative when $x < -2$ and $x > 0$, and positive when $-2 < x < 0$; $y \to -\infty$ as $x \to -\infty$ and $y \to -\infty$ as $x \to +\infty$.
3. 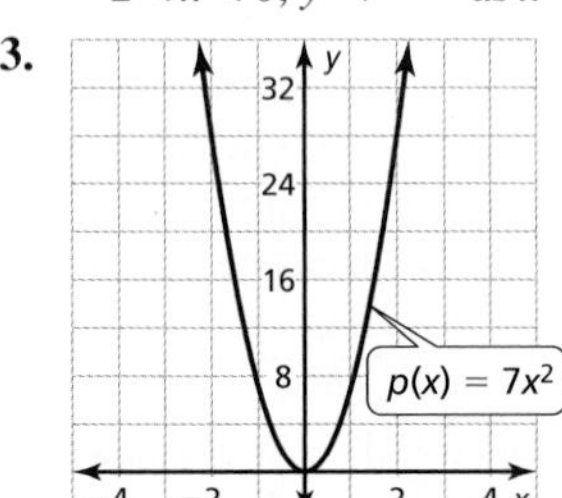

Both graphs have the same vertex, (0, 0), and axis of symmetry, $x = 0$. The graph of p is a vertical stretch by a factor of 7 of the graph of f.
4. 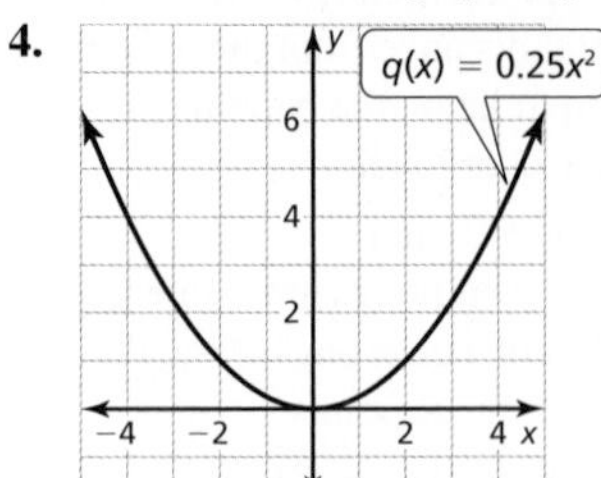

Both graphs have the same vertex, (0, 0), and axis of symmetry, $x = 0$. The graph of q is a vertical shrink by a factor of 0.25 of the graph of f.

5. 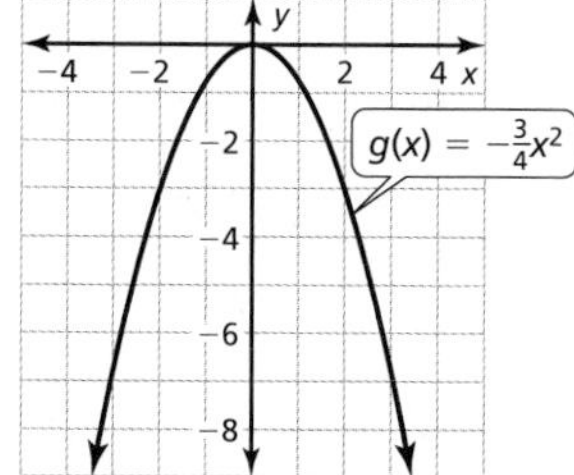

Both graphs have the same vertex, (0, 0), and axis of symmetry, $x = 0$. The graph of g is a vertical shrink by a factor of $\frac{3}{4}$, and a reflection in the x-axis of the graph of f.

6. 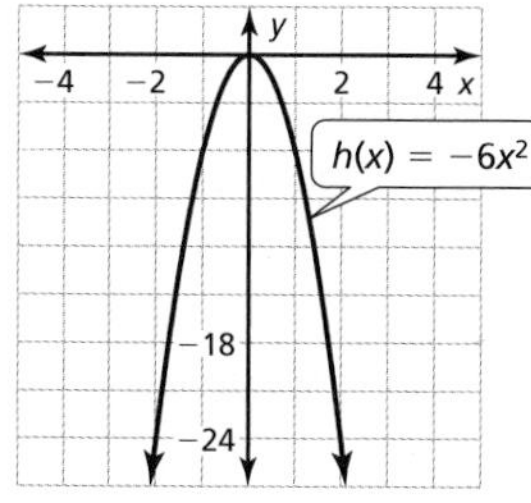

Both graphs have the same vertex, (0, 0), and axis of symmetry, $x = 0$. The graph of h is a vertical stretch by a factor of 6, and a reflection in the x-axis of the graph of f.

7. 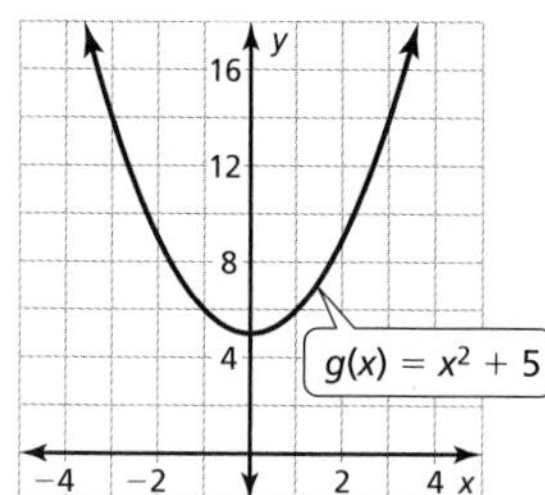

The graph of g is a vertical translation 5 units up of the graph of f.

8. 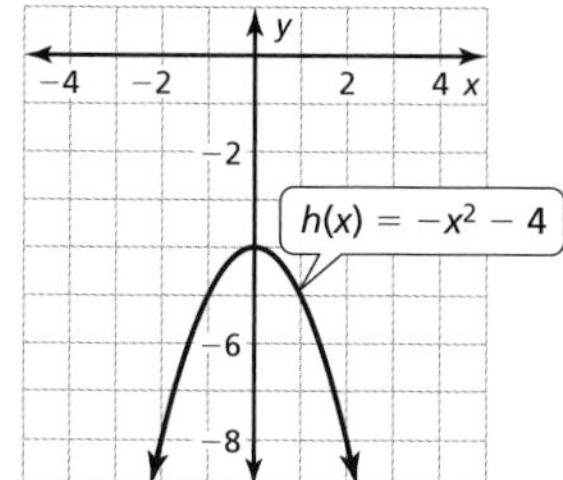

The graph of h is a reflection in the x-axis, and a vertical translation 4 units down of the graph of f.

9. 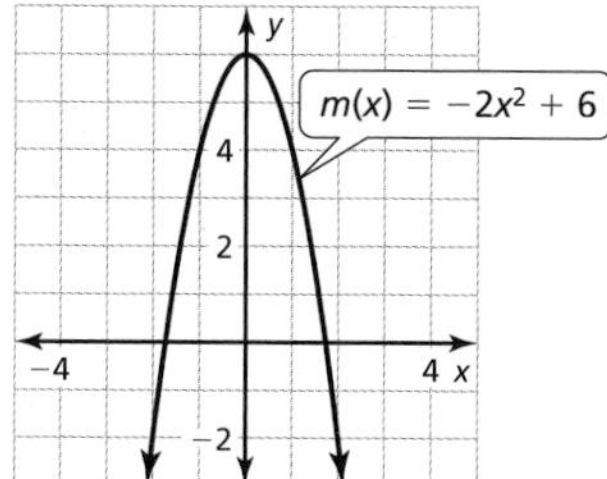

The graph of m is a vertical stretch by a factor of 2, a reflection in the x-axis, and a vertical translation 6 units up of the graph of f.

10. 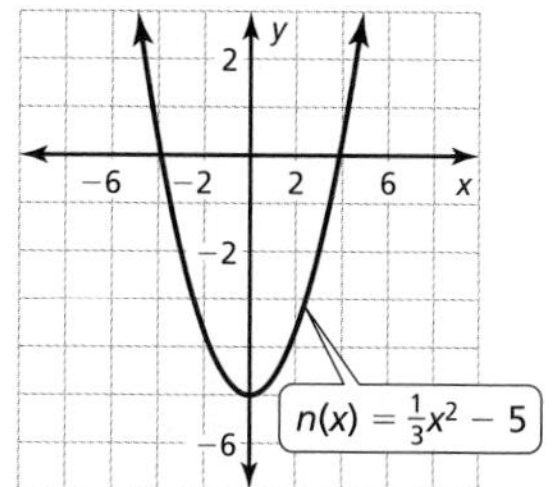

The graph of n is a vertical shrink by a factor of $\frac{1}{3}$, and a vertical translation 5 units down of the graph of f.

11. The graph of g is a vertical translation $ac - c$ units of the graph of f.

12. The x-intercepts are -4 and 4. $x = -4$ is not in the domain and $x = 4$ represents the number of seconds it takes your sandal to fall to the ground. The y-intercept is 256 and represents the height at which the sandal falls off your foot.

13. a. $x = -1$
b. $(-1, -5)$

14. a. $x = 12$
b. $(12, 39)$

15. 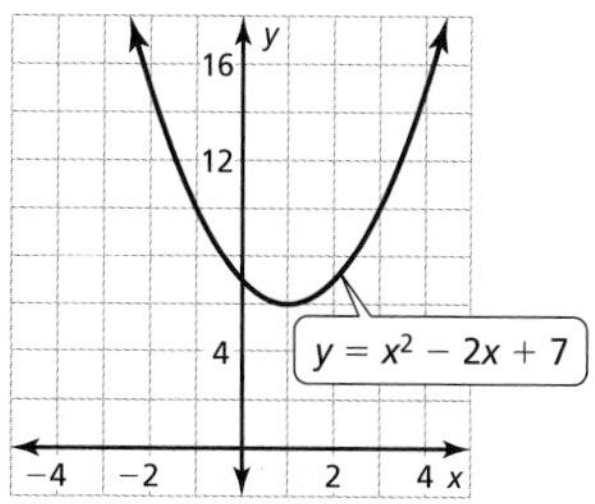

domain: all real numbers, range: $y \geq 6$

16. 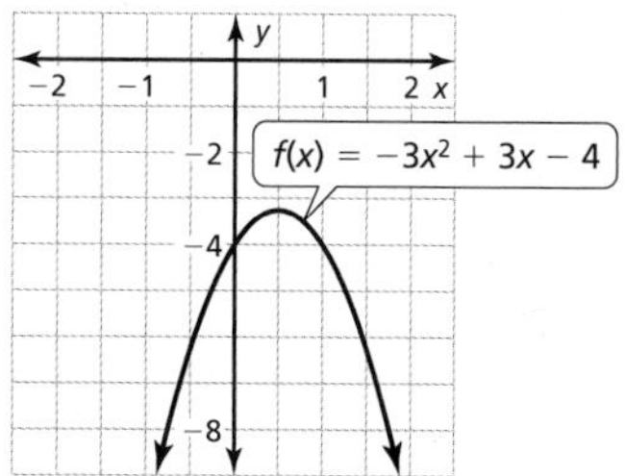

domain: all real numbers, range: $y \leq -\frac{13}{4}$

17. 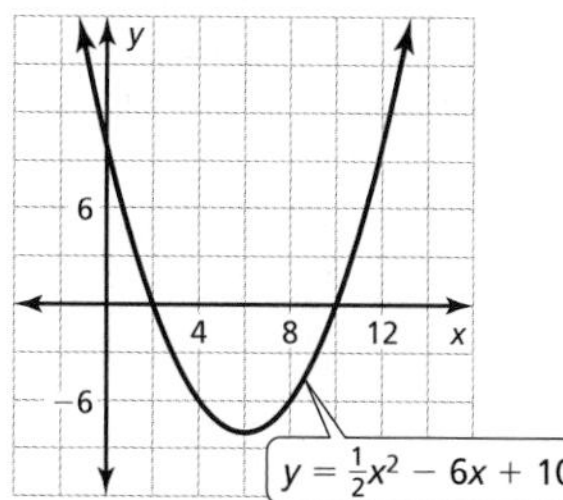

domain: all real numbers, range: $y \geq -8$

18. 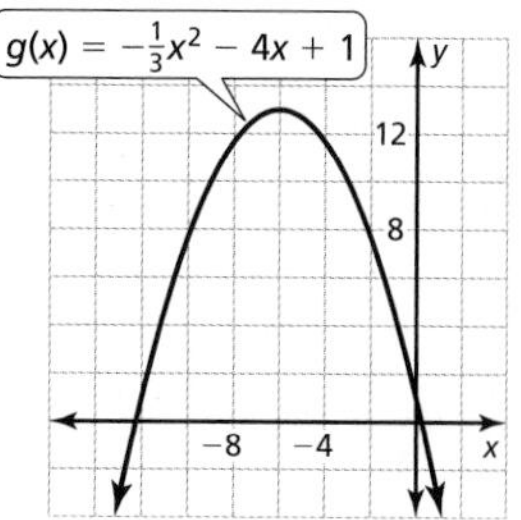

domain: all real numbers, range: $y \leq 13$

19. $a < 0$ because the graph opens down, $b > 0$ because a is negative and the axis of symmetry, $x = -\frac{b}{2a}$, is positive, $c > 0$ because the y-intercept is above the x-axis.

20. 2.75 sec; 133 ft

21. odd

22. even

23. even

24. neither

25.

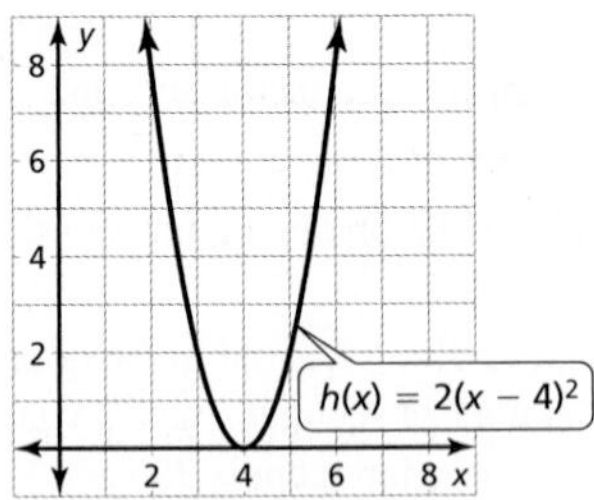

The graph of h is a vertical stretch by a factor of 2 and a horizontal translation 4 units right of the graph of f.

26.

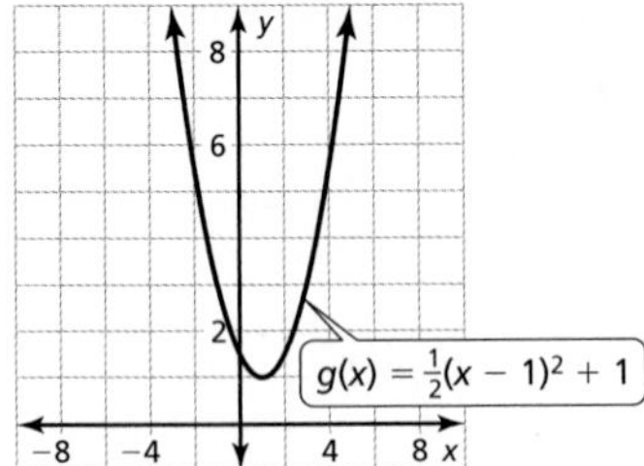

The graph of g is a vertical shrink by a factor of $\frac{1}{2}$, and a translation 1 unit right and 1 unit up of the graph of f.

27.

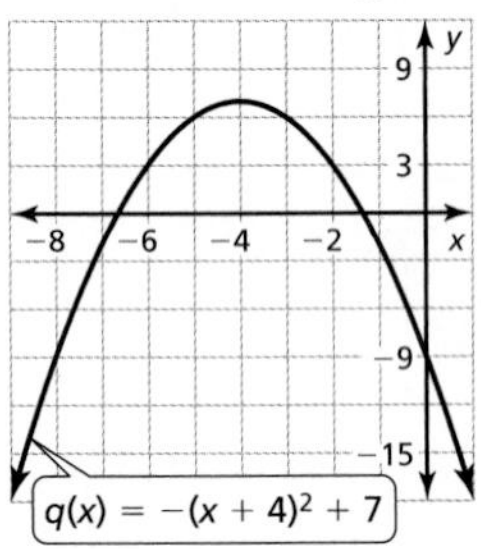

The graph of q is a reflection in the x-axis, and a translation 4 units left and 7 units up of the graph of f.

28.

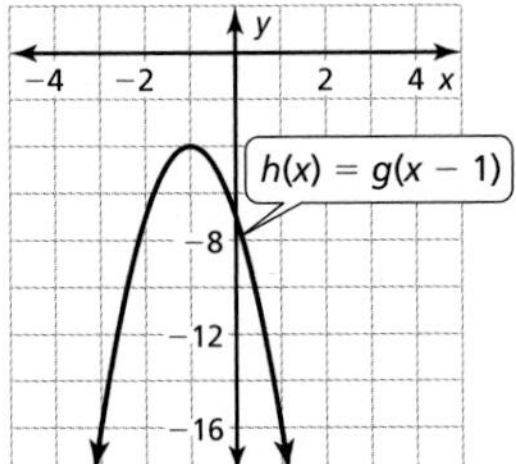

29. $f(x) = 5(x - 3)^2 + 2$

30. $y = -\frac{1}{36}x^2 + \frac{2}{3}x + 4$

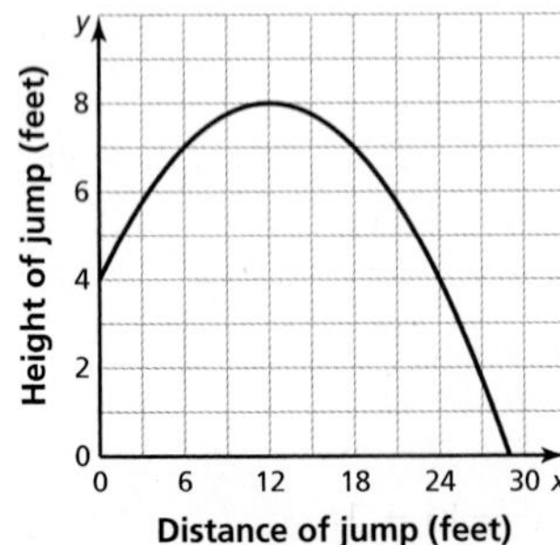

31. $f(x) = (x - 3)^2 - 2$

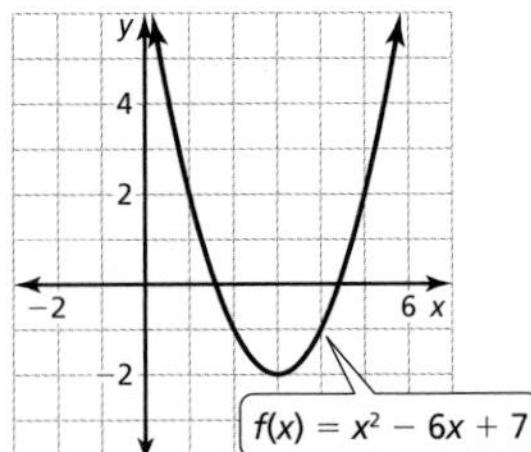

32.

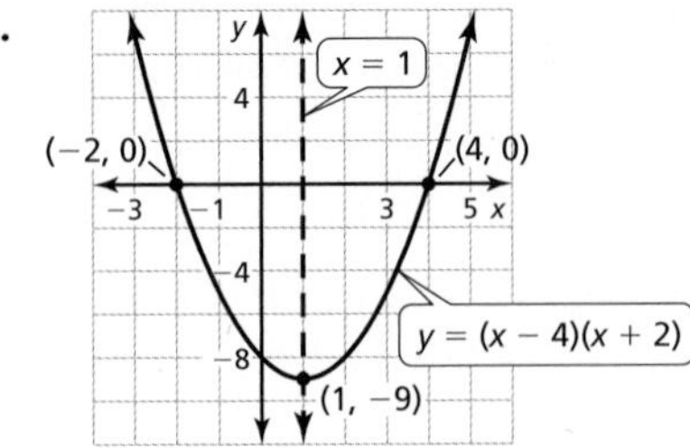

domain: all real numbers, range: $y \geq -9$

33.

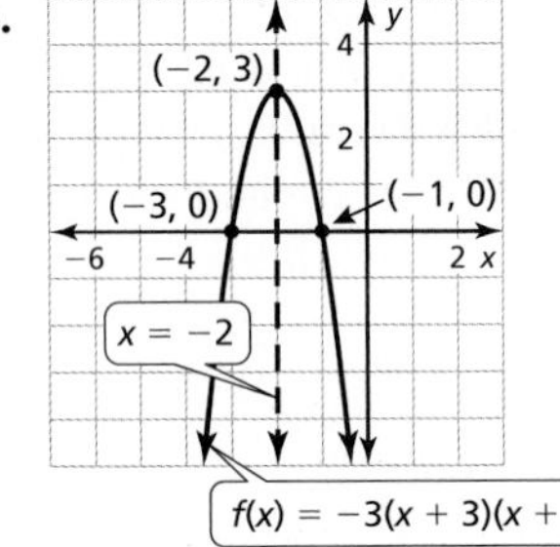

domain: all real numbers, range: $y \leq 3$

34.

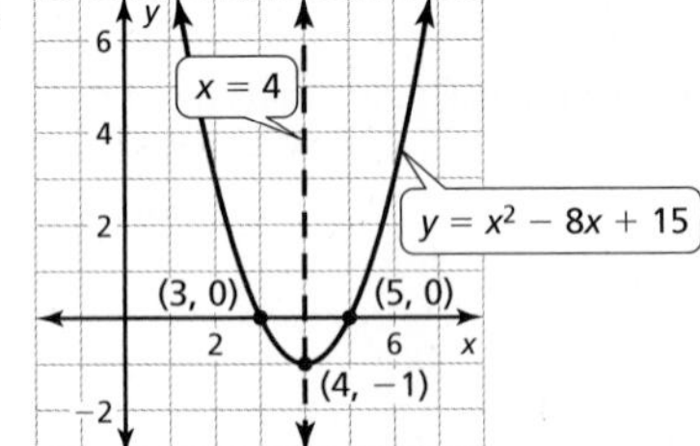

domain: all real numbers, range: $y \geq -1$

35.

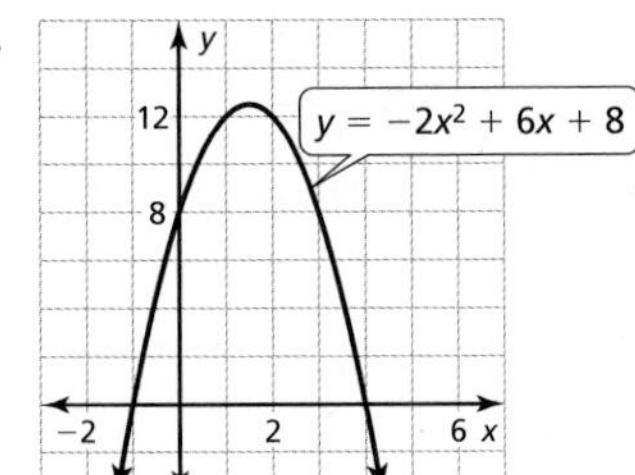

36.

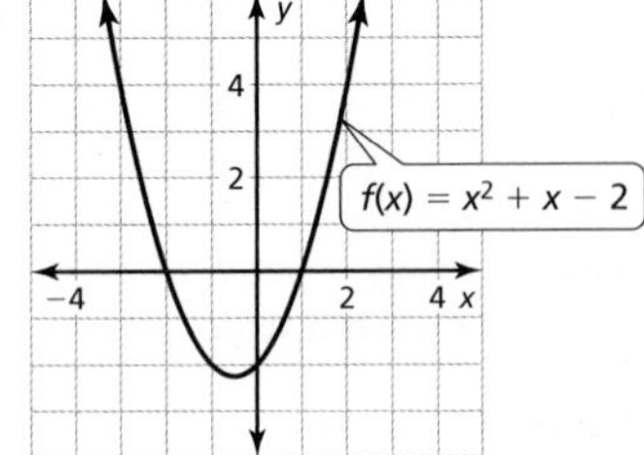

37. 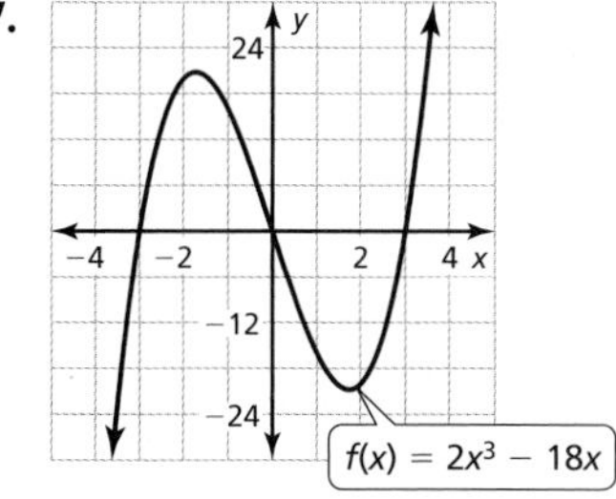

38. *Sample answer:* $x^2 - 10x + 24$

39. $y = x^3 + 4x^2 - 5.25x - 13.5$

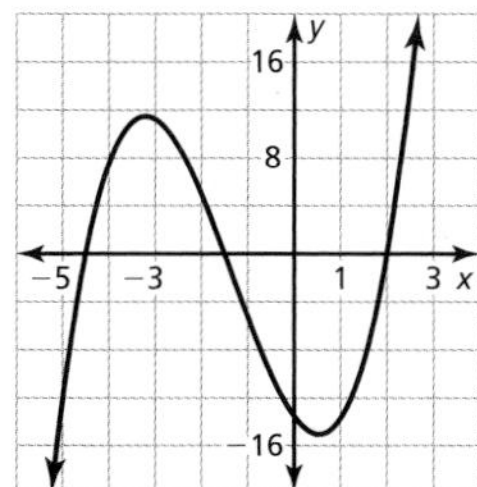

40. quadratic; $y = -4x^2 + 8x + 12$

41. linear; $y = 5x + 1$

42. quadratic; $y = -x^2 + 2x + 1$

43. exponential; $y = 128\left(\frac{1}{4}\right)^x$

44. **a.** your friend's account

b. your account; After 30 years, the exponential growth function will exceed the linear function.

Chapter 8 Mathematical Practices (Chapter Review)

1. *Sample answer:* You can use the horizontal and vertical translations of the graph of $y = ax^2$ to find the values of h and k for $f(x) = a(x - h)^2 + k$.

2. *Sample answer:* To find the maximum or minimum value, use the midpoint of the zeros to solve for y.

Chapter 8 Practice Test

1. 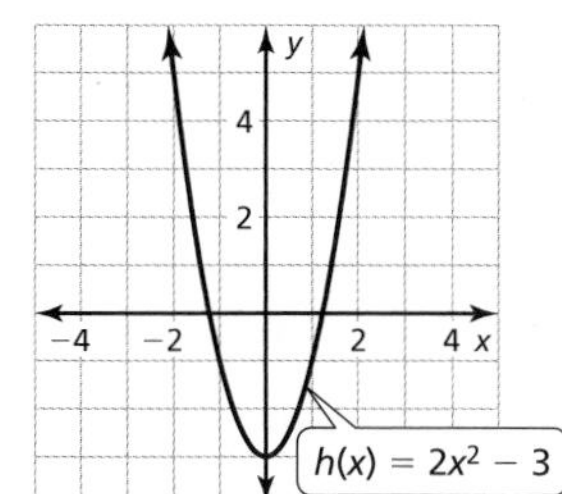

The graph of h is a vertical stretch by a factor of 2 and a vertical translation 3 units down of the graph of f.

2. 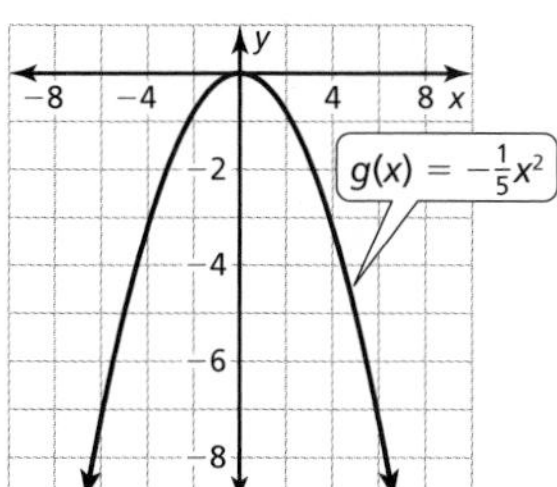

The graph of g is a reflection in the x-axis, and a vertical shrink by a factor of $\frac{1}{5}$ of the graph of f.

3. 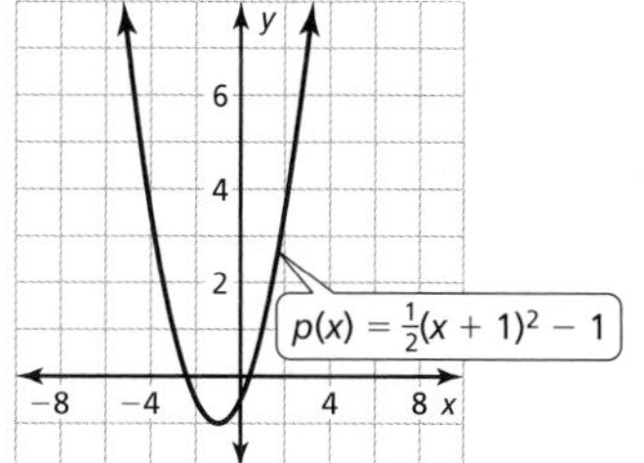

The graph of p is a vertical shrink by a factor of $\frac{1}{2}$, and a translation 1 unit left and 1 unit down of the graph of f.

4. **a.** domain: all real numbers, range: $y \leq 8$; 3, 7

b. $f(x) = -2x^2 + 20x - 42$

c. The graph of f is a vertical stretch by a factor of 2, a reflection in the x-axis, and a translation 5 units right and 8 units up of the graph of g.

d. 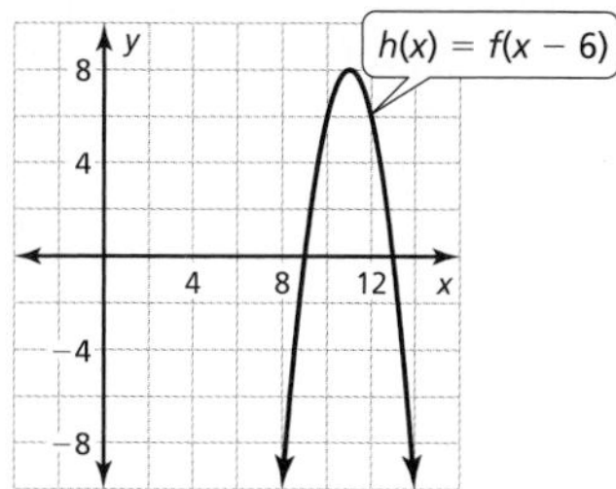

5. 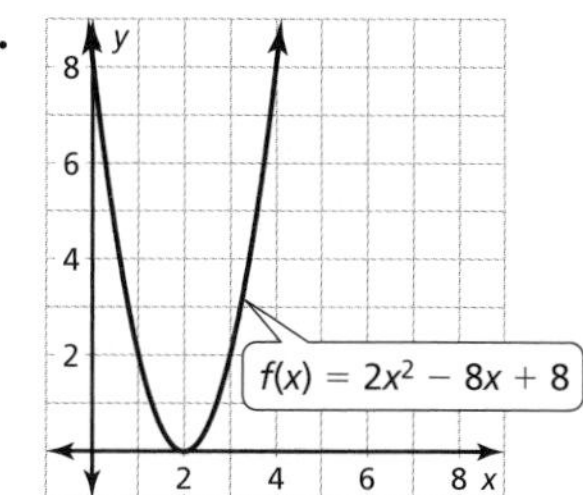

domain: all real numbers, range: $y \geq 0$

6. 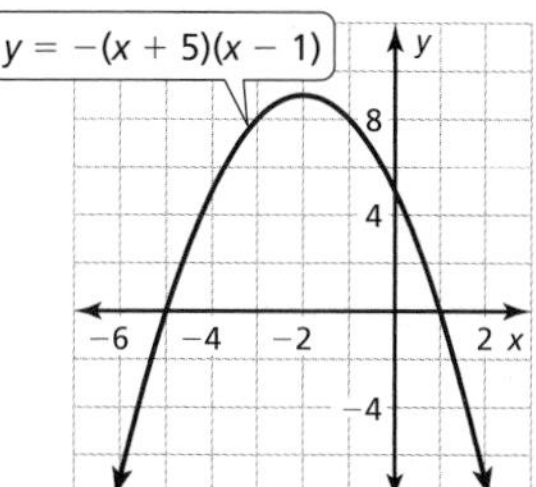

domain: all real numbers, range: $y \leq 9$

7. 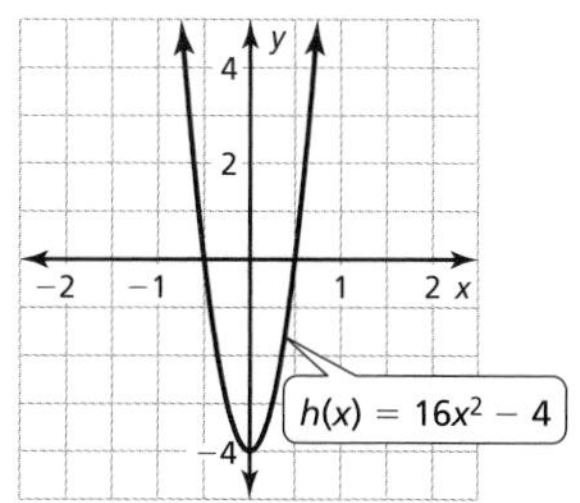

domain: all real numbers, range: $y \geq -4$

8. exponential; The y-values increase by a constant factor; $y = 8(2)^x$

9. quadratic; The second differences increase by a constant amount; $y = -2x^2$

10. 20 cm

11. *Sample answer:* $f(x) = x^2 + 3$

12. *Sample answer:* $f(x) = x^2 - 8x + 16$

13. **a.** App B

b. App B; The number of downloads for App A is represented by a linear function and the number of downloads for App B is represented by an exponential function, so the number of downloads for App B will eventually exceed the number of downloads for App A.

14. **a.** *Sample answer:* $a = 1, b = 0, c = 0$

b. *Sample answer:* $a = 0, b = 1, c = 0$

c. *Sample answer:* $a = 1, b = 2, c = 3$

15. $y = -2x^2 + 8x$

Chapter 8 College and Career Readiness

1. C
2. A
3. one solution; infinitely many solutions; no solution; The two equations in the first system are perpendicular. In the second system, the second equation is 3 times the first equation. In the third system, the right sides of each equation are equal, but the left side of the equations are not.
4. D
5. C
6. B
7. **a.** +; +

b. −; +

c. +; −

d. −; +; − or −; −; +

8. A, B, E
9. **a.** linear; *Sample answer:* The first difference is constant.

b. domain: whole numbers; discrete

c. $y = 45x$

d. no; *Sample answer:* If y is 500, x is $11\frac{1}{9}$, which is not in the domain.

10. $m = -\frac{8}{3}$; y-intercept: -1

Chapter 9

Chapter 9 Prepare

1. $(x + 5)^2$
2. $(x - 10)^2$
3. $(x + 6)^2$
4. $(x - 9)^2$
5. $(x + 8)^2$
6. $(x - 15)^2$
7. $(1, -2)$
8. $(4, 4)$
9. $(-2, 3)$
10. $\left(\frac{b}{2}\right)^2$

9.1 Practice

1. yes
3. yes
5. yes
7. $2\sqrt{5}$
9. $8\sqrt{2}$
11. $5\sqrt{5b}$
13. $-9m\sqrt{m}$
15. $\frac{2}{7}$
17. $-\frac{\sqrt{23}}{8}$
19. $\frac{a\sqrt{a}}{7}$
21. $\frac{5}{x}$
23. $2\sqrt[3]{2}$
25. $-4x\sqrt[3]{x^2}$
27. $-\frac{\sqrt[3]{6c}}{5}$
29. $-\frac{3\sqrt[3]{3y^2}}{10x}$
31. The radicand 18 has a perfect square factor of 9; $\sqrt{72} = \sqrt{36 \cdot 2} = 6\sqrt{2}$
33. $\frac{\sqrt{6}}{\sqrt{6}}$
35. $\frac{\sqrt[3]{x}}{\sqrt[3]{x}}$
37. $\frac{\sqrt{5} + 8}{\sqrt{5} + 8}$
39. $\sqrt{2}$
41. $\frac{\sqrt{15}}{12}$
43. $\frac{3\sqrt{a}}{a}$
45. $\frac{d\sqrt{15}}{5}$
47. $\frac{4\sqrt[3]{5}}{5}$
49. $\frac{\sqrt{7} - 1}{6}$
51. $\frac{70 + 10\sqrt{2}}{47}$
53. $\sqrt{5} + \sqrt{2}$
55. **a.** about 1.85 sec

b. about 0.41 sec

57. about 5.42 amperes
59. $5\sqrt{2}$, about 7.07
61. $\frac{\sqrt{2}}{3}$, about 0.47
63. $2\sqrt{2}$, about 2.83
65. $-6\sqrt{2}$, about -8.49
67. about 3.71 in.
69. $\sqrt{3} + 4\sqrt{2}$
71. $-13\sqrt{6}$
73. $8\sqrt{3} + 2\sqrt{6}$
75. $\sqrt[3]{3}$
77. $4\sqrt{10}$
79. $-2\sqrt{30x}$
81. 18
83. $3\sqrt[3]{12}$
85. $\frac{\sqrt{21} - 3}{4}$
87. about 114 ft
89. $\frac{\sqrt[4]{10}}{3}$
91. $2x\sqrt[5]{5x}$
93. $9\sqrt[4]{9} - \sqrt[5]{9}$
95. odd; even; When m is even, 2^m is a perfect square.
97. $a^2 < ab < b^2$ when $a < b$.
99. *Sample answer:* $f(x) = x^2 - 10x + 18$
101. **a.** irrational; Six is not a perfect square.

b. rational; Four is a rational number.

c. irrational; Twelve is not a perfect square.

d. irrational; Three and seven are not perfect squares.

e. irrational; Two and ten are not perfect squares.

f. rational; $\frac{1}{b}$ is rational when b is a positive integer.

103. $\frac{2\sqrt[3]{x^2} - 2\sqrt[3]{x} + 2}{x + 1}$; Multiplying the numerator and denominator by $\sqrt[3]{x^2} - \sqrt[3]{x} + 1$ rationalizes the denominator.

9.1 Review & Refresh

104.

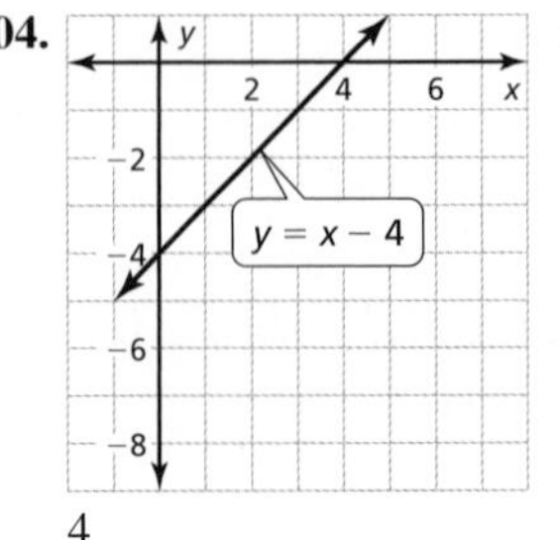

4

105.

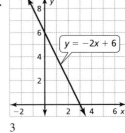

3

106.

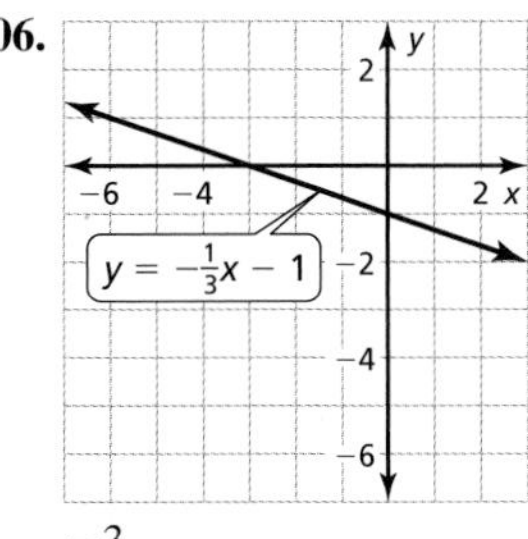

-3

107.

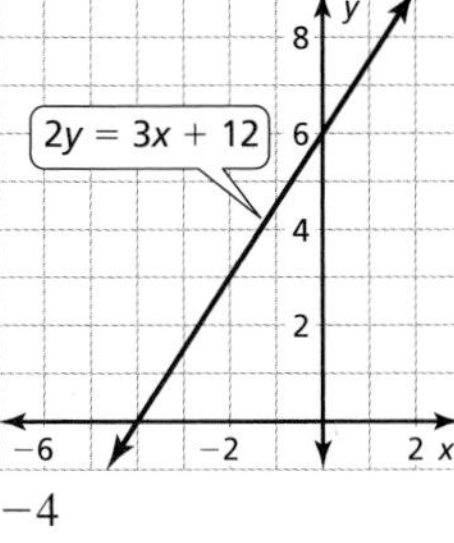

-4

108. $x = 2$

109. $x = -3$

110. $x = -\frac{2}{3}$

111. $x = 3$

112. a. $y = 3x - 11$

b. $y = -\frac{1}{3}x - 1$

113. $2x^2 - x - 15$

114.

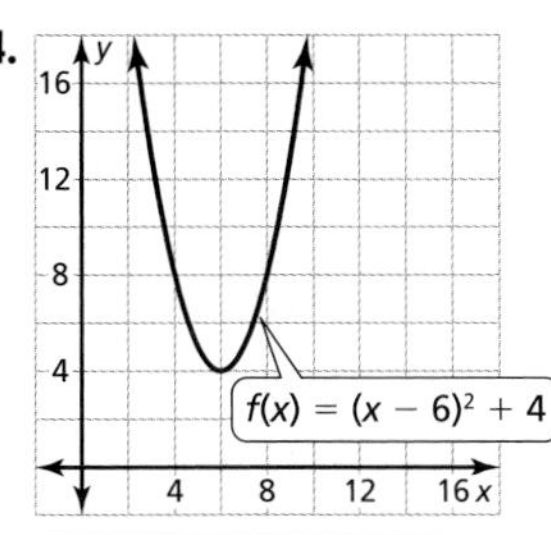

115.

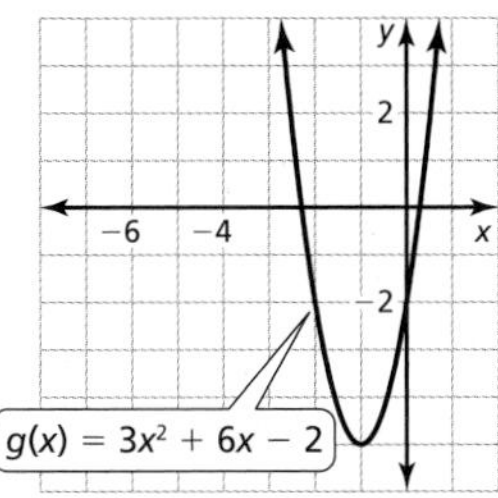

116.

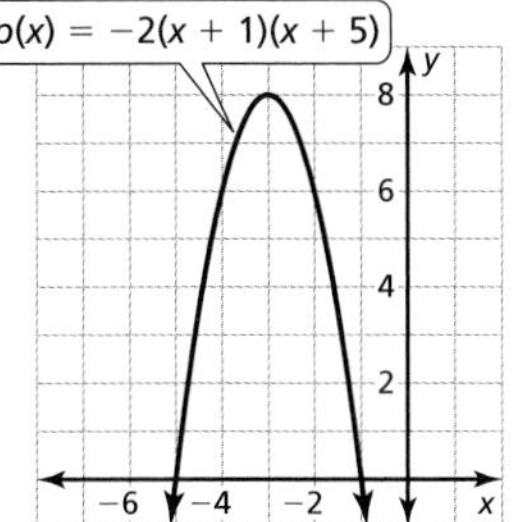

117. 5 months

118. $10\sqrt{2}$

119. $\frac{3x\sqrt[3]{2x}}{7y^2}$

120. $\frac{3\sqrt{2}}{2}$

121. $30\sqrt{2}$

122. $n = -10, n = 5$

123. $b = -3, b = 15$

124. $x = -11$

125. $t = \frac{3}{2}, t = -\frac{5}{2}$

126. 15 winning tickets

127.

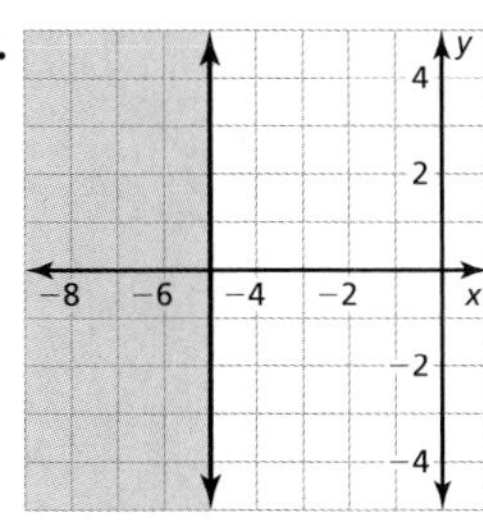

128.

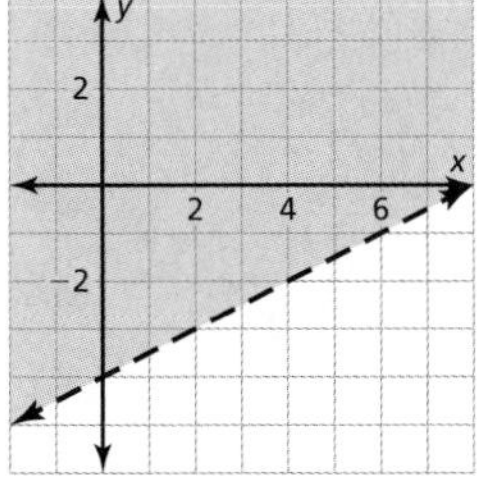

129. exponential

130. linear

9.2 Practice

1. $x = 3, x = -1$

3. $4x^2 - 12 = 0$ or $-4x^2 + 12 = 0$

5. $2x^2 + 5x = 0$ or $-2x^2 - 5x = 0$

7. $x^2 - 2x + 1 = 0$ or $-x^2 + 2x - 1 = 0$

9. $x = 0, x = 5$

11. no real solution

13. $x = 3$

15. $x = -1$

17. $x = -6, x = 2$

19. $x = -2, x = 1$

21. The equation needs to be in standard form; $x^2 + 3x - 18 = 0$

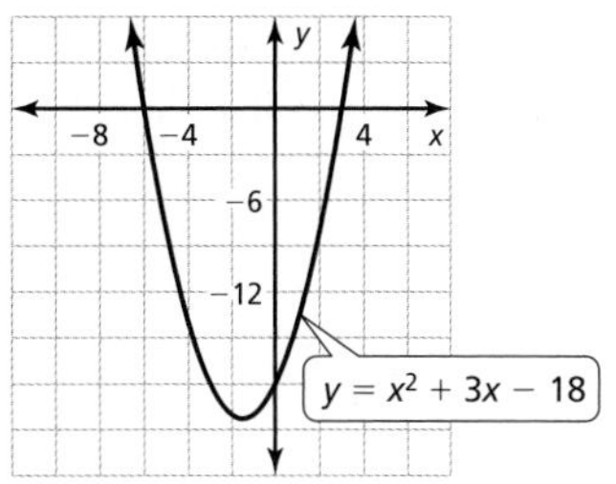

The solutions are $x = -6$ and $x = 3$.

23. a. The x-intercepts are the distances at which the height is 0 yards.

b. 5 yd

25. $x = -5, x = 2$

27. no real solution

29. $x = -10, x = -2$

31. no real solution

33. 2, 0, -1

35. about 4.3, about 0.7

37. $-2, 2, -3, 1$

39. about 2.4, about -0.4

41.

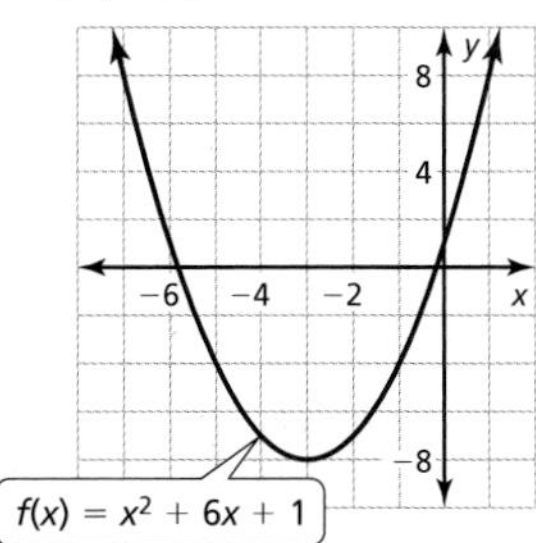

about -0.2, about -5.8

43.

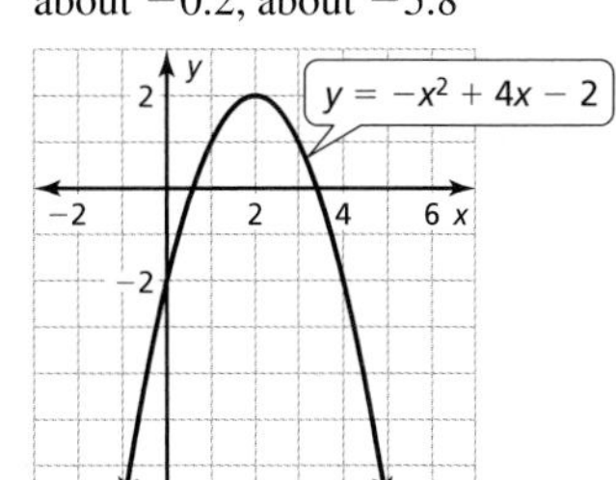

about 3.4, about 0.6

45.

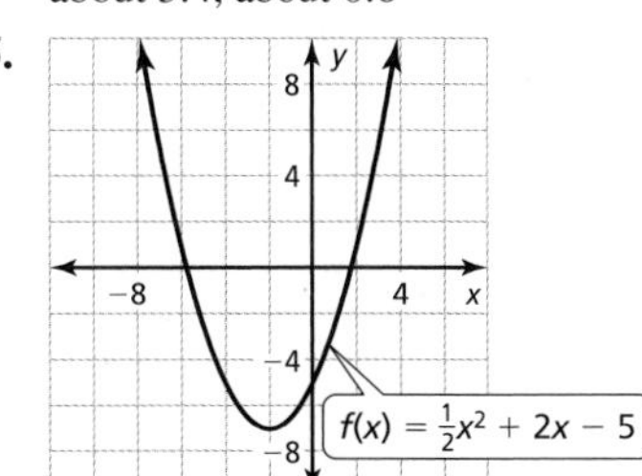

about 1.7, about -5.7

47. Graph the function to determine which integers the solutions are between. Then make tables using x-values between the integers with an interval of 0.1. Look for a change of sign in the function values, then select the value closest to zero.

49. a. 118 ft, 198 ft, 246 ft, 262 ft, 246 ft, 198 ft, 118 ft, 6 ft

b. about 1.5 sec, about 6.5 sec

c. about 1.4 sec, about 6.6 sec

51. a. $y = -0.7494x^2 + 15.000x - 27.02$; The model is a good fit for the data.
b. about \$8
c. no; The quadratic model shows the company with maximum revenue when the selling price is \$10, after that the revenue decreases.

53. a. 6; 10; 15; Check students' work.
b. $y = 0.5x^2 - 0.5x$; Yes, the graph of the equation passes through all of the data points.

55. A, C

57. 3.7 ft

59. 24.1 ft

61. yes; When $x = 57$, $y = 26.313$.

63. always; The sign of y does not change.

9.2 Review & Refresh

65. exponential decay function; As x increases by 1, y is multiplied by $\frac{1}{6}$.

66. exponential growth function; As x increases by 1, y is multiplied by 4.

67. no real solution

68. $x = -6$

69. no real solution

70. $y = \frac{1}{2}x^3 - 2x^2 - \frac{1}{2}x + 2$

71. $6x\sqrt{x}$

72. $2x^2\sqrt[3]{x^2}$

73. $-\frac{\sqrt{21}}{9}$

74. $\frac{\sqrt{30}}{5}$

75.

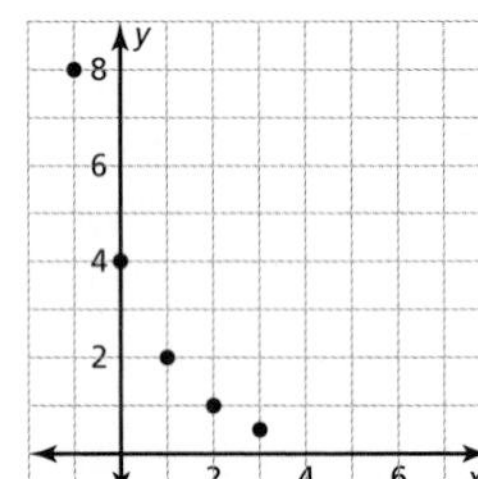

exponential

76. The sum and difference pattern and the difference of two squares pattern form an identity.

77. no

78. $\left(6, \frac{5}{2}\right)$; Explanations will vary.

79. a. \$90
b. 32 gigabytes
c. the price increases

80. $(a + 7)(a - 4)$

81. $(3b + 1)(b - 5)$

82. $(c - 12)(c + 12)$

83. $-x(2x + 7)(x - 2)$

9.3 Practice

1. 2; $x = 5, x = -5$

3. 1; $x = 0$

5. $x = 4, x = -4$

7. no real solutions

9. $x = 7, x = -7$

11. $x = 0$

13. $x = \frac{1}{2}, x = -\frac{1}{2}$

15. $x = -3$

17. $x = 5, x = -4$

19. $x = \frac{1}{3}, x = -\frac{7}{3}$

21. $x \approx 2.65, x \approx -2.65$

23. $x \approx 3.16, x \approx -3.16$

25. $x \approx 4.24, x \approx -4.24$

27. The number 36 has both a positive and negative square root; $x = \pm 6$

29. $\sqrt{\frac{3}{2}}$ sec, or about 1.2 sec

31. length: about 77.5 in., width: about 38.7 in.

33. a. $r = \sqrt{\frac{A}{\pi}}$
b. about 6 ft; about 24 in., about 13 m
c. The steps for solving only need to be completed once.

35. $(3, 9), (-3, 9)$; When $y = 9, x = \pm 3$

37. $x = 1.2, x = -1.2$; $1.2^2 = 1.44$

39. $x = 6, x = -2$

9.3 Review & Refresh

41. $(x + 9)^2$

42. $(x - 11)^2$

43. $(x + 4)(x - 2)$

44. $(2x + 5)(x - 7)$

45. $2 < q < 10.5$

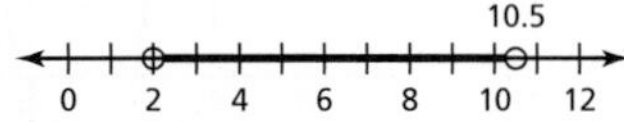

46. 0; no real solutions

47. 2; $x = 20, x = -20$

48. $x = 0$

49. $x = -6, x = 9$

50. linear; The graph is a line because it can be written in the form $y = mx + b$.

51. no real solution

52. $-7\sqrt[3]{4x}$

53. $118 - 48\sqrt{6}$

54. $\frac{4\sqrt{10x}}{5x}$

55. $7\sqrt{5} + 14$

56. quadratic; $f(x) = x^2 - 2x - 8$

57. $y = 500\left(\frac{1 + 0.04}{4}\right)^{4t}$

58.

Sample answer: $(0, 5)$

59. $t = -12$

60. $c = 35$

61. $g = -3$

62. no solution

63. 15

9.4 Practice

1. 16

3. 36

5. $x^2 - 10x + 25$; $(x - 5)^2$

7. $x^2 + 16x + 64$; $(x + 8)^2$

9. $x^2 + 5x + \frac{25}{4}$; $\left(x + \frac{5}{2}\right)^2$

11. $x = 1, x = -15$

13. $x = 2 \pm \sqrt{2}$

15. $x = \frac{5 \pm \sqrt{57}}{2}$

17. a. $x^2 + 6x = 216$
b. width: 12 ft, length: 18 ft

19. $x = 5, x = 3$

21. $x = -5 \pm \sqrt{3}$

23. $x = 8, x = -1$

25. The number 16 should be added to each side of the equation; $x^2 + 8x + 16 = 10 + 16$; $x = -4 \pm \sqrt{26}$

27. $y = (x + 3)^2 - 6$; D

29. $y = -(x + 2)^2 + 2$; B

31. minimum value; -6

33. maximum value; -5

35. maximum value; -6

37. yes; The graph has two negative x-intercepts and it opens down.

39. no; The x-intercepts are both positive.

41. f, m; The graph has two negative x-intercepts and it opens up.

43. a. 36 ft

b. $x = \frac{3}{2}$; On the left side of $x = \frac{3}{2}$, the height increases as time increases. On the right side of $x = \frac{3}{2}$, the height decreases as time increases.

45. 3 ft

47. A

49. 12

51. $x = -1 \pm \sqrt{5}$

53. $x = 2 \pm \frac{\sqrt{21}}{2}$

55. 40 mi/h

57. $b = 10$, $b = -10$; In a perfect square trinomial $c = \left(\frac{b}{2}\right)^2$, so $b = \pm 2\sqrt{c}$.

59. a. $x = -6 \pm \sqrt{46}$; $x \approx -12.782$, $x \approx 0.782$

b. *Sample answer:* completing the square; The result is more accurate.

61. length: 66 in., width: 6 in.

63. $x(x + 2) = 195$; $x = -15$ and $x = -13$

65. 0; If $c < -\left(\frac{b}{2}\right)^2$, then $\left(\frac{b}{2}\right)^2 + c < 0$, so there are no real solutions.

9.4 Review & Refresh

66. $x = -11$, $x = 11$

67. $x = 9$, $x = 7$

68. $a_1 = 10$, $a_n = a_{n-1} + 5$

69. $a_1 = 3$, $a_n = 2a_{n-1}$

70. $x = -\frac{3}{2} \pm \frac{\sqrt{13}}{2}$

71. $x < -\frac{5}{2}$

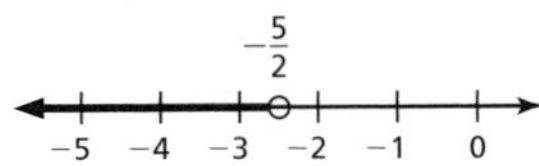

72. no solution

73. $-1 < x < -\frac{1}{2}$

74. $x \leq -8$ *or* $x > -5$

75. length: $\sqrt{46}$ m, width: $\frac{\sqrt{46}}{2}$ m

76. mean: 67, median: 66.5, mode: 68

77. $x = -7$, $x = -2$

78. no real solutions

79.

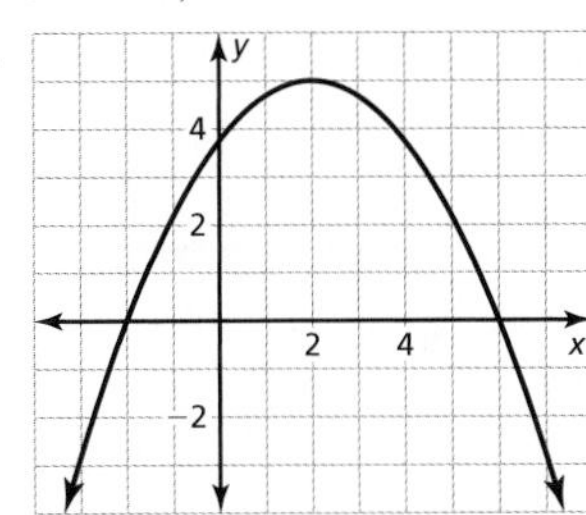

80. Factor out 3 from the terms on the left side of the equation so that the coefficient of the x^2-term is 1.

81. $\frac{1}{5}$

82. undefined

83. $2\sqrt{3}$

84. $6\sqrt{2}$

85.

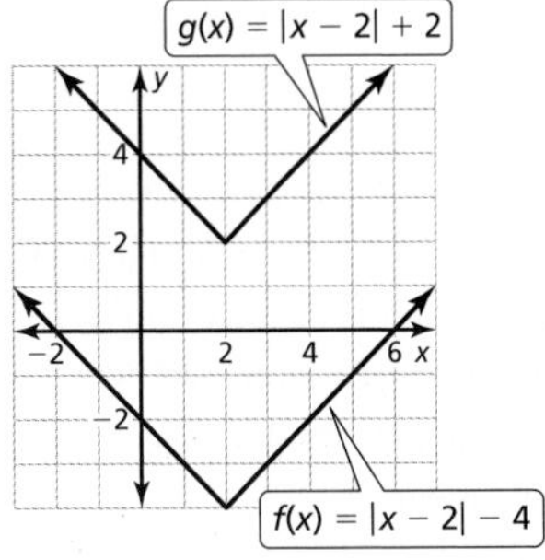

The graph of g is a vertical translation 6 units up of the graph of f.

86.

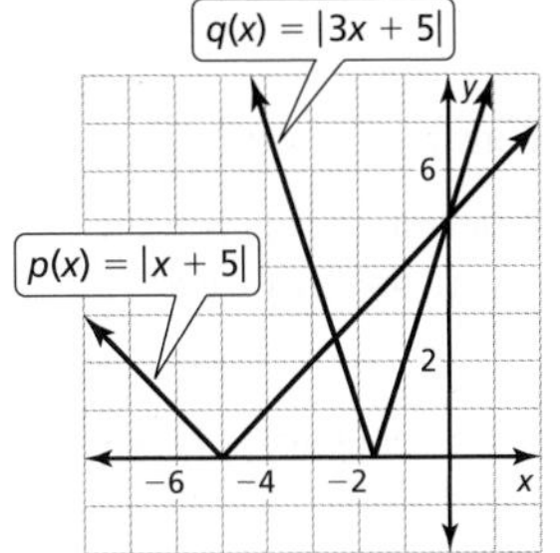

The graph of q is a horizontal shrink by a factor of $\frac{1}{3}$ of the graph of p.

87. $y = \begin{cases} 0.5x - 1, & \text{if } x \leq 2 \\ 2x - 3, & \text{if } x > 2 \end{cases}$

88. $y = \begin{cases} 1, & \text{if } 0 \leq x < 2 \\ 3, & \text{if } 2 \leq x < 4 \\ 5, & \text{if } 4 \leq x < 6 \end{cases}$

89. maximum; -12

90. no

9.5 Practice

1. $x = 6$

3. $x = 1$, $x = -\frac{1}{2}$

5. $x = \frac{1}{3}$

7. $x = \frac{3}{2}$, $x = \frac{2}{3}$

9. no real solutions

11. $x = -1 \pm \sqrt{10}$

13. $x = \frac{2 \pm \sqrt{14}}{5}$

15. about 0.2 sec, about 1.4 sec

17. no real solutions

19. one real solution

21. two real solutions

23. two x-intercepts

25. no x-intercepts

27. two x-intercepts

29. $x = \frac{1}{2}$, $x = \frac{4}{5}$; *Sample answer:* The equation is not easily factorable and $a \neq 1$, so solve using the Quadratic Formula.

31. $x = -3 \pm \sqrt{14}$; *Sample answer:* The equation is not easily factorable and $a = 1$, so solve by completing the square.

33. $x = -4$, $x = 3$; *Sample answer:* The equation is easily factorable, so solve by factoring.

35. $x = 1$, $x = -7$; *Sample answer:* The left side is a perfect square trinomial, so solve using square roots.

37. $-b$ should be $-(-7)$, not -7;

$x = \frac{-(-7) \pm \sqrt{(-7)^2 - 4(3)(-6)}}{2(3)}$; $x = 3$ and $x = -\frac{2}{3}$

39. yes; about 42 ft, about 158 ft

41. 5; length: 13 m, width: 7 m

43. a–c. $x = -2$

Sample answer: factoring; The equation is easily factorable.

45. 2; When a and c have different signs, ac is negative, so the discriminant is positive.

47. about 31 mi/h, about 65 mi/h

49. below the x-axis; The discriminant is positive and $a > 0$.

51. above the x-axis; The discriminant is negative and $a > 0$.

53. above the x-axis; The discriminant is positive and $a < 0$.

55. about 22 sec; The height is 30,800 feet after about 20.8 seconds and after about 42.8 seconds.

57. length: about 54 ft, width: about 278 ft; length: about 209 ft, width: about 72 ft

59. a. *Sample answer:* $\frac{1}{2}$

b. 1

c. *Sample answer:* 2

61. $-\frac{b}{2a}$; The mean of the solutions is the x-coordinate of the vertex; The mean of the solutions is equal to the graph's axis of symmetry, which is where the vertex lies.

63. about 24.7 ft/sec

65. $x = \frac{-1 \pm \sqrt{1 - 4ac}}{2a}$; $x \approx -1.77$, $x \approx 2.27$

67. a. $k < \frac{1}{24}$

b. $k = \frac{1}{24}$

c. $k > \frac{1}{24}$

69. a. $k > -\frac{25}{64}$

b. $k = -\frac{25}{64}$

c. $k < -\frac{25}{64}$

9.5 Review & Refresh

70. (4, 0); Explanations will vary.

71. (−4, 5); Explanations will vary.

72. (5, 3); Explanations will vary.

73. (−2, 7); Explanations will vary.

74. $x = 4 \pm \sqrt{19}$

75. $x = \frac{3}{2}$

76. $x = -\frac{1}{3}$

77. $x = \frac{7 \pm \sqrt{5}}{2}$

78. no real solution

79. no real solution

80. arithmetic sequence; The common difference is 6.

81. geometric sequence; The common ratio is 6.

82. $x = 10$

83. $d = 21$

84. $z = \frac{25}{2}$

85. $y = \frac{32}{3}$

86. $x = \pm 15$

87. $x = \pm 11$

88. $x = -5$

89. $x = \pm 3$

90. a. $y = 0.21x^2 + 53.8x - 18$; The model is a good fit for the data.

b. 18 days

91. $12.25m^2$

92. $\frac{8}{p^3}$

93. The function is negative when $x < 0$ and $0 < x < 3$, and positive when $x > 3$. The function is increasing when $x < 0$ and $x > 2$, and decreasing when $0 < x < 2$. As $y \to -\infty$, $x \to -\infty$. As $y \to +\infty$, $x \to +\infty$.

94. $x^2 - 20x + 100$; $(x - 10)^2$

95. $x^2 + 18x + 81$; $(x + 9)^2$

9.6 Practice

1. B; (0, 1), (3, 4)

3. A; (0, −1)

5. (2, 9), (−1, 6)

7. (−1, 2)

9. (3, 6), (−3, −6)

11. (0, −5), (−3, −8)

13. no real solutions

15. (0, 5)

17. (4, −11), (−4, 29)

19. (0, 2), (−6, −22)

21. (1, 1)

23. about (0.87, −1.74), about (−6.87, 13.74)

25. The graph does not show both solutions.

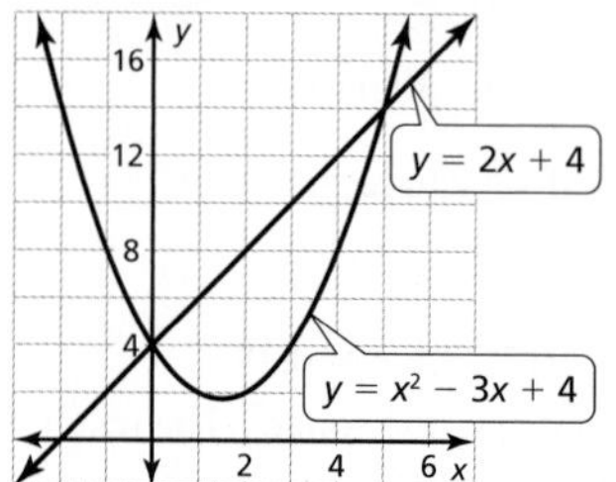

The solutions are (0, 4) and (5, 14).

27. between −4 and −3, between 0 and 1

29. (2.350, 13.225)

31. (−2.543, −0.941), (0.185, 1.586), (1.854, 25.152)

33. (0.840, 3.454), (−3.174, −1.898)

35. $x \approx 0.45$, $x \approx -4.45$

37. no real solutions

39. $x \approx -0.36$

41. $x \approx 1.13$, $x \approx 2.40$

43. 5 days and 35 days after the movie opened

45. $\left(\frac{-7 + \sqrt{145}}{6}, \frac{7 + 2\sqrt{145}}{9}\right), \left(\frac{-7 - \sqrt{145}}{6}, \frac{7 - 5\sqrt{145}}{9}\right)$; They are about the same.

47. no; The curve of a parabola does not lie on a straight line.

49. a–c. (2, 11), (−2, −5); Explanations will vary.

51. $y = 30x + 290$; (1, 320), (34, 1310) are solutions of the system

53. a. after 84 years

b. yes; after 115 years

55. no; The graph of the line could be on the outside of the parabola and touch the parabola at one point so that there is only one solution of the system.

57. (1, −6)

9.6 Review & Refresh

58. no real solutions

59.

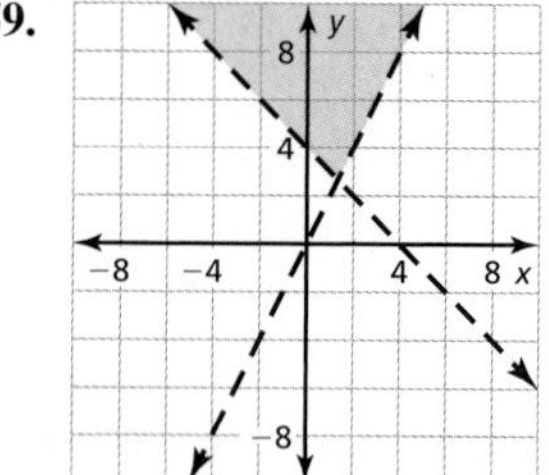

60.

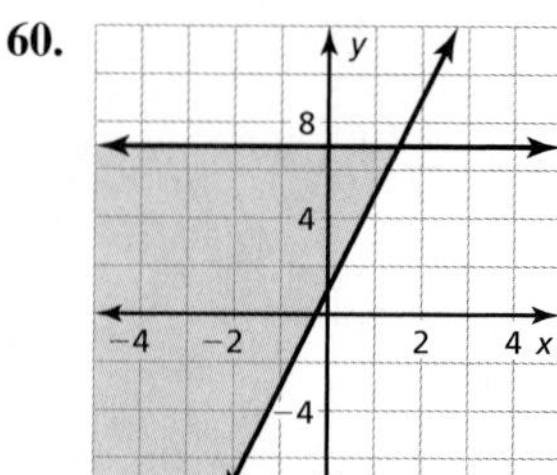

61.

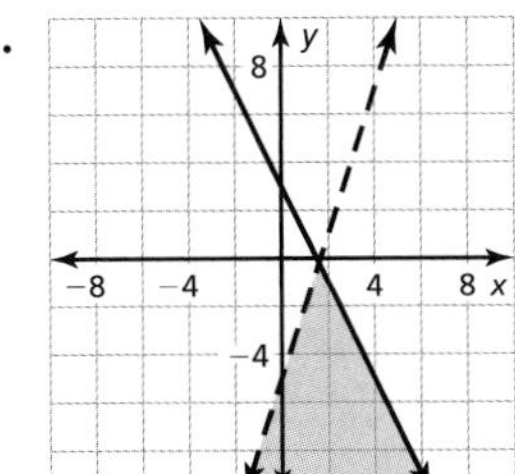

62.

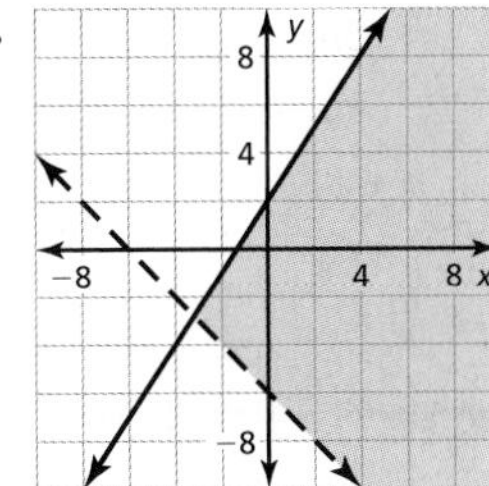

63.

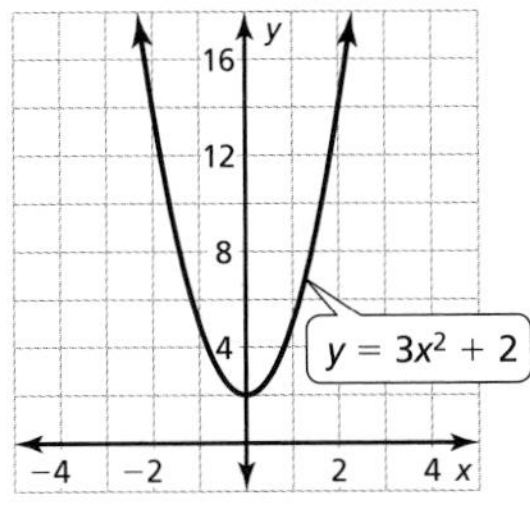

domain: all real numbers; range: $y \geq 2$

64.

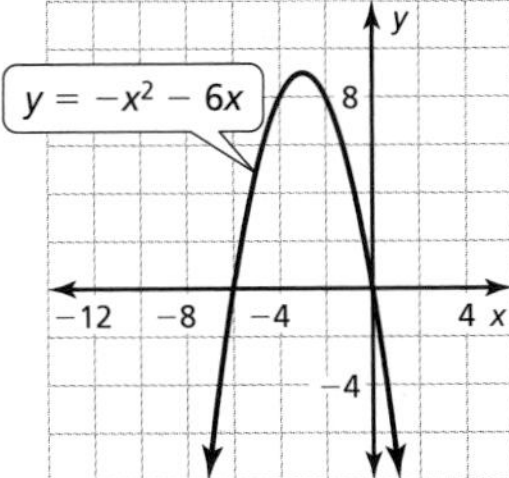

domain: all real numbers; range: $y \leq 9$

65.

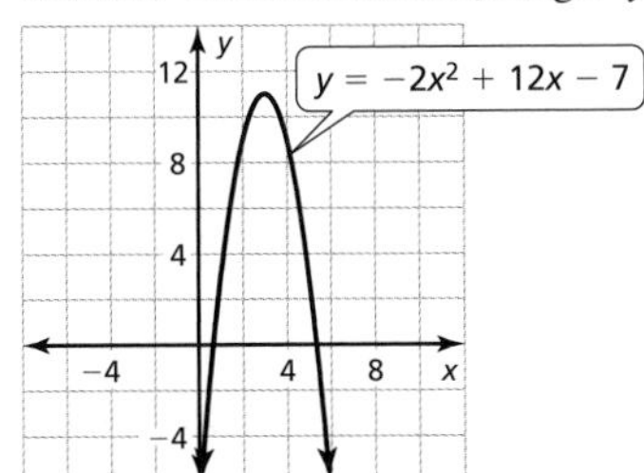

domain: all real numbers; range: $y \leq 11$

66.

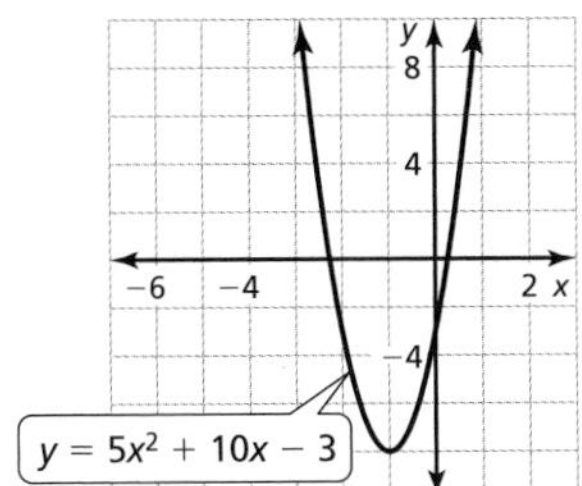

domain: all real numbers; range: $y \geq -8$

67. $x = -5$

68. -8

69. 4

70. $x = 6$

71. $x = \frac{4}{3}, x = -2$

72. $x = \frac{3 \pm \sqrt{57}}{4}$

73. $x < -8$

74. $x \leq -2$ *or* $x > 3$

75. $y = 4x - 13$

76. $y = -\frac{3}{4}x + 9$

77. a. 68 ft

b. $x = 2$; When $x < 2$, the ball is going up, and when $x > 2$, the ball is falling down.

78. $(-1, 0), (4, 5)$

79. $(-2, 3)$

Chapter 9 Review

1. $6p^3\sqrt{2p}$

2. $\frac{3\sqrt{35y}}{7y}$

3. $\frac{5x^3\sqrt[3]{2x^2}}{2}$

4. $4\sqrt{6} - 8$

5. $14\sqrt{3}$

6. $10\sqrt{3}$

7. 9.3 ft

8. rational; $\frac{3 - \sqrt{8}}{12d - \sqrt{128d^2}} = \frac{3 - \sqrt{8}}{12d - 4d\sqrt{8}} = \frac{3 - \sqrt{8}}{4d(3 - \sqrt{8})} = \frac{1}{4d}$, which is rational.

9. $x = -4, x = -1$

10. $x = 6, x = 3$

11. no real solutions

12. $x = 5$

13. $-3, -1, 1$

14.

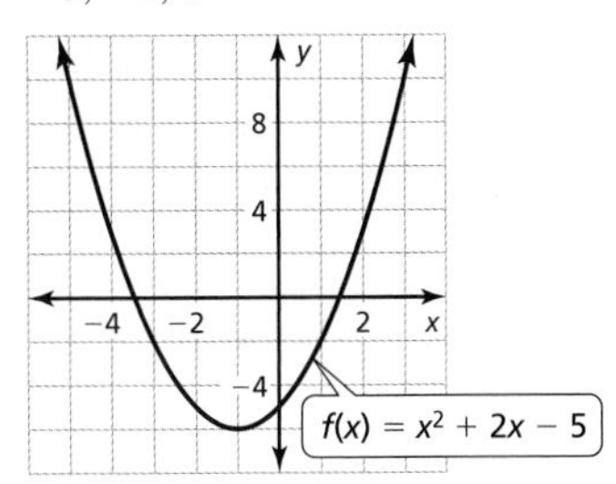

$-3.4, 1.4$

15. $x = \pm 2\sqrt{3}$

16. $x = 0$

17. $x = 6, x = -10$

18. $x = 1$

19. no real solutions

20. $\pm\frac{\sqrt{55}}{5}$

21. $6\sqrt{10}$ ft, or about 18.98 ft

22. length: $4\sqrt{19}$ m, or about 17.4 m, width: $\sqrt{19}$ m, or about 4.4 m

23. $x = 4, x = -10$

24. $x = -1$

25. $x = 1 \pm \sqrt{6}$

26. maximum value; 8

27. minimum value; 7

28. minimum value; -33

29. about 1.3 in.

30. $8

31. $x = 3, x = -5$

32. $x = \frac{1 \pm \sqrt{65}}{4}$

33. $x = 1$

34. one x-intercept

35. no x-intercepts

36. two x-intercepts

37. $k = -28$ or $k = 28$

38. 2015

39. $(1, -5)$

40. $\left(-\frac{1}{2}, \frac{3}{2}\right), (3, 5)$

41. $(-1, 10), (4, 0)$

42. about $(4.87, 14.75)$, about $(-2.87, -0.75)$

43. about $(1.54, -2.40)$

44. about $(-1.88, 2.35)$, about $(2.48, -4.64)$

45. a. 0; 4; The points have the same y-value, so the line is horizontal.

b. $x = -1$; Because the points of intersection have the same y-value, the axis of symmetry is the midpoint of the x-coordinates of the points of intersection.

46. *Sample answer:* $y = 1$ and $y = (x - 4)^2 + 1$

Chapter 9 Mathematical Practices (Chapter Review)

1. The given solution and the Quadratic Formula have a similar structure. So, the values of a, b, and c can be found by using the parts of the Quadratic Formula and setting them equal to the values of the solution.

2. no real solutions; On the right side of the equation, a is negative, so the parabola opens down. The maximum value occurs at $x = -\frac{b}{2a} = -\frac{12}{-6} = 2, f(2) = -6$, and $-6 < -4$, so the graphs will never intersect.

Chapter 9 Practice Test

1. $\frac{\sqrt{11}}{5}$
2. $\frac{\sqrt{6}}{4}$
3. $-2(\sqrt{6} + \sqrt{10})$
4. $x = 11, x = -11$; *Sample answer:* The equation can be written in the form $x^2 = d$, so solve using square roots.
5. $x = 3 \pm \sqrt{19}$; *Sample answer:* Solve by completing the square.
6. $x = 4, x = 3$; *Sample answer:* The equation is easily factorable, so solve by factoring.
7. $x = \frac{1}{4}, x = -\frac{7}{4}$; *Sample answer:* The equation is in the form $x^2 = d$ where x is a binomial, so solve using square roots.
8. $x = \frac{4}{5}, x = -1$; *Sample answer:* The equation is not easily factorable and $a \neq 1$, so solve using the Quadratic Formula.
9. $x = \frac{3 \pm \sqrt{65}}{4}$; *Sample answer:* The equation is not easily factorable and $a \neq 1$, so solve using the Quadratic Formula.
10. The equation can be put in vertex form $y = 2(x + 1)^2 - 8$. The vertex $(-1, -8)$, is in the third quadrant, so the function cannot be represented by the graph shown.
11. *Sample answer:* $\frac{1}{2 + \sqrt{3}}$; $2 - \sqrt{3}$
12. $(2, -6), (-2, 10)$
13. $(-1, -7), \left(\frac{6}{5}, -7\right)$
14. $(1, 3)$
15. 55 points
16. about 3.16 sec
17. $36x^3\sqrt{10x}$ in.^{2}
18. $x = -2, x = 20$
19. after 8 h; before 8 h

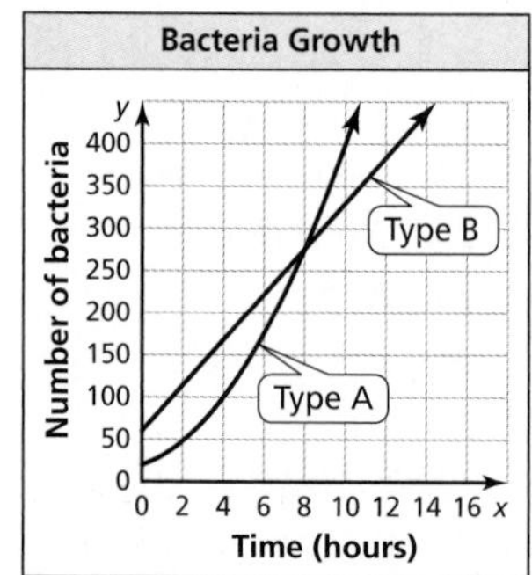

Chapter 9 College and Career Readiness

1. y-intercept: -12; x-intercepts: $-\frac{4}{3}$ and $\frac{3}{2}$; minimum: $-\frac{289}{24}$
2. D
3. $(-2, -13), (-1, -9), (0, -5), (1, -1), (2, 3), (3, 7)$
4. The slope, -0.6, represents the rate at which the number of cups of hot chocolate sold change as the temperature changes. The y-intercept, 42, shows that 42 cups of hot chocolate are likely to be sold when the temperature is 0°F.
5. A
6. B
7. A, D

8. **a.** *Sample answer:* $a = 400, b = 1.15$
   b. *Sample answer:* $a = 800, b = 1.15$
   c. *Sample answer:* $a = 600, b = 1.05$

Chapter 10

Chapter 10 Prepare

1. 45
2. -10
3. -20
4. -44
5. 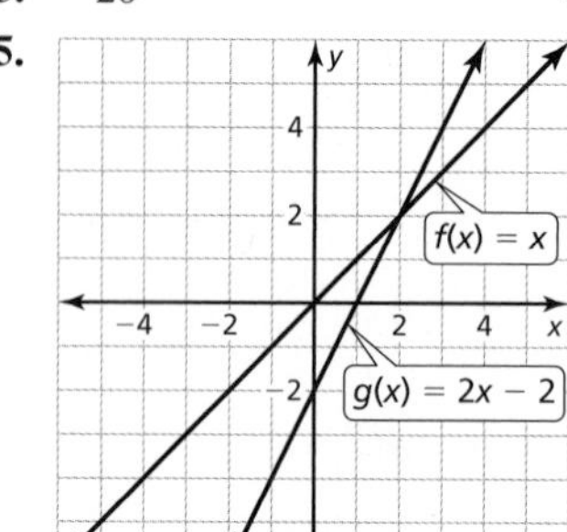

The graph of g is a vertical stretch by a factor of 2, then a vertical translation 2 units down of the graph of f.

6. 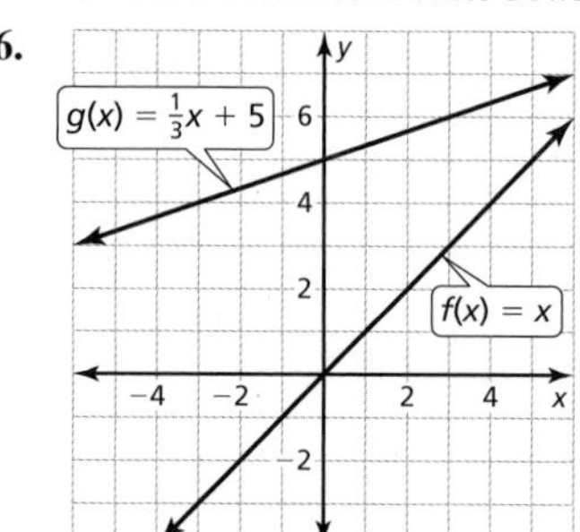

The graph of g is a vertical shrink by a factor of $\frac{1}{3}$, then a vertical translation 5 units up of the graph of f.

7. 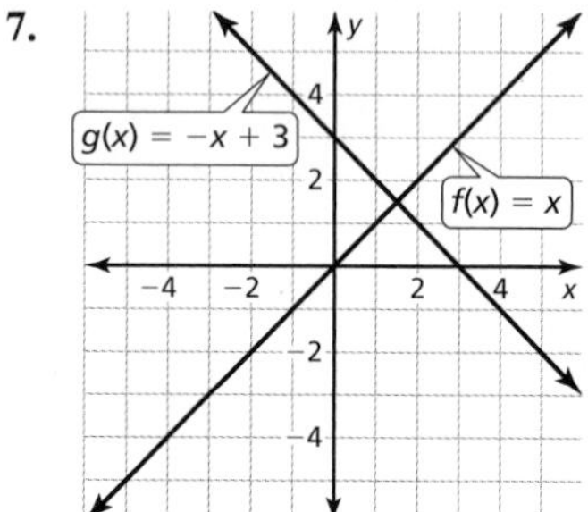

The graph of g is a reflection in the x-axis, then a vertical translation 3 units up of the graph of f.

8. The graph of n is a vertical stretch by a factor of 2, a reflection in the x-axis, then a vertical translation $2b$ units down of the graph of m.

10.1 Practice

1. $x \geq 0$
3. $x \leq 0$
5. $x \geq 4$
7. $x \leq 8$
9. $x \geq -4$

11. 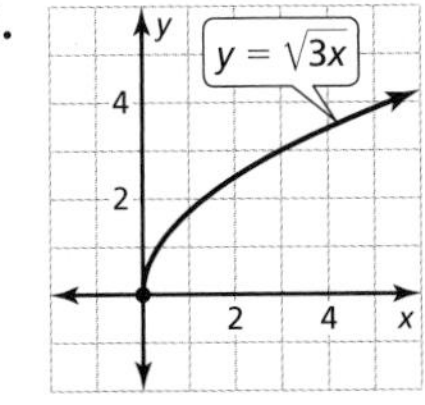

$y \geq 0$

13. 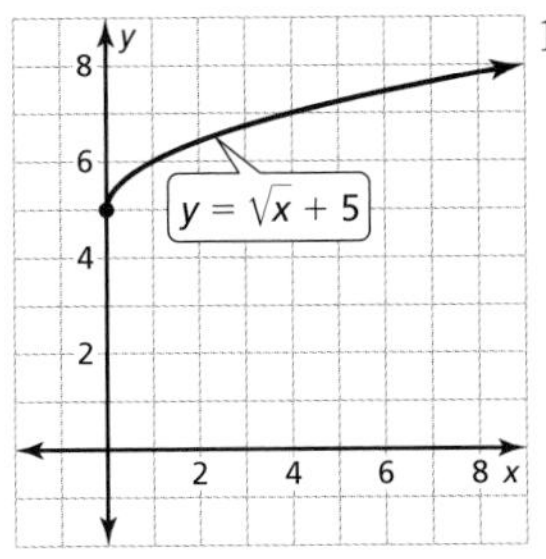

$y \geq 5$

15. 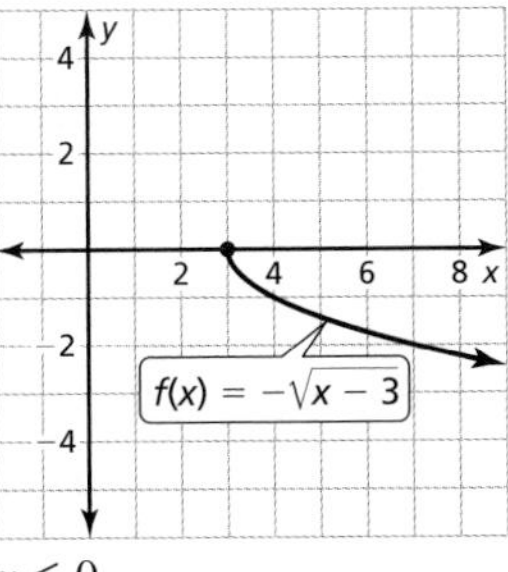

$y \leq 0$

17. 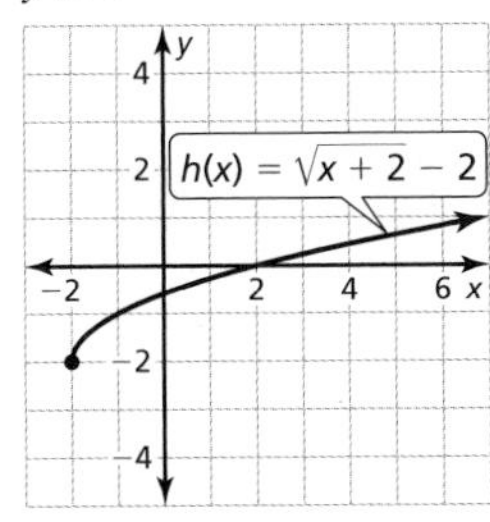

$y \geq -2$

19. 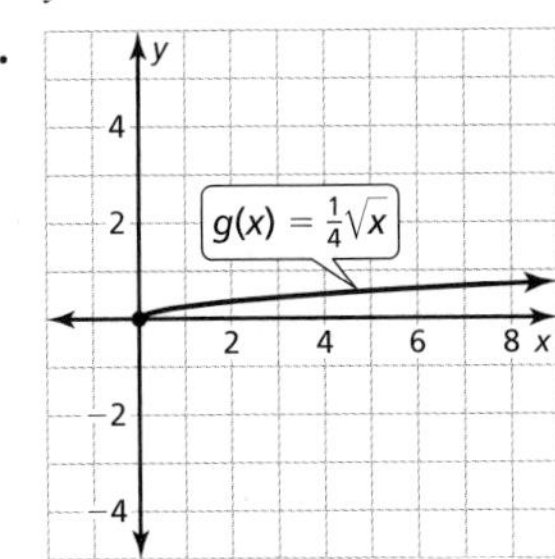

The graph of g is a vertical shrink by a factor of $\frac{1}{4}$ of the graph of f.

21. 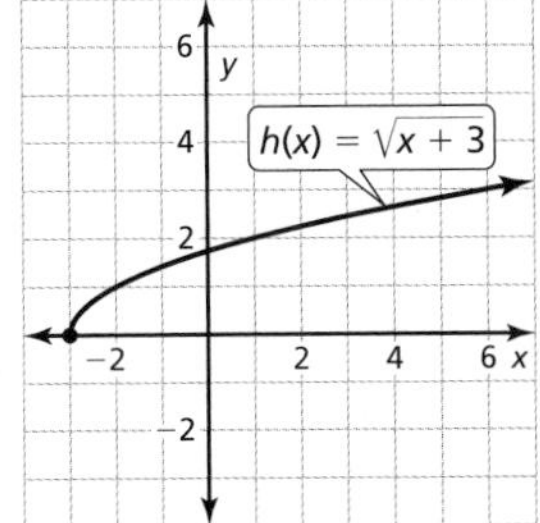

The graph of h is a translation 3 units left of the graph of f.

23. 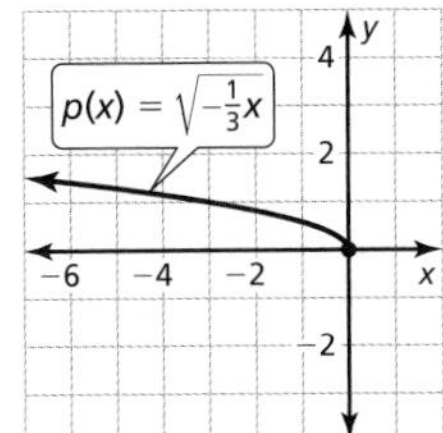

The graph of p is a horizontal stretch by a factor of 3 and a reflection in the y-axis of the graph of f.

25. 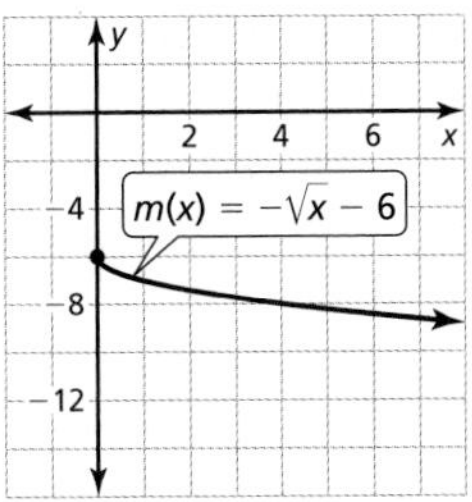

The graph of m is a reflection in the x-axis and a translation 6 units down of the graph of f.

27. 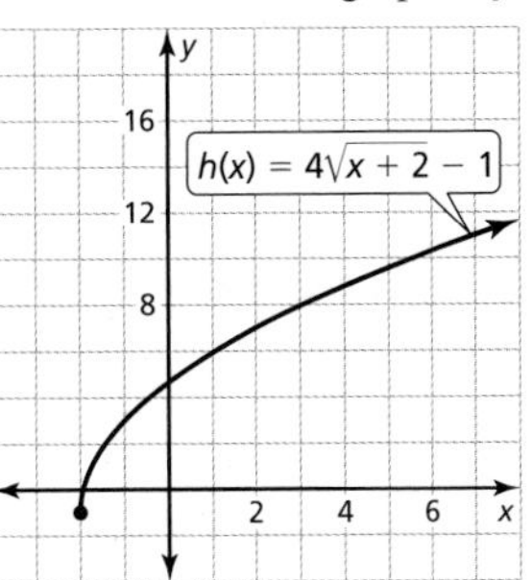

The graph of h is a horizontal translation 2 units left, a vertical stretch by a factor of 4, and a translation 1 unit down of the graph of f.

29. 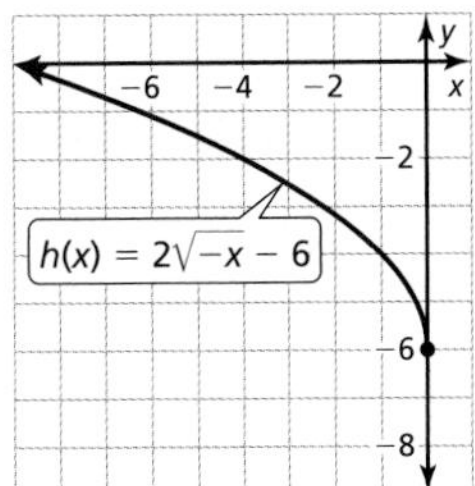

The graph of h is a reflection in the y-axis, a vertical stretch by a factor of 2, and a translation 6 units down of the graph of f.

31. 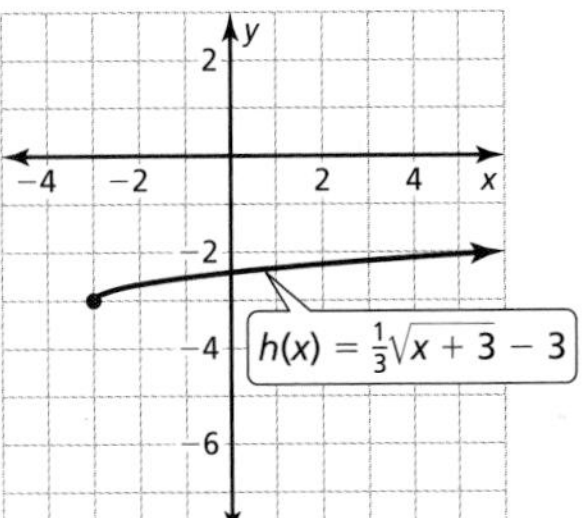

The graph of h is a horizontal translation 3 units left, a vertical shrink by a factor of $\frac{1}{3}$, and a translation 3 units down of the graph of f.

33. 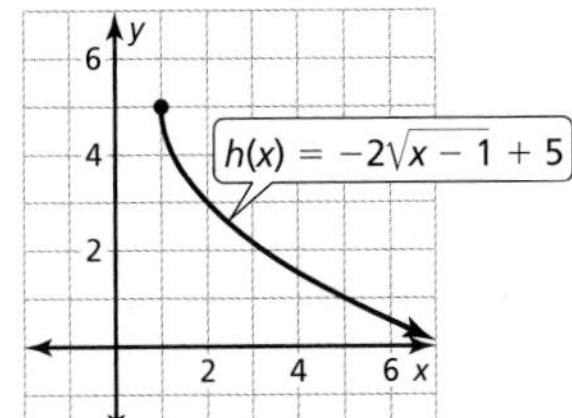

The graph of h is a horizontal translation 1 unit right, a vertical stretch by a factor of 2, a reflection in the x-axis, and a translation 5 units up of the graph of f.

35. vertical stretch; The y-coordinates increase by a factor of 1.25.

37. The graph of $y = \sqrt{x}$ is translated 1 unit up instead of 1 unit left.

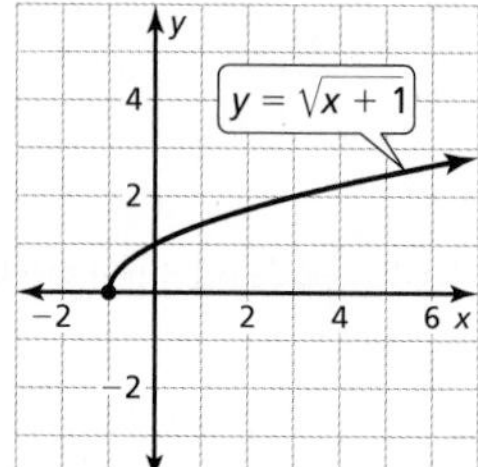

39. A

41. As skid mark lengths increase from 0 to 15 feet, the initial van speeds increase at an average rate of about 1.22 miles per hour per foot on Road Surface A and about 1.00 mile per hour per foot on Road Surface B.

43. a.

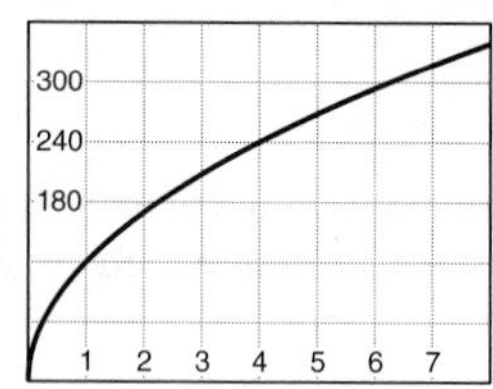

6.25 lb/in.^{2}

b. decreases

45. a. A > 0

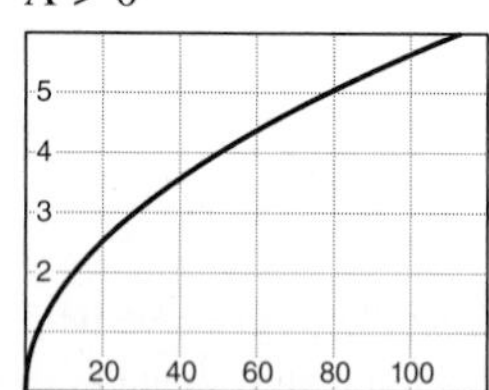

b. about 91.6 in.^{2}

47. yes; yes; no; A square root function has a minimum value when a is positive and a maximum value when a is negative. Because a square root function is either always increasing or always decreasing, it cannot have both a minimum and maximum value.

49. *Sample answer:* $f(x) = 3 - \sqrt{x + 5}$

51. Answers will vary. Check students' work.

10.1 Review & Refresh

52. 7

53. −4

54. $\frac{1}{3}$

55. $\frac{2}{5}$

56. a. $y = -0.4x + 100$

b. The slope, −0.4, shows the battery decreases by 0.4% every minute it is used. The y-intercept, 100, shows your phone starts with 100% battery before it is used.

57. $(x + 1)(x + 6)$

58. $(d - 4)(d - 7)$

59. $(y - 8)(y + 5)$

60. $6n^2\sqrt{3n}$

61. $14\sqrt{3} - \sqrt{7}$

62. $-\frac{\sqrt[3]{c}}{10}$

63. $-5\sqrt{2} + 5\sqrt{6}$

64. nonlinear; The graph is an absolute value function which is not a line.

65. $x = -9, x = 3$; Explanations will vary.

66. $x = \frac{11 \pm \sqrt{17}}{4}$; Explanations will vary.

67.

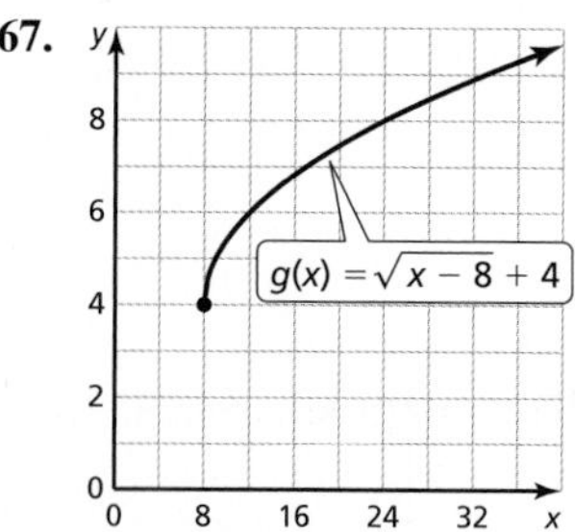

The graph of g is a horizontal translation 8 units right and a vertical translation 4 units up of the graph of f.

68. *Sample answer:* $y = 5(x - 1)^2 + 2$

69. (−0.386, 1.307), (4.638, 0.040)

70. (−0.717, 2.260), (0.300, −0.030)

71. $4 \leq z < 10$

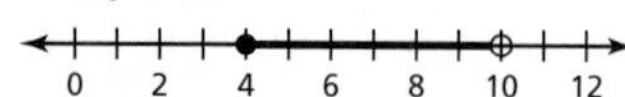

10.2 Practice

1.

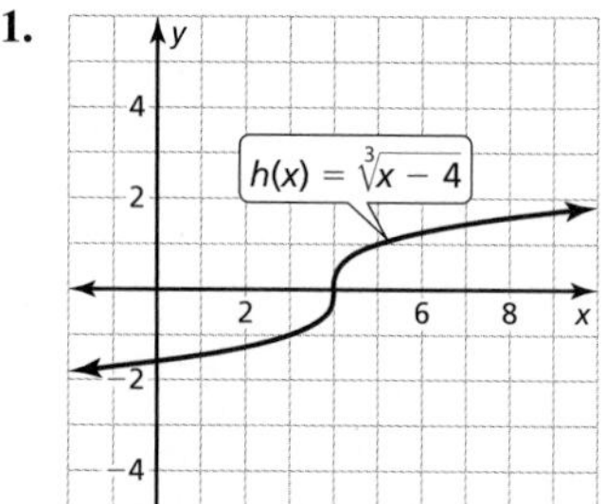

The graph of h is a translation 4 units right of the graph of f.

3.

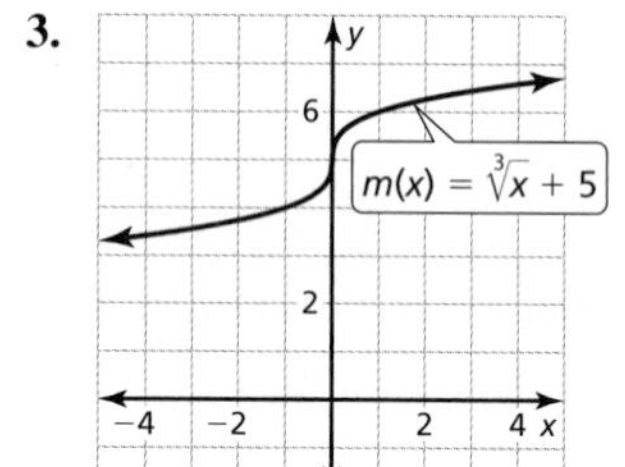

The graph of m is a translation 5 units up of the graph of f.

5.

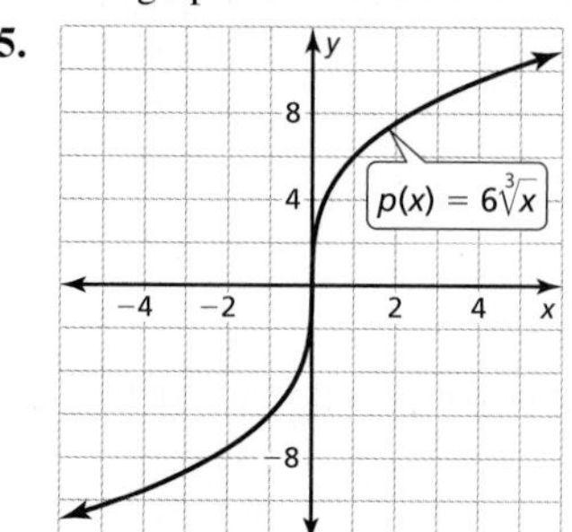

The graph of p is a vertical stretch by a factor of 6 of the graph of f.

7. The graph of q is a translation 5 units left of the graph of f; $h = -5$

9. The graph of v is a translation 6 units down of the graph of f; $k = -6$

11. 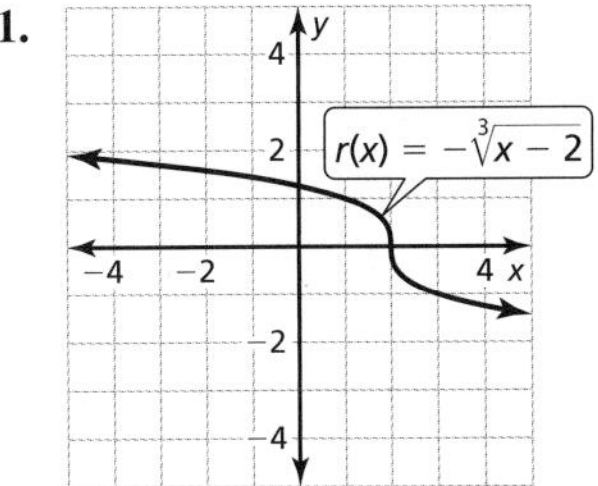

The graph of r is a reflection in the x-axis and a translation 2 units right of the graph of f.

13. 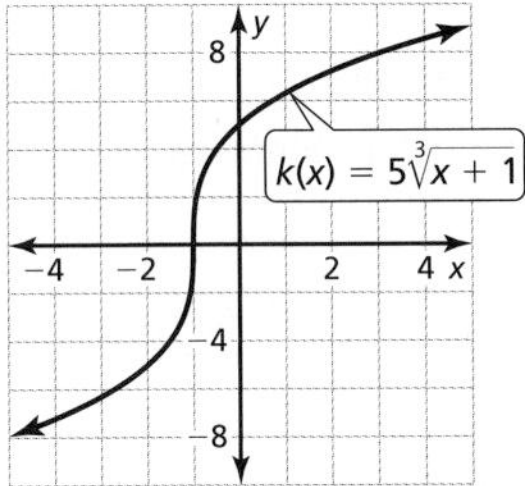

The graph of k is a vertical stretch by a factor of 5 and a translation 1 unit left of the graph of f.

15. 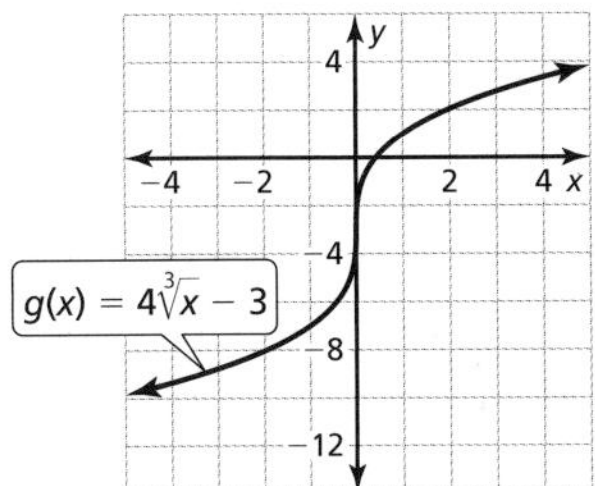

The graph of g is a vertical stretch by a factor of 4 and a translation 3 units down of the graph of f.

17. 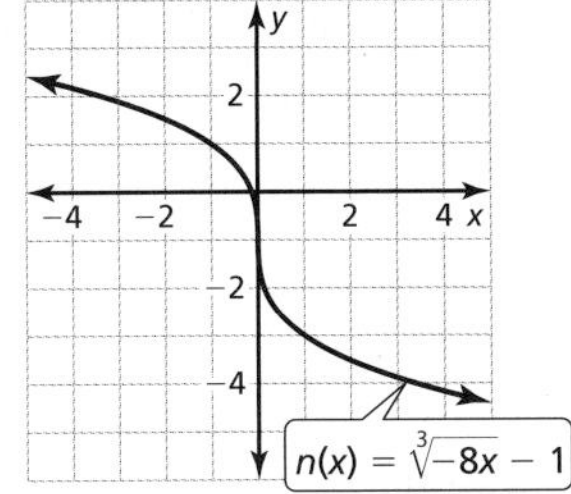

The graph of n is a horizontal shrink by a factor of $\frac{1}{8}$, a reflection in the y-axis, and a translation 1 unit down of the graph of f.

19. 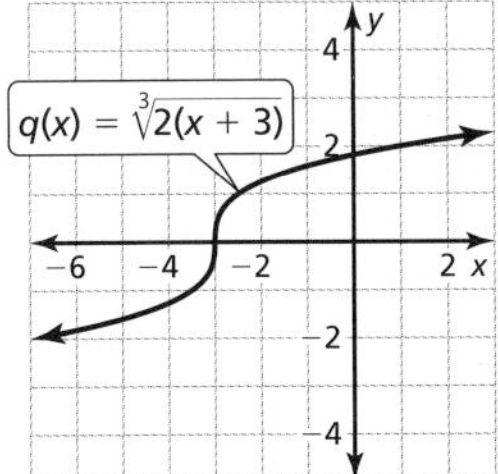

The graph of q is a horizontal shrink by a factor of $\frac{1}{2}$ and a translation 3 units left of the graph of f.

21. 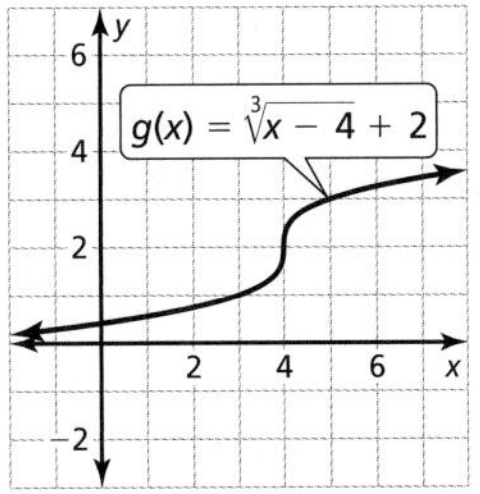

The graph of g is a horizontal translation 4 units right and 2 units up of the graph of f.

23. 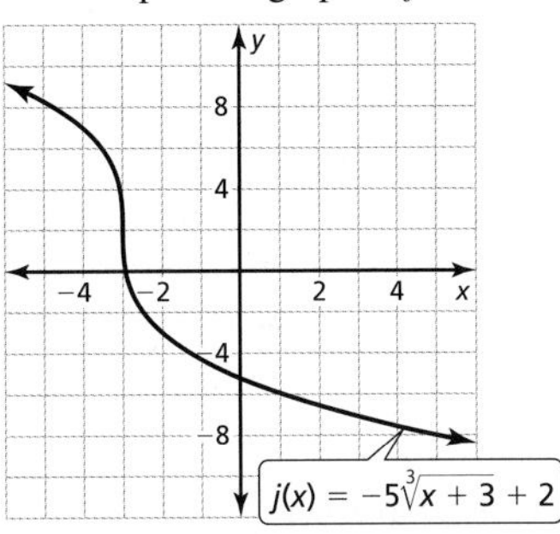

The graph of j is a horizontal translation 3 units left, a vertical stretch by a factor of 5, a reflection in the x-axis, and a translation 2 units up of the graph of f.

25. 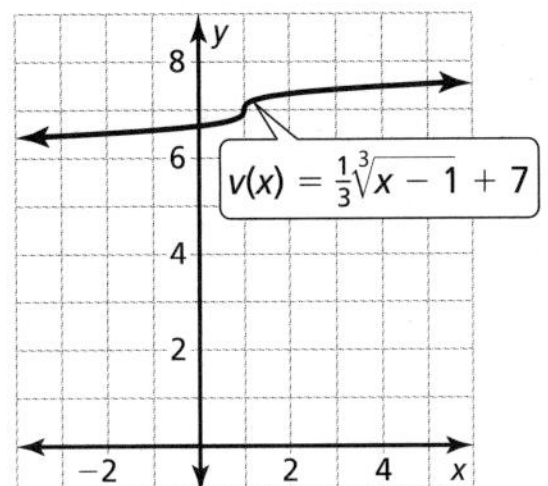

The graph of v is a horizontal translation 1 unit right, a vertical shrink by a factor of $\frac{1}{3}$, and a translation 7 units up of the graph of f.

27. The graph should be a translation 3 units right, not a translation 3 units left, of the graph of $y = \sqrt[3]{x}$.

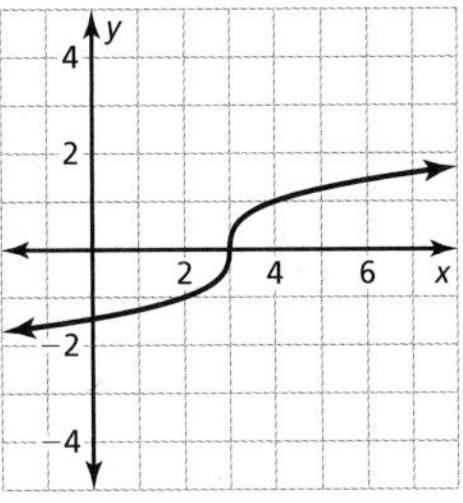

29. Because $0.91 > 0.167$, the average rate of change of f is greater than the average rate of change of q.

31. 14.1 ft^3

33. no; A function f is an odd function when $f(-x) = -f(x)$ for each x in the domain of f. *Sample answer:* A cube root function, such as $f(x) = \sqrt[3]{x} + 1$, is not an odd function because $f(-x) = \sqrt[3]{-x} + 1 = -\sqrt[3]{x} + 1$ and $-f(x) = -(\sqrt[3]{x} + 1) = -\sqrt[3]{x} - 1$. $f(-x) \neq -f(x)$.

35. no; A cube root function is always increasing or always decreasing.

37. $f(x) = 2\sqrt[3]{x-1}$

SELECTED ANSWERS

10.2 Review & Refresh

39. $(x - 5)(x - 15)$ **40.** $3(x + 6)(x - 2)$

41. $(x - 1)(2x - 9)$ **42.** $(x + 3)(4x - 5)$

43. $x \geq 0$ **44.** $x \leq 3$

45. no; A vertical line can be drawn through more than one point on the graph.

46. at most 3.76 gigabytes **47.** The value is 0.

48. $x = -6, x = 6$ **49.** no real solutions

50. $x = -13, x = 5$ **51.** $x = \frac{7}{5}, x = \frac{13}{5}$

52.

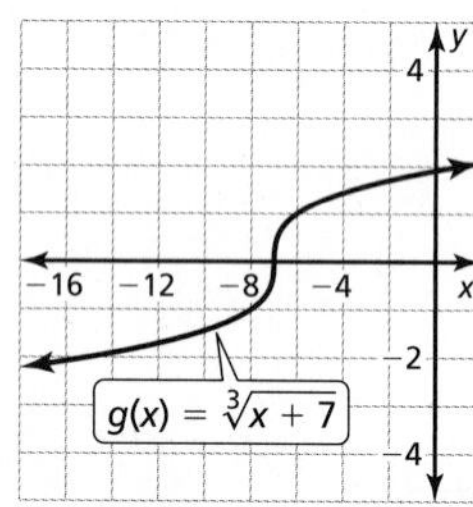

The graph of g is a horizontal translation 7 units left of the graph of f.

53.

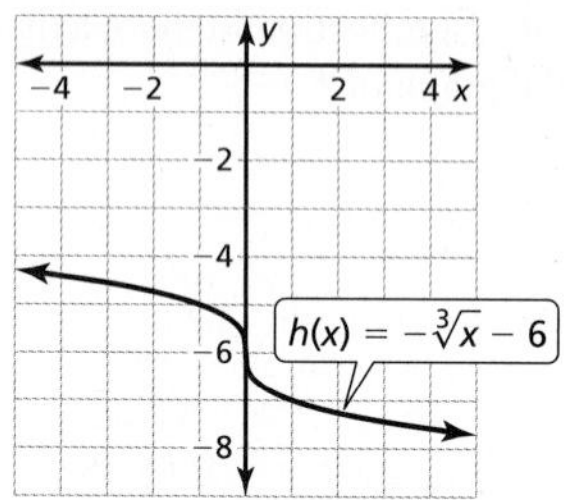

The graph of h is a reflection in the x-axis and a vertical translation 6 units down of the graph of f.

54. $f(x) = -3x^3 - 6x^2 + 9x$ **55.** $x = 0.31, x = 1.88$

56. $x = -0.65$

10.3 Practice

1. $x = 81$ **3.** $m = 144$

5. $c = 121$ **7.** $a = 4$

9. $y = 25$ **11.** $a = 19$

13. $x = 60$ **15.** $r = 7$

17. $p = 15$ **19.** 144 ft

21. $x = 1$ **23.** $x = 9$

25. $g = 5$ **27.** $p = 12$

29. $c = \frac{1}{2}$ **31.** $x = 64$

33. $g = 27$ **35.** $s = -18$

37. $y = 2$

39. Because the x-coordinate of the points where the graphs of the equations intersect is the value of x that makes both equations true

41. neither **43.** $p = 4$

45. $y = 1, y = 4$ **47.** $a = \frac{1}{4}$

49. no real solution **51.** $m = 7$

53. no real solution

55. An error was made in squaring both sides because the radical was not isolated. The third equation should be $\sqrt{x} = 2$, and the fourth equation should be $x = 4$.

57. In Step 2, a positive square root cannot equal a negative number, so there is no real solution.

59. yes; The resistance is $\frac{7.68}{30.72} = \frac{1}{4}$ as much for a 120-volt circuit than for a 240-volt circuit.

61. true

63. false; When $b = -a$, then $a^2 = (-a)^2$, but $a \neq -a$.

65. C

67. first cone: $r = 2$ units; second cone: $2r = 4$ units

69. $m = 5$ **71.** $y = \frac{16}{5}$

73. $h = 0$

75. *Sample answer:* $\sqrt{x - 4} = 1$

77. no; Because $\sqrt{(2x + 5)^2}$ cannot be negative, the equation is true only for $x \geq -\frac{5}{2}$, where $2x + 5$ is nonnegative.

79. **a.** about 71.5 N

b. more; To keep the same ratio $\frac{T}{m}$, if m is increased, then T must be increased also.

10.3 Review & Refresh

80. $-8y^3 + 20y$ **81.** $x^2 + 6x - 16$

82. $12p^2 + 11p - 5$ **83.** $s^3 + 5s^2 + 2s - 8$

84. $x = 2$

85.

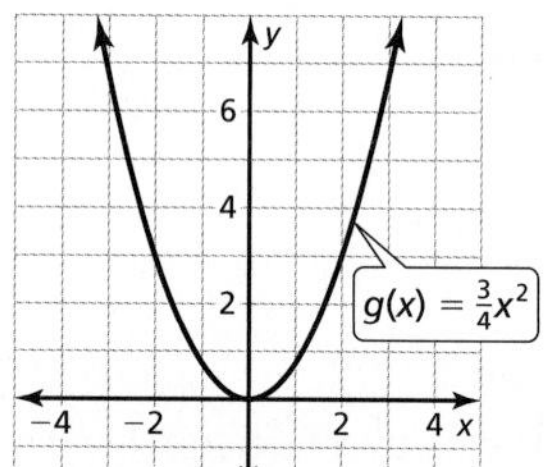

Both graphs open up and have the same vertex, (0, 0), and axis of symmetry, $x = 0$. The graph of g is wider than the graph of f because the graph of g is a vertical shrink by a factor of $\frac{3}{4}$ of the graph of f.

86.

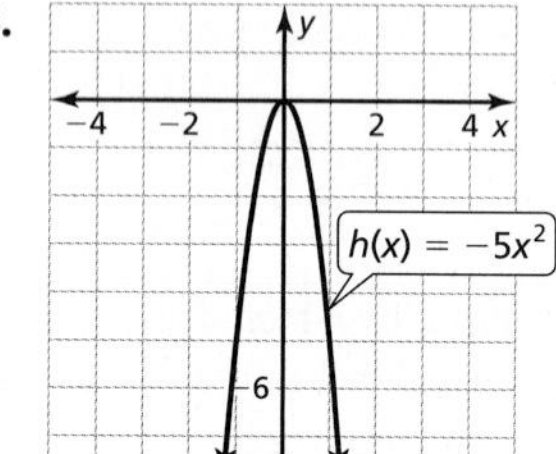

Both graphs have the same vertex, (0, 0), and axis of symmetry, $x = 0$, but the graph of h opens down and is narrower than the graph of f, because the graph of h is a vertical stretch by a factor of 5 and a reflection in the x-axis of the graph of f.

87.

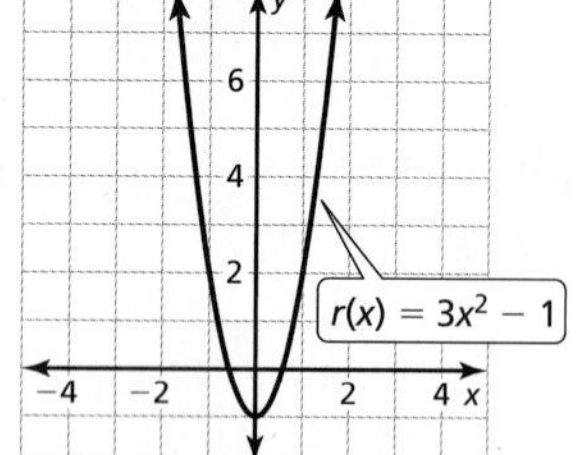

The graph of r is a vertical stretch by a factor of 3 and a vertical translation 1 unit down of the graph of f.

88.

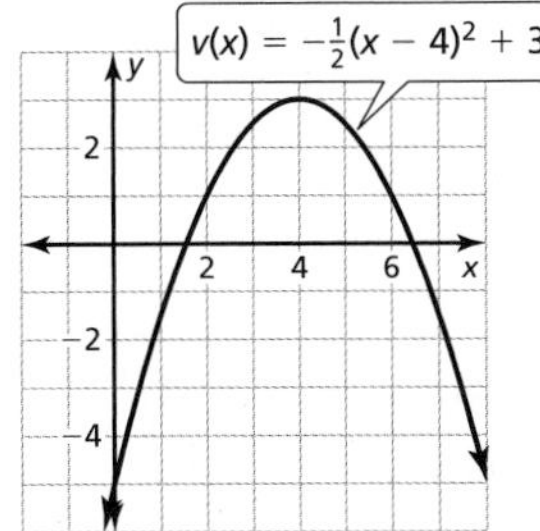

The graph of v is a horizontal translation 4 units right, a vertical shrink by a factor of $\frac{1}{2}$, a reflection in the x-axis, and a translation 3 units up of the graph of f.

89. no real solution

90. $z = \frac{5}{2}$

91. $-\frac{2}{3}$

92.

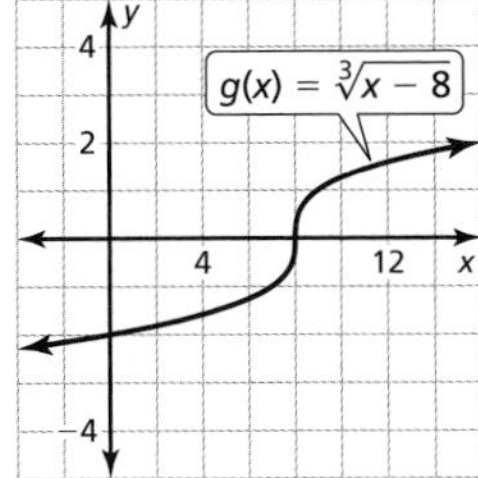

The graph of g is a horizontal translation 8 units right of the graph of f.

93.

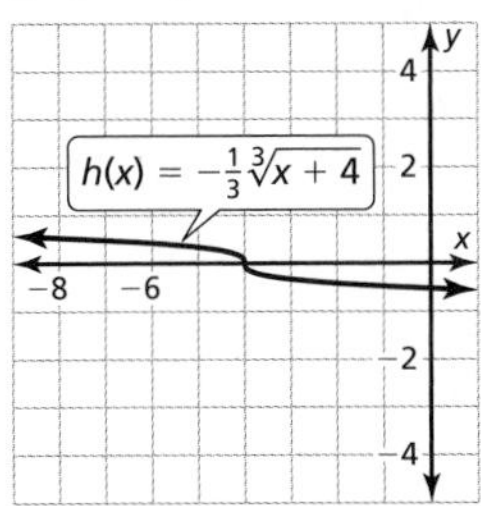

The graph of h is a horizontal translation 4 units left, a vertical shrink by a factor of $\frac{1}{3}$, and a reflection in the x-axis of the graph of f.

94. domain: $x \leq 0$, range: $y \geq 0$

95. domain: $x \geq 1$, range: $y \geq 6$

96. $y = 40\left(\frac{3}{2}\right)^x$; 304 visitors

97. (1, 5); Explanations will vary.

98. (−5, 12), (2, 5); Explanations will vary.

99. $\frac{\sqrt{15}}{2}$

100. $\frac{\sqrt{21y}}{7}$

101. $-16\sqrt{6}$

102. 6

10.4 Practice

1. (0, 1), (−8, 3), (−3, 4), (−5, 7), (−1, 9)

3.

Input	8	6	0	6	8
Output	−10	−5	0	5	10

5. Input Output

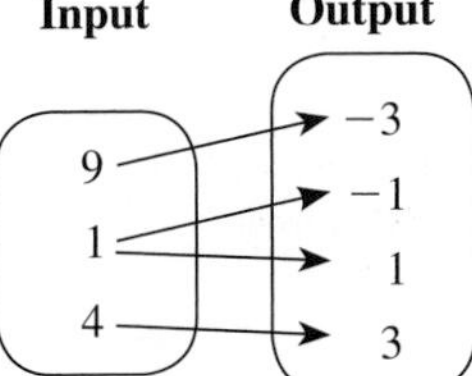

7. $x = y - 11$; -9

9. $x = 4y + 20$; 28

11. $x = \pm\frac{\sqrt{y}}{3}$; $\pm\frac{\sqrt{2}}{3}$

13.

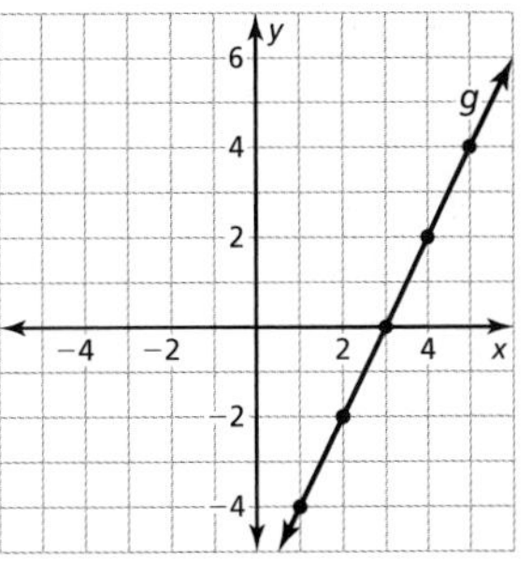

domain of inverse: all real numbers; range of inverse: all real numbers

15. $g(x) = \frac{x+1}{4}$

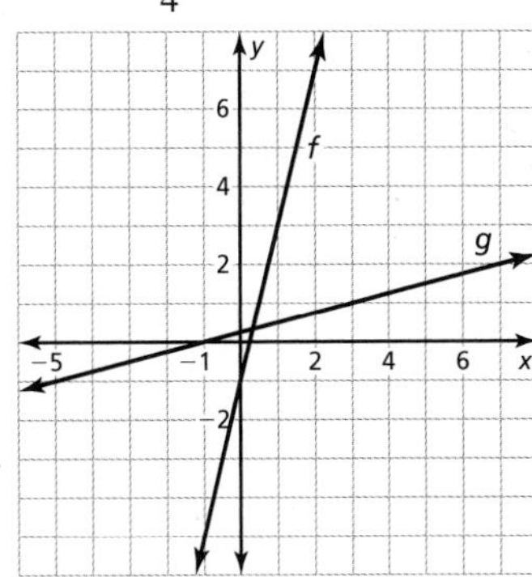

17. $g(x) = -\frac{x+2}{3}$

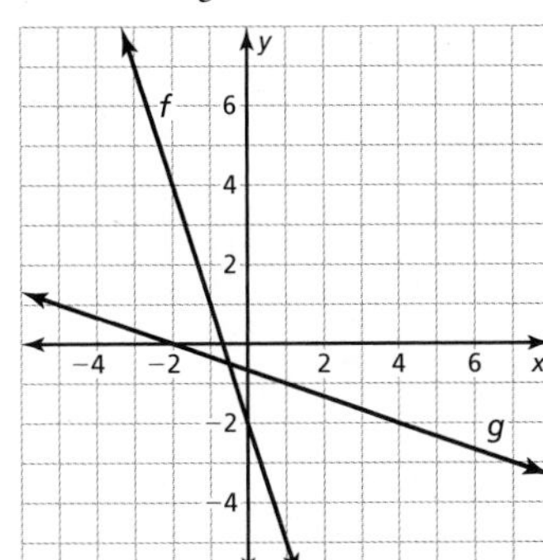

19. $g(x) = 3x - 24$

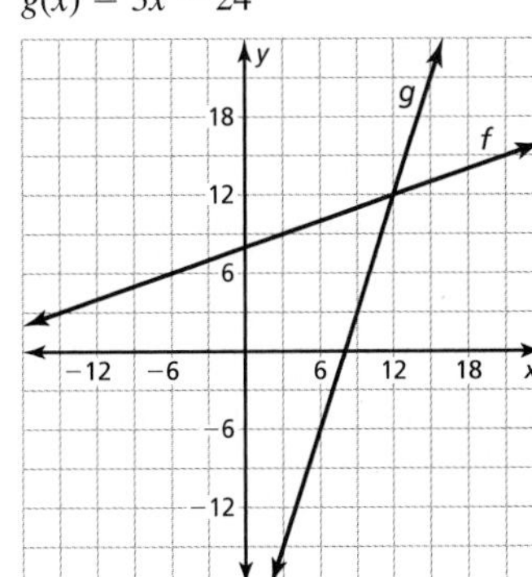

SELECTED ANSWERS

21. $g(x) = \frac{\sqrt{x}}{2}$

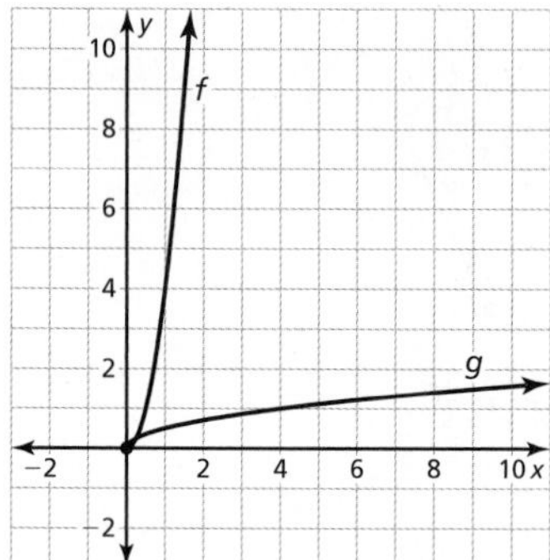

23. $g(x) = -\sqrt{10 - x}$

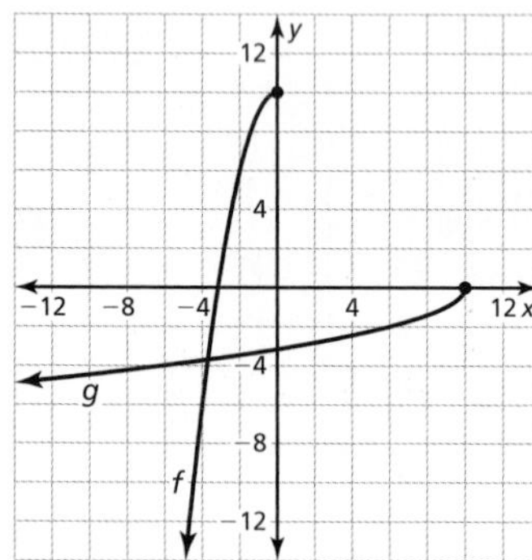

25. $g(x) = 3\sqrt{x - 2}$

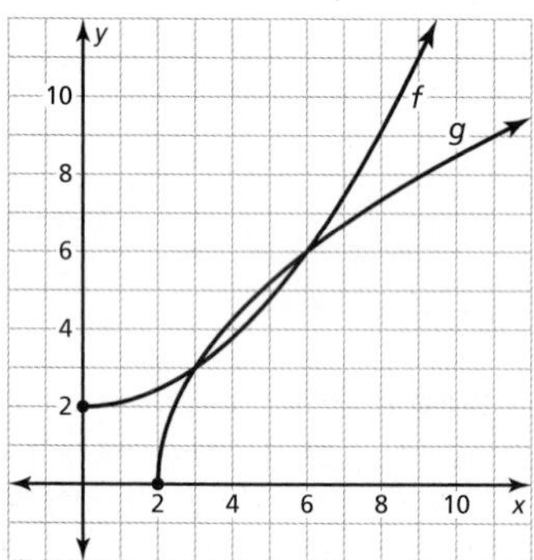

27. not a function

29. function

31. yes; $g(x) = x^2 - 3, x \geq 0$

33. yes; $g(x) = \frac{x^2 + 6}{2}, x \geq 0$

35. yes; $g(x) = \frac{x^2}{9} + 8, x \geq 0$

37. yes; $g(x) = \frac{(-x - 2)^2 - 5}{3}; x \leq -2$

39. no; $y = \pm \sqrt{\frac{x}{2}}$

41. x and y were not switched in the equation; The inverse of f is $g(x) = \frac{x - 5}{3}$ or $g(x) = \frac{x}{3} - \frac{5}{3}$.

43. $D = 1.1352E$; \$283.80

45. $s = \frac{2\sqrt{3}}{3}h$; $s \approx 18.48$ in.

47. $g(x) = \sqrt[3]{\frac{x}{2}}$

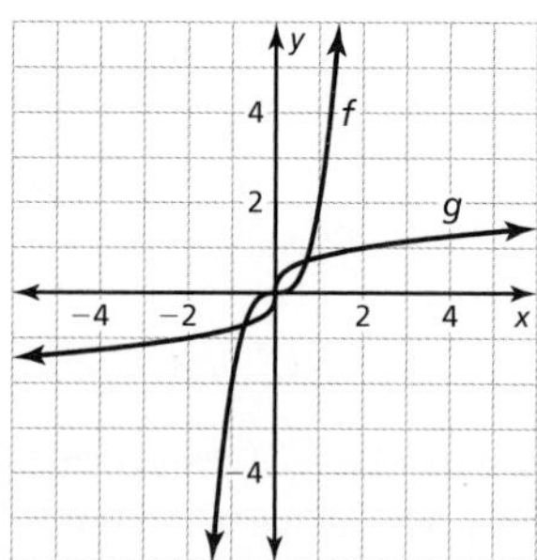

49. $g(x) = \sqrt[3]{x} + 5$

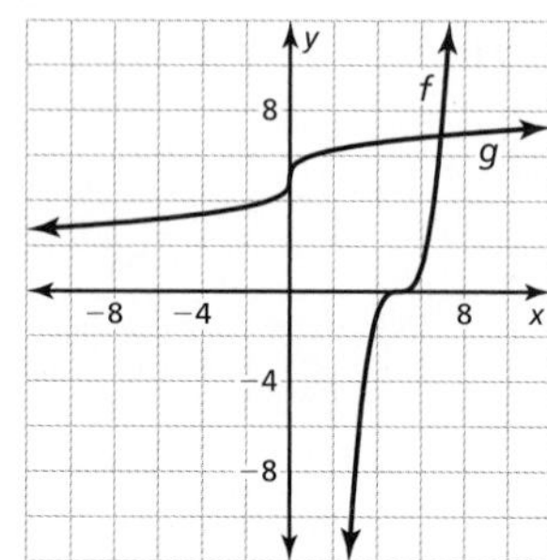

51. $g(x) = \left(\frac{x}{4}\right)^3$

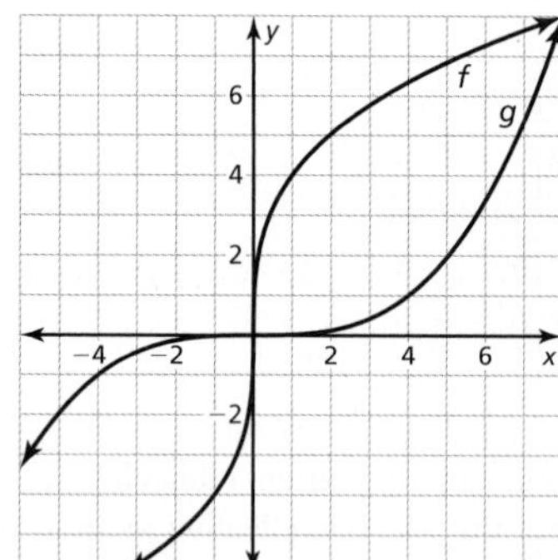

53. no; The function $f(x) = b$ does not pass the Horizontal Line Test. Its inverse is the vertical line $x = b$ and is not a function.

55. B, D

57. **a.**

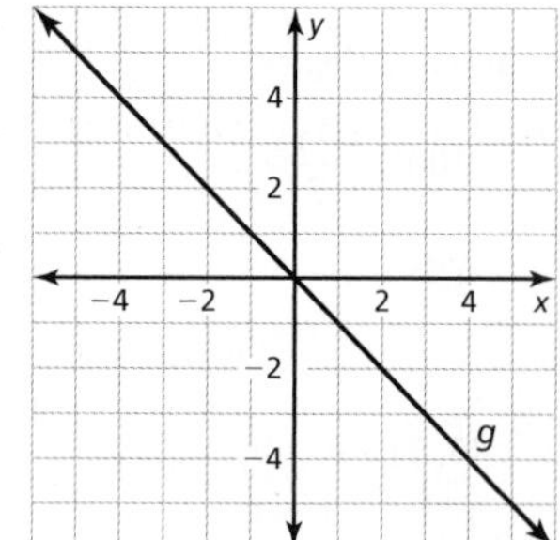

For each point $(a, -a)$ that is on the graph of $g(x) = -x$, the point $(-a, a)$ is also on the graph.

b.

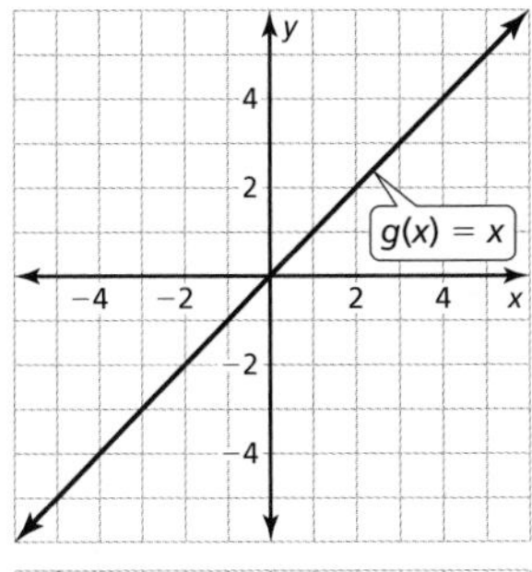

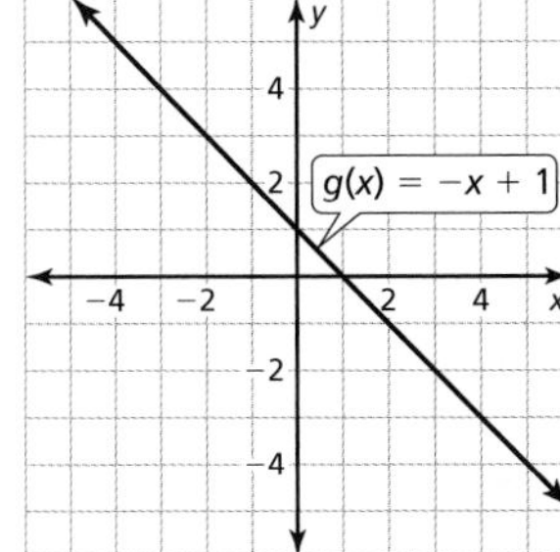

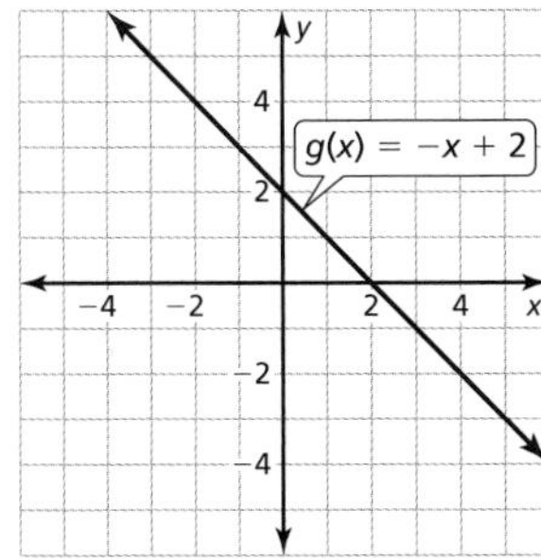

c. The linear function $f(x) = mx + b$ is its own inverse when $m = -1$ and b is any real number or when $m = 1$ and $b = 0$.

59. no; no; For any values of h, k, and a, a horizontal line intersects the graph of f more than once.

10.4 Review & Refresh

61. $-4x - 14$

62. $7y - 11$

63. $8t^2 + 8t - 1$

64. $-10d^2 + 11d - 2$

65. $\frac{7}{a^{10}}$

66. $625x^{24}$

67. y^6

68. $\frac{1}{32r^{35}}$

69. The graph of g is a horizontal translation 2 units right of the graph of f; $h = 2$

70.

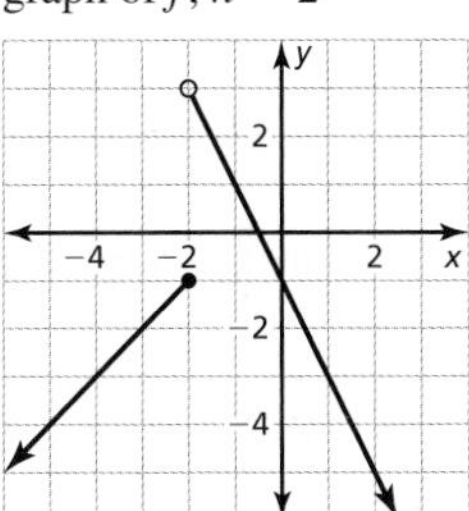

domain: all real numbers, range: $y < 3$

71. $g(x) = \frac{1}{5}x + 3$

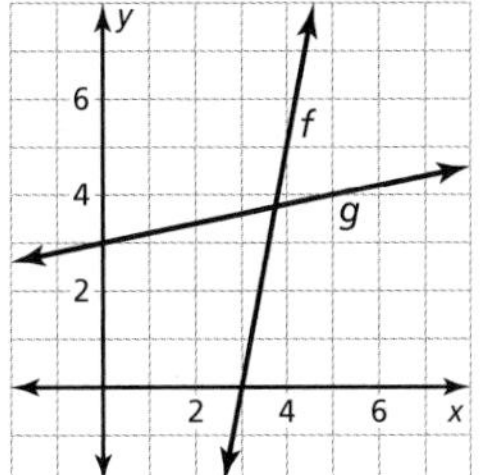

72. $g(x) = -2\sqrt{x}$

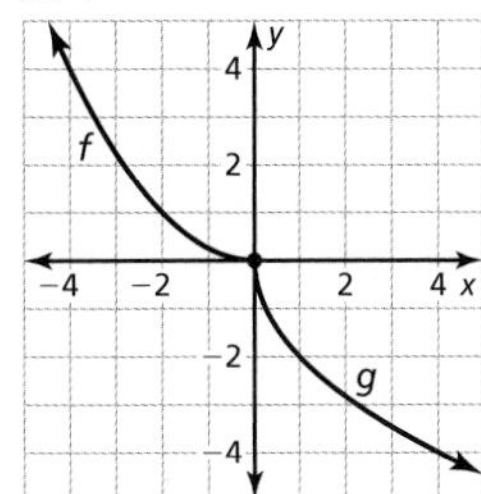

73. 8 teams, 4 teams, 2 teams

74. $b = 64$

75. $x = -113$

76. $t = 7$

77. $p = 5$

78. quadratic

79. $\left(-1, \frac{1}{2}\right)$; Explanations will vary.

80. $(-5, 7)$; Explanations will vary.

81.

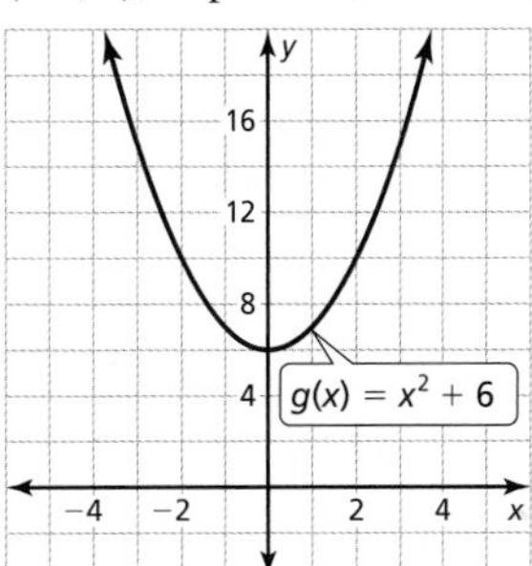

Both the graph of f and the graph of g open up and have the same axis of symmetry, $x = 0$. The vertex of the graph of g, $(0, 6)$, is above the vertex of the graph of f, $(0, 0)$, because the graph of g is a vertical translation 6 units up of the graph of f.

82.

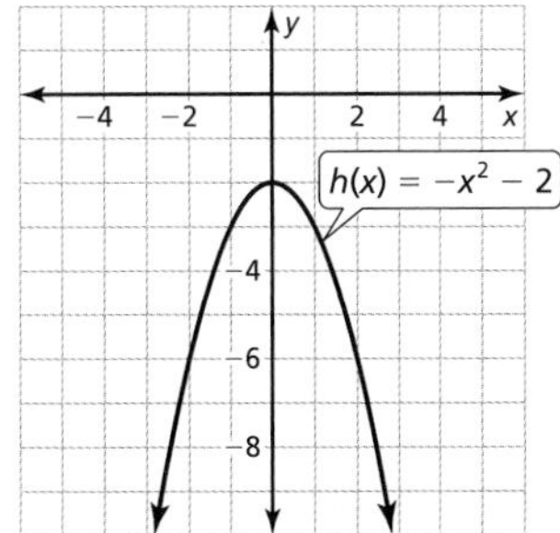

Both the graph of f and the graph of h have the same axis of symmetry, $x = 0$, but the graph of f opens up and the graph of h opens down . The vertex of the graph of f is $(0, 0)$, and the vertex of the graph of h is $(0, -2)$. So, the graph of h is a reflection in the x-axis and a vertical translation 2 units down of the graph of f.

83. 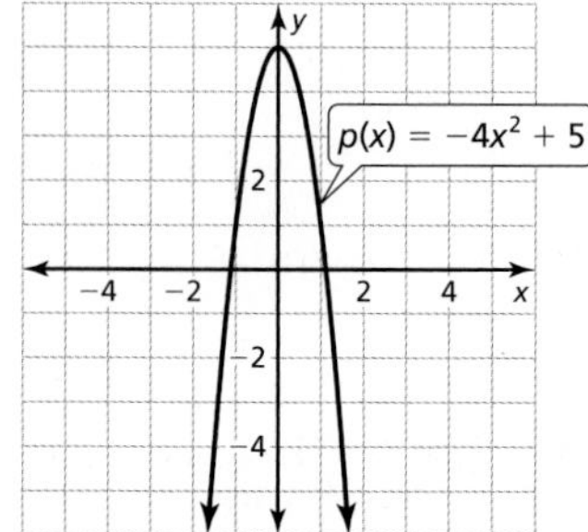

Both the graph of f and the graph of p have the same axis of symmetry, $x = 0$, but the graph of p is narrower than the graph of f. The graph of p opens down but the graph of f opens up, and the vertex of the graph of p is (0, 5) but the vertex of the graph of f is (0, 0). The graph of p is a vertical stretch by a factor of 4, a reflection in the x-axis, and a vertical translation 5 units up of the graph of f.

84. 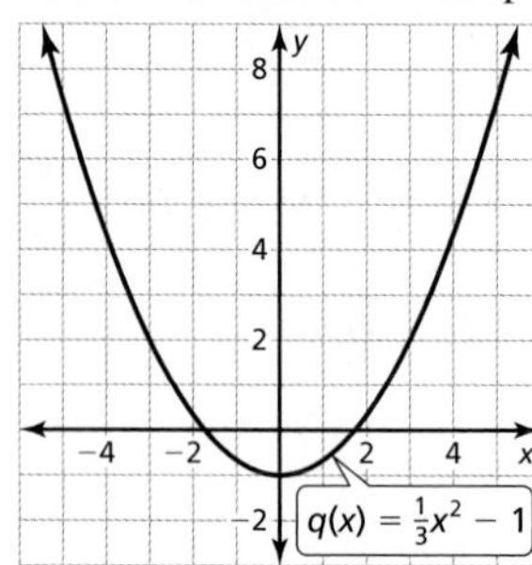

Both the graph of f and the graph of q open up and have the same axis of symmetry, $x = 0$, but the graph of q is wider than the graph of f. Also, the vertex, $(0, -1)$, of the graph of q is below the vertex, (0, 0), of the graph of f. The graph of q is a vertical shrink by a factor of $\frac{1}{3}$ and a vertical translation 1 unit down of the graph of f.

85. The graph of h is a vertical shrink by a factor of $\frac{1}{2}$ and a horizontal translation 3 units down from the graph of f.

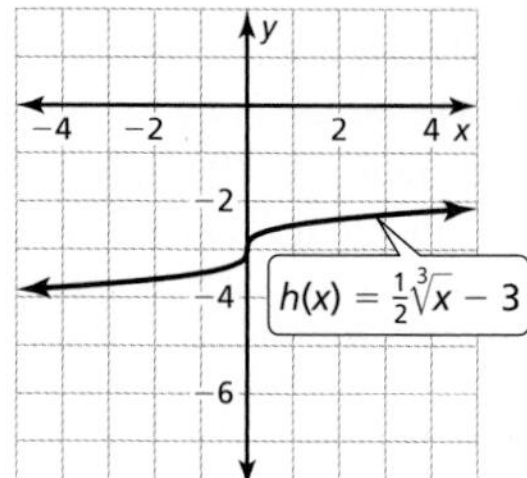

Chapter 10 Review

1. 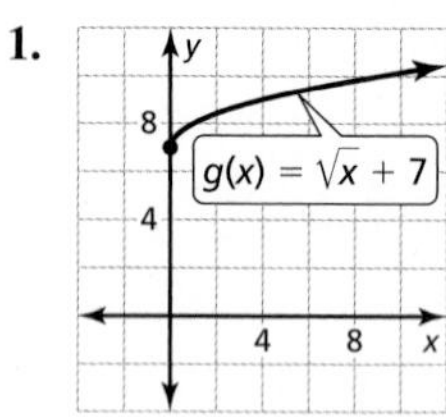

$x \geq 0$; $y \geq 7$; The graph of g is a translation 7 units up of the graph of f.

2. 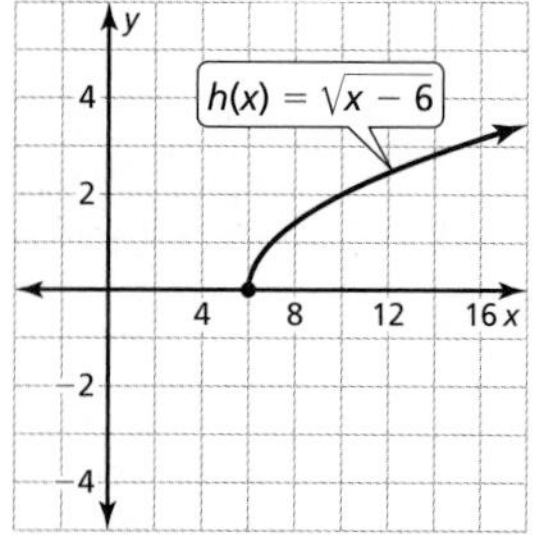

$x \geq 6$; $y \geq 0$; The graph of h is a translation 6 units right of the graph of f.

3. 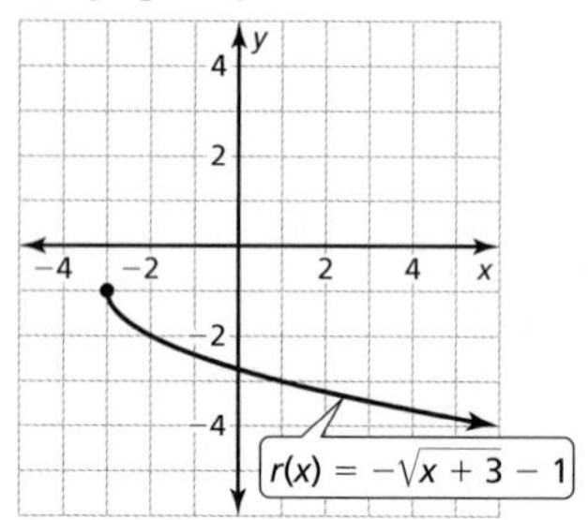

$x \geq -3$; $y \leq -1$; The graph of r is a translation 3 units left, a reflection in the x-axis, and a translation 1 unit down of the graph of f.

4. 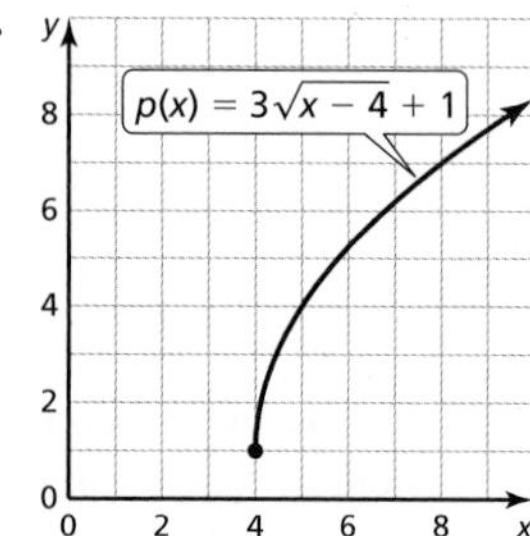

$x \geq 0$; $p(x) \geq 0$; The graph of p is a horizontal translation 4 units right, a vertical stretch by a factor of 3, and a translation 1 unit up of the graph of f.

5. 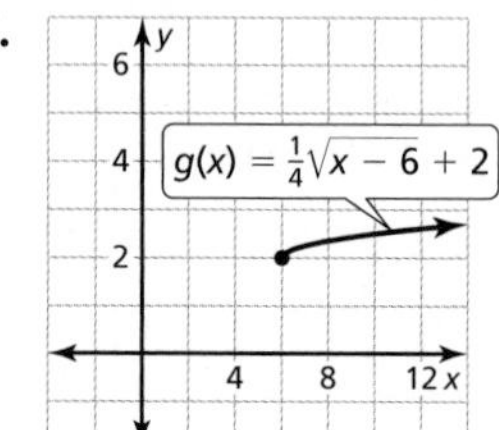

The graph of g is a horizontal translation 6 units right, a vertical shrink by a factor of $\frac{1}{4}$, and a translation 2 units up of the graph of f.

6. **a.** D; The graph is a horizontal translation 2 units right of the graph of $f(x) = \sqrt{x}$.

b. A; The graph is a horizontal translation 2 units left and a reflection in the x-axis of the graph of $f(x) = \sqrt{x}$.

c. C; The graph is a reflection in the x-axis and a vertical translation 2 units down of the graph of $f(x) = \sqrt{x}$.

d. B; The graph is a vertical translation 2 units up of the graph of $f(x) = \sqrt{x}$.

7. a.

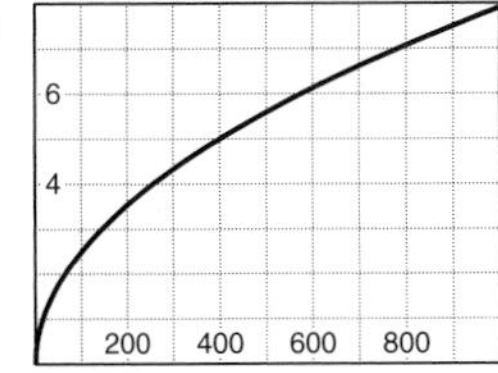

$h \geq 0, t \geq 0$

b. 876 ft

8.

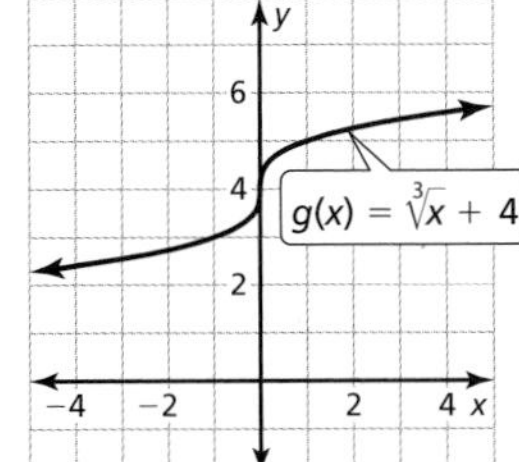

The graph of g is a translation 4 units up of the graph of f.

9.

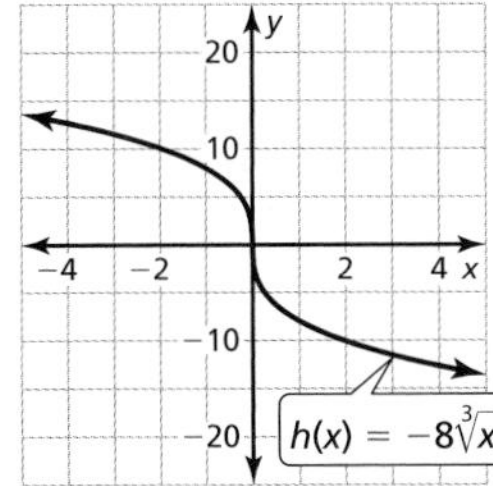

The graph of h is a vertical stretch by a factor of 8 and a reflection in the x-axis of the graph of f.

10.

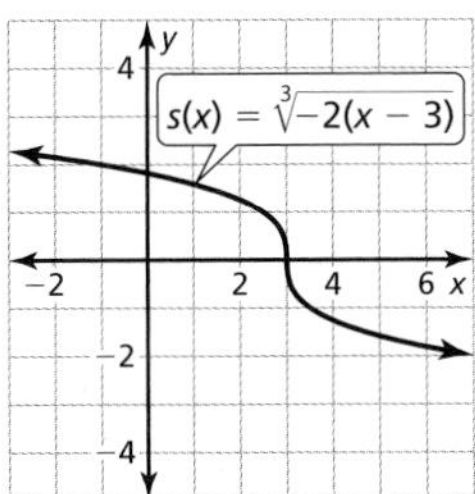

The graph of s is a reflection in the y-axis, a translation 3 units right, and a horizontal shrink by a factor of $\frac{1}{2}$ of the graph of f.

11.

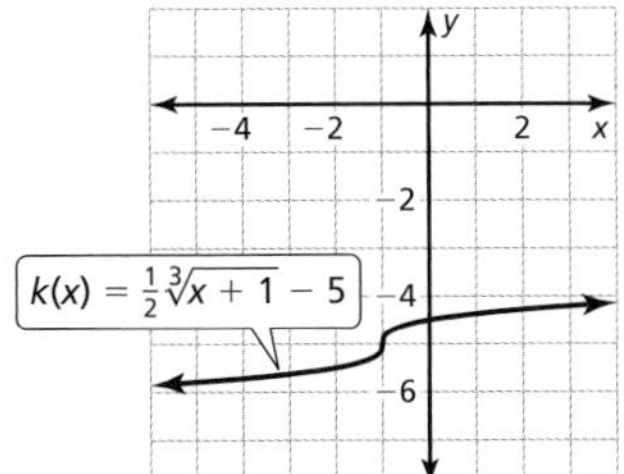

The graph of g is a horizontal translation 1 unit left, a vertical shrink by a factor of $\frac{1}{2}$, and a vertical translation 5 units down of the graph of f.

12.

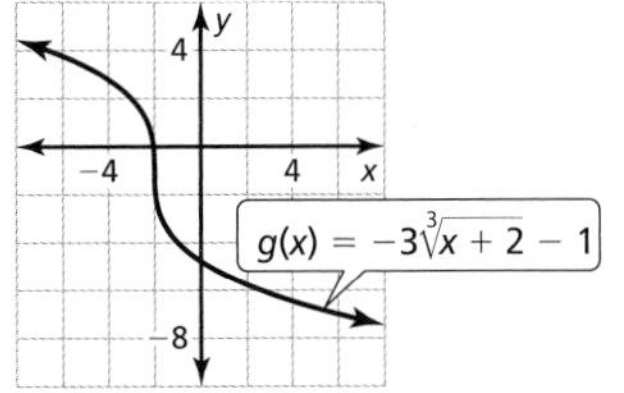

The graph of g is a horizontal translation 2 units left, a vertical stretch by a factor of 3, a reflection in the x-axis, and a translation 1 unit down of the graph of f.

13. The average rate of change of r is about $0.625 \div \left(\frac{\sqrt[3]{4}}{8}\right) \approx 3.15$ times greater than the average rate of change of p over the interval $x = 0$ to $x = 8$.

14. $x = 4$

15. $x = 2$

16. $x = 100$

17. $x = 28$

18. $x = 9$

19. $x = 4$

20. $x = 14$

21. no real solution

22. $16\pi \approx 50.3 \text{ in.}^3$

23. yes; Rewrite $v = \sqrt{19.6h}$ as $h = \frac{v^2}{19.6}$. Because $h_1 = \frac{5^2}{19.6}$ and $h_2 = \frac{15^2}{19.6}$, $\frac{h_2}{h_1} = \frac{\frac{15^2}{19.6}}{\frac{5^2}{19.6}} = \frac{15^2}{5^2} = \frac{225}{25} = 9$.

24. $(-10, 1), (-4, 3), (4, 5), (14, 7), (26, 9)$

25.

Input	6	3	0	−3	−6
Output	−4	−2	0	2	4

26. $x = y + 11$; 14

27. $x = 4y - 8$; 4

28. $x = \frac{y^2 + 5}{7}$; 2

29. $x = \pm\sqrt{12 - y}$; ± 3

30. $g(x) = \frac{10 - x}{5}$

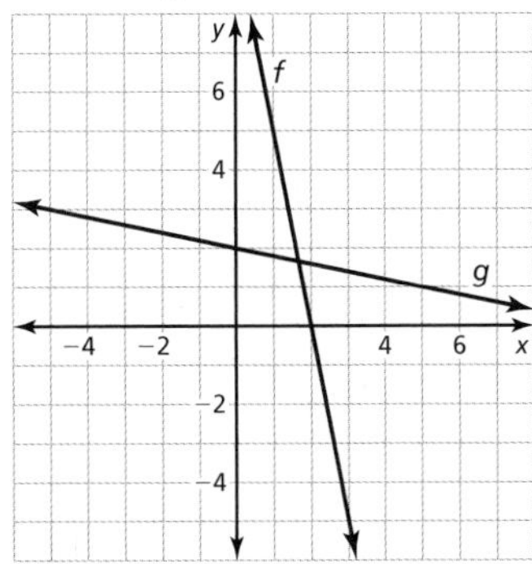

31. $g(x) = \frac{1}{3}\sqrt{3(x + 1)}$

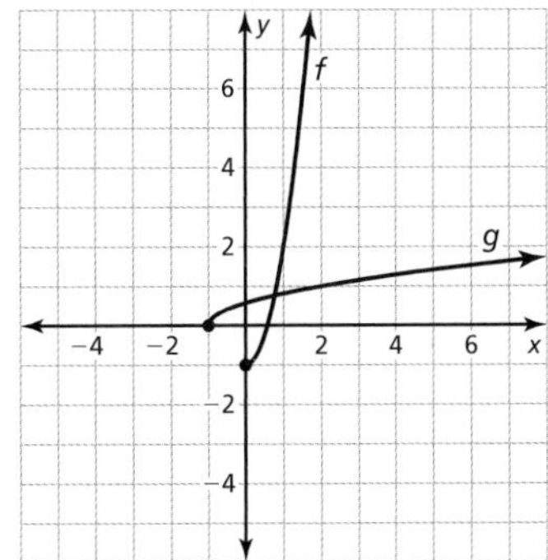

32. $g(x) = 2x^2 - 3, x \geq 0$

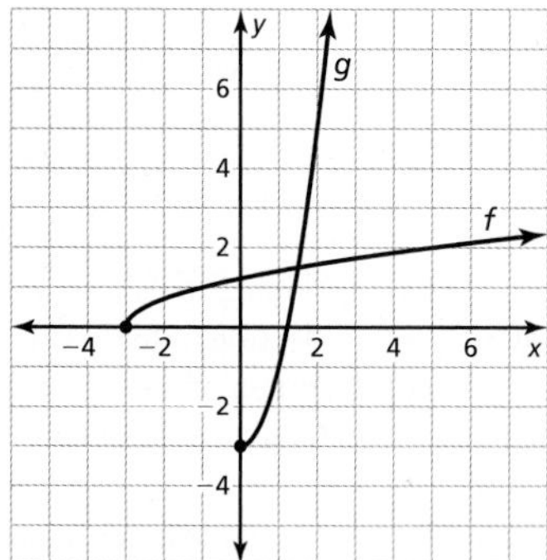

33. not a function

34. The domain of f is $x \geq -3$, and the range is $y \geq -2$. So, the domain of the inverse of f is $x \geq -2$, and the range is $y \geq -3$. The domain of g is $x \leq -3$, and the range is $y \geq -2$. So, the domain of the inverse of g is $x \geq -2$, and the range is $y \leq -3$.

35. $a = \dfrac{125h}{113} + 69.6$; The formula for using the golfer's average score to find the golfer's handicap

Chapter 10 Mathematical Practices (Chapter Review)

1. The context of the problem may be confusing, and focusing on the given values of the variables can help determine which information you need and do not need to solve the problem.
2. Because the values of the input and output must make sense within the context; *Sample answer:* The area of a circle is given by $A = \pi r^2$, where $r > 0$ and $A > 0$. The inverse gives an equation for the area of a circle in terms of the radius. So, $r = \sqrt{\dfrac{A}{\pi}}$. Because $r > 0$, only the positive square root is given.

Chapter 10 Practice Test

1.

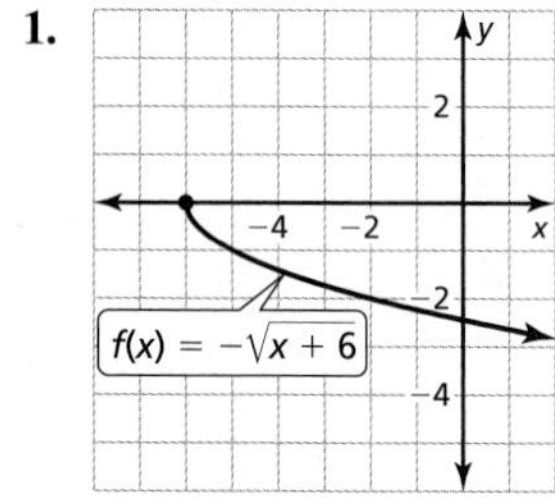

$x \geq -6$; $y \leq 0$; The graph of f is a translation 6 units left and a reflection in the x-axis of the graph of g.

2.

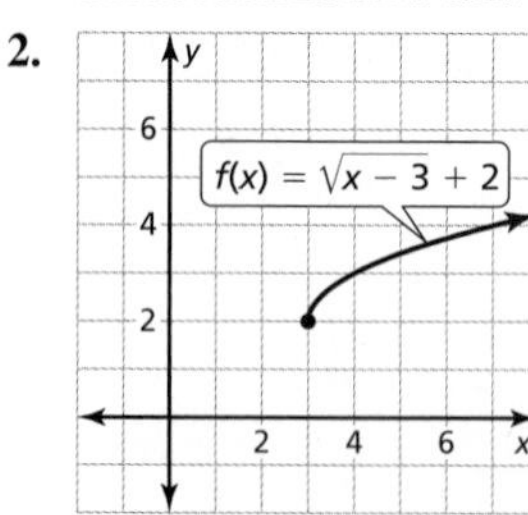

$x \geq 3$; $y \geq 2$; The graph of f is a translation 3 units right and 2 units up of the graph of g.

3.

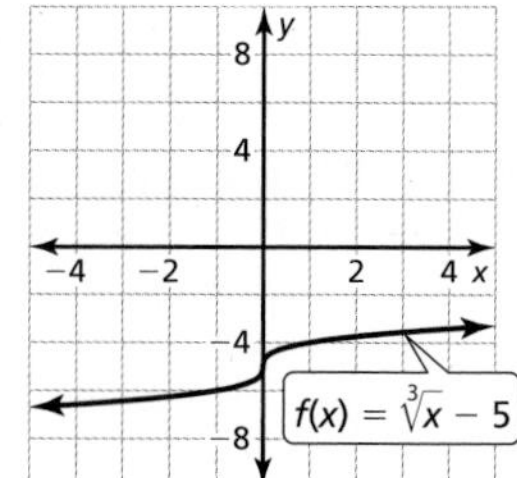

all real numbers; all real numbers; The graph of f is a translation 5 units down of the graph of g.

4.

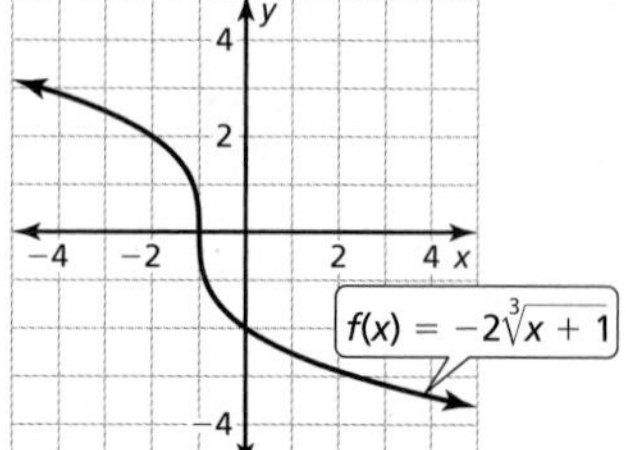

all real numbers; all real numbers; The graph of f is a vertical stretch by a factor of 2, a reflection in the x-axis, and a translation 1 unit left of the graph of g.

5. $x = 36$

6. $x = 8$

7. $x = 3$

8. $x = 4$

9. $g(x) = \dfrac{x + 8}{5}$

10. $g(x) = \left(\dfrac{x + 1}{2}\right)^2 - 3, x \geq -1$

11. $g(x) = \sqrt{12 - 3x}$

12. The solution $x = 3$ is extraneous, because it gives a value of $3 - 5 = -2$ on the left side, which cannot equal the radical expression on the right side of the equation.

13. The graph of v is a translation 3 units up of the graph of f; $k = 3$

14. The graph of p is a translation 1 unit left of the graph of f; $h = -1$

15. The graph of g is a vertical stretch by a factor of 2 and a reflection in the x-axis of the graph of f; $a = -2$

16. a.

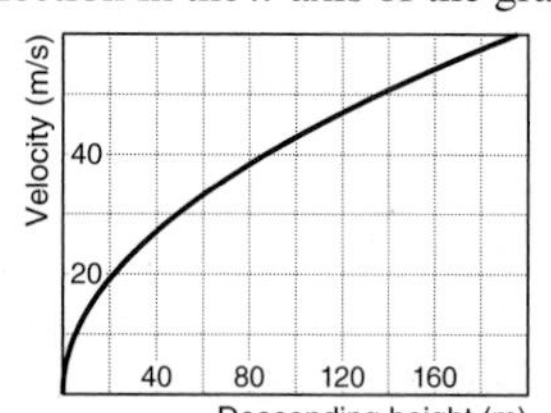

b. about 93.6 m

c. As the height of the hill increases, the average rate of change of the velocity decreases.

17. 5.5 sec

18. $(-4, 2), (4, 6)$

Chapter 10 College and Career Readiness

1. −; 1; 2

2. a. *Sample answer:* $-\frac{1}{6}$; $\frac{23}{6}$

b. *Sample answer:* $\frac{1}{2}$; -4

c. $-\frac{1}{4}$; $\frac{25}{4}$

3. B
4. A
5. $-3, 6$
6. The graph of g is always increasing; The average rate of change of g is greater than the average rate of change of f over the interval $x = 0$ to $x = 8$.
7. a. $8x + 56$
   b. $4x^2 + 56x + 192$
   c. 1, 1.5, 2, 2.5
8. D
9. $y = 11.2x + 112$; The slope, 11.2, represents the change in the average number of daily campsite reservations at the park each year, and the intercept, 112, shows the average number of daily campsite reservations when the park opened.
10. A

Chapter 11

Chapter 11 Prepare

1. 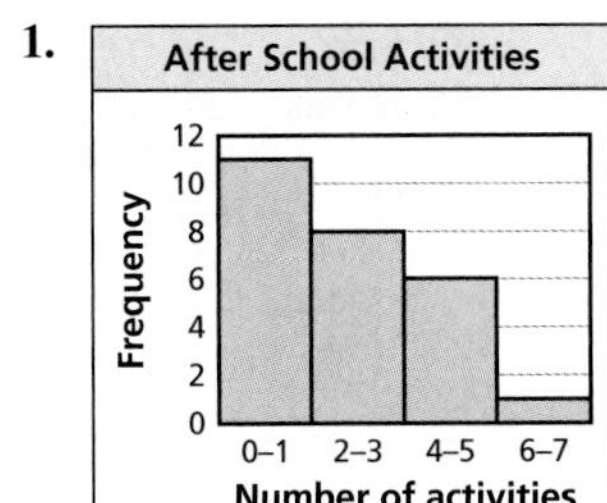

2. 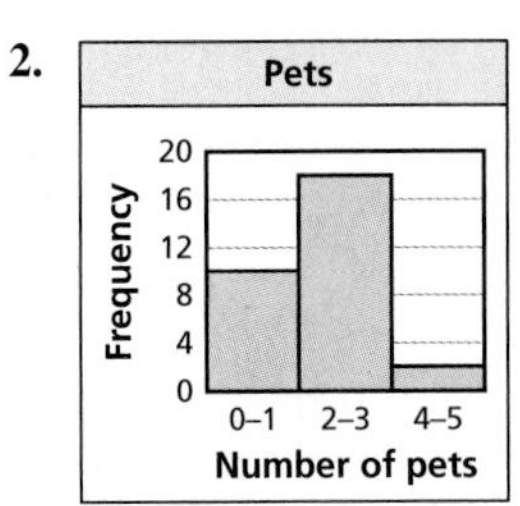

3. 40%
4. 80
5. 96
6. 200%
7. $133\frac{1}{3}\%$; If $0.75y = x$, then $y = \frac{4}{3}x$.

11.1 Practice

1. a. mean: 4, median: 3, mode: 1
   b. median; The mean is greater than most of the data and the mode is less than most of the data.
3. a. mean: 22, median: 21, mode: none
   b. mean and median; Both are about the same and in the middle of the data.
5. a. mean: about 1.96, median: 2, modes: $1\frac{2}{3}$ and 2
   b. mean and median; Both are about the same and in the middle of the data.
7. 4
9. 16
11. a. 62; The outlier decreases the mean and median and does not affect the mode.
    b. *Sample answer:* The outlier could be the mass of a baby polar bear.
13. Golfer A: 15; Golfer B: 8; The range for Golfer A is greater.
15. a. 25
    b. about 9.27
17. a. 2
    b. about 0.65
19. a. about 4.6; The typical score differs from the mean by about 4.6 points.
    b. about 2.5; The typical score differs from the mean by about 2.5 points.
    c. The standard deviation for Golfer A is greater, so the scores are more spread out.
21. mean: 76, median: 69, mode: 63, range: 46, standard deviation: 15.5
23. \$10; \$10
25. When a number is added to each value in a data set, the range stays the same; The range is 26.
27. Both processes involve comparing the mean to each data value and dividing by the number of values in the data set.
29. mean: 89, median: 104, mode: 62, range: 123, standard deviation: 27
31. C, D
33. a. Answers will vary.
    b. *Sample answer:* The mean, median, range, and standard deviation increase.
35. a. mean: 16.5, median: 16, mode: 16
    b. 30; It increases the mean, but does not affect the median or mode.
    c. mean: 18.5, median: 18, mode: 18

11.1 Review & Refresh

36. $x \le -5$

−8 −7 −6 −5 −4 −3

37. all real numbers

−8 −4 0 4 8

38. no solution
39. $w < \frac{3}{2}$

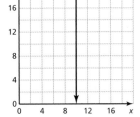

$\frac{3}{2}$

−2 −1 0 1 2 3

40. 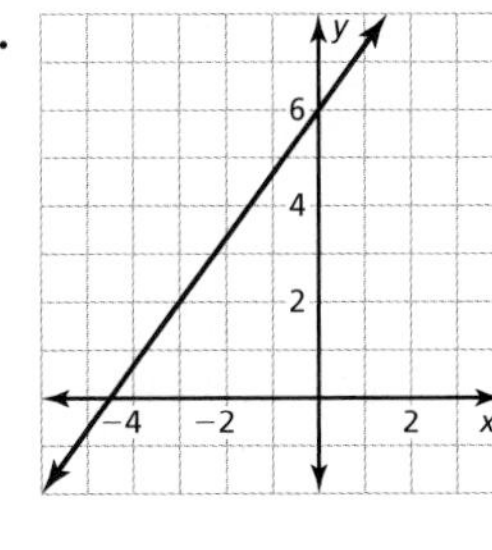

41. y 6 4 2 −4 −2 2 x

42. 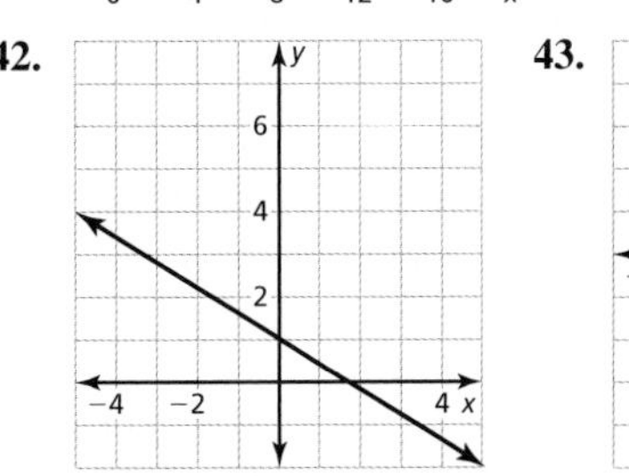

43. 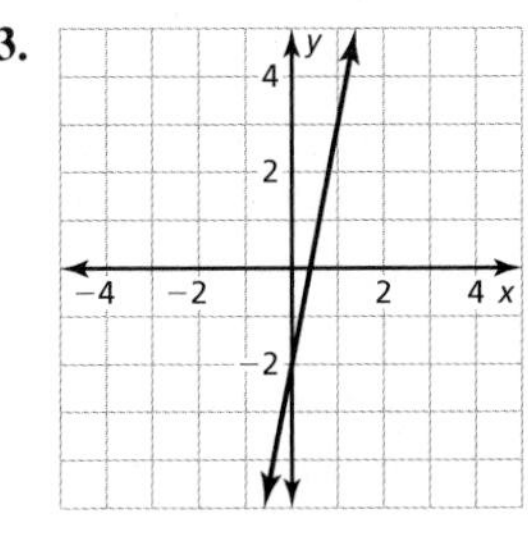

44. Input: 6, 1, 0, −2, −5; Output: −10, −7, −1, 2, 3
45. length: 10 ft, width: 4 ft
46. $\frac{1}{49}$
47. −162

48.

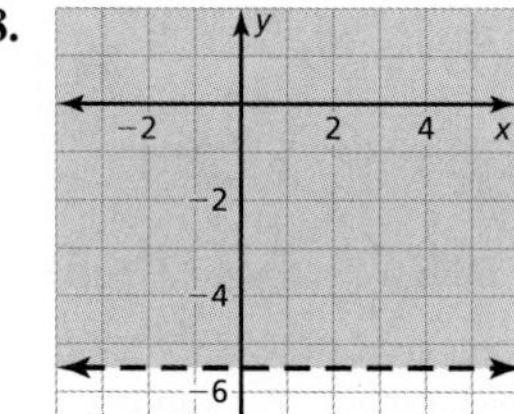

49.

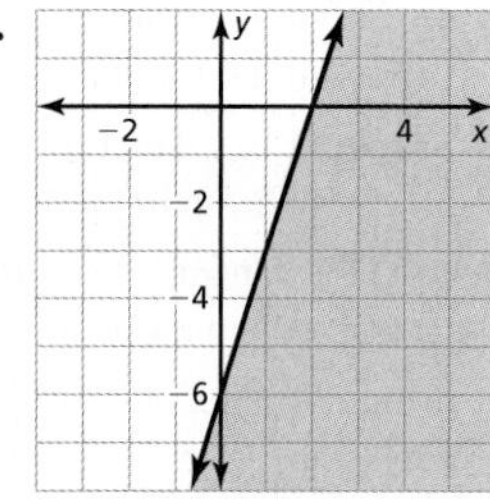

50. *Sample answer:* $g(x) = -\sqrt[3]{x-3}$

51. mean: 105, median: 104, mode: none, range: 10, standard deviation: about 3.58

52. mean: 32.5, median: 34, mode: 21, range: 23, standard deviation: about 8.96

53. The function is positive when $-5 < x < -2$ and $x > -2$ and negative when $x < -5$. The function is increasing when $x < -4$ and $x > -2$ and decreasing when $-4 < x < -2$. $y \to -\infty$ as $x \to -\infty$, and $y \to +\infty$ as $x \to +\infty$.

54. $x = 39$

55. no real solution

56. Lines a and c are perpendicular; The slope of Line a is -7, and the slope of Line c is $\frac{1}{7}$, which are opposite reciprocals.

11.2 Practice

1. 3

3. 11

5. 8

7.

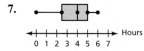

Hours

9.

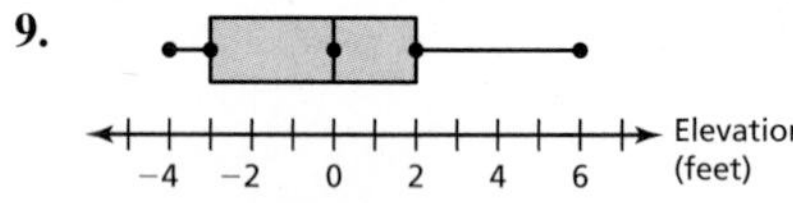

11.

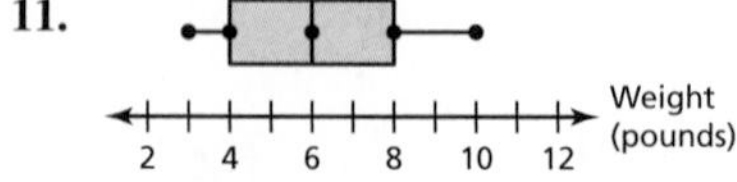

13.

Hours

15. **a.** 9.5; The prices vary by no more than \$9.50.

b. 25% of the prices are between \$8.75 and \$10.50, 50% of the prices are between \$10.50 and \$14.75, and 25% of the prices are between \$14.75 and \$18.25.

c. 4.25; The middle half of the prices vary by no more than \$4.25.

d. above Q3; the whisker is longer

17. **a.** Sales Rep A: symmetric; Sales Rep B: skewed right

b. Sales Rep B; The range and interquartile range are greater.

c. Sales Rep B; The least value is 4.

19. The median is the average of the two middle values 13 and 14, so Q2 should be 13.5.

21. range: 36, interquartile range: 12; The range is greater.

23. **a.**

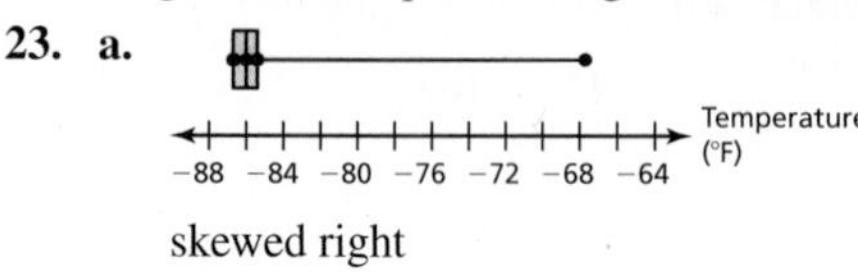

skewed right

b. -67.7

25. **a.** Both distributions are skewed right.

b. Brand A: 3.5, Brand B: 2.5

c. The interquartile range of Brand A is greater.

d. Brand A; The range is greater.

e. Brand A; 75% of the battery lives are greater than 5.5 hours.

27. yes; *Sample answer:*

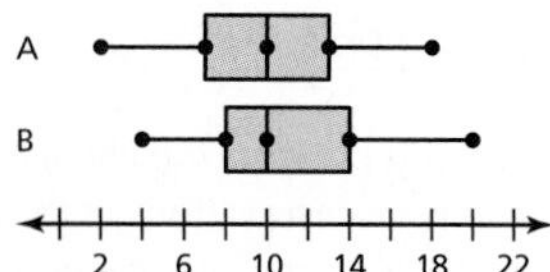

11.2 Review & Refresh

29. $y = 36$

30. $z = \frac{4}{3}$

31. $n = -11$

32. $p = 1$

33.

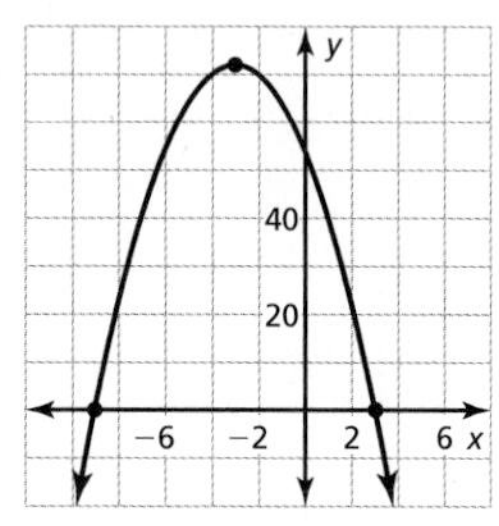

34.

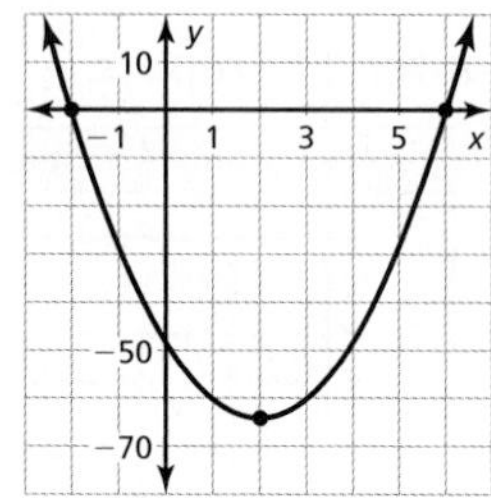

35. C

36. A

37. D

38. B

39. mean: 66, median: 68, mode: 54; mean and median

40. $g(x) = -4x + 24$

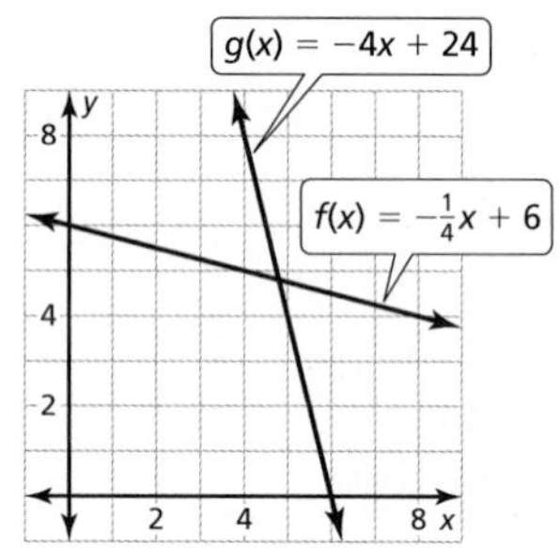

41. $g(x) = \sqrt{\frac{x+8}{2}}$

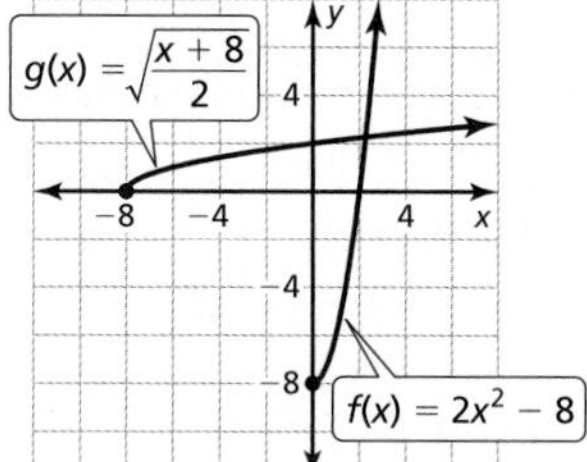

42. yes; Each input is paired with exactly one output.

43. $k \le 6$

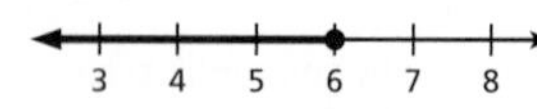

44. $z < 4$

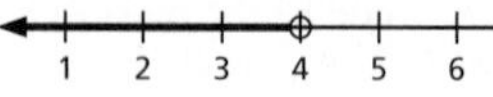

45. a.

10 20 30 40 50 60 Time (minutes)

skewed right

b. yes, 57

46. $\frac{4}{x}$

47. $\frac{\sqrt{3}}{3}$

48. $\frac{3a^2b\sqrt[3]{a}}{7}$

49. $\frac{4\sqrt{11} - \sqrt{33}}{13}$

50. $-d^2 + 11d + 3$

51. $5g^3 + 2g^2 - 3g - 18$

11.3 Practice

1.

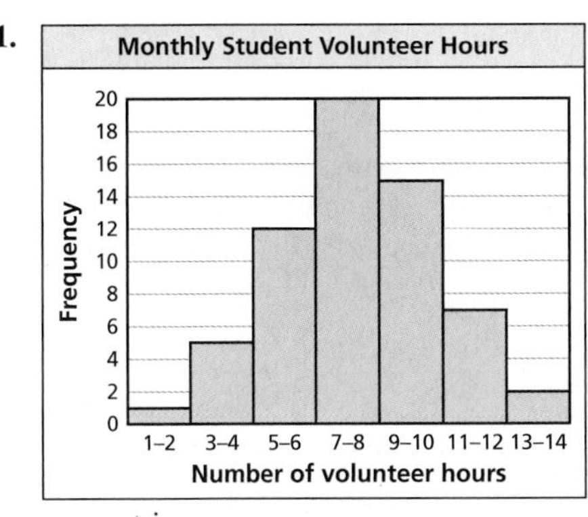

symmetric

3. skewed right; Most of the data are on the first two stems.

5. mean, standard deviation; The distribution is symmetric.

7. a.

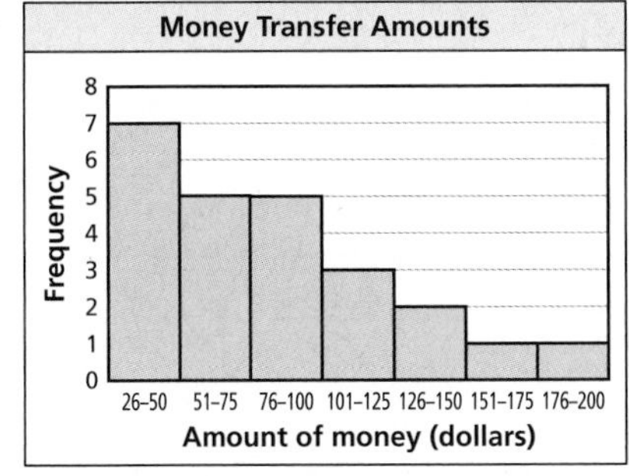

b. median, five-number summary; The distribution is skewed right.

9. histogram; You do not need to list every value.

11. When most of the data are on the right, the distribution is skewed left, not right.

13. *Sample answer:* salaries of employees at a large company

15. Town A usually has a greater daily high temperature, and the daily high temperature tends to differ more for town B.

17. a.

Teenagers

Adults

200 500 800 1100 1400 1700 2000 2300 Amount of storage (megabytes)

The distribution of data for teenagers is symmetric. The distribution of data for adults is skewed left.

b. The amount if storage used by teenagers tends to be less than the amount of storage used by adults.

c. about 31 teenagers; about 95 teenagers

19. symmetric; yes; The measures of center and variation double.

21. a.

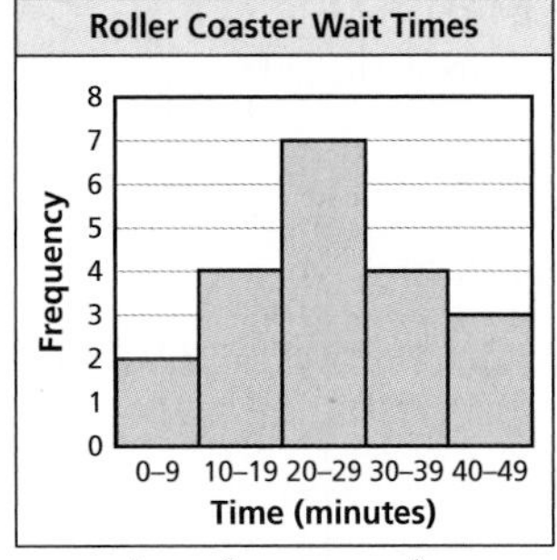

approximately symmetric

b.

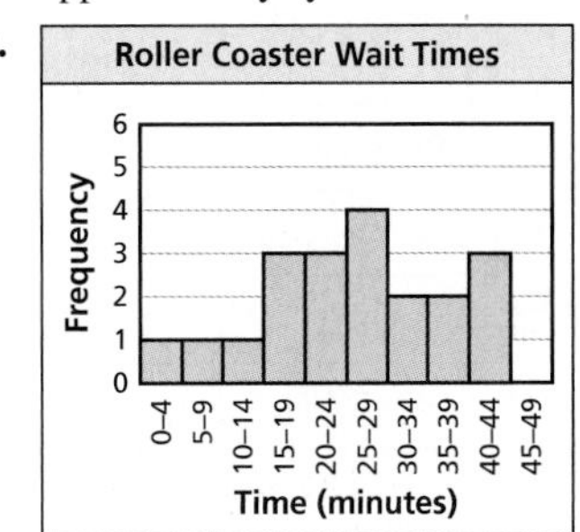

The distribution becomes skewed left.

c. part (b); More intervals show the spread of the data better.

11.3 Review & Refresh

23. $x \geq -6$

24. $x \geq 0$

25. domain: $0 \leq t \leq 2$, range: $0 \leq h \leq 18$; 18 ft

26.

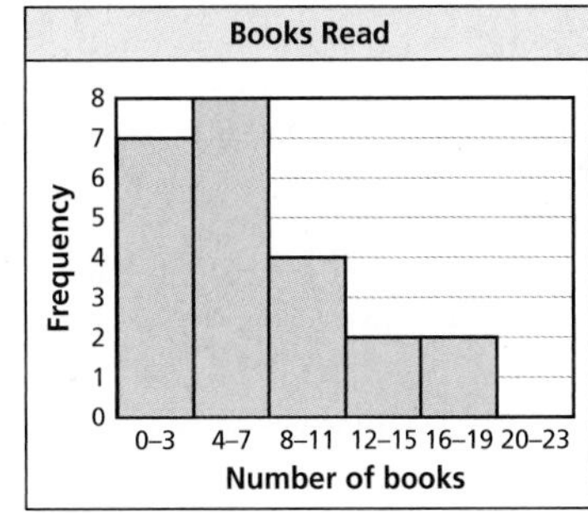

skewed right

27. $(-5)^5$

28. $81z^{32}$

29. n^3

30. $\frac{d^5}{4c^2b^3}$

31.

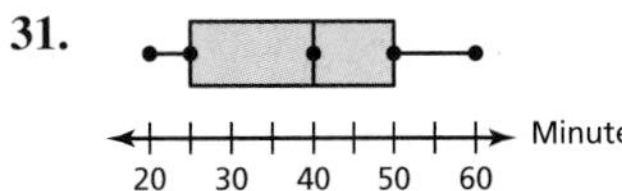

32. Input: 9, 8, 7, 6, 5; Output: $-3, -1, 1, 3, 5$

33. no real solution

34. $k = -\frac{4}{7}, k = 2$

35. $x = -1$

36. $x = -3$

37. yes; yes; The longer the school concert the more time that will be spent practicing.

38. female; range $= 4$, standard deviation ≈ 1.3; male: range $= 6$, standard deviation ≈ 1.9; Male absences are more spread out.

11.4 Practice

1. 178

3. 208

5. 310 students have set academic goals, 118 students have not set academic goals, 232 males responded, 196 females responded, 428 students were surveyed.

7. 244 students rated good, 90 students rated fair, 120 students rated poor, 224 males responded, 230 females responded, 454 students were surveyed.

9. 90; 152; 16; 200; 78

11.

		Spanish Class		
		Yes	No	Total
French Class	Yes	45	54	99
	No	64	82	146
	Total	109	136	245

13.

		Exercise Preference		
		Aerobic	Anaerobic	Total
Gender	Male	0.25	0.31	0.56
	Female	0.27	0.17	0.44
	Total	0.52	0.48	1

15. 52%; 31%

17. This number is only the number of freshmen who participated in the fundraiser; 272 freshmen responded to the survey.

19. a.

		Exercise Preference	
		Aerobic	Anaerobic
Gender	Male	0.45	0.55
	Female	0.61	0.39

b. about 61%

21. yes; About 85% of students who live off campus have a car and about 75% of students who live on campus do not have a car.

23. no; There is no trend in the conditional relative frequencies, so there is no association.

25. Answers will vary. Check students' work.

27.

		Seat Location		
		Main Floor	Balcony	Total
Ticket Type	Adult	$2x + y$	$x + 2y$	$3x + 3y$
	Child	$x - 40$	$3x - y - 80$	$4x - y - 120$
	Total	800	1009	1809

about 57%; about 73%

11.4 Review & Refresh

29. a. 55; The wait times vary by no more than 55 minutes.

b. 15; The middle half of the wait times vary by no more than 15 minutes.

c. below Q1; The left whisker is longer than the right.

30. exponential

31. quadratic

32. Increased by 40%: mean: 16.8, median: 19, mode 16.2, range: 25.2, standard deviation: 8.4

Increased by 5: mean: 21.8, median: 19, mode: 16.2, range: 25.2, standard deviation: 8.4

33. 2

34. 0

35.

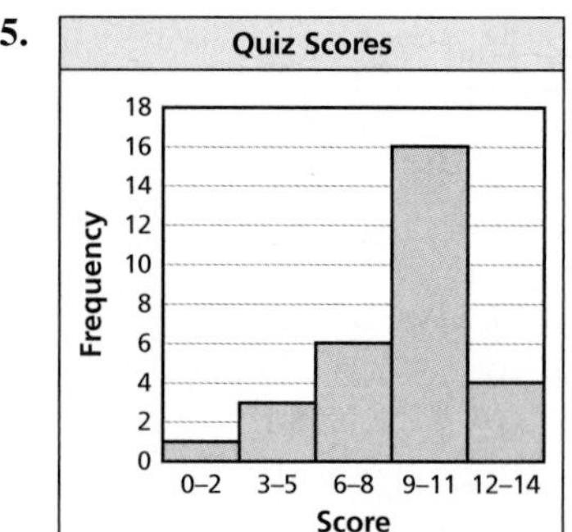

skewed left

36. $h = -\frac{4}{3}, h = 13$

37. $a_n = -13n + 49; -107$

38. $a_n = 7n - 19; 65$

39. 28 people have visited a foreign country, 122 people have not visited a foreign country, 70 people ages 14–15 responded, 80 people ages 16–17 responded, 150 people were surveyed

		Visited a Foreign Country		
		Yes	No	Total
Age	14-15	0.07	0.4	0.47
	16-17	0.12	0.41	0.53
	Total	0.19	0.81	1

40. $x = 4$

41. $x = -2, x = 1$

11.5 Practice

1. qualitative; Brands of cars are nonnumerical.

3. quantitative; Budgets are numerical values.

5. quantitative; Shoe sizes are numerical values.

7. *Sample answer:* line graph; It shows data values over time.

9. *Sample answer:* bar graph; It shows data in each specific category.

11. *Sample answer:*

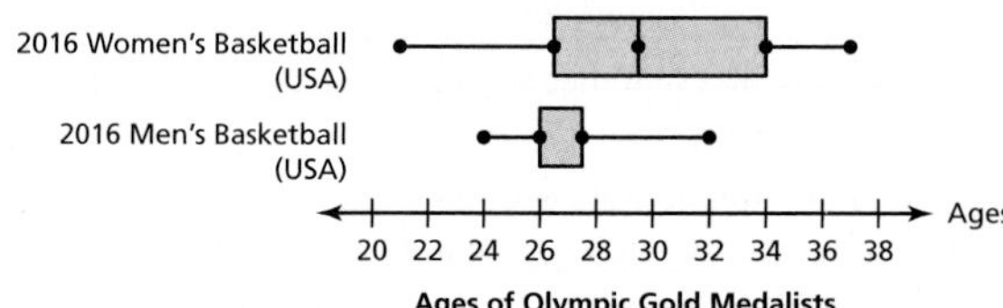

A box-and-whisker plot uses the five-number summary of each data set to display the quantitative data.

13. *Sample answer:*

Grades (out of 100) on a Test

Stem	Leaf
5	2 3 9
6	2 3
7	4 5 7
8	0 1 3 4 5 7 8 9
9	5 6 7
10	0

Key: 5 | 3 = 53 out of 100

A stem-and-leaf plot shows how the grades are distributed.

15. *Sample answer:*

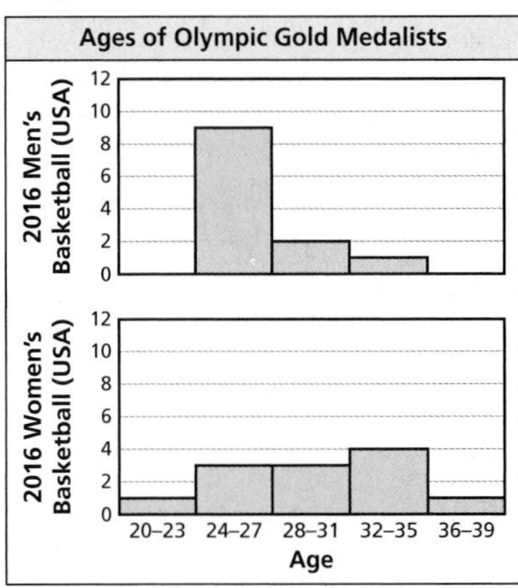

17. *Sample answer:*

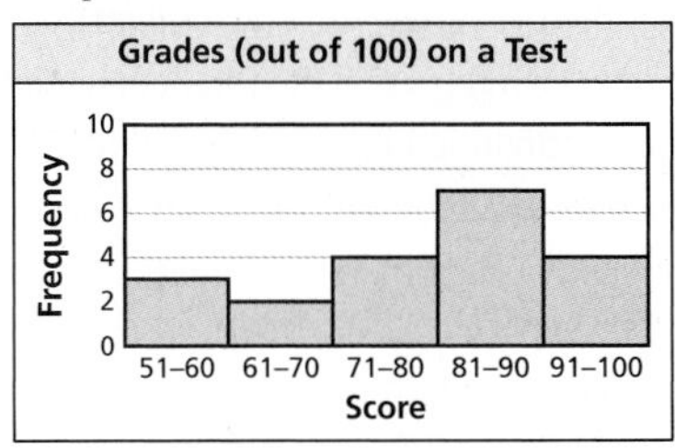

19. The scale on the vertical axis has very small increments; Someone might believe that the annual sales more than tripled from 2017 to 2020.

21. *Sample answer:*

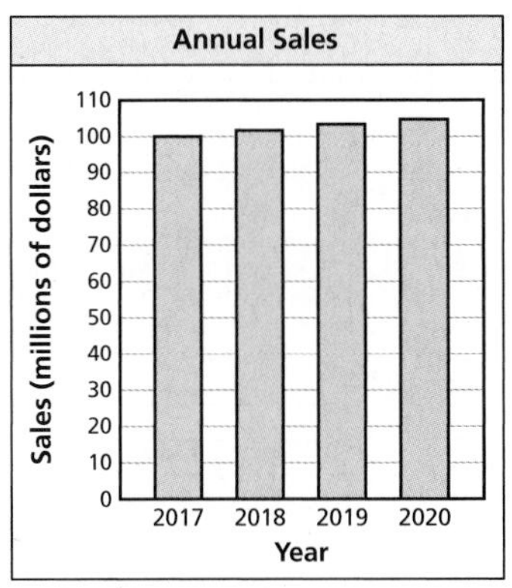

23. histogram; The data are quantitative, not qualitative.

25. dot plot, pictograph, bar graph, stem-and-leaf plot

27. *Sample answer:*

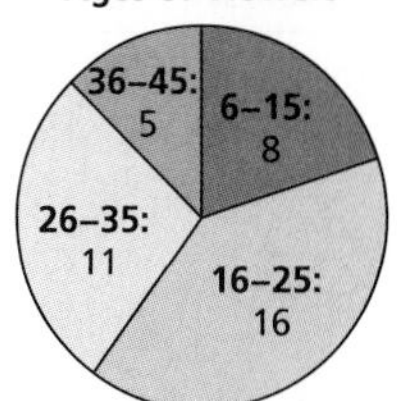

yes; 40% of the viewers are 16–25 years old.

11.5 Review & Refresh

28. no; The input, −5, has two outputs, −1 and 1.

29. yes; Every input has exactly one output.

30. mean and median; The data distribution is more symmetric than it is skewed.

31. $(x - 10)(x + 3)$

32. $(x - 8)^2$

33. $(4x - 1)(x + 7)$

34. $(x - 9)(x^2 - 2)$

35. no; A box-and-whisker plot shows the distribution of the data set but does not show the actual values.

36.

		Class		
		Freshman	Sophomore	Total
Candidates	Candidate A	23	29	52
	Candidate B	27	41	68
	Total	50	70	120

37. (2, 0); Explanations will vary.

38. no solution; Explanations will vary.

39. The graph of g is a vertical translation 4 units up of the graph of f.

40. The graph of g is a reflection in the y-axis of the graph of f.

41. *Sample answer:*

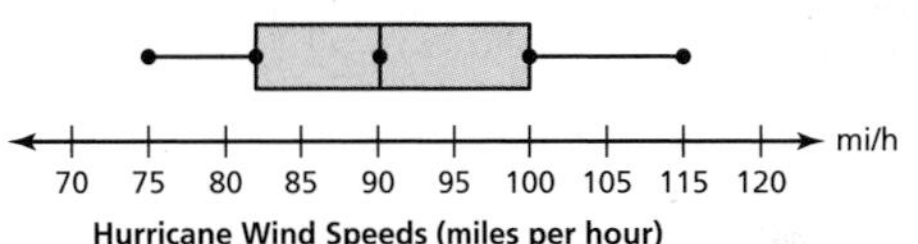

A box-and-whisker plot shows how the wind speeds are distributed.

Chapter 11 Review

1. mean: 1.7, median: 1, mode: 1

2. mean: 4, median: 3, mode: 10

3. a. mean: 3.7, median: 4.05, mode: 4.3
   b. 1.0; It decreases the mean and median, but does not affect the mode.

4. Player A: range = 45, standard deviation: ≈ 13.56; Player B: range = 86, standard deviation ≈ 31.24; The scores for Player B are more spread out.

5. Store A: range = \$110, standard deviation ≈ \$39.37; Store B: range = \$150, standard deviation ≈ \$48.09; The prices at Store B are more spread out.

6. mean: 134, median: 129, mode: 121, range: 45, standard deviation: 3.6

7. mean: 65.4, median: 62.4, mode: 57.6, range: 27, standard deviation: 2.16

8. 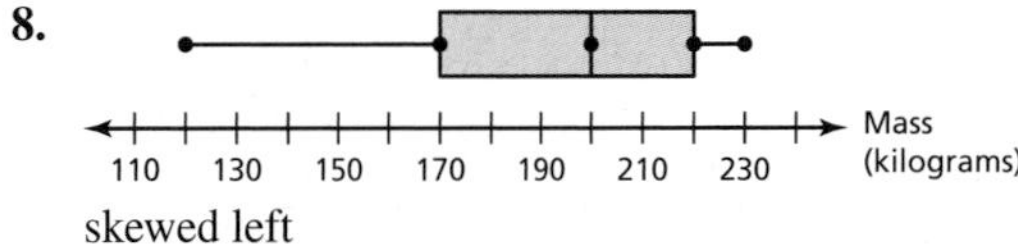

skewed left

9. 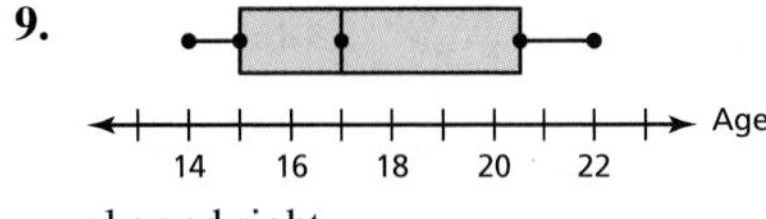

skewed right

10. a. 9; The weights vary by no more than 9 pounds.
    b. skewed right
    c. 4; The middle half of the weights vary by no more than 4 pounds.
    d. above Q3; The right whisker is longer.

11. a. 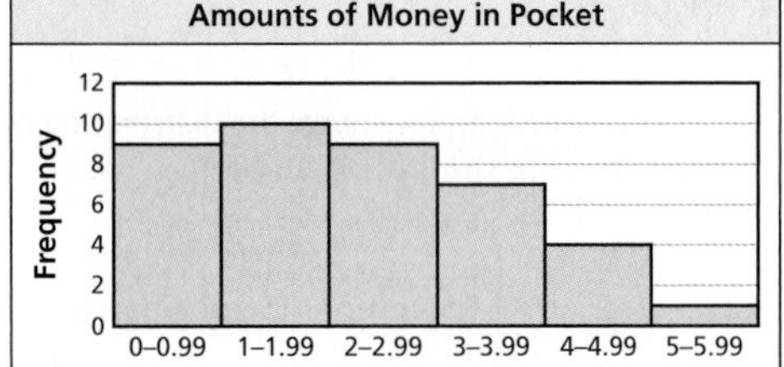

skewed right; median, five-number summary

b. The adults typically have more money in their pockets and the amounts vary more.

12. mean: 32, standard deviation: 4; The graph is symmetric, so the mean is in the middle of the data and 95% of data falls between 2 standard deviations of the mean.

13. a. greater than; The distribution is skewed right.

b. less than; The distribution is skewed left.

14.

		New Food Court		
		Like	Dislike	Total
Age	Teenagers	96	4	100
	Adults	21	79	100
	Total	117	83	200

15.

		New Food Court		
		Like	Dislike	Total
Age	Teenagers	0.48	0.02	0.50
	Adults	0.105	0.395	0.50
	Total	0.585	0.415	1

16.

		New Food Court	
		Like	Dislike
Age	Teenagers	0.82	0.05
	Adults	0.18	0.95

17. yes; As age increases people are less likely to see the movie.

18. *Sample answer:*

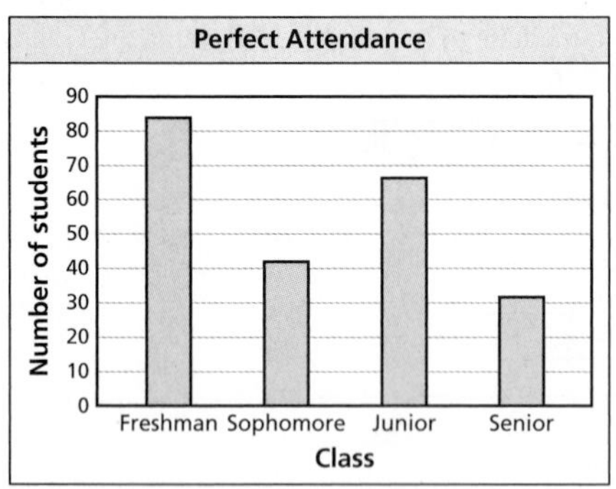

A bar graph shows data in specific categories.

19. *Sample answer:* box-and-whisker plot; A box-and-whisker plot uses the five-number summary of each data set to display the quantitative data.

20. *Sample answer:* circle graph; A circle graph shows the data as parts of a whole.

Chapter 11 Mathematical Practices (Chapter Review)

1. *Sample answer:* More freshman were surveyed. About 50% of freshman plan to participate in spirit week. About 21% of students are undecided whether they will participate in spirit week or not. About 46% of the students in the survey were sophomores.

2. *Sample answer:* line graph and box-and-whisker plot; A line graph shows the change in the number of books read each year. A box-and-whisker plot shows the distribution of the data.

Chapter 11 Practice Test

1. symmetric; mean, standard deviation

2. skewed right; median, five-number summary

3. skewed left; median, five-number summary

4. a. always; The marginal frequencies in the "total" row and the "total" column each represent the total population.

b. sometimes; The distribution might not be symmetric.

c. sometimes; Telephone numbers are qualitative data.

5. mean = \$15.00, median ≈ \$13.88, mode: none, range = \$15.70, standard deviation ≈ \$5.46

6. mean = \$12.00, median ≈ \$11.10, mode: none, range = \$12.56, standard deviation ≈ \$4.37

7. a. 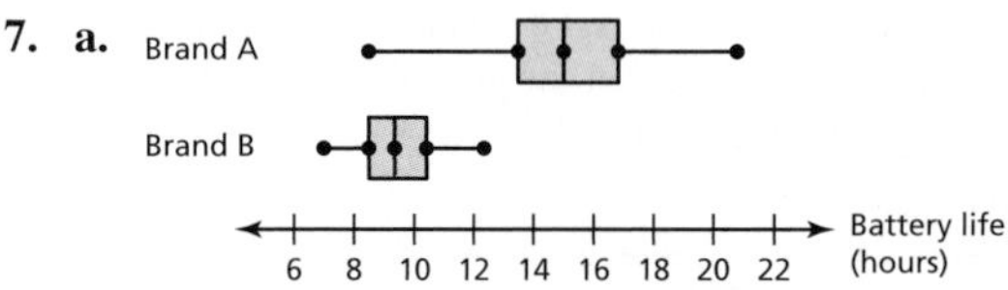

b. Brand A: approximately symmetric; Brand B: skewed right

c. Brand A: The range and interquartile range of the Brand A data are greater.

d. The battery life for Brand A is longer and varies more.

8. *Sample answer:*

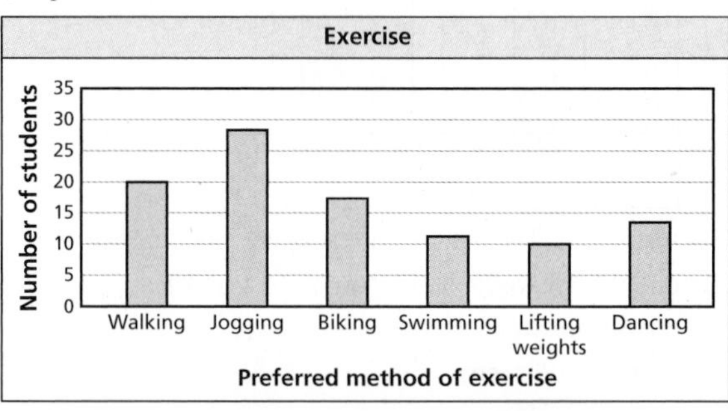

A bar graph shows data in specific categories.

9. a.

		Attending Field Trip		
		Yes	No	Total
Gender	Male	92	29	121
	Female	119	31	150
	Total	211	60	271

211 students are attending the field trip, 60 students are not attending the field trip, 121 males responded, 150 females responded, 271 students were surveyed.

b. about 79.3%

10. mean: 7.5, standard deviation: 3.2

Chapter 11 College and Career Readiness

1. A, D
2. a. yes; $f(x)$ eventually increases more rapidly than $h(x)$.
   b. yes; $g(x)$ eventually increases more rapidly than $f(x)$.
   c. yes; $g(x)$ eventually increases more rapidly than $h(x)$.
3. A
4. a. 38
   b. 46
   c. 63
   d. 99
5. $y = -3x^2, x \geq 0, y = \sqrt{-\frac{1}{3}x}$; $y = -x + 7, y = -x + 7$; $y = 2x - 4, y = \frac{1}{2}x + 2$; $y = x^2 - 5, x \geq 0, y = \sqrt{x + 5}$
6. -3; -2
7. C
8. D, E, F, G, H
9. B
10. a. 500; The traveler is about 500 feet from the starting point after 2 minutes.
    b. $x = 15$; It takes the traveler 15 minutes to travel 3500 feet.
    c. 8 min
    d. 2000 ft
    e. 1500 ft

English-Spanish Glossary

English / Spanish

A

absolute deviation *(p. 98)* The absolute value of the difference of a number x and a given value.

desviación absoluta *(p. 98)* El valor absoluto de la diferencia entre un número x y un valor dado

absolute value equation *(p. 38)* An equation that contains an absolute value expression.

ecuación de valor absoluto *(p. 38)* Una ecuación que contiene una expresión de valor absoluto

absolute value function *(p. 168)* A function that contains an absolute value expression.

función de valor absoluto *(p. 168)* Una función que contiene una expresión de valor absoluto

absolute value inequality *(p. 96)* An inequality that contains an absolute value expression.

desigualdad de valor absoluto *(p. 96)* Una desigualdad que contiene una expresión de valor absoluto

accuracy *(p. 27)* How close a measured value is to the actual value

exactitud *(p. 27)* Cuánto se aproxima un valor medido al valor real

arithmetic sequence *(p. 220)* An ordered list of numbers in which the difference between each pair of consecutive terms is the same.

secuencia aritmética *(p. 220)* Una lista ordenada de números en donde la diferencia entre cada par de términos consecutivos es la misma

asymptote *(p. 315)* A line that a graph approaches more and more closely

asíntota *(p. 315)* Una línea a la cual un gráfico se cerca cada vez más

average rate of change *(p. 467)* The slope of the line through $(a, f(a))$ and $(b, f(b))$ of a function $y = f(x)$ between $x = a$ and $x = b$.

tasa de variación media *(p. 467)* La pendiente de la línea a través de $(a, f(a))$ y $(b, f(b))$ de una función $y = f(x)$ entre $x = a$ y $x = b$

axis of symmetry *(p. 426)* The vertical line that divides a parabola into two symmetric parts.

eje de simetría *(p. 426)* La línea vertical que divide una parábola en dos partes simétricas

B

binomial *(p. 365)* A polynomial with two terms

binomio *(p. 365)* Un polinomio con dos términoso

box-and-whisker plot *(p. 596)* A graph that shows the variability of a data set along a number line using the least value, the greatest value, and the quartiles of the data

diagrama de cajas y bigotes *(p. 596)* Un gráfico que muestra la variabilidad de un conjunto de datos a lo largo de una línea de números usando el valor menor, el valor mayor y los cuartiles de los datos

C

categorical data *(p. 620)* Data that consist of labels or nonnumerical entries that can be separated into different categories

datos categóricos *(p. 620)* Datos que consisten en etiquetas o valores no numéricos que pueden separarse en categorías distintas

causation *(p. 215)* When a change in one variable causes a change in another variable

causalidad *(p. 215)* Cuando un cambio en una variable causa un cambio en otra variable

closed *(p. 366)* When an operation performed on any two numbers in the set results in a number that is also in the set

operación interna *(p. 366)* Cuando una operación efectuada en dos números cualesquiera del conjunto da como resultado un número que también está en el conjunto

common difference *(p. 220)* The difference between each pair of consecutive terms in an arithmetic sequence

diferencia común *(p. 220)* La diferencia entre cada par de términos consecutivos en una secuencia aritmética

common ratio *(p. 338)* The ratio between each pair of consecutive terms in a geometric sequence

razón común *(p. 338)* La razón entre cada par de términos consecutivos en una secuencia geométrica

completing the square *(p. 510)* To add a constant c to an expression of the form $x^2 + bx$ so that $x^2 + bx + c$ is a perfect square trinomial

completando el cuadrado *(p. 510)* Agregar una constante c a una expresión de la forma $x^2 + bx$ para que $x^2 + bx + c$ sea un trinomio de cuadrado perfecto

compound inequality *(p. 90)* An inequality formed by joining two inequalities with the word "and" or the word "or"

desigualdad compuesta *(p. 90)* Una desigualdad formada por dos desigualdades con la palabra "y" o la palabra "o"

compound interest *(p. 325)* The interest earned on the principal and on previously earned interest

interés compuesto *(p. 325)* El interés obtenido en el principal y en intereses previamente obtenidos

conditional relative frequency *(p. 614)* The ratio of a joint relative frequency to the marginal relative frequency

frecuencia relativa condicional *(p. 614)* La razón de una frecuencia relativa conjunta a una frecuencia relativa marginal

conjugates *(p. 486)* Binomials of the form $a\sqrt{b} + c\sqrt{d}$ and $a\sqrt{b} - c\sqrt{d}$, where a, b, c, and d are rational numbers

conjugados *(p. 486)* Binomios de la forma $a\sqrt{b} + c\sqrt{d}$ y $a\sqrt{b} - c\sqrt{d}$, donde a, b, c y d son números racionales

constant function *(p. 150)* A linear equation written in the form $y = 0x + b$ or $y = b$

función constante *(p. 150)* Una ecuación lineal escrita bajo la forma $y = 0x + b$ o $y = b$

continuous domain *(p. 128)* A set of input values that consists of all numbers in an interval

dominio continuo *(p. 128)* Un conjunto de valores que consiste en todos los números en un intervalo

correlation *(p. 207)* A relationship between data sets

correlación *(p. 207)* Una relación entre conjuntos de datos

correlation coefficient *(p. 213)* A value r that tells how closely the equation of the line of best fit models the data

coeficiente de correlación *(p. 213)* Un valor r que indica cuán fielmente la ecuación de la línea de mejor ajuste modela los datos

cube root function *(p. 556)* A radical function with an index of 3

función de raíz cúbica *(p. 556)* Una función radical con un índice de 3

data transformation *(p. 591)* A procedure that uses a mathematical operation to change a data set into a different data set

transformación de datos *(p. 591)* Un procedimiento que usa una operación matemática para cambiar un conjunto de datos en un conjunto de datos diferentes

decreasing *(p. 121)* A function's graph moves down as x moves to the right

en disminución *(p. 121)* Una función cuyo gráfico desciende a medida que x avanza hacia la derecha

degree of a monomial *(p. 364)* The sum of the exponents of the variables in the monomial

grado de un monomio *(p. 364)* La suma de los exponentes de las variables en el monomio

degree of a polynomial *(p. 365)* The greatest degree of the terms in a polynomial

grado de un polinomio *(p. 365)* El grado mayor de los términos en un polinomio

dependent variable *(p. 115)* The variable that represents the output values of a function

variable dependiente *(p. 115)* La variable que representa los resultados de una función

discrete domain *(p. 128)* A set of input values that consists of only certain numbers in an interval

dominio discreto *(p. 128)* Un conjunto de valores que consiste en solamente ciertos números en un intervalo

discriminant *(p. 522)* The expression $b^2 - 4ac$ in the Quadratic Formula

discriminante *(p. 522)* La expresión $b^2 - 4ac$ en la Fórmula Cuadrática

domain *(p. 114)* The set of all possible input values of a function

dominio *(p. 114)* El conjunto de todos los valores de entrada posibles de una función

GLOSSARY

end behavior *(p. 121)* The behavior of the graph of a function as x approaches positive infinity $(+\infty)$ or negative infinity $(-\infty)$

comportamiento de extremo *(p. 121)* El comportamiento del gráfico de una función según x se aproxima al infinito positivo $(+\infty)$ o al infinto negativo $(-\infty)$

equation *(p. 4)* A statement that two expressions are equal

ecuación *(p. 4)* Una afirmación de que dos expresiones son iguales

equivalent equations *(p. 4)* Equations that have the same solution(s)

ecuaciones equivalentes *(p. 4)* Ecuaciones que tienen las mismas soluciones

equivalent inequalities *(p. 72)* Inequalities that have the same solutions

desigualdades equivalentes *(p. 72)* Desigualdades que tienen las mismas soluciones

even function *(p. 446)* A function $y = f(x)$ is even when $f(-x) = f(x)$ for each x in the domain of f.

par función *(p. 446)* Una función $y = f(x)$ es par cuando $f(-x) = f(x)$ para cada x en el dominio de f.

explicit rule *(p. 346)* A rule to define arithmetic and geometric sequences that gives a_n as a function of the term's position number n in the sequence

regla explícita *(p. 346)* Una regla para definir secuencias aritméticas y geométricas que da a_n como función del número de posición del término n en la secuencia

exponential decay *(p. 323)* When a quantity decreases by the same factor over equal intervals

decaimiento exponencial *(p. 323)* Cuando una cantidad disminuye por el mismo factor sobre intervalos iguales

exponential decay function *(p. 323)* A function of the form $y = a(1 - r)^x$, where $a > 0$ and $0 < r < 1$

función de decaimiento exponencial *(p. 323)* Una función de la forma $y = a(1 - r)^x$, donde $a > 0$ y $0 < r < 1$

exponential equation *(p. 332)* An equation in which variable expressions occur as exponents

ecuación exponencial *(p. 332)* Una ecuación en donde las expresiones de una variable ocurren como exponentes

exponential function *(p. 314)* A nonlinear function of the form $y = ab^x$, where $a \neq 0$, $b \neq 1$, and $b > 0$

función exponencial *(p. 314)* Una función no lineal de la forma $y = ab^x$, donde $a \neq 0$, $b \neq 1$, y $b > 0$

exponential growth *(p. 322)* When a quantity increases by the same factor over equal intervals

crecimiento exponencial *(p. 322)* Cuando una cantidad se incrementa por el mismo factor sobre intervalos iguales

exponential growth function *(p. 322)* A function of the form $y = a(1 + r)^x$, where $a > 0$ and $r > 0$

función de crecimiento exponencial *(p. 322)* Una función de la forma $y = a(1 + r)^x$, donde $a > 0$ y $r > 0$

extraneous solution *(p. 41)* An apparent solution that must be rejected because it does not satisfy the original equation

solución extraña *(p. 41)* Una solución aparente que debe ser rechazada porque no satisface la ecuación original

extrapolation *(p. 215)* To predict a value outside the range of known values using a graph or its equation

extrapolación *(p. 215)* Predecir un valor fuera del rango de valores conocidos usando un gráfico o su ecuación

F

factored completely *(p. 410)* A polynomial that is written as a product of unfactorable polynomials with integer coefficients

factorizado completamente *(p. 410)* Un polinomio que se escribe como un producto de polinomios no factorizables con coeficientes de números enteros

factored form *(p. 386)* A polynomial that is written as a product of factors

forma factorizada *(p. 386)* Un polinomio que se escribe como un producto de factores

factoring by grouping *(p. 410)* To use the Distributive Property to factor a polynomial with four terms

factorización por agrupamiento *(p. 410)* Uso de la propiedad distributiva para factorizar un polinomio con cuatro términos

family of functions *(p. 158)* A group of functions with similar characteristics

familia de funciones *(p. 158)* Un grupo de funciones con características similares

five-number summary *(p. 596)* The five numbers that make up a box-and-whisker plot

resumen de cinco números *(p. 596)* Los cinco números que componen un diagrama de cajas y bigotes

FOIL Method *(p. 374)* A shortcut for multiplying two binomials by finding the sum of the products of the first terms, outer terms, inner terms, and last terms

método FOIL o de multiplicación de binomios *(p. 374)* Un método rápido para multiplicar dos binomios encontrando la suma de los productos de los primeros términos, los segundos términos, los terceros términos y los últimos términos

formula *(p. 47)* A literal equation that shows how one variable is related to one or more other variables

fórmula *(p. 47)* Una ecuación literal que muestra cómo una variable está relacionada con una o más variables

function *(p. 112)* A relation that pairs each input with exactly one output

función *(p. 112)* Una relación que asocia cada valor exactamente con un resultado

function notation *(p. 136)* Another name for y denoted as $f(x)$ and read as "the value of f at x" or "f of x"

notación de función *(p. 136)* Otro nombre para y que se denota como $f(x)$ y que se lee como "el valor de f en x" o "f de x"

geometric sequence *(p. 338)* An ordered list of numbers in which the ratio between each pair of consecutive terms is the same

secuencia geométrica *(p. 338)* Una lista ordenada de números en donde la razón entre cada par de términos consecutivos es la misma

graph of an inequality *(p. 66)* A graph that shows the solution set of an inequality on a number line

gráfico de una desigualdad *(p. 66)* Un gráfico que muestra el conjunto de soluciones de una desigualdad en una línea numérica

graph of a linear inequality *(p. 276)* The graph in two variables that shows all the solutions of the inequality in a coordinate plane

gráfico de una desigualdad lineal *(p. 276)* El gráfico en dos variables que muestra todas las soluciones de la desigualdad en un plano coordenado

graph of a system of linear inequalities *(p. 283)* The graph of all the solutions of the system of linear inequalities

gráfico de un sistema de desigualdades lineales *(p. 283)* El gráfico de todas las soluciones del sistema de desigualdades lineales

half-planes *(p. 276)* Two regions of the coordinate plane divided by a boundary line

semiplanos *(p. 276)* Dos regiones del plano coordenado divididas por una línea limítrofe

horizontal shrink *(p. 160)* A transformation that causes the graph of a function to shrink toward the y-axis when all the x-coordinates are multiplied by a factor a, where $a > 1$

reducción horizontal *(p. 160)* Una transformación que hace que el gráfico de una función se reduzca hacia el eje y cuando todas las coordenadas x se multiplican por un factor a, donde $a > 1$

horizontal stretch *(p. 160)* A transformation that causes the graph of a function to stretch away from the y-axis when all the x-coordinates are multiplied by a factor a, where $0 < a < 1$

ampliación horizontal *(p. 160)* Una transformación que hace que el gráfico de una función se amplíe desde el eje y cuando todas las coordenadas x se multiplican por un factor a, donde $0 < a < 1$

identity *(p. 33)* An equation that is true for all values of the variable

identidad *(p. 33)* Una ecuación que es verdadera para todos los valores de la variable

increasing *(p. 121)* A function's graph moves up as x moves to the right

en aumento *(p. 121)* Una función cuyo gráfico asciende a medida que x avanza hacia la derecha

independent variable *(p. 115)* The variable that represents the input values of a function

variable independiente *(p. 115)* La variable que representa los valores de entrada de una función

index of a radical *(p. 308)* The value of n in the radical $\sqrt[n]{a}$

índice de un radical *(p. 308)* El valor de n en el radical $\sqrt[n]{a}$

inequality *(p. 64)* A mathematical sentence that compares expressions

desigualdad *(p. 64)* Una oración matemática que compara expresiones

intercept form *(p. 454)* A quadratic function written in the form $f(x) = a(x - p)(x - q)$, where $a \neq 0$

forma factorizada *(p. 454)* Una ecuación cuadrática escrita en la forma $f(x) = a(x - p)(x - q)$, donde $a \neq 0$

interpolation *(p. 215)* To approximate a value between two known values using a graph or its equation

interpolación *(p. 215)* Aproximar un valor entre dos valores conocidos usando un gráfico o su ecuación

interquartile range *(p. 597)* A measure of variation for a data set, which is the difference of the third quartile and the first quartile

rango de intercuartiles *(p. 597)* Una medida de variación para un conjunto de datos, el cual es la diferencia del tercer cuartil y el primer cuartil

inverse function *(p. 571)* Functions that undo each other

función inversa *(p. 571)* Funciones que se anulan entre sí

inverse relation *(p. 570)* A relation that switches the inputs and outputs of the original relation

relación inversa *(p. 570)* Las entradas y salidas de la relación original

J

joint frequency *(p. 612)* Each entry in a two-way table

frecuencia conjunta *(p. 612)* Cada valor en una tabla de doble entrada

joint relative frequency *(p. 613)* The ratio of a joint frequency to the total number of values or observations

frecuencia relativa conjunta *(p. 613)* La razón de una frecuencia conjunta al número total de valores u observaciones

L

leading coefficient *(p. 365)* The coefficient of the first term of a polynomial written in standard form

coeficiente principal *(p. 365)* El coeficiente del primer término de un polinomio escrito en forma estándar

like radicals *(p. 488)* Radicals with the same index and radicand

radicales semejantes *(p. 488)* Radicales con el mismo índice y radicando

line of best fit *(p. 213)* A line that best models a set of data

línea de mejor ajuste *(p. 213)* Una línea que mejor modela un conjunto de datos

line of fit *(p. 208)* A line drawn on a scatter plot that is close to most of the data points

línea de ajuste *(p. 208)* Una línea dibujada en un diagrama de dispersión que está cerca a la mayoría de los puntos de datos

linear equation in one variable *(p. 4)* An equation that can be written in the form $ax + b = 0$, where a and b are constants and $a \neq 0$

ecuación lineal en una variable *(p. 4)* Una ecuación que puede escribirse en la forma $ax + b = 0$, donde a y b son constantes y $a \neq 0$

linear equation in two variables *(p. 126)* An equation that can be written in the form $y = mx + b$, where m and b are constants

ecuación lineal en dos variables *(p. 126)* Una ecuación que puede escribirse en la forma $y = mx + b$, donde m y b son constantes

linear function *(p. 126)* A function whose graph is a nonvertical line

función lineal *(p. 126)* Una función cuyo gráfico es una línea no vertical

linear inequality in two variables *(p. 276)* An inequality written in the form $ax + by < c$, $ax + by \leq c$, $ax + by > c$, or $ax + by \geq c$, where a, b, and c are real numbers

desigualdad lineal en dos variables *(p. 276)* Una desigualdad escrita en la forma $ax + by < c$, $ax + by \leq c$, $ax + by > c$, o $ax + by \geq c$, donde a, b y c son números reales

linear model *(p. 190)* A linear function that models a real-life situation

modelo lineal *(p. 190)* Una función lineal que modela una situación de la vida real

linear regression *(p. 213)* A method that uses technology to find a precise line of fit that models a set of data

regresión lineal *(p. 213)* Un método que emplea tecnología para hallar una línea precisa de ajuste que modela un conjunto de datos

literal equation *(p. 46)* An equation that has two or more variables

ecuación literal *(p. 46)* Una ecuación que tiene dos o más variables

M

marginal frequency *(p. 612)* The sums of the rows and columns in a two-way table

frecuencia marginales *(p. 612)* Las sumas de las hileras y columnas en una tabla de doble entrada

marginal relative frequency *(p. 613)* The sum of the joint relative frequencies in a row or a column

frecuencia relativa marginal *(p. 613)* La suma de las frecuencias relativas conjuntas en una hilera o columna

maximum value *(p. 439)* The y-coordinate of the vertex of the graph of $f(x) = ax^2 + bx + c$, where $a < 0$

valor máximo *(p. 439)* La coordenada y del vértice del gráfico de $f(x) = ax^2 + bx + c$, donde $a < 0$

mean *(p. 588)* The sum of a numerical data set divided by the number of data values

media *(p. 588)* La suma de un conjunto de datos numéricos divididos entre el número de valores de datos

measure of center *(p. 588)* A measure that represents the center, or typical value, of a data set

medida del centro *(p. 588)* Una medida que representa el centro, o valor típico, de un conjunto de datos

measure of variation *(p. 589)* A measure that describes the spread, or distribution, of a data set

medida de variación *(p. 589)* Una medida que describe la extensión, o distribución, de un conjunto de datos

median *(p. 588)* The middle number of a numerical data set when the values are written in numerical order

mediana *(p. 588)* El número medio de un conjunto de datos numéricos cuando los valores se escriben en orden numérico

minimum value *(p. 439)* The y-coordinate of the vertex of the graph of $f(x) = ax^2 + bx + c$, where $a > 0$

valor mínimo *(p. 439)* La coordenada y del vértice del gráfico de $f(x) = ax^2 + bx + c$, donde $a > 0$

misleading graph *(p. 622)* A statistical graph that is not drawn appropriately

gráfico engañoso *(p. 622)* Un gráfico estadístico que no está dibujado apropiadamente

mode *(p. 588)* The value or values that occur most often in a data set

modo *(p. 588)* El valor o valores que ocurren con mayor frecuencia en un conjunto de datos

monomial *(p. 364)* A number, a variable, or the product of a number and one or more variables with whole number exponents

monomio *(p. 364)* Un número, una variable o el producto de un número y una o más variables con exponentes en números enteros

N

nonlinear function *(p. 126)* A function that does not have a constant rate of change and whose graph is not a line

función no lineal *(p. 126)* Una función que no tiene una tasa constante de cambio y cuyo gráfico no es una línea

nth root of a *(p. 308)* For an integer n greater than 1, if $b^n = a$, then b is an nth root of a.

raíz de orden n de a *(p. 308)* Para un número entero n mayor que 1, si $b^n = a$, entonces b es una raíz de orden n de a.

O

odd function *(p. 446)* A function $y = f(x)$ is odd when $f(-x) = -f(x)$ for each x in the domain of f.

función impar *(p. 446)* Una función $y = f(x)$ es impar cuando $f(-x) = -f(x)$ para cada x en el dominio de f.

outlier *(p. 589)* A data value that is much greater than or much less than the other values in a data set

valor atípico *(p. 589)* Una valor de datos que es mucho mayor o mucho menor que los otros valores en un conjunto de datos

P

parabola *(p. 426)* The U-shaped graph of a quadratic function

parábola *(p. 426)* El gráfico en forma de U de una función cuadrática

parallel lines *(p. 200)* Two lines in the same plane that never intersect

líneas paralelas *(p. 200)* Dos líneas en el mismo plano que nunca se intersectan

parent function *(p. 158)* The most basic function in a family of functions

función principal *(p. 158)* La función más básica en una familia de funciones

perpendicular lines *(p. 201)* Two lines in the same plane that intersect to form right angles

líneas perpendiculares *(p. 201)* Dos líneas en el mismo plano que se intersectan para formar ángulos rectos

piecewise function *(p. 228)* A function defined by two or more equations

función por tramos *(p. 228)* Una función definida por dos o más ecuaciones

point-slope form *(p. 194)* A linear equation written in the form $y - y_1 = m(x - x_1)$

forma punto-pendiente *(p. 194)* Una ecuación lineal escrita en la forma $y - y_1 = m(x - x_1)$

polynomial *(p. 365)* A monomial or a sum of monomials

polinomio *(p. 365)* Un monomio o una suma de monomios

precision *(p. 26)* The level of detail of a measurement

precisión *(p. 26)* El nivel de detalle de una medición

proportion *(p. 20)* An equation stating that two ratios are equivalent

proporción *(p. 20)* Una ecuación que afirma que dos razones son equivalentes

Q

quadratic equation *(p. 494)* A nonlinear equation that can be written in the standard form $ax^2 + bx + c = 0$, where $a \neq 0$

ecuación cuadrática *(p. 494)* Una ecuación no lineal que puede escribirse en la forma estándar $ax^2 + bx + c = 0$, donde $a \neq 0$

Quadratic Formula *(p. 520)* The real solutions of the quadratic equation $ax^2 + bx + c = 0$ are

$x = \dfrac{-b \pm \sqrt{b^2 - 4ac}}{2a}$, where $a \neq 0$ and $b^2 - 4ac \geq 0$.

fórmula cuadrática *(p. 520)* Las soluciones reales de la ecuación cuadrática $ax^2 + bx + c = 0$ son

$x = \dfrac{-b \pm \sqrt{b^2 - 4ac}}{2a}$, donde $a \neq 0$ y $b^2 - 4ac \geq 0$.

quadratic function *(p. 426)* A nonlinear function that can be written in the standard form $y = ax^2 + bx + c$, where $a \neq 0$

función cuadrática *(p. 426)* Una ecuación no lineal que puede escribirse en la forma estándar $y = ax^2 + bx + c$, donde $a \neq 0$

qualitative data *(p. 620)* Data that consist of labels or nonnumerical entries that can be separated into different categories

datos cualitativos *(p. 620)* Datos que consisten en etiquetas o valores no numéricos que pueden separarse en categorías distintas

quantitative data *(p. 620)* Data that consist of numbers that represent counts or measurements

datos cuantitativos *(p. 620)* Datos que consisten en números que representan conteos o medidas

quartiles *(p. 596)* Values of a box-and-whisker plot that divide a data set into four equal parts

cuartiles *(p. 596)* Valores de un diagrama de cajas y bigotes que dividen un conjunto de datos en cuatro partes iguales

R

radical *(p. 308)* An expression of the form $\sqrt[n]{a}$

radical *(p. 308)* Una expresión de la forma $\sqrt[n]{a}$

radical equation *(p. 562)* An equation that contains a radical expression with a variable in the radicand

ecuación radical *(p. 562)* Una ecuación que contiene una expresión radical con una variable en el radicando

radical expression *(p. 484)* An expression that contains a radical

expresión radical *(p. 484)* Una expresión que contiene un radical

radical function *(p. 549)* A function that contains a radical expression with the independent variable in the radicand

función radical *(p. 549)* Una ecuación que contiene una expresión radical con la variable independiente en el radicando

range of a data set *(p. 589)* The difference of the greatest value and the least value of a data set

rango de un conjunto de datos *(p. 589)* La diferencia del valor mayor y el valor menor de un conjunto de datos

range of a function *(p. 114)* The set of all possible output values of a function

rango de una función *(p. 114)* El conjunto de todos los resultados posibles de una función

rate *(p. 21)* A ratio of two quantities using different units

relación o tasa *(p. 21)* Una razón de dos cantidades que emplean unidades diferentes

ratio *(p. 20)* A comparison of two quantities

razón *(p. 20)* Una comparación de dos cantidades

rationalizing the denominator *(p. 486)* To eliminate a radical from the denominator of a fraction by multiplying by an appropriate form of 1

racionalización del denominador *(p. 486)* Eliminar un radical del denominador de una fracción multiplicando por una forma apropiada de 1

recursive rule *(p. 346)* A rule to define arithmetic and geometric sequences that gives the beginning term(s) of a sequence and a recursive equation that tells how a_n is related to one or more preceding terms

regla recursiva *(p. 346)* Una regla para definir las secuencias aritméticas y geométricas que da el(los) primer(os) término(s) de una secuencia y una ecuación recursiva que indica cómo se relaciona a_n a uno o más términos precedentes

reflection *(p. 159)* A transformation that flips a graph over a line called the *line of reflection*

reflexión *(p. 159)* Una transformación que voltea un gráfico sobre una línea llamada la *línea de reflexión*

relation *(p. 112)* A pairing of inputs with outputs

relación *(p. 112)* Una pareja de valores con resultados

repeated roots *(p. 387)* Two or more roots of an equation that are the same number

raíces repetidas *(p. 387)* Dos o más raíces de una ecuación que son el mismo número

residual *(p. 212)* The difference of the y-value of a data point and the corresponding y-value found using the line of fit

residual *(p. 212)* La diferencia del valor y de un punto de datos y el valor y correspondiente usando la línea de ajuste

rise *(p. 148)* The change in y between any two points on a line

desplazamiento vertical *(p. 148)* El cambio en y entre cualesquiera dos puntos en una recta

roots *(p. 386)* The solutions of a polynomial equation

raíces *(p. 386)* Las soluciones deuna ecuación de polinomios

run *(p. 148)* The change in x between any two points on a line

desplazamiento horizontal *(p. 148)* El cambio en x entre cualesquiera dos puntos en una recta

S

scatter plot *(p. 206)* A graph that shows the relationship between two data sets

diagrama de dispersión *(p. 206)* Un gráfico que muestra la relación entre dos conjuntos de datos

sequence *(p. 220)* An ordered list of numbers

secuencia *(p. 220)* Una lista ordenada de números

simplest form of a radical *(p. 484)* An expression involving a radical with index n that has no radicands with perfect nth powers as factors other than 1, no radicands that contain fractions, and no radicals that appear in the denominator of a fraction

mínima expresión de un radical *(p. 484)* Una expresión que conlleva un radical con índice n que no tiene radicandos con potencias perfectas de orden n como factores distintos a 1, que no tiene radicandos que contengan fracciones y que no tiene radicales que aparezcan en el denominador de una fracción

slope *(p. 148)* The rate of change between any two points on a line

pendiente *(p. 148)* La tasa de cambio entre dos puntos cualesquiera en una línea

slope-intercept form *(p. 150)* A linear equation written in the form $y = mx + b$

forma intersección-pendiente *(p. 150)* Una ecuación lineal escrita en la forma $y = mx + b$

solution of an equation *(p. 4)* A value that makes an equation true

solución de una ecuación *(p. 4)* Un valor que hace que una ecuación sea verdadera

solution of an inequality *(p. 65)* A value that makes an inequality true

solución de una desigualdad *(p. 65)* Un valor que hace que una desigualdad sea verdadera

solution of a linear equation in two variables *(p. 128)* An ordered pair (x, y) that makes an equation true

solución de una ecuación lineal en dos variables *(p. 128)* Un par ordenado (x, y) que hace que una ecuación sea verdadera

solution of a linear inequality in two variables *(p. 276)* An ordered pair (x, y) that makes the inequality true

solución de una desigualdad lineal en dos variables *(p. 276)* Un par ordenado (x, y) que hace que la desigualdad sea verdadera

solution set *(p. 65)* The set of all solutions of an inequality

conjunto de soluciónes *(p. 65)* El conjunto de todas las soluciones de una desigualdad

solution of a system of linear equations *(p. 246)* An ordered pair that is a solution of each equation in the system

solución de un sistema de ecuaciones lineales *(p. 246)* Un par ordenado que es una solución de cada ecuación en el sistema

solution of a system of linear inequalities *(p. 282)* An ordered pair that is a solution of each inequality in the system

solución de un sistema de desigualdades lineales *(p. 282)* Un par ordenado que es una solución de cada desigualdad en el sistema

square root function *(p. 548)* A function that contains a square root with the independent variable in the radicand

función de raíz cuadrada *(p. 548)* Una función que contiene una raíz cuadrada con la variable independiente en el radicando

standard deviation *(p. 590)* A measure of how much a typical value in a numerical data set differs from the mean

desviación estándar *(p. 590)* Una medida de cuánto difiere un valor típico en un conjunto de datos numéricos de la media

standard form of a linear equation *(p. 142)* A linear equation written in the form $Ax + By = C$, where A, B, and C are real numbers and A and B are not both zero

forma estándar de una ecuación lineal *(p. 142)* Una ecuación lineal escrita en la forma $Ax + By = C$, donde A, B y C son números reales y ni A ni B son cero

standard form of a polynomial *(p. 365)* A polynomial in one variable written with the exponents of the terms decreasing from left to right

forma estándar de un polinomio *(p. 365)* Un polinomio en una variable escrita con los exponentes de los términos decreciendo de izquierda a derecha

step function *(p. 230)* A piecewise function defined by a constant value over each part of its domain

función escalón *(p. 230)* Una función por tramos definida por un valor constante sobre cada parte de su dominio

system of linear equations *(p. 246)* A set of two or more linear equations in the same variables

sistema de ecuaciones lineales *(p. 246)* Un conjunto de dos o más ecuaciones lineales en las mismas variables

system of linear inequalities *(p. 282)* A set of two or more linear inequalities in the same variables

sistema de desigualdades lineales *(p. 282)* Un conjunto de dos o más desigualdades lineales en las mismas variables

system of nonlinear equations *(p. 530)* A system in which at least one of the equations is nonlinear

sistema de ecuaciones no lineales *(p. 530)* Un sistema en donde al menos una de las ecuaciones no es lineal

T

term of a sequence *(p. 220)* Each number in a sequence

término de una secuencia *(p. 220)* Cada número en una secuencia

transformation *(p. 158)* A change in the size, shape, position, or orientation of a graph

transformación *(p. 158)* Un cambio en el tamaño, forma, posición u orientación de un gráfico

translation *(p. 158)* A transformation that shifts a graph horizontally and/or vertically but does not change the size, shape, or orientation of the graph

traslación *(p. 158)* Una transformación que desplaza un gráfico horizontal y/o verticalmente pero no cambia el tamaño, forma u orientación del gráfico

trinomial *(p. 365)* A polynomial with three terms

trinomio *(p. 365)* Un polinomio con tres términos

two-way table *(p. 612)* A frequency table that displays data collected from one source that belong to two different categories

tabla de doble entrada *(p. 612)* Una tabla de frecuencia que muestra los datos recogidos de una fuente que pertenece a dos categorías distintas

V

vertex *(p. 168)* The point where a graph changes direction

vértice *(p. 168)* El punto en donde un gráfico cambia de dirección

vertex form of an absolute value function *(p. 170)* An absolute value function written in the form $g(x) = a|x - h| + k$, where $a \neq 0$

forma de vértice de una función de valor absoluto *(p. 170)* Una función de valor absoluto escrita en la forma $g(x) = a|x - h| + k$, donde $a \neq 0$

vertex form of a quadratic function *(p. 448)* A quadratic function written in the form $f(x) = a(x - h)^2 + k$, where $a \neq 0$

forma de vértice de una función cuadrática *(p. 448)* Una función cuadrática escrita en la forma $f(x) = a(x - h)^2 + k$, donde $a \neq 0$

vertex of a parabola *(p. 426)* The lowest point on a parabola that opens up or the highest point on a parabola that opens down

vértice de una parábola *(p. 426)* El punto más bajo de una parábola que se abre hacia arriba o el punto más alto de una parábola que se abre hacia abajo

vertical shrink *(p. 160)* A transformation that causes the graph of a function to shrink toward the x-axis when all the y-coordinates are multiplied by a factor a, where $0 < a < 1$

reducción vertical *(p. 160)* Una transformación que hace que el gráfico de una función se reduzca hacia el eje x cuando todas las coordenadas y se multiplican por un factor a, donde $0 < a < 1$

vertical stretch *(p. 160)* A transformation that causes the graph of a function to stretch away from the x-axis when all the y-coordinates are multiplied by a factor a, where $a > 1$

ampliación vertical *(p. 160)* Una transformación que hace que el gráfico de una función se amplíe desde el eje x cuando todas las coordenadas y se multiplican por un factor a, donde $a > 1$

x-intercept *(p. 120)* The x-coordinate of a point where the graph intersects the x-axis

intersección x *(p. 120)* La coordenada x de un punto donde el gráfico interseca el eje x

y-intercept *(p. 120)* The y-coordinate of a point where the graph intersects the y-axis

intersección y *(p. 120)* La coordenada y de un punto donde el gráfico interseca el eje y

zero of a function *(p. 434)* An x-value of a function f for which $f(x) = 0$

cero de una función *(p. 434)* Un valor x de una función f para el cual $f(x) = 0$

Zero-Product Property *(p. 386)* If the product of two real numbers is 0, then at least one of the numbers is 0.

propiedad de producto cero *(p. 386)* Si el producto de dos números reales es 0, entonces al menos uno de los números es 0.

Index

INDEX

INDEX

Q

R

S

T

Reference

Properties

Properties of Equality

Addition Property of Equality
If $a = b$, then $a + c = b + c$.

Subtraction Property of Equality
If $a = b$, then $a - c = b - c$.

Multiplication Property of Equality
If $a = b$, then $a \cdot c = b \cdot c, c \neq 0$.

Division Property of Equality
If $a = b$, then $a \div c = b \div c, c \neq 0$.

Properties of Inequality

Addition Property of Inequality
If $a > b$, then $a + c > b + c$.
If $a < b$, then $a + c < b + c$.

Subtraction Property of Inequality
If $a > b$, then $a - c > b - c$.
If $a < b$, then $a - c < b - c$.

Multiplication Property of Inequality ($c > 0$)
If $a > b$ and $c > 0$, then $ac > bc$.
If $a < b$ and $c > 0$, then $ac < bc$.

Division Property of Inequality ($c > 0$)
If $a > b$ and $c > 0$, then $\frac{a}{c} > \frac{b}{c}$.
If $a < b$ and $c > 0$, then $\frac{a}{c} < \frac{b}{c}$.

Multiplication Property of Inequality ($c < 0$)
If $a > b$ and $c < 0$, then $ac < bc$.
If $a < b$ and $c < 0$, then $ac > bc$.

Division Property of Inequality ($c < 0$)
If $a > b$ and $c < 0$, then $\frac{a}{c} < \frac{b}{c}$.
If $a < b$ and $c < 0$, then $\frac{a}{c} > \frac{b}{c}$.

* The Properties of Inequality are also true for $\geq$ and $\leq$.

Properties of Exponents

Zero Exponent
$a^0 = 1$, where $a \neq 0$

Negative Exponent
$a^{-n} = \frac{1}{a^n}$, where $a \neq 0$

Product of Powers Property
$a^m \cdot a^n = a^{m+n}$

Quotient of Powers Property
$\frac{a^m}{a^n} = a^{m-n}$, where $a \neq 0$

Power of a Power Property
$(a^m)^n = a^{mn}$

Power of a Product Property
$(ab)^m = a^m b^m$

Power of a Quotient Property
$\left(\frac{a}{b}\right)^m = \frac{a^m}{b^m}$, where $b \neq 0$

Rational Exponents
$a^{m/n} = a^{(1/n) \cdot m} = (a^{1/n})^m = (\sqrt[n]{a})^m$ or $a^{m/n} = a^{m \cdot (1/n)} = (a^m)^{1/n} = \sqrt[n]{a^m}$

Properties of Absolute Value

$|a| \geq 0$

$|-a| = |a|$

$|ab| = |a||b|$

$\left|\frac{a}{b}\right| = \frac{|a|}{|b|}, b \neq 0$

Properties of Radicals

Product Property of Square Roots
$\sqrt{ab} = \sqrt{a} \cdot \sqrt{b}$, where $a \geq 0$ and $b \geq 0$

Quotient Property of Square Roots
$\sqrt{\frac{a}{b}} = \frac{\sqrt{a}}{\sqrt{b}}$, where $a \geq 0$ and $b > 0$

Other Properties

Property of Equality for Exponential Equations
If $b > 0$ and $b \neq 1$, then $b^x = b^y$ if and only if $x = y$.

Zero-Product Property
If a and b are real numbers and $ab = 0$, then $a = 0$ or $b = 0$.

Patterns

Square of a Binomial Pattern
$(a + b)^2 = a^2 + 2ab + b^2$
$(a - b)^2 = a^2 - 2ab + b^2$

Sum and Difference Pattern
$(a + b)(a - b) = a^2 - b^2$

Difference of Two Squares Pattern
$a^2 - b^2 = (a + b)(a - b)$

Perfect Square Trinomial Pattern
$a^2 + 2ab + b^2 = (a + b)^2$
$a^2 - 2ab + b^2 = (a - b)^2$

Formulas

Slope
$m = \frac{y_2 - y_1}{x_2 - x_1}$

Slope-intercept form
$y = mx + b$

Point-slope form
$y - y_1 = m(x - x_1)$

Standard form of a linear equation
$Ax + By = C$, where A and B are not both 0

Vertex form of an absolute value function
$f(x) = a|x - h| + k$, where $a \neq 0$

Standard form of a quadratic function
$f(x) = ax^2 + bx + c$, where $a \neq 0$

Vertex form of a quadratic function
$f(x) = a(x - h)^2 + k$, where $a \neq 0$

Intercept form of a quadratic function
$f(x) = a(x - p)(x - q)$, where $a \neq 0$

Quadratic Formula
$x = \frac{-b \pm \sqrt{b^2 - 4ac}}{2a}$, where $a \neq 0$ and $b^2 - 4ac \geq 0$

Exponential growth
$y = a(1 + r)^t$, where $a > 0$ and $r > 0$

Exponential decay
$y = a(1 - r)^t$, where $a > 0$ and $0 < r < 1$

Explicit rule for an arithmetic sequence
$a_n = a_1 + (n - 1)d$

Explicit rule for a geometric sequence
$a_n = a_1 r^{n-1}$

Recursive equation for an arithmetic sequence
$a_n = a_{n-1} + d$

Recursive equation for a geometric sequence
$a_n = r \cdot a_{n-1}$

Standard deviation

$$\sigma = \sqrt{\frac{(x_1 - \bar{x})^2 + (x_2 - \bar{x})^2 + \cdots + (x_n - \bar{x})^2}{n}}$$

Characteristics of Functions

Positive and Negative
A function is positive when its graph lies above the x-axis. A function is negative when its graph lies below the x-axis.

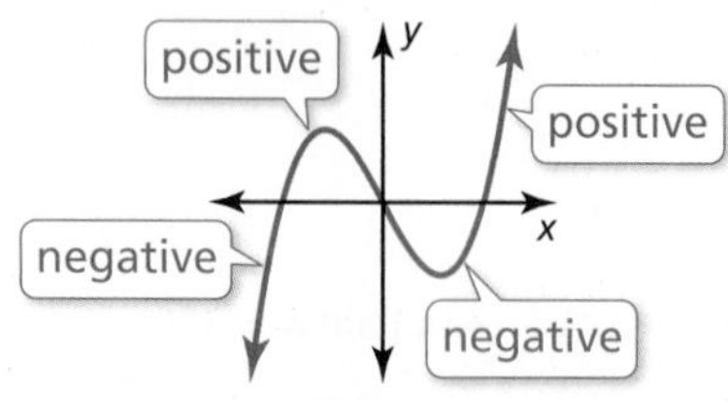

Increasing and Decreasing
A function is increasing when its graph moves up as x moves to the right. A function is decreasing when its graph moves down as x moves to the right.

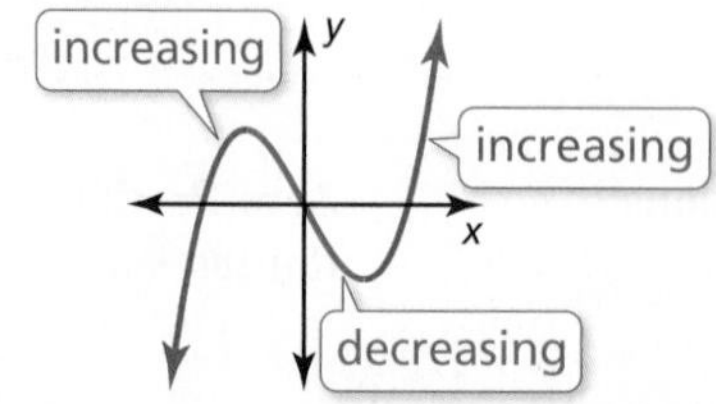

End Behavior
The end behavior of a function is the behavior of the graph as x approaches positive infinity ($+\infty$) or negative infinity ($-\infty$).

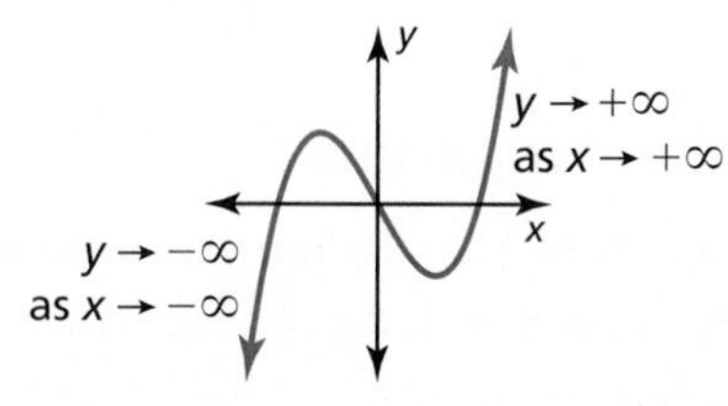

Perimeter, Area, and Volume Formulas

Square

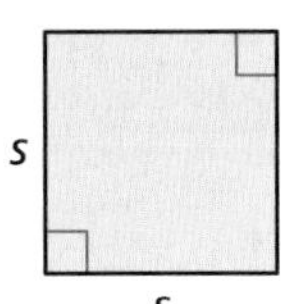

$P = 4s$
$A = s^2$

Rectangle

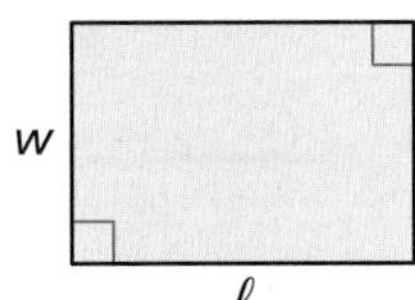

$P = 2\ell + 2w$
$A = \ell w$

Triangle

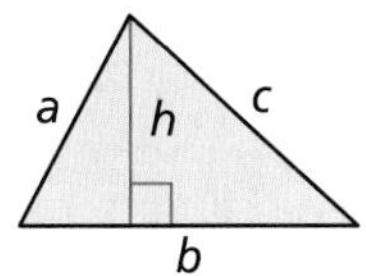

$P = a + b + c$
$A = \frac{1}{2}bh$

Circle

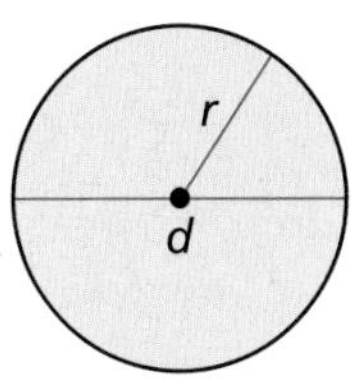

$C = \pi d$ or $C = 2\pi r$
$A = \pi r^2$

Parallelogram

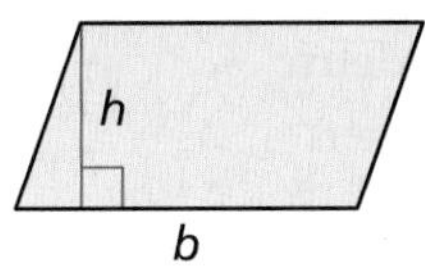

$A = bh$

Trapezoid

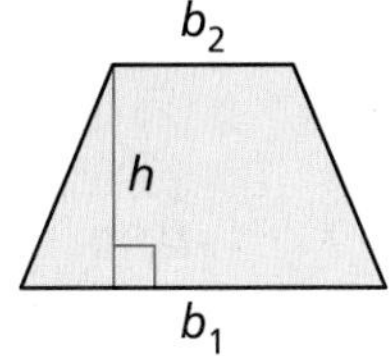

$A = \frac{1}{2}h(b_1 + b_2)$

Rhombus/Kite

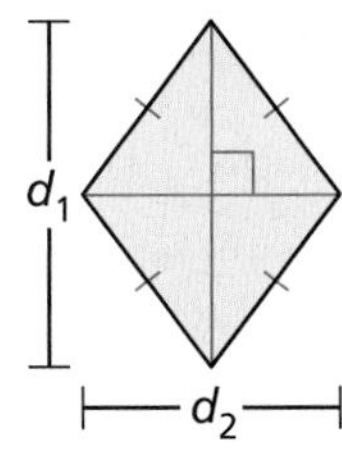

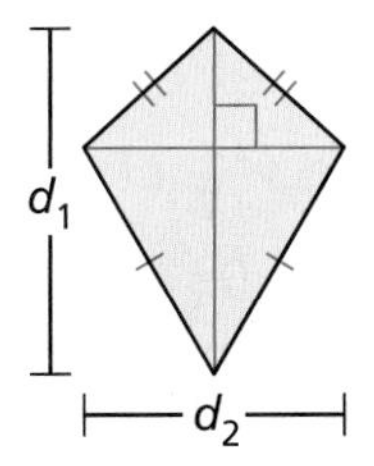

$A = \frac{1}{2}d_1d_2$

Regular *n*-gon

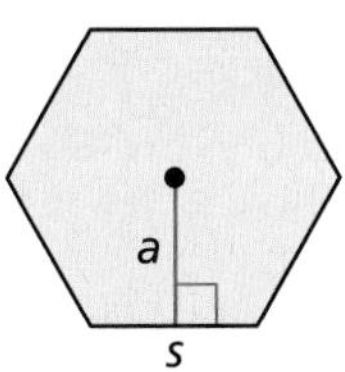

$A = \frac{1}{2}aP$ or $A = \frac{1}{2}a \cdot ns$

Prism

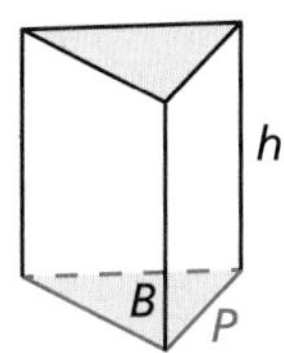

$L = Ph$
$S = 2B + Ph$
$V = Bh$

Cylinder

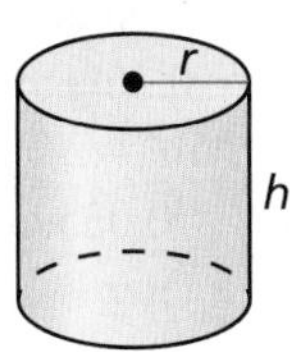

$L = 2\pi rh$
$S = 2\pi r^2 + 2\pi rh$
$V = \pi r^2h$

Pyramid

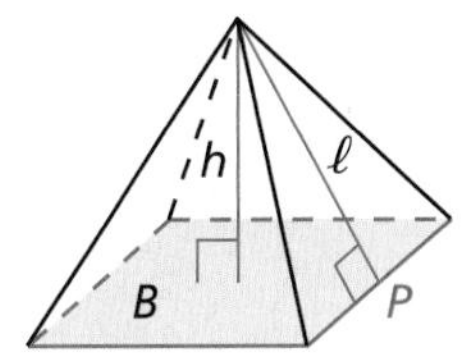

$L = \frac{1}{2}P\ell$
$S = B + \frac{1}{2}P\ell$
$V = \frac{1}{3}Bh$

Cone

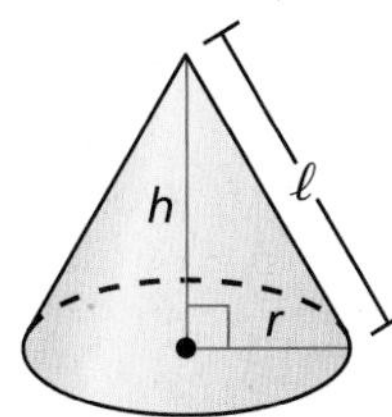

$L = \pi r\ell$

$S = \pi r^2 + \pi r\ell$

$V = \frac{1}{3}\pi r^2h$

Sphere

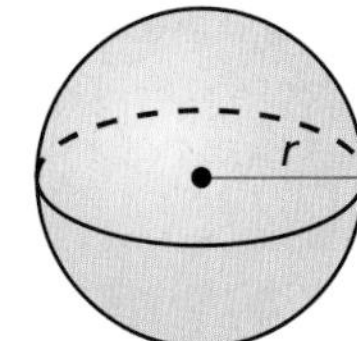

$S = 4\pi r^2$

$V = \frac{4}{3}\pi r^3$

Other Formulas

Pythagorean Theorem
$a^2 + b^2 = c^2$

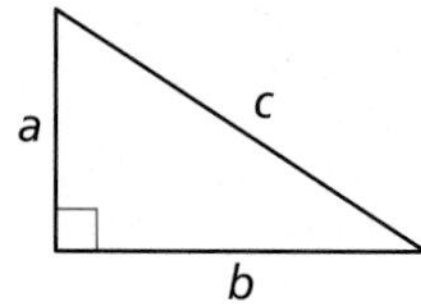

Simple Interest
$I = Prt$

Compound Interest
$y = P\left(1 + \frac{r}{n}\right)^{nt}$

Distance
$d = rt$

Conversions

U.S. Customary
1 foot = 12 inches
1 yard = 3 feet
1 mile = 5280 feet
1 mile = 1760 yards
1 acre = 43,560 square feet
1 cup = 8 fluid ounces
1 pint = 2 cups
1 quart = 2 pints
1 gallon = 4 quarts
1 gallon = 231 cubic inches
1 pound = 16 ounces
1 ton = 2000 pounds
1 cubic foot ≈ 7.5 gallons

U.S. Customary to Metric
1 inch = 2.54 centimeters
1 foot ≈ 0.3 meter
1 mile ≈ 1.61 kilometers
1 quart ≈ 0.95 liter
1 gallon ≈ 3.79 liters
1 cup ≈ 237 milliliters
1 pound ≈ 0.45 kilogram
1 ounce ≈ 28.3 grams
1 gallon ≈ 3785 cubic centimeters

Time
1 minute = 60 seconds
1 hour = 60 minutes
1 hour = 3600 seconds
1 year = 52 weeks

Temperature
$C = \frac{5}{9}(F - 32)$

$F = \frac{9}{5}C + 32$

Metric
1 centimeter = 10 millimeters
1 meter = 100 centimeters
1 kilometer = 1000 meters
1 liter = 1000 milliliters
1 kiloliter = 1000 liters
1 milliliter = 1 cubic centimeter
1 liter = 1000 cubic centimeters
1 cubic millimeter = 0.001 milliliter
1 gram = 1000 milligrams
1 kilogram = 1000 grams

Metric to U.S. Customary
1 centimeter ≈ 0.39 inch
1 meter ≈ 3.28 feet
1 meter ≈ 39.37 inches
1 kilometer ≈ 0.62 mile
1 liter ≈ 1.06 quarts
1 liter ≈ 0.26 gallon
1 kilogram ≈ 2.2 pounds
1 gram ≈ 0.035 ounce
1 cubic meter ≈ 264 gallons

Credits

Front Matter

xviii Pixel-Shot/Shutterstock.com; **xx** Nikolay 007/Shutterstock.com; **xxi** Roberto Caucino/Shutterstock.com; **xxii** David Kirkland/Media Bakery; **xxiii** ic36006/Shutterstock.com; **xxiv** George W. Bailey/Shutterstock.com; **xxv** Billion Photos/Shutterstock.com; **xxvi** Dotted Yeti/Shutterstock.com; **xxvii** Wira SHK/Shutterstock.com; **xxviii** FlashMovie/Shutterstock.com; **xxix** Rich Carey/Shutterstock.com; **xxx** Ociacia/Shutterstock.com; **xxxi** aldomurillo/iStock/Getty Images Plus

Chapter 1

0 *top* ©Randall Scott/National Geographic Image Collection; *bottom* Nikolay 007/Shutterstock.com; **1** jurisam/iStock/Getty Images Plus; **3** GlobalP/iStock/Getty Images Plus; **6** Petr Toman/Shutterstock.com; **7** *top* Harper 3D/Shutterstock.com; *bottom* lunamarina/Shutterstock.com; **8** 4FR/E+/Getty Images; **9** *top* adogslifephoto/iStock/Getty Images Plus; *bottom* cowardlion/Shutterstock.com; **10** Willard/iStock/Getty Images Plus; **11** *right* MPFphotography/Shutterstock.com; *left* agrobacteriStock/Getty Images Plus; **14** Tom Saga/Shutterstock.com; **15** *top* B toy Anucha/Shutterstock.com; *bottom* Dora Zett/Shutterstock.com; **16** ggyykk/iStock/Getty Images Plus; **19** Gregory_DUBUS/E+/Getty Images; **21** Image Source/Photodisc/Getty Images; **22** *top* BlueRingMedia/Shutterstock.com; *bottom* ©Solar Impulse/ Jean Revillard / Rezo.ch; **23** Liudmyla Liudmyla/iStock/Getty Images Plus; **25** Molnia/iStock/Getty Images Plus; **27** jiangdi/Shutterstock.com; **28** *right* tarras79/iStock/Getty Images Plus; *left* Joel Carillet/E+/Getty Images; **29** *top left* borojoint/iStock/Getty Images Plus; *bottom left* Zenobillis/iStock/Getty Images Plus; *right* Anadmist/iStock/Getty Images Plus; **31** Ljupco/iStock/Getty Images Plus; **34** mrdoomits/iStock/Getty Images Plus; **35** Vdovychenko Yurii/iStock/Getty Images Plus; **37** CiydemImages/iStock/Getty Images Plus; **39** Holyshyn Oleh/Shutterstock.com; **42** Nerthuz/iStock/Getty Images Plus, stephane106/iStock/Getty Images Plus; **45** Cimmerian/iStock/Getty Images Plus; **48** *bottom* guardiano007/Shutterstock.com; *top* Nerthuz/Istock/Getty Images Plus; **50** OSTILL/iStock/Getty Images Plus; **51** *top* heinteh/iStock/Getty Images Plus; *bottom* Obradovic/iStock/Getty Images Plus; **52** *top* kurtlichtenstein/iStock/Getty Images Plus; *bottom* kontur-vid/iStock/Getty Images Plus; **54** franckreporter/E+/Getty Images; **56** *top* zoooma/iStock/Getty Images Plus; *bottom* sdecoret/Shutterstock.com; **57** *top* AlessandroMassimiliano/iStock/Getty Images Plus; *background* pinkomelet/iStock/Getty Images Plus; **58** My Life Graphic/Shutterstock.com

Chapter 2

60 *top* ©Jimmy Chin/National Geographic Image Collection; *bottom* Roberto Caucino/Shutterstock.com; **61** gutiiev/iStock/Getty Images Plus; **67** Bertl123/Shutterstock.com; **68** *bottom* saiko3p/iStock Editorial/Getty Images Plus; *top* Bet_Noire/iStock/Getty Images Plus; **69** Morozov67/iStock/Getty Images Plus; **71** Photodisc/Photodisc/Getty Images; **74** Roman Voloshyn/Shutterstock.com; **77** aldomurillo/iStock/Getty Images Plus; **80** *top* Courtesy Peter Hutchinson Designs Ltd.; *bottom* amanalang/iStock/Getty Images Plus; **81** Picsfive/iStock/Getty Images Plus; **82** GlobalP/iStock/Getty Images Plus; **83** Dean Drobot/iStock/Getty Images Plus; **89** pkline/E+/Getty Images; **92** Symonenko Viktoriia/Shutterstock.com; **93** *left* benedek/E+/Getty Images; *right* andegro4ka/iStock/Getty Images Plus; **95** PORTRAIT IMAGES ASIA BY NONWARIT/Shutterstock.com; **98** Oleksiy Mark/Shutterstock.com; **99** GlobalP/iStock/Getty Images Plus; **101** nidwlw/iStock/Getty Images Plus; **102** *left* Dean Mitchell/E+/Getty Images; *right* skynesher/E+/Getty Images; **103** thedafkish/iStock/Getty Images Plus; **104** Paolo Bona/Shutterstock.com; **105** *bottom* Historic Images/Alamy Stock Photo; *background* hadynyah/E+/Getty Images; **107** *left* TPopova/iStock/Getty Images Plus; *right* Piotr Polaczyk/iStock/Getty Images Plus

Chapter 3

108 *top* ©Marco Grob/National Geographic Image Collection; *bottom* David Kirkland/Media Bakery; **109** cosmin4000/iStock/Getty Images Plus, Valentyna Chukhlyebova/Shutterstock.com; **111** ©iStockphoto.com/sorbetto; **115** *top* Konstantin G/Shutterstock.com; *bottom* Npeter/Shutterstock.com; **116** Nerthuz/iStock/Getty Images Plus; **119** xua/iStock/Getty Images Plus; **122** Safar Aslanov/Shutterstock.com, max dallocco/Shutterstock.com; **125** domin_domin/iStock/Getty Images Plus; **129** GlobalP/iStock/Getty Images Plus; **130** Ljupco Smokovski/Shutterstock.com; **132** OSTILL/iStock/Getty Images Plus; **133** Coprid/Shutterstock.com; **135** track5/E+/Getty Images; **136** Africa Studio/Shutterstock.com; **139** Nerthuz/iStock/Getty Images Plus; **141** hatman12/iStock/Getty Images Plus; **145** robertsrob/iStock/Getty Images Plus; **147** michaeljung/iStock/Getty Images Plus; **152** Andrey Suslov/Shutterstock.com; **154** oneblink-cj/iStock/Getty Images Plus; **157** Venera Salman/Shutterstock.com; **163** Africa Studio/Shutterstock.com; **164** 5 second Studio/Shutterstock.com; **167** michaeljung/iStock/Getty Images Plus; **177** *top* scanrail/iStock/Getty Images Plus; *bottom* OSTILL/iStock/Getty Images Plus; **180** White Space Ukraine/Shutterstock.com; **181** *left* Global_Pics/E+/Getty Images; *right* Pixelfeger/Shutterstock.com; **183** Es sarawuth/Shutterstock.com

Chapter 4

184 *top* ©Rebecca Hale/ National Geographic Image Collection; *bottom* ic36006/Shutterstock.com; **185** vencavolrab/iStock/Getty Images Plus; **187** PeopleImages/iStock/Getty Images Plus; **190** pedrosala/Shutterstock.com; **191** wundervisuals/E+/Getty Images; **193** DragonImages/iStock/Getty Images Plus; **196** Valerie Loiseleux/E+/Getty Images; **197** LongQuattro/iStock/Getty Images Plus, Archiwiz/iStock/Getty Images Plus; **199** Galina Zhigalova/iStock/Getty Images Plus; **205** AlexandreNunes/Shutterstock.com; **209** Slavun/Shutterstock.com; **211** Ljupco/iStock/Getty Images Plus; **214** Melissa Schalke/Shutterstock.com; **216** snvv/iStock/Getty Images Plus; **219** 4x6/iStock/Getty Images Plus; **227** tashka2000/iStock/Getty Images Plus; **230** Rawpixel/iStock/Getty Images Plus; **232** Tatomm/iStock/Getty Images Plus; **239** Mkstudi/Shutterstock.com

Chapter 5

242 *top* ©Mark Thiessen/National Geographic Creative; *bottom* George W. Bailey/Shutterstock.com; **248** Christina Richards/Shutterstock.com; **249** *Exercise 23 left* neamov/iStock/Getty Images Plus; *Exercise 23 right* tiler84/iStock/Getty Images Plus; *bottom* pilipphoto/iStock/Getty Images Plus; **251** aldomurillo/iStock/Getty Images Plus; **254** New Africa/Shutterstock.com; **255** Odua Images/Shutterstock.com; **257** Lenasirena/Shutterstock.com; **260** Nerthuz/iStock/Getty Images Plus; **261** MileA/iStock/Getty Images Plus; **263** HomePixel/iStock/Getty Images Plus; **266** damedeeso/iStock/Getty Images Plus; **267** final09/iStock/Getty Images Plus, venimo/iStock/Getty Images Plus, Yeko Photo Studio/Shutterstock.com; **269** Iakov Filimonov/Shutterstock.com; **272** goinyk/iStock/Getty Images Plus; **273** Africa Studio/Shutterstock.com; **274** *right* nata_zhekova/iStock/Getty Images Plus; *left* iko636/iStock/Getty Images Plus; **275** *left* photka/iStock/Getty Images Plus; *right* Arthito/iStock/Getty Images Plus; **278** harneshkp/iStock/Getty Images Plus, PixaHub/Shutterstock.com; **279** fergregory/iStock/Getty Images Plus; **281** londoneye/E+/Getty Images; **285** Supertrooper/Shutterstock.com; **287** eye-blink/Shutterstock.com; **289** *left* Irina Rogova/Shutterstock.com; *right* Kostyantyn Ivanyshen/Shutterstock.com; **292** *left* choness/iStock/Getty Images Plus; *right* Vonkara1/iStock/Getty Images Plus; **293** *in order from top to bottom* Harvepino/Shutterstock.com; Steve Nicklas/NOS; ©Mark Thiessan/National Geographic; katykin/iStock/Getty Images Plus; best works/Shutterstock.com; *background* divedog/Shutterstock.com, Global_Pics/iStock/Getty Images Plus

Chapter 6

296 *top* ©Rebecca Hale/National Geographic Image Collection; *bottom* Billion Photos/Shutterstock.com, Rost-9D/iStock/Getty Images Plus; **297** Kasia/Shutterstock.com; **299** LUNAMARINA/iStock/Getty Images Plus; **303** CoreyFord/iStock/Getty Images Plus; **304** dankuhs/iStock/Getty Images Plus; **305** *top* photo5963/iStock/Getty Images Plus; *bottom* AlexLMX/iStock/Getty Images Plus; **307** *top* Mint Fox/Shutterstock.com; *left* kurhan/Shutterstock.com; *bottom* ryasick/E+/Getty Images Plus; **310** JUN2/Stock/Getty Images Plus; **311** cybrain/iStock/Getty Images Plus; **313** DragonImages/iStock/Getty Images Plus; **319** *top right* Naughty_Vitus/Shutterstock.com; **320** miakievy/DigitalVision Vectors/Getty Images; **321** Hannamariah/Shutterstock.com; **322** DenisProduction.com/Shutterstock.com; **326** Vladimiroquai/iStock/Getty Images Plus; **327** MYALA88/Alamy Stock Photo; **329** *top* U.S. Department of Energy; *bottom* Dominique-Grosse/iStock/Getty Image Plus; **331** Africa Studio/Shutterstock.com; **335** rudigobbo/E+/Getty Images; **337** huronphoto/E+/Getty Images Plus; **341** Andrei Stanescu/iStock/Getty Images Plus; **345** *left* Litvalifa/iStock/Getty Images Plus; *right* chengyuzheng/iStock/Getty Images Plus, Voren1/iStock/Getty Images Plus; **347** bonchan/iStock/Getty Images Plus, mayer kleinostheim/Shutterstock.com, ©iStockphoto.com/Matej Michelizza, Refat/Shutterstock.com; **349** Jpecha/E+/Getty Images; **350** *top* jovan vitanovski/Shutterstock.com; *bottom* GlobalP/iStock/Getty Images Plus; **353** © Leerobin | Dreamstime.com; **357** polesnoy/iStock/Getty Images Plus

Chapter 7

360 *top* ©Randall Scott/National Geographic Image Collection; *bottom* Dotted Yeti/Shutterstock.com; **361** josefkubes/iStock/Getty Images Plus; **363** Ebtikar/Shutterstock.com; **367** *top* ©iStockphoto.com/edge69; *bottom* andresr/E+/Getty Images; **368** Marek R. Swadzba/Shutterstock.com; **369** Owen Smith/iStock/Getty Images Plus; **370** ©iStockphoto.com/edge69; **375** *top* Dmytro Aksonov/iStock/Getty Images Plus; *bottom* Fejas/Shutterstock.com; **377** *top* FatCamera/E+/Getty Images; *Exercise 63* koya79/iStock/Getty Images Plus; *Exercise 65* fergregory/iStock/Getty Images Plus, Rodrusoleg/iStock /Getty Images Plus; **378** Yana Korolenko/iStock/Getty Images Plus, abadonian/iStock /Getty Images Plus; **382** *top* Zoonar/E.Lam/iStock/Getty Images Plus; *bottom* cynoclub/iStock/Getty Images Plus; **384** Tamara Kulikova/Shutterstock.com; **385** ferlistockphoto/iStock/Getty Images Plus; **388** Alex/iStock/Getty Images Plus, Lana_M/iStock/Getty Images Plus; **389** Rudy Balasko/Shutterstock.com; **394** Floortje/iStock/Getty Images Plus; **395** *left* urfinguss/iStock/Getty Images Plus; *right* hadynyah/E+/Getty Images; **397** The_Molostock/Shutterstock.com; **400** ugniz/iStock/Getty Images Plus; **401** zokru/iStock/Getty Images Plus; **406** GlobalP/iStock/ Getty Images Plus; **407** *left* Shahrul Azmi/Shutterstock.com; *right* Ljupco/iStock/Getty Images Plus; **409** Ebtikar/Shutterstock.com; **412** *top* Lady Shmidt-Studio/Shutterstock.com; *bottom* Lara Hata/iStock/Getty Images Plus; **416** ©iStockphoto.com/tirc83; **417** AlbertoChagas/iStock/Getty Images Plus; **419** *top* Macrovector/Shutterstock.com; *bottom* fergregory/iStock/Getty Images Plus, Elen11/iStock/Getty Images Plus; *background* Misha Kaminsky/E+/Getty Images

Chapter 8

422 *top* ©Rebecca Hale/National Geographic Image Collection; *bottom* Wira SHK/Shutterstock.com; **425** ASDF_MEDIA/Shutterstock.com; **428** zhengzaishuru/iStock/Getty Images Plus; **430** julichka/iStock/Getty Images Plus, ©iStockphoto.com/PLAINVIEW; **431** Dean Drobot/Shutterstock.com; **434** GoodStudio/Shutterstock.com; **437** Dean Drobot/Shutterstock.com**440** 3DMI/Shutterstock.com; **441** ScantyNebula/iStock/Getty Images Plus; **442** Dmytro Aksonov/iStock/Getty Images Plus; **453** Victoria Kisel/Shutterstock.com; Flashon Studio/Shutterstock.com; **449** Matej Kastelic/Shutterstock.com; **451** *left* Mexitographer/iStock/Getty Images Plus; *right* chromatika/iStock/Getty Images plus; **460** janniwet/iStock/Getty Images Plus; **461** bernardbodo/iStock/Getty Images Plus; **463** Vladimiroquai/iStock/Getty Images Plus; **468** dive-hive/Shutterstock.com; **470** mel-nik/iStock/Getty Images Plus; **474** OSTILL/iStock/Getty Images Plus; **476** sergeyskleznev/iStock/Getty Images Plus; **477** ShaneMyersPhoto/iStock/Getty Images Plus; **478** Willard/iStock/Getty Images Plus

Chapter 9

480 *top* ©Randall Scott/National Geographic Image Collection; *bottom* FlashMovie/Shutterstock.com; **481** Pat Corkery, United Launch Alliance; **483** amanalang/iStock / Getty Images Plus; **487** *top* goce/E+/Getty Images; *bottom* ©iStockphoto.com/MinistryOfJoy; **490** *top left* enot-poloskun/E+/Getty Images; *bottom left* ChrisGorgio/iStock/Getty Images Plus; *Exercise 67* malerapaso/iStock/Getty Images Plus; **493** 4x6/iStock/Getty Images Plus; **497** joeygil/iStock Editorial/Getty Images Plus; **499** Wavebreakmedia/iStock/Getty Images Plus; **500** Michael Burrell/iStock/Getty Images Plus; **501** pikepicture/iStock/Getty Images Plus, scanrail/iStock/Getty Images Plus; **503** AndreyPopov/iStock/Getty Images Plus; **506** Olga Konstantinova/iStock/Getty Images Plus; **509** pepifoto/iStock/Getty Images Plus; **516** *top* Adriana Molas Serra/Shutterstock.com, drbimages/iStock/Getty Images Plus; *bottom* farosofa/iStock/Getty Images Plus; **517** *left* Artur Didyk/Shutterstock.com, *right* Natalia7/Shutterstock.com; **519** Hemera Technologies/PhotoObjects.net/Getty Images; **521** BirdImages/iStock/Getty Images Plus; **525** DrPAS/iStock/Getty Images Plus; **526** *top* ©iStockphoto.com/edhor; *bottom* kokoroyuki/iStock/Getty Images Plus; **527** Rtimages/iStock/Getty Images Plus; **529** stockyimages/Shutterstock.com; **539** ChubarovY/iStock/Getty Images Plus; **540** agsandrew/iStock/Getty Images Plus; **541** *top* shoo_arts/iStock/Getty Images Plus, *background* AlxeyPnferov/iStock/Getty Images Plus; **542** Africa Studio/Shutterstock.com

Chapter 10

544 *top* ©Elora Hayter López; *bottom* Rich Carey/Shutterstock.com; **545** Vold77/iStock/Getty Images Plus; **547** aldomurillo/iStock/Getty Images Plus; **550** danielvfung/iStock/Getty Images Plus; **551** Alexander Izmaylov/Shutterstock.com; **553** *left* EduardHarkoneniStock/Getty Images Plus; *right* Stefan Holm/Shutterstock.com; **555** Hugo Felix/Shutterstock.com; **558** defun/iStock/Getty Images Plus; **559** Velvetfish/iStock/Getty Images Plus; **561** Elnur/Shutterstock.com; **565** EdnaM/iStock/Getty Images Plus; **566** zanariahsalam/iStock Editorial/Getty Images Plus; **567** Satoshi-K/E+/Getty Images; **569** Ollyy/Shutterstock.com; **575** GlobalP/iStock/Getty Images Plus; **579** Alex Kravtsov/Shutterstock; **581** *In order from left to right* coffeekai/iStock/Getty Images Plus; atlantic-kid/iStock Editorial/Getty Images Plus; Reniw-Imagery/iStock/Getty Images Plus; Eloi_Omella/iStock/Getty Images Plus; *background* jonnysek/iStock/Getty Images Plus; **583** IvonneW/iStock/Getty Images Plus

Chapter 11

584 *top* ©Rebecca Drobis/National Geographic Image Collection; *bottom* Ociacia/Shutterstock.com; **587** OSTILL is Franck Camhi/Shutterstock.com; **593** ozanuysal/iStock/Getty Images Plus; **595** track5/E+/Getty Images; **596** Jupiterimages/PHOTOS.com>>/Getty Images; **597** rgbspace/iStock/Getty Images Plus; **599** Linda Bucklin/Shutterstock.com; **600** hdagli/E+/Getty Images; **601** PaulFleet/iStock/Getty Images Plus; **603** JanaShea/iStock Editorial/Getty Images Plus; **606** Dezein/iStock/Getty Images Plus; **607** Violanda/Shutterstock.com; **608** pixdeluxe/iStock/Getty Images Plus; **611** MJFelt/iStock/Getty Images Plus; **612** Eshma/iStock/Getty Images Plus; **613** Cristian Mircea Balate/iStock/Getty Images Plus; **615** FabrikaSimf/Shutterstock.com; **617** Ljupco/iStock/Getty Images Plus; **618** Cheremuha/iStock/Getty Images Plus; **619** GlobalP/iStock/Getty Images Plus; **621** muratart/Shutterstock.com; **626** boitano/iStock / Getty Images Plus; **629** *in counterclockwise order* AlfazetChronicles/iStock/Getty Images Plus; all_is_magic/iStock/Getty Images Plus; Jesussanz/iStock/Getty Images Plus; Rawpixel/iStock/Getty Images Plus; eestingnef/iStock/Getty Images Plus; freestylephoto/iStock/Getty Images Plus; PhonlamaiPhoto/iStock/Getty Images Plus; *background* Apoorva Patel/DigitalVision Vectors/Getty Images

Design Elements

mikimad/iStock/Getty Images Plus; saicle/Shutterstock.com